Dietary Reference Intakes: Recommended Intakes for Individuals: Vitamins

Life Stage Group	Vitamin A (μg/day)[a]	Vitamin C (mg/day)	Vitamin D (μg/day)[b,c]	Vitamin E (mg/day)[d]	Vitamin K (μg/day)	Thiamin (mg/day)	Riboflavin (mg/day)	Niacin (mg/day)[e]	Vitamin B6 (mg/day)	Folate (μg/day)[f]	Vitamin B12 (μg/day)	Pantothenic Acid (mg/day)	Biotin (μg/day)	Cholin (mg/d
INFANTS														
0–6 mo	400*	40*	5*	4*	2.0*	0.2*	0.3*	2*	0.1*	65*	0.4*	1.7*	5*	125
7–12 mo	500*	50*	5*	5*	2.5*	0.3*	0.4*	4*	0.3*	80*	0.5*	1.8*	6*	150
CHILDREN														
1–3 y	**300**	**15**	5*	**6**	30*	**0.5**	**0.5**	**6**	**0.5**	**150**	**0.9**	2*	8*	200
4–8 y	**400**	**25**	5*	**7**	55*	**0.6**	**0.6**	**8**	**0.6**	**200**	**1.2**	3*	12*	250
MALES														
9–13 y	**600**	**45**	5*	**11**	60*	**0.9**	**0.9**	**12**	**1.0**	**300**	**1.8**	4*	20*	375
14–18 y	**900**	**75**	5*	**15**	75*	**1.2**	**1.3**	**16**	**1.3**	**400**	**2.4**	5*	25*	550
19–30 y	**900**	**90**	5*	**15**	120*	**1.2**	**1.3**	**16**	**1.3**	**400**	**2.4**	5*	30*	550
31–50 y	**900**	**90**	5*	**15**	120*	**1.2**	**1.3**	**16**	**1.3**	**400**	**2.4**	5*	30*	550
51–70 y	**900**	**90**	10*	**15**	120*	**1.2**	**1.3**	**16**	**1.7**	**400**	**2.4**[h]	5*	30*	550
> 70 y	**900**	**90**	15*	**15**	120*	**1.2**	**1.3**	**16**	**1.7**	**400**	**2.4**[h]	5*	30*	550
FEMALES														
9–13 y	**600**	**45**	5*	**11**	60*	**0.9**	**0.9**	**12**	**1.0**	**300**	**1.8**	4*	20*	375
14–18 y	**700**	**65**	5*	**15**	75*	**1.0**	**1.0**	**14**	**1.2**	**400**[i]	**2.4**	5*	25*	400
19–30 y	**700**	**75**	5*	**15**	90*	**1.1**	**1.1**	**14**	**1.3**	**400**[i]	**2.4**	5*	30*	425
31–50 y	**700**	**75**	5*	**15**	90*	**1.1**	**1.1**	**14**	**1.3**	**400**[i]	**2.4**	5*	30*	425
51–70 y	**700**	**75**	10*	**15**	90*	**1.1**	**1.1**	**14**	**1.5**	**400**	**2.4**[h]	5*	30*	425
> 70 y	**700**	**75**	15*	**15**	90*	**1.1**	**1.1**	**14**	**1.5**	**400**	**2.4**[h]	5*	30*	425
PREGNANCY														
≤18 y	**750**	**80**	5*	**15**	75*	**1.4**	**1.4**	**18**	**1.9**	**600**[j]	**2.6**	6*	30*	450
19–30 y	**770**	**85**	5*	**15**	90*	**1.4**	**1.4**	**18**	**1.9**	**600**[j]	**2.6**	6*	30*	450
31–50 y	**770**	**85**	5*	**15**	90*	**1.4**	**1.4**	**18**	**1.9**	**600**[j]	**2.6**	6*	30*	450
LACTATION														
≤ 18 y	**1200**	**115**	5*	**19**	75*	**1.4**	**1.6**	**17**	**2.0**	**500**	**2.8**	7*	35*	550
19–30 y	**1300**	**120**	5*	**19**	90*	**1.4**	**1.6**	**17**	**2.0**	**500**	**2.8**	7*	35*	550
31–50 y	**1300**	**120**	5*	**19**	90*	**1.4**	**1.6**	**17**	**2.0**	**500**	**2.8**	7*	35*	550

Note: This table (taken from the DRI reports, see www.nap.edu) presents Recommended Dietary Allowances (RDAs) in **bold** type and Adequate Intakes (AIs) in ordinary type followed by an asterisk (*). RDAs and AIs may both be used as goals for individual intakes. RDAs are set to meet the needs of almost all (97 to 98 percent) individuals in a group. For healthy breastfed infants, the AI is the mean intake. The AI for all other life stage and gender groups is believed to cover needs of all individuals in a group, but lack of data or uncertainty in the data prevent being able to specify with confidence the percentage of individuals covered by this intake.

[a]As retinol activity equivalents (RAEs). 1 RAE = 1 μg retinol, 12 μg β-carotene, 24 μg α-carotene,or 24 μg β-cryptoxanthin in foods. To calculate RAEs from REs of provita A carotenoids in foods, divide REs by 2. For preformed vitamin A in foods or supplements and for provitamin A carotenoid in supplements 1 RE = 1 RAE.

[b]Cholecalciferol. 1 μg cholecalciferol = 40 IU vitamin D.

[c]In the absence of exposure to adequate sunlight.

[d]As α-tocopherol, which includes RRR-α-tocopherol, the only form of α-tocopherol that occurs naturally in foods, and the 2R-stereoisomeric forms of α-tocopherol (RRR-, RSR-, RRS, and RSS-α-tocopherol) that occur in fortified foods and supplements. It does not include the 2S-stereoisomeric forms of α-tocopherol (SRR-, SSR-, SRS-, and SSS-α-tocopherol), also found in fortified foods and supplements.

[e]As niacin equivalents (NEs). 1 mg niacin = 60 mg tryptophan; 0–6 months = preformed niacin (not NE).

[f]As dietary folate equivalents (DFE) 1 DFE = 1 μg food folate = 0.6 μg folic acid from fortified food or as a supplement consumed with food = 0.5 μg of a supplement take on an empty stomach.

[g]Although AIs have been set for choline, there are few data to assess whether a dietary supply of choline is needed at all stages of the lifecycle, and it may be that the choli requirement can be met by endogenous synthesis at some of these stages.

[h]Because 10–30% of older people may malabsorb food-bound B12, it is advisable for those older than 50 years to meet their RDA mainly by consuming foods fortified with B a supplement containing B12.

[i]In view of evidence linking folate intake with neural tube defects in the fetus, it is recommended that all women capable of becoming pregnant consume 400 μg from supplements or fortified foods in addition to intake of food folate from a varied diet.

[j]It is assumed that women will consume 400 μg from supplements or fortified foods until their pregnancy is confirmed and they enter prenatal care, which ordinarily occurs the end of the periconceptional period—the critical time for neural tube formation.

Source: Dietary Reference Intake Tables: The Complete Set. Institute of Medicine, National Academies of Sciences available online at www.nap.edu.

Nutrition
Science & Applications

Smolin • Grosvenor

Second Edition

WILEY *Custom*
LEARNING SOLUTIONS

ISBN   978-0-470-90391-9

Printed and bound by IPAK.

10 9 8 7 6 5 4 3

AGE	CALCIUM (mg/day)	CHROMIUM (μg/day)	COPPER (μg/day)	FLUORIDE (mg/day)	IODINE (μg/day)	IRON (mg/day)	MAGNESIUM (mg/day)	MANGANESE (mg/day)	MOLYBDENUM (μg/day)	PHOSPHORUS (mg/day)	SELENIUM (μg/day)	ZINC (mg/day)	SODIUM (g/day)	CHLORIDE (g/day)	POTASSIUM (g/day)
INFANTS															
6 mo	210*	0.2*	200*	0.01*	110*	0.27*	30*	0.003*	2*	100*	15*	2*	0.12*	0.18*	0.4*
12 mo	270*	5.5*	220*	0.5*	130*	**11**	75*	0.6*	3*	275*	20*	**3**	0.37*	0.57*	0.7*
CHILDREN															
3 y	500*	11*	**340**	0.7*	**90**	**7**	**80**	1.2*	**17**	**460**	**20**	**3**	1.0*	1.5*	3.0*
8 y	800*	15*	**440**	1*	**90**	**10**	**130**	1.5*	**22**	**500**	**30**	**5**	1.2*	1.9*	3.8*
MALES															
13 y	1,300*	25*	**700**	2*	**120**	**8**	**240**	1.9*	**34**	**1,250**	**40**	**8**	1.5*	2.3*	4.5*
–18 y	1,300*	35*	**890**	3*	**150**	**11**	**410**	2.2*	**43**	**1,250**	**55**	**11**	1.5*	2.3*	4.7*
–30 y	1,000*	35*	**900**	4*	**150**	**8**	**400**	2.3*	**45**	**700**	**55**	**11**	1.5*	2.3*	4.7*
–50 y	1,000*	35*	**900**	4*	**150**	**8**	**420**	2.3*	**45**	**700**	**55**	**11**	1.5*	2.3*	4.7*
–70 y	1,200*	30*	**900**	4*	**150**	**8**	**420**	2.3*	**45**	**700**	**55**	**11**	1.3*	2.0*	4.7*
70 y	1,200*	30*	**900**	4*	**150**	**8**	**420**	2.3*	**45**	**700**	**55**	**11**	1.2*	1.8*	4.7*
FEMALES															
13 y	1,300*	21*	**700**	2*	**120**	**8**	**240**	1.6*	**34**	**1,250**	**40**	**8**	1.5*	2.3*	4.5*
–18 y	1,300*	24*	**890**	3*	**150**	**15**	**360**	1.6*	**43**	**1,250**	**55**	**9**	1.5*	2.3*	4.7*
–30 y	1,000*	25*	**900**	3*	**150**	**18**	**310**	1.8*	**45**	**700**	**55**	**8**	1.5*	2.3*	4.7*
–50 y	1,000*	25*	**900**	3*	**150**	**18**	**320**	1.8*	**45**	**700**	**55**	**8**	1.5*	2.3*	4.7*
–70 y	1,200*	20*	**900**	3*	**150**	**8**	**320**	1.8*	**45**	**700**	**55**	**8**	1.3*	2.0*	4.7*
70 y	1,200*	20*	**900**	3*	**150**	**8**	**320**	1.8*	**45**	**700**	**55**	**8**	1.2*	1.8*	4.7*
PREGNANCY															
18 y	1,300*	29*	**1,000**	3*	**220**	**27**	**400**	2.0*	**50**	**1,250**	**60**	**13**	1.5*	2.3*	4.7*
–30 y	1,000*	30*	**1,000**	3*	**220**	**27**	**350**	2.0*	**50**	**700**	**60**	**11**	1.5*	2.3*	4.7*
–50 y	1,000*	30*	**1,000**	3*	**220**	**27**	**360**	2.0*	**50**	**700**	**60**	**11**	1.5*	2.3*	4.7*
LACTATION															
18 y	1,300*	44*	**1,300**	3*	**290**	**10**	**360**	2.6*	**50**	**1,250**	**70**	**14**	1.5*	2.3*	5.1*
–30 y	1,000*	45*	**1,300**	3*	**290**	**9**	**310**	2.6*	**50**	**700**	**70**	**12**	1.5*	2.3*	5.1*
–50 y	1,000*	45*	**1,300**	3*	**290**	**9**	**320**	2.6*	**50**	**700**	**70**	**12**	1.5*	2.3*	5.1*

This table (taken from the DRI reports, see www.nap.edu) presents Recommended Dietary Allowances (RDAs) in **bold** type and Adequate Intakes (AIs) in ordinary type followed by an asterisk (*). RDAs and AIs may both be used as goals for individual intakes. RDAs are set up to meet the needs of almost all (97–98%) individuals in a group. For healthy breastfed infants, the AI is the mean intake. The AI for all other life stage and gender groups is believed to cover needs of all individuals in the group, but lack of data or uncertainty in the data prevent being able to specify with confidence the percentage of individuals covered by this intake.

Source: Dietary Reference Intake Tables: The Complete Set. Institute of Medicine, National Academies of Sciences. Available online at www.nap.edu.

	CARBOHYDRATE	ADDED SUGARS	TOTAL FAT	LINOLEIC ACID	α-LINOLENIC ACID	PROTEIN
y	45–65	≤ 25	30–40	5–10	0.6–1.2	5–20
3 y	45–65	≤ 25	25–35	5–10	0.6–1.2	10–30
9 y	45–65	≤ 25	20–35	5–10	0.6–1.2	10–35

Source: Institute of Medicine, Food and Nutrition Board. "Dietary Reference Intakes for Energy, Carbohydrates, Fiber, Fat, Protein, and Amino Acids." Washington, D.C.: National Academies Press, 2002.

DIETARY REFERENCE INTAKES: RECOMMENDED INTAKES FOR INDIVIDUALS: CARBOHYDRATES, FIBER, FAT, FATTY ACIDS, PROTEIN, AND WATER

Life Stage Group	Carbohydrate (g/day)	Fiber (g/day)	Fat (g/day)	Linoleic Acid (g/day)	α-Linolenic Acid (g/day)	Protein (g/kg/day)	(g/day)	Water (liters)
INFANTS								
0–6 mo	60*	ND	31*	4.4*†	0.5*‡	1.52*	9.1*	0.7*
7–12 mo	95*	ND	30*	4.6*†	0.5*‡	1.5	13.5	0.8*
CHILDREN								
1–3 y	130	19*	ND	7*	0.7*	1.10	13	1.3*
4–8 y	130	25*	ND	10*	0.9*	0.95	19	1.7*
MALES								
9–13 y	130	31*	ND	12*	1.2*	0.95	34	2.4*
14–18 y	130	38*	ND	16*	1.6*	0.85	52	3.3*
19–30 y	130	38*	ND	17*	1.6*	0.80	56	3.7*
31–50 y	130	38*	ND	17*	1.6*	0.80	56	3.7*
51–70 y	130	30*	ND	14*	1.6*	0.80	56	3.7*
> 70 y	130	30*	ND	14*	1.6*	0.80	56	3.7*
FEMALES								
9–13 y	130	26*	ND	10*	1.0*	0.95	34	
14–18 y	130	26*	ND	11*	1.1*	0.85	46	2.1*
19–30 y	130	25*	ND	12*	1.1*	0.80	46	2.3*
31–50 y	130	25*	ND	12*	1.1*	0.80	46	2.7*
51–70 y	130	21*	ND	11*	1.1*	0.80	46	2.7*
> 70 y	130	21*	ND	11*	1.1*	0.80	46	2.7*
PREGNANCY	175	28*	ND	13*	1.4*	1.1	RDA + 25g	3.0*
LACTATION	210	29*	ND	13*	1.3*	1.1	RDA + 25g	3.8*

ND = not determined *Values are AI (Adequate Intakes) † Refers to all ω-6 polyunsaturated fatty acids ‡ Refers to all ω-3 polyunsaturated fatty acids

Source: Institute of Medicine, Food and Nutrition Board. "Dietary Reference Intakes for Energy, Carbohydrates, Fiber, Fat, Fatty Acids, and Protein." Washington, D.C.: National Academies Press, 2002.

Nutrition: Science and Applications

Second Edition

Lori A. Smolin, Ph.D.

University of Connecticut

Mary B. Grosvenor, M.S., R.D.

WILEY

John Wiley & Sons, Inc.

Vice President & Executive Publisher	Kaye Pace
Executive Editor	Bonnie Roesch
Senior Editor	Kevin Witt
Project Editor	Lorraina Raccuia
Production Manager	Dorothy Sinclair
Senior Production Editor	Valerie A. Vargas
Executive Marketing Manager	Clay Stone
Creative Director	Harry Nolan
Interior Design	Amy Rosen
Cover Design	Wendy Lai
Production Management Services	Furino Production
Senior Illustration Editor	Anna Melhorn
Manager, Photo Department	Hilary Newman
Senior Media Editor	Linda Muriello
Media Project Manager	Svetlana Barskaya
Program Assistant	Lauren Morris
Cover Photo Credit	© Ottmar Diez/Getty Images, Inc.

This book was set in Palatino by GGS Higher Education Resources, a Divison of PreMedia Global, Inc. and printed and bound by Courier-Kendallville. The cover was printed by Courier-Kendallville.

ISBN-13 978- 0-470-52474-9

Printed in the United States of America

10 9 8 7 6 5 4

About the Authors

Lori A. Smolin received a bachelor of science degree from Cornell University, where she studied human nutrition and food science. She received a doctorate from the University of Wisconsin at Madison, where her doctoral research focused on B vitamins, homocysteine accumulation, and genetic defects in homocysteine metabolism. She completed post-doctoral training both at the Harbor–UCLA Medical Center, where she studied human obesity, and at the University of California—San Diego, where she studied genetic defects in amino acid metabolism. She has published articles in these areas in peer-reviewed journals. Dr. Smolin is currently at the University of Connecticut, where she teaches in the Department of Nutritional Science. Courses she has taught include introductory nutrition, life cycle nutrition, food preparation, nutritional biochemistry, general biochemistry, and introductory biology.

Mary B. Grosvenor holds a bachelor of arts in English and a master of science in Nutrition Science, affording her an ideal background for nutrition writing. She is a registered dietitian and has worked in clinical as well as research nutrition, in hospitals and communities large and small in the western United States. She teaches at the community college level and has published articles in peer-reviewed journals in nutritional assessment and nutrition and cancer. Her training and experience provide practical insights into the application and presentation of the science in this text.

Dedication

To my sons, Zachary and Max, and to my husband, David Knecht, who help me maintain perspective and recognize and appreciate the important things in life.

LAS

To my boys, in appreciation for the time this work takes from them and the inspiration (and in recent years, editorial assistance) they give to me.

MBG

Preface

Sugar

Carbohydrate (starch)

Fatty acids

Lipid (Triglyceride)

Amino acids

Protein

Nutrition: Science and Applications, Second Edition, is intended as an introductory text for a science-oriented nutrition course. The material is appropriate for a college student at any level, freshman to senior, taking this course to fulfill a science requirement. The clear, concise writing style–reinforced visually with colorful, engaging illustrations—makes the science accessible. The strong metabolism coverage, clinical flavor, and in-depth approach to science and nutrition research make this a text that will also prepare nutrition and other science majors for their future studies and careers. The nutrition science presented in this text ties together information that students may have studied in chemistry, physiology, biology, and biochemistry courses.

This up-to-date text includes the most recent recommendations from the DRIs and MyPyramid and is extensively referenced with current literature. Recent advances in nutrition science, such as nutrigenomics, the relationship between genetics and body weight regulation, the ecological impact of genetically modified foods and organic food production, and the nutritional and health impact of phytochemicals and dietary supplements are discussed. The examples used throughout the text reflect the diverse ethnic and cultural mix of the American population.

Critical Thinking Enhances Problem-Solving Skills

Nutrition: Science and Applications, Second Edition, takes a critical thinking approach to understanding and applying human nutrition. Like other introductory texts it offers students the basics of nutrition by exploring the nutrients, their functions in the body, and sources in the diet. But, its unique critical thinking approach gives students an understanding of the "whys" and the "hows" behind nutrition processes and clarifies the issues that surround nutrition controversies. In each chapter, highlighted Critical Thinking exercises introduce nutrition-related problems and lead students through the logical questions and thought processes needed to find solutions and to make healthy food and nutrition decisions. "Applications" at the end of each chapter then ask students to use this same process of logical scientific inquiry, along with the information in the chapter, to assess their own diets and modify them to promote health and to reduce the risk of nutrient deficiencies and nutrition-related chronic diseases. This critical thinking approach gives students the tools they need to bring nutrition out of the classroom and apply the logic of science to their own nutrition concerns—both as consumers and as future scientists and health professionals.

Integrated Metabolism Reinforces Understanding

Nutrition: Science and Applications, Second Edition, is distinctive in its integrated approach to the presentation of nutrient metabolism. Metabolism is one of the most challenging topics for students, but it is a topic that applies to each nutrient and is intimately linked to its function and its impact on human health. The text includes a comprehensive discussion of metabolism as it applies to each of the energy-yielding nutrients, shows how the micronutrients are involved, and then ties it all together in discussions of energy metabolism during weight management and physical activity. Integrating discussions of metabolism throughout appropriate chapters in the text makes metabolism more manageable and memorable for students because it presents this challenging material in smaller segments and illustrates its relevance to the nutrient being discussed. It also reinforces understanding of metabolic processes by revisiting key concepts with each nutrient and adding relevant new information. For example, *Nutrition: Science and Applications* introduces a simple overview of metabolism in Chapter 3 and then builds on this base with a more complex discussion of carbohydrate metabolism in Chapter 4. This information is added to and reviewed in chapters covering lipids, proteins, micronutrients, energy balance, and exercise. Each discussion of metabolism is highlighted by a metabolism icon. To tie the concepts together, the illustrations use the same basic diagram with new information superimposed over familiar portions to demonstrate how each nutrient fits into the process. The nutrients and steps of metabolism are also color coded for easier recognition.

Integration of Health and Disease Relationships Holds Interest

Can I help my mom manage her blood cholesterol?

Why have I gained 10 pounds?

What should I eat to reduce my risk of cancer?

How can I change my diet to better support my athletic training?

These are some of the questions students want answered when they enroll in nutrition classes. To answer these and other health-related questions and to continuously fuel student interest, discussions of the relationships among nutrition, health, and disease are integrated throughout the text. The integration helps students recognize that a nutrient's function in metabolism is related to its role in health and disease. Discussing health concerns with the topic or nutrient most related to the concern continuously reinforces the applicability of nutrition science to the student's lives. This understanding helps them appreciate how and why their diets affect their health.

The Total Diet, Rather than Individual Foods is the Focus

Nutrition: Science and Applications, Second Edition, presents the message that each nutrient and food choice makes up only a small part of a person's total diet and that it is the overall dietary pattern that determines the healthfulness of the diet. Each of the macronutrient chapters begins with a section that discusses the role of that nutrient in the modern diet—factors that affect intake of the nutrient and the overall nutritional contribution made by different food sources of the nutrient. For example, choosing whole-wheat bread provides a more nutrient-dense source of carbohydrate than choosing a slice of chocolate cake. However, this does not mean people should never have chocolate cake. No one food is a bad one as long as the sum of the food choices over a period of days or weeks makes up a healthy overall diet. To reinforce this, these chapters end with a discussion of how students can meet their need for that specific nutrient while taking into consideration other dietary recommendations that promote health.

Distinctive Features

This text includes a number of features that both spark student interest and help them learn the basics of nutrition.

Case Study

Each chapter begins with a short case study. These health- and disease-oriented vignettes help spur student curiosity and provide a taste of some of the concepts that will be explained in the chapter. For example, the case study for Chapter 6 discusses the experiences of a Peace Corps volunteer observing protein-energy malnutrition for the first time and wondering why Songe, a malnourished child would have a swollen abdomen. Chapter 9 examines the case of a toddler adopted from China who has rickets, and Chapter 10 recounts the story of an athlete who experienced dehydration during an Olympic marathon. These intriguing stories link the material in the chapter with everyday nutrition issues.

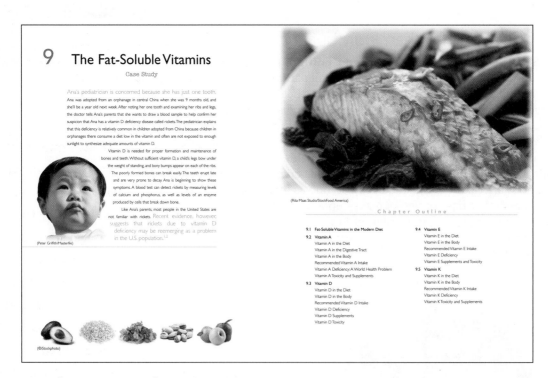

Chapter Outline

This brief outline of the chapter's content provides students and instructors with an overview of the major topics presented in the chapter

Outcome

Each chapter ends with the "outcome," which completes the case study stories begun in the chapter introduction. For example, the outcome at the end of Chapter 6 describes how young Songe's protein deficiency symptoms improve when his diet is supplemented with protein, and discusses the Peace Corps worker's efforts to improve protein nutrition by educating the people in the community. These "outcomes" review concepts covered in the chapter and illustrate the application of nutrition knowledge to clinical situations.

Learning Objectives

Each chapter section begins with one or more learning objectives. These present brief clear descriptions of what the student should be able to do to demonstrate mastery of the material once they have read the section.

7.2 Exploring Energy Balance

Learning Objectives

- Explain the principle of energy balance.
- Describe the processes involved in generating ATP from food.
- Describe the components of energy expenditure.
- Indicate how excess dietary energy is stored in the body.

The principle of **energy balance** states that when energy consumption equals energy expenditure, body weight remains constant. Energy balance can be achieved at any weight—fat, thin, or in between (**Figure 7.2**); it simply means that body weight is not changing. If, however, less energy is taken in than expended, energy balance is negative and weight will be lost. On the other hand, if the amount of energy taken in

Critical Thinking

Critical Thinking
Eating Healthier Fats

Background

Isabel has a busy schedule—working full-time and attending college—and has little time to cook meals at home. Currently, for breakfast and lunch she relies on things she can pick up on the way to school or between classes. She makes a quick dinner when she gets home in the evening. She is concerned about the fat in her diet and wants to know how to make healthier choices.

Data

Isabel analyzes her original diet and then modifies it to try to meet the recommendations for a healthy mix of fats (see table).

(Hola Images/Getty Images, Inc.)

| | | ORIGINAL DIET | | | | | | MODIFIED DIET | | | |
FOOD	SERVING	FAT (G)	SAT (G)	TRANS (G)	CHOLESTEROL (MG)	FOOD	SERVING	FAT (G)	SAT (G)	TRANS (G)	CHOLESTEROL (MG)
Breakfast						**Breakfast**					
Bran muffin	1 large	6	2.6	0.5	24	Bran muffin	1 large	6	2.6	0.5	24
Margarine	2 tsp	8	1.3	2	0	Orange	1 medium	0.2	0	0	0
Coffee	1 cup	0	0	0	0	Coffee	1 cup	0	0	0	0
Whole milk	1 cup	8	5	0.2	33	Low-fat milk	1 cup	2.6	1.6	0	10
Lunch						**Lunch**					
Big Mac	1	31	12.5	1	80	Rice noodles	1 cup	0	0	0	0
French fries	medium order	22	5	5	0	Stir-fry vegetables	1 cup	0.3	0	0	0
						in peanut oil	1 tsp	5	0.8	0	0
Water	1 bottle	0	0	0	0	Water	1 bottle	0	0	0	0
Snack						**Snack**					
Apple	1	0	0	0	0	Apple	1 medium	0	0	0	0
						Pretzels	1 oz	1	0	0	0
Dinner						**Dinner**					
Fish sticks	5	17	2.4	2	33	Trout	3 oz	12	1.2	0	63
Tater tots	10	8	6	4	0	Baked potato w/sour cream	1 medium	0.2	0	0	0
						Green beans	1/2 cup	0	0	0	10
						Salad w/oil & vinegar	1 cup	10	1.2	0	0
						Melon	1 cup	0	0	0	0
Tea	1 cup	0	0	0	Tea	1 cup	0	0	0	0
Coconut cookies	2	13	3.4	3.3	0	Frozen yogurt	2/3 cup	1.8	1.2	0	5
Totals		113	38.2	18	170	**Totals**		42.1	10.3	0.5	112

Critical Thinking Questions

Assuming Isabel is eating 2250 kcalories per day, calculate the percent of energy from fat and saturated fat (sat) in her original diet. How do these percentages compare to recommendations? What foods are the biggest contributors to her saturated fat intake? To her trans fat intake? To her cholesterol intake?

▼

Now look at the changes she has made. Assuming her kcalorie intake stayed the same calculate the percent of energy from fat and saturated fat in her modified diet.

▼

Fat is not the only concern in choosing a healthy diet. How does her modified diet stack up to the MyPyramid recommendations in terms of grains, fruits, and vegetables?

iProfile Use iProfile to find fast food choices that are low in saturated fat.

197

Critical Thinking

These exercises, which appear in each chapter, use a critical thinking approach to making decisions and solving problems regarding nutrition. They help students apply their nutrition knowledge to everyday situations by presenting a nutrition-related problem and then asking a series of questions that lead the student through the logical progression of thought processes needed to solve the problem. Many of these exercises focus on modifying a diet to reduce disease risk or maintain health. For example, one of the exercises in Chapter 5 takes the student through the process of evaluating the risk of developing heart disease. The exercise in Chapter 6 shows the students how to use complementary proteins in a vegetarian diet that is based on traditional Indian cuisine.

Your Choice

These boxed features included in each chapter provide a critical review of products and issues that are the focus of individual nutrtion-related consumer choices. For example, the Your Choice box in Chapter 1 discusses how grabbing breakfast on the run can affect your waistline and your wallet. The Your Choice box in Chapter 4 discusses the challenge of choosing whole-grain products and the box in Chapter 5 discusses foods that can lower your blood cholesterol.

Off the Label

"Off the Label" boxes present in-depth information on food, supplement, and drug labels. Off the Label is designed to show students how to use labels to make wise choices. For example, the boxes in Chapter 4 shows how food labels can be used to choose whole grain products and avoid foods that are high in added sugars. Chapter 6 has an Off the Label box that discusses how someone with food allergies can use food labels to avoid ingesting particular ingredients, and in Chapter 3 the box "Antacids: Getting the Drug Facts" points out that taking some medications can add nutrients to the diet and explains how the drug facts label can be used to assess the nutrient contribution made by a medication.

Science Applied

These boxed features included in every chapter highlight nutrition research studies that have led to discoveries key to our current understanding of nutrition. These help students appreciate the research process and expose them to the rich, colorful history of nutrition. For example, in Chapter 1, the Seven Countries Study is discussed. This classic study, begun in 1958, identified the relationship between saturated fat intake and heart disease. Other Science Applied topics include how weightlessness in space is used to study bone loss, how the obesity gene leptin was identified, how pellagra was determined to be a nutritional deficiency, and how LDL receptors, which help remove LDL cholesterol from the blood, were discovered.

SCIENCE APPLIED
ScienceAppliedScienceApplied
ScienceAppliedScienceApplied
ScienceAppliedScienceApplied

(DNJ/Getty Images, Inc.) (www.victorianglassworks.com/Getty Images, Inc.) (Elena Schweitzer/Shutterstock)

Leptin: Discovery of an Obesity Gene

A discovery made by Dr. Jeffrey Friedman and colleagues in 1994 brought hope to millions of people. Perhaps the cause of obesity had been found and a cure might be close behind. Was relief in sight for those who suffer from the physical and social consequences of obesity?

Dr. Friedman's work began with a strain of mice called *ob* for obese. *Ob* mice become grossly obese, gaining up to three times the normal body weight. The ob strain arose spontaneously in 1950 in the mouse colony at the Jackson Laboratory in Bar Harbor, Maine. Friedman and colleagues unraveled the cause for the obesity in this strain of mice when they identified and cloned the one gene that was responsible.[1]

Researchers used a series of breeding experiments to localize the gene to a particular stretch of DNA. They then looked to see if any of the genes in this stretch of DNA were expressed in adipose tissue. The search yielded a single gene. Evidence that this gene was involved in the regulation of body weight was obtained by examining the gene and the protein it codes for in the ob mice. Researchers found that this protein, which they named leptin, was either not produced or produced in an inactive form in the obese mice. Soon afterward a similar gene was identified in humans.

Optimism about the role of the protein hormone leptin in human obesity was so great that a biotechnology firm (Amgen) paid $25 million for the commercial rights to leptin in the hope that it could be used to treat human obesity. Those hopes grew even higher when Friedman and colleagues were able to demonstrate that injections of the hormone could restore the genetically obese mice to normal weight (see figure).[2,3] Unfortunately, the role of leptin in human obesity has not lived up to expectations. Mutations in this gene are not responsible for most human obesity.[4] In fact, obese humans generally have high blood leptin levels.[5] High doses of leptin administered to obese humans produces only modest weight loss.[6]

The leptin receptor—a protein in the brain to which leptin must bind to produce weight reduction—was also identified.[7] The fact that obese humans have high levels of leptin

A mouse with a defect in the leptin gene (ob) may weigh three times as much as a normal mouse. Both of these mice have defective ob genes but the one on the right was treated with leptin injections. (© AP/Wide World Photos)

suggested that the cause of human obesity might involve an abnormality in leptin receptors. If leptin receptors were defective, the leptin produced would have no place to bind and would not be able to signal mechanisms to promote weight reduction. Thus far, however, defective leptin receptors have not been found to be an important cause of human obesity.[8]

Continued study of the role of leptin in obesity has confirmed that it is an important signal involved in the long-term regulation of body fat, but it does not act alone. There are many steps, involving many genes, that occur between the production of leptin and alterations in food intake and energy expenditure. Researchers have discovered about a dozen molecules that interact with leptin in the brain to control appetite.[9] For example, neuropeptide Y and melanin-concentrating hormone boost appetite, whereas alpha-melanocyte stimulating hormone blunts appetite, and a protein called SOCS3 reduces the sensitivity of leptin receptors.

Despite the fact that the identification of leptin has not produced a cure for human obesity, its discovery lit up the field. This research was an important advance in our understanding of the genetics of body weight regulation. Continued work will someday answer the questions that remain about why some of us are obese and some of us are lean.

[1]Zhang, Y., Proenca, R., Maffei, M. et al. Positional cloning of the mouse obese gene and its human homologue. Nature 372:425–432, 1994.
[2]Halaas, J. L., Gajiwala, K. S., Maffei, M. et al. Weight-reducing effects of the plasma protein encoded by the obese gene. Science 269:543–546, 1995.
[3]Pelleymounter, M. A., Cullen, M. J., Baker, M. B. et al. Effects of the obese gene product on body weight regulation in ob/ob mice. Science 269:540–543, 1995.
[4]Montague, C. T., Farooqi, I. S., Whitehead, J. P. et al. Congenital leptin deficiency is associated with severe early onset obesity in children. Nature 387:903–908, 1997.
[5]Considine, R. V., Sinha, M. K., Heiman, M. L. et al. Serum immunoreactive-leptin concentrations in normal weight and obese humans. N. Engl. J. Med. 334:292–295, 1996.
[6]Gura, T. Obesity research: Leptin not impressive in clinical trial. Science 286:881–882, 1999.
[7]Tartaglia, L. A., Dembski, M., Weng X. et al. Identification and expression cloning of a leptin receptor, OB-R. Cell 83:1263–1271; 1995.
[8]Tsigos, C., Kyrou, I., and Raptis, S. A. Monogenic forms of obesity and diabetes mellitus. J. Pediatr. Endocrinol. Metab. 15:241–253, 2002.
[9]Gura, T. Tracing leptin's partners in regulating body weight. Science 287:1738–1741, 2000.

(©iStockphoto)

286

Process Diagrams

Sometimes the hardest part of understanding an illustration is knowing where to start. To help students start at the beginning and understand the information presented in the more complex line art, the steps in the processes are numbered and include a narrative describing what happens at each step. Process diagrams for metabolism help students reduce this often intimidating topic to a series of easy-to-follow steps.

6.3 Protein in the Digestive Tract **223**

How it Works

View in your Wiley Plus
www.wileyplus.com

1. In the mouth, chewing begins the mechanical breakdown of protein.

2. In the stomach, hydrochloric acid and the enzyme pepsin begin the chemical digestion of protein.

3. In the small intestine, protein-digesting enzymes secreted from the pancreas, along with those in the brush border, break down polypeptides into amino acids, dipeptides, and tripeptide

4. A variety of transport proteins move the products of protein digestion into the mucosal cell. Some amino acids share the same transport system. In this figure, the larger number of purple amino acids means that more purple than green ones cross the membrane into the cell.

5. Dipeptides and tripeptides can enter the mucosal cell. Once inside, they are broken down into single amino acids.

6. Amino acids pass from the mucosal cell into the blood and travel to the liver, which regulates the distribution of amino acids to the rest of the body.

7. Little dietary protein is lost in the feces.

Salivary glands
Liver
Stomach
Pancreas
Small intestine
Large intestine
Blood

Figure 6.7 Protein digestion and absorption
Protein must be broken down into small peptides and amino acids before it can be absorbed into the mucosal cells.

Applications

These exercises, which appear at the end of each chapter, are divided into two parts; one that focuses on the student's personal diet and nutrition concerns and a second that relates to more general nutrition issues. Both require the student to think critically and apply key nutrition concepts. Some of these exercises feature clinical applications and therefore also help reinforce the importance of nutrition in health promotion and disease prevention. Some of these can be done as collaborative learning exercises, which encourage students to work together and learn from each other to solve a problem.

Chapter Summary

Each chapter ends with a summary that highlights important concepts addressed in each section of the chapter.

Review Questions

A set of questions appears at the end of each chapter to test students' understanding of the key points covered. It can be used by students as a study tool to test their understanding of the important information in the chapter.

Focus On

There are a number of topics of great interest to students that have a close relationship with nutrition but are not part of a pure nutrition curriculum. For example, eating disorders have nutritional symptoms, but are really psychological disorders; alcohol is consumed in the diet and affects nutrient metabolism, but is not itself a nutrient; and herbal supplements are not nutrients but may affect health and are sold alongside vitamin and mineral supplements. To provide adequate coverage of these fascinating topics, they are discussed in sections called Focus On. These sections allow instructors to cover this material or skip it if they feel it is not pertinent to their curriculum. There are 5 of these throughout the book: Focus on Alcohol, Focus on Eating Disorders, Focus on Phytochemicals, Focus on Nonvitamin/Nonmineral Supplements, and Focus on Biotechnology.

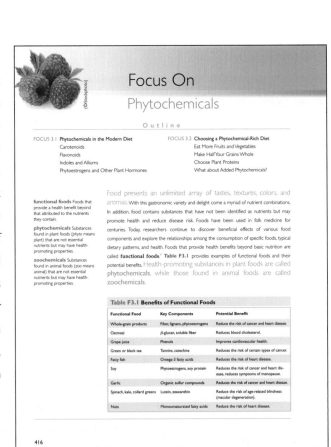

Marginal Features

The text includes a number of marginal features that aid student comprehension, enhance interest, and point out where particular types of information can be found.

Definitions of New Terms

New terms are highlighted in bold and defined in the margin. This provides easy access to new terms as they appear in the text. These and other terms are included in an extensive glossary at the back of the text.

The Scientific Method

Advances in nutrition are made using the **scientific method**. The scientific method offers a systematic, unbiased approach to evaluating the relationships among food, nutrients, and health. The first step of the scientific method is to make an observation and ask questions about the observation. The next step is to propose a **hypothesis**, or explanation for the observation. Once a hypothesis has been proposed, experiments can be designed to test it. The experiments must provide objective results that can be measured and repeated. If the experimental results do not prove the hypothesis to be

scientific method The general approach of science that is used to explain observations about the world around us.

hypothesis An educated guess made to explain an observation or to answer a question.

How It Works Icons These icons appear by figures or concepts that students can explore further through animations in WileyPLUS.

iProfile icons These point students to places where they can use the iProfile software to answer questions about the nutrient composition of foods and diets.

Video Icons These icons appear by topics that students can explore further by watching a BBC or CBS video on WileyPlus.

Metabolism icons These highlight the discussions of how each nutrient fits into the metabolic processes of nutrition.

Lifecycle icons These highlight passages that address how life stage affects nutrient needs and concerns. This information helps students understand why nutrient requirements differ with life stage as well as offers information relevant to students in all phases of life. Lifecycle nutrition is also covered in depth in separate chapters (Chapters 14, 15, and 16).

New to this Edition

New and Enhanced Art

Visuals show students a process rather than just describe it. To make sure students "see" the processes of nutrition many illustrations have been redesigned and converted to process diagrams. Fonts and figures layouts have been clarified to make illustrations more attractive and easier to read and to emphasize steps that occur at the physiological versus cellular levels. To make metabolism more intuitive metabolism illustrations have been redesigned. The new layout makes the steps involved in generating ATP more straightforward. Each step is distinguished by the color of the arrow and a numbered description. Repeated use of the same basic figure allows symbols such as the blue circle of the citric acid cycle and the descending purple steps of the electron transport chain to become immediately recognizable.

4.4 Carbohydrates in the Body **131**

How it Works

View in your Wiley Plus
www.wileyplus.com

1. Glycolysis splits glucose, a 6-carbon molecule, into two molecules of pyruvate, a 3-carbon molecule. This step produces high-energy electrons (e⁻) and a small amount of ATP. Each pyruvate is then either broken down to produce more ATP or used to make glucose via gluconeogenesis.

2. When oxygen is available, pyruvate can be used to produce more ATP. The first step is to remove one carbon as carbon dioxide from each pyruvate. This produces a 2-carbon molecule that combines with coenzyme A to form acetyl-CoA and releases high-energy electrons.

3. Each acetyl-CoA enters the citric acid cycle, where two carbons are lost as carbon dioxide, high-energy electrons are released, and a small amount of ATP is produced.

4. In the final step of cellular respiration, the electron transport chain accepts the high-energy electrons released in previous steps and uses the energy to synthesize ATP. The electrons are combined with oxygen and hydrogen to form water.

Figure 4.16 Glucose Metabolism
The reactions of cellular respiration split the bonds between carbon atoms in glucose, releasing energy that is used to synthesize ATP. ATP is used to power the energy-requiring processes in the body.

Citric Acid Cycle In the third stage, acetyl-CoA combines with oxaloacetate, a 4-carbon molecule derived from carbohydrate, to form a 6-carbon molecule called citric acid and begin the citric acid cycle (Figure 4.16). The reactions of the citric acid cycle then remove one carbon at a time, to produce carbon dioxide. After two carbons have been removed in this manner, a 4-carbon oxaloacetate molecule is re-formed and the cycle can begin again. These chemical reactions produce two ATP molecules per glucose molecule and also remove electrons, which are passed to shuttling molecules for transport to the fourth and last stage of cellular respiration, the electron transport chain.

Electron Transport Chain The electron transport chain consists of a series of molecules, most of which are proteins, associated with the inner membrane of the mitochondria. These molecules accept electrons from the shuttling molecules and pass them from one to

Updated Off the Label and Your Choice boxes.

This boxed material provides interesting up-to-date information on topics that are side bars to the necessary textual material but enhance the interest of students as consumers in the U.S. market place. For example, a Your Choice box in chapter 5 discusses foods that are so highly fortified that they resemble supplements and an Off the Label in chapter 13 looks at what you are getting in sports energy bars.

Enhanced Critical Thinking Exercises.

These critical thinking exercises present students with background information and data, which define a nutritional problem. Data may include clinical information such as blood cholesterol values or body weight as well as diet records. Student thought is then provoked with a series of questions that lead them through the issues that need to be addressed to solve the problem.

BBC and CBS Videos.

Video

Available in WileyPlus, these videos help students explore topics like the Mediterranean diet, the environmental impact of eating locally grown foods, diet myths, and other relevant topics.

Chapter-by-Chapter Overview

CHAPTER 1 - "Nutrition: Food for Health," begins by discussing the American diet—how it has changed, and how healthy it is. It emphasizes that food choices affect current and future health. This chapter provides an overview of the nutrients and their roles in the body, and defines the basic principles of balance, variety, and moderation that are key to a healthy diet. It also introduces the scientific method and the steps students need to follow to sort accurate from inaccurate nutrition information.

CHAPTER 2 - "Nutrition Guidelines: Applying the Science of Nutrition," takes the science out of the laboratory and shows how advances in nutrition knowledge have been used to develop the Dietary Reference Intakes (DRIs), the Dietary Guidelines for Americans, and tools for diet planning, including MyPyramid, food labels, and exchange lists. The final section of this chapter discusses how these and other tools can be used to assess the nutritional health of populations and individuals.

CHAPTER 3 - "Digestion, Absorption, and Metabolism," discusses how food is digested; how nutrients from foods are absorbed into the body and transported to the cells where they are broken down to provide energy or used to synthesize structural or regulatory molecules, and finally how wastes are removed. This chapter provides an overview of metabolism that serves as a launching pad for the more in-depth metabolism information presented in subsequent chapters.

CHAPTERS 4, 5, AND 6 feature the energy-yielding nutrients carbohydrates, lipids, and proteins. Each begins with a discussion of the respective macronutrient in the modern diet. The body of each chapter discusses dietary sources of the nutrient and it's functions, digestion and absorption, and metabolism. Each chapter ends with a discussion of how to choose a diet that meets recommendations. Emphasis is placed on the types and proportions of these that are optimal for health.

Chapter 4, "Carbohydrates: Sugars, Starches, and Fiber," discusses the health impact of refined grains and foods high in added sugar versus whole grains and unrefined sources of sugars. Chapter 5, "Lipids," points out that Americans are not eating too much fat, but are typically choosing the wrong types of fat for a healthy diet. Chapter 6, "Proteins and Amino Acids," discusses animal and plant sources of protein and points out that either plant or animal proteins can meet protein needs, but these protein sources bring with them different combinations of nutrients. In addition to discussing how to meet protein needs, this chapter includes information on how to plan a healthy vegetarian diet.

Focus on Alcohol, discusses alcohol metabolism and the health risks associated with excessive alcohol consumption and the cardiovascular benefits associated with moderate intake.

CHAPTER 7 - "Energy Balance and Weight Management," introduces energy balance and shows how small changes in diet and behavior can alter long-term energy balance. It discusses the obesity epidemic and the effect excess body fat has on health. It presents the most up-to-date information on how body weight is regulated and the role of genetic versus environmental factors in determining body fatness. The chapter includes recommendations for healthy body weight and composition and equations for determining energy needs. It also discusses weight loss options that range from simple energy restriction to risky surgical approaches.

Focus on Eating Disorders includes a comprehensive discussion of the different types of eating disorders, their causes, consequences, and treatment. This focus also addresses the sociocultural factors that influence body ideal as well as what to do if you have a friend or relative you suspect has an eating disorder.

CHAPTER 8 - "The Water-Soluble Vitamins," begins with a general overview of the vitamins—where they are found in the diet, factors affecting their bioavailability, and how they function. Each of the B vitamins and vitamin C are then discussed individually, providing information on sources in the diet, functions in the body, impact on health, recommended intakes, use as dietary supplements, and potential for toxicity. This chapter also discusses choline, a substance that is not currently classified as a vitamin but one for which DRIs have been established.

CHAPTER 9 - "The Fat-Soluble Vitamins," introduces the fat-soluble vitamins within the context of the modern diet and then presents each one with a discussion of their sources in the diet, functions in the body, impact on health, recommended intakes, use as dietary supplements, and potential for toxicity.

Focus on Phytochemicals discusses the role of phytochemicals in nutrition and health. These substances are not dietary essentials but can positively impact health. Different categories of phytochemicals are presented, along with a discussion of how to maximize their intake.

CHAPTER 10 - "Water and the Electrolytes," addresses water, a nutrient often overlooked, and the electrolytes because they help regulate the distribution of body water. This chapter presents information on where these nutrients are found in the diet and discusses their functions in the body and their relationship to health and disease. A discussion of hypertension illustrates the importance of sodium, potassium, and other minerals and dietary components in blood pressure regulation. Advances in our understanding of how dietary patterns affect hypertension is stressed by a discussion of the DASH diet, a dietary pattern that has been shown to lower blood pressure.

CHAPTER 11 - "Major Minerals and Bone Health," discusses the remaining major minerals, calcium, phosphorus, magnesium, and sulfur. This chapter discusses their functions in the body and availability in the diet as well as their relationship to health and disease. Because most of these play an important role in bone health, this chapter also includes a section on the relationship between nutrition and the development of osteoporosis.

CHAPTER 12 - "The Trace Elements," discusses the trace elements in a format similar to that used for other micronutrients. An emphasis is placed on the unique roles of some minerals as well as the similarities that some have in their functions and the interactions that exist among them. Discussions of the health issues related to these nutrients help create interest, as do discussions of the pros and cons of trace element supplements.

Focus on Nonvitamin/Nonmineral Supplements targets dietary supplements that contain substances other than micronutrients. Micronutrient supplements are discussed in Chapters 8 through 12 with the appropriate nutrient, but many of the supplements Americans are taking include ingredients that are not vitamins or minerals. This focus will help students evaluate the benefits and risks associated with supplements containing substances such as coenzyme Q, glucosamine, and echinacea.

CHAPTER 13 - "Nutrition and Physical Activity," discusses the relationships among physical activity, nutrition, and health. It emphasizes the importance of exercise for health maintenance as well as the impact nutrition can have on exercise performance. Because nutrients fuel activity, this chapter serves as a review of energy metabolism. By this point in the text, students have studied all the essential nutrients, so a complete discussion of the macronutrients and micronutrients needed for energy metabolism can be included. An expanded discussion of ergogenic aids directs students to use a risk-benefit analysis of these products before deciding whether or not to use them.

CHAPTER 14 - "Nutrition During Pregnancy and Lactation," addresses the role of nutrition in human development by discussing the nutritional needs of women during pregnancy and lactation as well as the nutritional needs of infants. The benefits breastfeeding are discussed.

Life Cycle

CHAPTER 15 - "Nutrition from Infancy to Adolescence," begins with a discussion of the rising rates of childhood obesity and other chronic diseases and the importance of learning healthy eating habits early in life. The chapter discusses nutrient needs and how they change from infancy through adolescence.

CHAPTER 16 - "Nutrition and Aging: The Adult Years," addresses how nutrition affects health and how the physiological changes that occur with aging affect nutritional needs and the ability to meet them. The impact that chronic disease, medications, and socioeconomic changes have on the risk of malnutrition is discussed.

CHAPTER 17 - "Food Safety," discusses the risks and benefits associated with the U.S. food supply and includes information on the impact of microbial hazards, chemical toxins, food additives, irradiation, and food packaging. The directives of the Food Safety Initiative are addressed, including the use of HACCP (Hazard Analysis Critical Control Point) to ensure safe food and advanced technology to help prevent and track food-borne illness.

Focus on Biotechnology explains how plants are genetically modified and addresses the potential benefits and risks associated with this expanding technology.

CHAPTER 18 - "World Hunger and Malnutrition," discusses the coexistence of hunger and malnutrition along with obesity in both developed and developing nations around the world. It examines the causes of world hunger and solutions that can impact on the amounts and types of food and nutrients that are available.

Student Resources in WileyPLUS

Video

BBC and CBS Videos

Videos produced by BBC and CBS spark discussion and allow students to explore current and relevant topics in nutrition.

How It Works Animations

How it Works

View in your Wiley Plus
www.wileyplus.com

Wiley has developed a new set of animations for Nutrition students and professors. We surveyed professors across North America, to find out what topics were the most difficult to teach and learn and what processes were most essential to the introductory nutrition course. After much research and reviewing, we developed animations on these topics, to make these difficult processes easier for students to learn and bring the process diagrams from the book to life.

Absorption of Nutrients

Flow of Blood During Absorption

Digestion and Absorption of Carbohydrates

Glucose Metabolism

Regulation of Glucose Metabolism

Maintaining Normal Blood Glucose Levels

Blood Glucose Regulation

Digestion and Absorption of Lipids

Lipid Transport

Metabolism of Lipids

Digestion and Absorption of Proteins

Metabolism of Proteins

Role of B Vitamins in Metabolism

Action of Antioxidants Against Free Radicals

Action of Vitamins as Coenzymes

Acid-Base Balance

These animations and accompanying quiz questions are available in WileyPLUS.

iProfile

- **iProfile 2.0: Assessing Your Diet and Energy Balance** This new version of iProfile features an enhanced search engine, which allows foods to be found more easily. Available both online and on a multi-platform CD-ROM, this dynamic assessment software contains nutrient values for over 26,000 foods, including fast food and brand name products, as well as ethnic and cultural choices. If a food is not in the database, iProfile allows users to add foods to the database to keep pace with the ever-growing market of available products. To make calculating energy expenditure easier, this new software includes an easy-to-use section on physical activity. In addition to the ability to track and analyze diets and exercise, some distinctive features of the software include serving size animations, a quick self-quiz, single nutrient reports, menu planning, and a user-friendly design.
- **Energy Acquisition: The Digestive System and Metabolism 2.0** [0-471-70754-6]— This CD-ROM from the popular series, Interactions: Exploring the Functions of the Human Body, uses animations, interactivity, and clinical correlations to enhance student understanding of the difficult concepts of metabolism and the structures and functions of the digestive system.

Your Learning Styles

A questionnaire allows students to discover their preferred learning styles. This resource provides descriptions of all learning styles and study tips designed for each learning style.

Nutrition News Finder

This searchable resource provides links to nutrition-related news articles from major publications from around the world, updated every 15 minutes.

Resources for Instructors

- **Instructor Companion Website** [www.wiley.com/college/smolin]—A dedicated companion website for instructors provides many resources for preparing and presenting lectures. Included are additional Critical Thinking Exercises. Also available are all of the illustrations and tables in the text already placed within **PowerPoint Slides**, as well as a set of **Lecture PowerPoints** that combine important images with major concepts from each chapter. Questions for use with **Clicker Systems** are also provided.
- **Testbank**—Available online, the Test Bank includes multiple-choice questions as well as short case studies with questions.
- **Computerized Test Bank**—This computerized version of the Test Bank makes preparing clear, concise tests quick and easy. It is available in both Windows and Macintosh formats.
- **Nutrition Visual Library 4.0** This resource includes all of the illustrations from the textbook in labeled, unlabeled, and unlabeled with leader line formats. In addition, select illustrations and photographs from Wiley's Anatomy and Physiology textbooks are included. Search for images by chapter, or by using keywords. It is also available through WileyPLUS.

iProfile Sample Profile and Assignments

Sample Profile: Kelly Watson's 3 Days of Food Intakes and Activities

A sample profile that students and instructors can import into their own iProfile program is now available in WileyPLUS. The sample profile includes profile, food journal, and activity journal for a fictional 20-year old woman called Kelly Watson. Kelly's diet and activity habits are not perfect; her food journal is based on student food journals. WileyPLUS contains automatically gradable assessment questions about Kelly Watson's reports. Since every student report is different, using Kelly Watson's reports provides a standard way to teach and learn the concepts needed to analyze the reports from food and activity journals.

iProfile Essay Questions in WileyPLUS

Essay questions that ask about students' individual reports based on their food and activity journals are available in WileyPLUS. These essay questions ask students to reflect on their own diets and activities. For example, students are asked to look at their fiber intakes, compare it to the recommendations for fiber and suggest foods that could increase the amount of fiber in their diets.

TO THE STUDENT

Nutrition is a subject that all of you have a personal interest in, whether you are concerned about your own nutritional health, a parent with diabetes, or a friend with an eating disorder. You may enroll in a nutrition course to learn what to eat and how to choose healthy foods and then be surprised when the course talks about protein synthesis, lipid transport, and anaerobic metabolism. A good course and textbook should do both.

As authors, our goal is to provide you with tools that can be used throughout your life. We could tell you what makes a healthy breakfast, but if you didn't understand why the foods in the breakfast were healthy choices you would not be able to make healthy choices from a different set of breakfast foods or use the same principles to choose a healthy dinner. On the other hand, for example, if you understand why saturated fat affects blood cholesterol you will not forget how to choose a heart-healthy diet.

The critical thinking approach we have used in this text will help you understand the science of nutrition and give you the decision-making skills you need to navigate the scores of choices you face when deciding what to eat and which of the latest nutrition headlines to believe. By becoming a knowledgeable consumer, you will be able to make informed choices about diet and lifestyle, whether you use this information to improve your own health or to pursue a career in nutrition.

Acknowledgments

The authors wish to thank the many professors and students who helped in the development of this text. Their endless hours of careful reading and their many thoughtful suggestions from diverse viewpoints have helped to make this text the best available on today's market. In particular we wish to offer a special thank you to those who have worked on the preparation of the many support materials found on the companion websites, as well as the testbank. They are Nancy Berkoff, Los Angeles Trade Tech College; Jo Carol Chezem, Ball State University; Leonard Gerber, University of Rhode Island; Lisa Gurule, Central New Mexico Community College; Kathleen Melanson, University of Rhode Island; Elizabeth Quintana, West Virginia University; Tammy Stephenson, University of Kentucky Lexington; Sandra M. Walz, West Chester University; Catherine Weinstein, Nassau Community College; Daryle Wane, Pasco-Hernando Community College; and Shahla Wunderlich, Montclair State University.

The reviewers and focus group attendees, who offered comments and suggestions on both the presentation and the accuracy of this information, include the following:

Roger Adams, *Richland College*

Janet Anderson, *Utah State University*

Nancy Berkoff, *Los Angeles Trade Technical College*

Linda Brown, *Kaplan University/Florida State University*

Emily Boldrin, *Oklahoma State University*

Paula Cochrane, *Central New Mexico Community College*

Sylvia Crixell, *Texas State University*

George F. Estabrook, *University of Michigan*

Mary Flynn, *Brown University*

Andrea Grim, *Idaho State University*

Melissa Gutschall, *Radford University*

Theresa Han-Markey, *University of Michigan Ann Arbor*

Susan N. Hawk, *Central Washington University*

Shanil Juma, *Texas Womens' University*

Deepinder Kaur, *Wayne State University*

Amy L. Kelly, *Bradley University*

Gina Kraft, *Oklahoma Baptist University*

Colleen Loveland, *Dallas County Community College*

Mary Martinez, *Central New Mexico Community College*

Kathleen Melanson, *University of Rhode Island*

Owen Murphy, *University of Colorado Boulder*

Jillann Neely, *Onondaga Community College*

Anna M. Page, *Johnson County Community College*

Janet T. Peterson, *Linfield College*

Daniel Rowlson, *Oakland Community College*

Denise Russo, *Cabrillo College/West Valley College*

Carole Sloan, *Henry Ford Community College*

Susan Sharaga Swadener, *Cal Poly, San Luis Obispo*

Lydia Steinman, *University of Texas Austin*

Sarah Tringle, *Mississippi Gulf Coast Community College*

Elizabeth Vargo, *Community College of Allegheny County*

Daryle Wane, *Pasco Hernando Community College*

Catherine Weinstein, *Nassau Community College*

Peggie L. Williamson, *Central Texas College*

We are grateful to the editorial and production staff at John Wiley & Sons for their help and support. We thank our Executive Editor Bonnie Roesch for originally signing this book, our Senior Editor, Kevin Witt, for his enthusiasm and excitement about publishing in the field of nutrition, our Project Editor Lorraina Raccuia for the endless hours she devoted to the book, our Senior Media Editor Linda Muriello for her help with creating the media, our Executive Marketing Manager, Clay Stone, for coordinating the advertising, marketing, and sales efforts for the book and its supplements, and our Program Assistant Lauren Morris for all her help and support. We also thank our Photo Editor, Hilary Newman, for ensuring the outstanding quality of the photos in this text, our Illustration Editor, Anna Melhorn, for assuring high-quality artwork, even when last minute corrections were needed, our Design Director, Harry Nolan, for delivering an attractively designed text, our cover designer, Wendy Lai, and our Production Editors Valerie Vargas and Jeanine Furino, of Furino Production, for their patience and efficiency in guiding this project through production.

The Wiley Nutrition Advisory Board

Wiley Nutrition—Right for You!

Wiley is deeply committed to nutrition education. Through our teaching and learning materials, we aspire to excellence in nutrition by providing students with engaging resources that will help them to understand the most difficult concepts in nutrition. Our goal is to provide you and your students with the right resources for your course, such as animations that teach tough topics in nutrition. To ensure that we are producing the highest-quality resources for nutrition, we have assembled an expert advisory board to guide the direction of our materials—to review all data, art, references, and media before publication.

What Is the Nutrition Advisory Board?

The mission of the Wiley Nutrition Advisory Board (NAB) is to provide a voice that helps shape and guide Wiley's vision for nutrition and message to the intended markets.

Selected by the Wiley editorial team, NAB members are called on to participate in the following ways:

- Guide Wiley's vision for nutrition and help develop the message to the market
- Serve as expert reviewers and contributors
- Be available for phone conversations or email exchanges on specific topics
- Contribute ideas and resources for best practices initiative and faculty development
- Oversee the accuracy of our nutrition products, including review of manuscript, scientific art, and supplements
- Align textbook learning objectives with course and discipline objectives
- Assist in the development of animation storyboards

NAB Members

NANCY BERKOFF
California State University–Los Angeles and Los Angeles Trade Technical College

LINDA BROWN
Florida State University and Kaplan

The Wiley Nutrition Advisory Board

JAYNE L. BYRNE
*College of St. Benedict/
St. John's University*

SYLVIA CRIXELL
Texas State University

KAREN ISRAEL
*Anne Arundel
Community College*

SHANIL JUMA
Texas Women's University

YOUNGHEE KIM
Bowling Green University

OWEN MURPHY
University of Colorado

JUDY MYHAND
Louisiana State University

JOHN ORTA
*California State
University–Los Angeles*

JANET PETERSON
Linfield College

DIANA SPILLMAN
University of Ohio–Miami

PRIYA VENKATASEN
Pasadena City College

SHAHLA WUNDERLICH
Montclair State University

Brief Contents

Contents

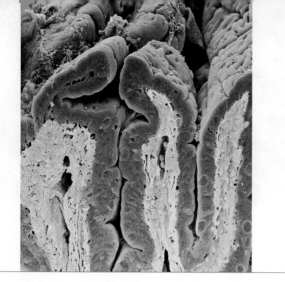

3 Digestion, Absorption, and Metabolism   76

10   Water and the Electrolytes   426

11   Major Minerals and Bone Health   456

13 Nutrition and Physical Activity 536

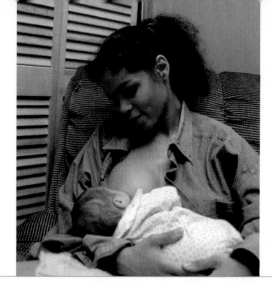

14 Nutrition During Pregnancy
and Lactation   582

17 Food Safety   700

Nutrition: Science and Applications

Second Edition

1 Nutrition:

Food for Health

Case Study

Kaitlyn knew the potato chips in the dorm vending machine weren't a good choice—but aside from candy, they were her only option. Kaitlyn had been in classes and at work until late in the evening. When she finally sat down to study, she realized that she had missed dinner. She needed to eat something to keep her going until she finished that chapter in her nutrition book, but her dorm offered few food choices late at night. So she opted for the chips and fruit punch from the vending machine—they seemed to be the healthiest choices available.

As a college freshman away from home for the first time, Kaitlyn has gained a few pounds and is beginning to be concerned about her weight. Her father recently had cardiac bypass surgery, and her mother takes medication for high blood pressure. Kaitlyn knows that because of this family history, her diet is a particularly important part of her future health. The dorm cafeteria, although not great, does offer a variety of choices. The problem is that Kaitlyn doesn't know how to choose a healthy diet. She tries to keep some healthy snacks in her dorm room, but her options are limited because she doesn't have a refrigerator. Several of her friends have started taking supplements like Mega B to give them more energy and ginkgo biloba to improve their memories. Kaitlyn is tempted to start taking them herself but remembers that her high school soccer coach told her that some supplements can be dangerous. To optimize her health Kaitlyn needs to learn the basics of nutrition science and perfect the art of making nutritionally sound decisions and healthy food choices—a goal that is a little overwhelming at first.

(PhotoAlto/Sigrid Olsson/Getty Images, Inc.)

(©iStockphoto)

(M. Elsing Food Photography/StockFood America)

1.1 Nutrition and the Modern Diet

Learning Objectives

- Discuss how American eating habits have changed over the past 50 years.
- Compare Americans' intake of milk, vegetables, and fruit to recommendations for a healthy diet.

nutrition A science that studies the interactions that occur between living organisms and food.

nutrients Chemical substances in foods that provide energy and structure and help regulate body processes.

Nutrition is a science that studies all the interactions that occur between living organisms and food. Food provides **nutrients** and energy, which are needed to keep us alive and healthy, to support growth, and to allow reproduction. Sometimes, however, fast-paced lifestyles and food choices made available through modern technology contribute to a diet that contains too much or too little of some of the nutrients we need (**Figure 1.1**).

The Changing American Food Supply

For much of human history, in order to get enough to eat people needed to spend most of their day obtaining food ingredients and preparing meals. Even 100 years ago, the time spent for meal preparation was measured in hours—hours spent peeling, chopping, baking, roasting, stewing, and then cleaning. Today, a microwavable dinner that includes meat, rice, vegetables, and dessert can be ready in 5 minutes.

Our modern food supply includes an endless assortment of eating options. Many of these choices are foods that have been part of the human diet for centuries—fresh fruits and vegetables, meats, and grains. But others are newer additions—frozen vegetables, canned soups, packaged meats, frozen prepared meals, and snack foods. Fifty years ago people ate most of their meals at home, with their families, at a leisurely pace. Today more single-parent households and families with both parents working means the woman of the house is no longer at home in the afternoon preparing meals and waiting for the kids to come home from school. After-school activities often impinge on family meal times. Few young adults even know how to prepare a full meal and shoppers of all ages are choosing to buy more convenient, **processed foods** that can be boiled or microwaved rather than raw ingredients that need to be chopped, seasoned, and cooked. The increase in the availability and variety of processed foods has made it easier and quicker to get something to eat. Meals that used to take hours can be prepared in minutes. A multitude of convenient snack foods are available to keep us full and replace missed meals. In addition, Americans today are replacing more and more home-cooked meals with meals from fast food restaurants.[1]

processed foods Foods that have been specially treated or changed from their natural state.

These changes in the American food supply have made it easier and faster to obtain a meal or snack but they have not necessarily improved our nutritional health. Over the past century the major nutrition concerns in the United States have shifted from providing enough nutrients to meet people's needs to limiting overconsumption and the chronic diseases related to excesses of energy and certain nutrients (see Your Choice: Convenience Has Its Costs).

Figure 1.1 The availability of fast food has changed the American diet, but at what price? (Jeff Greenberg/ Age Fotostock America, Inc.)

(©iStockphoto)

Convenience Has Its Costs

It's Monday morning, and you're exhausted. As you lie in bed, you decide that you'll stop for a muffin and coffee on your way to school to save a couple of minutes. You won't have to turn on your coffee pot, wait for the toaster, or clean up after you eat. But what is the cost of this convenience?

You may pay a higher price than you think, in terms of both dollars and nutrition. At home you might pour yourself an 8-ounce mug of coffee with whole milk and sugar, which would cost about 20 cents and provide about 50 kcalories along with a little protein and calcium. Toast or an English muffin with butter would add about 30 cents to the cost, along with 150 kcalories and some B vitamins and iron. If instead you stop for a 16-ounce mocha and a healthy-looking bran muffin at Dunkin' Donuts or the corner coffee bar, you will spend around $4.00 and ingest about 850 kcalories without getting many more nutrients than the toast and coffee at home would provide. The impact of stopping for coffee and a muffin once in a while when you are running late is minimal, but making it an everyday habit can break your dollar and kcalorie budget.

The cost of convenience as measured in money and kilocalories applies to any meal or snack you eat out. For lunch, a homemade turkey sandwich would cost about $2.00 and provide approximately 320 kcalories. A 12-inch sub from the shop on the corner, in comparison, costs two or three times as much and may contain an additional 500 kcalories—even more if you add a soft drink and cookie. Dropping $2.00 into the vending machine for an afternoon snack will get you a soft drink and a bag of chips, for a total of more than 300 kcalories with few vitamins or minerals. Instead, a snack of fruit and baby carrots from

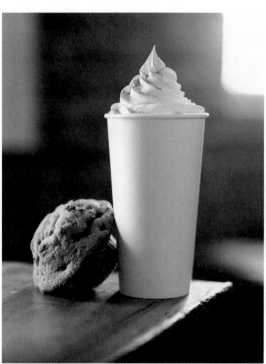

(P. Mittongtare/FoodPix/Jupiter Images Corp)

home costs only about 50 cents and provides an assortment of essential nutrients for only about 100 kcalories. Although the modern American lifestyle tempts us with convenience, we need to consider the costs to our wallets and our waistlines.

How Healthy is the American Diet?

The American diet isn't as healthy as it could be. As it has become easier to obtain and prepare food, the amount of food consumed has increased.[2] American adults eat more kcalories than they did 30 years ago, primarily due to larger portion sizes, especially from fast foods, and an increase in the consumption of salty snacks, soft drinks, and pizza.[3] Americans today get 32% of their kcalories from meals eaten away from home; these meals tend to be higher in kcalories than foods prepared at home.[4]

In addition to eating more kcalories than we need, we are not eating enough of the foods that make up a healthy diet. Recommendations suggest a diet based on whole grains, vegetables, and fruits, with smaller amounts of low-fat dairy products and lean meats and limited amounts of sweets and certain types of fats. As a population, we don't eat enough whole grains, **legumes**, fruits, or dairy foods. We frequently

legumes The starchy seeds of plants belonging to the pea family; includes peas, peanuts, beans, soybeans, and lentils.

choose potatoes, often fried, for a vegetable but consume few nutrient-rich dark green and deep yellow vegetables. Our diets are high in snack foods and desserts that supply us with more salt and sugar than is recommended (**Table 1.1**).[1,5] Instead of milk we are choosing sweetened beverages, especially carbonated soft drinks.[1,6] This dietary pattern along with a lack of physical activity increases the risk of developing chronic diseases, such as diabetes, obesity, heart disease, and cancer, which are the major causes of illness and death in our population.[7] It has been estimated that over 16% of all deaths in the United States can be attributed to a poor diet and a sedentary lifestyle (**Figure 1.2**).[8] Recommendations for reducing disease risk focus on changes in the foods we choose and the amount of exercise we get.[5,9]

Table 1.1 How Healthy Is the Typical American Diet?

Recommended Diet	Typical Diet
Eat 6 to 11 servings of grains daily—half should be whole grains.	50% do not eat even 6 servings. Most people only eat 1 serving of whole grains.
Eat 3 to 5 servings of vegetables daily—include legumes, leafy greens, and yellow-orange vegetables.	59% do not meet recommendations—33% of vegetable servings are white potatoes, only 3% are leafy greens, and 6% are legumes.
Have 2 to 4 servings of fruit daily.	76% do not meet recommendations—48% do not eat any fruit at all.
Consume 2 to 3 dairy servings daily.	77% of all people and 80% of women do not meet recommendations.
Eat 2 to 3 servings of meat or a total of only 5 to 7 ounces.	52% of men and 25% of women consume more servings than recommended.
Consume less than 30% of your kcalories from fat and limit added sugars.	The typical diet contains 33% fat and includes 19 teaspoons of added sugars per day.

Source: Adapted from Cleveland, L. E., Cook, A. J., Wilson, J. E., et al. Pyramid Servings Data, ARS Food Survey Research Group. Available online at www.barc.usda.gov/bhnrc/foodsurvey/home.htm/. Accessed January 25, 2006.

A healthy diet does not need to exclude processed convenience foods, but it must involve wise choices. To choose a healthy diet that provides the right amounts of energy and each nutrient, we need to understand how our bodies obtain nutrients from food, which nutrients are essential, how much we need, and which foods provide healthy sources of nutrients. We also need to recognize which nutrition information to believe.

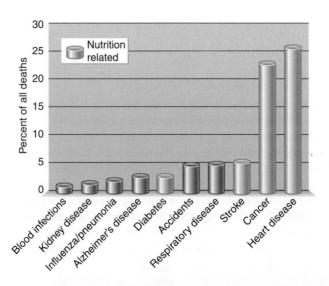

Figure 1.2 Leading causes of death

Of the ten leading causes of death in the United States, the top three are nutrition-related.

1.2 Food Provides Nutrients

Learning Objectives

* Define the term *essential nutrient* and list the six classes of nutrients.
* Describe the three general functions of nutrients.
* Define *malnutrition*.

To date, approximately 45 nutrients have been determined to be essential to human life. **Essential nutrients** must be supplied in the diet to support life; they either cannot be made by the body or cannot be made in large enough quantities to meet needs. For example, our bodies cannot synthesize vitamin C, but we need it to stay healthy. If we do not consume vitamin C in the foods we eat we will begin to show signs of a vitamin C deficiency. If not added back to the diet, vitamin C deficiency will eventually be fatal.

Our intake of essential nutrients is determined by our food choices. Some foods are naturally high in nutrients and some contain nutrients added during processing. Foods to which nutrients have been added are called **fortified foods**. Some fortified foods like milk with added vitamin A and grains with added B vitamins and iron have been a part of our food supply for decades. The purpose of this fortification is to eliminate nutrient deficiencies in the population, and the amounts and types of nutrients added to these foods are specified by government fortification programs. Other fortified foods, such as orange juice with added calcium and flavored water with added vitamins and minerals, are not part of mandated fortification programs. These nutrients are added to increase sales by meeting consumer demand for nutrient-rich foods. The amounts and types of nutrients added to these foods are at the discretion of the manufacturer. **Dietary supplements** are another source of nutrients in the American food supply. National surveys indicate that over 50% of adults in the United States take some type of vitamin or mineral supplement to boost their nutrient intake.[10]

In addition to nutrients, food contains substances that are needed by the body but are not essential in the diet. Lecithin, for example, is a substance found in egg yolks that is needed for nerve function. It is not considered an essential nutrient because it can be manufactured in the body in adequate amounts. The diet also contains substances that are not made by the body and are not necessary for life, but that have health-promoting properties. Those that come from plants are called **phytochemicals**; those that come from animal foods are called **zoochemicals**. For example, a phytochemical found in broccoli called sulforaphane is not essential in the diet but has effects in the body that may help reduce the risk of cancer.

Classes of Nutrients

Chemically, there are six classes of nutrients: carbohydrates, lipids, proteins, water, vitamins, and minerals. These classes can be grouped in a variety of ways—by whether they provide energy to the body, by how much is needed in the diet, and by their chemical structure. Carbohydrates, lipids, and proteins provide energy and thus are referred to as **energy-yielding nutrients**. Alcohol also provides energy but is not considered a nutrient because it is not needed to support life (see Focus on Alcohol). Along with water, the energy-yielding nutrients constitute the major portion of most foods and are required in relatively large amounts by the body. Therefore, they are referred to as **macronutrients** (*macro* means large). Their requirements are measured in kilograms (kg) or grams (g). Vitamins and minerals are classified as **micronutrients**, because they are needed in small amounts in the diet (*micro* means small). The amounts required are expressed in milligrams (1 mg = 1/1000 g) or micrograms (1 μg = 1/1,000,000 g) (see Appendix N). Structurally, carbohydrates, proteins, lipids, and vitamins are **organic molecules** so they are referred to as organic nutrients. Minerals and water are **inorganic molecules** so they are referred to as inorganic nutrients.

---

essential nutrients Nutrients that must be provided in the diet because the body either cannot make them or cannot make them in sufficient quantities to satisfy its needs.

fortified foods Foods to which one or more nutrients have been added.

dietary supplement A product intended for ingestion in the diet that contains one or more of the following: vitamins, minerals, plant-derived substances, amino acids, or concentrates or extracts.

phytochemicals Substances found in plant foods (*phyto* means plant) that are not essential nutrients but may have health-promoting properties.

zoochemicals Substances found in animal foods (*zoo* means animal) that are not essential nutrients but may have health-promoting properties.

energy-yielding nutrients Nutrients that can be metabolized to provide energy in the body.

macronutrients Nutrients needed by the body in large amounts. These include water and the energy-yielding nutrients; carbohydrates, lipids, and proteins.

micronutrients Nutrients needed by the body in small amounts. These include vitamins and minerals.

organic molecules Those containing carbon bonded to hydrogen.

inorganic molecules Those containing no carbon-hydrogen bonds.

kilocalorie (kcalorie, kcal)
The unit of heat that is used to express the amount of energy provided by foods. It is the amount of heat required to raise the temperature of 1 kilogram of water 1 degree Celsius (1 kcalorie = 4.18 kjoules).

kilojoule (kjoule, kJ)
A unit of work that can be used to express energy intake and energy output. It is the amount of work required to move an object weighing 1 kilogram a distance of 1 meter under the force of gravity (4.18 kjoules = 1 kcalorie).

Nutrition Facts

Serving Size 1 cup (236ml)
Servings Per Container 1

Amount Per Serving

Calories 120   Calories from Fat 45

            % Daily Value*

Total Fat 5g   **8%**

   Saturated Fat 3g   **15%**

   Trans Fat 0g

Cholesterol 20   **7%**

Figure 1.3 Kilocalories on food labels
The "Calories" listed near the top of the Nutrition Facts panel of a food label technically refers to the number of kilocalories (kcalories) in a serving.

The Energy-Yielding Nutrients The energy provided by carbohydrates, lipids, and proteins is measured in **kilocalories** (abbreviated as kcalories or kcals) or in **kilojoules** (abbreviated as kjoules or kJs). The more common term, "calorie," is technically 1/1000 of a kilocalorie, but when it is spelled with a capital "C," it indicates kilocalories. For instance, the term "Calories" on food labels actually refers to kilocalories (**Figure 1.3**). However, in the popular press, the term "calorie" (small "c") is often used to express the kcalorie content of a food or diet.

Carbohydrates provide a readily available source of energy to the body. They contain 4 kcalories per gram (**Table 1.2**). Carbohydrates include sugars such as those in table sugar, fruit, and milk, and starches such as those in vegetables and grains. Sugars are the simplest form of carbohydrate, and starches are more complex carbohydrates made of many sugars linked together (**Figure 1.4**). Most fiber is also carbohydrate. Fiber cannot be digested and therefore provides very little energy. However, it is important for gastrointestinal health. Fiber is found in vegetables, fruits, legumes, and whole grains.

Lipids, commonly called fats and oils, provide 9 kcalories per gram. They are a concentrated source of energy in food and a lightweight storage form of energy in the body. There are several types of lipids that are important in nutrition. Triglycerides are the type that is most abundant in foods and in the body. The fat on the outside of a steak, the butter and oil that is added to food during cooking, and the layer of fat under a person's skin are all comprised almost entirely of triglycerides. Triglycerides are made up of fatty acids (see Figure 1.4). Different types of fatty acids have different health effects. Diets high in saturated fatty acids increase the risk of heart disease whereas those high in monounsaturated and polyunsaturated fatty acids may reduce risks. Cholesterol is another type of lipid; high levels in the blood can increase heart disease risk (see Chapter 5).

Protein is needed for growth and maintenance of body structures and regulation of body processes. It can also be used to provide energy—4 kcalories per gram. Meat, fish, poultry, milk, grains, vegetables, and legumes all provide protein. Like carbohydrate and lipid, protein is not a single substance. There are thousands of different proteins in the human body and in the diet. All of these are made up of units called amino acids. Different combinations of amino acids are linked together to form different types of proteins (see Figure 1.4). Some amino acids can be made by the body, and others are essential in the diet. The proteins in animal products better match our need for amino acids than do plant proteins but, both plant and animal proteins can provide all the amino acids we need.

Water Water is a nutrient in a class by itself. It is a macronutrient that does not provide energy. Water makes up about 60% of the human body by weight and is required in kilogram amounts in the daily diet. Water serves many functions in the body, including acting as a lubricant, a transport fluid, and a regulator of body temperature.

Micronutrients Vitamins and minerals are needed in small amounts. Vitamins are organic molecules that do not provide energy, but are needed to regulate body processes. Thirteen substances have been identified as vitamins. Each has a unique structure and provides a unique function in the body. Many are involved in providing energy from carbohydrates, lipids, and proteins; others function in processes

Table 1.2 Energy Provided by Macronutrients and Alcohol

	Kcalories/Gram	Kjoules/Gram
Carbohydrate	4	16.7
Protein	4	16.7
Lipid	9	37.6
Alcohol	7	29.3

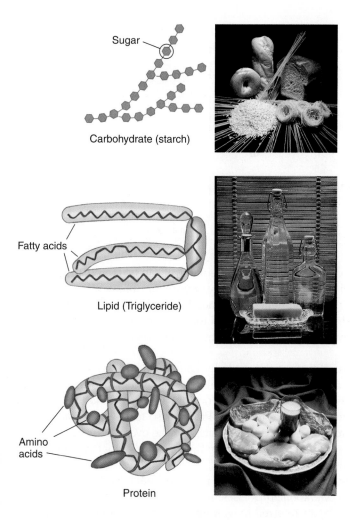

Figure 1.4
Carbohydrates, lipids, and proteins
Starches are a type of carbohydrate made of sugars linked together; most lipids, such as the triglyceride shown here, contain fatty acids; proteins are made of amino acids linked together. (Photographs, Charles D. Winters)

such as bone growth, vision, blood clotting, oxygen transport, and tissue growth and development.

Minerals are inorganic molecules. Like vitamins they do not provide energy. Many have regulatory roles and some are important structurally. They are needed for bone strength, the transport of oxygen, the transmission of nerve impulses, and numerous other functions. Requirements have been established for many of the minerals, but some are required in such small amounts that their role in maintaining health is still not fully understood.

Vitamins and minerals are found in most foods. Fresh foods are a good natural source and many processed foods are fortified with vitamins and minerals. Food processing and preparation can also cause vitamin losses because some are destroyed by exposure to light, heat, and oxygen. Minerals are more stable but can still be lost along with vitamins in the water used in cooking and processing. Nevertheless, frozen, canned, and otherwise processed foods can still be good sources of micronutrients.

Functions of Nutrients

Together, the macronutrients and micronutrients provide energy, structure, and regulation, which are needed for growth, maintenance and repair, and reproduction. Each nutrient provides one or more of these functions, but all nutrients together are needed to maintain health.

Providing Energy Inside the body, biochemical reactions release the energy contained in carbohydrates, lipids, and proteins. Some of this energy is used to synthesize new compounds and maintain basic body functions, some is used to fuel physical activity, and some is lost as heat. When the energy in the carbohydrates, lipids, and

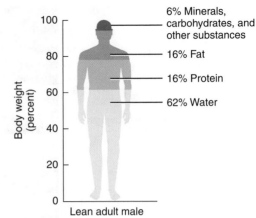

Figure 1.5 Composition of the human body
Water, protein, and fat are the most abundant nutrients in the human body.

proteins consumed in the diet is not needed immediately it can be stored, primarily as fat. These stores can provide energy when dietary sources are unavailable. Over the long term, if more energy is consumed than is needed, body stores get larger, and body weight increases. If less energy is consumed than is needed, the body will burn its stores to meet its energy needs, and body weight will decrease.

Forming Structures Most of the weight of the human body is due to water, protein, and fat (**Figure 1.5**). These nutrients, along with minerals, are needed to form and maintain the shape and structure of the body. Proteins form the ligaments and tendons that hold bones together and attach muscles to bones. Protein also forms the framework of bones and teeth that is hardened by mineral deposits, and the overall structure of muscles. At the cellular level, lipids and proteins make up the membranes that surround cells.

Regulating Body Processes Together all of the reactions that occur in the body are referred to as **metabolism**. Metabolic processes must be regulated to maintain a stable environment inside the body, referred to as **homeostasis**. All six classes of nutrients have important regulatory roles (**Table 1.3**). For example, water helps to regulate body temperature. When body temperature increases, water lost through sweat helps to cool the body. Proteins, vitamins, and minerals help to speed up or slow down the reactions of metabolism as needed to maintain homeostasis.

metabolism The sum of all the chemical reactions that take place in a living organism.

homeostasis A physiological state in which a stable internal body environment is maintained.

Table 1.3 Examples of Nutrient Functions in the Body

Function	Nutrient	Example
Energy	Carbohydrate	Glucose is a carbohydrate that provides energy to body cells.
	Lipid	Fat is the most plentiful source of stored energy in the body.
	Protein	Protein consumed in excess of protein needs will be used for energy.
Structure	Lipid	Lipids are the principal component of the membranes that surround each cell.
	Protein	Protein in connective tissue holds bones together and holds muscles to bones. Protein in muscles defines their shape.
	Minerals	Calcium and phosphorus are minerals that harden teeth and bones.
Regulation	Lipid	Estrogen is a lipid hormone that helps regulate the female reproductive cycle.
	Protein	Leptin is a protein that helps regulate the size of body fat stores.
	Carbohydrate	Sugar chains attached to proteins circulating in the blood signal whether the protein should remain in the blood or be removed by the liver.
	Water	Water in sweat helps cool the body to regulate body temperature.
	Vitamins	B vitamins regulate the use of macronutrients for energy.
	Minerals	Sodium is a mineral that helps regulate blood volume.

Nutrition and Health

What we eat has an enormous impact on how much we weigh, how healthy we are now, and how likely we are to develop chronic diseases like heart disease and diabetes in the future. Consuming either too little or too much of one or more nutrients or energy can cause **malnutrition**. Malnutrition can affect our health today and can impact on our health 20, 30, or 40 years from now.

malnutrition Any condition resulting from an energy or nutrient intake either above or below that which is optimal.

Dietary Deficiencies **Undernutrition** is a form of malnutrition caused by a deficiency of energy or nutrients. It may be caused by a deficient intake, increased requirements, or an inability to absorb or use nutrients. Starvation, the most severe form of undernutrition, is a deficiency of energy that causes weight loss, poor growth, the inability to reproduce, and if severe enough, death (**Figure 1.6a**). Deficiencies of individual nutrients can also cause serious health problems. These health problems often reflect the body functions that rely on the deficient nutrient. For example, vitamin A is necessary for vision; a deficiency of vitamin A can result in blindness. Vitamin B_{12} is needed for normal nerve function. A deficiency of this vitamin, which is more common in older adults because absorption often decreases with age, causes changes in mental status.

undernutrition Any condition resulting from an energy or nutrient intake below that which meets nutritional needs.

Some nutrient deficiencies cause symptoms quickly. In only a matter of hours an athlete exercising in hot weather may become dehydrated due to a deficiency of water. Drinking water relieves the headache, fatigue, and dizziness caused by dehydration almost as rapidly as these symptoms appeared. Other nutritional deficiencies may take weeks, months, or even years to become apparent. The symptoms of the vitamin C deficiency disease scurvy do not occur until the diet has been deficient in vitamin C for weeks or months. Too little calcium in the teenage years causes no immediate symptoms but can cause bones to be weak and break too easily when people reach their fifties or sixties.

Dietary Excesses **Overnutrition**, an excess of energy or nutrients, is also a form of malnutrition. When excesses of specific nutrients are consumed, an adverse or toxic reaction may occur. For example, a single excessive dose of iron can cause liver failure and too much vitamin B_6 over a few weeks or months can cause nerve damage. Most nutrient toxicities are due to excessive intakes of vitamin and mineral supplements. Foods generally do not contain high enough concentrations of nutrients to cause toxic reactions.

overnutrition Poor nutritional status resulting from an energy or nutrient intake in excess of that which is optimal for health.

The kinds of overnutrition that are most common in the United States today do not have immediate toxic effects but contribute to the development of chronic diseases in the long term. Diets providing more energy than needed have resulted in a population where over 65% of adults are overweight (**Figure 1.6b**).[11] Diets high in

(a)   (b)

Figure 1.6 Malnutrition includes both (a) undernutrition and (b) overnutrition. (Photo on left, Tom Koene/Peter Arnold, Inc. Photo on right, Stockbyte/Getty Images, Inc.)

The genes you inherit may give you a greater or lesser tendency to develop conditions like obesity, heart disease, high blood pressure, or diabetes.

The nutrients and food components you consume and the amount of exercise you get can increase or decrease your risk of developing nutrition-related diseases.

Figure 1.7 Diet and genes
Your actual risk of disease results from the interplay between the genes you inherit and the diet and lifestyle choices you make.

salt contribute to high blood pressure. Diets high in saturated fat and cholesterol play a role in heart disease. Diets high in sugar and other refined carbohydrates are associated with an increased risk of diabetes, and diets high in red meats and saturated fats and low in fruits and vegetables and fiber may increase the risk of colon cancer.[12]

Diet–Gene Interactions

Diet affects your health, but diet alone does not determine whether you will develop a particular disease. Each of us inherits a unique combination of **genes**. Some of these genes affect your risk of developing chronic diseases such as heart disease, cancer, high blood pressure, and diabetes, but their impact is affected by what you eat (**Figure 1.7**). Your genetic makeup determines the impact a certain nutrient will have on you. For example, some people inherit a combination of genes that results in a tendency to have high blood pressure. When these individuals consume even an average amount of sodium, their blood pressure increases (discussed further in Chapter 10). Others inherit genes that allow them to consume more sodium without a rise in blood pressure. Those whose genes dictate a rise in blood pressure with a high-sodium diet can reduce their blood pressure, and the complications associated with high blood pressure, by eating a diet that is low in sodium.

Our increasing understanding of human genetics has given rise to the discipline of **nutritional genomics** or **nutrigenomics**, which explores the interaction between genetic variation and nutrition.[13] This research has led to the development of the concept of "personalized nutrition," the idea that a diet based on the genes an individual has inherited can be used to prevent, moderate, or cure chronic disease. Although today we do not know enough to take a sample of your DNA and use it tell you what to eat to optimize your health, we do know that certain dietary patterns can reduce the risk of many chronic diseases.

genes Units of a larger molecule called DNA that are responsible for inherited traits.

nutritional genomics or **nutrigenomics** The study of how diet affects our genes and how individual genetic variation can affect the impact of nutrients or other food components on health.

1.3 Food Choices for a Healthy Diet

Learning Objectives

- List factors other than nutrition that affect food choices.
- Explain the importance of variety, balance, and moderation in selecting a healthy diet.

Each of the food choices we make contributes to our diet as a whole. This diet must provide enough energy to fuel the body and all the essential nutrients and other food components—in the right proportions—to prevent deficiencies, promote health, and protect against chronic disease. No single food choice is good or bad in and of itself, but all of our choices combined make up a dietary pattern that is either healthy or not so healthy.

Factors that Affect Food Choices

There are hundreds of food choices to make and hundreds of reasons for making them (**Figure 1.8**). Even though the foods we eat provide the nutrients and energy necessary to maintain health, the foods we choose are not necessarily determined by the nutrients these foods contain. Our food choices and food intake are affected not only by nutrient needs but also by what is available to us, where we live, what is within our budget and compatible with our lifestyle, what we like, what is culturally acceptable, what our emotional and psychological needs are, and what we think we should eat.

Figure 1.8 What factors influence the foods you purchase at the supermarket? (Marnie Burkhart/ Masterfile)

Availability The food available to an individual or a population is affected by geography, socioeconomics, and health status. Geography is important in developing parts of the world, where dietary choices are often limited to foods produced locally. Nutrients that are lacking in local foods will be lacking in the population's diet. This is less of a factor in more developed countries, because the ability to store, transport, and process food allows year-round access to seasonal foods and foods grown and produced at distant locations (**Figure 1.9**).

Even if foods are available in the store, it doesn't mean that they are available to all individuals. Socioeconomic factors such as income level, living conditions, and lifestyle as well as education affect the types and amounts of foods that are available. Individuals with limited incomes can choose only the types and amounts of foods that they can afford. Individuals who don't own cars can only purchase what they can carry home. Those without refrigerators or stoves are limited in what foods can be prepared at home. And those who can't or don't have time to cook are limited to prepared foods and restaurant meals.

Health status also affects the availability of food. People who cannot carry heavy packages are limited in what they can purchase. People with food allergies, digestive problems, and dental disease are limited in the foods that are safe and comfortable for them to eat. People consuming special diets to manage disease conditions are limited to foods that meet their dietary prescriptions.

Figure 1.9 The fresh produce you buy in your local store may come from across the street or across the ocean. (David Frazier/ Stone/Getty Images)

Cultural and Family Background Food preferences and eating habits are learned as part of each individual's family, cultural, national, and social background. They are among the oldest and most entrenched features of every culture. In Japan rice is the focus of the meal, whereas in Italy pasta is included with every meal. Curries characterize Indian cuisine and we expect refried beans and tortillas when we go out for Mexican food. The foods we are exposed to as children influence what foods we buy and cook as adults. If your mother never served artichokes or Swiss chard you may not consider eating them as an adult. If you grew up in Asia or Africa, you might consider grasshoppers or termites an acceptable food choice, but in American culture insects are considered food contaminants (**Figure 1.10**). If you didn't grow up in a culture that eats insects you may be unwilling to try them now.

What would a birthday be without a cake, or Thanksgiving without a turkey? Each of us associates holidays such as Christmas, Easter, Passover, New Year's Day, and Kwanza with specific foods that are traditional in our family, religion, and culture. Seventh-Day Adventists are vegetarians; Jews and Muslims do not eat pork; Sikhs and Hindus do not eat beef. Even for those who choose not to observe religious dietary rules, habit may dictate many mealtime decisions. Jewish kosher laws prohibit the consumption of meat and milk in the same meal. Often Jews who do not follow kosher law as adults may choose not to serve milk at dinner because they never had it as children.

Figure 1.10 A plate of silkworms such as these being sold in a Vietnamese market may not seem very appetizing to you, but insects are a part of the diet in many parts of the world. (AFP/Getty Images)

Social Acceptability In addition to being part of our cultural heritage, food is the centerpiece of our everyday social interactions. We get together with friends for a meal or for a cup of coffee and dessert. The dinner table is often the focal point for communication within the family—a place where the experiences of the day are shared. Social events dictate our food choices in a number of ways. When invited to a friend's house for dinner we may eat foods we don't like out of politeness to our hosts. We sometimes alter our food choices because of peer pressure. For exmple, an adolescent may feel that stopping for a cheeseburger or taco after school is an important part of being accepted by his or her peers.

Video

Personal Preference We eat what we like. Tradition, religion, and social values may dictate what foods we consider appropriate, but personal preferences for taste, smell, appearance, and texture affect which foods we actually consume. How would you feel about giving up your favorite foods? Probably not too good, and you are not alone. Even though most Americans understand that nutrition is important to their health, many do not choose a healthy diet because they don't want to give up their favorite foods and they don't want to eat foods they don't like.[14] Personal convictions also affect food choices; a vegetarian would not choose a meal that contains meat, and an environmentalist may not buy foods packaged in non-recyclable containers.

Psychological and Emotional Factors Food represents comfort, love, and security. We learn to associate food with these feelings as infants suckling while cradled in our mothers' arms. As children and as adults, comfort foods such as hot tea and chicken soup help us to feel better when we are sick (**Figure 1.11**). We use food as a reward when we are good—A's on a report card are celebrated with an ice cream cone. We sometimes take away food as punishment—a child who misbehaves is sent to bed without dinner. We consider ourselves good when we eat healthy foods and bad when we order a decadent dessert. We celebrate milestones and reward life's accomplishments with food. Food may also be an expression and a moderator of mood and emotional states. When we are upset some of us turn to chocolate or overeat in general while others eat less or stop eating altogether.

Health Concerns An individual's perceptions of what makes a healthy diet affect their food and nutrition choices. For example, someone may choose low-carbohydrate foods if they believe that these choices will help them lose weight. They may limit red meat intake to reduce their risk of heart disease, or they may purchase organically produced foods if they believe that reducing pesticide exposure will prevent illness. In a recent survey of attitudes about diet and nutrition, 43% of respondents said that they have made changes in their eating behavior to achieve a healthful, nutritious diet and 38% felt they knew what healthy eating was but for one reason or another were not able to do it.[14]

Figure 1.11 What foods make you feel better when you are sad, tired, or lonely? (Masterfile)

nutrient density An evaluation of the nutrient content of a food in comparison to the kcalories it provides.

Choosing a Healthy Diet

A healthy diet is one that provides the right amount of energy to keep weight in the desirable range; the proper types and balance of carbohydrates, proteins, and fats; plenty of water; and sufficient but not excessive amounts of essential vitamins and minerals. A healthy diet is rich in nutrient-dense foods. **Nutrient density** is a measure of the nutrients a food provides compared to its energy content. Nutrient-dense foods contain more nutrients per kcalorie. For example, broccoli is more nutrient-dense than french fries (**Figure 1.12**). The broccoli is a good source of calcium, vitamin C, vitamin A, and folate and only contributes about 20 kcalories per half cup serving. The french fries provide little vitamin A and much smaller amounts of vitamin C, calcium, and folate and contribute about 80 kcalories per half cup. The french fries also provide less fiber and more fat than the broccoli. This doesn't mean you should never have french fries, but it does mean that if many of your choices throughout the day are foods that are low in nutrient density, such as soft drinks, snack foods, and baked goods, it will be hard to meet your nutrient needs. On the other hand if you

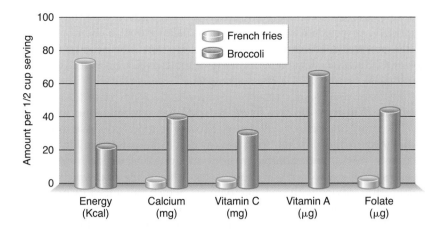

Figure 1.12 Nutrient density Choosing broccoli instead of french fries will provide fewer kcalories and more calcium, vitamin C, vitamin A, and folate.

know how to choose nutrient-dense foods you can meet all your nutrient needs and have kcalories left over for occasional treats that are low in nutrients and high in kcalories (**Table 1.4**). A healthy diet is based on variety, balance, and moderation. Using these principles you can develop a personal strategy for making better choices and maintain your health for the long term.

Table 1.4 Choices to Boost Nutrient Density

Lower Nutrient Density Choice	Higher Nutrient Density Choice
Instead of this . . .	*Have this . . .*
Soft drink	Low-fat milk
Chocolate candies	Fruit and nut trail mix
Apple pie	Fresh apple
Potato chips and sour cream dip	Baked tortilla chips and salsa
Triple fudge brownie	Oatmeal raisin cookie
Fried chicken	Roasted chicken without skin
French fries	Oven-baked potato wedges

Eat a Variety of Foods No one food can provide all the nutrients the body needs for optimal health. Eating a variety of foods, however, helps ensure an adequate nutrient intake. Variety means including grains, vegetables, fruits, dairy products, and meats in the diet. Some of these foods are rich in protein and minerals, others in vitamins and phytochemicals. All are important. Variety also means choosing many different foods from within each food group. For instance, if you choose three servings of vegetables a day and they are all carrots, it is unlikely that you will meet your nutrient needs. Carrots provide fiber and vitamin A but are a poor source of vitamin C. If instead you have carrots, peppers, and broccoli, you will be getting vitamin C along with more vitamin A, vitamin K, fiber, and phytochemicals than carrots alone would provide. Likewise, if you always choose red meat as a protein source you will be missing out on the fiber in beans and the healthy fats in nuts and fish. Variety comes not only from choosing different foods each day, but also each week, and each season. If you had apples and grapes today, have blueberries and cantaloupe tomorrow. If tomatoes don't look appetizing in the winter, replace them with a winter vegetable like squash.

Choosing a varied diet is also important because there are interactions between different foods and nutrients. These interactions may be positive, enhancing nutrient utilization, or negative, inhibiting nutrient use. For example, consuming iron with orange juice enhances iron absorption, while consuming iron with milk may reduce its absorption. In a varied diet these interactions balance out. In addition, some foods may contain natural toxins or residues of pesticides, fertilizers, and other toxic substances (see Chapter 17). Choosing a variety of foods avoids an excess of any one of these substances.

Balance Your Choices Do you like fast food? Are you someone who can't live without chocolate? Balancing your choices allows the foods you love to be included in your diet. Any food can be part of a healthy diet as long as overall intake over the course of days, weeks, and months provides enough of all of the nutrients needed without excesses of any. When you choose a food, like white rice, which is lacking in fiber, balance this choice with one, like oatmeal, which provides lots of fiber. When you choose a food that is high in fat, like chocolate, then balance that choice with a low-fat one, like a piece of fruit. Balance involves mixing and matching foods in proportions that allow you to get enough of the nutrients you need and not too much of ones that might harm your health. A balanced diet provides plenty of whole grains, fruits, and vegetables. It contains enough but not too much of each of the vitamins and minerals, as well as protein, carbohydrate, fat, and water. It also balances the energy taken in with the energy used up in daily activities so body weight stays in the healthy range (**Figure 1.13**). Balancing your choices allows foods that would not usually be considered healthy choices to fit into an overall healthy diet. For example, baked goods, snack foods, and sodas should be balanced with nutrient-dense choices such as salads, fresh fruit, and low-fat dairy products. If your favorite meal is a burger, french fries, and a milkshake, enjoy it but balance it with asparagus, brown rice, and baked chicken at the next meal. There is no such thing as a good food or a bad food—only healthy diets and unhealthy diets.

If you have a Big Mac for lunch instead of a smaller plain burger, you will have to increase your energy expenditure by 300 kcalories.

You could do this by playing golf for about a hour, carrying your own club

If you have a grande mocha frappuccino instead of a regular iced coffee, you will have to increase your energy expenditure by 370 kcalories.

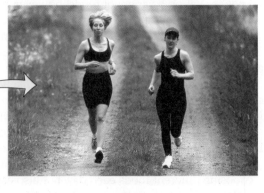

You could do this by jogging for about 30 minutes.

Figure 1.13 Balance kcalories in with kcalories out
Extra kcalories you consume during the day can be balanced by increasing the kcalories you burn in physical activity. (Top left, Andy Washnik; top right, Picturenet/Blend Images/Getty Images, Inc.; bottom left, Andy Washnik; bottom right, Kate Thompson/NG Image Collection)

Everything in Moderation Moderation means everything is okay, as long as you don't overdo it. It means watching your portions and passing up the super sizes. Have you ever sat down in front of the TV with a bag of chips and before you knew it half the bag was gone? If you have, then you know how easy it is to let portion sizes get out of control. Moderation means not consuming too much energy, too much fat, too much sugar, too much salt, or too much alcohol. Choosing moderately will help you maintain a healthy weight and help prevent some of the chronic diseases like heart disease and cancer that are on the rise in the U.S. population. The fact that more Americans are obese than ever before demonstrates that we have not been practicing moderation when it comes to energy intake. Moderation will make it easier to balance your diet and will allow you to enjoy a greater variety of foods.

1.4 Understanding Science Helps Understand Nutrition

Learning Objectives

- List the steps of the scientific method.
- Discuss experimental controls, including control groups, placebos, and blinded studies.

Nutrition, like all science, continues to develop as new discoveries provide clues to the right combination of nutrients needed for optimal health. As knowledge and technology advance, new nutrition principles are developed. Sometimes, established beliefs and concepts must give way to new ideas, and recommendations change. Today more and more consumers are seeking information about nutrition and how to improve their diets.[14] But, they may find this frustrating because the experts seem to change their minds so often. One day consumers are told margarine is better for them than butter; the next day a report says that it is just as bad. Developing an understanding of the process of science and how it is used to study the relationship between nutrition and health can help consumers make wise nutrition decisions whether it involves what to have for breakfast or whether a headline about vitamin E supplements is true.

The Scientific Method

Advances in nutrition are made using the **scientific method**. The scientific method offers a systematic, unbiased approach to evaluating the relationships among food, nutrients, and health. The first step of the scientific method is to make an observation and ask questions about the observation. The next step is to propose a **hypothesis**, or explanation for the observation. Once a hypothesis has been proposed, experiments can be designed to test it. The experiments must provide objective results that can be measured and repeated. If the experimental results do not prove the hypothesis to be wrong, a **theory**, or a scientific explanation based on experimentation, can be established. Scientific theories are accepted only as long as they cannot be disproved and continue to be supported by all new evidence that accumulates. Even a theory that has been accepted by the scientific community for years can be proved wrong.

The discovery of the relationship between nutrition and pellagra, a disease now known to be caused by a deficiency of the vitamin niacin, is an example of how the scientific method has been used to study nutrition (**Figure 1.14**). The events leading to this discovery began with the observation in 1914 that in institutions such as hospitals, orphanages, and prisons residents suffered from pellagra, but the staff did not. If pellagra was an infectious disease, both populations would be affected. The hypothesis proposed was that pellagra was due to a dietary deficiency. To test this hypothesis, nutritious foods such as fresh meats and vegetables were added to the

scientific method The general approach of science that is used to explain observations about the world around us.

hypothesis An educated guess made to explain an observation or to answer a question.

theory An explanation based on scientific study and reasoning.

Figure 1.14 The scientific method
The scientific method is a process used to ask and answer scientific questions through observation and experimentation.

residents' diet. The symptoms of pellagra disappeared, supporting the hypothesis that pellagra was due to a deficiency of something in the diet. This experiment and others led to the theory that pellagra is caused by a dietary deficiency. This theory, further developed by the discovery of the vitamin niacin, still holds today (see Chapter 9: Science Applied: Pellagra: Infectious Disease or Dietary Deficiency?).

What Makes a Good Experiment?

For the scientific method to generate reliable theories, the experiments done to test hypotheses must generate reliable results and be interpreted accurately. The first step is to understand what makes a good experiment. A well-conducted experiment must collect quantifiable data from the right experimental population and use proper experimental controls.

Quantifiable Data Scientific experiments are designed to provide measurable data that can be quantified and repeated. Measurements of body weight and blood pressure for example, are parameters that can be quantified reliably. Feelings or impressions on the other hand are more difficult to assess. Individual testimonies or opinions, referred to as anecdotal, have not been measured objectively. In order to be useful in science feelings and opinions must be quantified using standardized questionnaires. For example, if a person taking a supplement to build muscle reports that they feel stronger after taking it, this is anecdotal information that has not been quantified. However, if perceptions of strength are assessed with a questionnaire or changes in muscle mass are documented by measuring muscle mass or strength, these are objective measurements that can be quantified and repeated.

Appropriate Experimental Population For an experiment to produce useful results, the right experimental population must be studied. For example, a food or supplement that claims to improve performance in trained athletes, must be tested using trained athletes.

The number of subjects included in a study is also important. Statistical methods should be applied before a study is conducted to determine how many subjects are needed to demonstrate the effect of the experimental treatment. The number of subjects will depend on the type of study and the effect being tested. The fewer variables included in a study, the fewer experimental subjects needed to demonstrate an effect. To be successful, an experiment must show that the treatment being tested causes a result to occur more frequently than it would occur by chance. Fewer subjects are needed to demonstrate an effect that rarely occurs by chance. For example, if only one person in a million can increase his muscle mass by weight training for 4 weeks, then an experiment to see if a supplement increases muscle mass in athletes weight training for 4 weeks would require only a few subjects to demonstrate an effect. However, if 1 in 4 athletes can improve his muscle mass by weight training for 4 weeks, then many more subjects are needed to show that the supplement further increases muscle mass.

Proper Controls Experimental controls are used to ensure that each factor or **variable** studied can be compared with a known situation. A **control group** acts as a standard of comparison for the treatment being tested. A control group is treated in the same way as the experimental groups except no experimental treatment is implemented. For example, in an experiment testing the effect of a protein supplement on athletic performance the experimental group would consist of athletes consuming the supplement. An appropriate control group would consist of athletes of similar age, gender, and ability eating similar diets and following similar workout regimens, but not consuming the supplement. Both groups would have their performance measured before and after the experimental period.

In order to make the control and experimental groups indistinguishable, a **placebo** is sometimes used. A placebo is identical in appearance to the actual treatment but has no therapeutic value. If for example, in the muscle mass study described above, the experimental group is consuming a protein drink, an appropriate placebo for the control group would be a drink that looks and tastes just like the protein drink but doesn't contribute any nutrients. Using a placebo prevents participants in the experiment from knowing whether or not they are receiving the actual supplement. When the subjects do not know which treatment they are receiving, the study is called a **single-blind study**. Using a placebo in a single-blind study helps to prevent the expectations of subjects from biasing the results. For example, if the athletes think they are taking the protein supplement, they may be convinced that they are getting stronger and as a result work harder in their training and develop bigger muscles even without the supplement. Errors can also occur if investigator's expectations bias the results or the interpretation of the data. This type of error can be avoided by designing a **double-blind study** in which neither the subjects nor the investigators know who is in which group until after the results have been analyzed.

Interpretation of Experimental Results

In science, the interpretation of results is as important as the way studies are done. If the impact of a supplement on muscle strength is tested in experienced weight lifters, the study cannot conclude that it will help novices in the gym. One way to ensure that experiments are correctly interpreted is to use a peer-review system. Most scientific journals require that prior to publication, two or three experts (who did not take part in the research that is being evaluated) agree that the experiment under review was well conducted and that the results were interpreted fairly. Nutrition articles can be found in peer-reviewed journals such as the *American Journal of Clinical Nutrition*, the *Journal of Nutrition*, the *Journal of the American Dietetic Association*, the *New England Journal of Medicine*, and the *International Journal of Sport Nutrition*.

variable A factor or condition that is changed in an experimental setting.

control group A group of participants in an experiment that is identical to the experimental group except that no experimental treatment is used. It is used as a basis of comparison.

placebo A fake medicine or supplement that is indistinguishable in appearance from the real thing. It is used to disguise the control from the experimental groups in an experiment.

single-blind study An experiment in which either the study participants or the researchers are unaware of who is in a control or an experimental group.

double-blind study An experiment in which neither the study participants nor the researchers know who is in a control or an experimental group.

1.5 Nutrition Research

Learning Objectives

- Compare the type of information obtained from epidemiology to that obtained from human intervention studies.
- Explain the rationale behind balance studies and depletion-repletion studies.
- Discuss how the ethics of human and animal studies is monitored.

Nutrition research studies are done to determine nutrient requirements, to learn more about the metabolism of nutrients, and to understand the role of nutrition in health and disease. Perfect tools do not exist for addressing all these questions. However, there are many types of research studies that can be useful in understanding the relationships between humans and their nutrient intake.

Types of Nutrition Studies

Some of our nutrition knowledge has been obtained by observing relationships between diet and health in different populations throughout the world. This study of diet, health, and disease patterns is called **epidemiology**. The observations and hypotheses that arise from epidemiology can be tested using **human intervention studies** often referred to as **clinical trials**. This type of experiment actively intervenes in the lives of a population and examines the effect of this intervention.

Observational Studies Epidemiology does not determine cause and effect relationships—it just identifies patterns (**Figure 1.15**) (see Science Applied: From Seven Countries to the Mediterranean Diet). For instance, by comparing diets in different countries with the incidence of cancer, scientists were able to identify an association, or **correlation**, between diets high in fruits and vegetables and a lower incidence of cancer. Some epidemiological studies collect data from a cross section of the population at one point in time whereas others collect data from the same individuals over a long period of time.

Case-control studies are a type of epidemiological study that compares individuals with a particular condition to similar individuals without the condition. For example, a case-control study of colon cancer might include a comparison of the dietary intake of a 45-year-old African-American man with colon cancer to a man of the same age and ethnic background who is free of the disease. If a pattern, such as a higher fat intake among the cancer patients, is found in comparing cases to controls, a hypothesis can be proposed. Hypotheses based on case control studies and other types of epidemiology must then be tested by controlled intervention and laboratory studies.

epidemiology The study of the interrelationships between health and disease and other factors in the environment or lifestyle of different populations.

human intervention study or **clinical trial** A study of a population in which there is an experimental manipulation of some members of the population; observations and measurements are made to determine the effects of this manipulation.

correlation Two or more factors occurring together.

case-control study A type of observational study that compares individuals with a particular condition under study with individuals of the same age, sex, and background who do not have the condition.

Figure 1.15 Association between saturated fat intake and heart disease This graph shows that populations with high intakes of saturated fat have a higher incidence of coronary heart disease, but it does not tell us if the high incidence of heart disease is caused by the high intake of saturated fat. (Reprinted by permission of the publisher from SEVEN COUNTRIES: A MULTIVARIATE ANALYSIS OF DEATH AND CORONARY HEART DISEASE by Ancel Keys, p. 253, Cambridge, Mass.: Harvard University Press, Copyright © 1980 by the President and Fellows of Harvard College.)

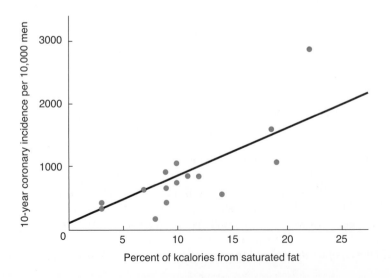

SCIENCE

ScienceAppliedScienceApplied
Science**AppliedScience**Applied
ScienceAppliedScienceApplied

APPLIED

(DAJ/Getty Images, Inc.)

(www.victorianoizquierdo.com/Getty Images, Inc.)

(Elena Schweitzer/Shutterstock)

From "Seven Countries" to the Mediterranean Diet

In 1916, Dutch physician C. D. de Langen hypothesized that a cholesterol-rich diet was associated with high blood cholesterol levels and coronary heart disease. But, it was not until the 1950s that the associations among diet, blood cholesterol, and coronary heart disease were investigated. In 1958, Professor Ancel Keys initiated the Seven Countries Study, designed to test the hypothesis that coronary heart disease was a nutritional problem related to fat intake. Between 1958 and 1964 the study enrolled 12,763 men from 40 to 59 years of age from 16 different regions within 7 countries on 3 continents.

The study evaluated health status, dietary intake, body weight, blood pressure, blood cholesterol level, and other health-related parameters at regular intervals. Patterns began to emerge. In northern European countries, the diet was high in dairy products; in the United States, it was high in meat; in southern Europe, it was high in vegetables, legumes, fish, and wine; and in Japan, it was high in cereals, soy products, and fish.[1] After 10 years, 1512 of the study participants were dead—413 of them from coronary heart disease[2]—but mortality differed strikingly with location. The Isle of Crete had only one coronary death out of 686 men studied, whereas eastern Finland had 78 coronary deaths among 817 participants.[3]

The coronary death rate was correlated with the average percentage of kcalories from saturated fat. In countries such as Japan, where the diet was low in total and saturated fat, blood cholesterol levels were lower, as was the risk of dying from heart disease. In countries such as Finland, where the diet was rich in saturated fat and cholesterol, blood cholesterol levels were higher, as was the incidence of heart disease. The results showed that blood cholesterol was strongly correlated with coronary heart disease deaths both for populations and for individuals.

A closer examination of the data revealed some paradoxes. In different populations, the same blood cholesterol level represented different degrees of cardiovascular risk. For example, someone living in northern Europe with a blood cholesterol level of 200 had five times the risk of dying of heart disease as someone with a blood cholesterol level of 200 living in Mediterranean southern Europe.[4] The data suggested that blood cholesterol was not the only risk factor in heart disease. When other dietary and lifestyle factors were examined, pat-

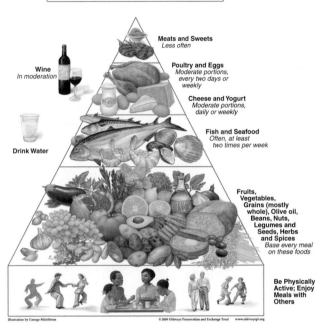

Mediterranean Diet Pyramid
A contemporary approach to delicious, healthy eating

Meats and Sweets
Less often

Wine
In moderation

Poultry and Eggs
Moderate portions, every two days or weekly

Cheese and Yogurt
Moderate portions, daily or weekly

Drink Water

Fish and Seafood
Often, at least two times per week

Fruits, Vegetables, Grains (mostly whole), Olive oil, Beans, Nuts, Legumes and Seeds, Herbs and Spices
Base every meal on these foods

Be Physically Active; Enjoy Meals with Others

Illustration by George Middleton   © 2009 Oldways Preservation and Exchange Trust   www.oldwayspt.org

terns related to the risk of coronary heart disease emerged. In southern Europe around the Mediterranean Sea—where the incidence of coronary heart disease was low—the diet was plentiful in vegetables and whole grains, and olive oil was the source of fat. In addition, the lifestyle was not stressful and wine was routinely, but not excessively, consumed with meals. This dietary pattern became known as the "Mediterranean diet."

Many features of the Mediterranean diet have been included in current population-wide recommendations for reducing the risk of coronary heart disease (see figure). The standard prescription for reducing heart disease risk includes consuming olive oil and other unsaturated oils as the source of dietary fat, including plenty of whole grains and fruits and vegetables, exercising, not smoking, and reducing stress.

After more than 50 years, subjects of the Seven Countries Study are still being studied and epidemiological data collected, analyzed, and used as the basis for countless laboratory studies and intervention trials. As more and more pieces of the coronary heart disease puzzle fall into place, scientists and government agencies no doubt will continue to modify their recommendations.

[1]Menotti, A., Kromhout, D., Blackburn, H., et al. Food intake patterns and 25-year mortality from coronary heart disease: Cross-cultural correlations in the Seven Countries Study. The Seven Countries Research Group. *Eur. J. Epidemiol.* 15:507–515, 1999.

[2]The diet and all-causes death rate in the Seven Countries Study. *Lancet* 2:58–61, 1981.

[3]Keys, A. *Seven Countries: A Multivariate Analysis of Death and Coronary Heart Disease.* A Commonwealth Fund book. Cambridge, MA: Harvard University Press, 1980.

[4]Kromhout, D. Serum cholesterol in cross-cultural perspective: The Seven Countries Study. *Acta. Cardiol.* 45:155–158, 1999.

Human Intervention Studies Nutrition intervention studies generally explore the effects that result from altering people's diets. For example, if it is determined by epidemiology that populations that eat a diet low in saturated fat have a lower incidence of heart disease, an intervention trial may be designed with an experimental group that consumes a diet lower in saturated fat than is typical in the population and a control group that consumes the typical diet. The groups can be monitored to see if the dietary intervention affects the incidence of heart disease over the long term (see Critical Thinking: Using the Scientific Method).

Laboratory Studies Laboratory studies are conducted in research facilities such as hospitals and universities. They are used to learn more about how nutrients function and to evaluate the relationships among nutrient intake, levels of nutrients in the body, and health. They may study nutrient requirements and functions in whole organisms—either humans or animals—or they may focus on nutrient functions at the cellular, biochemical, or molecular levels.

Studies Using Whole Organisms Many nutrition studies are done by feeding a specific diet to a person or animal and monitoring the physiological effects of that diet. **Depletion-repletion studies** are a classic method for studying the functions of nutrients and estimating the requirement for a particular nutrient. This type of study involves depleting a nutrient by feeding experimental subjects a diet devoid of that nutrient. After a period of time, if the nutrient is essential, symptoms of a deficiency will develop. The symptoms provide information on how the nutrient functions in the body. The nutrient is then added back to the diet, or repleted, until the symptoms are reversed. The requirement for that nutrient is the amount needed to reverse the deficiency symptoms. An example of a depletion-repletion study might be to feed animals a diet devoid of vitamin A for several weeks and examine the deficiency symptoms that appear. Then, if vitamin A is incrementally added back to the diet, the amount that prevents deficiency symptoms can be identified.

Another method for determining nutrient functions and requirements is to compare the intake of a nutrient with its excretion. This type of study is known as a **balance study**. If more of a nutrient is consumed than is excreted, balance is positive and it is assumed that the nutrient is being used or stored by the body. If more of the nutrient is excreted than is consumed, balance is negative, indicating that some is being lost from the body. When the amount consumed equals the amount lost, the body is neither gaining nor losing that nutrient and is said to be in a steady state or in balance (**Figure 1.16**). By varying the amount of a nutrient consumed and then measuring the amount excreted,

depletion-repletion study A study that feeds a diet devoid of a nutrient until signs of deficiency appear, and then adds the nutrient back to the diet to a level at which symptoms disappear.

balance study A study that compares the total amount of a nutrient that enters the body with the total amount that leaves the body.

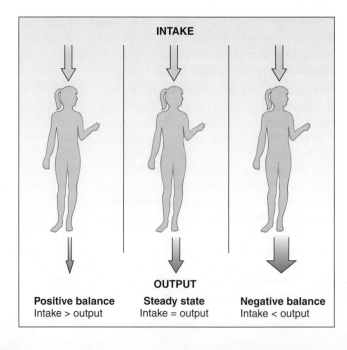

Figure 1.16 Nutrient balance Nutrient balance studies compare the amount of a nutrient that is consumed with the amount excreted to determine whether the body is in positive balance, steady state, or negative balance.

INTAKE

OUTPUT

Positive balance
Intake > output

Steady state
Intake = output

Negative balance
Intake

Critical Thinking
Using the Scientific Method

Observation

While analyzing some epidemiological data, Dr. Tanaka notices that the incidence of colon cancer is much greater in the United States than it is in Japan. He proposes two hypotheses to explain this observation.

Hypotheses

1. The difference may occur because the Japanese people inherit genetic factors that protect against colon cancer.
2. The difference may be due to differences between the diet in the United States and in Japan.

Experiment #1

To generate data to support or refute each of his hypotheses, Dr. Tanaka reviews the medical records and dietary intakes of second-generation Japanese Americans. These individuals are not different genetically from Japanese living in Japan, but they have been consuming a typical American diet for all or most of their lives. The results of his study indicate that second-generation Japanese Americans have an incidence of colon cancer that is similar to that of the rest of the U.S. population.

(Lori Smolin)

Experiment #2

To further explore why the incidence of colon cancer is lower in Japan than in the U.S., Dr. Tanaka designs a human intervention trial. One group of Japanese Americans is instructed to consume a traditional Japanese diet and a control group is instructed to continue eating a typical American diet. Those who adopt the traditional diet are monitored for 10 years. The results indicate that the incidence of colon cancer is lower in this group when compared to Japanese Americans who continue to eat an American-style diet.

Critical Thinking Questions

Review the 2 experiments discussed here. Which hypothesis is supported? Which is refuted?

▼

Could you propose other experiments to obtain more information about the causes of colon cancer in the United States?

▼

Based on the evidence presented here, propose a theory to explain the difference in the incidence of colon cancer in the U.S. and Japan.

it is possible to determine the minimum amount of that nutrient needed to replace body losses. This type of study can be used to determine protein requirements because protein is not stored in the body. It is not useful for determining the requirements for nutrients such as fat and iron that are stored when an excess is available.

Using Animals to Study Human Nutrition Ideally, studies of human nutrition would be done in humans. However, because studying humans is costly, time consuming, inconvenient for subjects, and in some cases impossible for ethical reasons, many studies are done using experimental animals.

An ideal animal model is one with metabolic and digestive processes similar to humans. For example, cows are rarely used in human nutrition research because they digest their food in four stomach-like chambers as opposed to a single stomach. Pigs, on the other hand, are a good model because they digest food in a manner similar to that of humans. In addition to digestion and metabolism, factors such as cost and time must be considered. Pigs and other large animals are expensive to use, and they take a long time to develop nutrient deficiencies. Smaller laboratory animals, such as rats and mice, are therefore the most common experimental animals. They are inexpensive, have short life spans, reproduce quickly, and the effects of nutritional changes develop rapidly. Their food intake can be easily controlled, and their excretions can be measured accurately using special cages. Even when using small animals, the species of animal must be carefully chosen. For example, rats are more resistant to heart disease than are humans, so they are not a good model for studying the effect of diet on heart disease. Rabbits, on the other hand, do develop heart disease and can be used to study diet–heart disease relationships. Both rabbits and rats, however, are poor choices for a study of vitamin C requirements because they can synthesize this vitamin in their bodies. Guinea pigs would be a better choice because the guinea pig is one of the few animals, other than humans, that cannot make vitamin C in its body (**Figure 1.17**). Even the best animal model is not the same as a human, and care must be taken when extrapolating the results to the human population. For example, a study that uses rats to show that a calcium supplement increases bone density can hypothesize, but not conclude, that the supplement will have the same effect in humans.

Studies Using Cells Another alternative to conducting studies in humans is to study cells either extracted from humans or animals or grown in the laboratory (**Figure 1.18**). Biochemistry can be used to study how nutrients are used to provide energy and how

Figure 1.17 What are the advantages and disadvantages of using guinea pigs and other laboratory animals to study human nutrition? (Courtesy Lori Smolin)

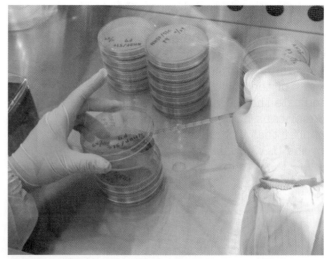

Figure 1.18 The ability to grow cells in the laboratory allows scientists to study nutrients without using whole organisms. (Medicimage/Visuals Unlimited)

they regulate biochemical reactions in cells. Molecular biology can be used to study how genes regulate cell functions. The types and amounts of nutrients available to cells can affect the action of genes. For example, vitamin A can directly activate or inactivate certain genes. Knowledge gained from biochemical and molecular biological research can be used to study nutrition-related conditions that affect the entire organism. Molecular biology can help us understand the hereditary basis of diseases like heart disease, cancer, diabetes, and obesity and is helping us to identify individuals who have a genetic susceptibility to specific diseases so that intervention can begin early.

Ethical Concerns in Scientific Study

Ethical issues are often raised in the process of conducting nutrition research. Whenever possible researchers use alternatives to human subjects or experimental animals. For example, studying body fluids, cells grown in the laboratory, and even computer models can help predict how changes in nutrient intake affect body processes. However, such alternatives cannot always be used; human and animal experimentation is still necessary to answer many questions. To avoid harm and protect the rights of humans and animals used in experimental research, government guidelines have been developed.

Human Subjects Before an experiment involving human subjects can be conducted, the study must first be reviewed by a committee of scientists and nonscientists to ensure that the rights of the subjects are respected and that the risk of physical, social, and psychological injury is balanced against the potential benefit of the research. Before subjects participate in a study, the researchers must explain to them the purpose of the research, the procedures used, and the possible risks and benefits. In addition to an oral explanation of the study, each subject must be given a written description of the study and its risks and benefits. Those who choose to participate must then sign a consent stating exactly what they have agreed to do. Signing a consent form doesn't mean a subject must complete the study if it turns out to be more than they bargained for—subjects can leave a study at any time. This informed consent process is part of the strict safety and ethical regulations that must be followed when research involves human subjects. This protects subjects, but limits the type of study that can be done on humans. For example, much of what we know today about the effects of starvation in humans was determined during World War II by conducting depletion-repletion studies using conscientious objectors as experimental subjects. These subjects were monitored physically and psychologically while they were starved and then re-fed. These individuals experienced some level of suffering during the trials and risked longer lasting physical and psychological harm. It is unlikely that this study would be approved if researchers wanted to repeat it today.

Animal Studies As with experiments involving humans, the federal government mandates that panels of scientists review experiments that propose to use animals. These panels consider whether the need for animals is justified and whether all precautions will be taken to avoid pain and suffering. Animal housing and handling are strictly regulated, and a violation of these guidelines can close a research facility.

Genetic Modification The development of the techniques of molecular biology has given rise to ethical issues regarding the manipulation of genes. Guidelines for manipulating genes have been developed and are constantly being revised to stay abreast of advances in this field.

1.6 Sorting Out Nutrition Information

Learning Objectives

- Name three points to consider when evaluating the reliability of nutritional information.
- Discuss why individual testimonies are not considered reliable sources of information.

We are bombarded with nutrition information. Some of what we hear is accurate and based on science and some of it is incorrect or exaggerated to sell products or make news headlines more enticing: oat bran lowers cholesterol, antioxidants prevent cancer, low-carb diets promote weight loss, vitamin C cures the common cold, vitamin E slows aging. Sifting through this information and distinguishing the useful from the useless can be overwhelming. Just as scientists use the scientific method to expand their understanding of the world around us, each of us can use an understanding of how science is done to evaluate nutrition claims by asking the questions discussed below and summarized in **Table 1.5**.

Does the Information Make Sense?

The first question to ask yourself when evaluating nutrition information is does the claim being made make sense? Some claims are too outrageous to be true. For example, the hypothetical advertisement for StayWell illustrated in **Figure 1.19** states that this product will make illness a thing of the past. This is certainly appealing, but it is hard to believe, and common sense should tell you that it is too good to be true. The claim that StayWell will reduce cold symptoms, however, is not so outrageous.

Table 1.5 Ask These Questions BEFORE You Believe it

- Does the claim presented make sense?
  - If it is too outrageous to believe, disregard it.

- Where did the information come from?
  - If it is based on personal opinions, be aware that one person's perception does not make something true.
  - Information from government agencies, universities, and nonprofit organizations is generally sound.
  - Check the credentials of the person providing the information. If they do not have a legitimate degree in nutrition or medicine view the material with skepticism. If no credentials are listed, there is no way to determine if they are qualified to give this information.

- Was the information based on well-designed experiments?
  - Reliable information is based on scientific studies that use proper controls, include enough experimental subjects to get reliable results, and collect quantifiable data.
  - Studies published in peer-reviewed journals have been evaluated for accuracy before they are published.

- Were the experimental results interpreted accurately?
  - Compare news reports to study results to see if the importance of the study has been exaggerated to make the headline more attractive.
  - If the study was done in animals, consider carefully whether the results will also apply to humans.

- Who stands to benefit?
  - If the information is helping to sell a product, it may be biased toward that product.
  - If the information is making a magazine cover or newspaper headline more appealing, the claims may be exaggerated to promote sales.

- Has it stood the test of time?
  - If the study is the first to support a particular finding, wait before changing your diet based on the result.
  - If the finding has been shown repeatedly in different studies over a period of years, it will become the basis for reliable nutrition recommendations.

- Does it pose a risk?
  - Be sure the expected benefit of the product is worth the risk associated with using it.

StayWell

Make illness a thing of the past!
Naturally enhances your immune system and
improves overall health

**Users report high energy levels and
an increased sense of health
and well-being**

Contains:
**Vitamin B$_6$ –An immune system
  stimulator**
Vitamin C –A potent antioxidant
**Echinachea –A natural herb
  with immune stimulating,
  antiviral, and antibacterial
  activity**

A study at a prestigious university compared college students who   took **StayWell** twice a day for six months
to those who took a placebo. The students taking **StayWell** had milder cold symptoms and recovered faster then
those taking the placebo.

Figure 1.19 This hypothetical supplement advertisement illustrates the types of nutrition claims that consumers must be prepared to evaluate. (© Hernera/ Age Fotostock America, Inc.)

Where Did the Information Come From?

If the claim seems reasonable, look to see where it came from. Was it a personal testimony, a government recommendation, or advice from a health professional? Was it the result of a research study? Is it in a news story or an advertising promotion? Is it on television, in a magazine, or on a Web page?

Although dietitians and physicians are viewed as the most valuable source of nutrition information, Americans today get most of their food and nutrition information from the mass media.[13] Mass media are very powerful tools in promoting health and nutrition messages. Information that would take individual health-care workers years to disseminate can reach millions of individuals in a matter of hours or days. Much of this information is reliable, but some can be misleading. The motivation for news stories is often to sell subscriptions or improve ratings, not to promote the nutritional health of the population. Some nutrition and health information originates from food manufacturers. It is usually in the form of marketing and advertising designed to sell existing products or target new ones. This promotional information can be confusing to the consumer, who may not know how to interpret it. For instance, in the 1990s the recommendation to reduce fat intake to protect against heart disease and help maintain a healthy weight created a demand for products low in fat. Food manufacturers responded by creating fat-free, low-fat, and reduced-fat products at an astonishing rate. Weight- and health-conscious consumers responded by increasing their consumption of these foods, but the girth of American waists continued to increase. The message that reducing fat intake promotes health was received, but consumers did not understand that fat-free foods are not kcalorie-free and simply adding low-fat foods to the diet was not a prescription for good health. Knowing what information to believe and how to use this information to choose a diet can be challenging (see Off the Label: Look Beyond the Banner on the Label).

Individual Testimonies Claims that come from individual testimonies have not been tested by experimentation. For example, the claim in Figure 1.19 that StayWell improves energy levels and overall sense of health and well-being is based on the comments of supplement users and is therefore anecdotal, and not based on measured parameters.

Off The Label

Look Beyond the Banner on the Label

(©iStockphoto)

Healthy! Fresh! Lite! The large-print banner advertising a nutritious feature on a food package stands out and catches your eye. Food labels can be misleading, however, even though they must conform to federal guidelines and use standard definitions for most terms. Understanding the meaning of terms on food labels will help you know what you are choosing and how a food fits into your diet.

Many food label descriptors highlight individual nutrients. But, because no single nutrient makes a food good or bad for you, you must look beyond these descriptors to understand the overall contribution that the food makes to your diet. For example, chocolate cookies labeled "fat free" may not be your best choice if you are trying to reduce your sugar intake or increase your fiber consumption. A food labeled "fresh" may sound appealing, but actually, any raw food that has not been frozen, heat processed, or otherwise preserved can be labeled fresh. The term doesn't provide any information about the nutrient content of the food or how long it took the product to travel from the farm to the grocery store shelf. "Healthy" is another appealing term that implies that a product is wholesome and nutritious. In fact, to use the term "healthy," a food must be low in fat and saturated fat, contain no more than 360 mg of sodium and 60 mg of cholesterol per serving, and be a good source of one or more important nutrients. Although all these qualities are indeed part of a healthy diet, foods that fit this definition are not necessarily the basis for a healthy diet. For instance, many fruit drinks fit the labeling definition of healthy. They are low in fat, saturated fat, cholesterol, and sodium, and they supply at least 10% of the recommended intake for vitamin C. But they are a good choice only in limited quantities because they are high in added refined sugars and contain few other nutrients. Likewise, a food that doesn't meet the labeling definition of healthy is not necessarily a poor choice. Vegetable soup, for example, contains more sodium than the definition of healthy will allow, but if the rest of your diet is not high in sodium, the soup can be a healthy choice.

Healthy-sounding product names can also be misleading. Product names must comply with legal definitions, but they don't have to make sense to consumers. Unless you have memorized the U.S. Department of Agriculture (USDA) and Food and Drug Administration (FDA) labeling regulations, you have no way of knowing how much beef is needed for a product to be called a beef enchilada, for example, or how much chicken must be in chicken soup and how much fruit is in a Fruit Roll-Up. "Lasagna with meat sauce" must be 6% meat, but "lasagna with meat and sauce" must be 12% meat.

To get the whole picture, then, you need to look beyond the healthy-sounding descriptors and the product name. Read the label, which must include the food's nutrient content and information on how it fits into the diet as a whole. Chapter 2 and Off the Label boxes throughout this book provide more information on how to read food labels.

Information from Government, Nonprofit, and Educational Institutions

Government recommendations regarding healthy dietary practices are developed by committees of scientists who interpret the latest well-conducted research studies and use their conclusions to develop recommendations for the population as a whole. The government provides information about food safety and recommendations on food choices and the amounts of specific nutrients needed to avoid nutrient deficiencies and excesses and to prevent chronic diseases. These recommendations are used to develop food-labeling regulations and are the basis for public health policies and programs. They are published in pamphlets and brochures and available on Web sites designed for consumers.

Nonprofit organizations such as the American Dietetic Association, the American Medical Association, and the American Institute for Cancer Research are also a good source of nutrition information. The purpose of the information they provide to the public is to improve health. Reports that come from universities are supported by research and are also a reliable place to look for information. Many universities provide information that targets the general public and university research studies are usually published in peer-reviewed journals and are well-scrutinized. The StayWell ad in Figure 1.19 cites a university research study that demonstrated reduced cold symptoms. If the study was published in a peer-reviewed journal the information is probably reliable.

Qualified Individuals Knowing who is providing the information can help you decide whether or not to believe it. What are the credentials of the individual providing the information? Where do they work? Do they have a degree in nutrition or medicine? If you are looking at an article or a Web site check the credentials of the author. Care must be taken even when obtaining information from nutritionists. Although "nutritionists" and "nutrition counselors" may provide accurate information, these terms are not legally defined and are used by a wide range of people from college professors with doctoral degrees from reputable universities to health food store clerks with no formal training. One reliable source of nutrition information is registered dietitians. Registered dietitians (RDs) are nutrition professionals who have completed a 4-year college degree in a nutrition-related field and who have met established criteria to certify them in providing nutrition counseling.

Is the Information Based on Well-Designed, Accurately Interpreted Research Studies?

If the source of the information seems reliable, ask if the study was well designed and if the results were interpreted accurately. Even well-designed, carefully executed, peer-reviewed experiments can be a source of misinformation if the experimental results are interpreted incorrectly or if the implications of the results are exaggerated. For example, the headline in Figure 1.19 states that StayWell improves overall health. However, the study only investigates cold symptoms; overall health is not addressed.

For some nutrition claims not enough information is given to evaluate the validity of the studies on which they are based. Others, however, do provide the details of how a study was done. For example, the university study described in the StayWell ad compares the severity of cold symptoms and the cold recovery time (quantifiable parameters) of college students who took the StayWell supplement (experimental group) with the same parameters in a similar group of students who took a placebo (control group). The results indicate that the experimental group had milder cold symptoms and shorter recovery times than the control or placebo group. This then supports the claim that the product can reduce cold symptoms.

Who Stands to Benefit?

Another important question to ask when judging nutrition claims is who stands to benefit from the information? If a person or company will profit from the information presented, you should be wary. Information presented in newspapers and magazines and on television may be biased or exaggerated because it must help sell magazines or boost ratings. Consider whether the claim is making a magazine cover or newspaper headline more appealing. Claims that are part of an advertisement should be viewed skeptically because advertisements are designed to increase product sales and the company stands to profit from your belief in that claim. For example, in an advertisement for a vitamin E supplement a company may cite a study that shows that rats fed a diet high in vitamin E live longer than those consuming less vitamin E. However, the fact that a diet high in vitamin E increased longevity does not mean that supplements will have the same effect. In addition, this study was done in rats. Can the result be extrapolated to human health? Just because rats consuming diets high in vitamin E live longer does not mean that vitamin E supplements will extend human life. Information on the Internet is also likely to be biased toward a product or service if it comes from a site where you can buy the product.

Has It Stood the Test of Time?

Often the results of a new scientific study are on the morning news the same day they are published in a peer-reviewed journal. Sometimes this information is accurate, but a single study is never enough to develop a reliable theory. Results need to be reproducible before they can be used as the basis for nutrition decisions or used to make dietary recommendations. Headlines based on a single study should therefore be viewed skeptically. The information may be accurate, but there is no way to know because there has not been time to repeat the work and reaffirm the conclusions. If, for example, someone has found the secret to easy weight loss, the information will undoubtedly appear again if the finding is valid. If it is not, it will fade away with all the other weight loss cures that have come and gone.

Outcome

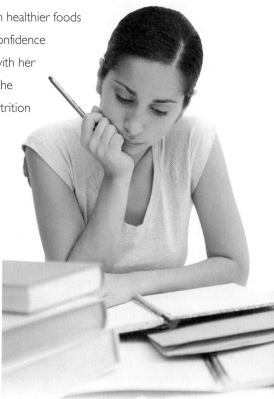

Kaitlyn found it hard to eat a healthy diet during the first semester of her freshman year. Her choices were limited by living in a college dorm and eating meals in the cafeteria, but the biggest problem was figuring out what a healthy diet was. Now that she's read this chapter, she knows that a healthy diet includes a variety of foods. She aims for an assortment of choices from within each of the food groups. She recognizes that eating a healthy diet involves using moderation, so she doesn't consume too much of any one food or food group. Kaitlyn now knows how to balance less healthy choices, like study snacks, with healthier foods at other times of the day. She is gaining confidence in her ability to balance her food intake with her activity. In addition, her understanding of the scientific method and how to evaluate nutrition information has given her the tools she needs to make decisions about following fads and using dietary supplements. Now, in the middle of her second semester, Kaitlyn is maintaining a healthy weight and using the principles of variety, balance, and moderation to choose a nutrient-dense diet that minimizes her risks of developing heart disease and high blood pressure.

APPLICATIONS

1. **How healthy is your diet?**
   a. How many different vegetables and fruits did you eat today? How about this week? If you average fewer than 5 a day make some suggestions that would increase the fruit and vegetable variety in your diet.
   b. If you had a treat such as a doughnut or an extravagant dessert, did you balance it with some healthier choices at other times during the day or the next day? Suggest a healthy choice you could have to balance two of your favorite treats.
   c. Do you order large portions? Use iProfile to look up how many more kcalories are in a large burger, fries, and drink than in a medium-size order.
   d. Do you ever eat foods right out of the package? If you do, it is hard to tell how much you really ate. Suggest some things you could do to control your portion size.

2. **What factors affect your food choices?**
   a. List four food items you ate today or yesterday.
   b. For each food listed, indicate the factor or factors that influenced your selection of that particular food. For example, if you ate a candy bar before your noon class, did you choose it because it was available in the vending machine outside the lecture hall, because you didn't have enough money for anything else, because you just like candy bars, because you were depressed, because all of your friends were eating them, because it is good for you, or for some other reason?
   c. For each food, indicate what information you used in making the selection. For example, did you read the label on the product, or consider something you had read or heard recently in the news media?
   d. List three types of information you regularly use to make your food choices.

1. The Good Heart Study is evaluating the relationship between a new miracle drug and heart disease. The study involves 200 participants, who are divided into two equal groups. Pills identical in appearance are administered to all participants. Group 1 receives two tablets per day of the miracle drug and group 2 receives two placebo tablets per day. After 1 month, half of the subjects in group 1 have blood cholesterol levels at or below the recommended level. In group 2, 49 of the subjects have blood cholesterol levels at or below the recommended level.
   a. Is the study blinded?
   b. What factors would you consider when dividing the subjects between the experimental and control groups?
   c. Does the miracle drug lower cholesterol?

2. **Does this nutritional supplement live up to its claims?**
   a. Examine a nutritional supplement ad provided by your instructor or select one from a health- or fitness-related magazine or Web site. What is the claim made about this product and is it believable?
   b. Does the ad refer to any research studies? If so, do they seem well controlled? Were the results based on objective measurements? Were the conclusions consistent with the results obtained? Were they published in peer-reviewed journals?
   c. Were claims based on anecdotal reports of individual users?
   d. Who stands to benefit if you spend money on this product?
   e. Based on this ad alone, would you choose to take this supplement? Why or why not?

Summary

1.1 Nutrition and the Modern Diet

- Nutrition is a science that encompasses all the interactions that occur between living organisms and food. Americans today are eating more fast food, processed foods, and prepared foods and spending less time preparing meals and eating at home than 50 years ago. This is affecting the healthfulness of the diet.
- The typical American diet does not meet the recommendations for a healthy diet and contributes to the incidence of chronic diseases such as diabetes, obesity, and heart disease.

1.2 Food Provides Nutrients

- About 45 nutrients are essential to human life. Nutrients consumed come from those naturally present in foods, those added to fortified foods, and those contained in dietary supplements. In addition to nutrients, food provides phytochemicals and zoochemicals, nonessential substances, which may provide health benefits. There are six classes of nutrients: carbohydrates, lipids, proteins, water, vitamins, and minerals.

- Food contains nutrients that are needed by the body for growth, maintenance and repair, and reproduction. Carbohydrates, lipids, and proteins are energy-yielding nutrients. The energy they provide to the body is measured in kcalories or kjoules. Carbohydrates, lipids, protein, water, and minerals provide structure to the body, and all nutrient classes help regulate the biochemical reactions of metabolism to maintain homeostasis.

- When energy or one or more nutrients are deficient or excessive in the diet, malnutrition may result. Malnutrition includes both undernutrition and overnutrition. Undernutrition is caused by a deficiency of energy or nutrients. Overnutrition may be caused by a toxic dose of a nutrient or chronic overconsumption of energy or of nutrients that increases the risk of chronic disease. Depending on the cause, the symptoms of malnutrition can occur in the short term or over the course of many weeks, months, or even years.

- The diet you consume can affect your genetic predisposition for developing a variety of chronic diseases.

1.3 Food Choices for a Healthy Diet

- Food choices are affected by food availability, sociocultural influences, personal tastes, emotional factors, and what we think we should eat to stay healthy. No one food choice is good or bad, and no one choice can make a diet healthy or unhealthy—each choice contributes to the diet as a whole.

- A healthy diet includes a variety of nutrient-dense foods from each food group as well as a variety of foods from within each group. It balances energy and nutrient intake with needs and moderates choices to keep intakes of energy, fat, sugar, salt, and alcohol within reason.

 Video

- *Go to WileyPLUS to view a video clip on the local food movement.*

1.4 Understanding Science Helps Understand Nutrition

- The science of nutrition uses the scientific method to determine the relationships between food and the nutrient needs and health of the body. The scientific method involves making observations of natural events, formulating hypotheses to explain these events, designing and performing experiments to test the hypotheses, and developing theories that explain the observed phenomenon based on the experimental results.

- To be valid, nutrition information should be based on experiments that use quantifiable measurements, the right type and number of experimental subjects, appropriate controls, and a careful interpretation of experimental results.

1.5 Nutrition Research

- The science of nutrition uses many different types of experimental approaches to determine nutrient functions and requirements. Observational studies identify relationships between diet and health. Intervention trials can test hypotheses developed from epidemiology. Laboratory studies use biochemical and molecular methods to study whole organisms or cells.

- Ethical guidelines protect humans and animals involved in research studies, but limit the type of experiment that can be done.

1.6 Sorting Out Nutrition Information

- When judging nutrition claims, first consider whether the information makes sense and whether it comes from a reliable source, such as educational institutions and government and nonprofit organizations. Individual testimonies cannot be trusted because they have not been tested by experimentation.

- If information is based on experimentation, determine if the studies were well designed and accurately interpreted.

- Information that promotes a product or in any other way benefits the person or organization providing it should be viewed with skepticism.

- Accurate information will be supported by more than a single research study.

Review Questions

1. How does the typical U.S. diet compare to recommendations for a healthy diet?

2. What does the science of nutrition study?

3. What is an essential nutrient?

4. List six classes of nutrients and indicate which provide energy.

5. List three functions provided by nutrients.

6. List three ways in which what you eat today can affect your health.

7. What is malnutrition?

8. List three factors other than biological need that influence what we eat.

9. Why is it important to choose a variety of foods?

10. How does moderation help maintain a healthy weight?

11. List the steps of the scientific method.

12. What is a control group?

13. What is a placebo?

14. What is a double-blind study?

15. What type of information can be obtained using epidemiology?

16. Why are animals used to study human nutrition?

17. What factors should be considered when judging nutrition claims?

References

1. Briefel, R. R., and Johnson, C. L. Secular trends in dietary intake in the United States. *Annu. Rev. Nutr.* 24:401–431, 2004.

2. Nielsen, S. J., Siega-Riz, A. M., and Popkin, B. M. Trends in energy intake in U.S. between 1977 and 1996: Similar shifts seen across age groups. *Obes. Res.* 10:370–378, 2002.

3. Nielsen, S. J., and Popkin, B. M. Patterns and trends in food portion sizes, 1977–1998. *JAMA.* 289:450–453, 2003.

4. USDA Office of Communications Agriculture Fact Book, 2001–2002. Food consumption in America. Available online at http://www.usda.gov/factbook/2002factbook. pdf. Accessed May 14, 2009.

5. US Department of Health and Human Services, US Department of Agriculture. *Dietary Guidelines for Americans 2005*, 6th ed. Washington, DC, 2005.

6. French, S. A., Lin, B. H., and Guthrie, J. F. National trends in soft drink consumption among children and adolescents age 6 to 17 years: Prevalence, amounts, and sources, 1977/1978 to 1994/1998. *J. Am. Diet. Assoc.* 103:1326–1331, 2003.

7. Frazao, E. America's Eating Habits: Changes and Consequences. Agriculture Information Bulletin No. 750. ERS, USDA. Beltsville, MD: 1999. Available online at www.ers.usda.gov/publications/aib750/ Accessed May 21, 2009.

8. Mokdad, A. H., Marks, J. S., Stroup, D. F., and Gerberding, J. L. Actual causes of death in the United States, 2000. *JAMA.* 291:1238–1245, 2004.

9. US Department of Health and Human Services. Physical Activity Guidelines for Americans, 2008. Available online at www.health.gov/paguidelines/ pdf/paguide.pdf. Accessed May 13, 2009.

10. Picciano, M. F. Office of Dietary Supplements, National Institutes of Health. Who is using Dietary Supplements. What are They Using? Available online at http://ods.od.nih.gov/pubs/fnce2005/ M%20F%20Picciano-Who%20Is%20Using%20Dietary% 20Supplements%20and%20What%20are%20They%20 Using.pdf. Accessed May 14, 2009.

11. Ogden, C. L., Caroll, M. D., Curtin, L. R. et al. Prevalence of overweight and obesity in the United States. 1999–2004. *JAMA* 295:1549–1555, 2006.

12. Diet, Nutrition and the Prevention of Chronic Diseases. Report of a Joint WHO/FAO Expert Consultation. Available online at http://whqlibdoc.who.int/trs/ WHO_TRS_916.pdf. Accessed May 14, 2009.

13. Kaput, J. Nutrigenomics–2006 update. *Clin. Chem. Lab. Med.* 45:279–287, 2007.

14. American Dietetic Association. Nutrition and You: Trends 2008. Available online at www.eatright.org/trends/2008. Accessed May 14, 2009.

2 Nutrition Guidelines:

Applying the Science of Nutrition

Case Study

Kareem was starting his freshman year at college on an athletic scholarship. Although it was only September, he wanted to make sure he ate well to stay in shape for track season in March. Now that he was away from home and had to make his own food choices at the dorm cafeteria, Kareem was overwhelmed. Should breakfast be oatmeal, doughnuts, an omelet, or just fruit? He liked burgers and fries for lunch, but thought he should choose a salad and a cold sandwich. Dinner offered even more choices—there was always some type of meat dish, a pasta choice, fish, and a vegetarian entrée. For dessert there were cakes, pies, and big vats of scoop-your-own ice cream to tempt him. Many of his friends piled their plates and served themselves two or three desserts, but he knew those choices were not the best. His track coach suggested he talk to the team nutrition advisor, who was also a professor in the university's department of nutritional sciences.

Kareem was surprised when the professor suggested that he go online to find out how to choose a healthy diet. There he could look up how many cups of vegetables and fruit, how many ounces of meats and grains, and how many cups of milk would meet his needs based on his age and activity level. The professor also advised him that making healthy choices from each food group and choosing a variety of foods were just as important as the amounts of food he ate. If he chose foods that were high in fat and sugar, he might exceed his energy needs even if he ate the right amounts from each group. The professor explained which foods Kareem should emphasize to maximize his nutrient intake. He also showed Kareem how to use food labels to choose foods to meet his goals.

(Photodisc/Getty Images, Inc.)

(©iStockphoto)

e/Triolo Productions/FoodPix)

Chapter Outline

Figure 2.1 An individual's nutritional needs depend on age, gender, and genetic makeup. (Bob Thomas/Stone/Getty Images)

2.1 Nutrition Recommendations for the Modern Diet

Learning Objectives

- Give some reasons why population-wide nutrition recommendations are developed.
- Describe the early nutrition recommendations in the U.S.

People need to eat to survive, but health-conscious individuals want to do more than survive. They want to choose diets that will optimize their health. An optimal diet would contain just the right amount of each nutrient to prevent deficiencies and maintain health and, for some people, to maintain a healthy pregnancy or to allow for growth. What is optimal for each individual also depends on a variety of other factors such as their genetic background, their activity level, and the other nutrients in their diet (**Figure 2.1**).

The science of nutrition has determined which nutrients are necessary to keep humans alive and how the amounts needed vary at different stages of life, such as pregnancy or infancy. But it is not currently possible to determine the optimal amount of each nutrient that should be included in the diet of each individual. Instead, the methods of science have been used to establish general recommendations for the types and amounts of nutrients that will maintain the health of individuals and populations. To be useful to health-conscious consumers, these amounts have been translated into recommendations about food choices. These recommendations are also used as a standard of comparison to assess whether populations and individuals are consuming diets that promote health.

Early Nutrition Recommendations

Some of the first nutrition recommendations were made in England in the 1860s when the Industrial Revolution caused a rise in urban populations with large numbers of homeless and hungry people. The government wanted to know the least expensive way to keep these people alive and maintain the workforce. As a result, a dietary standard was established based on what the average working person ate in a typical day. This method of estimating nutrient needs was used until World War I, when the British Royal Society made specific recommendations about foods that not only would sustain life but also would be protective of health. They recommended that fruits and green vegetables be included in a healthy diet and that milk be included in the diets of all children. Since then, the governments of many countries have established their own sets of dietary standards based on the nutritional problems and dietary patterns specific to their populations and the interpretations of their scientists. Generally, the differences between guidelines from country to country are small. The World Health Organization and the Food and Agriculture Organization of the United Nations, organizations concerned with international health, publish a set of dietary standards to apply worldwide[1] (see Appendix F).

Nutrition Recommendations in the United States

Because nutrition recommendations must satisfy a variety of needs, a number of different types of guidelines have been developed in the United States. Some describe the amounts of individual nutrients that are needed and some suggest patterns of food intake that promote health and prevent disease. The nature of each set of guidelines depends on the population it is targeting, who is developing it, what its goals are, and how it will be used. These recommendations are updated periodically as the science of nutrition evolves and new information becomes available.

The original dietary standards in the United States were the Recommended Dietary Allowances (RDAs). First published in 1943, they were developed in response to the widespread food limitations created by World War II (**Figure 2.2**). Recommendations were made for the intake of energy and nutrients at risk for deficiency—protein, vitamins, and minerals. Levels of intake were based on amounts

Figure 2.2 World War II nutrition poster
Food shortage was a national concern in the United States during World War II. People were expected to cooperate with rationing efforts and to plant home gardens, called victory gardens. The food that could be produced from a plot of land was too valuable to waste. (U.S. National Archives)

that would prevent nutrient deficiencies.[2] Over the years since these first standards were developed, our knowledge of nutrient needs has increased and patterns of dietary intake and disease have changed. Overt nutrient deficiencies are now rare in the United States, but the incidence of diet-related chronic diseases such as heart disease, cancer, and obesity has increased. In response to these changes in our diet and health, these original RDAs have been replaced by a set of energy and nutrient intake recommendations called the **Dietary Reference Intakes**, or DRIs for short. These are designed to promote health as well as prevent nutrient deficiencies. The United States and Canada have collaborated to develop the DRIs, which have replaced both the 1989 RDAs in the United States and the Recommended Nutrient Intakes (RNIs) in Canada. This joint United States–Canadian effort has helped to standardize recommendations for North America.

In addition to the DRIs there are a number of other types of recommendations designed to help Americans choose the foods that make up a healthy diet. The Dietary Guidelines for Americans provide diet and lifestyle recommendations to promote health and reduce chronic disease risk in the population. MyPyramid: Steps to a Healthier You is designed to translate recommendations about nutrient intakes into food choices. Food labels show consumers which nutrients are provided by packaged foods and how the amounts contained in a serving compare with the recommendations for an overall healthy diet.

dietary reference intakes (DRIs) A set of reference values for the intake of energy, nutrients, and food components that can be used for planning and assessing the diets of healthy people in the United States and Canada.

2.2 Dietary Reference Intakes

Learning Objectives

- Describe the types of nutrient intake recommendations included in the Dietary Reference Intakes (DRIs) and explain the purpose of each.
- List the variables used to calculate the EERs.

The DRIs are designed to be used for planning and assessing the diets of healthy people. They include recommendations not only for energy, protein, and micronutrients but also for macronutrients (carbohydrate, fat, and protein) and food components that affect health, such as phytochemicals. The amounts recommended by the DRIs are chosen to promote health and reduce the incidence of chronic disease as well as prevent deficiencies. They are not requirements that must be consumed each day but recommendations for what should be consumed on an average daily basis.

The DRIs have been developed for six nutrient groups:

- Calcium, phosphorus, magnesium, vitamin D, and fluoride
- B vitamins and choline
- Antioxidants (vitamin C, vitamin E, selenium, and beta-carotene)
- Vitamins A and K and the trace elements (e.g., iron, zinc, copper)
- Energy and macronutrients
- Electrolytes and water

A seventh group, which includes other food components that affect health such as phytochemicals, is also planned. At the time of publication the report from this seventh group had not yet been released.

The DRIs include values for different **life-stage groups**. These have been established to account for the physiological differences among infants, children, adolescents, adults, older adults, and pregnant and lactating women. The pregnancy and lactation recommendations are divided into age categories to distinguish the unique nutritional needs of pregnancy and lactation in teenagers and older mothers (see inside cover).

Life Cycle

life-stage groups Groupings of individuals based on stages of growth and development, pregnancy, and lactation that have similar nutrient needs.

Nutrient Recommendations

The DRIs for macronutrients and micronutrients include four different sets of reference values.[3] One of these, the **Estimated Average Requirements (EARs)** can be used to evaluate the nutrient intake of populations. Two sets of values, the **Recommended Dietary Allowances (RDAs)** and the **Adequate Intakes (AIs)** recommend specific amounts of nutrients that can be used as goals for individual intake and to plan or evaluate individual diets. The fourth set of values, the **Tolerable Upper Intake Levels (ULs)**, helps individuals prevent nutrient toxicities.

Estimated Average Requirements (EARs) These are the amount of a nutrient that is estimated to meet the needs of 50% of people in the same gender and life-stage group (**Figure 2.3**). EAR values are useful for evaluating the adequacy of, and planning for, the nutrient intake of population groups. For example, the prevalence of low iron intake in a population can be estimated by looking at the proportion of the population with iron intakes below the EAR.

To set an EAR, scientists must establish a measurable functional marker of adequacy. These **criteria of adequacy** are typically things like the activity of an enzyme or the level of a nutrient or metabolite in the blood, which can be evaluated to determine the biological effect of a level of nutrient intake. Appropriate criteria of adequate intake must be established for each nutrient in each life-stage and gender group.

Recommended Dietary Allowances (RDAs) The RDA values are higher than the EARs because they are calculated to meet the needs of nearly all healthy individuals in each gender and life-stage group. They are determined by starting with the EAR value and using the variability in the requirements among individuals to increase it to an amount that meets the needs of 97% to 98% of healthy individuals (see Figure 2.3). Because the RDA is set higher than the needs of most people, it serves as a target for individual intake. An intake less than the RDA does not necessarily indicate that the needs of that particular person have not been met, however, the risk of a deficiency is low if intake meets the RDA and increases as intake falls below the RDA.[4]

estimated average requirements (EARs) Intakes that meet the estimated nutrient needs of 50% of individuals in a gender and life-stage group.

recommended dietary allowances (RDAs) Intakes that are sufficient to meet the nutrient needs of almost all healthy people in a specific life-stage and gender group.

adequate intakes (AIs) Intakes that should be used as a goal when no RDA exists. These values are an approximation of the average nutrient intake that appears to sustain a desired indicator of health.

tolerable upper intake levels (ULs) Maximum daily intakes that are unlikely to pose a risk of adverse health effects to almost all individuals in the specified life-stage and gender group.

criteria of adequacy Functional indicators, such as the level of a nutrient in the blood or the appearance of a deficiency symptom, that can be measured to determine the biological effect of a level of nutrient intake.

The RDA is set by adding a safety factor to the EAR. About 97% of the population meets its needs by consuming this amount (shown as yellow shading).

An EAR is the average amount of a nutrient required for good health. If everyone in the population consumed this amount, only 50% (shown as diagonal lines) would obtain enough of the nutrient to meet their requirements.

The UL is set well above the needs of everyone in the population and represents the highest amount of the nutrient that will not cause toxicity symptoms in the majority of healthy people.

EAR RDA UL

Number of people

Daily nutrient requirement

Figure 2.3 Understanding EARs, RDAs, and ULs
An EAR and RDA are determined by assessing the amount of a nutrient required by different individuals in a population group and plotting the resulting values. Because a few individuals in the group need only a small amount, a few need a large amount, and most need an amount that falls between the extremes, the result is a bell-shaped curve like the one shown here.

Adequate Intakes (AIs) Although the AIs are also used as a guide for individual intake they are not based on EAR values. These are estimates used when there is insufficient scientific evidence to set an EAR and calculate an RDA. The AIs are based on observed or experimentally determined approximations of the average nutrient intake by a healthy population. When an AI value rather than an RDA is set, it targets the need for more research on the requirement of that nutrient. A healthy individual whose intake of a specific nutrient is at or above the AI is unlikely to be deficient in that nutrient. In order to set an AI a criterion of adequacy must be established. For example, the AI for calcium for children is based on the amount needed for maximal calcium accumulation to support bone growth.

Tolerable Upper Intake Levels (ULs) The fourth set of values, the Tolerable Upper Intake Levels, represent the maximum level of daily intake of a nutrient that is unlikely to pose a risk of adverse health effects to almost all individuals in the specified group. These are not a recommended levels, but levels of intake that probably be tolerated (see Figure 2.3). ULs are used as a guide for limiting intake when planning diets and evaluating the possibility of overconsumption. The exact level of intake that will cause an adverse effect cannot be known with certainty for each individual, but if a person's intake is below the UL, there is good assurance that an adverse effect will not occur.

To establish a UL, a specific adverse effect or indicator of excess is considered. The lowest level of intake that causes the adverse effect is determined, and the UL is set far enough below this level that even the most sensitive people in the population are unlikely to be affected. If adverse effects have been associated only with intake from supplements, the UL is based only on this source. Therefore, for some nutrients these values represent intake from supplements alone; for some, intake from supplements and fortified foods; and for others, total intake from food, fortified food, water, nonfood sources, and supplements. For many nutrients, data are insufficient to establish a UL value.

Energy Recommendations

The DRIs make two types of recommendations regarding energy intake. One provides an estimate of how much energy is needed to maintain body weight and the other provides information about the proportion of each of the energy-yielding nutrients from which this energy should come.

estimated energy requirements (EERs) Average energy intakes predicted to maintain body weight in healthy individuals.

Estimated Energy Requirements (EERs) The recommendations for energy intake are called **Estimated Energy Requirements (EERs)**.[5] They can be used to calculate the number of kcalories needed to keep weight stable in a healthy person. Variables in the calculations include age, gender, weight, height, and level of physical activity (see inside cover). Changing any of these variables changes the EER. For example, a 17-year-old girl who is 5'4" tall and weighs 127 lbs and gets no exercise needs to eat only 1730 kcalories a day to maintain her weight. If she adds an hour of moderate activity to her daily routine her EER will increase to 2380 kcalories and she will need to increase her food intake by about 650 kcalories per day to maintain her weight. If she grows taller or gains weight, these factors will also increase her energy needs. The EERs are discussed in more depth in Chapter 7.

acceptable macronutrient distribution ranges (AMDRs) Ranges of intake for energy-yielding nutrients, expressed as a percentage of total energy intake, that are associated with reduced risk of chronic disease while providing adequate intakes of essential nutrients.

Acceptable Macronutrient Distribution Ranges (AMDRs) The proportion of each of the energy-yielding nutrients in the diet is just as important as the total amount of energy consumed. Therefore, the DRIs make recommendations for the proportions of carbohydrate, fat, and protein that make up a healthy diet. These are called **Acceptable Macronutrient Distribution Ranges (AMDRs)**. These recommendations are expressed as ranges because healthy diets can contain many different combinations of carbohydrate, protein, and fat.[5] According to the AMDRs, a healthy diet for an adult can contain from 45% to 65% of kcalories from carbohydrate, 20% to 35% from fat, and 10% to 35% from protein. When kcalorie intake stays the same, changing the proportion of one of these will change the proportion of the others as well. So for example, in a diet that provides 2000 kcalories with 50% of kcalories from carbohydrate, the other 50% will come from protein and fat. If the kcalories are kept the same but carbohydrate intake is decreased, the percentage of fat and/or protein will increase (**Figure 2.4**). The AMDRs allow flexibility in food choices based on individual preferences while still providing a diet that minimizes disease risk. AMDR values have also been set for specific amino acids and fatty acids (Appendix A).

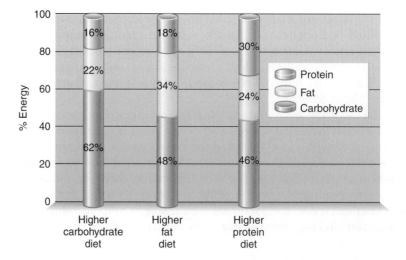

Figure 2.4 Proportions of energy-yielding nutrients Changing the proportion of one of the energy-yielding nutrients in the diet changes the proportions of the others.

Applications of the Dietary Reference Intakes

The DRIs have many uses. They provide a set of standards that can be used to plan diets, to assess the adequacy of diets, and to make judgments about excessive intakes for individuals and populations.[3] For example, they can be used as a standard for meals prepared for schools, hospitals, and other health-care facilities; for government feeding programs for the elderly; and even for meals for space-shuttle astronauts. They can be used to determine standards for food labeling and to develop practical tools for diet planning, such as food group systems. They can also be used to interpret information gathered about the food consumed by a population to help identify potential nutritional inadequacies that may be of public health concern.

Despite their many uses, dietary standards cannot be used to identify with certainty whether a specific person has a nutritional deficiency or excess. To ascertain this, an evaluation of an individual's nutritional status using dietary, clinical, biochemical, and body-size measurements is needed, as discussed later in this chapter.

2.3 The Dietary Guidelines for Americans

Learning Objectives

- Explain the purpose of the Dietary Guidelines.
- Discuss how the Dietary Guidelines address the problem of obesity.

The **Dietary Guidelines for Americans** is a set of diet and lifestyle recommendations designed to promote health and reduce chronic disease risks in the American population. Unlike the DRIs, which provide recommendations for specific amounts of nutrients and food components, the Dietary Guidelines suggest overall diet and lifestyle choices that will promote health.

Dietary Guidelines for Americans A set of nutriution and lifestyle recommendations designed to promote population-wide dietary changes to reduce the incidence of nutrition-related chronic disease.

Development of the Dietary Guidelines

The concept of providing broad-based recommendations for health promotion has evolved over the past 40 years. In 1977, the "Dietary Goals for the United States" was established by the Senate Select Committee on Human Needs.[6] This was the first set of recommendations that considered health promotion, rather than just deficiency prevention. The Dietary Goals were subsequently modified and published as the Dietary Guidelines for Americans in 1980 by the U.S. Department of Agriculture (USDA) and the U.S. Department of Health and Human Services (USDHHS). Since then, they have been revised every 5 years to reflect advances in our scientific understanding of what constitutes a diet that promotes health. The current (sixth) edition was released in 2005.[7] The next set of Dietary Guidelines are expected to be released in late 2010.

Recommendations of the Dietary Guidelines

The Dietary Guidelines for Americans, 2005 include 23 recommendations in 9 categories targeted to all healthy Americans 2 years of age or older (**Table 2.1**). Additional recommendations target specific subpopulations (Appendix G). The following sections outline the general concepts presented in the Dietary Guidelines: get more nutrients in fewer kcalories; improve the balance between food intake and exercise; limit dietary components that contribute to chronic disease; and keep food safe.

Table 2.1 Key Recommendations of the 2005 Dietary Guidelines for Americans

Adequate Nutrients within Kcalorie Needs

- Consume a variety of nutrient-dense foods and beverages within and among the basic food groups while choosing foods that limit the intake of saturated and *trans* fats, cholesterol, added sugars, salt, and alcohol.
- Meet recommended intakes within energy needs by adopting a balanced eating pattern, such as MyPyramid or the DASH Eating Plan (see Chapter 10).

Weight Management

- Maintain body weight in a healthy range; balance kcalories consumed from foods and beverages with kcalories expended.
- Prevent gradual weight gain over time; make small decreases in food and beverage kcalories and increase physical activity.

Physical Activity

- Engage in regular physical activity (at least 60 to 90 minutes most days of the week) and reduce sedentary activities.
- Include cardiovascular conditioning, stretching exercises, and resistance exercises or calisthenics for muscle strength and endurance.

Food Groups to Encourage

- Consume a sufficient amount of fruits and vegetables while staying within energy needs. Two cups of fruit and 2½ cups of vegetables per day are recommended for a reference 2000-kcalorie intake, with higher or lower amounts depending on the kcalorie level.
- Choose a variety of fruits and vegetables each day. In particular, select from all five vegetable subgroups (dark green, orange, legumes, starchy vegetables, and other vegetables) several times a week.
- Consume 3 or more ounce-equivalents of whole-grain products per day, with the rest of the recommended grains coming from enriched or whole-grain products. In general, at least half the grains should come from whole grains.
- Consume 3 cups per day of nonfat or low-fat milk or equivalent milk products.

Fats

- Consume less than 10% of kcalories from saturated fatty acids and less than 300 mg/day of cholesterol, and keep *trans* fatty acid consumption as low as possible.
- Keep total fat intake between 20% to 35% of kcalories, with most fats coming from sources of polyunsaturated and monounsaturated fatty acids, such as fish, nuts, and vegetable oils.
- When selecting and preparing meat, poultry, dry beans, and milk or milk products, make choices that are lean, low-fat, or fat-free.
- Limit intake of fats and oils high in saturated and/or *trans* fatty acids, and choose products low in such fats and oils.

Carbohydrates

- Choose fiber-rich fruits, vegetables, and whole grains often.
- Choose and prepare foods and beverages with little added sugars or kcaloric sweeteners, such as amounts suggested by MyPyramid and the DASH Eating Plan.
- Reduce dental caries through good oral hygiene and consuming sugar- and starch-containing foods and beverages less frequently.

Sodium and Potassium

- Consume less than 2300 mg (approximately 1 tsp of salt) of sodium per day.
- Choose and prepare foods with little salt and consume potassium-rich foods, such as fruits and vegetables.

Alcoholic Beverages

- Those who choose to drink alcoholic beverages should do so in moderation—defined as the consumption of up to 1 drink per day for women and up to 2 drinks per day for men.
- Alcoholic beverages should not be consumed by some individuals, including those who cannot restrict their alcohol intake, women of childbearing age who may become pregnant, pregnant and lactating women, children and adolescents, individuals taking medications that can interact with alcohol, and those with specific medical conditions.
- Alcoholic beverages should be avoided by individuals engaging in activities that require attention, skill, or coordination.

Food Safety

- Know how to prepare, handle, and store food safely to keep you and your family safe.

Source: Dietary Guidelines, 2005.

Make Nutrient-Dense Choices Many Americans today are eating more food than they need but still come up short on essential nutrients. As a result, they weigh more than is healthy, but are still at risk for nutrient deficiencies. To address this, the Dietary Guidelines recommend choosing a variety of nutrient-dense foods—foods that are high in essential nutrients relative to the kcalories they provide. The Guidelines direct Americans to improve their nutrient intake by eating more vegetables, fruits, whole grains, low-fat milk products, and lean meats and beans. The vegetables, fruits, whole grains, and beans are rich in fiber, micronutrients, and phytochemicals. Low-fat dairy products provide calcium and protein without too much saturated fat. Choosing more fish, beans, peas, nuts, and seeds, along with lean meats provides nutrient-dense protein sources.

Balance Food and Physical Activity To address the problem of overweight and obesity, the Guidelines recommend that Americans balance the kcalories they consume in food and beverages with the kcalories they expend in activity. This balance is key to weight management.

Preventing weight gain is easier than losing weight. For most people, small changes in their kcalorie intake and activity level will prevent weight gain. A reduction of 50 to 100 kcalories of intake or an increase of 50 to 100 kcalories of activity a day will prevent weight gain in most people (**Figure 2.5**). For those who are overweight, a change of about 500 kcalories a day may be needed. The guidelines emphasize that consuming the appropriate number of kcalories, not the proportion of carbohydrate, fat, or protein in the diet, is the important factor in weight management.

Exercise is important for weight loss and for keeping weight in a healthy range. At least 30 minutes of moderate activity on most days is recommended, and greater health benefits can be obtained by engaging in more vigorous intensity activity or

(a)   (b)

Figure 2.5 (a) To promote a healthy weight, the Dietary Guidelines for Americans recommend moderating kcalorie intake by limiting portion sizes and reducing consumption of added sugars, solid fats, and alcohol, which provide kcalories but few essential nutrients. (b) Exercise is important for weight management and overall health. To optimize the health benefits, exercise should include aerobic activities to strengthen the heart, stretching exercises for flexibility, and weight lifting for muscle strength and endurance. (Left, Picture India/Getty Images, Inc.; right, iStockphoto)

activity of longer duration. Sixty minutes of moderate to vigorous intensity activity on most days of the week is recommended to help manage body weight and prevent weight gain. For those who have lost weight and want to keep it off, 60 to 90 minutes of moderate intensity activity is recommended.

Limit Nutrients that Increase Health Risks Although we need fats and carbohydrates in our diet, not all types of fat and carbohydrate are as healthy as others. The Guidelines recommend reducing intake of saturated fats, *trans* fat, and cholesterol. These types of fats increase the risk of heart disease and other chronic illnesses (see Chapter 5). Most of the fats in our diets should come from plant and fish oils because of the positive effects they have on heart health. The Guidelines also recommend minimizing intake of added sugars by choosing and preparing foods and beverages with little added sugar. Added sugars provide kcalories but contribute few nutrients (see Chapter 4). Sodium should also be limited. In general, the more sodium people consume, the higher their blood pressure will be. Blood pressure can be reduced by eating less sodium, increasing potassium intake, losing weight, exercising more, and eating an overall healthy diet (see Chapter 10). Food labels can be helpful in determining the number of kcalories, the types of fat, and the amounts of sugar and sodium in packaged food products.

The Dietary Guidelines also advise those who drink alcohol to do so in moderation. Consuming one or two drinks per day is associated with lowest all cause mortality as well as lowest coronary heart disease mortality. Alcohol consumption is not recommended for those who cannot restrict their intake, women of childbearing age who may become pregnant, pregnant and lactating women, children and adolescents, those taking medications that interact with alcohol, those with specific medical conditions, and those engaged in activities that require attention, skill, or coordination (see Focus on Alcohol).

Keep Food Safe Paying attention to food safety is part of healthful eating (see Chapter 17). To prevent microbial food-borne illness, the 2005 Dietary Guidelines encourage Americans to clean hands, food contact surfaces, fruits, and vegetables; to separate raw, cooked, and ready-to-eat foods; to cook foods to a safe temperature; and to refrigerate perishable foods. Avoiding unpasteurized milk or products made with unpasteurized milk, raw eggs, raw or undercooked meat or poultry, unpasteurized juices, and raw sprouts is also advised.

2.4 MyPyramid: Applying the Dietary Guidelines

Learning Objectives

- Discuss the MyPyramid recommendations for activity, variety, proportionality, and moderation.
- Look up the MyPyramid recommendations for someone of your age, gender, and activity level.

To help individuals apply the recommendations of the Dietary Guidelines to their own food choices, the USDA has developed MyPyramid: Steps to a Healthier You (**Figure 2.6**).[8] This educational tool translates the Dietary Guidelines recommendations into the choices that make up a healthy dietary and lifestyle pattern. Like previous food guides, MyPyramid is a food group system; it divides foods into groups based on the nutrients they supply most abundantly. The amounts recommended from each food group for an individual depends on their energy needs.

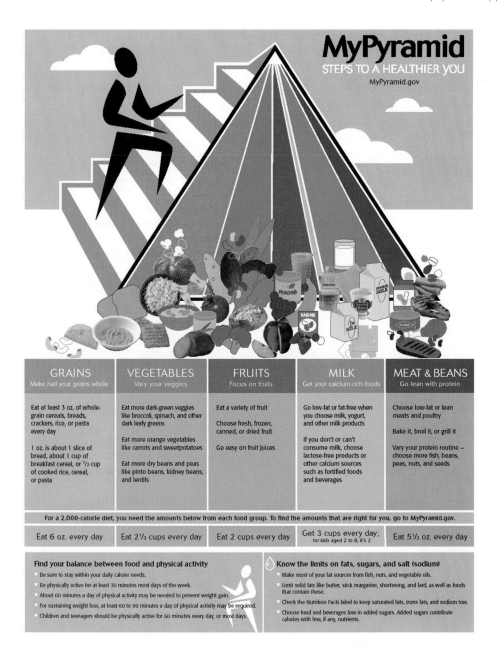

**Figure 2.6 MyPyramid:
Steps to a Healthier You**
MyPyramid is a food group system
designed to help Americans apply
the recommendations of the
Dietary Guidelines to their
individual diets.

The Food Group Concept

Food groups have been used to guide the dietary choices of Americans since the early twentieth century. During the Great Depression of the 1930s a food guide was released that consisted of 12 food groups and focused on responding to food scarcities. In 1943, influenced by World War II, a food guide called the "Basic Seven" was released. In 1956, the seven food groups were condensed to the "Basic Four" and presented in the USDA publication *Essentials of an Adequate Diet*.[9] In 1992 the food groups were organized into a pyramid shape and released as the Food Guide Pyramid. The pyramid shape helped to emphasize the relative contribution of each food group.

Food guides developed in other countries have adopted different shapes to emphasize the proportions of choices that should come from different food groups. Korea and China use a pagoda shape, Mexico, Australia, and most European countries use a pie or plate shape, and Canada uses a rainbow (see Appendix E). America's current food guide, MyPyramid, retains the pyramid shape and the concept that the types of foods at the base should make up the largest proportion of the diet, but the shapes and arrangement of the individual food groups are different from the Food Guide Pyramid.

MyPyramid Food Groups and Amounts

MyPyramid is built around five main food groups—grains, vegetables, fruits, milk, and meat and beans (see Figure 2.6). Although fats are not considered a food group, MyPyramid also includes recommendations on the amounts and types of fats that should be included in the diet.

Table 2.2 What Counts as an Ounce or Cup?

Grains

One cup of rice is the size of a baseball.

Food	Amount that counts as an ounce
Bagel	1/4 large or one mini bagel
Bread	1 regular slice
Crackers	5 whole wheat or 7 square or round
Cooked cereal, rice, or pasta	1/2 cup (A typical serving size is 1 cup)
Popcorn	3 cups, 1/4 microwave bag
Ready-to-eat breakfast cereal	1 cup flakes or rounds, 1¼ cup puffed

Vegetables

A medium potato is the size of computer mouse

Food	Amount that counts as a cup
Broccoli	1 cup chopped or 3 spears 5" long
Carrots	1 cup strips, 2 medium carrots, or 12 baby carrots
Greens (collards, mustard greens, turnip greens, kale, spinach)	1 cup cooked
Raw leafy greens (spinach, romaine, dark green leafy lettuce, endive)	2 cups raw
Sweet potato	1 large baked (2¼" or more diameter)
Corn on the cob	1 large ear (8" to 9" long)
Dry beans	1 cup cooked whole or mashed
White potatoes	1 medium boiled or baked (2½ to 3" diameter) french fried: 20 medium to long strips (2½ to 4" long)
Tomatoes	1 large whole (3" diameter), 1 cup chopped raw, canned, or cooked, 1 cup juice

Fruits

A medium apple is the size of a baseball

Food	Amount that counts as a cup
Apple	1/2 large or 1 small
Banana	1 large (8" to 9" long), 1 cup sliced
Orange	1 large (3" diameter)
Strawberries	8 large
Grapes	32 seedless grapes
Dried fruit	1/2 cup
100% fruit juice	1 cup

Milk

An ounce of cheese is the size of 4 dice

Food	Amount that counts as a cup
Milk and yogurt	1 cup
Cheese	2 slices or 1½ ounces hard cheese, 1/3 cup shredded, 1/2 cup ricotta, 2 cups cottage cheese
Pudding or frozen yogurt	1 cup
Ice cream	1½ cups or 3 scoops

Meat and Beans

3 ounces of meat or tofu is the size of a deck of cards

Food	Amount that counts as an ounce
Meat, poultry, fish	1 ounce cooked, 1/3 small steak, 1/2 small hamburger, 1/3 chicken breast, 1/3 can tuna (A typical serving size is 3 oz)
Eggs	1 egg
Nuts and seeds	1/2 ounce, 12 almonds, 24 pistachios, 7 walnut halves, 1 Tbsp peanut butter
Dry beans or peas	1/4 cup cooked black, kidney, or pinto beans, 1/4 cup cooked chick peas, lentils, or split peas, 1/2 cup lentil soup, 1/4 cup tofu, 2 Tbsp hummus

(Photos by Andy Washnik)

Figure 2.7 Discretionary kcalories
If nutrient-dense foods are chosen, nutrient needs can be met with fewer kcalories than are needed to maintain weight. The "extra" kcalories needed to maintain weight make up the discretionary kcalorie allowance.

The amounts recommended from each food group are expressed in consumer-friendly measures like cups, ounces, and teaspoons. For example, for a 2000-kcalorie diet, MyPyramid recommends 2 cups of fruits, 2½ cups of vegetables, and 6 ounce-equivalents of grains. An ounce-equivalent of grains is a slice of bread, a half bagel, or a half cup of pasta or rice. Amounts recommended from the meat and beans group are also expressed in ounce-equivalents; one ounce-equivalent is an ounce of meat, fish, or poultry; one egg; a tablespoon of peanut butter; a quarter cup of beans; or one-half ounce of nuts or seeds. **Table 2.2** provides examples of amounts of foods that are equivalent to a cup of vegetables, fruits, or milk, or an ounce-equivalent of grains or meat and beans. The number of teaspoons of oils recommended for different kcalorie levels is also provided by MyPyramid. Some of these oils are components of foods and some are added to foods during cooking or as spreads and sauces. Fats that are solid at room temperature, like butter and margarine, are not part of this oils recommendation because high intakes are related to increased disease risk.

Discretionary Kcalories

If your diet is made up of nutrient-dense foods you will be able to meet your nutrient needs with fewer kcalories than are needed to maintain your weight (**Figure 2.7**). The kcalories remaining after you have met your nutrient needs by

Table 2.3 *Finding Discretionary Kcalories*

Food Group	Foods with few or no discretionary kcalories	Foods with about half their energy from discretionary kcalories
Grains	Whole-wheat bread Brown rice Plain bagel Whole-wheat crackers	Blueberry muffin Croissant Doughnut Chocolate chip cookies
Vegetables	Steamed broccoli Sweet potatoes Green beans	Broccoli and cream sauce Candied sweet potatoes Green bean casserole
Fruits	Raw apple Strawberries Fresh peaches	Apple pie Frozen sweetened strawberries Canned peaches in heavy syrup
Milk	Fat-free or low-fat milk Nonfat plain yogurt Nonfat mozzarella	Whole milk Fruit-flavored low-fat yogurt Cheddar cheese
Meat and Beans	Extra lean ground beef Roasted chicken breast without skin Kidney beans	Sausage Fried chicken with skin Bologna

discretionary kcalories
The energy left over after an individual has consumed all the food needed to meet their nutrient needs.

consuming nutrient-dense foods from each of the food groups are called **discretionary kcalories**. If you imagine your energy intake as a kcalorie budget, discretionary kcalories are the kcalories you have left over after having made nutrient-dense choices according to the MyPyramid recommendations. In a typical diet some of these discretionary kcalories come from foods within the food groups such as cookies, cakes, and doughnuts that contain solid fats and added sugars (**Table 2.3** on previous page). Others come from dietary substances not in a food group such as butter and margarine, added table sugar, sweetened carbonated beverages, and alcohol. For a 2000-kcalorie diet the discretionary kcalories remaining after the specified number of nutrient-dense choices have been made from each food group is about 265 kcalories. You could spend these extra kcalories on a candy bar, or a 20-oz soda, or a cup of ice cream—but you wouldn't have enough discretionary kcalories to eat all these foods in the same day. The more active a person is, the more discretionary kcalories they are allowed and the more of these "splurge" foods they can fit into their diet.

Key Messages of MyPyramid

MyPyramid stresses the key concepts of moderation, proportionality, and variety in choosing foods, but unlike its food guide predecessors it also emphasizes activity. The following sections outline the general messages promoted by MyPyramid and symbolized by the MyPyramid icon (**Figure 2.8**).

Activity Many Americans have sedentary lifestyles, getting little or no exercise on a daily basis. The figure climbing the side of the pyramid illustrates the activity component in MyPyramid. The activity recommendations match those of the Dietary Guidelines: 30 minutes of moderate to vigorous physical activity on most days of the week to reduce the risk of chronic disease and improve physical fitness, up to 60 minutes of exercise on most days to manage weight and prevent unhealthy weight gain, and 60 to 90 minutes of exercise per day to sustain a weight loss. Increasing activity increases energy needs and makes weight loss and weight maintenance easier.

Variety Variety is important for a healthy diet because no one type of food provides all the nutrients and food components needed. Variety is shown in MyPyramid by six slender colored triangles; which represent the five food groups and oils. Variety is also emphasized by recommendations regarding the consumption of different types of vegetables—more leafy greens, orange vegetables, and legumes.

Physical activity is represented by the figure climbing the stairs.

Proportionality is represented by the different widths of the colored triangles.

Moderation is represented by the triangle shapes. The wide base of each triangle includes the most nutrient-dense choices, which should be selected more often.

Variety is symbolized by the six colored triangles representing the five food groups plus oils.

Figure 2.8 MyPyramid Messages
The MyPyramid icon symbolizes the key messages of variety, proportionality, moderation, and activity.

Proportionality Proportionality may be a new word when it comes to food pyramids, but it is not a new concept. Proportionality means that we need to eat more of some types of food than others. In MyPyramid proportionality is represented by the different widths of the colored food group bands. The widest groups are the ones to choose the most of—grains, vegetables, fruits, and milk. The meat and beans band is narrower and the band representing oils is the thinnest. The exact amount you should choose from each group depends on how many kcalories you expend each day.

Moderation Dietary moderation means avoiding excesses of food components that increase health risks. Practicing moderation means that most of your choices should be from foods that are low in saturated fat, *trans* fat, cholesterol, added sugars, salt, and alcohol. Foods that are higher in these should be consumed in limited amounts. The message of moderation is symbolized by the narrowing of each food group from bottom to top. The wider base represents the nutrient-dense whole foods that should be chosen most often. The narrower tip represents the foods that should be eaten less often—those with more discretionary kcalories from added sugars and solid fats. For example, at the base of the grains group would be cooked plain oatmeal, as you move up would be sweetened instant oatmeal, and at the tip would be oatmeal chocolate chip cookies. At the base of the fruits group is a fresh apple. As you move up you would find a sweetened baked apple and at the tip a slice of apple pie. At the base of the milk group is low-fat milk and yogurt and at the tip is ice cream. The www.MyPyramid.gov Web site provides examples and suggestions to help you consume more of the nutrient-dense choices from the broader base of each food group.

Finding Your Pyramid Plan

MyPyramid is a personalized approach to healthy eating and physical activity. To obtain an individualized pyramid plan go to, www.MyPyramid.gov. After entering your age, gender, and activity level, it will give you "Your Pyramid", based on the amount of food from each group that will meet your energy needs. **Figure 2.9**

Figure 2.9 Individualized MyPyramid Plan
A MyPyramid plan shows the recommended amounts from each food group and oils and indicates the number of discretionary kcalories allowed to meet kcalorie needs. It also gives advice on making nutrient-dense choices from within each group.

Table 2.4 *Estimated Energy Needs*

Age (Yrs)	Males			Females		
	Inactive	Moderately Active	Active	Inactive	Moderately Active	Active
			Kcalories			
16–18	2400	2800	3200	1800	2000	2400
19–20	2600	2800	3000	2000	2200	2400
21–25	2400	2800	3000	2000	2200	2400
26–30	2400	2600	3000	1800	2000	2400
31–35	2400	2600	3000	1800	2000	2200
36–40	2400	2600	2800	1800	2000	2200
41–45	2200	2600	2800	1800	2000	2200
46–50	2200	2400	2800	1800	2000	2200
51–55	2200	2400	2800	1600	1800	2200
56–60	2200	2400	2600	1600	1800	2200
61–65	2000	2400	2600	1600	1800	2000
66–70	2000	2200	2600	1600	1800	2000

Inactive = less than 30 minutes a day of moderate activity.

Moderately active = between 30 and 60 minutes of moderate activity a day.

Active = 60 minutes or more of moderate activity a day.

Source: www.mypyramid.gov

shows the Pyramid plan for an 18-year old female who exercises between 30 and 60 minutes a day and therefore needs to eat 2000 kcalories per day. The kcalorie needs and recommended amounts from each food group for adults are summarized in **Tables 2.4** and **2.5**. To find your pyramid plan look up your kcalorie needs in Table 2.4 and then match them to your recommended food group amounts in Table 2.5. Once you know how much to choose from each group, you can plan your meals and snacks for the day. **Table 2.6** shows a sample day's menu for a 2000-kcalorie diet. The variety of vegetables recommended over the course of a week can be seen by looking at the 7 days of menus for a 2000-kcalorie food pattern shown in Appendix G.

The MyPyramid Web site also includes MyPyramid Tracker and Menu Planner. The Tracker is an interactive program that allows you to analyze the nutrient content of your diet and the energy you burn in activity. You can enter the foods you eat each day and analyze them in terms of their energy and nutrient intake and how well they

Table 2.5 *Food Group Choices for Different Kcalorie Levels*

Energy Level (Kcal)	1800	2000	2200	2400	2600	2800	3000	3200
Grains (ounce equivalents)	6	6	7	8	9	10	10	10
Vegetables (cups)	2.5	2.5	3	3	3.5	3.5	4	4
Fruits (cups)	1.5	2	2	2	2	2.5	2.5	2.5
Milk (cups)	3	3	3	3	3	3	3	3
Meat & Beans (ounce equivalents)	5	5.5	6	6.5	6.5	7	7	7
Oils (tsp)	5	6	6	7	8	8	10	11
Discretionary kcalorie allowance (kcals)	195	267	290	362	410	426	512	648

Source: www.mypyramid.gov

Table 2.6 *Sample Menu for a 2000-Kcalorie Day*

Breakfast

Hot Cereal
- *1/2 cup cooked oatmeal*
- *2 Tbsp raisins*
- *1 tsp soft margarine*

1/2 cup fat-free milk

1 cup orange juice

Lunch

Taco salad
- *2 ounces tortilla chips*
- *2 ounces chopped turkey, sauteed in*
- *2 tsp sunflower oil*
- *1/2 cup black beans*
- *1/2 cup iceberg lettuce*
- *2 slices tomato*
- *1 ounce low-fat cheddar cheese*
- *2 Tbsp salsa*
- *1/2 cup avocado*
- *1 tsp lime juice*

1 unsweetened beverage

Dinner

Spinach lasagna
- *1 cup lasagna noodles, cooked*
- *(2 oz dry)*
- *2/3 cup cooked spinach*
- *1/2 cup ricotta cheese*
- *1/2 cup tomato sauce*
- *1 ounce part-skim mozzarella cheese*

1 ounce whole-wheat dinner roll

1 cup fat-free milk

Snacks

1/2 ounce dry-roasted almonds

1/4 cup pineapple

1 apple

match the recommendations of the Dietary Guidelines and MyPyramid. You can also enter your daily activities to determine if your activity level meets recommendations, how your energy output compares with your energy input, and obtain tips on how to improve your activity profile (see Critical Thinking: The Personalized Pyramid). The MyPyramid Menu Planner at www.mypyramind.gov allows you to compare your intake with the recommendations for a healthy diet (**Figure 2.10**).

Figure 2.10 MyPyramid Menu Planner
This interactive tool (at www.mypyramid.gov) helps you visualize each food's contribution to your diet. It can be used to evaluate up to a week's worth of meals and snacks.

Critical Thinking
The Personalized Pyramid

Background

For the first time in his life, Jarad is living on his own. He has gained a few pounds and is beginning to realize that he needs to pay more attention to the kinds of foods he eats. Jarad is 22 years old. He spends less than 30 minutes walking from class to class each day and gets little other exercise. To evaluate his intake he keeps a record of everything he consumes for one day. Then he compares his intake to the "MyPyramid Plan" at www.MyPyramid.gov for someone his age, gender, and activity level.

Data:

FOOD	AMOUNT	FOOD GROUP
Breakfast		
Corn flakes	1 cup	Grains
Whole milk	1/2 cup	Milk (contains discretionary kcalories)
Orange juice	1 cup	Fruits
Coffee	1 cup	
with cream	1 Tbsp	(all discretionary kcalories)
and sugar	1 tsp	(all discretionary kcalories)
Snack		
Whole-grain crackers	5	Grains (whole)
Swiss cheese	1 slice	Milk (contains discretionary kcalories)
Lunch		
Hamburger		
roll	1 whole	Grains
regular-fat ground beef patty	2 oz	Meat and Beans (contains discretionary kcalories)
onions, tomatoes, lettuce	1/2 cup	Vegetables
sauce	1 Tbsp	(contains discretionary kcalories)
French fries	20 pieces	Vegetables, Oils
Milk shake		
whole milk	1 cup	Milk (contains discretionary kcalories)
ice cream	1/3 cup	Milk (contains discretionary kcalories)
Snack		
Soda	1 can	(all discretionary kcalories)
Dinner		
Frozen lasagna		
noodles	1 cup	Grains
tomato sauce	1/2 cup	Vegetables
regular-fat ground beef	4 oz	Meat and Beans (contains discretionary kcalories)
low-fat mozzarella cheese	1/6 cup	Milk
ricotta cheese	1/4 cup	Milk (contains discretionary kcalories)
olive oil	2 tsp	Oils
Soda	1 can	(all discretionary kcalories)
Chocolate chip cookies	3 cookies	Grains (contains discretionary kcalories)

(©iStockphoto)

(©iStockphoto)

(©iStockphoto)

Critical Thinking Questions

How does Jarad's diet compare to the MyPyramid recommendations? Does he eat enough whole grains? Do his vegetable choices meet the recommendations for types of vegetables?

▼

Based on his food choices, why do you think he is gaining weight?

▼

Use the MyPyramid Web site to determine how Jarad's kcalorie needs would change if he begins exercising for 50 minutes per day.

 iProfile   Use iProfile to find nutrient-dense substitutions for foods that are high in discretionary kcalories.

2.5 Food and Supplement Labels

Learning Objectives

- Use the Nutrition Facts on a food label to select a food that is considered low in saturated fat.
- Use a food label to distinguish which ingredients in the product are present in the greatest and least amounts.
- Use a dietary supplement label to determine the types and amounts of ingredients the product provides.

Food labels are a tool that can help plan diets that meet the recommendations of the DRIs, Dietary Guidelines, and MyPyramid. They are designed to help consumers make healthy food choices by providing information about the nutrient composition of foods and how a food fits into the overall diet. Checking the food label can help you select a food that is a good source of fiber, or one that is low in saturated fat, or high in vitamin C. To make this information uniform and easy to use, food labeling standards are specified by the Nutrition Labeling and Education Act of 1990. Dietary supplements are required to carry a similar label to help consumers know what supplemental nutrients and other ingredients they are choosing.

Food Labels

More than 98% of all processed, packaged foods sold in the United States carry standard food labels.[10] The Food and Drug Administration (FDA) regulates the labeling of all foods except meat and poultry products, which are regulated by the USDA. All packaged foods except those produced by small businesses and those in packages too small to fit the information must be labeled. Some restaurant food and ready-to-eat food, such as that served in bakeries and delicatessens, is also exempt, but if a claim about a food's nutritional content or health benefits such as "low-fat" or "heart healthy" is included on a menu, the eating establishment must provide nutritional information about this food when requested[11] (See Your Choice: How Can You Eat Out and Still Eat Well). Raw fruits, vegetables, fish, meat, and poultry are not required to carry individual labels. The FDA has asked grocery stores to voluntarily provide nutrition information for the raw fruits, vegetables, and fish most frequently eaten in the United States and the USDA encourages voluntary nutrition labeling of raw meat and poultry (**Figure 2.11**).

All labels are required to contain basic product information such as the name of the product; the net contents or weight; the date by which the product should be sold; and the name and place of business of the manufacturer, packager, or distributor. In addition, most food labels contain a "Nutrition Facts" panel and a list of the food's ingredients.

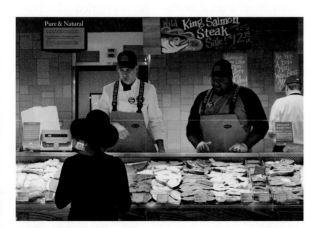

Figure 2.11 Labeling of raw fruits, vegetables, meat, poultry, and fish is voluntary. The information can appear on large placards or in consumer pamphlets or brochures (© AP/Wide World Photos)

How Can You Eat Out and Still Eat Well?

Restaurant meals are typically higher in kcalories, saturated fat, cholesterol, and salt, and lower in fiber, vitamin A, and other micronutrients than the meals we prepare at home.[1] Our eat-on-the-run lifestyle has made choosing healthy foods from restaurant menus an important skill—but it can be a challenge.

Some healthy choices are easy. Skip the fried fish and have it broiled instead. Minimize sauces and spreads that add fat, sugar, and kcalories. Ask that salad dressing be served on the side. Take some of the meal home for tomorrow's lunch. Other restaurant choices are more difficult to make. Items that sound like part of a healthy diet are not always what they seem. What's in that house special turkey tetrazzini, beef lo mein, or a fajita wrap?

Many restaurants have responded to consumer concern about healthy diets by highlighting healthy items on their menus with nutrient content claims such as "low-fat" or "low-salt." The food labeling laws that regulate packaged foods also apply to menus so these terms mean the same thing they do on food labels. For example, if you order a "low-fat" tostado, you can assume that low fat means that it contains 3 grams or less of fat per serving, as it would on a food label. Menus may also offer general dietary guidance and make claims about the relationship between a nutrient and a disease or health condition, as long as they follow the labeling laws (see Appendix J).

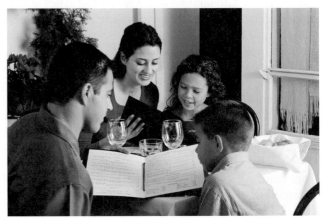

(Banana Stock/Age Fotostock America, Inc.)

Nutrient content claims and health claims about items on the menu must be backed up with appropriate written or recited nutrition information when requested.

When choosing from a menu, look for items that fit into an overall healthy diet. Choose foods you like, and remember that a high-fat or high-kcalorie meal now and then doesn't make your overall diet unhealthy. If you eat out often, though, choose carefully, because these meals make up a greater part of your overall diet.

[1] Frazao, E. (Ed.). America's Eating Habits: Changes and Consequences. USDA/Economic Research Service, Agricultural Information Bulletin No. AIB750, May 1999. Available online at www.ers.usda.gov/publications/aib750/. Accessed May 16, 2009.

Nutrition Facts The nutrition information section of the label is entitled "Nutrition Facts" (**Figure 2.12**). It provides information about serving size; total kcalories (on food labels the term "Calorie" is used to represent kcalories); kcalories from fat; the amounts of total fat, saturated fat, *trans* fat, cholesterol, sodium, total carbohydrate, dietary fiber, sugars, and protein per serving; and how the food fits into the overall diet.

Serving Size The serving size of a food product is given in common household and metric measures and is followed by the number of servings per container. Serving size is based on a standard list of serving sizes. The use of standard serving sizes allows comparisons to be made easily between products. For example, comparing the energy content of different types of cookies is simplified because all packages list energy values for a standard serving size of about an ounce and tell you the number of

Nutrition Facts

Start Here

Serving Size 1 cup (228g)
Servings Per Container 2

Amount Per Serving

Calories 250   Calories from Fat 110

% Daily Value*

Limit these
nutrients

Total Fat 12g	**18**%
Saturated Fat 3g	**15**%
Trans Fat 1.5g	
Cholesterol 30mg	**10**%
Sodium 470mg	**20**%
Total Carbohydrate 31g	**10**%
Dietary Fiber 0g	**0**%
Sugars 5g	
Protein 5g	

Quick guide
to % Daily Value
5% or less is low
20% or more is
high

Get enough
of these
nutrients

Vitamin A	4%
Vitamin C	2%
Calcium	20%
Iron	4%

Footnote

* Percent Daily Values are based on a 2,000 calorie
diet. Your daily values may be higher or lower
depending on your calorie needs:

	Calories:	2,000	2,500
Total Fat	Less than	65g	80g
Sat. Fat	Less than	20g	25g
Cholesterol	Less than	300mg	300mg
Sodium	Less than	2,400mg	2,400mg
Total Carbohydrate		300g	375g
Dietary Fiber		25g	30g

Figure 2.12 Nutrition Facts
This Nutrition Facts panel from a macaroni and cheese label illustrates how the information can be used to make wise food choices.

cookies per serving. These serving sizes are not always the same as the portions you put on your plate. If you eat two servings you are consuming twice as many kcalories.

Daily Values Food labels list the amounts of most nutrients as a percentage of a standard called the **Daily Value**. Daily Values help consumers determine how a food fits into their overall diet. The % Daily Value is the amount of a nutrient in a food as a percentage of the recommendation for a 2000-kcalorie diet. For example, if a food provides 10% of the Daily Value for dietary fiber, then the food provides 10% of the recommended daily intake for dietary fiber in a 2000-kcalorie diet. This helps people assess whether an individual food provides a little or a lot of a particular nutrient. As a general rule, a Daily Value of 5% or less indicates that the food is low in that nutrient and a Daily Value of 20% or more indicates that it is high. For most nutrients, the Daily Value is a target for intake, but for some, such as total fat, saturated fat, and cholesterol, it is a maximum recommended amount. For these you would want to select foods with a low % Daily Value. So, for example, if a food contains 15% of the Daily Value for saturated fat, then it contains 15% of the maximum amount recommended for a 2000-kcalorie diet. Food labels must list the Daily Value for total fat, saturated fat, cholesterol, sodium, total carbohydrate, and dietary fiber, as well as for vitamin A, vitamin C, calcium, and iron.

Because the Daily Values are a single set of standards for everyone, they may overestimate the amount of a nutrient needed for some groups, but they do not underestimate the requirement for any group (except pregnant and lactating women). Daily Values are based on two sets of standards, the **Reference Daily Intakes (RDIs)** and the **Daily Reference Values (DRVs)** (**Table 2.7**). To avoid confusion, only the term "Daily Value" appears on food labels.

daily value A nutrient reference value used on food labels to help consumers see how foods fit into their overall diets.

reference daily intakes (RDIs) Reference values established for vitamins and minerals that are based on the highest amount of each nutrient recommended for any adult age group by the 1968 RDAs.

daily reference values (DRVs) Reference values established for protein and seven nutrients for which no original RDAs were established. The values are based on dietary recommendations for reducing the risk of chronic disease.

Table 2.7 *Standards that Make up the Daily Values*

Nutrient	Daily Reference Value	Amount in 2000-Kcalorie Diet	Amount in 2500-Kcalorie Diet
Total fat	<30% of kcalories	65 g	80 g
Saturated fat	<10% of kcalories	20 g	25 g
Total carbohydrate	60% of kcalories	300 g	375 g
Dietary fiber	11.5 g/1000 kcalories	25 g	30 g
Protein	10% of kcalories	50 g	63 g
Cholesterol	<300 mg	<300 mg	<300 mg
Sodium	<2400 mg	<2400 mg	<2400 mg
Potassium	3500 mg	3500 mg	3500 mg

Nutrient	Reference Daily Intake*	Nutrient	Reference Daily Intake*
Vitamin A	5000 IU†	Vitamin E	30 IU†
Biotin	300 µg	Riboflavin	1.7 mg
Vitamin C	60 mg	Niacin	20 mg
Vitamin B$_6$	2.0 mg	Vitamin B$_{12}$	6 µg
Thiamin	1.5 mg	Chromium	120 µg
Folic acid	400 µg	Phosphorus	1000 mg
Pantothenic acid	10 mg	Selenium	70 µg
Vitamin K	80 µg	Calcium	1000 mg
Iodine	150 µg	Magnesium	400 mg
Molybdenum	75 µg	Manganese	2 mg
Iron	18 mg	Zinc	15 mg
Vitamin D	400 IU†	Chloride	3400 mg
Copper	2 mg		

*Based on National Academy of Sciences' 1968 Recommended Dietary Allowances.

†The Reference Daily Intakes for some fat-soluble vitamins are expressed in International Units (IU). The DRIs use a newer system of measurement.

Ingredient List The ingredients section of the label lists the contents of the product in order of their prominence by weight. For example, many juice drinks are mostly water and sugar. The ingredient list shown in **Figure 2.13** indicates that water and the sweetener high-fructose corn syrup are the first two ingredients and thus are the most abundant ingredients by weight. An ingredient list is required on all products containing more than one ingredient. Food additives, including food colors and

INGREDIENTS: Water, high fructose corn syrup, pear and grape juice concentrates, citirc acid, water extracted orange and pineapple juice concentrates, natural flavor

Figure 2.13 Interpreting an ingredient list
You can tell from the ingredient list that the greatest proportion of the weight of this juice drink is water, followed by the sweetener high-fructose corn syrup.

flavorings, must be listed among the ingredients (see Off the Label: Using Food Labels to Choose Wisely).

Dietary Supplement Labels

There are thousands of types of dietary supplements and about half of all American adults take some kind of supplement.[12] These products, which can include vitamins; minerals; herbs, botanicals, or other plant-derived substances; amino acids; enzymes; concentrates; and extracts, must carry a standard label that meets the specifications of the Dietary Supplement Health and Education Act of 1994.[13] Each product must include the words "dietary supplement" on the label and carry a "Supplement Facts" panel similar to the "Nutrition Facts" panel found on most processed foods (**Figure 2.14**). This panel lists the recommended serving size and the name and quantity of each ingredient per serving. The source of the ingredient may be given with its name in the Supplement Facts panel or in the ingredient list below the panel. The nutrients for which Daily Values have been established are listed first, followed by other dietary ingredients for which Daily Values have not been established.[13]

The serving size tells you the recommended dose.

Supplement Facts

Serving Size 3 Capsules — Servings Per Container 33

	Amount Per Serving	% Daily Value*
Calories	20	
Calories from Fat	20	
Total Fat	2 g	3%
Total Omega-3 Fatty Acids	1100 mg	
EPA (Eicosapentaenoic Acid)	450 mg	†
DHA (Docosahexaenoic Acid)	500 mg	†
DPA (Docosapentaenoic Acid)	60 mg	†
Stearidonic, Eicosatrienoic, Eicosatetraenoic, Heneicosapentaenoic, and Alpha-Linolenic Acids	90 mg	†

* Percent Daily Values are based on 2,000 calorie diet
† Daily Value not established

INGREDIENTS: Salmon Oil, UHPO3 Omega-3 Fatty Acid Concentrate (Sardines, Tuna, Anchovies), Gelatin, Glycerin and Water.

Each serving of Fish Oil Omega A–C provides the complete spectrum of healthful Omega-3 fatty acids equivalent to approximately one serving of fresh salmon.

*Research shows Omega-3 fatty acids play a role in the health and function of the cardiovascular system, central nervous system, vision, connective tissue, and the inflammatory response.

*These statements have not been evaluated by the Food and Drug Administration. This product is not intended to diagnose, treat, cure or prevent any disease.

FISH OIL
OMEGA A-C

DIETARY SUPPLEMENT
100 soft gel caps

The name, quantity per serving, and % Daily Values for nutrients are listed. You can use these to assess how that amount compares to the recommended intake and UL for each nutrient. Nutrients with Daily Values are listed first, followed by ingredients without Daily Values.

All ingredients must be listed on the label either in the Supplement Facts panel or in the ingredient list below the panel. Ingredients are listed in descending order of prominence.

All these products must include the words *dietary supplement* on the label.

Because structure/function claims are based on the manufacturer's interpretation and are not approved by the FDA, products with these claims must include this disclaimer.

Figure 2.14 Dietary supplement label
Unlike food labels, dietary supplement labels must provide directions for use and must frequently provide information about ingredients that are not nutrients and for which Daily Values have not been established.

Off the Label
Using Food Labels to Choose Wisely

Food labels can't help you include more vegetables and fruits in your diet each day, or ensure that you select a varied diet, but they do provide you with a good source of nutrition information. For example, for breakfast you might choose granola with whole milk or oatmeal made with nonfat milk. Which is the best choice if you want your diet to be moderate in sugar and fat, and high in nutrient density? You can see on the label that a cup of whole milk provides 150 kcalories and 5 grams of saturated fat. This 5 grams of saturated fat represents 25% of the Daily Value—that is, 25% of the total amount of saturated fat recommended per day for a 2000-kcalorie diet. A cup of nonfat milk, in contrast, contains no saturated fat and only 90 kcalories. Both are good sources of calcium and vitamins A and D, and both are in the milk group. But nonfat milk contributes no discretionary kcalories and better meets the Dietary Guidelines recommendation to choose a diet low in saturated fat and cholesterol.

Granola and oatmeal each provide a serving from the grains group—both contain whole grains—but the amounts of fat and added sugars differs. A serving of granola provides 230 kcalories and 9 grams of fat, whereas a serving of oatmeal has only 150 kcalories and 3 grams of fat. The ingredient list reveals that oatmeal contains only rolled oats. No sugars are added. In contrast, the granola contains rolled oats plus brown sugar and honey in addition to other ingredients. The oatmeal is lower in both fat and added sugar so is higher in nutrient density.

Knowing how to interpret the information on food labels can help you choose a diet that meets the recommendations of the Dietary Guidelines and follows the selection tips of MyPyramid. However, this doesn't mean you can never have a doughnut for breakfast because the label identifies it as high in fat and kcalories. Even a high-fat food choice can be part of a healthy diet as long as it is balanced with healthy low-fat choices throughout the day. Remember, it is your total diet—not each choice—that counts.

Nonfat Milk

Nutrition Facts
Serving Size 1 cup (236 ml)
Servings Per Container 16

Amount Per Serving

Calories 90 Calories from Fat 0	
	% Daily Value*
Total Fat 0g	0%
Saturated Fat 0g	0%
Trans Fat 0g	
Cholesterol less than 5mg	1%
Sodium 125mg	5%
Total Carbohydrate 13g	4%
Dietary Fiber 0g	0%
Sugars 12g	
Protein 9g	17%

INGREDIENTS: GRADE A FAT FREE SKIM MILK. VITAMIN A PALMITATE AND VITAMIN D3

Whole Milk

Nutrition Facts
Serving Size 1 cup (236 ml)
Servings Per Container 16

Amount Per Serving

Calories 150 Fat Cal. 70	
	% Daily Value*
Total Fat 8g	12%
Saturated Fat 5g	25%
Trans Fat 0g	
Cholesterol 35mg	11%
Sodium 125mg	5%
Total Carbohydrate 12g	4%
Dietary Fiber 0g	0%
Sugars 12g	
Protein 8g	16%

INGREDIENTS: MILK

Old Fashioned Oats

Nutrition Facts
Serving Size ½ cup (40g) dry
Servings Per Container about 13

		Cereal with ½ cup
Amount Per Serving	Dry	Skim Milk
Calories	150	190
Calories from Fat	25	30
	% Daily Value**	
Total Fat 3g	5%	5%
Saturated Fat 0.5g	3%	3%
Trans Fat 0g		
Cholesterol 0mg	0%	0%
Sodium 0mg	0%	3%
Total Carbohydrate 27g	9%	11%
Dietary Fiber 4g	16%	16%
Sugars 0g		
Protein 5g		

INGREDIENTS: 100% ROLLED OATS

Natural Granola

Nutrition Facts
Serving Size ½ cup (51g)
Servings Per Container about 16

Amount Per Serving

Calories 230 Calories from Fat 80	
	% Daily Value*
Total Fat 9g	13%
Saturated Fat 3.5g	18%
Trans Fat 1g	
Polyunsaturated Fat 1g	
Monounsaturated Fat 4g	
Cholesterol 0mg	0%
Sodium 20mg	1%
Potassium 250mg	7%
Total Carbohydrate 34g	11%
Other Carbohydrate 15g	
Dietary Fiber 3g	13%
Sugars 16g	
Protein 5g	

INGREDIENTS: Whole grain rolled oats, whole grain rolled wheat, brown sugar, raisins, dried coconut, almonds, partially hydrogenated cottonseed and soybean oils, nonfat dry milk, glycerin, honey.

Supplements are classified as foods and not drugs, so they are not bound by the strict laws that regulate drug manufacturing. To help ensure that these products contain the right ingredients and the right amount per dose, the FDA established dietary supplement "current Good Manufacturing Practice" (cGMP) regulations. These require manufacturers to test their products to ensure identity, purity, strength, and composition.[14] The U.S. Pharmacopeia (USP) Convention, which sets the standards for drug manufacturing, has also developed the USP Dietary Supplement Verification Program (DSVP).[15] This voluntary program evaluates and confirms the contents of dietary supplements, the manufacturing processes, and compliance with standards of purity. Products that have been reviewed and meet USP criteria can use the DSVP verification mark on the label or the statement "made to US Pharmacopeia (USP) quality, purity, and potency standards" (**Figure 2.15**). Consumers can be assured that products that have been USP-verified contain the ingredients in the amounts as listed on the label, will disintegrate or dissolve effectively to release nutrients for absorption, meet requirements for limits on contaminants, and comply with good manufacturing practices.

Products that carry the DSVP verification mark must meet certain manufacturing standards, but they are not necessarily safe or effective. Dietary supplements do not need to be approved by the FDA for safety and effectiveness before they are marketed. According to the Dietary Supplement Health and Education Act, the manufacturer is responsible for ensuring that a supplement is safe before it is sold. If a problem arises after the supplement is on the market, it is the responsibility of the FDA to prove that the supplement represents a risk and that it should be removed from the market (see Focus on Nonvitamin Nonmineral Supplements).

Figure 2.15 The Dietary Supplement Verification Program mark
This symbol indicates that the supplement has been verified as manufactured according to the quality, purity, and potency standards set by the U.S. Pharmacopeia (USP) Convention.

Label Claims

Three different types of claims can be used on food and dietary supplement labels: nutrient content claims, health claims, and structure/function claims. The responsibility for ensuring the validity of these claims rests with the manufacturer, the FDA, or, in the case of advertising, with the Federal Trade Commission.[16]

Nutrient Content Claims Food and supplement labels often highlight the level of a nutrient or dietary substance in a product that might be of interest to the consumer, such as "low Calorie" or "high fiber." Definitions for nutrient content descriptors such as "free," "high," and "reduced" have been established by the FDA. In selecting a product labeled with a descriptor such as "fat free," consumers can be assured that the food meets the defined criteria, in this case that the product contains less than 0.5 gram of fat per serving. Likewise, when selecting a supplement, the claim "excellent source of vitamin C" means that a serving of the product must contain at least 20% of the Daily Value for vitamin C. Terms like "high potency" or "antioxidant" used on supplement labels are also considered nutrient content claims. The specific definition of each of these descriptors is given in **Table 2.8** and their use in relation to specific nutrients is discussed in Off the Label features throughout this text.

Health Claims Food and supplement labels are also permitted to include a number of health claims if they are relevant to the product. Health claims refer to a relationship between a food, food component, or dietary supplement ingredient and the risk of a disease or health-related condition. They can help consumers choose products that will meet their dietary needs or health goals. For example, low-fat milk, a good source of calcium, might include on the package label a statement indicating that a diet high in calcium will reduce the risk of developing osteoporosis.

All health claims are reviewed by the FDA but there are three different paths that can lead to the authorization of a health claim. The first is the most stringent.

Table 2.8 *Descriptors Commonly Used on Food Labels*

Free	Product contains no amount of, or a trivial amount of, fat, saturated fat, cholesterol, sodium, sugars, or kcalories. For example, "sugar free" and "fat free" both mean less than 0.5 g per serving. Synonyms for "free" include "without," "no," and "zero."
Low	Used for foods that can be eaten frequently without exceeding the Daily Value for fat, saturated fat, cholesterol, sodium, or kcalories. Specific definitions have been established for each of these nutrients. For example, "low fat" means that the food contains 3 g or less per serving, and "low cholesterol" means that the food contains less than 20 mg of cholesterol per serving. Synonyms for "low" include "little," "few," and "low source of."
Lean and Extra Lean	Used to describe the fat content of meat, poultry, seafood, and game meats. "Lean" means that the food contains less than 10 g fat, less than 4.5 g saturated fat, and less than 95 mg of cholesterol per serving and per 100 g. "Extra lean" means that the food contains less than 5 g fat, less than 2 g saturated fat, and less than 95 mg of cholesterol per serving and per 100 g.
High	Used for foods that contain 20% or more of the Daily Value for a particular nutrient. Synonyms for "high" include "rich in" and "excellent source of."
Good Source	Food contains 10% to 19% of the Daily Value for a particular nutrient per serving.
Reduced	Nutritionally altered product contains 25% less of a nutrient or of energy than the regular or reference product.
Less	Food, whether altered or not, contains 25% less of a nutrient or of energy than the reference food. For example, pretzels may claim to have "less fat" than potato chips. "Fewer" may be used as a synonym for "less."
Light	Used in different ways. It can be used on a nutritionally altered product that contains one-third fewer kcalories or half the fat of a reference food. It can be used when the sodium content of a low-kcalorie, low-fat food has been reduced by 50%. The term "light" can also be used to describe properties such as texture and color as long as the label explains the intent—for example, "light and fluffy."
More	Serving of food, whether altered or not, contains a nutrient that is at least 10% of the Daily Value more than the reference food. This definition also applies to foods using the terms "fortified," "enriched," or "added."
Healthy	Used to describe foods that are low in fat and saturated fat and contain no more than 360 mg of sodium and no more than 60 mg of cholesterol per serving and provide at least 10% of the Daily Value for vitamins A or C, or iron, calcium, protein, or fiber.
Fresh	Used on foods that are raw and have never been frozen or heated and contain no preservatives.
High Potency	Used on foods or supplements to describe individual vitamins or minerals that are present at 100% or more of the Daily Value or on multi-ingredient foods or supplement products that contain 100% or more of the Daily Value for at least two-thirds of the vitamins and minerals present in significant amounts (e.g., "High-potency multivitamin, multimineral dietary supplement tablets").
Antioxidant	Used to describe foods or supplements that are "a good source of" or "high in" a nutrient for which there is an established Daily Value and for which there is scientific evidence of its function as an antioxidant.

Source: U.S. Food and Drug Administration.

These health claims, such as the one in **Figure 2.16**, are authorized after an extensive review of the scientific evidence and are said to meet the *significant scientific agreement* standard. A second way to authorize a health claim on foods (but not supplements) is based on a statement of support, called an *authoritative statement*, from an appropriate scientific body of the United States government or the National Academy of Sciences. Finally, some health claims are approved when there is emerg-

Figure 2.16 Health claims on food labels
Oatmeal contains enough soluble fiber to be permitted to include on the label a health claim about the relationship between soluble fiber and the risk of heart disease.

ing, but not well-established evidence for a relationship between a food, food component, or dietary supplement and reduced risk of a disease or health-related condition. These are called *qualified health claims* and must be accompanied by a statement explaining this so they do not mislead the consumer. The claims listed in **Table 2.9** are those that currently meet significant scientific agreement for use on food and supplement labels.[17] A complete table of health claims can be found in Appendix J.

Structure/Function Claims Structure/function claims describe the role of a nutrient or dietary ingredient in maintaining normal structure or function in humans. For example, a structure/function claim about calcium may state that "calcium builds strong bones." These claims may also describe the general well-being that arises from consumption of a nutrient or dietary supplement, such as "fiber maintains bowel regularity." Some structure/function claims also describe a benefit in relation to a nutrient-deficiency disease, such as "vitamin C prevents scurvy." These statements must also tell how widespread the disease is in the United States. Structure/function claims are not approved by the FDA. They are based on the manufacturer's review and interpretation of the scientific literature and must not be untrue or misleading. They must be accompanied by the disclaimer that "This statement has not been evaluated by the Food and Drug Administration. This product is not intended to diagnose, treat, cure, or prevent any disease" (see Figure 2.14).

2.6 Other Guidelines

Learning Objectives

- List the parameters that foods in the same Exchange List have in common.
- Describe the purpose of the Healthy People Initiative.

In addition to the guidelines discussed in the previous section, there are a number of other types of recommendations made to promote a healthy diet and lifestyle. The **Exchange Lists** is a food group system that is useful in planning diets to meet specific energy and macronutrient goals. The **Healthy People Initiative** is a health promotion program that includes nutrition in its recommendations. Other diet and lifestyle recommendations are made by special interest groups, which make recommendations for reducing the risks of specific diseases such as heart disease and cancer.

exchange lists A food group system that groups foods according to energy and macronutrient content. It is used extensively in planning diabetic and weight loss diets.

healthy people initiative A set of national health promotion and disease prevention objectives for the U.S. population.

Table 2.9 *Health Claims Used on Food Labels**

Calcium and osteoporosis	Adequate calcium intake throughout life helps maintain bone health and reduce the risk of osteoporosis.
Sodium and hypertension (high blood pressure)	Diets low in sodium may reduce the risk of high blood pressure in some people.
Dietary fat and cancer	Diets low in fat may reduce the risk of some types of cancer.
Saturated fat and cholesterol and risk of coronary heart disease	Diets low in saturated fat and cholesterol help reduce blood cholesterol and, thus, the risk of heart disease.
Fiber-containing grain products, fruits, and vegetables, and cancer risk	Diets low in fat and rich in fiber-containing grain products, fruits, and vegetables may reduce the risk of some types of cancer.
Fruits, vegetables, and grain products that contain fiber, particularly soluble fiber, and risk of coronary heart disease	Diets low in saturated fat and cholesterol and rich in fruits, vegetables, and grain products that contain fiber, particularly soluble fiber, may reduce the risk of coronary heart disease.
Fruits and vegetables and cancer	Diets low in fat and rich in fruits and vegetables may reduce the risk of some types of cancer.
Folic acid and neural tube birth defects	Adequate folic acid intake by the mother reduces the risk of birth defects of the brain or spinal cord in her baby.
Soluble fiber from certain foods and risk of coronary heart disease	Diets low in fat, saturated fat, and cholesterol that include soluble fiber from whole oats or psyllium seed husk may reduce the risk of heart disease.
Dietary sugar alcohol and dental caries (cavities)	Sugar-free foods that are sweetened with sugar alcohols do not promote tooth decay and may reduce the risk of dental caries.
Soy protein and risk of coronary heart disease	Soy protein included in a diet that is low in saturated fat and cholesterol may reduce the risk of coronary heart disease.
Plant sterol/stanol esters and risk of coronary heart disease	Plant sterols and plant stanols included in a diet that is low in saturated fat and cholesterol may reduce the risk of coronary heart disease by lowering blood cholesterol levels.

*The health claims included in this table are those that meet the significant scientific agreement standard. A food carrying a health claim must be a naturally good source (10% or more of the Daily Value) for one of six nutrients (vitamin A, vitamin C, protein, calcium, iron, or fiber) and must not contain more than 20% of the Daily Value for fat, saturated fat, cholesterol, or sodium.

Exchange Lists

The Exchange Lists were first developed in 1950 by the American Dietetic Association and the American Diabetes Association as a meal-planning tool for individuals with diabetes. Since then, its use has been expanded to planning weight-loss diets and diets in general. The latest revision of the Exchange Lists divides foods into three main groups based on their macronutrient content: the carbohydrate group, the meat and meat-substitute group, and the fat group.[18] The carbohydrate group includes exchange lists for foods that are sources of carbohydrates: starches, fruits, milk, and vegetables. It also defines a list of other high-carbohydrate foods and indicates how to fit these foods into a diet based on exchanges. The meat and meat-substitute group includes an exchange list with four subgroups: very lean, lean, medium-fat, and high-fat meat. The fat group includes an exchange list with subgroups of monounsaturated, polyunsaturated, and saturated fats (**Table 2.10**) (see Appendix I).

Table 2.10 *Energy and Macronutrient Values of the Exchange Lists*

Exchange Group/Lists	Serving Size	Energy (kcals)	Carbohydrate (g)	Protein (g)	Fat (g)
Carbohydrate Group					
Starch	1/2 cup pasta, cereal; 1 slice bread	80	15	3	0–1
Fruit	1 small apple, peach, or pear; 1/2 banana; 1/2 cup canned fruit (in juice)	60	15	0	0
Milk					
Nonfat	1 cup milk or yogurt	90	12	8	0
Low-fat		110	12	8	3
Reduced fat		120	12	8	5
Whole		150	12	8	8
Other carbohydrates	Serving sizes vary	Varies	15	Varies	Varies
Vegetables	1/2 cup cooked vegetables, 1 cup raw	25	5	2	0
Meat/Meat Substitute Group	1 oz meat or cheese				
Very lean		35	0	7	0–1
Lean		55	0	7	3
Medium fat		75	0	7	5
High fat		100	0	7	8
Fat Group	1 tsp butter, margarine, or oil; 1 Tbsp salad dressing	45	0	0	5

The exchanges are designed so that each serving within a list contains approximately the same amount of energy, carbohydrate, protein, and fat. For instance, each fruit serving in the fruit exchange list provides about 60 kcalories, 15 grams of carbohydrate, no protein, and no fat, whereas choices in the starch list provide about 80 kcalories, 15 grams of carbohydrate, 3 grams of protein, and 0 to 1 gram of fat. The food groupings of the Exchange Lists differ from the MyPyramid groups because the lists are designed to meet energy and macronutrient criteria, whereas the MyPyramid groups are designed to be good sources of certain nutrients regardless of their energy content. For example, a potato is included in the starch exchange list because it contains about the same amount of energy, carbohydrate, protein, and fat as breads and grains, but in MyPyramid a potato is in the vegetable group because it is a good source of vitamins, minerals, and fiber.

The Exchange Lists can be used to design diets to meet individual tastes and preferences at specific energy and macronutrient levels. For instance, a diet could be calculated to provide 1600 kcalories with 80 grams of protein, 207 grams of carbohydrate, and 50 grams of fat. The consumer would meet these nutrient criteria by consuming a prescribed number of servings from each of the exchanges. For example, he or she would be instructed to choose 6 starch exchanges, 2 milk exchanges, 3 vegetable exchanges, and so on.

The Healthy People Initiative

The U.S. Public Health Service along with hundreds of private and public organizations has developed a set of public health objectives called Healthy People. The first set, Healthy People 2000, developed in 1990, was directed toward the year 2000. The most recent objectives, Healthy People 2010, target the current decade. The purpose of Healthy People 2010 is to promote health and prevent illness, disability, and premature death. To achieve this it defines two overarching goals—increase quality and years of healthy life, and eliminate health disparities. These goals served as a guide for developing objectives that can be used to measure progress. Healthy People 2010 includes 467 objectives designed to improve the health of all people in the United States by promoting healthy behaviors, protecting health, assuring access to quality health care, and strengthening community prevention.[19] Many of the objectives of Healthy People 2010 address improving the nutritional status of the population (see Appendix G). For instance, Healthy People is working toward reducing the number of cancer and heart disease deaths and the prevalence of obesity in adults by promoting active lifestyles and diets low in fat and sodium and high in fiber. It promotes a reduction in growth retardation in children by encouraging healthy feeding practices, including breast-feeding for infants. Other nutrition-related objectives are designed to improve the delivery of nutrition information and services. The newest version of these objectives, Healthy People 2020, will be released in 2010.

Recommendations for Reducing Risks for Specific Diseases

In addition to guidelines for a healthy diet for the general population, recommendations to populations at risk for certain diseases have been published by groups such as the American Heart Association, the American Diabetes Association, and the American Institute for Cancer Research. These groups base their recommendations on sound scientific literature, but because of their special interest in preventing a specific disease, their recommendations may differ slightly from one another in emphasis and focus. In general, however, recommendations that protect against one chronic disease such as cancer, heart disease, or diabetes, will also reduce the risk of the others.

2.7 Assessing Nutritional Health

Learning Objectives

- Name three types of information used in assessing nutritional status.
- Discuss the pros and cons of a dietary recall versus a dietary record for assessing food intake.
- Explain the types of tools used to assess the nutritional health of populations.

To be healthy, people need to consume combinations of foods that provide appropriate amounts of nutrients. Scientists have developed standards for the amounts of nutrients needed and tools for planning diets to meet these needs. But how do we know if the nutritional needs of an individual or the population are being met? Evaluating the **nutritional status** of individuals and populations can identify nutritional needs and be used to plan diets to meet these needs.

nutritional status State of health as it is influenced by the intake and utilization of nutrients.

Individual Nutritional Health

What is your nutritional status? Are you losing weight? Gaining weight? Do you have a history of heart disease in your family? Are you at risk for a nutrient deficiency because you can't get to the store, can't afford to buy healthy foods, or you don't know what to eat or how to cook? An individual **nutritional assessment** helps to determine if a person has a nutrient deficiency or excess or is at risk of one, or if that individual is at risk of chronic diseases that are affected by diet. It requires a review of past and present dietary intake, a clinical assessment that evaluates body size and includes a medical history and physical exam, and laboratory measurements. Even with all these tools, diagnosing a nutritional deficiency or excess is not trivial. Estimates of dietary intake are not always accurate, and symptoms may be indistinguishable from other medical conditions.

nutritional assessment An evaluation used to determine the nutritional status of individuals or groups for the purpose of identifying nutritional needs and planning personal healthcare or community programs to meet those needs.

SCIENCE
ScienceAppliedScienceApplied
Science**AppliedScience**Applied
ScienceAppliedScienceApplied
APPLIED

(DAJ/Getty Images, Inc.)

(www.victorianoizquierdo.com/Getty Images, Inc.)

(Elena Schweitzer/Shutterstock)

The Art of Assessing Food Intake

What did you have for dinner last night? How about last week? To study nutrient requirements and functions, scientists need to know exactly how much of each nutrient their subjects are consuming. To identify possible nutrient deficiencies or excesses, a dietitian needs to know a client's typical diet. To make nutrition recommendations for a population, public health officials need to know what the population is eating.

The most accurate way to know what people in a research study are eating is to control it. Subjects typically are housed in a research facility where all the food they consume is specially prepared and served to them. The nutrient content of the diet is calculated to meet the study needs; the food is weighed before it is served; and everything that is served must be consumed. This method, though, is only practical for small numbers of subjects. Larger studies can be managed if a research facility prepares all food and subjects consume it in their homes or workplaces—but only if the subjects are compliant with the diet, resist urges for a candy bar or bag of chips not included in the diet, and are honest about what they consume. Also, these techniques do not provide information on what people typically eat.

Food frequencies, food records, and 24-hour recalls can be used to evaluate what individuals typically eat, to assess a population's nutritional health, or to study the relationships between nutrient intake and disease. The tool used depends on the type of information needed and the time and cost constraints. The goal is to collect the most reliable data in the fastest and most cost-effective manner. For instance, a study of fruit and vegetable consumption could use a food frequency questionnaire, which is easy for participants and relatively inexpensive for researchers to analyze. Food frequencies are often used in large epidemiological studies of food intake patterns. When more specific information is required, food frequencies may not be the best tool.[1]

Food records and 24-hour recalls can provide more detailed information. Food records created as subjects consume their meals can be very reliable. However, the act of recording can affect intake. Subjects may decide to skip the handful of chips they would have eaten rather than record that they ate it. In addition, food records are time-consuming for subjects and can be costly for researchers to collect and analyze. The 24-hour recall method, in contrast, can survey large numbers of people in

a short time and can be conducted by telephone.[2] The process is easy for the subjects; also, it can provide information that is more comprehensive than a food frequency and more accurate than a food record because subjects are less likely to change their intake.

All these methods involve the possibility for error, as they depend on the memories and reliability of study subjects. The most common error in food intake data is underreporting of intake. Subjects may not remember all the foods they have consumed or choose not to report them all. Portion sizes can be hard to accurately assess, and it can be difficult to know what ingredients are included in foods prepared away from home.

To recognize these biases, improve accuracy, and decrease or control for error in estimates of intake, researchers have studied methods of evaluating food intake and have come up with unique ways of validating accuracy. People can be placed in settings where they are allowed to choose the types and amounts of foods they wish to eat and their choices secretly observed and recorded. This type of observational study can generate general estimates on how well individuals report their intake. More recent methods to test the accuracy of food intake data rely on measuring energy balance (see Chapter 7). In people who are not losing or gaining weight, the energy they eat will equal the energy they expend. A comparison of an individual's energy expenditure, which can be accurately measured, with his or her energy intake can be used to evaluate the reliability of that person's reported intake.[3] These types of investigations have found that underreporting of food intake is common. It occurs more often in women than in men and more in persons who are older, overweight, or trying to lose weight.[4]

Assessments of what people typically eat are used to make and evaluate nutrition recommendations and plan the food supply. Inaccurate dietary intake data can give a misleading view of the public's nutritional status or of the effectiveness of nutritional guidelines. For example, the incidence of childhood obesity has increased over the last few decades. If food intake data indicate that American children have not increased their energy intake over this time, scientists might conclude that the increase in obesity is due to a decrease in physical activity and recommend that they increase their activity level. How might this conclusion and recommendation change if it were determined that the children were underreporting their food intake?

[1]Schaefer, E. J., Augustin, J. L., Schaefer, M. M., et al. Lack of efficacy of food frequency questionnaire in assessing dietary macronutrient intakes in subjects consuming diets of known composition. *Am. J. Clin. Nutr.* 71:746–751, 2000.

[2]Godwin, S. L., Chambers, E., 4th, and Cleveland, L. Accuracy of reporting dietary intake using various portion-size aids in-person and via telephone. *J. Am. Diet. Assoc.* 104:585–594, 2004.

[3]Black, A. E., Welch, A. A., and Bingham, S. A. Validation of dietary intakes measured by diet history against 24 h urinary nitrogen excretion and energy expenditure measured by the doubly-labeled water method in middle-aged women. *Br. J. Nutr.* 83:341–354, 2000.

[4]Becker, W., and Welten, D. Underreporting in dietary surveys–implications for development of food-based dietary guidelines. *Public Health Nutr.* 4:683–687, 2003.

Figure 2.17 Keeping an accurate food diary requires recording the precise amounts of all food and drink consumed. (Tony Freeman/PhotoEdit)

24-hour recall A method of assessing dietary intake in which a trained interviewer helps an individual remember what he or she ate during the previous day.

food diary A method of assessing dietary intake that involves an individual keeping a written record of all food and drink consumed during a defined period.

food frequency questionnaire A method of assessing dietary intake that gathers information about how often certain categories of food are consumed.

Estimating Dietary Intake A good place to start when evaluating nutritional status is to determine what a person typically eats. This can be done by observing all the food and drink consumed by the individual for a specified period of time or by asking them to record or recall their intake. Neither option is ideal. Being observed can affect an individual's intake and recording and recalling intake are imprecise measures because these methods rely on the memory and reliability of the consumer. For instance, a person who is attempting to lose weight may tend to report smaller portions than were actually eaten.[20] Despite this problem, the commonly used methods described here are the best tools available for evaluating dietary intake to predict nutrient deficiencies or excesses (see Science Applied: The Art of Assessing Food Intake).

24-Hour Recall The most common method of assessing dietary intake is a **24-hour recall** in which a trained interviewer asks a person to recall exactly what they ate during the preceding 24-hour period. A detailed description of all food and drink, including descriptions of cooking methods and brand names of products, is recorded. Since food intake varies from day to day, repeated 24-hour recalls on the same individual provide a more accurate estimate of typical intake.

Food Diary or Food Intake Record Food intake information can also be gathered by having a consumer keep a **food diary**, or record, of all the food and drink consumed for a set period of time. Typically, this is done for 2 to 7 days including at least one weekend day, since most people eat differently on weekends than during the school or work week. Foods may be weighed or measured or portion sizes just estimated (**Figure 2.17**). The record should be as complete as possible, including all beverages, condiments, and the brand names and preparation methods. The tedious nature of this type of record can be a disadvantage because in some cases it may cause the consumer to change his or her intake rather than record certain items.

Food Frequency A **food frequency questionnaire** lists a variety of foods, and the consumer is asked to estimate the frequency with which he or she consumes each item or food group. For example, "How often do you drink milk?" or "How many times a week do you eat red meat?" This method cannot be used to itemize a specific day's intake, but it can give a general picture of a person's typical pattern of food intake (**Figure 2.18**).

Figure 2.18 Food Frequency This section of a sample food frequency questionnaire can be used to obtain information about dairy product consumption patterns.

Food Frequency Questionnaire

On the following pages, please check the appropriate column indicating how often you consume each food.

	Once a day	Twice or more a day	Once a week	Twice or more a week	Once a month	Twice or more a month
Milk						
Whole						
Reduced fat						✔
Nonfat	✔					
Yogurt						
Whole						
Reduced fat			✔			
Nonfat						
Cheese						
Hard					✔	
Soft						✔
Reduced fat						
Ice cream						
Regular						
Reduced fat	✔					

Diet History A **diet history** collects information about dietary patterns. It may review eating habits: Do you cook your own meals? Do you skip lunch? It may also include a combination of methods to assess food intake such as a 24-hour recall along with a food frequency questionnaire. The combination of two or more methods often provides more complete information than one method alone. For instance, if an individual's 24-hour recall does not include milk, but a food frequency questionnaire suggests that the individual usually drinks milk 5 days a week, the two can be combined to provide a more accurate picture of this individual's typical intake.

Analyzing Nutrient Intake Once information on food intake has been obtained, the nutrient content of the diet can be compared to recommended intakes. This can be done in a number of ways. To get a general picture of dietary intake, an individual's food record can be compared with a guide for diet planning such as MyPyramid. For example, does the individual consume the recommended amount of milk each day? If an evaluation of the energy and macronutrient content of the diet is needed, it can be estimated using the Exchange Lists. A more precise and extensive analysis of dietary intake can be done by totaling the nutrients contributed by each food item.

Information on the nutrient composition of foods is available on food labels, in published food composition tables, and in computer databases. Food labels provide information only for some nutrients, and they are not available for all foods. Food composition tables generated by government and industry laboratories can provide more extensive information on food composition (see Nutrient Content of Foods Supplement for an abbreviated list). The major source of food composition data in the United States is the USDA Nutrient Database for Standard Reference, which is available online.[21] Computer programs with food composition databases, such as iProfile, are available for professionals and for home use. An easy-to-use online nutrient analysis can be done by using MyPyramid Tracker which uses the USDA database to analyze foods and diets entered into the program.

To analyze nutrient intake correctly using a computer program, each food and the exact portion consumed must be entered into the program. If a food is not found in the computer database, an appropriate substitute can be used or the food can be broken down into its individual ingredients. For example, homemade vegetable soup could be entered as generic vegetable soup, or as vegetable broth, carrots, green beans, rice, and so on. If a new product has come on the market, the information from the food label can be added to the database. The advantage of computer diet analysis is that it is fast and accurate. A program can calculate the nutrients for each day or average them over several days. It can also compare nutrient intake to recommended amounts. However, the information generated by computer diet analysis is only useful if it is entered correctly and interpreted appropriately. Also, a nutrient intake that is below the recommended amount does not always indicate a deficiency, and intake that meets recommendations does not ensure adequate nutritional status. **Figure 2.19** illustrates how iProfile diet analysis software compares the nutrients in a diet with recommendations.

Diet History Information about dietary habits and patterns. It may include a 24-hour recall, a food record, or a food frequency questionnaire to provide information about current intake patterns

Nutrient	DRI	Intake	Percent of Recommendation 0% 50% 100%		
Vitamin A (RAE)	700 µg	525	75%		
Vitamin C	75 mg	86	115%		
Iron	18 mg	9.7	54%		
Calcium	1000 mg	750	75%		
Saturated fat	< 23.8 g	31.9	134%		

Figure 2.19 Computerized diet analysis
In this example of an iProfile printout, which shows only a few nutrients, intake of vitamin C and saturated fat is above the recommended amounts and intake of vitamin A, calcium, and iron is below the recommended amounts.

anthropometric measurements External measurements of the body, such as height, weight, limb circumference, and skinfold thickness.

Figure 2.20 Height, weight, and body circumference are examples of anthropometric measurements. (Blair Seitz/Photo Researchers)

Life Cycle

Anthropometric Measurements Evaluating nutritional health also involves an assessment of an individual's height, weight, and body size. These **anthropometric measurements** can be compared with population standards (see Appendix B) or used to monitor changes in an individual over time (**Figure 2.20**). If an individual's measurements differ significantly from standards, it could indicate a nutritional deficiency or excess; however, this information should be evaluated only within the context of that person's personal and family history. For example, children who are small for their age may have a nutritional deficiency or may simply have inherited their small body size. Individuals who weigh less than the standard may be adequately nourished if they have never weighed more than their current weight and are otherwise healthy.

Medical History and Physical Exam A medical history is an important component of a nutritional assessment because dietary needs depend on genetic background, life stage, and health status. Family history is important because the risk of developing some nutrition-related diseases is affected by an individual's genes. If your mother died of a heart attack at age 50, you have a higher than average risk of developing heart disease. If you have a family history of diabetes, you have an increased risk of developing this disease. If both of your parents are overweight it increases the chances that you, too, will have a weight problem.

Life stage is important because nutrient needs vary at different stages. Pregnant women need more of some nutrients and energy to support the development of a healthy newborn. Young infants have higher energy and protein needs per unit body weight than at any other time of life. The needs of older adults change as their body composition changes and the ability to digest and absorb certain nutrients declines.

Existing health conditions also affect dietary needs. Some conditions, such as arthritis, affect the ability to acquire and prepare food. Others affect the kinds of foods that should be consumed or the way nutrients are handled by the body. For example, gastrointestinal disorders may decrease the ability to digest foods and absorb nutrients. Kidney disease alters the ability to excrete nitrogen and so affects the amount of protein that should be consumed.

In conjunction with personal and family medical history, a careful physical exam can detect the symptoms of, and risk factors for, nutrition-related diseases. In a physical exam all areas of the body including the mouth, skin, hair, eyes, and fingernails are examined for indications of poor nutritional status. Symptoms, such as dry skin, cracked lips, or lethargy may indicate a nutritional deficiency, but these types of symptoms are nonspecific and may be due to factors unrelated to nutritional status. Determining whether the symptoms noted in a physical exam are due to malnutrition or another disease requires that they be evaluated not only within the context of each individual's medical history, but in conjunction with the results of laboratory measurements.

Laboratory Measurements Measures of nutrients or their by-products in body cells or fluids such as blood and urine can be used to detect nutrient deficiencies and excesses (see Appendix C). For instance, levels of the blood protein albumin are often used to assess protein status. Newly absorbed nutrients are carried to the cells of the body in the blood, therefore the amounts of some nutrients in the blood may reflect the amount in the current diet rather than the total body status of the nutrient. To assess the status of these nutrients, it may be necessary to measure nutrient functions rather than just nutrient amounts. For example, vitamin B_6 is needed for chemical reactions involved in amino acid metabolism. Measuring the rates of chemical reactions that require vitamin B_6 can be used to assess B_6 status.

Laboratory data can also be used to evaluate risk for nutrition-related chronic diseases. For instance, heart disease risk can be assessed by measuring cholesterol levels in the blood. Measuring the amount of glucose in the blood can be used to diagnose diabetes. More sophisticated medical tests can be used to obtain additional information about the risk and progression of nutrition-related diseases. For example, procedures are available to determine the extent of coronary artery blockage in an individual with heart disease or to assess bone density in someone at risk for osteoporosis.

Stages of Nutrient Deficiency A nutritional deficiency usually takes time to develop. For example, an individual who is not meeting the requirement for protein may not suffer any physical signs of protein deficiency for months. Deficiencies generally progress through a number of stages. Appropriate nutritional assessment tools can identify deficiencies at any of these stages and allow intervention to restore nutritional health (**Figure 2.21**).

The earliest stage of nutrient deficiency is intake that is inadequate to meet needs. This may occur due to a deficient diet, poor absorption, increased need, or increased losses from the body. Assessment of dietary intake can help identify low levels in the diet and a physical exam and medical history can identify conditions that might reduce absorption or increase need or losses. The next stage of deficiency is declining nutrient stores in the body. Anthropometric measures that assess body weight and body fat can be used to monitor energy stores. Laboratory tests that measure levels of nutrients and their by-products in blood and tissues can be used to detect decreases in nutrient stores. For instance, measuring levels of the iron-containing protein ferritin in the blood can be used to detect low iron stores. The next stage of deficiency is altered biochemical or physiological functions, such as low enzyme activities or reduced amounts of regulatory or structural molecules. Finally, if a deficiency persists, function is disrupted enough that physical signs and symptoms, referred to as clinical symptoms, become apparent. For instance, a deficiency of iron causes fatigue, weakness, and decreased work capacity (see Critical Thinking: Assessing Nutritional Health).

Nutritional Health of the Population

We know that there is enough food available in the United States to meet the needs of the population. We also know that poor nutritional choices from this food supply result in diets high in some nutrients and low in others. This kind of information is obtained by monitoring what foods are available and what is consumed. In the United States, the National Nutrition Monitoring and Related Research Program is responsible for providing an ongoing description of nutrition conditions in the population by collecting information about food availability and consumption; food composition; and the eating behaviors, health, and nutritional status of the population.[22] These epidemiological data are gathered from population surveys. These surveys are key in establishing relationships among diet, nutritional status, and the health of the U.S. population. The information is used for the purpose of planning nutrition-related policies and programs and predicting future trends of public health importance. For example they may help identify the need for nutrition education, food assistance programs, or the addition of a specific nutrient to the food supply.

Stages of Deficiency	Inadequate intake	Decreased stores and tissue levels	Altered biochemical and physiological functions	Physical signs and symptoms of deficiency
Assessment Tools	**Dietary evaluation:** assess nutrient intake **Medical history, Physical exam, and Laboratory tests:** assess problems due to poor nutrient absorption, increased need, or increased losses	**Laboratory tests:** assess nutrient levels in blood, urine, and tissues **Anthropometrics:** assess body weight and composition	**Laboratory tests:** assess nutrient-dependent functions in the body	**Physical exam and Anthropometrics:** assess outward symptoms of deficiency

Figure 2.21 Assessing different stages of nutrient deficiency Different assessment tools yield different types of information that can be used to evaluate the severity of a nutrient deficiency.

Critical Thinking
Assessing Nutritional Health

Background

Darra is a 23 year-old freshman in college. Recently, she has been feeling tired and has had difficulty concentrating in class. She goes to the health clinic where she is weighed and measured. A physician does a physical exam and asks about her medical history. She suspects that Darra is anemic so she orders a blood sample for laboratory analysis. Darra is referred to a dietitian to assess her dietary intake.

Clinical assessment

The physician notes that Darra appears thin and pale. Anthropometric measurements of height and weight tell us that she is 5'4" tall and weighs 114 lbs. She recalls that a year ago she weighed 120 lbs and hasn't been trying to lose weight. Although her body weight is in the normal range, her unintentional weight loss is a concern.

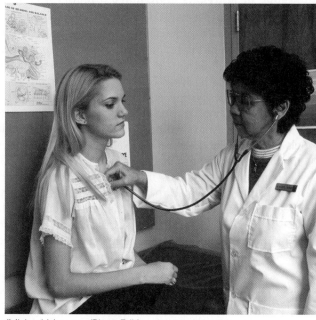

(Michael Newman/PhotoEdit)

Dietary assessment

Darra tells the dietitian that she stopped eating red meat last year. Using information from a 24-hour recall, the dietitian enters her diet into a computer program. A portion of the analysis is shown below.

DIET ANALYSIS

NUTRIENT	VALUE	% OF RECOMMENDATION
Kcalories	1500	68%
Protein	46 g	100%
Vitamin C	110 mg	146%
Vitamin A	1028 mg	147%
Iron	6 mg	33%
Calcium	1300 mg	130%

Laboratory assessment

The results of her blood test indicate that blood hemoglobin level is 11.2 g per 100 mL of blood and that her hematocrit, which measures the total volume of blood cells, is 35 mL per 100 mL of blood.

Critical Thinking Questions

Do you think Darra has iron deficiency anemia? Evaluate this by looking up the normal values for hemoglobin and hematocrit in Appendix C.

▼

What about her iron intake? Compare her iron intake to the recommendations for a woman of her age.

▼

Should Darra be concerned about the nutrients she is consuming in excess of the recommended amount? Use the DRI tables to determine if they are likely to pose a risk.

 iProfile Use iProfile to find foods that are good sources of iron.

Monitoring the Food Supply The food available to a population is estimated using **food disappearance surveys**. The food supply includes all that is grown, manufactured, or imported for sale in the country. Food use or "disappearance" is estimated by measuring what food is sold. These types of surveys are used to estimate what is available to the population, provide year-to-year comparisons, and identify trends in the diet; but they tend to overestimate actual intake because they do not consider losses that occur during processing, marketing, and home use. Also, the surveys do not consider how food is distributed throughout the population. For example, **Figure 2.22** illustrates the food disappearance data on milk consumption between 1909 and 1999. It shows that the consumption of whole milk, which is high in fat, has declined since the 1950s and the consumption of lower-fat milks has increased. From this it can be concluded that fat intake from milk has declined. But the graph also indicates that total milk consumption has been declining. This may alert the government that calcium intake from milk has decreased and that there may be a risk for low calcium intake in the population. The numbers in this graph do not give any information about how much milk each person is drinking or who is at risk of inadequate calcium intake.

food disappearance surveys Surveys that estimate the food use of a population by monitoring the amount of food that leaves the marketplace.

Monitoring Nutritional Status The nutritional status of the population is monitored by examining and comparing trends in food intake and health. This is done by interviewing individuals within the population to determine what food is actually consumed, and collecting information on health and nutritional status. The Department of Health and Human Services conducts the **National Health and Nutrition Examination Survey (NHANES)**, which combines information on food consumption with medical histories, physical examinations, and laboratory measurements to monitor both nutritional and health information. Data on food, energy, and nutrient intake can be assessed by comparing population intakes with reference values such as the DRIs or with other guidelines such as the recommendations of the Dietary Guidelines. For example, the NHANES data has indicated that few people eat the recommended amounts of fruits and vegetables, that there has been a slight drop in dietary fat intake since the 1950s, and that the number of people who are overweight has increased in all adult age groups in the past decade.

A system that has been developed to evaluate the adequacy of the diet of Americans is the Healthy Eating Index (HEI).[23] This provides a measure that summarizes overall diet quality by scoring 12 components of the diet. An individual who carefully follows the Dietary Guidelines would have an HEI score of 100. An HEI score over 80 implies that a person has a good diet; a score between 51 and 80, a diet that needs improvement; and a score less that 51, a poor diet. The typical American diet has not changed much since it was evaluated in 1994.[23] The average score was 58.2 for 2001–2002, suggesting a diet that needs improvement.

national health and nutrition examination survey (NHANES) A survey that collects information about the health and nutritional status of individuals in the population.

Figure 2.22 Trends in U.S. milk consumption
Food disappearance data illustrates that there was an increase in the consumption of lower-fat milks and a decrease in whole milk consumption during the second half of the 20th century. (Source: USDA Economic Research Service, Major trends in the U.S. food supply, 1909–1999, Food Review 23:12, 2000. Available online at www.ers.usda.gov/epubs/pdf/foodrevw/jan2000/ Accessed January 30, 2008.)

Outcome

Kareem wanted to make sure that he was not only making nutritious food choices, but also that he was choosing a diet to optimize his fitness for the track season. The dorm cafeteria offered a seemingly endless variety of selections, and he didn't know how much of which foods to choose. He was tempted by all those great desserts but knew that he would regret the extra pounds when it came time to run track. To construct his training diet, he learned to use MyPyramid, which promotes a diet that meets the recommendations of the DRIs and incorporates the Dietary Guidelines for Americans. By comparing his diet to his MyPyramid recommendations, he figured out what he was consuming in excess and what types of foods he needed more of. When he bought snacks, he used the information on food labels to determine nutritional benefits and deficiencies.

By the time the track season started, Kareem was in excellent physical as well as nutritional health. He had kept his weight where he wanted it and felt fit to compete. His diligence paid off, and he qualified for the state championships.

APPLICATIONS

Personal Nutrition

1. **What do you eat?** To find out, make a form similar to the sample food record shown below or use one provided by your instructor to keep a food diary of everything you eat for 3 consecutive days. Since you may eat differently on weekends, record for 2 weekdays and 1 weekend day. To make sure you don't forget anything, carry your record with you and record food as it is consumed. This record will be used in Applications throughout this book to focus on particular nutrients. Make the record as complete as possible by using the following tips:

a. Include all food and drink, and be as specific as possible. For example, did you eat a chicken breast or thigh?

b. Measure or estimate as carefully as possible the portion size that you ate; for example, 1/2 cup of rice, 10 potato chips, 2 ounces of tofu, and 6 ounces of milk.

c. Record the preparation or cooking method. For example, was your potato peeled? Was your chicken skinless? Was it baked or fried?

d. Include anything added to your food, for instance, butter, ketchup, or salad dressing.

e. Don't forget snacks, beverages, and desserts.

f. If the food is from a fast-food chain, list the name.

g. You may have to break down mixed dishes into their ingredients. For example, a tuna sandwich can be listed as 2 slices of whole-wheat bread, 1 tablespoon of mayonnaise, and 3 ounces of tuna packed in water.

h. Use iProfile to analyze your food record.

SAMPLE FOOD RECORD

FOOD OR BEVERAGE	KIND/HOW PREPARED	AMOUNT
Chicken salad sandwich:		
wheat bread		2 slices
chicken	skinless breast	2 oz
mayonnaise	low-fat	1 Tbsp
Diet cola		1 12-oz can

2. Does your diet meet the recommendations of your individual MyPyramid plan? To find out go to www.MyPyramid.gov. Enter your age, gender, and activity level and then record the number of kcalories listed for your Pyramid plan. Click on "For Professionals" and print out a Food Tracking Worksheet for your kcalorie level.

a. List the foods and amounts from one day of your food intake record on the left side of the form.

b. On the right side of the form record each food next to the Pyramid food group to which it belongs. In the far right column record the total amount of food you consumed from each group in cups or ounce equivalents. (Hint: Entering foods into MyPyramid Menu Planner can help determine this information)

c. How do the amounts you consumed from each food group compare to the recommendations? Are there any food groups you need to eat more or less of?

d. Are your food choices consistent with the selection tips listed on the worksheet for each group? How might you modify your food choices to more closely follow these suggestions?

e. List foods you consumed that are mostly solid fat or sugar.

f. List the foods you consumed from each group that contribute discretionary kcalories.

3. What's in your packaged foods? Select three packaged foods and check the label.

a. What is the percent of kcalories from fat in each of these foods?

b. How much total carbohydrate, total fat, and fiber are in a serving of each?

c. How does each of these foods fit into your overall daily diet with regard to total carbohydrate? total fat? dietary fiber?

 iProfile

d. If you consumed a serving of each of these three foods, how much more fat could you consume during the day without exceeding the Daily Value? How much more total carbohydrate and fiber should you consume that day to meet the Daily Value for a 2000-kcalorie diet?

General Nutrition Issues

1. To encourage healthy eating in her family, a nutrition student hangs the MyPyramid poster on the refrigerator. Her family is enthusiastic, but don't know how much they should eat from each group. Use the MyPyramid Web site to find out the kcalorie level and the amounts of food recommended from each of the food groups for the following family members:

a. Her 45-year-old inactive mother?

b. Her 12-year-old sister who plays outside for about 45 minutes a day?

c. Her 16-year-old brother who spends 2 hours a day practicing with the track team?

d. Her 70-year-old grandmother who is inactive?

2. Are "health foods" different than standard products?

a. Compare the label from a product such as cereal, crackers, or cookies purchased at the grocery store to the label from a comparable product from a "health" or "natural" food store.

b. Which is higher in total fat? saturated fat? *trans* fat? cholesterol?

c. Which has more kcalories per serving?

d. Which has more sugars?

e. How do the ingredients differ?

f. What other differences or similarities do you notice?

3. Food intake data from population surveys provided the following information about the intake of milk and soda in 1977–1978 and 1994–1996:

POPULATION	YEAR	MILK CONSUMPTION (OUNCES PER DAY)	SODA CONSUMPTION (OUNCES PER DAY)
Teenage boys (ages 12–19)	1977–1978	16	7
	1994–1996	10	20
Teenage girls (ages 12–19)	1977–1978	10	7
	1994–1996	6	14

a. How might these trends have affected the number of kcalories from added sugars in the teen diet?

b. How might these trends affect calcium intake in teenagers?

Summary

2.1 Nutrition Recommendations for the Modern Diet

- Nutrition recommendations made to the public for health promotion and disease prevention are based on available scientific knowledge.

- Dietary standards such as the Dietary Reference Intakes (DRIs) provide recommendations for intakes of nutrients and other food components that can be used to plan and assess the diets of individuals and populations. Intakes at these levels will avoid deficiencies and excesses and prevent chronic diseases in the majority of healthy persons.

2.2 Dietary Reference Intakes

- The DRIs include four sets of nutrient intake recommendations. The Estimated Average Requirements (EARs) are amounts of nutrients estimated to meet the needs of half of the people in a particular gender and life-stage group. The Recommended Dietary Allowances (RDAs), which are based on the EARs, are recommendations calculated to meet the needs of nearly all healthy individuals (97%–98%) in a specific group. Adequate Intakes (AIs) estimate nutrient needs based on average intakes by healthy populations when there is insufficient scientific evidence to calculate an EAR and RDA. Tolerable Upper Intake Levels (ULs) provide a guide for a safe upper limit of intake.

- Energy Recommendations of the DRIs include Estimated Energy Requirements (EERs), which provide a recommendation for energy intakes that will maintain body weight and Acceptable Macronutrient Distribution Ranges (AMDRs), which recommend the proportions of energy intake that should come from carbohydrate, protein, and fat.

- The Dietary Reference Intakes can be used to evaluate and plan nutrient intakes for populations, as a guide for individual intake, and to make judgments about excessive intakes for individuals and populations.

2.3 The Dietary Guidelines for Americans

- The Dietary Guidelines for Americans makes dietary and lifestyle recommendations that promote good health and help reduce the risk of chronic diseases.

- The Dietary Guidelines, 2005, recommend that Americans get more nutrients in fewer kcalories, improve the balance between the amount of food they eat and the amount of exercise they get, limit dietary components that contribute to chronic disease, and keep food safe.

2.4 MyPyramid: Applying the Dietary Guidelines

- Food guides translate nutrient intake recommendations into food intake recommendations by making recommendations on how much to eat from various food groups.

- MyPyramid: Steps to a Healthier You is a food guide that recommends amounts from five main food groups and oils, based on individual energy needs. It also makes recommendations about the number of discretionary kcalories allowed in an individual's diet and includes activity recommendations.

- MyPyramid stresses the key concepts of activity, moderation, proportionality, and variety. The wider bottom of each triangle represents nutrient-dense foods from each food group that should be chosen more often. The narrower tip represents foods high in solid fats and added sugars that should be consumed in moderation.

2.5 Food and Supplement Labels

- Food labels follow a standard format and are designed to provide consumers with the information they need to make wise food choices. The % Daily Values show how foods fit into the recommendations for a healthy diet.

- Labels on dietary supplements are designed to help consumers make educated decisions about these products. The safety of dietary supplements is not evaluated by the FDA before they are marketed.

- Only FDA-approved nutrient content and health claims can appear on food and supplement labels.

2.6 Other Guidelines for Health Promotion and Disease Prevention

- The Exchange Lists are used to plan individual diets that provide specific amounts of energy, carbohydrate, protein, and fat.

- The Healthy People Initiative establishes a set of health promotion and disease prevention objectives for the U.S. population.

2.7 Assessing Nutritional Health

- Individual nutritional status is assessed by evaluating dietary intake, examining clinical parameters such as body size, and interpreting laboratory values within the context of an individual's medical history.

- The nutritional status of populations is monitored by measuring what foods are available, what foods are consumed, and how nutrient intake is related to overall health.

Review Questions

1. Which types of DRI standards can be used as a goal for individual intake?
2. What type of DRI standard can be used to evaluate the adequacy of nutrient intake in a population?
3. Which DRI standard can help you determine if a supplement contains a toxic level of a nutrient?
4. What is the purpose of the Dietary Guidelines?
5. What aspect of the MyPyramid graphic illustrates variety?
6. Why is variety important to a healthy diet?
7. Explain what is meant by proportionality.
8. List two foods from each food group that are low in discretionary kcalories and two foods that are high in discretionary kcalories.
9. How much food from each group does a 56-year-old moderately active man need to meet his nutritional needs?
10. Why are serving sizes standardized on food labels?
11. How do the Daily Values help consumers determine how foods fit into their overall diets?

12. What determines the order in which food ingredients are listed on a label?

13. How are the Exchange Lists used in planning diets?

14. What is nutritional status?

15. List the components of individual nutritional assessment.

16. How does food disappearance data help monitor the nutritional health of populations?

References

1. Diet, nutrition and the prevention of chronic diseases. Report of a Joint WHO/FAO Expert Consultation. Available online at http://whqlibdoc.who.int/trs/WHO_TRS_916.pdf. Accessed May 20, 2009.

2. National Research Council, Food and Nutrition Board. *Recommended Dietary Allowances*, 10th ed. Washington, DC: National Academies Press, 1989.

3. Institute of Medicine, Food and Nutrition Board. *Dietary Reference Intakes for Calcium, Phosphorus, Magnesium, Vitamin D, and Fluoride*. Washington, DC: National Academies Press, 1997.

4. Institute of Medicine, Food and Nutrition Board. *Dietary Reference Intakes for Thiamin, Riboflavin, Niacin, Vitamin B-6, Folate, Vitamin B-12, Pantothenic Acid, Biotin, and Choline*. Washington, DC: National Academies Press, 1998.

5. Institute of Medicine, Food and Nutrition Board. *Dietary Reference Intakes for Energy, Carbohydrates, Fiber, Fat, Protein, and Amino Acids*. Washington, DC: National Academies Press, 2002.

6. Report of the Select Committee on Nutrition and Human Needs, U.S. Senate. *Eating in America: Dietary Goals for the United States*. Cambridge, MA: MIT Press, 1977.

7. U.S. Department of Health and Human Services, U.S. Department of Agriculture. Dietary Guidelines for Americans, 2005. Available online at www.healthierus.gov/dietaryguidelines. Accessed December 7, 2008

8. U.S. Department of Agriculture. MyPyramid: Steps to a Healthier You. Available online at www.mypyramid.gov/ Accessed May 19, 2009.

9. USDA, Food and Nutrition Information Center Historical Food Guides Background and Development Available online at http://www.nal.usda.gov/fnic/history/index.html. Accessed May 23, 2009.

10. Legault, L., Brandt, M. B., McCabe, N. et al. 2000–2001 Food Label and Package Survey: An Update on Prevalence of Nutrition Labeling and Claims on Processed, Packaged Foods. *J. Am. Diet. Assoc.* 104:952–958, 2004.

11. U.S. Food and Drug Administration Center for Food Safety and Applied Nutrition. Food Labeling Questions and Answers: A Guide for Restaurants and Other Retail Establishments, August, 1995; Modified March, 2001. Available online at www.cfsan.fda.gov/~frf/qaintro.html/ Accessed March 4, 2006.

12. Picciano, M. F., Office of Dietary Supplements, National Institutes of Health. Who is Using Dietary Supplements and What are they Using? Available online at http://ods.od.nih.gov/pubs/fnce2005/M%20F%20 Picciano-Who%20Is%20Using%20Dietary%20 Supplements%20and%20What%20are%20They%20 Using.pdf. Accessed May 14, 2009.

13. U.S. Food and Drug Administration, Center for Food Safety and Applied Nutrition /Office of Nutrition, Labeling, and Dietary Supplements. April 2005. Guidance for food industry, A Dietary Supplement Labeling Guide. Available at http://www.cfsan.fda.gov/~dms/dslg-toc.html. Accessed May 24, 2009

14. Food and Drug Administration. Current good manufacturing practice in manufacturing, packaging, labeling, or holding operations for dietary supplements; final rule. *Fed Regist* 72(121):34751–34958, June 25, 2007. Available online at www.cfsan.fda.gov/~lrd/fr07625a.html Accessed May 27, 2008.

15. USP Dietary Supplement Verification Program. Available online at www.usp-dsvp.org/ Accessed May 23, 2009.

16. U.S. Food and Drug Administration, Center for Food Safety and Applied Nutrition. Label Claims. Available online at www.cfsan.fda.gov/~dms/lab-hlth.html. Accessed December 7, 2008.

17. Food and Drug Administration, Center for Food Safety and Applied Nutrition. Health Claims that Meet Significant Scientific Agreement. Available online at www.cfsan.fda.gov/~dms/lab-ssa.html/ Accessed May 23, 2009.

18. The American Diabetes Association, Inc., the American Dietetic Association. Exchange Lists for Meal Planning, Alexandria, VA, 2003.

19. Office of Disease Prevention and Health Promotion. U.S. Department of Health and Human Services. Healthy People. Available online at www.healthypeople.gov Accessed August 6, 2009.

20. Johansson, L., Solvoll, K., Bjørneboe, G-E. A., and Drevon, C. A. Under- and overreporting of energy intake related to weight status and lifestyle in a nationwide sample. *Am. J. Clin. Nutr.* 68:226–274, 1998.

21. USDA. USDA Nutrient Database for Standard Reference. Available online at www.nal.usda.gov/ Accessed May 15, 2009.

22. Interagency Board of Nutrition Monitoring and Related Research. Bialostosky, K., ed. Nutrition Monitoring in the United States: The Directory of Federal and State Nutrition Monitoring and Related Research Activities, Hyattsville, MD: National Center for Health Statistics, 2000. Available online at www.cdc.gov/nchs/data/misc/direc-99.pdf/ Accessed May 23, 2009.

23. USDA, Center for Nutrition Policy and Promotion Diet Quality of Americans in 1994–96 and 2001–02 as Measured by the Healthy Eating Index-2005. Available online at http://www.cnpp.usda.gov/Publications/NutritionInsights/Insight37.pdf. Accessed May 23, 2009.

3

Digestion, Absorption, and Metabolism

Case Study

Sheila was worried as she left the doctor's office. She had just learned that now, in addition to having high blood pressure and high cholesterol, her blood sugar levels were elevated. Her weight was seriously affecting her health, and the doctor had suggested gastric bypass surgery.

Shelia had been overweight since she was 18, and now at 38, she was heavier than she had ever been—289 lb on her 5'10" frame. She felt fat and miserable and even simple things in her life were difficult. She hated squeezing into restaurant booths and airplane seats, and shopping for clothes was depressing. She had tried every diet, but when she did manage to lose weight, she would gain it back—and then some. Exercise was challenging because she was too embarrassed to put on a bathing suit and her knees hurt too much to walk very far.

The surgical procedure Sheila was considering would alter her digestive tract in two ways. First, it would reduce the size of her stomach so it could hold less food; second, it would shorten the length of her intestines so her body could not absorb as much of what she ate. She knew it would be a drastic move—the surgical procedure itself would carry risks and permanently alter the amounts and types of foods she could eat. She would have to eat very small meals throughout the day. Overeating or choosing the wrong foods could result in pain, sweats, chills, and nausea. Even if she were careful, diarrhea could be a constant problem. Bypassing part of her intestines would also put her at risk for vitamin deficiencies. On the plus side, though, she would feel less hungry, eat less, and lose weight. Should she choose a procedure so drastic that it would permanently change her digestive tract?

(Digital Vision/Getty Images, Inc.)

(©iStockphoto)

(erfile)

3.1 Food Becomes Us

Learning Objective

- Describe the organization of life from atoms to organisms.

The old adage that you are what you eat is not literally true, but biochemically it is a fact. The food we eat provides all of the energy we need to stay alive and active and all the raw materials we need to build and maintain our body structures and synthesize regulatory molecules.

Atoms and Molecules

To be useful to us the food we eat must be broken into smaller components, absorbed into the body, and then converted into forms that can be used. Our bodies and the food we eat, like all matter on Earth, are made of units called **atoms**. Atoms cannot be further broken down by chemical means. Atoms of different **elements** have different characteristics. Carbon, hydrogen, oxygen, and nitrogen are the most abundant elements in our bodies and in the foods we eat. These atoms can be linked by forces called **chemical bonds** to form **molecules** (**Figure 3.1** and Appendix L). The chemistry of all life on Earth is based on organic molecules, which are those that contain carbon bonded to hydrogen. As discussed in Chapter 1, carbohydrates, lipids, proteins, and vi-

atoms The smallest units of an element that still retain the properties of that element.

elements Substances that cannot be broken down into products with different properties.

chemical bonds Forces that hold atoms together.

molecules Units of two or more atoms of the same or different elements bonded together.

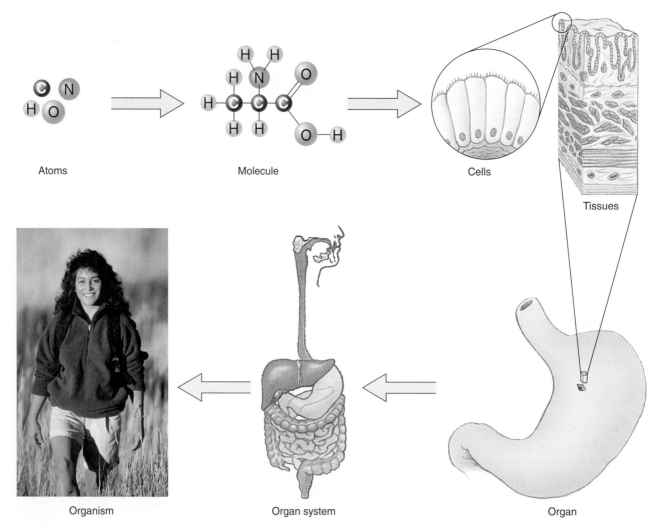

Atoms   Molecule   Cells

Tissues

Organism   Organ system   Organ

Figure 3.1 Organization of life
The organization of life begins with atoms that form molecules, which are then organized into cells to form tissues, organs, organ systems, and whole organisms. (Photo: Brian Bailey/Getty Images, Inc.)

tamins are nutrient classes that are made up of organic molecules, whereas water and minerals are inorganic nutrients because they do not contain carbon hydrogen bonds.

Cells, Tissues, and Organs

In any living system, molecules are organized into structures that form **cells**, the smallest unit of life. Cells of similar structure and function are organized into tissues. The human body contains four types of tissue: muscle, nerve, epithelial, and connective. These tissues are organized in varying combinations into **organs**, which are discrete structures that perform specialized functions in the body (see Figure 3.1). The stomach is an example of an organ; it contains all four types of tissue.

cells The basic structural and functional units of plant and animal life.

organs Discrete structures composed of more than one tissue that perform a specialized function.

Organ Systems

Most organs do not function alone but are part of a group of cooperative organs called an *organ system*. The organ systems in humans include the nervous system, respiratory system (lungs), urinary system (kidneys and bladder), reproductive system, cardiovascular system (heart and blood vessels), lymphatic/immune system, muscular system, skeletal system, endocrine system (hormones), integumentary system (skin and body linings), and digestive system (**Table 3.1**). An organ may be part of more than one organ system. For example, the pancreas is part of the endocrine system as well as the digestive system. Organ systems work together to support the entire organism.

Table 3.1 Organ Systems and Their Functions

Organ System	What It Includes	What It Does
Nervous	Brain, spinal cord, and associated nerves	Responds to stimuli from the external and internal environments; conducts impulses to activate muscles and glands; integrates activities of other systems.
Respiratory	Lungs, trachea, and air passageways	Supplies the blood with oxygen and removes carbon dioxide.
Urinary	Kidneys and their associated structures	Eliminates wastes and regulates the balance of water, electrolytes, and acid in the blood.
Reproductive	Testes, ovaries, and their associated structures	Produces offspring.
Cardiovascular	Heart and blood vessels	Transports blood, which carries oxygen, nutrients, and wastes.
Lymphatic/Immune	Lymph and lymph structures, white blood cells	Defends against foreign invaders, picks up fluid leaked from blood vessels, transports fat-soluble nutrients.
Muscular	Skeletal muscles	Provides movement and structure.
Skeletal	Bones and joints	Protects and supports the body, provides a framework for the muscles to use for movement.
Endocrine	Pituitary, adrenal, thyroid, pancreas, and other ductless glands	Secretes hormones that regulate processes such as growth, reproduction, and nutrient use.
Integumentary	Skin, hair, nails, and sweat glands	Covers and protects the body; helps control body temperature.
Digestive	Mouth, pharynx, esophagus, stomach, intestines, pancreas, liver, and gallbladder	Ingests and digests food, absorbs nutrients into the blood, eliminates unabsorbed food residues and other wastes.

Source: Adapted from Marieb, E. N., and Hoehn, K. *Human Anatomy and Physiology*, 7th ed. Menlo Park, CA: Benjamin Cummings, 2007.

The digestive system is the organ system primarily responsible for the movement of nutrients into the body; however, several other organ systems are also important in the process of using these nutrients. The endocrine system secretes chemical messengers that help regulate food intake and absorption. The nervous system aids in digestion by sending nerve signals that help control the passage of food through the digestive tract. Once absorbed, nutrients are transported to individual cells by the cardiovascular system. The body's urinary, respiratory, and integumentary systems allow for the elimination of metabolic waste products.

3.2 An Overview of the Digestive System

Learning Objectives

- Define *digestion* and *absorption*.
- Explain the roles of mucus, enzymes, nerves, and hormones in digestion.

digestion The process of breaking food into components small enough to be absorbed into the body.

absorption The process of taking substances into the interior of the body.

feces Body waste, including unabsorbed food residue, bacteria, mucus, and dead cells, which is excreted from the gastrointestinal tract by passing through the anus.

gastrointestinal tract A hollow tube consisting of the mouth, pharynx, esophagus, stomach, small intestine, large intestine, and anus, in which digestion and absorption of nutrients occurs.

transit time The time between the ingestion of food and the elimination of the solid waste from that food.

mucosa The layer of tissue lining the GI tract and other body cavities.

The digestive system provides two major functions: **digestion** and **absorption**. Most food must be digested in order for the nutrients it contains to be absorbed into the body. For example, a slice of whole-wheat bread does not travel through the digestive system intact. First it is broken apart, releasing its carbohydrate, protein, and fat. Most of the carbohydrate is digested to sugars, the protein to amino acids, and the fat to fatty acids. Sugars, amino acids, and fatty acids can be absorbed. The fiber from the bread is carbohydrate that cannot be digested and therefore is not absorbed into the body. Fiber and other unabsorbed substances pass through the digestive tract and are excreted in the **feces**.

Structure of the Gastrointestinal Tract

The main part of the digestive system is the **gastrointestinal tract**. It is also referred to as the GI tract, gut, digestive tract, intestinal tract, or alimentary canal. It can be thought of as a hollow tube, about 30 feet in length, that runs from the mouth to the anus. The organs of the gastrointestinal tract include the mouth, pharynx, esophagus, stomach, small intestine, large intestine, and anus (**Figure 3.2a**). The inside of the tube that these organs form is called the *lumen* (**Figure 3.2b**). Food within the lumen of the gastrointestinal tract has not been absorbed and is therefore technically still outside the body. Therefore, if you swallow something that cannot be digested, such as an apple seed, it will pass through your digestive tract and exit in the feces without ever being broken down or entering your blood or cells. Only after food is transferred into the cells that line the intestine by the process of absorption is it actually "inside" the body.

Transit Time The amount of time it takes for food to pass the length of the GI tract from mouth to anus is referred to as **transit time**. In a healthy adult, transit time is about 24 to 72 hours. It is affected by the composition of the diet, physical activity, emotions, medications, and illnesses. To measure transit time, researchers add a non-absorbable dye to a meal and measure the time between consumption of the dye and its appearance in the feces. The shorter the transit time, the more rapid the passage through the digestive tract.

Structure of the Gut Wall The wall of the GI tract contains four layers of tissue (see Figure 3.2b). Lining the lumen is the **mucosa**, a layer of mucosal cells that serves as a protective layer and is responsible for the absorption of the end products of digestion. The cells of the mucosa are in direct contact with churning food and harsh digestive secretions. Therefore, these cells have a short life span—only about 2 to 5 days. When these cells die, they are sloughed off into the lumen, where

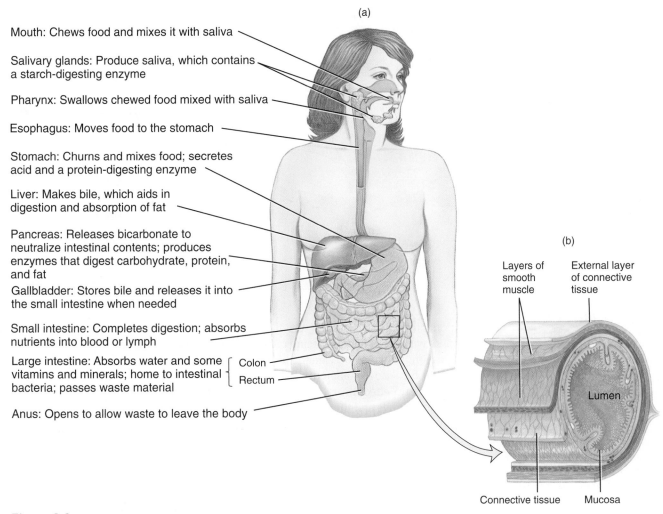

(a)

Mouth: Chews food and mixes it with saliva

Salivary glands: Produce saliva, which contains a starch-digesting enzyme

Pharynx: Swallows chewed food mixed with saliva

Esophagus: Moves food to the stomach

Stomach: Churns and mixes food; secretes acid and a protein-digesting enzyme

Liver: Makes bile, which aids in digestion and absorption of fat

Pancreas: Releases bicarbonate to neutralize intestinal contents; produces enzymes that digest carbohydrate, protein, and fat

Gallbladder: Stores bile and releases it into the small intestine when needed

Small intestine: Completes digestion; absorbs nutrients into blood or lymph

Large intestine: Absorbs water and some vitamins and minerals; home to intestinal bacteria; passes waste material

Colon
Rectum

Anus: Opens to allow waste to leave the body

(b)

Layers of smooth muscle

External layer of connective tissue

Lumen

Connective tissue

Mucosa

Figure 3.2 Structure of the digestive system
(a) The digestive system consists of the organs of the gastrointestinal tract, as well accessory organs that include the salivary glands, liver, gallbladder, and pancreas.
(b) A cross-section through the wall of the small intestine shows the four tissue layers: mucosa, connective tissue, smooth muscle layers, and outer connective tissue layer. (Source: Adapted from E. P. Solomon, R. R. Schmidt, and P. J. Adragna, Human Anatomy and Physiology, 2nd ed. Philadelphia: Saunders College Publishing, 1990.)

some components are digested and absorbed and the remainder are excreted in the feces. Because mucosal cells reproduce rapidly, the mucosa has high nutrient requirements and is therefore one of the first parts of the body to be affected by nutrient deficiencies. Surrounding the mucosa is a layer of connective tissue containing nerves and blood vessels. This layer provides support, delivers nutrients to the mucosa, and provides the nerve signals that control secretions and muscle contractions. Layers of smooth muscle—the type over which we do not have voluntary control—surround the connective tissue. The contraction of smooth muscles mixes food, breaks it into smaller particles, and propels it through the digestive tract. The final, external layer is also made up of connective tissue and provides support and protection.

Digestive Secretions

Digestion inside the lumen of the GI tract is aided by digestive secretions. One of these substances is **mucus**, a viscous material produced by cells in the mucosal lining of the gut. Mucus moistens, lubricates, and protects the digestive tract. **Enzymes**, another

mucus A viscous fluid secreted by glands in the GI tract and other parts of the body. It acts to lubricate, moisten, and protect cells from harsh environments.

enzymes Protein molecules that accelerate the rate of specific chemical reactions without being changed themselves.

Smaller carbohydrate molecules

Large carbohydrate molecule

Figure 3.3 Enzyme action
Enzymes speed up chemical reactions without themselves being altered by the reaction. In this example, the enzyme amylase breaks a large carbohydrate molecule into two smaller ones.

component of digestive system secretions, are protein molecules that speed up chemical reactions without themselves being consumed or changed by the reactions (**Figure 3.3**). In digestion, enzymes accelerate the breakdown of nutrients. Different enzymes are needed to breakdown different nutrients. For example, an enzyme that digests carbohydrate has no effect on fat, and one that digests fat has no effect on carbohydrate. Digestive enzymes and their actions are summarized in **Table 3.2**.

Table 3.2 Enzyme Functions

Enzyme	Where it is Found	What it Does
Salivary amylase	Mouth	Breaks starch into shorter chains of glucose.
Rennin	Stomach	Causes the milk protein casein to curdle.
Pepsin		Breaks proteins into polypeptides and amino acids.
Trypsin	Pancreas	Breaks proteins and polypeptides into shorter polypeptides.
Chymotrypsin		Breaks proteins and polypeptides into shorter polypeptides.
Carboxypeptidase		Breaks polypeptides into amino acids.
Lipase		Breaks triglycerides into monoglycerides, fatty acids, and glycerol.
Pancreatic amylase		Breaks starch into shorter glucose chains and maltose.
Carboxypeptidase, aminopeptidase, and dipeptidase	Small intestine	Breaks polypeptides and dipeptides into amino acids.
Lipase		Breaks monoglycerides into fatty acids and glycerol.
Sucrase		Breaks sucrose into glucose and fructose.
Lactase		Breaks lactose into glucose and galactose.
Maltase		Breaks maltose into glucose.
Dextrinase		Breaks short chains of glucose into individual glucose molecules.

Regulation of Gastrointestinal Function

Nerve signals help regulate activity in the GI tract. The sight and smell of food, as well as the presence of food in the gut, stimulate nerves throughout the GI tract. For example, food in the mouth can trigger a nerve impulse that signals the stomach to prepare itself for the arrival food. Nerve signals cause muscle contractions that churn, mix, and propel food through the gut at a rate that allows for optimal absorption of nutrients. Nerve signals also stimulate or inhibit digestive secretions. For example, food in the mouth stimulates digestive secretions in the stomach. After food has passed through a section of the digestive tract, digestive secretions decrease and muscular activity slows to conserve energy and resources for other body processes. The nerves in the GI tract can also communicate with the brain so digestive activity can be coordinated with other body needs.

Activity in the digestive tract is also regulated by **hormones** released into the bloodstream. Hormones that affect gastrointestinal function are produced both by cells lining the digestive tract and by a number of accessory organs. Hormonal signals help prepare different parts of the gut for the arrival of food and thus regulate the digestion of nutrients and the rate that food moves through the system. Some of the hormones released by the GI tract and their functions are summarized in **Table 3.3**.

hormones Chemical messengers that are produced in one location, released into the blood, and elicit responses at other locations in the body.

Table 3.3 Digestive Hormone Functions

Hormone	Where it Comes From	What it Does
Gastrin	Stomach mucosa	Stimulates secretion of HCl and pepsinogen by gastric glands in the stomach and increases gastric motility and emptying.
Somatostatin	Stomach and duodenal mucosa	Inhibits the following: stomach secretion, motility, and emptying; pancreatic secretion; absorption in the small intestine; gallbladder contraction; and bile release.
Secretin	Duodenal mucosa	Inhibits gastric secretion and motility; increases output of water and bicarbonate from the pancreas; increases bile output from the liver.
Cholecystokinin (CCK)		Stimulates contraction of the gallbladder to expel bile; increases output of enzyme-rich pancreatic juice.
Gastric inhibitory peptide		Inhibits gastric secretion and motility.

The Gastrointestinal Tract and Immune Function

The GI tract is an important part of the immune system, which protects the body from infection by foreign invaders. The GI tract limits the absorption of toxins and disease-causing organisms, but if an invading substance, or **antigen**, does get past the intestinal cells, the immune system has a number of weapons stationed in the gut that can destroy it before it spreads to other parts of the body (**Figure 3.4**). Some of these are cells and some are chemicals released into the blood. The cells of the immune system consist of the different types of white blood cells. Because many of these reside in the GI tract, a foreign substance or harmful organism that enters the body through the mucosa can be destroyed quickly. The first types of cells to come to the body's defense are called *phagocytes*. They target any invader and engulf and destroy it. These cells also release chemicals that signal other immune system cells called *lymphocytes* to come join the fight. Lymphocytes are very specific about what they will attack. Some lymphocytes bind directly to a specific invader or antigen and destroy it. This type of lymphocyte helps eliminate cancer cells, foreign tissue, and cells that have been infected by viruses and bacteria. Other lymphocytes produce and secrete protein molecules called **antibodies**. Antibodies bind to invading antigens and help to destroy them. Each antibody is designed to fight off only one specific antigen. Once the body has made antibodies to a specific antigen, it remembers and can rapidly produce these antibodies to fight that antigen any time it enters the body.

antigen A foreign substance (almost always a protein) that, when introduced into the body, stimulates an immune response.

antibodies Proteins produced by cells of the immune system that destroy or inactivate foreign substances in the body.

The immune system protects us from many invaders without our even being aware that the battle is going on. Unfortunately, the response of the immune system to a

Figure 3.4
Peyer's patches, which consist of immune system tissue, are embedded throughout the mucosa of the small intestine. They help prevent harmful organisms or materials present in the GI tract from making us ill. (George Wilder/Visuals Unlimited)

Peyer's patch

allergen A substance that causes an allergic reaction.

foreign substance is also responsible for allergic reactions. An allergic reaction occurs when the immune system produces antibodies to a substance, called an **allergen**, that is present in our diet or environment. For example, a food allergy occurs when proteins absorbed from food are seen as foreign and trigger an immune response. The immune response causes symptoms that range from hives to life-threatening breathing difficulties (see Chapter 6). Food allergies affect less than 2% of adults and up to 6% of children under 3 years of age. They are responsible for 150 deaths each year. The most common sources of food allergens are seafood, peanuts, tree nuts, fish, soy, wheat, milk, and eggs.[1]

3.3 Digestion and Absorption

Learning Objectives

- Describe what happens in each of the organs of the gastrointestinal tract.
- Discuss factors that influence how quickly food moves through the gastrointestinal tract.
- Explain how the structure of the small intestine enhances its function.
- Distinguish simple diffusion, facilitated diffusion, and active transport.

To be used by the body, food must be eaten and digested, and the nutrients must be absorbed and transported to the cells of the body. Because most foods we consume are mixtures of carbohydrate, fat, and protein, the physiology of the digestive tract is designed to allow the digestion of all of these components without competition among them.

Sights, Sounds, and Smells

Activity in the digestive tract begins before food even enters the mouth. As the meal is being prepared, sensory input such as the clatter of the table being set, the sight of a chocolate cake, or the smell of freshly baked bread may make your mouth become moist and your stomach begin to secrete digestive substances. This response occurs when the nervous system signals the digestive system to ready itself for a meal. This cephalic (pertaining to the head) response occurs as a result of external cues, such as sight and smell, even when the body is not in need of food.

Mouth

saliva A watery fluid produced and secreted into the mouth by the salivary glands. It contains lubricants, enzymes, and other substances.

The mouth is the entry point for food into the digestive tract. Here, food is tasted and the mechanical breakdown and chemical digestion of food begin. The presence of food in the mouth stimulates the flow of **saliva** from the salivary glands located internally at the sides of the face and immediately below and in front of the ears (see Figure 3.2a). Saliva plays many roles: It moistens the food so that it can easily be tasted and swallowed; it begins the enzymatic digestion of starch; it cleanses the mouth and protects teeth from decay; and it lubricates the upper GI tract. By moistening food, saliva helps us taste because molecules dissolve in the saliva and are carried to the taste buds, most of which are located on the tongue. This contact between food molecules and taste buds allows the flavors of the meal to be tasted and enjoyed. Saliva begins the chemical digestion of carbohydrate because it contains the enzyme **salivary amylase**. Salivary amylase can break the long sugar chains of starch in foods like bread and cereal into shorter chains of sugars (see Figure 3.3). Saliva also protects against tooth decay because it helps wash away food particles and it contains **lysozyme**—an enzyme that inhibits the growth of bacteria that may cause tooth decay (see Chapter 4).

Digestive enzymes can act only on the surface of food particles. Therefore, chewing is important because it mechanically breaks food into small pieces, increasing the surface area in contact with digestive enzymes. Adult humans have 32 teeth, specialized for biting, tearing, grinding, and crushing foods. The tongue helps mix food with saliva and aids chewing by constantly repositioning food between the teeth. Chewing also breaks apart fiber that traps nutrients in some foods. If the fiber is not broken apart, some nutrients cannot be absorbed. For example, unless chewed thoroughly, a raisin or a kernel of corn will travel intact through the digestive tract and the vitamins and minerals in the fibrous skin and the nutrients within the raisin or corn kernel will be unavailable.

salivary amylase An enzyme secreted by the salivary glands that breaks down starch.

lysozyme An enzyme in saliva, tears, and sweat that is capable of destroying certain types of bacteria.

Pharynx

The tongue initiates swallowing by moving the bolus of chewed food mixed with saliva back toward the **pharynx**. The pharynx is shared by the digestive tract and the respiratory tract: Food and liquid pass through the pharynx on their way to the stomach, and air passes here on its way to and from the lungs. We are able to start the muscular contractions of swallowing by choice, but once initiated it becomes involuntary and proceeds under the control of nerves. During swallowing, the air passages are blocked by a valve-like flap of tissue called the **epiglottis**, which ensures that the bolus of food passes to the stomach, not the lungs (**Figure 3.5a**). Sometimes food can pass into an upper air passageway. It is usually dislodged with a cough, but if it becomes stuck it can block the flow of air and cause choking. A quick response is required to save the life of a person whose airway is completely blocked. The Heimlich maneuver, which forces air out of the lungs by using a sudden application of pressure just below the diaphragm, can blow an object out of the blocked air passage (**Figure 3.5b**).

pharynx A funnel-shaped opening that connects the nasal passages and mouth to the respiratory passages and esophagus. It is a common passageway for food and air and is responsible for swallowing.

epiglottis A piece of elastic connective tissue at the back of the throat that covers the opening of the passageway to the lungs during swallowing.

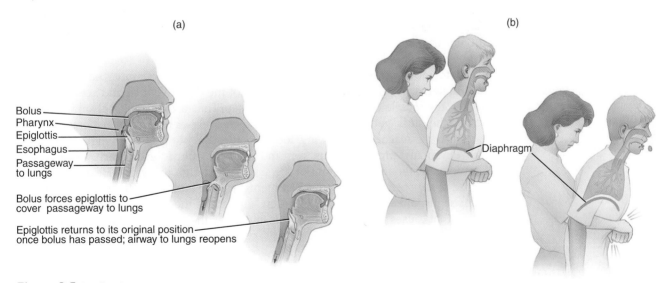

(a)

(b)

Bolus
Pharynx
Epiglottis
Esophagus
Passageway to lungs

Bolus forces epiglottis to cover passageway to lungs

Epiglottis returns to its original position once bolus has passed; airway to lungs reopens

Diaphragm

Figure 3.5 Swallowing
(a) When a bolus of food is swallowed, it pushes the epiglottis down over the opening to the air passageways. (b) If food becomes lodged in the airways it can be dislodged by the Heimlich maneuver.

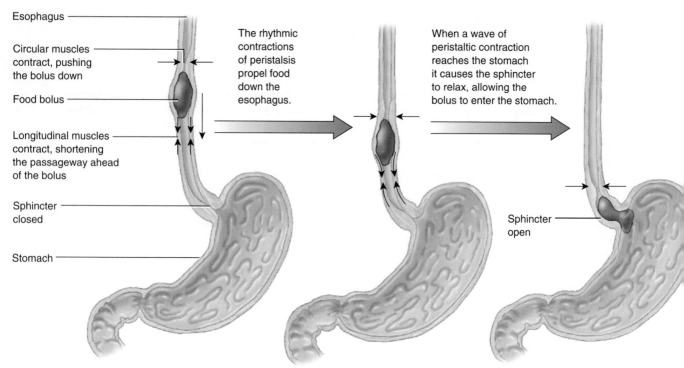

Esophagus

Circular muscles contract, pushing the bolus down

Food bolus

Longitudinal muscles contract, shortening the passageway ahead of the bolus

Sphincter closed

Stomach

The rhythmic contractions of peristalsis propel food down the esophagus.

When a wave of peristaltic contraction reaches the stomach it causes the sphincter to relax, allowing the bolus to enter the stomach.

Sphincter open

Figure 3.6 Peristalsis
The rhythmic contractions of peristalsis move the food bolus toward the stomach and stimulate the opening of the gastroesophageal sphincter.

Esophagus

esophagus A portion of the GI tract that extends from the pharynx to the stomach.

peristalsis Coordinated muscular contractions that move food through the GI tract.

The **esophagus** is a tube that passes through the diaphragm, a muscular wall separating the abdomen from the chest cavity where the lungs are located, to connect the pharynx and stomach. In the esophagus the bolus of food is moved along by rhythmic contractions of the smooth muscles, called **peristalsis** (**Figure 3.6**). Peristalsis is like an ocean wave that moves through the muscle, producing a narrowing in the lumen that pushes food and fluid in front of it. It takes only about 4 to 8 seconds for solid food to move from the pharynx down the esophagus to the stomach and even less time for liquids to make the trip. The peristaltic waves in the esophagus are so powerful that food and fluids will reach your stomach even if you are upside down. This contractile movement, which is controlled automatically by the nervous system, occurs throughout the GI tract, pushing the food bolus along from the pharynx through the large intestine.

sphincter A muscular valve that helps control the flow of materials in the GI tract.

To move from the esophagus into the stomach, food must pass through a **sphincter**, a muscle that encircles the tube of the digestive tract and acts as a valve. When the muscle contracts, the valve is closed. The gastroesophageal sphincter, also called the cardiac or lower esophageal sphincter, relaxes reflexively just before a peristaltic wave reaches it, allowing food to enter the stomach (see Figure 3.6). This valve normally prevents foods from moving back out of the stomach. Occasionally, however, materials do pass out of the stomach through this valve. Heartburn occurs when some of the acidic stomach contents leak up and out of the stomach into the esophagus, causing a burning sensation. Vomiting is the result of a reverse peristaltic wave that causes the sphincter to relax and allow the food to pass upward out of the stomach toward the mouth.

Stomach

chyme A mixture of partially digested food and stomach secretions.

The stomach is an expanded portion of the GI tract that serves as a temporary storage place for food. While held in the stomach, the bolus is mixed with highly acidic stomach secretions to form a semiliquid food mass called **chyme**. Some digestion takes place in the stomach, but, with the exception of some water, alcohol, and a few drugs, including aspirin and acetaminophen (Tylenol), very little absorption occurs here.

The Structure of the Stomach The stomach walls are thicker and have stronger muscles than other segments of the GI tract. Two layers of muscle, one running longitudinally down the tract and one running around it, surround most of the GI tract. The stomach has an additional layer that circles it diagonally, allowing for powerful contractions that thoroughly churn and mix the stomach contents (**Figure 3.7a**).

The surface of the stomach mucosa is covered with cells that produce large amounts of protective mucus. This surface is interrupted by millions of tiny openings called gastric pits. These pits lead to gastric glands, which contain several different types of cells that secrete substances into the stomach (**Figure 3.7b**). These stomach secretions are collectively referred to as *gastric juice*. Gastric glands also contain cells that secrete a variety of hormones and hormone-like compounds into the blood.

Composition of Gastric Juice Gastric juice consists of a number of substances, one of which is hydrochloric acid, produced by **parietal cells**. Hydrochloric acid acidifies the stomach contents and as a result kills most bacteria present in food. Parietal cells also produce intrinsic factor, which is needed for the absorption of vitamin B_{12} (see Chapter 8). Gastric juice also contains **pepsinogen**, produced by chief cells. Pepsinogen is an inactive form of the protein-digesting enzyme **pepsin**. Pepsin breaks proteins into shorter chains of amino acids called *polypeptides*. In children, the stomach glands also produce the enzyme rennin. Rennin acts on the milk protein casein to convert it into a curdy substance resembling sour milk.

Pepsin functions best in the acidic environment of the stomach. This acidic environment stops the function of salivary amylase. Therefore, the digestion of starch

parietal cells Cells in the stomach lining that make hydrochloric acid and intrinsic factor in response to nervous or hormonal stimulation.

pepsinogen An inactive protein-digesting enzyme produced by gastric glands and activated to pepsin by acid in the stomach.

pepsin A protein-digesting enzyme produced by the gastric glands. It is secreted in the gastric juice in an inactive form and activated by acid in the stomach.

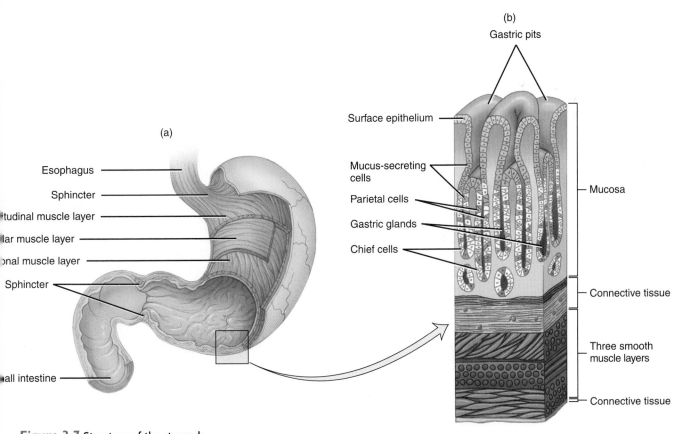

(b)
Gastric pits

(a)

Esophagus
Sphincter
tudinal muscle layer
lar muscle layer
onal muscle layer
Sphincter
all intestine

Surface epithelium
Mucus-secreting cells
Parietal cells
Gastric glands
Chief cells

Mucosa
Connective tissue
Three smooth muscle layers
Connective tissue

Figure 3.7 Structure of the stomach
(a) The stomach wall contains three layers of smooth muscle, which contract powerfully to mix food. (b) The lining of the stomach is covered with gastric pits. Inside these pits are the gastric glands, made up of different types of cells that produce the components of gastric juice.

from foods such as bread and potatoes stops in the stomach, and digestion of the protein from foods such as meat, milk, and legumes begins. The protein of the stomach wall is protected from the acid and pepsin by a thick layer of mucus. If the mucus layer is penetrated, pepsin and acid can damage the underlying tissues and cause a **peptic ulcer**, an erosion of the stomach wall or some other region of the GI tract. One of the leading causes of ulcers is acid-resistant bacteria called *Helicobacter pylori* that infect the lining of the stomach, destroying the protective mucosal layer and causing damage to the stomach wall.[2,3]

peptic ulcer An open sore in the lining of the stomach, esophagus, or small intestine.

Regulation by Nerves and Hormones How much your stomach churns and how much gastric juice is released is regulated by signals from both nerves and hormones. These signals originate from three different sites—the brain, the stomach, and the small intestine. The thought, smell, sight, or taste of food causes the brain to send nerve signals that stimulate gastric motility and secretion, preparing the stomach to receive food (**Figure 3.8**). Food entering the stomach stimulates the release of gastric secretions and an increase in motility. It does this by stretching local nerves, sending signals to the brain, and promoting the secretion of the hormone **gastrin**. Gastrin then triggers the release of gastric juice and increases stomach motility. Chyme moving out of the stomach must pass through the pyloric sphincter, which helps regulate the rate at which food empties from the stomach. Food entering the small intestine triggers hormonal and nervous signals that can decrease stomach motility and secretions and slow stomach emptying. This ensures that the amount of chyme entering the small intestine does not exceed the ability of the intestine to process it. Emotional factors can also affect gastric emptying. For example, sadness and fear tend to slow emptying, while aggression tends to increase gastric motility and speed emptying.

gastrin A hormone secreted by the stomach mucosa that stimulates the secretion of gastric juice.

The Rate of Stomach Emptying Chyme normally leaves the stomach in 2 to 6 hours but this rate is determined by the size and composition of the meal. A large meal will take longer to leave the stomach than a small meal, and a solid meal will leave the stomach more slowly than a liquid meal. The nutritional composition of a

1 The thought, smell, sight, or taste of food stimulates gastric secretions and increases stomach motility, thereby preparing the stomach to receive food.

2 Food entering the stomach increases the rate of gastric secretion and motility by stimulating local nerves, sending signals to the brain, and stimulating the secretion of gastrin.

3 Food entering the small intestine causes distention. This triggers hormonal and nervous signals that reduce stomach secretion and motility, slowing the entry of material into the intestine.

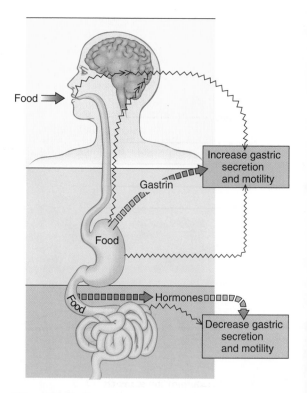

Figure 3.8 Regulation of stomach motility and secretion
Nerve signals (zigzag arrows) and hormonal signals (dashed arrows) from the brain, stomach, and small intestine regulate stomach activity.

meal also affects how long it stays in the stomach. A meal that is partly solid and partly liquid and contains about 25% of energy as protein, 45% as carbohydrate, and 30% as fat will be in the stomach for an average amount of time, about 4 hours. A high-fat meal will stay in the stomach the longest because fat entering the small intestine causes the release of hormones that slow GI motility, thus slowing stomach emptying. A meal that is primarily protein will leave more quickly, and a meal of mostly carbohydrate will leave the fastest. The reason you are often ready to eat again soon after a dinner of vegetables and rice is that this high-carbohydrate, low-fat meal leaves the stomach rapidly. What you choose for breakfast can also affect when you become hungry for lunch. Toast and coffee will leave your stomach far more quickly than a larger meal with more protein and some fat, such as bacon and eggs, toast with butter, and a glass of juice.

Small Intestine

The small intestine is the main site of digestion of food and absorption of nutrients. It is a narrow tube about 20 feet in length. It is divided into three segments. The first 12 inches are the duodenum, the next 8 feet are the jejunum, and the last 11 feet are the ileum. The structure of the small intestine is specialized to allow maximal absorption of the nutrients. In addition to its length, the small intestine has three other features that increase the area of its absorptive surface (**Figure 3.9**). First, the intestinal walls

Figure 3.9 Structure of the small intestine
The small intestine contains large circular folds, villi, and microvilli, all of which increase the absorptive surface area. (top/center: David M. Martin/Photo Researchers; right: S. Ito and D. W. Fawcett/Visuals Unlimited; bottom: SPL/Photo Researchers, Inc.)

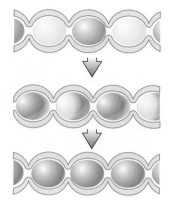

Figure 3.10 Segmentation
The alternating contraction and relaxation of segments of the small intestine moves food forward and backward, mixing it rather than propelling it forward.

villi (villus) Finger-like protrusions of the lining of the small intestine that participate in the digestion and absorption of nutrients.

microvilli or **brush border** Minute brush-like projections on the mucosal cell membrane that increase the absorptive surface area in the small intestine.

lacteal A small lymph vessel in the intestine that absorbs and transports the products of fat digestion.

segmentation Rhythmic local constrictions of the intestine that mix food with digestive juices and speed absorption by repeatedly moving the food mass over the intestinal wall.

pancreas An organ that secretes digestive enzymes and bicarbonate ions into the small intestine during digestion.

gallbladder An organ of the digestive system that stores bile, which is produced by the liver.

lipases Fat-digesting enzymes.

bile A substance made in the liver and stored in the gallbladder. It is released into the small intestine to aid in fat digestion and absorption.

secretin A hormone released by the duodenum that signals the release of pancreatic juice rich in bicarbonate ions and stimulates the liver to secrete bile into the gallbladder.

are arranged in large circular folds, which increase the surface area in contact with nutrients. Second, its entire inner surface is covered with finger-like projections called **villi** (singular, villus). And finally, each of these villi is covered with tiny **microvilli**, often referred to as the **brush border**. Together these features provide a surface area that is about the size of a tennis court (250 m^2 or 2700 ft^2). Each villus contains a blood vessel and a lymph vessel, called a **lacteal**, which are located only one cell layer away from the nutrients in the intestinal lumen. Nutrients must cross the mucosal cell layer to reach the bloodstream or lymphatic system for delivery to the tissues of the body.

Chyme is propelled through the small intestine by peristalsis, and the mixing of chyme with digestive secretions is aided in the small intestine by rhythmic local constrictions called **segmentation** (**Figure 3.10**). Segmentation also enhances absorption by repeatedly moving chyme over the surface of the intestinal mucosa.

Enzymes and Secretions in the Small Intestine The cells of the small intestine produce some digestive enzymes as well as a watery mucus-containing fluid called *intestinal juice*, that aids in absorption. However, normal digestion and absorption in the small intestine also require secretions from the **pancreas** and **gallbladder**. The pancreas secretes pancreatic juice, which contains both bicarbonate ions and digestive enzymes. The bicarbonate ions neutralize the acid in chyme, making the environment in the small intestine neutral rather than acidic as it is in the stomach. This neutrality allows enzymes from the pancreas and small intestine to function. The enzyme pancreatic amylase continues the job of breaking starch into sugars that was started in the mouth by salivary amylase. Pancreatic protein-digesting enzymes, including trypsin and chymotrypsin (see Table 3.2), continue to break protein into shorter and shorter chains of amino acids, and pancreatic fat-digesting enzymes, called **lipases**, break triglycerides into fatty acids. Intestinal digestive enzymes, found attached to or inside the cells lining the small intestine, are involved in the digestion of sugars into single sugar units and the digestion of small polypeptides into amino acids.

The gallbladder secretes **bile**, a substance produced in the liver and stored in the gallbladder that is necessary for fat digestion and absorption. Bile secreted into the small intestine mixes with fat and emulsifies it, or breaks it into smaller droplets, allowing lipases to more efficiently access the fat. Bile then helps form tiny droplets of digested fats, which move up against the mucosal lining, facilitating fat absorption (see Chapter 5).

Hormonal Control of Secretions The release of bile and pancreatic juice into the small intestine is controlled by two hormones secreted by the mucosal lining of the duodenum (see Table 3.3). **Secretin** signals the pancreas to secrete pancre-

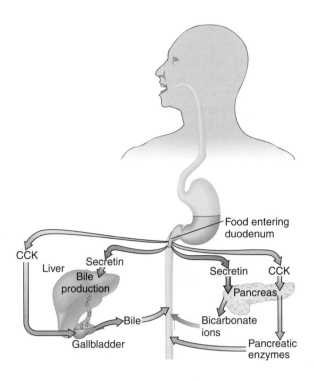

Figure 3.11 Hormonal control of secretions into the small intestine
Food entering the duodenum triggers the release of the hormones secretin (purple arrows) and cholecystokinin (CCK) (red arrows). These stimulate the secretion of bicarbonate ions, digestive enzymes, and bile into the small intestine.

atic juice rich in bicarbonate ions and stimulates the liver to secrete bile into the gallbladder. **Cholecystokinin (CCK)** signals the pancreas to secrete digestive enzymes and causes the gallbladder to contract and release bile into the duodenum (**Figure 3.11**).

cholecystokinin (CCK)
A hormone released by the duodenum that stimulates the release of pancreatic juice rich in digestive enzymes and causes the gallbladder to contract and release bile into the duodenum.

How Are Nutrients Absorbed? The small intestine is the primary site of absorption for water, vitamins, minerals, and the products of carbohydrate, fat, and protein digestion. To be absorbed these nutrients must pass from the lumen of the GI tract into the mucosal cells lining the tract and then into the blood or lymph. Several different mechanisms are involved (**Figure 3.12**). Some molecules are absorbed by diffusion—the process by which a substance moves from an area of higher concentration to an

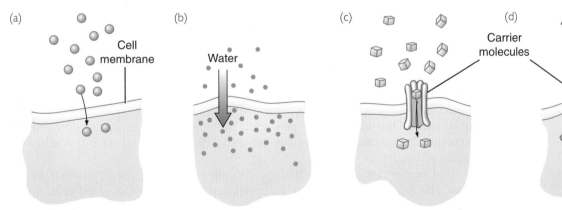

Figure 3.12 Absorption mechanisms

(a) Simple diffusion, which requires no energy, is shown here by the purple balls that move from an area of higher concentration to an area of lower concentration.

(b) Osmosis is the diffusion of water. The water molecules represented by the purple arrow move from an area with a lower concentration of dissolved substances (blue dots) to an area with a higher concentration of dissolved substances.

(c) Facilitated diffusion, which requires no energy, is shown here by the yellow cubes that move from an area of higher concentration to an area of lower concentration with the help of a carrier.

(d) Active transport, which requires energy and a carrier, is shown here by the red pyramids that move from an area of lower concentration to an area of higher concentration.

area of lower concentration. Substances that move from higher to lower concentrations are said to move down their concentration gradient. When a concentration gradient exists and the nutrient can pass freely from the lumen of the GI tract across the cell membrane into the mucosal cell, the process is called **simple diffusion**. This process does not require the input of energy. Vitamin E and fatty acids are absorbed by simple diffusion. Water is also absorbed by diffusion. The diffusion of water is called **osmosis**. In osmosis there is a net movement of water in a direction that will balance the concentration of dissolved substances on either side of a membrane. For example, if there is a high concentration of sugar in the lumen of the intestine, water will actually move from the mucosal cells into the lumen. As the sugar is absorbed, and the concentration of sugar in the lumen decreases, water will move back into the mucosal cells by osmosis.

Many nutrients, however, cannot pass freely across cell membranes; they must be helped across by carrier molecules in a process called **facilitated diffusion**. Even though these nutrients are carried across the cell membrane by other molecules, they still move down a concentration gradient from an area of higher concentration to one of lower concentration without requiring energy; the sugar fructose found in fruit is absorbed by facilitated diffusion.

Substances unable to be absorbed by diffusion must enter the body by **active transport**, a process that requires both a carrier molecule and the input of energy. This use of energy allows substances to be transported against their concentration gradient from an area of lower concentration to an area of higher concentration. The sugar glucose from the breakdown of the starch in a slice of bread and amino acids from protein digestion are absorbed by active transport. This allows these nutrients to be absorbed even when they are present in higher concentrations inside the mucosal cells. More specific information about the absorption of the products of carbohydrate, fat, and protein digestion will be discussed in Chapters 4, 5, and 6, respectively.

Large Intestine

Components of chyme that are not absorbed in the small intestine pass through the ileocecal valve to the large intestine, which includes the **colon** and **rectum**. Although most absorption occurs in the small intestine, water and some vitamins and minerals are also absorbed in the colon. Peristalsis here is slower than in the small intestine. Water, nutrients, and fecal matter may spend 24 hours in the large intestine, in contrast to the 3 to 5 hours it takes for chyme to move through the small intestine. This slow movement favors the growth of bacteria, referred to as the **intestinal microflora**. These bacteria are permanent beneficial residents of this part of the GI tract (see Your Choice: Should You Feed Your Flora?). The microflora act on unabsorbed portions of food, such as the fiber, producing nutrients that the bacteria themselves can use or, in some cases, that can be absorbed into the body. For example, the microflora synthesize small amounts of fatty acids, some B vitamins, and vitamin K, some of which can be absorbed. One additional by-product of bacterial metabolism is gas, which causes flatulence. In normal adult humans between 200 and 2000 mL of intestinal gas is produced per day.

Materials not absorbed in the colon are excreted as waste products in the feces. The feces are a mixture of undigested unabsorbed matter, dead cells, secretions from the GI tract, water, and bacteria. The amount of bacteria in the feces varies but can make up more than half the weight of the feces. The amount of water in the feces is affected by fiber and fluid intake. Fiber retains water, so when adequate fiber and fluid are consumed, feces have a high water content and are easily passed. When inadequate fiber or fluid is consumed, feces are hard and dry, and difficult to eliminate.

The end of the colon is connected to the rectum, where feces are stored prior to defecation. The rectum is connected to the **anus**, the external opening of the digestive tract. The rectum works with the colon to prepare the feces for elim-

simple diffusion The movement of substances from an area of higher concentration to an area of lower concentration. No energy is required.

osmosis The passive movement of water across a semipermeable membrane in a direction that will equalize the concentration of dissolved substances on both sides.

facilitated diffusion The movement of substances across a cell membrane from an area of higher concentration to an area of lower concentration with the aid of a carrier molecule. No energy is required.

active transport The transport of substances across a cell membrane with the aid of a carrier molecule and the expenditure of energy. This may occur against a concentration gradient.

colon The largest portion of the large intestine.

rectum The portion of the large intestine that connects the colon and anus.

intestinal microflora Microorganisms that inhabit the large intestine.

anus The outlet of the rectum through which feces are expelled.

YOUR CHOICE

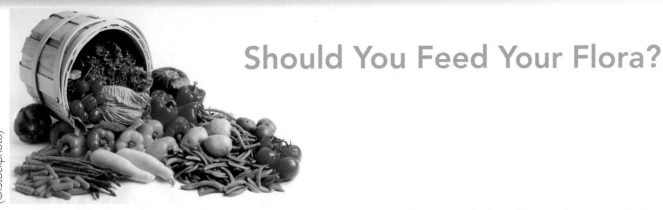

Should You Feed Your Flora?

The large intestine of a healthy adult is home to 300 to 500 different species of bacteria, and the gut has about 10 times more bacterial cells than the total number of cells in your entire body.[1] These bacteria are usually beneficial. They break down indigestible dietary substances, improve the digestion and absorption of essential nutrients, synthesize some vitamins, and metabolize harmful substances. They are important for intestinal immune function, proper growth and development of cells in the colon, and optimal intestinal motility and transit time.[2] A strong population of healthful bacteria can also inhibit the growth of harmful bacteria. If the wrong bacteria take over, they can cause diarrhea, infections, and perhaps an increased risk of cancer. In light of these benefits, should you supplement your diet with beneficial bacteria or eat certain foods to promote the growth of these good bugs?

Research supports the hypothesis that bacteria in fermented dairy products, such as *Bifidobacterium* and *Lactobacillus*, provide health benefits. Consuming products such as yogurt that naturally contain these bacteria, and supplements containing live bacteria, is referred to as *probiotic therapy*. When consumed, some of these organisms survive passage through the upper GI tract and live temporarily in the colon before they are excreted in the feces. Probiotics improve the digestion of the sugar lactose in lactose-intolerant people (see Chapter 4), prevent diarrhea associated with antibiotic use,[3] reduce the duration of diarrhea due to intestinal infections and other causes,[4] and have beneficial effects on immune function in the intestine.[5] There is also evidence that probiotics may relieve constipation, reduce allergy symptoms, modify the risk of colon cancer, and affect body weight.[6–8] One problem with probiotics is that when they are no longer consumed, the added bacteria are rapidly washed out of the colon. However, you can promote the growth of a healthy population of bacteria by consuming substances called *prebiotics*. Prebiotics are indigestible carbohydrates that pass into the colon where they serve as a food supply for bacteria, stimulating the growth or activity of certain types of bacteria. Prebiotics are found naturally in onions, bananas, garlic, and artichokes and are currently sold as dietary supplements.

Our understanding of probiotics and prebiotics is expanding. We know that the risks of using these products are negligible, but their specific health benefits are still being investigated. Meanwhile, eating a diet rich in fruits, vegetables, and whole grains gives you a wide variety of indigestible carbohydrates that promote the growth of healthful bacteria. It is not clear whether consuming additional probiotics or prebiotics is needed for optimal health.[9]

[1]Volker, M. Dietary modification of the intestinal microbiota. *Nutr. Rev.* 62:235–242, 2004.

[2]Guarner, F., and Malagelada, J. R. Gut flora in health and disease. *Lancet*. 361:512–519, 2003.

[3]D'Souza, L., Rajkumar, C., Cooke, J., and Bulpitt, C. J. Probiotics in prevention of antibiotic associated diarrhoea: Meta-analysis. *BMJ* 324:1361–1366, 2002.

[4]Johnston, B. C., Supina, A. L., Ospina, M., and Vohra, S. Probiotics for the prevention of pediatric antibiotic-associated diarrhea. *Cochrane Database Syst. Rev.* 18:CD004827, 2007.

[5]Gill, H., and Prasad, J. Probiotics, immunomodulation, and health benefits. *Adv Exp Med Biol* 606:423–454, 2008.

[6]Isolauri, E., and Salminen, S. Nutrition, Allergy, Mucosal Immunology, and Intestinal Microbiota (NAMI) Research Group Report: Probiotics: Use in allergic disorders: A Nutrition, Allergy, Mucosal Immunology, and Intestinal Microbiota (NAMI) Research Group Report. *J. Clin. Gastroenterol.* 42(Suppl 2):S91–S96, 2008.

[7]Rescigno, M. The pathogenic role of intestinal flora in IBD and colon cancer. *Curr. Drug. Targets* 9:395–403, 2008.

[8]Bäckhed, F., Ding, H., Wang, T. et al. The gut microbiota as an environmental factor that regulates fat storage. *Proc. Natl. Acad. Sci. USA* 101:18–23, 2004.

[9]Blaut, M. Relationship of prebiotics and food to intestinal microflora. *Eur. J. Nutr.* 41(Suppl. 1):111–116, 2002.

ination. Defecation is regulated by a sphincter that is under voluntary control. It allows the feces to be eliminated at convenient and appropriate times. The digestion and absorption of carbohydrate, fat, and protein are summarized in **Figure 3.13**.

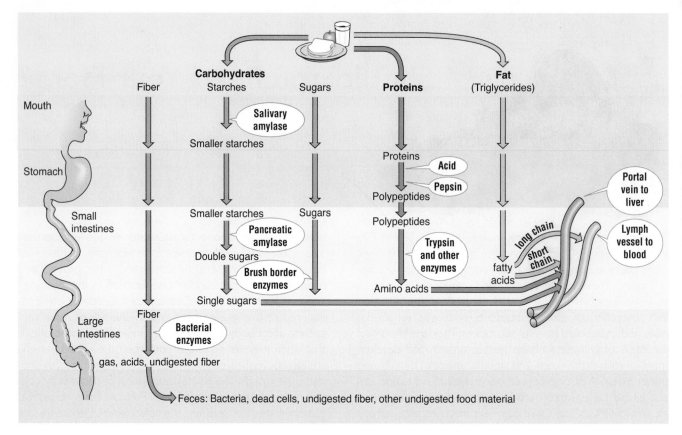

Figure 3.13 An overview of digestion and absorption
Some carbohydrate digestion occurs in the mouth and some protein digestion occurs in the stomach, but the majority of macronutrient digestion and the absorption of nutrients occur in the small intestine.

3.4 Digestion and Health

Learning Objectives

- Describe the cause of heartburn and GERD.
- Discuss when alternative feeding methods are needed to provide nutrients.
- Explain how changes in the digestive system throughout life affect digestion and absorption.

The digestive system is adaptable and able to handle a wide variety of foods. However, minor problems related to the digestive tract are common and almost everyone experiences some type of GI distress at one time or another. The types of food that can be consumed and the function of the digestive tract are also affected by certain stages of life. If gastrointestinal problems limit the ability to obtain adequate energy and nutrients alternative methods must be employed to provide the nutrients necessary for life.

Common Digestive Problems

Minor digestive problems, such as heartburn, constipation, and diarrhea, are common and, in most cases, have little effect on nutritional status. However, more long-term or severe problems can have serious consequences for nutrition and overall health. Some digestive problems and their causes, consequences, and solutions are given in **Table 3.4**.

Table 3.4 Digestive Problems and Nutritional Consequences

Problem	Causes	Consequences	Treatment/Management
Dry mouth	Disease, medications	Decreased food intake due to changes in taste, difficulty chewing and swallowing, increased tooth decay, and gum disease.	Change medications, use artificial saliva.
Dental pain and loss of teeth	Tooth decay, gum disease	Reduced food intake due to impaired ability to chew, reduced nutrient absorption due to incomplete digestion.	Change consistency of foods consumed.
Heartburn, Gastroesophageal reflux disease (GERD)	Stomach acid leaking into esophagus due to overeating, anxiety, stress, pregnancy, hiatal hernia, or disease processes	Pain and discomfort after eating; ulcers; increased cancer risk.	Reduce meal size, avoid high-fat foods, consume liquids between rather than with meals, remain upright after eating, take antacids and other medications.
Hiatal hernia	Pressure on the abdomen from persistent or severe coughing or vomiting, pregnancy, straining while defecating, or lifting heavy objects	Heartburn, belching, GERD, and chest pain	Reduce meal size, avoid high-fat foods, consume liquids between rather than with meals, remain upright after eating, take antacids and other medications, weight loss.
Ulcers	Infection of stomach by *H. pylori,* acid-resistant bacteria that penetrate the mucous layer and damage the epithelial lining; chronic use of drugs such as aspirin and ibuprofen that erode the mucosa; GERD	Pain, bleeding, and possible abdominal infection	Antibiotics to treat infection, antacids to reduce acid, change medications.
Vomiting	Bacterial and viral infections, medications, other illnesses, eating disorders, pregnancy, food allergies	Dehydration and electrolyte imbalance; if chronic, can damage the mouth, gums esophagus, and teeth.	Medications to treat infection, fluid and electrolyte replacement.
Diarrhea	Bacterial and viral infections, medications, food intolerance	Dehydration and electrolyte imbalance	Medications to treat infection, fluid and electrolyte replacement.
Constipation	Low fiber intake, low fluid intake, high fiber in combination with low fluid intake, weak intestinal muscles	Discomfort, intestinal blockage, formation of outpouchings in the intestinal wall (diverticula) (see Chapter 4)	High-fiber, high-fluid diet, exercise, medications.
Irritable bowel syndrome	Unusual pattern of muscle contractions in the intestines, may be stronger and last longer or slower and weaker than normal.	Abdominal pain or cramping and changes in bowel function—including bloating, gas, diarrhea, and constipation.	Manage stress and make changes in diet and lifestyle, fiber supplements, antidiarrheal medications, other medications.
Pancreatic disease	Cystic fibrosis or pancreatitis	Malabsorption of fat, fat-soluble vitamins, and vitamin B_{12} due to reduced availability of pancreatic enzymes and bicarbonate.	Oral supplements of digestive enzymes.
Gallstones	Deposits of cholesterol, bile pigments, and calcium in the gallbladder or bile duct	Pain and poor fat digestion and absorption.	Low-fat diet, surgical removal of the gallbladder.

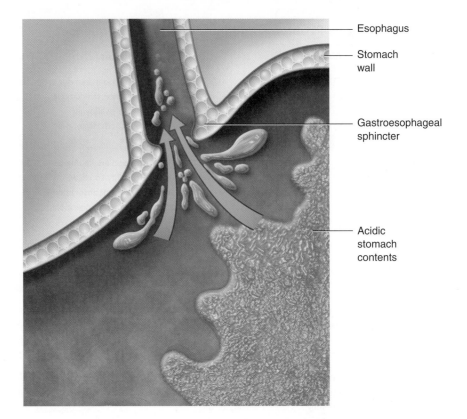

Esophagus

Stomach
wall

Gastroesophageal
sphincter

Acidic
stomach
contents

Figure 3.14 Gastroesophageal reflux
Heartburn and GERD occur when stomach acid leaks through the gastroesophageal sphincter, which separates the esophagus from the stomach, and irritates the lining of the esophagus.

Video

gastroesophageal reflux disease (GERD) A chronic condition in which acidic stomach contents leak back up into the esophagus causing pain and damaging the esophagus.

Heartburn Heartburn is one of the most common digestive complaints. It occurs when the acidic stomach contents leak back into the esophagus causing a burning sensation in the chest or throat (**Figure 3.14**). The more technical term for the leakage of stomach contents back into the esophagus is *gastroesophageal reflux*. Occasional heartburn from reflux is common but if it occurs more than twice a week it may indicate a condition called **gastroesophageal reflux disease (GERD)**. If left untreated GERD can eventually lead to more serious health problems such as ulcers and cancer. Whether you have occasional heartburn or GERD, it can cause discomfort after eating a large meal and limit the types and amounts of food you can consume. Symptoms can be reduced by eating small meals and avoiding spicy foods, fatty and fried foods, citrus fruits, chocolate, caffeinated beverages, tomato-based foods, garlic, onions, and mint. Remaining upright after eating, wearing loose clothing, avoiding smoking and alcohol, and losing weight may also help relieve symptoms. For many people medications are needed to manage symptoms (see Off the Label: Antacids: Learning the Drug Facts).

Heartburn and GERD are sometimes caused by a *hiatal hernia*. The opening in the diaphragm that the esophagus passes through is called the hiatus. A hiatal hernia occurs when the upper part of the stomach bulges through this opening into the chest cavity. Hiatal hernias are common, occurring in about one-quarter of people older than 50. They're more common in women, in smokers, and in people who are overweight. Most hiatal hernias cause no signs or symptoms, but larger ones may allow food and acid to back up into the esophagus causing heartburn and chest pain. It can usually be treated by heartburn medications, but in severe cases surgery may be needed.

Ulcers Ulcers can arise both in the esophagus and the stomach. They occur when the mucosa is eroded away, exposing the underlying tissues to the gastric juices (**Figure 3.15**). If the damage reaches the nerve layer, it causes pain, and if capillaries are damaged, gastrointestinal bleeding can occur. If the ulcer perforates the wall of the GI tract, a serious abdominal infection can occur. Ulcers can result from GERD or the chronic use of drugs such as aspirin and ibuprofen that erode the mucosa of the GI tract, but, as previously discussed, ulcers are more often caused by a bacterial infection in the stomach. Mild ulcers can affect nutrient intake by limiting food choices

Figure 3.15
Ulcers, such as this one in the lining of the stomach, are most often due to *Helicobacter Pylori* infection. (CNRI/SPL/Photo Researchers)

Off the Label
Antacids: Learning the Drug Facts

(©iStockphoto)

Did you know that over-the-counter heartburn remedies often contain nutrients? How can you determine whether a product will affect your nutritional health in addition to relieving your heartburn? When choosing a product to treat heartburn (or any other ailment), be sure to check the label. Drug Facts labels on nonprescription drugs are designed to help consumers take medications correctly, as well as understand the drug's benefits, risks, and nutritional impact. They must present information in a standardized, easy-to-follow format that is as readable and as consistent as the Nutrition Facts labels on food products. The active ingredients must be listed first, along with the purpose for each, followed by uses, warnings, directions, and then inactive ingredients.[1]

The label shown here indicates that Reducid contains famotidine, a drug that reduces the amount of acid secreted by the stomach. It also contains calcium carbonate and magnesium hydroxide, antacids that contribute minerals as well as neutralize the acidity of the stomach contents. The label tells you that a single tablet contains 800 mg of calcium carbonate and 165 mg of magnesium hydroxide. This is equivalent to about 320 mg of calcium (32% of the Daily Value) and 69 mg of magnesium (17% of the Daily Value). Both nutrients are typically low in the American diet, so this product can be a welcome supplement. Higher doses of magnesium can cause diarrhea.

Other antacids contain minerals that are not beneficial additions to the diet. For example, each tablet of Alka-Seltzer contains 567 mg of sodium, about 24% of the Daily Value. Aluminum is also found in a number of antacids, it binds phosphorus and limits its absorption and may cause constipation. The list of inactive ingredients shows that Reducid contains sugar and starch; important information for individuals who have diabetes or are consuming low-kcalorie diets.

If you are looking for an over-the-counter medication to treat occasional heartburn, understanding how to read the label will help you to use it correctly and to know if the product will affect your nutrient intake.

Drug Facts

Active ingredients (in each chewable tablet) — **Purpose**
Famotidine 10 mg . . . . Acid reducer
Calcium carbonate 800 mg . . . . Antacid
Magnesium hydroxide 165 mg . . . . Antacid

Use relieves heartburn associated with acid indigestion and sour stomach

Warnings
Allergy alert: Do not use if you are allergic to famotidine or other acid reducers

Do not use
• if you have trouble swallowing • with other famotidine products or acid reducers

Ask a doctor or pharmacist before use if you are presently taking a prescription drug. Antacids may interact with certain prescription drugs.

Stop use and ask a doctor if
• stomach pain continues • you need to take this product for more than 14 days

If pregnant or breast-feeding, ask a health professional before use.
Keep out of reach of children. In case of overdose, get medical help or contact a Poison Control Center right away.

Directions
• adults and children 12 years and over:
  • **do not swallow tablet whole: chew completely**
  • to relieve symptoms, chew 1 tablet before swallowing
  • do not use more than 2 chewable tablets in 24 hours
• children under 12 years: ask a doctor

Drug Facts (continued)
Other information
• read the directions and warnings before use
• keep the carton and package insert. They contain important information.
• store at 25–30°C (77-86°F) • protect from moisture

Inactive ingredients
cellulose acetate, corn starch, dextrates, flavors, hydroxypropyl cellulose, hydroxypropyl methylcellulose, lactose, magnesium stearate, pregelatinized starch, red iron oxide, sodium lauryl sulfate, sugar

Questions or comments? call toll-free 1–800–555–4008

---

[1] Nordenberg, T. New drug label spells it out simply, *FDA. Consumer*, July/August 1999.

to those that do not cause discomfort but more severe ulcers can cause bleeding that can be life threatening (see Science Applied: Discovering What Causes Ulcers).

Pancreatic and Gallbladder Problems Abnormalities in the pancreas and gallbladder can affect digestion and cause discomfort. If the pancreas is not functioning normally, the availability of enzymes needed to digest carbohydrate, fat, and protein may be reduced, limiting the ability to absorb these essential nutrients. If the gallbladder is not releasing bile, it can impair fat absorption. A common condition that affects the gallbladder is gallstones. These are clumps of solid material that form in the gallbladder or bile duct and can cause pain when the gallbladder contracts in response to fat in the intestine. Gallstones can interfere with bile secretion and reduce fat absorption. They are usually treated by removing the gallbladder. In this case, bile simply drips into the intestine as it is produced rather than being stored and squeezed out in larger amounts in response to fat in the intestine.

Diarrhea and Constipation Common discomforts that are related to problems in the intestines include diarrhea and constipation. Diarrhea refers to frequent watery stools. It occurs when material moves through the colon too quickly for sufficient water to be absorbed or when water is drawn into the lumen from cells lining the intestinal tract. Diarrhea may occur when the lining of the small intestine is inflamed so nutrients and water are not absorbed. The inflammation may be caused by infection with a microorganism or by other irritants. Constipation refers to hard, dry stools that are difficult to pass. Constipation can be caused by a diet that contains insufficient fluid or fiber, lack of exercise, or a weakening of the muscles of the large intestine. A condition that may cause either diarrhea or constipation is irritable bowel syndrome. Its cause is unknown, but it often results in abnormal contractions of the muscles in the intestinal wall. Symptoms include abdominal pain or cramping, bloating, gas, diarrhea, and constipation.

Alternate Feeding Methods

enteral or **tube-feeding**
A method of feeding by providing a liquid diet directly to the stomach or intestine through a tube placed down the throat or through the wall of the GI tract.

total parenteral nutrition (TPN) A technique for nourishing an individual by providing all needed nutrients directly into the circulatory system.

For individuals who are unable to consume food or digest and absorb the nutrients needed to meet their requirements, several alternative feeding methods have been developed. People who are unable to swallow can be fed a liquid diet through a tube inserted into the stomach or intestine. **Enteral or tube-feeding** can provide all the essential nutrients. Tube-feeding can be used in patients who are unconscious or have suffered an injury to the upper GI tract (**Figure 3.16a**). For individuals whose GI tract is not functional, nutrients can be provided directly into the bloodstream. This is referred to as **total parenteral nutrition (TPN)** (**Figure 3.16b**). Carefully planned TPN can provide all the nutrients essential to life. When all nutrients are not

(a)

(b)

Figure 3.16
People who are not able to eat enough to meet their nutrient and energy needs can be nourished with (a) enteral feeding (tube-feeding) if their GI tract is able to digest food and absorb nutrients or (b) total parenteral nutrition if their gut is not functional. (Left, Ed Eckstein/ Phototake; right, L. Steinmark/ Custom Medical Stock Photo, Inc.)

SCIENCE
ScienceAppliedScienceApplied
ScienceAppliedScienceApplied
ScienceAppliedScienceApplied
APPLIED

(DAJ/Getty Images, Inc.)

(www.victorianoizquierdo.com/Getty Images, Inc.)

(Elena Schweitzer/Shutterstock)

Discovering What Causes Ulcers

Peptic ulcers are lesions in the wall of the stomach or other part of the GI tract. They cause pain and, sometimes, bleeding. For many years they were thought to be caused by excess stomach acid. Treatments included milk to coat the GI lining, a bland diet, stress reduction, and drugs to neutralize acid or reduce its secretion. These treatments usually reduced irritation and decreased symptoms, but ulcers were a chronic condition even with treatment. Today, due to the observations and perseverance of Drs. B. J. Marshall and J. R. Warren, many ulcers can be cured.

Dr. Warren is a pathologist who observed curvy-shaped bacteria in some of the stomach biopsies he examined under the microscope. He noted that the bacteria were always present in tissue that was inflamed and that the number of organisms correlated with the degree of inflammation.[1] In 1982 he and Dr. Marshall isolated and grew this bacteria, later named *Helicobacter pylori* (*H. pylori*), in the laboratory.[2] They believed that the bacteria were the cause of peptic ulcers.

The hypothesis that ulcers were caused by bacteria however was not immediately embraced by the scientific community. At the time the accepted theory was that ulcers were caused by too much stomach acid and it was widely accepted that bacteria could not survive in the strong acid of the stomach. To persuade other scientists that the hypothesis was correct, more convincing evidence that the bacteria were the cause of ulcer symptoms, such as gastric inflammation, was needed. Therefore, Marshall decided to use himself as an experimental subject to gather data to support his theory.

Marshall's experiment involved first having a small sample of his gastric mucosa examined to confirm that it was not infected with bacteria. He then drank a vial containing *H. pylori* that had been isolated from a patient with chronic gastric inflammation. Ten days later he developed symptoms of gastric inflammation. A follow-up sample of his gastric mucosa confirmed that his stomach lining was now inflamed and *H. pylori* bacteria could be seen attached to the mucosa (see figure).[3] Fortunately, his symptoms resolved quickly with antibiotic therapy. This confirmed the connection between *H. pylori* and stomach inflammation, but since Marshall did not develop an ulcer, that link was still unproven. The connection between *H. pylori* and ulcers was eventually supported by epidemiologi-

This electron micrograph shows the helical-shaped bacteria *Helicobacter pylori* attached to the gastric mucosa. (© Science Photo Library/Photo Researchers)

cal studies that showed an increased incidence of ulcers in persons infected with the bacteria.[1]

As our understanding of how this organism survives in the acid environment of the stomach grew, the idea that bacteria caused ulcers became more universally accepted. In the stomach, *H. pylori* use a tail-like structure to swim through the protective mucus layer and adhere to the mucosal cells. Once attached to the mucosal cells, they use an enzyme to produce substances that neutralize the acid immediately around them.[4] The bacteria damage mucosal cells and increase the release of gastrin, which subsequently increases stomach acid secretion.[5] The presence of bacteria causes inflammation and other immune responses that lead to additional tissue damage. About 30% to 50% of the world's population is infected with *H. pylori*.[1] In the United States about 20% of people under 40 years old and half of those over 60 years old are infected.[6] Most people who are infected with *H. pylori* do not have symptoms and fewer than 20% go on to develop an ulcer, but infection with this organism is now known to also be associated with cancers of the stomach.[1,6]

Because of the observations and persistence of Drs. Warren and Marshall, a patient diagnosed with an ulcer today is given antibiotics rather than a bland diet and antacids. Successful antibiotic therapy combined with acid-suppression therapy can allow the ulcer to heal, eliminate the bacteria that caused the disease, and cure the patient. A hypothesis that was at first rejected by the scientific community is now a theory supported by scientific evidence.

[1]Lynch, N. A. *Helicobacter. pylori* and ulcers: A paradigm revised. Available online at http://opa.faseb.org/pdf/pylori.pdf. Accessed September 2, 2009.

[2]Marshall, B. J., and Warren, J. R. Unidentified curved bacilli on gastric epithelium in active chronic gastritis. *Lancet* I:1311–1315, 1984.

[3]Marshall, B. J., Armstrong, J. A., McGechie, D. B., and Glancy, R. J. Attempt to fulfill Koch's postulates for pyloric. *Campylobacter. Med. J. Aust.* 142:436–439, 1985.

[4]McGee, D. J., and Mobley, H. L. T. Mechanisms of *Helicobacter pylori* infection: Bacterial factors. *Curr. Top. Microbiol. Immunol.* 241:156–180, 1999.

[5] Joseph, I. M., and Kirschner, D. A. Model for the study of *Helicobacter pylori* interaction with human gastric acid secretion. *J. Theor. Biol.* 228:55–80, 2004.

[6]National Digestive Disease Information Clearinghouse, National Institutes of Diabetes and Digestive and Kidney Diseases. *H. pylori* and peptic ulcer. Available online at http://digestive.niddk.nih.gov/ddiseases/pubs/hpylori/ Accessed September 2, 2009.

provided in a TPN solution, nutrient deficiencies develop quickly. Inadvertently feeding patients incomplete TPN solutions has helped demonstrate the essentiality of several trace minerals.

The Digestive System Throughout Life

There are some differences in the way the digestive system functions during pregnancy and infancy and with advancing age. These changes affect the ability to ingest and digest food and absorb nutrients. However, if the diet is properly managed, nutritional status can be maintained at all stages of life.

Life Cycle

Pregnancy Physiological changes that occur during pregnancy may cause gastrointestinal problems. During the first three months, many women experience nausea, referred to as morning sickness. This term is a misnomer, because the nausea can occur at any time of the day. Morning sickness is believed to be due to pregnancy-related hormonal changes. In most cases, it can be dealt with by eating frequent small meals and avoiding foods and smells that cause nausea. Eating dry crackers or cereal may also help. In severe cases where uncontrollable vomiting occurs, nutrients may need to be given intravenously to maintain nutritional health.

Later in pregnancy, the enlarged uterus puts pressure on the stomach and intestines, which can make it difficult to consume large meals. In addition, the placenta produces the hormone progesterone, which causes the smooth muscles of the digestive tract to relax. The muscle-relaxing effects of progesterone may relax the gastroesophageal sphincter enough to allow the stomach contents to move back into the esophagus, causing heartburn. In the large intestine, relaxed muscles and the pressure of the uterus cause less efficient peristaltic movements and may result in constipation. Increasing water intake, eating a diet high in fiber, and exercising regularly can help prevent and relieve constipation (see Chapter 14).

Life Cycle

Infancy The digestive system is one of the last to fully mature in developing humans. At birth, the digestive tract is functional, but a newborn is not ready to consume an adult diet. The most obvious difference between the infant and adult digestive tracts is that newborns are not able to chew and swallow solid food. They are born with a suckling reflex that allows them to consume liquids from a nipple placed toward the back of the mouth. A protrusion reflex causes anything placed in the front of the mouth to be pushed out by the tongue. As head control increases, this reflex disappears, making spoon-feeding possible.

Digestion and absorption also differ between infants and adults. In infants, the digestion of milk protein is aided by rennin, an enzyme produced in the infant stomach that is not found in adults.[4] The stomachs of newborns also produce the enzyme gastric lipase. This enzyme is present in adults but plays a more important role in infants where it begins the digestion of the fats in human milk. The absorption of fat from the infant's small intestine is inefficient. Low levels of pancreatic enzymes in infants limit starch digestion; however, enzymes at the brush border of the small intestine allow the milk sugar lactose to be digested and absorbed.

The ability to absorb intact proteins is greater in infants than that in adults. The absorption of whole proteins can cause food allergies (see Chapter 15), but it also allows infants to absorb immune factors from their mothers' milk. These proteins provide temporary immunity to certain diseases.

The bacteria in the large intestine of infants are also different from those in adults because of the all-milk diet infants consume. This is the reason that the feces of breast-fed babies are almost odorless. Another feature of the infant digestive tract is the lack of voluntary control of elimination. Between the ages of 2 and 3, this ability develops and toilet training is possible.

Aging Although there are few dramatic changes in nutrient requirements with aging, changes in the digestive tract and other systems may affect the palatability of food and the ability to obtain proper nutrition. The senses of smell and taste are often diminished or even lost with age, reducing the appeal of food. A reduction in the amount of saliva may make swallowing difficult, decrease the taste of food, and also promote tooth decay. Loss of teeth and improperly fitting dentures may limit food choices to soft and liquid foods or cause solid foods to be poorly chewed. Gastrointestinal secretions may also be reduced, but this rarely impairs absorption because the levels secreted in healthy elderly adults are still sufficient to break down food into forms that can be absorbed. A condition called **atrophic gastritis** that causes a reduction in the secretion of stomach acid is also common in the elderly. This may decrease the absorption of several vitamins and minerals and may allow bacterial growth to increase (see Chapters 8 and 16). Constipation is a common complaint among the elderly. It may be caused by decreased motility and elasticity in the colon, weakened abdominal and pelvic muscles, and a decrease in sensory perception (see Critical Thinking: Gastrointestinal Problems Can Affect Nutrition).

Life Cycle

atrophic gastritis
An inflammation of the stomach lining that causes a reduction in stomach acid and allows bacterial overgrowth.

3.5 Transporting Nutrients to Body Cells

Learning Objectives

- Explain why the cardiovascular system is important in nutrition.
- Compare the path of an amino acid and a large fatty acid from absorption to delivery to a cell.

Nutrients absorbed into the mucosal cells of the intestine enter the blood circulation by either the **hepatic portal circulation** or the **lymphatic system**. The hepatic portal circulation is part of the cardiovascular system, which consists of the heart and blood vessels. Amino acids from protein digestion, simple sugars from carbohydrate digestion, and the water-soluble products of fat digestion are absorbed into **capillaries**, which are part of the hepatic portal circulation. The products of fat digestion that are not water-soluble are taken into lacteals, which are small vessels of the lymphatic system, before entering the blood.

hepatic portal circulation
The system of blood vessels that collects nutrient-laden blood from the digestive organs and delivers it to the liver.

lymphatic system The system of vessels, organs, and tissues that drains excess fluid from the spaces between cells, transports fat-soluble substances from the digestive tract, and contributes to immune function.

capillaries Small, thin-walled blood vessels where the exchange of gases and nutrients between blood and cells occurs.

veins Vessels that carry blood toward the heart.

arteries Vessels that carry blood away from the heart.

The Cardiovascular System

The cardiovascular system is a closed network of tubules through which blood is pumped. Blood carries nutrients and oxygen to the cells of all the organs and tissues of the body and removes waste products from these same cells. Blood also carries other substances, such as hormones, from one part of the body to another.

The heart is the workhorse of the cardiovascular system. It is a muscular pump with two circulatory loops—one that delivers blood to the lungs and one that delivers blood to the rest of the body (**Figure 3.17**). The blood vessels that transport blood and dissolved substances toward the heart are called **veins**, and those that transport blood and dissolved substances away from the heart are called **arteries**. As arteries carry blood away from the heart, they branch many times to form smaller and smaller blood vessels. The smallest arteries are called arterioles. Arterioles then branch to form capillaries. Capillaries are thin-walled vessels that are just large enough to allow one red blood cell to pass at a time. From the capillaries, oxygen and nutrients carried by the blood pass into the cells, and waste products pass from the cells into the blood. In the capillaries of the lungs, blood releases carbon dioxide to be exhaled and picks up oxygen to be delivered to the cells. Blood in capillaries in the villi of the small intestine picks up water-soluble nutrients absorbed from the diet. Blood then flows from capillaries into the smallest veins, the venules, which converge to form larger and larger veins for return to the heart. Therefore, blood starting in the heart is pumped through the arteries to the capillaries of the lungs where it picks up oxygen. It then returns to the heart via the veins and is pumped out again into the arteries that lead to the rest of the body. In the capillaries of the body, blood delivers oxygen and nutrients and removes wastes before returning to the heart via the veins.

Critical Thinking
Gastrointestinal Problems Can Affect Nutrition

Many factors affect how well we digest food and absorb nutrients. For each situation described below, consider how digestion and absorption are affected and what the consequences are for nutritional status.

Critical Thinking Questions

A 50-year old man is taking medication that reduces the amount of saliva produced.

▼

What effect would this have on his nutrition and health?

An 80-year-old woman has dentures that don't fit well; she likes raw carrots but can't chew them thoroughly.

▼

How will this affect the digestion and absorption of nutrients in the carrots?

For breakfast, a college student has cereal with skim milk and black coffee. His friend has scrambled eggs with sausage, biscuits with butter, and a glass of whole milk.

▼

Which person's stomach will empty faster? Why?

A 40-year-old woman weighing 350 lbs has undergone a surgical procedure that has reduced the size of her stomach and intestines.

▼

How will this affect food consumption and nutrient absorption?

A 63-year-old woman has a disease of the pancreas that causes a deficiency of pancreatic enzymes.

▼

What effect would this have on her ability to digest and absorb protein?

A 56-year-old man has gallstones, which cause pain when his gallbladder contracts.

▼

What type of foods should he avoid and why?

A 47-year-old woman undergoes treatment for colon cancer that requires that most of her large intestine be surgically removed.

▼

How would this affect fluid needs?

After reading about the benefits of a high-fiber diet, an 18-year-old man dramatically increases the amount of fiber he consumes.

▼

How might this affect the feces? The amount of intestinal gas?

(©iStockphoto)

 iProfile Use iProfile to find out how much fiber is in a cup of raw carrots.

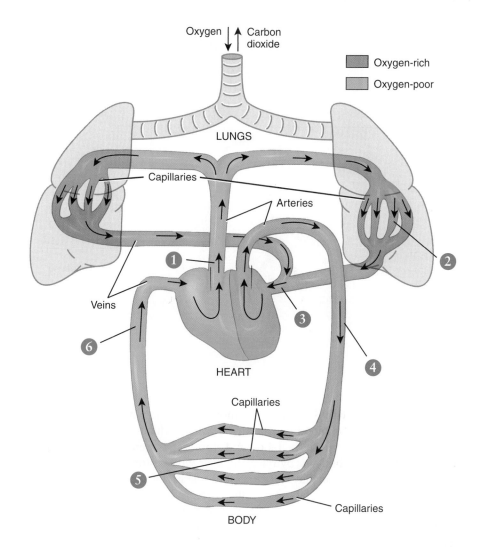

1. Oxygen-poor blood that reaches the heart from the rest of the body is pumped through the arteries to the capillaries of the lungs.

2. In the capillaries of the lungs, oxygen from inhaled air is picked up by the blood, and carbon dioxide is released into the lungs and exhaled.

3. Oxygen-rich blood returns to the heart from the lungs via veins.

4. Oxygen-rich blood is pumped out of the heart into the arteries that lead to the rest of the body.

5. In the capillaries of the body, nutrients and oxygen move from the blood to the body's tissues, and carbon dioxide and other waste products move from the tissues to the blood, to be carried away.

6. Oxygen-poor blood returns to the heart via veins.

Figure 3.17 Cardiovascular system
Blood pumped to the lungs picks up oxygen and delivers nutrients. Blood pumped to the rest of the body delivers oxygen and nutrients.

The volume of blood flow, and hence the amounts of nutrients and oxygen that are delivered to an organ or tissue, depends on the need. When a person is resting, about 25% of the blood goes to the digestive system, about 20% to the skeletal muscles, and the rest to the heart, kidneys, brain, skin, and other organs.[4] After a large meal, a greater proportion will go to the intestines to support digestion and absorption and to transport nutrients. When a person engages in strenuous exercise, about 85% of blood flow will be directed to the skeletal muscles to deliver nutrients and oxygen and remove carbon dioxide and waste products. Attempting to exercise after a large meal creates a conflict. The body cannot supply both the intestines and the muscles with enough blood to support their respective activities. The muscles win, and food remains in the intestines, often resulting in cramps.

The Hepatic Portal Circulation

In the small intestine, water-soluble molecules, including amino acids, sugars, water-soluble vitamins, and water-soluble products of fat digestion, cross the mucosal cells of the villi and enter capillaries. These capillaries merge to form venules at the base of the villi. The venules then merge to form larger and larger veins, which eventually form the **hepatic portal vein**. The hepatic portal vein transports blood directly to the liver, where absorbed nutrients are processed before they enter the general circulation (**Figure 3.18**).

The liver acts as a gatekeeper between substances absorbed from the intestine and the rest of the body. Depending on the immediate needs of the body some nutrients are stored in the liver, some are broken down or changed into different forms, and others are allowed to pass through unchanged for delivery to other body cells.

hepatic portal vein The vein that transports blood from the GI tract to the liver.

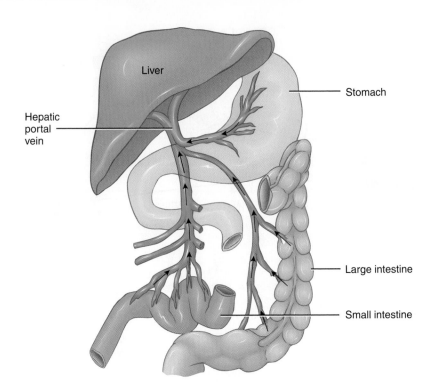

Figure 3.18 Hepatic portal circulation
The hepatic portal circulation carries blood from the stomach and intestines to the hepatic portal vein and then to the liver.

For example, the liver, with the help of hormones from the pancreas, keeps the concentration of sugar in the blood constant. The liver modulates blood glucose by removing absorbed glucose from the blood and storing it, by sending absorbed glucose on to the tissues of the body, or by releasing liver glucose (from stores or synthesis) into the blood. The liver also plays an important role in the synthesis and breakdown of amino acids, proteins, and fats. It modifies the products of protein breakdown to form molecules that can be safely transported to the kidneys for excretion. The liver also contains enzyme systems that protect the body from toxins that are absorbed by the GI tract.

The Lymphatic System

The lymphatic system consists of a network of tubules (lymph vessels), structures, and organs that contain infection-fighting cells. Fluid that has accumulated in tissues drains into the lymphatic system where it is filtered past a collection of infection-fighting lymphocytes and phagocytes. The cleansed fluid is then returned to the bloodstream. If the fluid contains a foreign substance it may trigger an immune response. By draining the excess fluid, and any disease-causing agents it contains, away from the spaces between cells, the lymphatic system provides immunity and prevents the accumulation of fluid from causing swelling.

In the intestine, fat soluble materials such as triglycerides, cholesterol, and fat-soluble vitamins are incorporated into particles that are too large to enter the intestinal capillaries (see Chapter 5). These pass from the intestinal mucosa into the lacteals, small lymph vessel in the villi, which drain into larger lymph vessels. Lymph vessels from the intestine and most other organs of the body drain into the thoracic duct, which empties into the bloodstream near the neck. Therefore, substances that are absorbed via the lymphatic system do not pass through the liver before entering the general blood circulation.

cell membrane The membrane that surrounds the cell contents.

selectively permeable Describes a membrane or barrier that will allow some substances to pass freely but will restrict the passage of others.

Body Cells

In order for nutrients to be used by the body, they must enter the cells. To enter a cell, substances must first cross the **cell membrane**. The cell membrane maintains homeostasis in the cell by controlling what enters and what exits. It is **selectively permeable**,

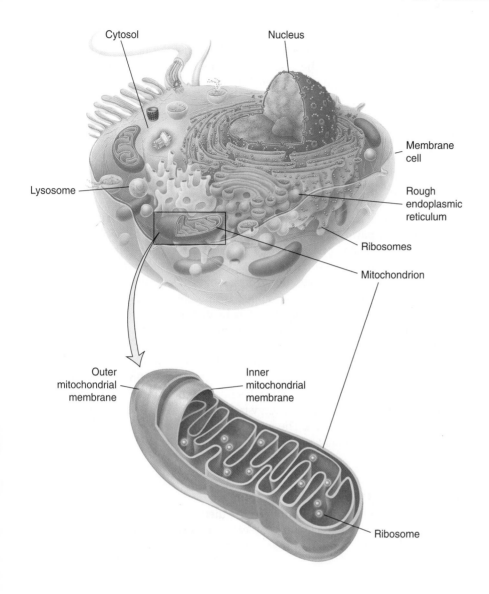

Figure 3.19 **Animal cell structure**
All human cells are surrounded by a cell membrane and most contain a nucleus, mitochondria, lysosomes, endoplasmic reticulum, and ribosomes in their cytosol.

allowing some substances, such as water, to pass freely back and forth, while limiting the passage of others. Nutrients and other substances are transported from the blood into cells by simple and facilitated diffusion and active transport. Inside the cell membrane are the **cytosol**, or cell fluid, and **organelles** that perform functions necessary for cell survival. The largest organelle is the nucleus, which contains the cell's genetic material. The organelle where metabolic reactions that provide energy occur is called the **mitochondrion** (plural, **mitochondria**) (**Figure 3.19**).

cytosol The liquid found within cells.

organelles Cellular organs that carry out specific metabolic functions.

mitochondrion (mitochondria) Cellular organelle responsible for providing energy in the form of ATP for cellular activities.

3.6 Metabolism of Nutrients: An Overview

Learning Objectives

- Explain how the respiratory system is related to cellular respiration.
- Name the dietary fuel sources used to produce ATP.

By the mechanisms described thus far, foods are digested and the products of digestion absorbed, transported, and delivered to body cells. Each nutrient plays a unique role in metabolism. If the proper amounts and types of nutrients are not delivered to cells, the reactions of metabolism cannot proceed optimally, resulting in poor health. The following discussion provides only a brief overview of how glucose, fatty acids, and amino acids are used by the cells. Details about the metabolism of each nutrient will be discussed in appropriate chapters throughout this text.

metabolic pathway A series of chemical reactions inside of a living organism that results in the transformation of one molecule into another.

coenzyme A small organic molecule (not a protein but sometimes a vitamin) that is necessary for the proper functioning of many enzymes.

catabolic The processes by which substances are broken down into simpler molecules releasing energy.

ATP (adenosine triphosphate) The high-energy molecule used by the body to perform energy-requiring activities.

anabolic Energy-requiring processes in which simpler molecules are combined to form more complex substances.

cellular respiration The reactions that break down glucose, fatty acids, and amino acids in the presence of oxygen to produce carbon dioxide, water, and energy in the form of ATP.

Metabolic Pathways

Depending on the body's needs, the glucose, fatty acids, and amino acids absorbed from the diet will be broken down to provide energy, be used to synthesize essential structural or regulatory molecules, or be transformed into energy-storage molecules. The conversion of one molecule into another often involves a series of reactions. The series of biochemical reactions needed to go from a raw material to the final product is called a **metabolic pathway** (see Appendix L). For each of the reactions of a metabolic pathway to proceed at an appropriate rate an enzyme is required. These enzymes often need help from **coenzymes**. The B vitamins are important coenzymes in metabolism.

Some metabolic pathways break large molecules into smaller ones. These **catabolic** pathways release energy trapped in the chemical bonds that hold molecules together. Some of this energy is lost as heat, but some is converted into a form that can be used by the body called **adenosine triphosphate (ATP)** (**Figure 3.20**). ATP can be thought of as the energy currency of the cell. The chemical bonds of ATP are very high in energy, and when they break, the energy is released and can be used to power body processes, such as circulating blood or conducting nerve impulses—or it can be used to synthesize new molecules needed to maintain and repair body tissues. Metabolic pathways that use energy from ATP to build body compounds are referred to as **anabolic** pathways. The anabolic and catabolic pathways of metabolism occur in the body continually and simultaneously (**Figure 3.21**).

Producing ATP

Carbohydrate, fat, and protein, both from the diet and from body stores, can be used to produce ATP via a catabolic pathway called **cellular respiration**. First carbohydrate, fat, and protein must be broken down into glucose, fatty acids, and amino

Figure 3.20 Structure of ATP
ATP consists of an adenosine molecule attached to three phosphate groups. The bonds between the phosphate groups are very high in energy, which is released when the bonds are broken.

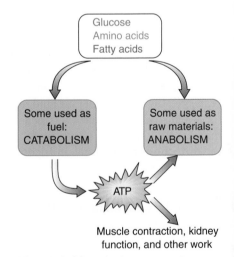

Figure 3.21 Catabolism and anabolism
Nutrients delivered to body cells can be used either in catabolic reactions to produce ATP or as raw materials in anabolic reactions that use ATP to synthesize molecules needed by the body.

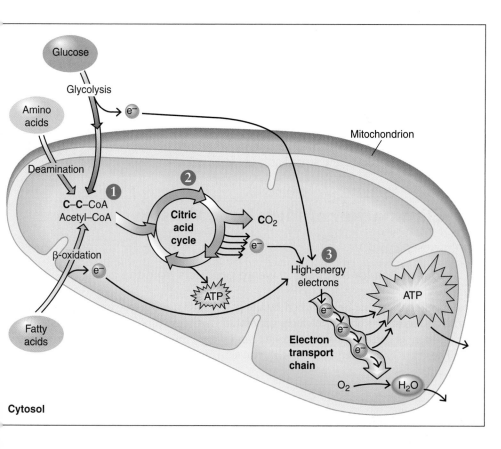

Figure 3.22 Cellular respiration
Cellular respiration uses oxygen to convert glucose, fatty acids, and amino acids into carbon dioxide, water, and energy, in the form of ATP.

① In the presence of oxygen, glucose, fatty acids, and amino acids can be metabolized to produce acetyl-CoA.

② Acetyl-CoA is broken down by the citric acid cycle to yield carbon dioxide (CO_2) and high-energy electrons.

③ The electrons are shuttled to the electron transport chain where their energy is used to generate ATP and they combined with oxygen and hydrogen to form water.

acids, respectively. Then they can be metabolized, producing ATP along with carbon dioxide and water. In cellular respiration, oxygen brought into the body by the respiratory system and delivered to cells by the circulatory system is used and carbon dioxide is released. This carbon dioxide is then transported to the lungs where it is eliminated in exhaled air.

The reactions of cellular respiration are central to all energy-yielding processes in the body. Without available oxygen, only glucose can be used to produce ATP (see Chapters 4 and 13). When oxygen is available, glucose, fatty acids, and amino acids can all be broken down to yield 2-carbon units that form a molecule called **acetyl-CoA** (**Figure 3.22**). To form acetyl-CoA from glucose it must first be split in half by a pathway called *glycolysis* (see Chapter 4). To form acetyl-CoA from fatty acids the carbon chains that make up fatty acids are broken into 2-carbon units by a pathway called *beta-oxidation* (see Chapter 5). Amino acids vary in structure but after the amino group is removed by *deamination*, they can be broken down into units that can form acetyl-CoA (see Chapter 6). Acetyl-CoA from all of these sources is broken down inside the mitochondria via the metabolic pathway known as the **citric acid cycle**. In this pathway, the two carbons of acetyl-CoA are removed one at a time, forming carbon dioxide molecules, releasing **electrons**, and generating a small amount of ATP. The electrons, which are high in energy, are passed to shuttling molecules for transport to the **electron transport chain**.

The electron transport chain consists of a series of molecules that accept electrons from the shuttling molecules and pass them from one to another down the chain. When one substance loses an electron, another must pick up that electron. A substance that loses an electron is said to be **oxidized** and one that gains an electron is said to be **reduced**. Reactions that transfer electrons are called *oxidation-reduction* reactions and are very important in energy metabolism. As electrons are passed along the electron transport chain, their energy is released and used to make ATP. The final molecule to accept electrons in the electron transport chain is oxygen. When oxygen accepts electrons it is reduced and forms a molecule of water (see Figure 3.22).

acetyl CoA A metabolic intermediate formed during the breakdown of glucose, fatty acids, and amino acids. It is a 2-carbon compound attached to a molecule of CoA.

citric acid cycle Also known as the Krebs cycle or the tricarboxylic acid cycle, this is the stage of cellular respiration in which two carbons from acetyl-CoA are oxidized, producing two molecules of carbon dioxide.

electron High-energy particle carrying a negative charge that orbits the nucleus of an atom.

electron transport chain The final stage of cellular respiration in which electrons are passed down a chain of molecules to oxygen to form water and produce ATP.

oxidized Refers to a compound that has lost an electron or undergone a chemical reaction with oxygen.

reduced Refers to a substance that has gained an electron.

Synthesizing New Molecules

Glucose, fatty acids, and amino acids that are not broken down for energy are used in anabolic pathways to synthesize structural, regulatory, or storage molecules. Glucose molecules can be used to synthesize glycogen, a storage form of carbohydrate. If the body has enough glycogen, glucose can also be used to synthesize fatty acids. Fatty acids can be used to synthesize triglycerides that are stored as body fat. Amino acids can be used to synthesize the various proteins that the body needs, such as muscle proteins, enzymes, protein hormones, and blood proteins. Excess amino acids can be converted into fatty acids and stored as body fat.

3.7 Elimination of Metabolic Wastes

Learning Objective

• List four routes for eliminating waste products from the body.

Substances that cannot be absorbed by the body, such as fiber, are excreted from the GI tract in feces. The waste products generated by the metabolism of absorbed substances, such as carbon dioxide, nitrogen, and water, must also be removed from the body. These are eliminated by the lungs, the skin, and the kidneys (**Figure 3.23**).

Figure 3.23 Taking in nutrients and oxygen and eliminating wastes The digestive system takes in nutrients and the respiratory system takes in oxygen, which are then distributed to all body cells by the circulatory system. The urinary, respiratory, and integumentary systems transfer metabolic wastes to the external environment.

Lungs and Skin

Carbon dioxide produced by cellular respiration leaves the cells and is transported to the lungs by red blood cells. At the lungs, red blood cells release their load of carbon dioxide, which is then exhaled. In addition to carbon dioxide, a significant amount of water is lost from the lungs by evaporation. Water, along with protein breakdown products and minerals, is also lost through the skin in perspiration or sweat.

Kidneys

The kidneys are the primary site for the excretion of water, metabolic waste products, and excess minerals. Each kidney consists of about 1 million **nephrons**. The nephrons consist of a **glomerulus** where the blood is filtered and a series of tubules where molecules that have been filtered out of the blood can be reabsorbed (**Figure 3.24**). As blood flows through the glomerulus most of the small dissolved molecules are filtered out. Protein molecules and blood cells are too large to be removed by the glomerulus. Filtered substances that are needed are then reabsorbed back into the blood. Components that are not needed are not reabsorbed but are passed down the ureters to the bladder and excreted in the urine. The amounts of water and other substances excreted in the urine are regulated so that homeostasis is maintained (see Chapter 10).

nephron The functional unit of the kidney which performs the job of filtering the blood and maintaining fluid balance.

glomerulus A ball of capillaries in the nephron that filters blood during urine formation.

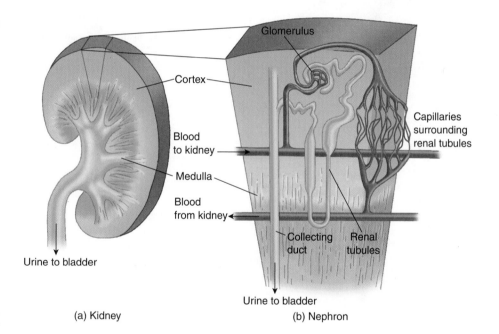

(a) Kidney

(b) Nephron

Figure 3.24 Kidney and nephron structure (a) A kidney consists of an outer cortex and a central medulla; (b) A nephron includes the glomerulus, where dissolved materials are filtered out of the blood, renal tubules, where some materials are reabsorbed into the blood, and a collecting duct, which transports unabsorbed materials to the bladder.

Outcome

Sheila's surgery went well and has allowed her to lose 100 pounds over the past year. The changes in Sheila's GI tract have caused some problems, though. First, she must carefully limit what and how much she eats because alterations in her stomach have bypassed the gastroesophageal sphincter, which regulates the rate at which material leaves her stomach. When she eats too much or chooses too many high-carbohydrate foods, her meal "dumps" into her intestines and draws in water, resulting in dizziness, sweating, and diarrhea. Second, her small intestine has less surface area for nutrient absorption now that a portion of it has been bypassed. To prevent vitamin and mineral deficiencies, Sheila must take supplements and get monthly vitamin B_{12} injections. Although she often longs to sit down to a large meal and not have to worry about the consequences of overeating, she believes the decision to have the procedure was the right one for her. Her blood pressure, blood cholesterol, and blood sugar have all decreased. She can now bend to tie her own shoes, and when she travels she can fit into a single airplane seat. By sticking to her diet and exercise program, she hopes to lose another 40 pounds and maintain the loss.

APPLICATIONS

Personal Nutrition

1. Look at the iProfile report from the food record you kept in Chapter 2 and review the protein, carbohydrate, and fat content of each food.

   a. List foods that would not begin chemical digestion until they have left the mouth.

   b. List foods that might require bile for digestion and explain why.

   c. List foods that dmight begin their digestion in your stomach and explain why.

2. Imagine you wake up on a Sunday morning and join some friends for a large breakfast consisting of a cheese omelet and sausage (foods high in fat and protein), a croissant with butter (which contains carbohydrate but is also very high in fat), and a small glass of orange juice. After the meal, you remember that you have plans to play basketball with a friend in just an hour.

   a. If you keep your plans and play basketball, what problems might you experience while exercising?

b. Had you remembered your plans for strenuous exercise before you had breakfast, what type of meal might you have selected to ensure that your stomach would empty more quickly?

General Nutrition Issues

1. There are hundreds of products available to aid digestion. Go to the drug store, or search the Internet and select a product claiming to aid digestion.
   a. List the claims made for the product.
   b. Use the information in Chapter 1 on judging nutritional claims to analyze the information given.
   c. What nutrients, if any, does the product provide?

 iProfile

d. What risks, if any, does it carry?
e. Would you take it if you were experiencing digestive problems? Why or why not?

2. Plan a lunch menu for a senior center. It should provide food from each MyPyramid food group. Assume that many of the diners have difficulty chewing.
   a. Evaluate whether your menu would be appropriate for someone with gallstones who needs to limit their intake of fat.
   b. Evaluate whether your menu would be appropriate for someone who is trying to increase their intake of fiber and fluid to prevent constipation.
   c. Evaluate whether your menu would be appropriate for someone who must restrict their salt intake.

Summary

3.1 Food Becomes Us

- Our bodies and the foods we eat are all made from the same building blocks—atoms. Atoms are linked by chemical bonds to form molecules.
- Molecules can form cells, which are the smallest unit of life. Cells of similar structure and function are organized into tissues, and tissues into organs and organ systems.

3.2 An Overview of the Digestive System

- The digestive system is the organ system primarily responsible for the movement of nutrients into the body. The digestive system provides two major functions: digestion and absorption. Digestion is the process by which food is broken down into units that are small enough to be absorbed. Absorption is the process by which nutrients are transported into the body.
- The gastrointestinal (GI) tract consists of a hollow tube that begins at the mouth and continues through the pharynx, esophagus, stomach, small intestine, and large intestine.
- The digestion of food and the absorption of nutrients in the lumen of the GI tract is aided by the secretion of mucus and enzymes.
- The passage of food and the secretion of digestive substances is regulated by nervous and hormonal signals.
- Immune system cells and tissues located in the gastrointestinal tract help eliminate disease-causing organisms or chemicals.

3.3 Digestion and Absorption

- The processes involved in digestion begin in response to the smell or sight of food and continue as food enters the digestive tract at the mouth.
- In the mouth, food is broken into smaller pieces by the teeth and mixed with saliva. Carbohydrate digestion is begun in the mouth by salivary amylase.
- From the mouth, food passes through the pharynx and into the esophagus. The rhythmic contractions of peristalsis propel it down the esophagus to the stomach.
- The stomach acts as a temporary storage tank for food. The muscles of the stomach mix the food into a semiliquid mass called chyme, and gastric juice containing hydrochloric acid and pepsin begins protein digestion. Stomach emptying is regulated by the amount and composition of food consumed and by nervous and hormonal signals from the stomach and small intestine.
- The small intestine is the primary site of nutrient digestion and absorption. In the small intestine, bicarbonate from the pancreas neutralizes stomach acid, and pancreatic and intestinal enzymes digest carbohydrate, fat, and protein. The digestion of fat in the small intestine is aided by bile from the gallbladder. Bile helps make fat available to fat-digesting enzymes by breaking it into small droplets and also facilitates fat absorption. Secretions from the pancreas and liver are regulated by the hormones secretin and cholecystokinin (CCK), produced by the duodenum.

- The absorption of food across the intestinal mucosa occurs by several different processes. Simple diffusion, osmosis, and facilitated diffusion do not require energy but depend on a concentration gradient. Active transport requires energy but can transport substances against a concentration gradient. The absorptive surface area of the small intestine is increased by folds, finger-like projections called *villi*, and tiny projections called *microvilli*, which cover the surface of the villi.

- Components of chyme that are not absorbed in the small intestine pass on to the large intestine, where some water and nutrients are absorbed. The large intestine is populated by bacteria that digest some of these unabsorbed materials, such as fiber, producing small amounts of nutrients and gas. The remaining unabsorbed materials are excreted in feces.

3.4 Digestion and Health

Video
- Heartburn and GERD are common digestive problems that are caused by the leakage of stomach contents into the esophagus. Ulcers are caused by infection with *Helicobacter pylori*, GERD, or medications that damage the mucosa. Gallstones can cause pain and interfere with fat digestion.

- Tube-feeding can nourish a patient who is unable to ingest or chew food on their own. Total parenteral nutrition is necessary when the gut is not able to digest and or absorb nutrients.

- Digestive system function is affected by lifestage. During pregnancy physiological changes cause morning sickness, heartburn, and constipation. During infancy the immaturity of the GI tract limits what foods can be ingested and digested. In older adults changes in the digestive tract may decrease the appeal of food and the ability to digest and absorb nutrients.

3.5 Transporting Nutrients to Body Cells

- Absorbed nutrients are delivered to the cells of the body by the cardiovascular system. The heart pumps blood to the lungs to pick up oxygen and eliminate carbon dioxide. From the lungs, blood returns to the heart and is pumped to the rest of the body to deliver oxygen and nutrients and remove carbon dioxide and other wastes before returning to the heart. Blood is pumped away from the heart in arteries and returned to the heart in veins. Exchange of nutrients and gases occurs at the smallest blood vessels, the capillaries.

- The products of carbohydrate and protein digestion and the water-soluble products of fat digestion enter capillaries in the intestinal villi and are transported to the liver via the hepatic portal circulation. The liver serves as a processing center, removing the absorbed substances for storage, converting them into other forms, or allowing them to pass unaltered. The liver also protects the body from toxic substances that may have been absorbed.

- The fat-soluble products of digestion enter lacteals in the intestinal villi. Lacteals join larger lymph vessels. The nutrients absorbed via the lymphatic system enter the blood circulation without first passing through the liver.

- Cells are the final destination of absorbed nutrients. To enter the cells, nutrients must be transported across cell membranes.

3.6 Metabolism of Nutrients: An Overview

- Within the cells, glucose, fatty acids, and amino acids absorbed from the diet can be broken down to provide energy in the form of ATP, used to power body activities and synthesize essential structural or regulatory molecules, or be transformed into energy storage molecules. The sum of all the chemical reactions of the body is called metabolism.

- The reactions that completely break down macronutrients in the presence of oxygen to produce water, carbon dioxide, and ATP are referred to as cellular respiration. Glucose, fatty acids, and amino acids can all be broken down into 2-carbon molecules that form acetyl-CoA. The reactions of the citric acid cycle and the electron transport chain complete the breakdown of acetyl-CoA to form carbon dioxide and water and generate ATP. Dietary glucose, fatty acids, and amino acids are used to synthesize structural, regulatory, or storage molecules.

3.7 Elimination of Metabolic Wastes

- Unabsorbed materials are excreted in the feces. Carbon dioxide is eliminated in exhaled air. Water is lost via the lungs and skin.

- Water, metabolic waste products, and excess minerals are excreted by the kidneys.

R e v i e w   Q u e s t i o n s

1. What is the smallest unit of plant and animal life?

2. List three organ systems involved in the digestion and absorption of food.

3. How do teeth function in digestion?

4. What is peristalsis? What is segmentation?

5. List two functions of the stomach.

6. How is the movement of material through the digestive tract regulated?

7. List three mechanisms by which nutrients are absorbed.

8. Where does most digestion and absorption occur?

9. How does the structure of the small intestine aid absorption?

10. What products of digestion are transported by the lymphatic system?

11. What path does an amino acid follow from absorption to delivery to the cell? Compare this to the path a large fatty acid would follow from absorption to delivery to the cell.

12. What is the form of energy used by cells?

13. Explain what occurs during the citric acid cycle and the electron transport chain.

14. What happens to material that is not absorbed in the small intestine?

15. How do the lungs and kidneys help eliminate metabolic waste products?

References

1. Formanek, R. Food allergies: When food becomes the enemy. *FDA Consumer*, July/Aug, 2001.

2. Konturek, S. J., Konturek, P. C., Konturek, J. W. et al. *Helicobacter pylori* and its involvement in gastritis and peptic ulcer formation. *J. Physiol. Pharmacol.* *57*(Suppl– 3):29–50, 2006.

3. Lynch, N. A. *Helicobacter pylori* and ulcers: A paradigm revisited. Available online at http://opa.faseb.org/pdf/pylori.pdf. Accessed December 20, 2008.

4. Marieb, E. N., and Hoehn, K. *Human Anatomy and Physiology*, 7th ed. Menlo Park, CA: Benjamin Cummings, 2007.

4

Carbohydrates:
Sugars, Starches, and Fiber

Case Study

Shamara's enthusiam for her low-carbohydrate diet was flagging, and the 15 pounds she had recently lost was slowly creeping back onto her 5'6" frame. She had always been heavier than she liked and had been delighted to lose some weight. Now, though, the 10 pounds she regained had brought her up to 153 pounds. This weight was still in the healthy range, so she decided to forget the low-carb weight-loss diet approach and just focus on eating healthy foods. Shamara looked up her MyPyramid recommendations and was surprised to find that not all carbohydrates are bad—MyPyramid recommended that she eat the equivalent of about six servings of grain products and that at least half of them be whole grains. She also saw that she needed to increase her intake of fruits and vegetables. These foods, too, contain carbohydrate and are high in fiber.

The first step Shamara took to improve her diet was to keep a bag of cut-up raw vegetables and a bowl of fruit salad in her refrigerator, ready for snacking or adding to a meal. To increase her intake of whole grains, she began to make smarter choices at the grocery store. She switched from white rice to brown rice and chose multi-grain breads and healthy-sounding cereals. A few weeks later, she had her diet analyzed at a health fair. She was dismayed to see that even after all the changes she made in her diet; her fiber intake was still below the recommended 25 grams per day. When she got home, she took a look at the food labels in her cupboard. She found that her seven-grain bread didn't actually contain any whole grains. Her breakfast cereal did contain whole wheat, but provided only 2 grams of fiber per cup—and it also contained 18 grams of sugars she hadn't intended to consume. Choosing healthy carbohydrates was turning out to be almost as difficult as eliminating them.

(Masterfile)

Group/Photodisc/Getty Images, Inc.

Chapter Outline

4.1 Carbohydrates in the Modern Diet

Learning Objectives

- Discuss the difference between refined and unrefined carbohydrates.
- Explain why added sugars are considered empty kcalories.

refined Refers to foods that have undergone processes that change or remove various components of the original food.

Carbohydrates are the basis of our diet. They are found in foods as diverse as whole-wheat bread, chocolate cake, fresh fruit, milk, and carbonated soft drinks. The carbohydrates in these foods are a readily available source of energy; they supply 4 kcalories per gram. However, the additional nutritional impact they deliver varies depending on whether the carbohydrate is **refined** or in its natural state. The carbohydrates in the whole-wheat bread, the fresh fruit, and the milk are considered unrefined or whole food sources of carbohydrate because they have not been altered from their natural state. These foods contain vitamins, minerals, and other health-promoting substances as well as carbohydrates. The cake and the soda provide carbohydrates that have been refined. Refining separates carbohydrates from many of the other essential nutrients and food components present in the whole food (**Table 4.1**).

Table 4.1 More and Less Refined Carbohydrate Food Choices

	Less Refined	More Refined	High in Added Sugars
Cereals	Oatmeal, shredded wheat, Kashi	Corn flakes, Rice Puffs, Cheerios	Lucky Charms, Frosted Shredded Wheat
Breads	Whole-wheat bread, whole-wheat bagel	White bread, English muffin, white bagel	Doughnut, Danish pastry
Grains	Whole-wheat pasta, brown rice, bulgur wheat, barley, quinoa	White pasta, white rice, rice cakes	Rice pudding, Rice Krispie treats, sweetened rice cakes
Fruit	Raspberries, apple, orange	Canned fruit, dried fruit, orange juice	Canned fruit in heavy syrup, fruit pies, sweetened dried fruit, candied fruit, fruit punch
Vegetables	Baked potato, zucchini	French fries, fried zucchini	Candied yams, sweet potato pie, pumpkin cake

Over the last century the amounts and sources of carbohydrates in the American diet have changed. Our total carbohydrate intake decreased between 1909 and 1963. Most of this drop was due to a decrease in the consumption of whole grains, and with it came a 40% drop in the amount of fiber consumed.[1] Since the 1960s our total carbohydrate intake has increased, but our fiber intake did not rise with it, suggesting an increase in the intake of refined carbohydrates. Much of the carbohydrate added back to our diet between 1960 and 2000 came from sugars; over this time period per capita sugar consumption rose by 33%.[2] Whole-grain breads, dried peas and beans, and bulgur had been replaced by white bread, snack foods, and sugared soft drinks. The type of sweetener also changed. In the 1960s we sweetened food with cane and beet sugar, but today most of the foods we buy are sweetened with corn sweeteners.

The carbohydrates in today's diet are more refined than they were earlier in the century. Recommendations for a healthy diet tell us to choose more of the carbohydrates we used to eat: more unrefined sources such as whole grains, vegetables, legumes, and fruits, and fewer foods high in refined carbohydrates and **added sugars** such as baked goods and soft drinks (**Figure 4.1**).

added sugars Sugars and syrups that have been added to foods during processing or preparation.

Refined Carbohydrates

Unrefined food sources of carbohydrate such as whole grains, legumes, vegetables, fruit, and milk contain a variety of nutrients in addition to carbohydrates. Whole grains, legumes, and vegetables provide B vitamins, some minerals, and fiber. Fruits provide vi-

Eat
Less

Eat
More

Figure 4.1 Carbohydrate recommendations for a healthy diet
Choose more unrefined sources of carbohydrates while limiting foods high in refined carbohydrates and added refined sugars. (© Andy Washnik)

tamins A and C along with fiber. Milk is a good source of the B vitamin riboflavin and the mineral calcium. In contrast, refined sources of carbohydrate such as the corn flakes you may have had for breakfast, are made from corn that has been ground, sieved, washed, cooked, extruded, and dried. During these refining steps, many of the nutrients and other healthful components of the corn kernel are lost. When we eat the entire kernel or seed of a grain, such as corn or wheat, we are eating an unrefined or **whole-grain** product. The whole-grain kernel includes three parts (**Figure 4.2**). The outermost **bran**

whole grain The entire kernel of grain including the bran layers, the germ, and the endosperm.

bran The protective outer layers of whole grains. It is a concentrated source of dietary fiber.

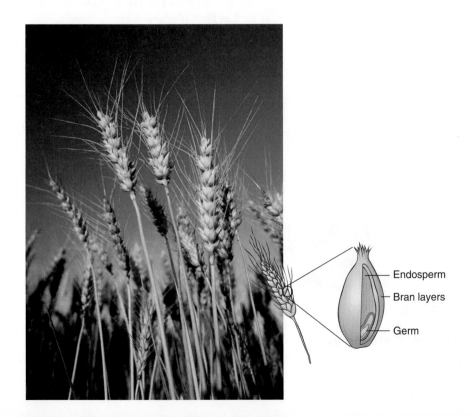

— Endosperm

— Bran layers

— Germ

Figure 4.2 Parts of a whole-grain kernel
A kernel of wheat contains outer layers of bran, the plant embryo (germ), and a carbohydrate-rich endosperm. (Kevin Morris/Stone/ © Getty Images)

germ The embryo or sprouting portion of a kernel of grain. It contains vegetable oil, protein, fiber, and vitamins.

endosperm The largest portion of a kernel of grain. It is primarily starch and serves as a food supply for the sprouting seed.

layers contain most of the fiber and are a good source of vitamins. The **germ**, which lies at the base of the kernel, is the plant embryo where sprouting occurs. It is the source of vegetable oils such as corn or safflower oil, and is rich in vitamin E. It also contains protein, fiber, and the B vitamins riboflavin, thiamin, and vitamin B_6. The remainder of the kernel is the **endosperm**, which is primarily starch but also contains most of the protein and some vitamins and minerals. During the milling of grain into flour, the grinding detaches the germ and bran from the endosperm. Whole-grain flours such as whole-wheat flour include most of the bran, germ, and endosperm (see Your Choice: Choosing Whole Grains). White flour however is produced from just the endosperm. Fiber and some vitamins, minerals, and phytochemicals naturally found in the whole grain are therefore lost. In order to restore some of the lost nutrients, refined grains sold in the United States are fortified with some, but not all, of the nutrients lost in processing. **Enriched grains** contain added thiamin, riboflavin, niacin, and iron and are fortified with folate. However, they do not contain added vitamin E, magnesium, vitamin B_6, or a number of other nutrients that are also removed by milling.

enriched grains Grains to which specific amounts of thiamin, riboflavin, niacin and iron have been added. Since 1998, folic acid has also been added to enriched grains.

Added Sugars

If you sprinkle some sugar on your corn flakes you are adding another refined source of carbohydrate. This added sugar was most likely extracted from a sugar beet, boiled, bleached, and purified. It adds kcalories without adding any nutrients other than carbohydrate and reduces the nutrient density of your breakfast. But the sugar you add to food isn't the only source of added sugars in the diet—much of the added sugar we consume comes from desserts, beverages, and snacks that we purchase already prepared. Refined added sugars make up about 16% of the kcalories in the American diet.[3] Added sugars are not nutritionally or chemically different from sugars occurring naturally in foods. The only difference is that they have been separated from their plant sources and therefore are not consumed with all of the fiber, vitamins, minerals, and other substances found in the original plant. Because added sugars provide few nutrients for the number of kcalories they contain they have a low nutrient density and are therefore thought of as **empty kcalories**. Unrefined or whole food sources of sugar such as fruit provide vitamins, minerals, and phytochemicals as well as kcalories. For example, a 12-ounce soda contains about 140 kcalories but almost no nutrients other than sugar. Three kiwis also have about 140 kcalories but contribute vitamin C, folate, potassium, and some calcium as well as fiber (**Figure 4.3**).

empty kcalories Refers to foods that contribute energy but few other nutrients.

Figure 4.3
Three kiwis and 12 ounces of soda provide about the same amounts of energy and carbohydrate, but the kiwis also contain fiber and a variety of micronutrients.
(© George Semple)

Nutrient	Soda (12 fluid oz)	Kiwi (3 medium)
Vitamin A (μg)	0	7
Vitamin C (mg)	0	171
Folate (μg DFE)	0	87
Potassium (mg)	7	757
Calcium (mg)	7	60
Protein (g)	0	2
Fiber (g)	0	8
Carbohydrate (g)	35	34
Sugars (g)	33	26
Energy (kcals)	136	139

4.2 Simple and Complex Carbohydrates

Learning Objectives

- Compare the structures of simple and complex carbohydrates.
- Distinguish between soluble and insoluble fiber and name food sources of each.

Chemically, carbohydrates are compounds that contain carbon (carbo), as well as hydrogen and oxygen in the same proportion as in water (hydrate). They are typically divided into **simple carbohydrates**, also known as sugars, and **complex carbohydrates**, which include starches and fibers. Both can provide a source of energy to fuel the body.

Simple Carbohydrates

The basic unit of carbohydrate is a single sugar unit, a **monosaccharide** (*mono* means one). When two sugar units combine, they form a **disaccharide** (*di* means two). Monosaccharides and disaccharides are known as simple sugars or simple carbohydrates. Fruits, vegetables, and milk are sources of simple carbohydrates. The sugars we add to food such as white table sugar, brown sugar, molasses, and confectioner's sugar are also simple carbohydrates. These are produced by refining the sugar from plants such as sugar cane and sugar beets.

Monosaccharides The three most common monosaccharides in the diet are glucose, galactose, and fructose. Each contains 6 carbon, 12 hydrogen, and 6 oxygen atoms but differ in their arrangement (**Figure 4.4**). **Glucose**, commonly referred to as blood sugar, is the most important carbohydrate fuel for the body. It is produced in plants by the process of photosynthesis, which uses energy from the sun to combine carbon dioxide and water (**Figure 4.5**). Glucose rarely occurs as a monosaccharide in food. It is most often found as part of a disaccharide or starch. **Galactose** is also rarely present as a monosaccharide in the food supply. It occurs most often as a part of lactose, the disaccharide in milk.

Fructose is a monosaccharide that tastes sweeter than glucose. It is found in fruits and vegetables and makes up more than half the sugar in honey. Because fructose does not cause as great a rise in blood glucose as other sugars, it is sometimes used in products for people with diabetes. However, because fructose causes an increase in blood lipids, its use should be limited. Fructose consumed in fruits or juices can also cause diarrhea in children. Most of the fructose in our diet comes from high-fructose corn syrup. This sweetener is produced by modifying starch extracted from corn to produce a syrup that is approximately half glucose and half fructose. High-fructose corn syrup is sweeter and less expensive than table sugar. It is now the most common kcaloric sweetener added to foods and beverages and is the kcaloric sweetener used in most soft drinks in the United States.[4] The dramatic increase in the use of high-fructose corn sweeteners that has occurred in the last few decades has been suggested to be related to the increased incidence of diabetes and obesity.[4]

simple carbohydrates Carbohydrates known as sugars that include monosaccharides and disaccharides.

complex carbohydrates Carbohydrates composed of sugar molecules linked together in straight or branching chains. They include glycogen, starches, and fibers.

monosaccharide A single sugar unit, such as glucose.

disaccharide A sugar formed by linking two monosaccharides.

glucose A monosaccharide that is the primary form of carbohydrate used to provide energy in the body. It is the sugar referred to as blood sugar.

galactose A monosaccharide that combines with glucose to form lactose or milk sugar.

fructose A monosaccharide that is the primary form of carbohydrate found in fruit.

Figure 4.4 Structures of common monosaccharides Glucose, galactose, and fructose have the same chemical formulas, but the atoms are arranged differently.

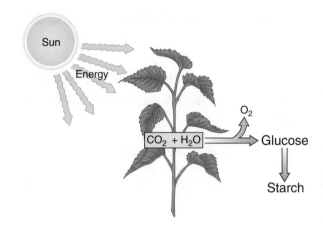

Figure 4.5 Photosynthesis
Photosynthesis uses energy from the sun to convert carbon dioxide and water into glucose, which can be stored as starch.

sucrose A disaccharide that is formed by linking fructose and glucose. It is commonly known as table sugar or white sugar.

lactose A disaccharide that is formed by linking galactose and glucose. It is commonly known as milk sugar.

maltose A disaccharide made up of 2 molecules of glucose. It is formed in the intestines during starch digestion.

Disaccharides Disaccharides are simple carbohydrates made up of two mono-saccharides linked together (**Figure 4.6**). **Sucrose**, or common white table sugar, is the disaccharide formed by linking glucose to fructose. It is found in sugar cane, sugar beets, honey, and maple syrup. Sucrose is the only sweetener that can be called "sugar" in the ingredient list on food labels in the United States. **Lactose**, or milk sugar, is glucose linked to galactose. Lactose is the only sugar found naturally in animal foods. It contributes about 30% of the energy in whole cow's milk and about 40% of the energy in human milk. **Maltose** is a disaccharide consisting of two molecules of glucose. This sugar is made whenever starch is broken down. For example, it is responsible for the slightly sweet taste experienced when bread is held in the mouth for a few minutes. As salivary amylase begins digesting the starch, some sweeter-tasting maltose is formed.

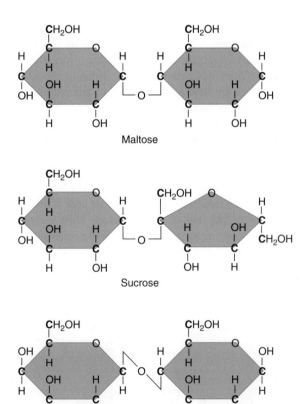

Figure 4.6 Structures of common disaccharides
Maltose, sucrose, and lactose are made up of different pairs of monosaccharides.

Figure 4.7 Hydrolysis and condensation reactions
In this hydrolysis reaction, a molecule of maltose is broken into its component glucose molecules; two glucose molecules are joined to form the disaccharide maltose in a condensation reaction.

Making and Breaking Sugar Chains The chemical reaction that breaks the bonds between sugar molecules is called a **hydrolysis reaction** (**Figure 4.7**). Hydrolysis reactions use water to add a hydroxyl group (OH) to one sugar and a hydrogen atom (H) to the other. The reaction that links two sugars together is called a **condensation reaction**. Condensation reactions release a molecule of water by taking a hydroxyl group from one sugar and a hydrogen atom from the other.

Complex Carbohydrates

Complex carbohydrates are made up of many monosaccharides linked together in chains. They are generally not sweet to the taste like simple carbohydrates. Short chains of three to ten monosaccharides are called **oligosaccharides**, and longer chains are called **polysaccharides** (*poly* means many). The polysaccharides include **glycogen** in animals and **starch** and fiber in plants (**Figure 4.8**).

Oligosaccharides Some oligosaccharides are formed in the gut during the breakdown of polysaccharides. These are then further digested to simple sugars. Other oligosaccharides are found naturally in foods such as beans and other legumes, onions, bananas, garlic, and artichokes. Many of these are not digested by human enzymes in the digestive tract and pass into the colon where they are broken down by the intestinal microflora. Therefore they can affect the types of bacteria that grow in the colon and have beneficial effects on gastrointestinal (GI) health. Oligosaccharides present in human milk make the infant stool easier to pass, help promote the growth of a healthy intestinal microflora, and may protect the infant from infections that cause diarrhea.[5]

Glycogen Glycogen is the storage form of carbohydrate in animals. It is a polysaccharide made up of highly branched chains of glucose molecules (see Figure 4.8). The branched structure allows it to be broken down quickly when glucose is needed. In humans, glycogen is stored in the muscles and in the liver. Muscle glycogen provides glucose to the muscle as a source of energy during activity; liver glycogen releases glucose into the bloodstream for delivery to cells throughout the body. We don't consume glycogen in our food because glycogen present in animal muscles is broken down soon after slaughter so is not present when the meat is consumed.

The amount of glycogen in the body is relatively small—about 200 to 500 grams. The amount of glycogen stored in muscle can be temporarily increased by a regimen

hydrolysis reaction A type of chemical reaction in which a large molecule is broken into two smaller molecules by the addition of water.

condensation reaction A type of chemical reaction in which two molecules are joined to form a larger molecule and water is released.

oligosaccharides Short chain carbohydrates containing 3 to 10 sugar units.

polysaccharides Carbohydrates containing many sugar units linked together.

glycogen A carbohydrate made of many glucose molecules linked together in a highly branched structure. It is the storage form of carbohydrate in animals.

starch A carbohydrate made of many glucose molecules linked in straight or branching chains. The bonds that hold the glucose molecules together can be broken by human digestive enzymes.

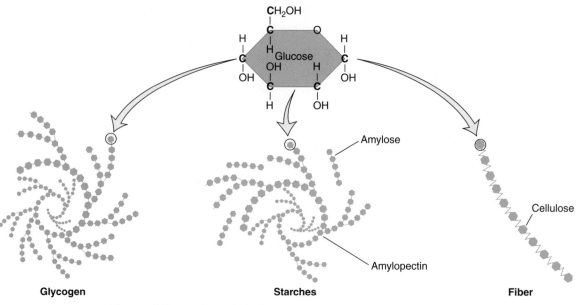

Figure 4.8 Complex carbohydrates
Glycogen, starches, and the fiber cellulose are made up of straight or branching chains of glucose.

called *carbohydrate loading* or *glycogen supercompensation*. This regimen is often used by endurance athletes to build up glycogen stores before an event. Extra glycogen can mean the difference between running only 20 miles or finishing a 26-mile marathon before exhaustion takes over. Glycogen supercompensation is discussed in more detail in Chapter 13.

Starches Starch is the storage form of carbohydrate in plants. Starch is made up of two types of molecules: amylose, which consists of long straight chains of glucose molecules, and amylopectin, which consists of branched chains of glucose molecules (see Figure 4.8). Starch accumulates in roots and tubers (the underground energy storage organ of some plants) where it provides energy for the growth and reproduction of the plant. Therefore we consume starch in roots and tubers such as potatoes, sweet potatoes, beets, turnips, and cassava (**Figure 4.9**). Starch accumulates in seeds as an energy source for the developing plant embryo. We consume the starch in grain seeds such as wheat, barley, and rye. We also consume starch in **legumes**, such as lentils, soybeans, and pinto and kidney beans.

In addition to the starch naturally present in foods, the diet also contains refined starch such as cornstarch, which is added to thicken foods such as sauces, puddings, and gravies. Starch can be used to thicken foods because the granules swell when heated in water (**Figure 4.10**). As a starch-thickened mixture cools, high-amylose

legumes Plants in the pea or bean family, which produce an elongated pod containing large starchy seeds. Examples include green peas, kidney beans, and peanuts.

Figure 4.9
This starchy root vegetable known as cassava or manioc is a dietary staple in some parts of Africa. (Magar-StockFood Munich/© StockFood America)

Figure 4.10
These starch granules inside a potato cell, like starch granules in all plant cells, have a unique size, shape, and organization that accounts for the properties of the starch during cooking. (© Eric V. Grave/Photo Researchers, Inc.)

Choosing Whole Grains

(©iStockphoto)

You know you should eat more whole-grain products, but how can you spot them at the store? Do you just put brown bread instead of white into your shopping cart? Unfortunately, it's not that easy. Bread may be brown because of ingredients such as molasses, not necessarily because it is made from whole grain ingredients. Product names can also be deceptive. Healthy-sounding terms like "multi-grain" or "seven-grain" simply mean the product contains more than one type of grain, not that these grains are necessarily whole grains. "Wheat" refers to the type of grain, not how refined it is; "stone ground" refers to how the grain was processed, not whether the bran and germ are included; and terms like "bran" and "oat" may refer to things added to the product, not whether the product is made predominantly from a whole grain.

To see if what you pull off the shelf is indeed a whole-grain product, look at the ingredient list. When a whole grain is listed first, the product is made with mostly whole-grain ingredients. Choose products whose labels include whole wheat, whole oats, oatmeal, rolled oats, whole-grain corn, popcorn, brown rice, whole rye, whole-grain barley, wild rice, buckwheat, triticale, bulgur, cracked wheat, millet, quinoa, or sorghum. Products whose first ingredient is wheat flour, enriched flour, or degerminated cornmeal are not made predominantly from whole grains. Also, foods to which wheat bran or oat bran has been added to increase the fiber content provide the benefits of ingredients but are not necessarily whole-grain products. Don't forget to look at the rest of the ingredient list, too. For example, Lucky Charms cereal is made with whole grains, but marshmallows are the second ingredient, making this choice high in sugar.

Whole-grain products can also be identified by looking for whole-grain stamps (see figure) and the whole-grain health claim. Foods that are low in fat and contain at least 51% of their weight as whole grains can include the health claim which states "Diets rich in whole grain foods and other plant foods and low in total fat, saturated fat, and cholesterol may help reduce the risk of heart disease and certain cancers."[1]

The Dietary Guidelines recommend consuming three servings of whole grains daily. To get the benefits of whole-grains look at more than the color and name of the product.

These whole-grain stamps were developed by the Whole Grains Council™ to help consumers identify products that provide either a half serving (8g) or a whole serving (16g) of whole grain.

THE BASIC STAMP
Product may contain some refined grain

THE 100% STAMP
All grain ingredients are whole grains

Courtesy oldways and the Whole Grains Council, wholegrainscouncil.org

(Courtesy Oldways and the Whole Grains Council, wholegrainscouncil.org.)

---

[1]U.S. Dept. of Health and Human Services, Food and Drug Administration Qualified Health Claims Subject to Enforcement Discretion, September 2003; Updated August 2005, November 2005, and April 2007 Washington, DC, 2005. Available online at http://www.cfsan.fda.gov/~dms/qhc-sum.html Accessed July 11, 2009.

starches form bonds between the molecules, forming a gel. Some starches are treated to enhance their ability to form a gel. These modified food starches are added to foods as thickeners.

Fiber Fiber includes certain complex carbohydrates and lignins (substances in plants that are not carbohydrates but are classified as fiber) that cannot be digested by human enzymes. Since they cannot be digested, they cannot be absorbed into the body. However, fiber consumed in the diet can have beneficial health effects, from reducing constipation to lowering blood cholesterol. The term **dietary fiber** is used to refer to fiber that is found intact in plants. Fiber that has been isolated from its plant source and has been shown to have beneficial physiological effects is called **functional fiber**. Functional fiber can be added to foods or supplements. For example, oat bran added to bread would be considered functional fiber. **Total fiber** is the sum of dietary fiber and functional fiber.[3]

Fiber includes a number of different chemical substances that have different physical and physiological properties. Some fibers can be digested by bacteria in the large intestine, producing gas and short-chain fatty acids, small quantities of which can be absorbed. These fibers also form viscous solutions when mixed with water and are therefore often referred to as **soluble fibers**. Soluble fibers are found around and inside plant cells. They include pectins, gums, and some hemicelluloses. Food sources of soluble fibers include oats, apples, beans, and seaweed. Fibers that cannot be broken down by bacteria in the large intestine and do not dissolve in water are called **insoluble fibers**. They are primarily derived from the structural parts of plants, such as the cell walls, and include cellulose, some hemicelluloses, and lignins. Food sources of insoluble fibers include wheat bran and rye bran, which are mostly hemicellulose and cellulose, and vegetables such as broccoli, which contain woody fibers composed partly of lignins. Most foods of plant origin contain mixtures of soluble and insoluble fibers (**Figure 4.11**).

In addition to the soluble and insoluble fibers found in whole grains, fruits, and vegetables, our diet contains fibers that are added to foods during processing. Pectin is a soluble fiber found in fruits and vegetables that forms a gel when sugar and acid are added. It is used to thicken yogurt and to form jams and jellies. Carbohydrate gums such as xanthan gum and locust bean gum are also soluble fibers. They combine with water and are used to keep solutions from separating. Gravies, puddings, reduced-fat salad dressings, and frozen desserts are examples of products that contain carbohydrate gums. Pectins and gums are also used in reduced-fat products to mimic the texture of fat (see Chapter 5). Insoluble fibers such as wheat bran are added to foods like breads and muffins to reduce kcalorie content and meet consumer demand for high-fiber foods.

dietary fiber A mixture of indigestible carbohydrates and lignin that is found intact in plants.

functional fiber Isolated indigestible carbohydrates that have been shown to have beneficial physiological effects in humans.

total fiber The sum of dietary fiber and functional fiber.

soluble fiber Fiber that dissolves in water or absorbs water to form viscous solutions and can be broken down by the intestinal microflora. It includes pectins, gums, and some hemicelluloses.

insoluble fiber Fiber that, for the most part, does not dissolve in water and cannot be broken down by bacteria in the large intestine. It includes cellulose, some hemicelluloses, and lignin.

Figure 4.11
How many good sources of dietary fiber do you include in your diet each day? (© Charles D. Winter)

4.3 Carbohydrates in the Digestive Tract

Learning Objectives

- Describe the steps of carbohydrate digestion.
- Define lactose intolerance and explain why it causes gas and bloating when milk is consumed.
- Discuss the effects of dietary fiber and other indigestible carbohydrates on gastrointestinal function and health.

Disaccharides and complex carbohydrates must be digested to monosaccharides to be absorbed. Some people are unable to digest the disaccharide lactose. It spills into the colon causing uncomfortable side effects. All humans lack the digestive enzymes needed to completely break down a variety of oligosaccharides, certain forms of starch, and fiber. These indigestible carbohydrates have important effects on the health and function of the digestive system and the body as a whole.

Digestible Carbohydrates

Digestion of starch begins in the mouth, where the enzyme salivary amylase starts breaking it into shorter polysaccharides. The majority of starch and disaccharide digestion occurs in the small intestine. Here, pancreatic amylases complete the job of breaking down starch into monosaccharides, disaccharides, and oligosaccharides. The digestion of disaccharides and oligosaccharides is completed by enzymes attached to the brush border of the villi in the small intestine (**Figure 4.12**). At the

1 In the mouth, the enzyme salivary amylase starts breaking starch into shorter polysaccharides.

2 In the stomach, salivary amylase is inactivated by acid so no carbohydrate digestion occurs.

3 In the small intestine, most starch digestion and breakdown of disaccharides occur. Here pancreatic amylases continue breaking down starch into monosaccharides, disaccharides, and oligosaccharides.

4 Enzymes attached to the brush border of the small intestinal villi complete the digestion of carbohydrates. Here, disaccharides and oligosaccharides are broken down into monosaccharides.

5 In the large intestine, fiber and other indigestible carbohydrates are partially broken down by bacteria to form short chain fatty acids and gas. Some fiber is excreted in the feces.

Salivary glands · Liver · Stomach · Pancreas · Small intestine · Large intestine

Oligosaccharide · Disaccharide · Monosaccharides · Intestinal villi · Capillaries · Vein · Artery · To liver

Figure 4.12 Overview of carbohydrate digestion and absorption
During digestion, enzymes break starches and sugars into monosaccharides, which are absorbed. Most of the fiber and other indigestible carbohydrates are excreted in the feces.

lactase An enzyme located in the brush border of the small intestine that breaks the disaccharide lactose into glucose and galactose.

brush border maltose is broken down into two glucose molecules by the enzyme maltase, sucrose is broken down by sucrase to yield glucose and fructose, and lactose is broken down by **lactase** to form glucose and galactose. The resulting monosaccharides—glucose, galactose, and fructose—are then absorbed and transported to the liver via the hepatic portal vein.

Lactose Intolerance

lactose intolerance The inability to digest lactose because of a reduction in the levels of the enzyme lactase. It causes symptoms including intestinal gas and bloating after dairy products are consumed.

Lactose intolerance is a condition in which there is not enough of the enzyme lactase in the small intestine to digest the milk sugar lactose. When this occurs the undigested lactose passes into the large intestine, where it draws in water and is metabolized by bacteria producing acids and gas. This causes symptoms that include abdominal distention, flatulence, cramping, and diarrhea. Human infants normally produce enough of the enzyme lactase to digest the lactose in their all-milk diet. Enzyme activity may begin to decrease at 2 years of age but the symptoms of lactose intolerance usually do not become apparent until after the age of 6 years and may not be evident until adulthood. Whether or not an individual retains the ability to digest lactose into adulthood depends on the genes they inherit.[6] Lactose intolerance may also occur as a result of an intestinal infection or other disease. It is then referred to as secondary lactose intolerance and may disappear when the other condition is resolved.

Incidence of Lactose Intolerance In the United States, it is estimated that 30 to 50 million adults cannot fully digest lactose. The incidence varies enormously depending on ethnic background. Lactose intolerance is more common in Asian, African, Native American, and Mediterranean populations than it is among northern and western Europeans. Nearly 100% of adults in Asian populations are lactose intolerant as opposed to just 5% or less of adults in northwestern European populations.[7] In the U.S. 90% of Asian Americans, 75% of African Americans, and about 15% of Caucasian Americans experience symptoms after consuming lactose.[8]

Meeting Calcium Needs In the United States, milk is an important source of calcium. The Dietary Guidelines recommend 3 cups of low-fat milk or milk products each day.[9] Because the degree of lactose intolerance varies, some individuals can consume small amounts of dairy products without symptoms and can meet their calcium needs by dividing the 3 cups into many smaller portions. Those who cannot tolerate any lactose can meet their calcium needs with foods like tofu, fish, and vegetables (**Figure 4.13**). These foods provide dietary calcium in cultures where lactose intolerance is common. For example, in Asia, tofu and fish consumed with bones supply calcium, and in the Near East, cheese and yogurt provide much of the calcium. These fermented products are more easily tolerated than milk because some of the lactose

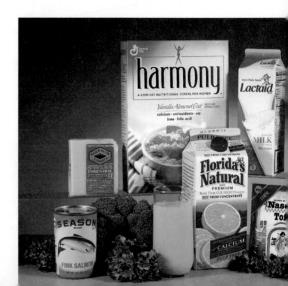

Figure 4.13
These foods are good natural or fortified sources of calcium that are low in lactose.
(© Andy Washnik)

originally present is digested by bacteria or lost in processing. Calcium-fortified foods, calcium supplements, milk treated with the enzyme lactase, and lactase tablets, which can be consumed with or before milk products, are also available for those with lactose intolerance.

Indigestible Carbohydrates

Carbohydrates that are not digested in the small intestine include fiber, some oligo-saccharides, and **resistant starch**. Fiber and oligosaccharides are not digested because human enzymes cannot break the bonds that hold their subunits together. Resistant starch is not digested because the natural structure of the grain protects it or because cooking and processing alter its digestibility. For instance, heating makes potato starch more digestible but cooling the cooked potato reduces the starch's digestibility. Foods high in resistant starch include legumes, unripe bananas, and cold cooked potatoes, rice, and pasta. The presence of indigestible carbohydrates in the diet affects GI motility, the type of intestinal microflora, nutrient absorption, and the amount of intestinal gas.

resistant starch Starch that escapes digestion in the small intestine of healthy people.

Indigestible Carbohydrates Stimulate GI Motility Indigestible carbohydrates affect GI motility because they increase the volume of material in the lumen of the intestine. Insoluble fibers, such as wheat bran, increase the bulk of material in the feces. Soluble fibers and resistant starch draw water into the intestine. The combination of the increased bulk and additional water allow for easier evacuation of the stool. Indigestible carbohydrates also promote healthy bowel function because the extra bulk stimulates peristalsis, causing the muscles of the colon to work more, become stronger, and function better. The increase in peristalsis reduces transit time—the time it takes food and fecal matter to move through the digestive tract. In African countries, where the diet contains 40 to 150 grams of fiber per day, the transit time is 36 hours or less. In the United States, where the usual fiber intake is only about 15 grams per day,[10] it is not uncommon for transit time to be as long as 96 hours (see Science Applied: Cereal Fibers and Health).

Indigestible Carbohydrates Promote a Healthy Microflora When soluble fibers, resistant starch, and oligosaccharides reach the colon they serve as a food source for the microflora that reside there. Diets high in these substances promote the maintenance of beneficial species of bacteria in the colon. When these carbohydrates are broken down it results in the production of short-chain fatty acids and the acidification of the colonic contents. The short-chain fatty acids serve as a fuel source for cells in the colon as well as other body tissues and may play a role in regulating cellular processes. The acid inhibits the growth of undesirable bacteria and favors the growth of *Lactobacilli* and *Bifidobacteria*, which are well adapted to acid conditions.[11] In addition to inhibiting the growth of disease-causing bacteria these short-chain fatty acids may help prevent and treat inflammation in the bowel, which causes diarrhea, as well as protect against colon cancer.[12,13] (See Chapter 3, Your Choice: Should You Feed Your Flora?)

Indigestible Carbohydrates Slow Nutrient Absorption Indigestible carbohydrates increase the volume of the intestinal contents and absorb water, forming viscous solutions. These effects slow nutrient absorption by affecting passage through the GI tract, by decreasing the amount of contact between nutrients and the absorptive surface of the small intestine, and by reducing contact between digestive enzymes and food. In the stomach, fiber causes distention and slows emptying. In the small intestine, the added volume and viscosity slows the absorption of sugars and other nutrients (**Figure 4.14**). This can be beneficial because it slows the absorption of glucose and thereby reduces fluctuations in blood glucose. Soluble fiber also binds cholesterol and bile, which is made from cholesterol, reducing their absorption. This is beneficial because it can lower blood cholesterol and help reduce the risk of heart disease.

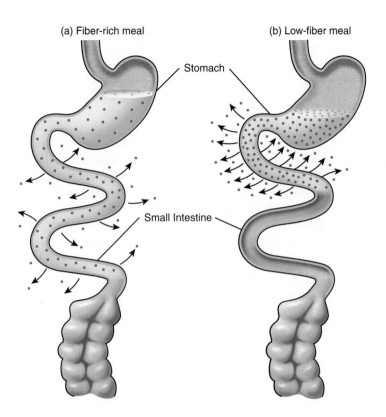

Figure 4.14 Effect of fiber on digestion and absorption
(a) A fiber-rich meal dilutes the stomach and small intestinal contents and slows the digestion and absorption of nutrients (green dots). (b) Nutrients from a low-fiber meal are more concentrated in the gastrointestinal tract, resulting in more rapid digestion and absorption.

Fiber also binds certain minerals, preventing their absorption. For instance, wheat bran fiber binds the minerals zinc, calcium, magnesium, and iron. Too much fiber can reduce the absorption of these essential minerals. However, when mineral intake meets recommendations, a reasonable intake of high-fiber foods does not compromise mineral status.

Life Cycle

A high-fiber diet also increases the volume of food needed to meet energy requirements. This is beneficial for someone who is trying to lose weight because they feel satiated after fewer kcalories are consumed. A high-fiber diet may be a disadvantage for someone with a small stomach capacity because they may satisfy their hunger before their nutrient requirements are met. Generally, this is a problem only when the diet is low in protein or micronutrients or when high-fiber diets are consumed by young children, whose small stomachs limit the amount of food they can eat.

Indigestible Carbohydrates Increase Intestinal Gas Anyone who has ever eaten beans knows of their potentially embarrassing side effect of flatulence. The reason beans cause gas is that they are particularly high in the oligosaccharides raffinose and stachyose, which cannot be digested by enzymes in the human stomach and small intestine. They pass into the large intestine where the bacteria that live there digest them, producing gas and other by-products. This gas can cause abdominal discomfort and flatulence. To alleviate the problem, over-the-counter enzyme tablets and solutions (such as Beano®) can be consumed to break down oligosaccharides before they reach the intestinal bacteria, thereby reducing the amount of gas produced.

As with oligosaccharides, intestinal gas is a by-product of the bacterial breakdown of fiber and resistant starch. A sudden increase in the fiber content of the diet can cause abdominal discomfort, gas, and diarrhea. Constipation can also be a problem if fiber intake is increased without an increase in fluid intake. To avoid these problems, the fiber content of the diet should be increased gradually and fluid intake should also be increased.

SCIENCE

ScienceAppliedScienceApplied
ScienceAppliedScienceApplied
ScienceAppliedScienceApplied

APPLIED

(DAJ/Getty Images, Inc.)   (www.victorianoizquierdo.com/Getty Images, Inc.)   (Elena Schweitzer/Shutterstock)

Cereal Fibers and Health

One hundred and fifty years ago, self-proclaimed health advocates Sylvester Graham, John Harvey Kellogg, and Charles W. Post promoted cereal foods as health tonics. These pioneers, of what are now Kellogg's and Post cereals, were not scientists. Often the health information they promoted was outlandish. Graham preached that food should never be eaten hot, that water should not be consumed with a meal, and that lewdness, along with chicken pie, was the cause of cholera. Kellogg told his patients that coffee could cripple the liver and that bouillon was a solution of poisons. And Post advertised that his whole grain cereal, called Grape Nuts, tightened up loose teeth and cured tuberculosis and malaria.[1] While these ideas have not held up over time, the suggestion that whole grains are healthy is part of current nutrition wisdom. The Dietary Guidelines and MyPyramid recommend a diet that is based on whole grains to promote gastrointestinal health and reduce the risks of heart disease, cancer, and diabetes.

Scientific support for the role of unrefined cereal grain consumption in health started to accumulate in the 1940s when scientists such as A. R. P. Walker and Denis Burkitt began observing and investigating the effects of high-fiber foods on health. At the time they began their studies fiber was referred to as roughage and many regarded it as a gastrointestinal irritant rather than a dietary component important for health.

Walker and colleagues began to relate a population's dietary pattern with their disease pattern—emphasizing the role of fiber.[2] They observed that in Western populations, where fiber intake was between 15 and 30 grams per day, feces were smaller and harder than in African populations consuming diets containing from 70 to more than 100 grams of fiber per day. They hypothesized that fiber increased stool weight and decreased transit time. This hypothesis was supported by studies that compared intestinal transit time and stool weight in Ugandan villagers, who ate a high-fiber diet to British subjects, who ate a lower-fiber diet (see figure). To further test this hypothesis, they added unprocessed bran to the diet of British subjects. The added fiber reduced transit time and increased stool weight.[3]

In 1956, Denis Burkitt, traveling in Africa, noticed that many diseases that were common among whites in Europe and Africa were rare among black African peasants. With

Ugandan villagers, who consume an unrefined diet high in fiber, have greater stool weights and shorter transit times than British subjects who consume a more refined, lower-fiber diet. (*Source:* Adapted from Burkitt, D. P., Walker, A. R. P., and Painter, N. S. Dietary fiber and disease. *JAMA* 229:1068–1074, 1974.)

these observations in mind, Burkitt proposed that a variety of conditions common in industrialized society, including diabetes, obesity, heart disease, constipation, diverticular disease, hemorrhoids, and varicose veins, were caused by the overconsumption of refined carbohydrates. He postulated that three manufactured foods—refined sugar, white flour, and white rice—caused virtually all the diseases of civilization.[2] Burkitt hypothesized that a deficiency of dietary fiber may underlie the development of these diseases.[3,4] This became known as the fiber hypothesis. Burkitt was often quoted as saying that the health of a country's people could be determined by the size of their stools and whether the stools floated or sank.[5]

The fiber hypothesis of Burkitt was the stimulus for much of today's research on fiber and its importance in maintaining normal gastrointestinal function and reducing the incidence of chronic disease. Today the whole-grain cereals promoted by Graham, Kellogg, and Post over a century ago are still considered a sort of health tonic, but this time scientific data are available to support the benefits.

[1]Deutsch, R. M. *The New Nuts Among the Berries.* Palo Alto, CA: Bull Publishing Company, 1977.

[2]Trowell, H. Dietary fibre: A paradigm. In: Trowell, H., Burkitt, D., and Heaton, K., eds. *Dietary Fibre, Fibre-Depleted Foods and Disease.* London: Academic Press, 1985, 1–20.

[3]Burkitt, D. P., Walker, A. R. P., and Painter, N. S. Dietary fiber and disease. *JAMA* 229:1068–1074, 1974.

[4]Burkitt, D. P., and Trowell, H. C. *Refined Carbohydrate and Disease: Some Implications of Dietary Fibre.* London: Academic Press, 1975.

[5]Story, J. A., and Kritchevsky, D. Denis Parsons Burkitt. *J. Nutr.* 124:1551–1554, 1994.

1 Glucose molecule

2 ATP

e⁻

2 Pyruvate molecules

Figure 4.15 Glycolysis
In the cytosol of the cell, glycolysis breaks glucose into two molecules of pyruvate, electrons are released, and two ATP molecules are produced.

cellular respiration
The reactions that break down carbohydrates, fats, and proteins in the presence of oxygen to produce carbon dioxide, water, and ATP.

glycolysis (also called **anaerobic metabolism**). Metabolic reactions in the cytosol of the cell that split glucose into two 3-carbon pyruvate molecules, yielding two ATP molecules.

aerobic metabolism
Metabolism in the presence of oxygen, which can completely break down glucose to yield carbon dioxide, water, and as many as 38 ATP molecules.

4.4 Carbohydrates in the Body

Learning Objectives

- Describe the steps involved in metabolizing glucose to produce ATP.
- Discuss how carbohydrate intake is related to ketone production.

Carbohydrates are central to energy production in the body and also provide other essential functions. The monosaccharide galactose is an important molecule in nervous tissue. It also combines with glucose to make lactose in women who are producing breast milk. Two other monosaccharides that are of great importance to the body are deoxyribose and ribose. These sugars are components of DNA and RNA (ribonucleic acid), respectively, which contain the genetic information for the synthesis of proteins. Deoxyribose and ribose can be synthesized by the body and are not found in significant amounts in the diet. Ribose is also a component of the vitamin riboflavin. Oligosaccharides are also important in our bodies. They are found attached to proteins or lipids on the surface of cells where they help to signal information about the cells. Another type of carbohydrate that is important in the body is mucopolysaccharides. They are a type of polysaccharide that functions with proteins in body secretions and structures. Mucopolysaccharides give mucus its viscous consistency and provide cushioning and lubrication in connective tissue.

Using Carbohydrate to Provide Energy

After absorption, monosaccharides travel to the liver. The monosaccharides fructose and galactose are metabolized for energy. Glucose may also be broken down to provide energy, or passed into the bloodstream for delivery to other body tissues that can use it to provide energy. It may also be stored in the liver as glycogen and, to a lesser extent, used to synthesize fat.

To generate ATP, glucose is metabolized through **cellular respiration**. Cellular respiration, uses 6 molecules of oxygen to convert 1 molecule of glucose into 6 molecules of carbon dioxide, 6 molecules of water, and about 38 molecules of ATP:

$$C_6H_{12}O_6 \;+\; 6O_2 \;\Rightarrow\; 6CO_2 \;+\; 6H_2O \;+\; ATP$$

Glucose   oxygen   carbon dioxide   water

The carbon dioxide produced by cellular respiration is transported to the lungs where it is eliminated in exhaled air. Providing energy through cellular respiration involves four interconnected stages (see Appendix L).

Glycolysis The first stage of cellular respiration takes place in the cytosol of the cell and is called **glycolysis**, meaning glucose breakdown. Because oxygen isn't needed for this reaction, glycolysis is sometimes called **anaerobic metabolism**. In glycolysis, the 6-carbon sugar glucose is broken into two 3-carbon molecules called pyruvate (**Figure 4.15**, **Figure 4.16**). The reactions generate two molecules of ATP for each molecule of glucose and release high-energy electrons that are passed to shuttling molecules which can transport them to the last stage of cellular respiration. When oxygen is limited, no further metabolism of glucose and production of ATP occurs.

Acetyl-CoA Formation When oxygen is present, **aerobic metabolism** can proceed. In the mitochondria, one carbon is removed from pyruvate and released as CO_2. The remaining 2-carbon compound combines with a molecule of coenzyme A (CoA) to form acetyl-CoA (Figure 4.16). High-energy electrons are released and passed to shuttling molecules for transport to the last stage of cellular respiration. Acetyl-CoA then enters the third stage of breakdown, the citric acid cycle.

1. Glycolysis splits glucose, a 6-carbon molecule, into two molecules of pyruvate, a 3-carbon molecule. This step produces high-energy electrons (e^-) and a small amount of ATP. Each pyruvate is then either broken down to produce more ATP or used to make glucose via gluconeogenesis.

2. When oxygen is available, pyruvate can be used to produce more ATP. The first step is to remove one carbon as carbon dioxide from each pyruvate. This produces a 2-carbon molecule that combines with coenzyme A to form acetyl-CoA and releases high-energy electrons.

3. Each acetyl-CoA enters the citric acid cycle, where two carbons are lost as carbon dioxide, high-energy electrons are released, and a small amount of ATP is produced.

4. In the final step of cellular respiration, the electron transport chain accepts the high-energy electrons released in previous steps and uses the energy to synthesize ATP. The electrons are combined with oxygen and hydrogen to form water.

Figure 4.16 Glucose Metabolism
The reactions of cellular respiration split the bonds between carbon atoms in glucose, releasing energy that is used to synthesize ATP. ATP is used to power the energy-requiring processes in the body.

Citric Acid Cycle In the third stage, acetyl-CoA combines with oxaloacetate, a 4-carbon molecule derived from carbohydrate, to form a 6-carbon molecule called citric acid and begin the citric acid cycle (Figure 4.16). The reactions of the citric acid cycle then remove one carbon at a time, to produce carbon dioxide. After two carbons have been removed in this manner, a 4-carbon oxaloacetate molecule is re-formed and the cycle can begin again. These chemical reactions produce two ATP molecules per glucose molecule and also remove electrons, which are passed to shuttling molecules for transport to the fourth and last stage of cellular respiration, the electron transport chain.

Electron Transport Chain The electron transport chain consists of a series of molecules, most of which are proteins, associated with the inner membrane of the mitochondria. These molecules accept electrons from the shuttling molecules and pass them from one to

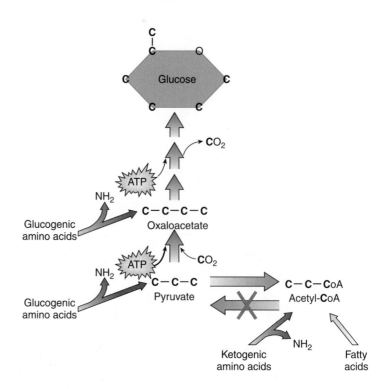

Figure 4.17 Gluconeogenesis
Gluconeogenesis uses 3-carbon molecules and energy from ATP to synthesize glucose. 2-carbon compounds, such as acetyl-CoA cannot be used to make glucose.

another down the chain until they are finally combined with oxygen to form water (Figure 4.16). As the electrons are passed along, their energy is trapped and used to make ATP. The reactions of cellular respiration are central to all energy-yielding processes in the body.

Carbohydrate and Protein Breakdown

When carbohydrate intake is low, some glucose can be obtained from the breakdown of glycogen. This glucose is released into the blood to prevent blood glucose from dropping below the normal range. Glucose is also supplied by a metabolic pathway called **gluconeogenesis** (production of new glucose). Gluconeogenesis, which occurs in liver and kidney cells, is an energy-requiring process that forms glucose from 3-carbon molecules. These 3-carbon molecules come primarily from amino acids derived from protein breakdown. Some amino acids, referred to as glucogenic amino acids, can form pyruvate and oxaloacetate. These can then be used to make glucose (**Figure 4.17**, Figure 4.16). Fatty acids and ketogenic amino acids cannot be used to make glucose because the reactions that break them down produce primarily 2-carbon molecules that form acetyl-CoA. Gluconeogenesis is essential for meeting the body's immediate need for glucose, particularly when carbohydrate intake is very low, but it uses amino acids from proteins that could be used for other essential functions such as growth and maintenance of muscle tissue. Since adequate dietary carbohydrate eliminates the need to use amino acids from protein to synthesize glucose, carbohydrate is said to spare protein.

gluconeogenesis The synthesis of glucose from simple noncarbohydrate molecules. Amino acids from protein are the primary source of carbons for glucose synthesis.

Carbohydrate and Fat Breakdown

Carbohydrate is also needed for the metabolism of fat, so when the supply of carbohydrate is limited, fat cannot be completely broken down. This is because fatty acids are broken into molecules of acetyl-CoA. Acetyl-CoA cannot be metabolized via the citric acid cycle unless it can combine with a 4-carbon oxaloacetate molecule derived from carbohydrate metabolism. When carbohydrate is in short supply, oxaloacetate is limited so acetyl-CoA cannot be broken down to form carbon dioxide and water and produce ATP. Instead, the liver converts it into compounds known as **ketones** or **ketone bodies**, which are released into the blood (**Figure 4.18**). Ketones can be used as an energy source by tissues, such as those in the heart, muscle, and kidney. Ketone production is a normal response to starvation or to a diet very low in carbohydrate. Even the brain, which requires glucose, can adapt to obtain a portion of its energy from ketones.

ketones or **ketone bodies** Molecules formed in the liver when there is not sufficient carbohydrate to completely metabolize the 2-carbon units produced from fat breakdown.

Figure 4.18 Ketone formation
When carbohydrate is available (right), acetyl-CoA from fatty acid breakdown can combine with oxaloacetate and enter the citric acid cycle and no ketones are formed; when carbohydrate (and thus oxaloacetate) is in short supply (left), acetyl-CoA molecules cannot enter the citric acid cycle, and the liver converts them to ketones.

Excess ketones are excreted by the kidney in urine. However, if fluid intake is too low to produce enough urine to excrete ketones, or if ketone production is high, ketones can build up in the blood, causing ketosis. Mild ketosis, which may arise during moderate energy restriction, such as might occur with a weight-loss diet, causes symptoms including headache, dry mouth, foul-smelling breath, and a reduction in appetite. High ketone levels, such as might occur with untreated diabetes (discussed later in the chapter), increase the acidity of the blood and can result in coma and death.

4.5 Blood Glucose Regulation

Learning Objectives

- Explain how insulin and glucagon are involved in regulating blood glucose.
- Compare the causes and consequences of type 1 and type 2 diabetes.

Blood glucose levels are normally tightly controlled by the liver and hormones secreted by the pancreas. If these hormones are not produced normally or if the body does not respond to them normally, blood glucose levels can rise too high or drop too low. **Diabetes mellitus** is a disease in which blood glucose levels are consistently above the normal range and **hypoglycemia** is a condition in which blood glucose levels drop below the normal range.

Regulating Blood Glucose

Normally, fasting blood glucose, measured after an 8- to 12-hour overnight fast, is maintained at about 60 to 100 mg per 100 mL of blood, or 70 to 110 mg per 100 mL of **plasma**. Maintaining this level ensures adequate glucose will be available to body

diabetes mellitus A disease caused by either insufficient insulin production or decreased sensitivity of cells to insulin. It results in elevated blood glucose levels.

hypoglycemia A low blood glucose level, usually below 40 to 50 mg of glucose per 100 mL of blood.

plasma The liquid portion of the blood that remains when the blood cells are removed.

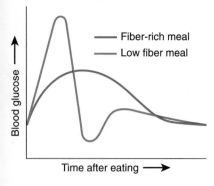

Figure 4.19 Effect of dietary fiber on blood glucose levels Blood glucose rises rapidly after a high-carbohydrate, low-fiber meal, whereas the rise in blood glucose is delayed and blunted after a high-carbohydrate meal that is rich in fiber.

glycemic response The rate, magnitude, and duration of the rise in blood glucose that occurs after a particular food or meal is consumed.

glycemic index A ranking of the effect on blood glucose of a food of a certain carbohydrate content relative to an equal amount of carbohydrate from a reference food such as white bread or glucose.

glycemic load An index of the glycemic response that occurs after eating specific foods. It is calculated by multiplying a food's glycemic index by the amount of available carbohydrate in a serving of the food.

insulin A hormone made in the pancreas that allows the uptake of glucose by body cells and has other metabolic effects such as stimulating protein and fat synthesis and the synthesis of glycogen in liver and muscle.

glucagon A hormone made in the pancreas that stimulates the breakdown of liver glycogen and the synthesis of glucose to increase blood sugar.

cells. A steady supply of glucose is particularly important for nerve cells, including those in the brain, and red blood cells because these cells rely almost exclusively on glucose as an energy source.

Glycemic Response The carbohydrate consumed in food is digested and absorbed and enters the bloodstream causing blood glucose to rise. How quickly and how high blood glucose rises after carbohydrate is consumed is referred to as **glycemic response**. It is affected by both the amount and type of carbohydrate eaten and the amount of fat and protein in that food or meal. Because carbohydrate must be digested and absorbed to enter the blood, how quickly a food leaves the stomach and how fast it is digested and absorbed in the small intestine all affect how long it takes glucose to get into the blood. Refined sugars and starches generally cause a greater glycemic response than unrefined carbohydrates containing fiber because sugars and starches consumed alone leave the stomach quickly and are rapidly digested and absorbed causing a sharp, swift rise in blood sugar. For example, when you drink a can of soda or a glass of juice on an empty stomach, your blood sugar increases within minutes. Fiber slows stomach emptying and intestinal absorption so whole grains and other unrefined carbohydrates, which contain fiber along with sugars and starches, cause a slower, lower increase in blood sugar (**Figure 4.19**). The presence of fat and protein also slow stomach emptying and, therefore, foods high in these macronutrients generally cause less of a glycemic response than foods containing sugar or starch alone. For example, ice cream is high in sugar, but also contains fat and some protein so it causes less of a rise in blood glucose than sorbet, which contains sugar, but no fat or protein.

The glycemic response of a specific food can be quantified by its **glycemic index**. Glycemic index is a ranking of how a food affects blood glucose compared to the response of an equivalent amount of carbohydrate from a reference food such as white bread or pure glucose. The reference food is assigned a value of 100 and the values for food samples are expressed relative to this. Foods that have a glycemic index of 70 or more compared to glucose are considered high glycemic index foods; those with an index of less than 55 are considered low glycemic index foods. Although glycemic index can be used to evaluate the effect of a specific food on blood glucose, it is not based on amounts of carbohydrate in a typical portion of food. For example, watermelon has a high glycemic index, but this is based on a larger piece of watermelon than is typically consumed. The actual rise in blood glucose after eating a slice of watermelon is not large. **Glycemic load** is a newer method of assessing glycemic response that takes into account both the glycemic index of the food and the amount of carbohydrate in a typical portion.[14] To calculate glycemic load, the grams of carbohydrate in a serving of food are multiplied by that food's glycemic index expressed as a percent. A glycemic load of 20 or more is considered high, whereas a value of less than 11 is considered low. A shortcoming of both glycemic index and glycemic load is that they are determined for individual foods, but we typically eat meals containing mixtures of foods. Knowing the glycemic index or glycemic load of a specific food does not tell us much about what blood glucose levels will be after eating this food as part of a mixed meal. For example, a slice of white bread has a high glycemic index and glycemic load, but if the bread is part of a peanut butter sandwich, the rise in blood glucose is much less.

Insulin A rise in blood glucose triggers the pancreas to secrete the hormone **insulin**, which allows glucose to be taken into the cells of the body. In the liver, insulin promotes the storage of glucose as glycogen and, to a lesser extent, fat. In muscle, insulin stimulates the uptake of glucose for energy production and the synthesis of muscle glycogen for energy storage (**Figure 4.20**). Insulin also stimulates protein synthesis and, in fat-storing cells, it increases glucose uptake from the blood and stimulates lipid synthesis. These actions remove glucose from the blood, decreasing levels.

Glucagon When no carbohydrate has been consumed for a few hours, the glucose level in the blood—and consequently the glucose available to the cells—begins to decrease. This triggers the pancreas to secrete the hormone **glucagon**. Glucagon signals

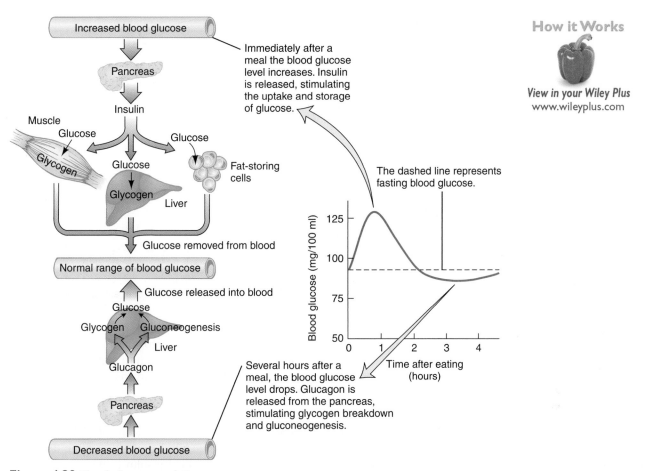

Figure 4.20 Blood glucose regulation
Blood glucose levels are regulated by the hormones insulin and glucagon, secreted by the pancreas.

liver cells to break down glycogen into glucose, which is released into the blood-stream. Glucagon also stimulates the liver to synthesize new glucose molecules by gluconeogenesis (see Figure 4.20). Newly synthesized glucose is released into the blood to prevent blood glucose from dropping below the normal range. Gluconeogenesis can also be stimulated by the hormone epinephrine, also known as adrenaline. This hormone, which is released in response to dangerous or stressful situations, enables the body to respond to emergencies. It causes a rapid release of glucose into the blood to supply the energy needed for action.

Diabetes Mellitus

Diabetes mellitus, commonly called diabetes, is a major public health problem in the United States. Over 23 million Americans have diabetes. This disease and its complications account for about $174 billion in direct medical costs and indirect costs due to disability, lost work, and premature death.[15] Diabetes is characterized by high blood glucose levels due to either a lack of insulin or an unresponsiveness or resistance to insulin (**Figure 4.21**). The elevated glucose causes damage to the large blood vessels, leading to an increased risk of heart disease and stroke. It also causes changes in small blood vessels and nerves. In the United States diabetes is the leading cause of blindness in adults and accounts for 44% of all new cases of kidney failure and over 60% of nontraumatic lower-limb amputations.[15] There are three main types of diabetes: type 1, type 2, and gestational diabetes, which occurs during pregnancy.

Type 1 Diabetes **Type 1 diabetes** is an autoimmune disease in which the body's own immune system destroys the insulin-secreting cells of the pancreas. Once these cells are destroyed, insulin is no longer made in the body. Type 1 diabetes is usually

Video

type 1 diabetes A form of diabetes that is caused by the autoimmune destruction of insulin-producing cells in the pancreas, usually leading to absolute insulin deficiency; previously known as insulin-dependent diabetes mellitus or juvenile-onset diabetes.

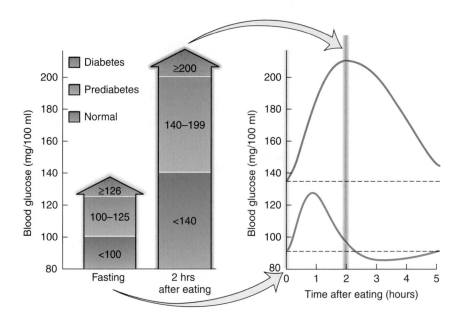

Figure 4.21 Blood glucose levels in diabetes
Blood glucose levels measured after an 8-hour fast and 2 hours after consuming 75 grams of glucose determine whether an individual has normal blood glucose levels, prediabetes, or diabetes. (*Source:* © American Diabetes Association.)

diagnosed before the age of 30 and accounts for only 5% to 10% of diagnosed cases of diabetes.[15] It is not known what causes the immune system to malfunction and attack its own cells but genetics, viral infections, exposure to toxins, and abnormalities in the immune system have been hypothesized to play a role.

Type 2 Diabetes Type 2 diabetes is the more common form of diabetes. It accounts for about 95% of all cases of diabetes in the United States. It is often the result of a decrease in the sensitivity of cells to insulin called insulin resistance; insulin is present, but the cells don't respond to it normally. As a result, only limited amounts of glucose can enter the cells and blood levels of glucose rise. Large amounts of insulin are therefore required to allow cells to take up enough glucose to meet their energy needs. Type 2 diabetes is believed to be due to a combination of genetic and lifestyle factors. Risk of developing this disease is increased in people with a family history of diabetes, in those who are overweight, particularly if they carry their extra body fat in the abdominal region, and those who have a sedentary lifestyle. The incidence of type 2 diabetes is higher among minority groups. The age-adjusted prevalence of diabetes is about 18% among Native Americans and Alaska Natives, 13% among non-Hispanic blacks, and 12% among Hispanic/Latino Americans, compared with only 8% among non-Hispanic whites.[15] Type 2 diabetes may occur as part of a combination of conditions called **metabolic syndrome**, which includes obesity, elevated blood pressure, altered blood lipid levels, and insulin insensitivity.

Type 2 diabetes is often preceded by a condition called **pre-diabetes** or **impaired glucose tolerance** in which blood glucose levels are above normal but not high enough to be diagnosed as diabetes (see Figure 4.21). An estimated 41 million adults between the ages of 40 and 74 have pre-diabetes and are therefore at increased risk for developing diabetes, as well as heart disease and stroke.[16] Progression to diabetes among those with pre-diabetes is not inevitable. Weight loss and increased physical activity among people with pre-diabetes can prevent or delay diabetes and may return blood glucose levels to normal.[16]

Type 2 diabetes has typically been diagnosed in persons over the age of 40, but its incidence is increasing among younger individuals. This change is thought to be due to the increasing incidence of obesity and overweight in younger age groups. Before 1994, less than 5% of children with newly diagnosed diabetes were classified as type 2, but recently this has increased to 30% to 50%.[17]

Gestational Diabetes Gestational diabetes is a form of diabetes that occurs in women during pregnancy. It may be caused by the hormonal changes of pregnancy. The high levels of glucose in the mother's blood increase the risk of complications for the un-

type 2 diabetes A form of diabetes that is characterized by insulin resistance and relative insulin deficiency; previously known as noninsulin-dependent diabetes mellitus or adult-onset diabetes.

metabolic syndrome
A collection of health risks, including excess fat in the abdominal region, high blood pressure, elevated blood triglycerides, low high-density lipoprotein (HDL) cholesterol, and high blood glucose that increases the chance of developing heart disease, stroke, and diabetes. The condition is also known by other names including Syndrome X, insulin resistance syndrome, and dysmetabolic syndrome.

pre-diabetes or impaired glucose tolerance A fasting blood glucose level above the normal range but not high enough to be classified as diabetes.

gestational diabetes A form of diabetes that occurs during pregnancy and resolves after the baby is born.

Life Cycle

born child (see Chapter 14). Gestational diabetes usually disappears once the pregnancy is complete and hormones return to nonpregnant levels. However, individuals who have had gestational diabetes have an increased risk for developing type 2 diabetes later in life.

Diabetes Symptoms The symptoms of diabetes result from the fact that without sufficient insulin, glucose cannot be used normally. Cells that require insulin for glucose uptake are starved for glucose, and cells that can use glucose without insulin are exposed to damaging high levels.

Immediate Symptoms The immediate symptoms of diabetes may include excessive thirst, frequent urination, blurred vision, and weight loss. Excessive thirst and frequent urination occur because blood glucose levels rise so high that the kidneys excrete glucose, which draws fluid with it, increasing the volume of urine. Blurred vision occurs when excess glucose enters the lens of the eye, drawing in water and causing the lens to swell. Weight loss, and impaired growth in children, occur because glucose cannot enter cells to be used for energy, so the body responds as it does in starvation, breaking down fat and protein to supply fuel. With limited carbohydrate for fatty acid metabolism, ketones are formed and released into the blood. Some ketones are used as fuel by muscle and adipose tissue, but in type 1 diabetes, they are produced more rapidly than they can be used and thus accumulate in the blood. This elevation of ketones causes an increase in the acidity of the blood called *ketoacidosis*. In type 2 diabetes, ketoacidosis usually does not develop because there is enough insulin to allow some glucose to be used so fewer ketones are produced.

Long-Term Complications The long-term complications of diabetes include damage to the heart, blood vessels, kidneys, eyes, and nerves. This damage is thought to be a result of prolonged exposure to high levels of blood glucose. When glucose is high it can bind to proteins contributing to blood vessel damage and abnormalities in blood cell function. Damage to the large blood vessels leads to an increased risk of heart disease and stroke. Heart disease is a major complication and the leading cause of premature death among people with diabetes. Changes in small blood vessels and nerves lead to kidney failure, blindness, and nerve dysfunction. For example, accumulation of glucose in the eye damages small vessels in the retina, leading to blindness (**Figure 4.22**). High glucose levels cause kidney failure by damaging kidney cells and small blood vessels in the kidney. Exposure to high glucose also affects the function of peripheral nerves, often causing numbness and tingling in the feet. In addition to these problems, infections are more common in diabetes because high blood glucose levels favor microbial growth; infections are usually the cause of amputations of the toes, feet, and legs.

Diabetes Treatment The goal of diabetes treatment is to keep blood glucose levels within the normal range. This involves diet, exercise, and, in many cases, medication. Blood glucose levels should be monitored frequently to assure that levels are staying in the healthy range. Adherence to this type of treatment regimen can reduce the incidence of elevated blood glucose levels and the complications it causes. To reduce

Figure 4.22
(Left) Damaged retinal blood vessels caused by diabetes. (right) Normal retinal blood vessels. (© SBHA/Stone/Getty Images)

disability and death associated with diabetes and its complications, the National Institutes of Health and the Centers for Disease Control and Prevention have established the National Diabetes Education Program. This program is designed to increase public awareness of the seriousness of diabetes, promote better management among individuals with diabetes, and improve the quality of and access to health care.[16]

Diet To help control blood glucose levels, carbohydrate intake should be distributed throughout the day. This can be done by estimating carbohydrate intake at each meal using the Exchange Lists or a system of carbohydrate counting.[18] Recommendations consider total carbohydrate consumption—whether sucrose, fructose (which causes a smaller rise in blood glucose than sucrose), or starch. Unrefined carbohydrates, which contain fiber, cause a slower rise in glucose than refined carbohydrates. Carbohydrate intake must be coordinated with medication and exercise schedules so that glucose and insulin are available in the proper proportions at the same time to maintain normal blood glucose levels. The diet should also be adequate in energy, protein, and micronutrients. To help prevent heart disease, fat intake should be limited to no more than 30% of energy, with no more than 10% from saturated fat. Overweight individuals may need to restrict energy intake to promote weight loss, which can be beneficial for maintaining blood glucose levels in the normal range.

Exercise Exercise is an important component of diabetes management because exercise increases the sensitivity of body cells to insulin. Therefore, more glucose can enter the cells with less insulin. It also promotes weight loss, which further reduces insulin resistance. Individuals with diabetes are encouraged to maintain regular exercise patterns. A change in the amount of exercise an individual participates in may change the amount of food and medication required to keep blood glucose in the normal range.

Medication When diet and exercise cannot keep blood glucose in the normal range, drug treatments are needed. In type 1 diabetes, insulin production is absent, so insulin must be injected. Insulin cannot be taken orally because it is a protein that would be broken down in the GI tract, losing its ability to function. Type 2 diabetes can often be treated with medications that increase pancreatic insulin production, decrease glucose production by the liver, enhance insulin action, or slow carbohydrate digestion to keep blood glucose in the normal range. In some cases of type 2 diabetes, injected insulin is needed to achieve normal blood glucose levels.

Hypoglycemia

Hypoglycemia is a condition in which blood sugar drops low enough to cause symptoms including irritability, nervousness, sweating, shakiness, anxiety, rapid heartbeat, headache, hunger, weakness, and sometimes seizure and coma. It can occur in people with diabetes as a result of over-medication or an imbalance between insulin level and carbohydrate intake. People with diabetes must learn to recognize the symptoms of hypoglycemia and immediately treat them by consuming a source of quickly absorbed carbohydrate, such as juice or hard candy. Following this, a meal should be consumed within about 30 minutes to keep glucose in the healthy range.

In individuals without diabetes, hypoglycemia can result from abnormalities in the production of or response to insulin or other hormones involved in blood sugar regulation. There are two forms of hypoglycemia. The first, reactive hypoglycemia occurs in response to the consumption of high-carbohydrate foods. The rise in blood glucose from the carbohydrate stimulates insulin release. However, too much insulin is secreted, resulting in a rapid fall in blood glucose to an abnormally low level. The treatment for reactive hypoglycemia is a diet that prevents rapid changes in blood glucose. Small, frequent meals low in simple carbohydrates and high in protein and fiber are recommended. A second form of hypoglycemia, fasting hypoglycemia, is not related to food intake. In this disorder, abnormal insulin secretion results in episodes of low blood glucose levels. This condition is often caused by pancreatic tumors.

4.6 Carbohydrates and Health

Learning Objectives

- Explain the health risks and benefits of diets high in unrefined carbohydrates and diets high in refined carbohydrates.
- Discuss the role of carbohydrates in weight management.

Carbohydrate-rich foods are the basis of healthy diets around the world.[3] They provide about half of the kcalories in the American diet and as much as two-thirds in developing countries. Nonetheless, the consumption of carbohydrates has been blamed for a host of chronic health problems, from dental caries and hyperactivity to obesity and heart disease. The incongruity relates to the health effects of different forms and sources of dietary carbohydrates: A dietary pattern that is high in unrefined carbohydrates, such as whole grains, fruits, and vegetables, has been associated with a lower incidence of a variety of chronic diseases, whereas diets high in refined carbohydrates, such as added sugars and white flour, may contribute to chronic disease risk.[19]

Dental Caries

The most well-documented health problem associated with a diet high in carbohydrates is **dental caries**, or tooth cavities. It is one of the most common childhood diseases in the United States; 85% of people 18 years of age and older have had caries.[20] Cavities are caused when bacteria that live in the mouth form colonies on the tooth surface known as plaque (**Figure 4.23**). If the plaque is not brushed, flossed, or scraped away the bacteria metabolize carbohydrate from the food we eat, producing acid. The acid can then dissolve the enamel and underlying structure of the teeth, forming cavities. Bacteria can metabolize both naturally occurring and added refined sugars and starches. Some types of food are more cavity-causing than others. Simple carbohydrate, particularly sucrose, is the most rapidly used food source for bacteria and therefore easily produces tooth-damaging acids. But, starchy foods that stick to the teeth can also promote tooth decay. Foods such as gummy candies, cereals, crackers, cookies, and raisins and other sticky dried fruits tend to remain on the teeth longer, providing a continuous supply of nutrients to decay-causing bacteria. Other foods, such as chocolate, ice cream, and bananas, are rapidly washed away from the teeth and therefore are less likely to promote cavities. Frequent snacking, sucking on hard candy, or slowly sipping soda can also increase the risk of cavities by providing a continuous food supply for the bacteria. Limiting sugar intake can help prevent dental caries, but other dietary factors and proper dental hygiene are important even if the diet is low in sugar. Dairy products, sugarless gums (sweetened with sugar alcohols), and fluoride reduce caries formation. Brushing teeth after eating reduces cavity risk no matter what food is consumed.

dental caries The decay and deterioration of teeth caused by acid produced when bacteria on the teeth metabolize carbohydrate.

Figure 4.23
The regions on these teeth that are stained brown indicate the presence of dental plaque. The main component of dental plaque is bacterial colonies. (SPL/Photo Researchers, Inc.)

Life Cycle

Does Sugar Cause Hyperactivity?

The consumption of sugary foods has been suggested as a cause of hyperactivity in children (see Chapter 15). The rise in blood glucose following a meal high in simple carbohydrates has been hypothesized to provide the energy for the excessive activity of a hyperactive child. However, a review of the research on sugar intake and behavior failed to support the hypothesis that sugar contributes to behavioral changes in most children.[21] Hyperactive behavior that is observed after sugar consumption is likely the result of other circumstances. For example, the excitement of a birthday party rather than the cake is more likely the cause of hyperactive behavior. Hyperactivity might also be caused by lack of sleep, overstimulation, caffeine consumption, the desire for more attention, or lack of physical activity.

Do Carbohydrates Affect Body Weight?

Carbohydrates in and of themselves are not "fattening." They provide 4 kcalories per gram compared with 9 kcalories per gram provided by fat. In fact, it is the fats that we often add to our high-carbohydrate foods that increase their kcalorie tally. A medium-sized baked potato provides about 160 kcalories, but the 2 tablespoons of sour cream you add brings the total to 225 kcalories (**Figure 4.24**). A plate of plain pasta has about 200 kcalories, but with a high-fat sauce, the kcalories rise to 300; add sausage and the meal is now 450 kcalories. This is not to say that carbohydrate consumed in excess of energy needs will not add pounds. Any energy source consumed in excess of requirements can cause weight gain. But carbohydrates are no more fattening than any other energy source. In fact, excess carbohydrate in the diet is less efficient at producing body fat than excess fat in the diet (see Chapter 7). But, even though carbohydrates are not high in kcalories, the type of carbohydrate affects the impact that carbohydrates have on body weight.

High-Fructose Corn Syrup and Body Weight High-fructose corn syrup accounts for over 40% of the sweeteners in the American diet, contributing on average about 132 kcalories per person per day. Because its introduction into the food supply in the 1970s correlates with the expansion of American waistlines it has been accused of being the cause of the increase in obesity rates. Fructose is handled by the body differently than glucose. It does not stimulate insulin production and has different effects on other hormonal signals that regulate food intake and body weight.[4] Fructose metabolism in the liver favors fat synthesis. Studies in mice indicate that dietary fructose produces a greater increase in body fat than the same amount of sucrose.[22] So, is high-fructose corn syrup making us fat? It certainly is adding kcalories to our diets but high-fructose corn syrup provides almost the same amount of fructose as does sucrose, which is broken down to glucose and fructose before it is absorbed. High-fructose corn syrup alone cannot account for the rise in obesity in the United States. The increase in total energy intake and reduction in physical activity remain the most significant factors contributing to the increased incidence of obesity.[23]

Low-Carbohydrate Weight Loss Diets The rationale behind consuming a low-carbohydrate diet for weight loss is that foods high in carbohydrate stimulate the release of insulin, which is a hormone that promotes energy storage. It is suggested that the more insulin you release, the more fat you will store. High-glycemic index foods, which increase blood sugar and consequently stimulate insulin release, are therefore hypothesized to shift metabolism toward fat storage. In contrast, a low-carbohydrate diet causes less of a rise in insulin and therefore is suggested to promote fat loss. Weight loss while consuming a low-carbohydrate diet may also be affected by ketone levels and the amount of protein in the diet. Ketones help suppress appetite and the high protein content of a low-carbohydrate diet can be satiating, so both help the dieter eat less. Studies on the effectiveness of low-carbohydrate diets for weight loss indicate that they result in greater short-term weight loss (6 months) than low-fat diets.[24] The weight loss on these diets, as with any weight loss diet, is caused by consuming less energy than is expended.[25–27]

Figure 4.24
High-carbohydrate foods like baked potatoes are not high in kcalories, but the toppings used on them can easily double their kcalorie count. (FoodCollection/© IndexStock)

Unrefined Carbohydrates and Weight Management Diets high in unrefined carbohydrates can help make weight maintenance and weight loss easier. Unrefined carbohydrates are good sources of fiber. Fiber can help reduce energy intake because it adds bulk to the GI tract and causes you to feel full after consuming less. It may also slow the absorption of energy-yielding nutrients by decreasing transit time, adding bulk, and forming viscous solutions, all of which reduce contact between digestion products and the absorptive surface. Unrefined foods that are good sources of fiber also have a lower glycemic response and therefore cause less of a rise in insulin than refined carbohydrates. Diets high in unrefined foods would therefore have glycemic effects similar to diets low in carbohydrate and high in protein.

Refined Carbohydrates and Diabetes

Evidence is accumulating that the type of dietary carbohydrate plays a role not only in the treatment of diabetes, but in the development of type 2 diabetes in susceptible individuals.[1] The risk of developing type 2 diabetes is lower in populations that consume diets high in whole grains than in populations that eat a diet high in refined starches and added sugars.[28–30] In particular a high intake of sugar-sweetened beverages has been associated with an increased risk for development of type 2 diabetes.[31] One mechanism that may explain this relationship is that a dietary pattern that is high in refined starches and added sugars causes a greater glycemic response and therefore increases the amount of insulin needed to maintain normal blood glucose levels. Over the long term, in susceptible individuals, the high demand for insulin eventually may wear out the insulin-producing cells in the pancreas. When the diet is lower in simple carbohydrates and refined starches and higher in fiber there is a more gradual rise in blood sugar and therefore a lower insulin demand. So, although a diet high in simple carbohydrates and refined starches does not cause diabetes, it does increase the demand for insulin required to maintain normal glucose levels and may increase the risk of developing diabetes.

Carbohydrates and Heart Disease

Just as with weight management and diabetes, when considering heart disease, some carbohydrates may be protective while others may increase risk. Evidence shows that a diet high in sugar can raise blood lipid levels and thereby increase the risk of heart disease.[32] On the other hand, diets high in whole grains have been found to reduce the risk of heart disease.[33–36] In an analysis of over 150,000 people, those with the highest dietary fiber intake had a 29% lower risk of coronary heart disease than those with the lowest intake.[37] In general, people with the highest intake of whole grains—about 3 servings a day—have a 20% to 30% lower risk of heart disease than those consuming the fewest whole grains. Whole grains provide fiber, resistant starch, oligosaccharides, omega-3 fatty acids, vitamins, minerals, antioxidants, and other phytochemicals that may be protective against heart disease (see Chapter 5).

One of the ways a diet high in whole grains and other unrefined carbohydrates may reduce the risk of heart disease is by reducing blood cholesterol levels. Soluble fiber binds cholesterol and bile acids, which are made from cholesterol, in the digestive tract. Normally, bile acids secreted into the GI tract are absorbed and reused. When bound to fiber, they are excreted in the feces rather than being absorbed (**Figure 4.25**). The liver must then use cholesterol from the blood to synthesize new bile acids. This provides a mechanism for eliminating cholesterol from the body and reducing blood cholesterol levels. Soluble fibers from legumes, oats, guar gum, pectin, flax seed, and psyllium (a grain used in bulk-forming laxatives such as Metamucil) are effective at reducing cholesterol, but insoluble fibers such as wheat bran or cellulose are not.[38] Soluble fiber may also reduce blood cholesterol by inhibiting cholesterol synthesis in the liver or by increasing the removal of cholesterol from the blood.[39]

Because of the beneficial effects of certain fibers on heart disease risk, the FDA permits a health claim on food products containing either soluble fiber from psyllium seed husk or beta-glucan (found in whole oats), which states that these products

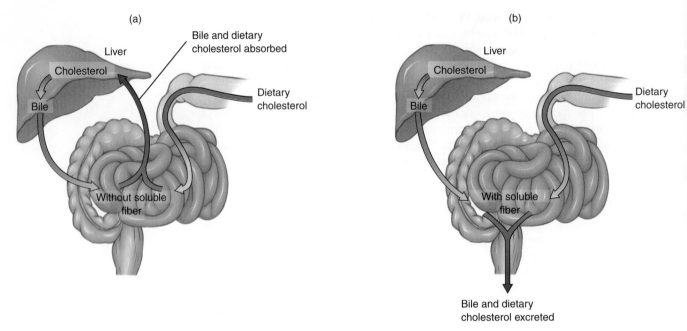

Figure 4.25 Effect of soluble fiber on cholesterol absorption
(a) Bile, which contains cholesterol and bile acids made from cholesterol, is absorbed and returned to the liver when soluble fiber is not present in the digestive tract. (b) When soluble fiber is present, the fiber binds cholesterol and bile acids so that they are excreted rather than absorbed.

may reduce the risk of coronary heart disease. In addition to lowering blood cholesterol levels whole grains help lower blood pressure, normalize blood glucose levels, prevent obesity, and affect a number of other parameters, all of which help reduce the risk of heart disease.[38]

Indigestible Carbohydrates and Bowel Disorders

Whole grains, fruits, and vegetables are good sources of fiber and also contain resistant starch and oligosaccharides. Diets high in these indigestible carbohydrates can relieve or prevent certain bowel disorders that are caused by pressure in the lumen of the colon.[40] As discussed earlier, a mixture of soluble and insoluble fibers in the colon adds bulk and absorbs water. This increases stool weight, speeds transit, and makes the feces larger and softer, thus reducing the amount of pressure needed for defecation. The presence of these fibers and other indigestible carbohydrates helps to reduce the incidence of constipation. Constipation makes muscles strain to move stool that is too hard and is the main cause of increased pressure in the colon. This excess pressure contributes to the formation of **hemorrhoids**, the swelling of veins in the rectal or anal area. Excess pressure is also believed to cause weak spots in the colon to bulge out and become **diverticula** (**Figure 4.26**). When these outpouchings form, the condition is called **diverticulosis**. A high-fiber diet reduces pressure in the lumen of the colon and therefore reduces the possibility of developing diverticulosis.[41,42] If diverticulosis does develop, fecal matter may occasionally accumulate in these outpouchings, causing irritation, pain, inflammation, and infection, a condition known as **diverticulitis**. Treatment of diverticulitis usually includes antibiotics to reduce bacterial growth and a temporary decrease in fiber intake to prevent irritation of the inflamed tissues. Once the inflammation is resolved however, a high-fiber intake is recommended to increase fecal bulk, decrease transit time, ease stool elimination, and reduce future attacks of diverticulitis.

Although fiber helps soften stools and prevent constipation, if fiber is consumed without sufficient fluid, it can also cause constipation. The more fiber there is in the diet, the more water is needed to keep the stool soft. When too little fluid is consumed, the stool becomes hard and difficult to eliminate. In severe cases when fiber intake is excessive and fluid intake is low, intestinal blockage can occur.

hemorrhoids Swollen veins in the anal or rectal area.

diverticula Sacs or pouches that protrude from the wall of the large intestine in the disease **diverticulosis**. When these become inflamed, the condition is called **diverticulitis**.

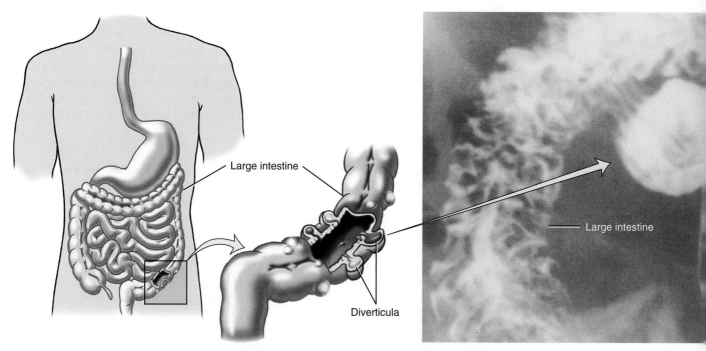

Figure 4.26 Diverticula
Diverticula (the singular is *diverticulum*) in the colon. (© L.V. Bergman/Project Masters, Inc.)

Indigestible Carbohydrates and Colon Cancer

Cancer is a disease that affects the way cells behave. Different cancers originate in different parts of the body and have different causes and effects. The type of cancer depends on the type of cell that is originally affected—for example, lung, breast, or colon—and on how the genetic material has been altered. Some people are more susceptible to cancer due to a genetic predisposition but the development of most cancers is also believed to be influenced by environmental **carcinogens** from the diet, tobacco smoke, or air pollution. In the case of colon cancer, substances consumed in the diet or produced in the GI tract that come in contact with mucosal cells may contribute to cancer development.

Characteristics of Cancer Cells Cells become cancerous as a result of **mutations** in their genetic material that allow them to reproduce without restraint and grow in abnormal locations. Normal body cells reproduce only to replace lost cells or to accommodate normal growth, but cancer cells divide continuously, forming enlarged cell masses known as tumors. Further mutations allow them to invade and colonize areas reserved for other cells, referred to as **malignancy (Figure 4.27)**. The cancer

carcinogens Cancer-causing substances.

mutations Changes in DNA caused by chemical or physical agents.

malignancy A mass of cells showing uncontrolled growth, a tendency to invade and damage surrounding tissues, and an ability to seed daughter growths to sites remote from the original growth.

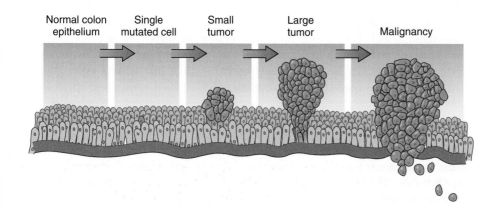

Figure 4.27 Development of colon cancer
Colon cancer, like other cancers, progresses from a single mutated cell to a tumor to a malignancy.

cells eventually crowd out the normal cells, robbing them of nourishment, and preventing them from functioning properly. Some carcinogens act by damaging DNA and inducing mutations. These are usually referred to as *tumor initiators* since the induction of mutations in key genes is thought to be the initiating event in cancer development. Other carcinogens contribute to cancer development by stimulating cells to divide. Such compounds are referred to as *tumor promoters*, since the increased cell division they induce enlarges the population of mutated cells, which is necessary for cancer to progress.

Fiber and Cancer Development Epidemiological studies have shown that the incidence of colon cancer is lower in populations consuming diets high in fiber.[41,43,44] Several hypotheses have been suggested to explain how fiber might affect the development of colon cancer. One is related to its ability to decrease contact between the mucosal cells of the large intestine and the fecal contents, which may contain tumor initiators or tumor promoters. Fiber decreases contact by increasing fecal bulk, diluting the colon contents, and speeding transit. Another relates to the effect of fiber on the intestinal microflora and the by-products of microbial metabolism, such as fatty acids, that accumulate there. These by-products may directly affect colon cells or may cause changes in the environment of the colon that can affect the development of colon cancer. It has also been hypothesized that high-fiber diets protect against colon cancer because of the antioxidant vitamins and phytochemicals that are present along with fiber in plant foods.

Recent intervention studies have not supported the epidemiological observations of a connection between fiber intake and colon cancer.[45-47] A number of reasons have been suggested for this discrepancy—the interventions were not long enough, the fiber dose was not high enough, the type of cancer monitored was not appropriate, or the fiber itself is not really protective, but rather some other component in the diet of the low-cancer populations may have a protective effect. Despite these results, the scientific consensus is still that there is enough evidence that diets high in fiber protect against colon cancer to recommend an increase in fiber intake.[41]

4.7 Meeting Carbohydrate Recommendations

Learning Objectives

- Modify a diet so it meets current recommendations for the types and amounts of carbohydrate.
- Discuss the role of alternative sweeteners in weight-loss.

The average American diet provides plenty of carbohydrate, but whether or not this carbohydrate promotes or harms our health depends on the food sources and types of carbohydrates we choose. A healthy diet is high in complex carbohydrates from whole grains, legumes, fruits, and vegetables and simple carbohydrates from unrefined foods such as fresh fruit and low-fat dairy products. This diet is high in fiber, micronutrients, and phytochemicals, and low in saturated fat and cholesterol. Unfortunately, the typical American diet is lower in whole grains, fruits, and vegetables and higher in added sugars than is recommended.

Types of Carbohydrate Recommendations

A small amount of carbohydrate is needed to fuel the brain. Additional carbohydrate provides an important source of energy in the diet and adequate fiber offers many health benefits. Therefore the DRIs make several kinds of recommendations for carbohydrate intake; an RDA for total carbohydrate, a range of acceptable carbohydrate intakes called the Acceptable Macronutrient Distribution Range (AMDR), and an AI for fiber. Because no specific toxicity is associated with high intakes of carbohydrate in general or of different types of carbohydrates, no UL has been established for total carbohydrate, added sugars, or fiber.

The RDA for Carbohydrate The RDA for carbohydrate for adults and children has been set at 130 grams per day based on the average minimum amount of glucose used by the brain.[3] In a diet that meets energy needs, this amount will provide adequate glucose and prevent ketosis. This amount of carbohydrate provides only 420 kcalories; that's about 25% of the energy in a 2000-kcalorie diet. It is equivalent to a breakfast of a cup of juice, two slices of toast with jam, and a bowl of cereal with half a banana and milk (**Figure 4.28**). Most people consume well in excess of this amount over the course of a day. A diet that includes only this much carbohydrate and meets kcalorie needs would be very high in protein and fat.

The Range of Healthy Carbohydrate Intakes No single ratio of macronutrients defines a perfect diet. Healthy diets can be made up of many different combinations of carbohydrate, protein, and fat. The AMDR for carbohydrate intake for a healthy diet has been set at 45% to 65% of energy. Choosing a diet in this range will allow you to meet your energy needs without consuming excessive amounts of protein or fat. The sources of carbohydrate are more important than the absolute amount. In order to promote a diet that meets needs for all nutrients, the DRIs recommend that most carbohydrate should come from unrefined food sources; no more than 25% of energy should come from added refined sugars. This percentage is based on the amount of added sugar that can be consumed without reducing the nutrient density of the diet so much that essential nutrient needs cannot be met. The Dietary Guidelines and

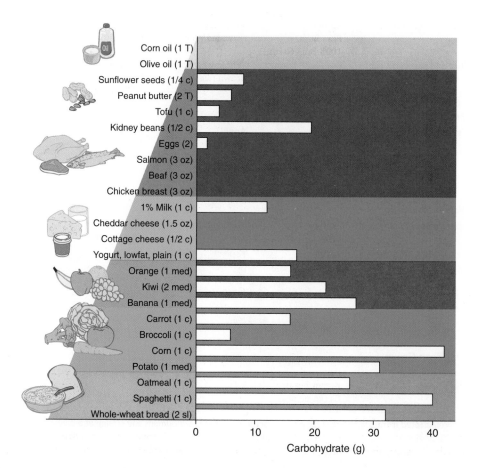

Figure 4.28 Carbohydrate content of MyPyramid food groups
Grains, vegetables, and legumes are the best sources of complex carbohydrates; fruits and milk are good sources of naturally occurring simple carbohydrates.

MyPyramid consider added sugar as one component of the discretionary kcalories—those kcalories left over once you have met your serving recommendations with healthy choices from all of the food groups. The amount allowed depends on the total kcalories that can be consumed without weight gain.[9] A diet that includes no more than the recommended number of discretionary kcalories will only include about 10% of kcalories from added sugars. This coincides with the recommendation from the World Health Organization that no more than 10% of energy come from added sugars.[48]

The AI for Fiber For fiber, an AI has been set at 38 and 25 grams per day for young adult men and women, respectively, based on the amount of fiber needed to reduce heart disease risk.[3] Eating a bowl of raisin bran with a half-cup of strawberries for breakfast, a sandwich on whole wheat bread with lettuce and tomatoes and an apple for lunch, eggplant parmesean for dinner and popcorn for a snack will provide about 25 grams of fiber. **Table 4.2** offers an exchange system for estimating fiber in foods. Specific AIs for fiber have been set for different life-stage groups (see Appendix A).

Table 4.2 Estimating the Fiber Content of Foods

Food Group/Serving	High Fiber	Medium Fiber	Low Fiber
Fiber per serving	*4–5 g*	*2–3 g*	*0.5–1 g*
Grain Group			
Breads (1 slice)	—	Whole wheat Rye	White bread Bagel (1/2) Tortilla Roll (1/2) English muffin (1/2) Graham crackers (2)
Cereals (1/2 cup)	All Bran Bran Buds 100% Bran Flakes	40% Bran Shredded Wheat	Cheerios Rice Krispies
Rice and pasta (1/2 cup)	—	Whole-wheat pasta Brown rice	Macaroni Pasta White rice
Fruit Group			
Fruits (1 medium or 1/2 cup)	Berries Prunes	Apple Apricot Banana Orange Raisins	Melon Canned fruit Juices
Vegetable Group			
Vegetables (1/2 cup)	Peas Broccoli Spinach	Green beans Carrots Eggplant Cabbage Potatoes with skin Corn	Asparagus Cauliflower Celery Lettuce Tomatoes Zucchini Peppers Potatoes without skin Onions
Dry Bean Group			
Beans (1/2 cup)	Pinto, red Kidney beans Blackeyed peas	—	—

Source: Adapted from Bright-See, E., Benda, C., Vartouhi, J., et al. Development and testing of a dietary fibre exchange system. *Can. Diet. Assoc. J.* 47:199–205, 1986; and Marlett, J. A. Content and composition of dietary fiber in 117 frequently consumed foods. *J. Am. Diet. Assoc.* 92:175–186, 1992.

Tools for Assessing Carbohydrate Intake

How does your diet compare to the recommendation of 45% to 65% of kcalories from carbohydrate? **Table 4.3** illustrates how to calculate carbohydrate intake as a percent of energy. This same calculation can be used to determine the percent of energy from carbohydrate in individual foods. To calculate the percent of energy from carbohydrate, you need to know the amount of carbohydrate in a food or in the diet. This can be estimated from the Exchange Lists or determined using values from food labels or food composition tables (see Nutrient Content of Foods Supplement).

Table 4.3 Calculating Percent Energy from Carbohydrate

Determine
- The total energy (kcalorie) intake for the day
- The grams of carbohydrate in the day's diet

Calculate Energy from Carbohydrate
- Carbohydrate provides 4 kcalories per gram
- Multiply grams of carbohydrate by 4 kcalories per gram

  Energy (kcalories) from carbohydrate = grams carbohydrate $\times$ 4 kcalories/gram carbohydrate

Calculate % Energy from Carbohydrate
- Divide energy from carbohydrate by total energy and multiply by 100 to express as a percent

$$\text{Percent of energy from carbohydrate} = \frac{\text{kcalories from carbohydrate}}{\text{Total kcalories}} \times 100$$

For example:

A diet contains 2500 kcalories and 350 grams of carbohydrate

$$350 \text{ grams of carbohydrate} \times 4 \text{ kcal/g} = 1400 \text{ kcal of carbohydrate}$$

$$\frac{1400 \text{ kcal of Carbohydrate}}{2500 \text{ kcal}} \times 100 = 56\% \text{ of energy (kcal) from Carbohydrate}$$

Carbohydrate Exchange Lists The Exchange Lists can be used to give a quick estimate of the total amount of carbohydrate in a food or in the diet (**Table 4.4**). One serving from the bread or fruit exchange provides 15 grams of carbohydrate, 1 milk serving provides 12 grams, and 1 vegetable serving provides about 5 grams. Meats and fats provide no carbohydrate (see Appendix I).

Table 4.4 Using Exchange Lists to Estimate Carbohydrate Content

Exchange Groups/Lists	Serving Size	Carbohydrates (g)
Carbohydrate Group		
Starch	1/2 cup pasta, cereal, potatoes; 1 slice bread	15
Fruit	1 small apple, peach, pear; 1/2 banana; 1/2 cup canned fruit (in juice)	15
Milk	1 cup milk or yogurt	
Nonfat		12
Lowfat		12
Reduced fat		12
Whole		12
Other carbohydrates	Serving sizes vary	15
Vegetables	1/2 cup cooked vegetables, 1 cup raw	5
Meat/Meat Substitute Group	1 oz meat or cheese	
Very lean		0
Lean		0
Medium-fat		0
High-fat		0
Fat Group	1 tsp butter, margarine, or oil; 1 Tbsp salad dressing	0

Off The Label
The Scoop on Sugar

Nutrition Facts
Serving Size 1 Container

Amount Per Serving	
Calories 190 Calories from Fat 30	

Amount/Serving	% DV*
Total Fat 3.5g	**5%**
Saturated Fat 2g	**10%**
Trans Fat 0g	
Cholesterol 15mg	**4%**
Sodium 100mg	**4%**
Potassium 310g	**9%**
Total Carbohydrate 32g	**11%**
Sugars 28g	
Protein 7g	**14%**

Vitamin A 15%	●	Calcium 30%

*Percent Daily Values (DV) are based on a 2,000 calorie diet.

INGREDIENTS: CULTURED PASTEURIZED GRADE A REDUCED FAT MILK, SUGAR, NONFAT MILK, HIGH FRUCTOSE CORN SYRUP, STRAWBERRY PUREE, MODIFIED CORN STARCH, KOSHER GELATIN, TRI-CALCIUM PHOSPHATE, NATURAL FLAVOR, COLORED WITH CARMINE, VITAMIN A ACETATE, VITAMIN D$_3$

Thick & Creamy
Lowfat Yogurt
STRAWBERRY

(©)iStockphoto)

Cutting down on the sugar you add to your morning coffee and cereal will reduce your sugar intake. You might be surprised to learn, though, that this strategy isn't cutting out the biggest sources of sugar in your diet. Most of the sugar you consume is from added sugars in prepared foods like sodas, cookies, and snacks. Recognizing foods high in added sugars is an important step toward cutting down on these empty kcalories.

Identifying packaged foods that are high in added refined sugar isn't always easy because food labels don't differentiate between added and natural sugar. As you can see in the strawberry yogurt label shown here, the Nutrition Facts lists the total grams of sugars (monosaccharides and disaccharides)—28 grams in this case. This amount includes both the sugar found naturally in the strawberries and milk and the sugar added for additional sweetness. Some food labels make it easier to identify foods that have not had sugar added in processing by including a nutrition claim such as "no added sugar" or "without added sugar". For products that do not contain descriptors such as these, you can sort out their sugar sources by reading the ingredient list.

To catch foods high in added sugar, check labels for sweeteners listed early in the ingredient list. The sooner they appear, the more the product contains by weight. Remember, though, that the sum of the added sweeteners hiding farther down in the ingredient list may be considerable. Recognizing added sugars can be a challenge. The only sweetener that can be called "sugar" on the ingredient list is sucrose; sucrose may come in the form of brown, powdered, granulated, or raw sugar. There are many other sugars added to foods. Invert sugar, dextrose, glucose, maltose, lactose, and fructose are sugars added in dry form. Corn syrup, honey, molasses, malt syrup, sugar syrup, fruit juice concentrates, and high-fructose corn syrup are added as syrups. The yogurt label shown here lists sugar as the second ingredient and high-fructose corn syrup as the fourth. Together these two contribute much of the sugar in this food.

Carbohydrates on Food Labels Food labels list the grams of total carbohydrate, fiber, and sugars in foods. The amounts of soluble and insoluble fiber may be listed if manufacturers choose to include them but are not required. Total carbohydrate and fiber are also listed as a percent of the Daily Value. The Daily Value for total carbohydrate is calculated as 60% of the energy. For a 2000-kcalorie diet, this represents 300 grams of carbohydrate ([2000 kcal × 0.6]/4 kcal/g of carbohydrate = 300 g). The Daily Value for fiber is 25 grams in a 2000-kcalorie diet. A slice of whole-wheat bread contains 2 grams of fiber per serving, which is 8% of the Daily Value. No Daily Value has been established for sugars, but labels can help identify products that are high in sugars (see Your Choice: The Scoop on Sugar).

Descriptors such as "high fiber" and "a good source of fiber" can help you find high-fiber products. Foods that contain 20% or more of the Daily Value for fiber per serving can state on the label that they are "high in dietary fiber." Products containing 10% to 19% of the Daily Value can state that they are "a good source of dietary fiber"

(Table 4.5). If you are looking for low-carbohydrate products, be aware that the terms "low carbohydrate" and "low carb" have not been defined by the FDA, so at the moment the definition is up to the manufacturer. Some products may also advertise the number of "net carbs" they provide. Again, there is no official definition of net carbs but usually this number is calculated by subtracting the grams of fiber, and sometimes other poorly absorbed carbohydrates, from the grams of total carbohydrate in the food.

Food labels may also carry health claims related to fiber and chronic disease risk. Fiber-containing grain products, fruits, and vegetables that contain at least 2.5 grams of fiber per serving and are low in fat may claim to reduce the risk of cancer. Fruits, vegetables, and grain products that are low in total fat, saturated fat, and cholesterol and that contain at least 0.6 gram of soluble fiber per serving, and foods that contain at least 0.75 gram of soluble fiber per serving from whole oats or psyllium husks, may claim to reduce the risk of heart disease (see Appendix J).

Table 4.5 Sugar and Fiber on Food Labels

Sugar-free	Product contains no amount, or a trivial amount, of sugars (less than 0.5 g per serving). Synonyms for "free" include "without," "no," and "zero."
Reduced sugar	Nutritionally altered product contains 25% less sugar than the regular or reference product.
Less sugar	Whether altered or not, a food contains 25% less sugar than the reference food. "Fewer" may be used as a synonym for "less."
No added sugars or without added sugars	No sugar or sugar-containing ingredient is added during processing.
High fiber	Food contains 20% or more of the Daily Value for fiber per serving. Synonyms for "high" include "rich in" and "excellent source of."
Good source of fiber	Food contains 10% to 19% of the Daily Value for fiber per serving. Synonyms for "good source of" include "contains" and "provides."
More fiber	Food contains 10% or more of the Daily Value for fiber per serving than an appropriate reference food. Synonyms for "more" include "added" (or "fortified" and "enriched"), "extra," or "plus."

Translating Recommendations into Healthy Diets

The typical North American diet meets some but not all of these carbohydrate recommendations. We consume about 50% of energy from carbohydrate but most of this comes from refined sources. We consume too little fiber, too few whole grains and other unrefined carbohydrate sources, and too much added sugar. Our average fiber intake is only 15 grams per day, which is well below the AI. In order to promote a healthy balance of carbohydrates, the Dietary Guidelines recommend an increase in whole grains, vegetables, and fruits, and a reduction in added sugars from foods such as bakery products, candy, and soft drinks.[9] MyPyramid helps translate these recommendations into food choices and healthy diets for individuals.

Eat More Whole Grains, Fruits, and Vegetables To encourage the consumption of healthy sources of carbohydrates the Dietary Guidelines and MyPyramid recommend that you choose half of your grains from whole sources or eat at least three servings of whole grains per day (see Your Choice: Choosing Whole Grains). Whole grains are good sources of fiber as well as micronutrients and phytochemicals. Fruits and vegetables are also excellent unrefined food sources of both complex and simple carbohydrates. For a 2000-kcalorie diet MyPyramid recommends 2 cups of fruit and 2½ cups of vegetables. To maximize fiber intake most fruit choices should be whole fruits rather than juices. An apple provides about 80 to 90 kcalories and 2.7 grams of fiber, whereas a cup of apple juice provides the same amount of energy but almost no fiber (0.2 gram). Choosing legumes as part of the vegetable servings will increase fiber intake—a half-cup of cooked black beans has about 7 grams of fiber.

Limit Added Sugars Foods that contain the most added sugars in the American diet include soft drinks, candy, cakes, cookies, pies, fruit drinks, and dairy desserts, but added sugars are also found in thousands of other processed products. Sugars are also added at home when we sprinkle sugar on our cereal or spoon honey into our tea. The greater your consumption of foods high in added sugars, the harder it is to consume enough nutrients without gaining weight. Added sugars provide kcalories with little if any of the essential nutrients. People who eat foods and beverages high in added sugars tend to eat more kcalories and fewer micronutrients.[9] To avoid exceeding your discretionary kcalorie limit added sugar intake must be kept to a minimum. For example, a 2000-kcalorie diet can include only about 270 discretionary kcalories. As seen in **Table 4.6**, a 12-ounce can of Coke has about 9 teaspoons of added sugar, which would use up 160 of your discretionary kcalories.

Table 4.6 How Much Added Sugar Do You Eat?

Food	Added sugar (tsp)[a]
Doughnut, 3-inch diameter	2
Cookies, 2 medium chocolate chip	3
Frosted corn flakes, 1 oz	3
Cake, frosted, 1 piece	6
Pie, fruit, 2 crust, 1 slice	6
Fruit, canned in heavy syrup, 1 cup	4
Chocolate milk, 2%, 1 cup	3
Low-fat fruit yogurt, 1 cup	7
Ice cream, vanilla, 1 cup	3
Chocolate bar, 1 oz	5
Fruit drink, 12 oz	12
Cola, not diet, 12 oz can	9
Cola, not diet, 20 oz bottle	15

[a] 1 tsp = 4 g dry weight

Putting It All Together To meet the recommendations for a healthy diet, refined carbohydrates should be replaced with unrefined sources of simple and complex carbohydrates (**Table 4.7**). For example, choosing a stir-fry meal of a few ounces of beef and plenty of vegetables on brown rice can provide the same kcalories but more fiber and less fat than a dinner of steak, white rice, and a small salad with dressing. To limit added sugars, foods high in added sugar should be replaced with natural sources of sugar such as fruits and dairy products. If instead of a 20-ounce bottle of soda you have an 8-ounce glass of low-fat milk, you will consume 140 fewer kcalories, no added sugar, as well as getting plenty of high-quality protein, calcium, and other micronutrients. Using fresh instead of canned fruit can also help increase fiber and decrease added refined sugars. For example, a half-cup of pear halves canned in heavy syrup provides 90 kcalories, 1 gram of fiber, and almost 20 grams of sugar, most of which is added in the syrup. One large fresh pear provides 90 kcalories, 4 grams of fiber, and no refined sugar (see Critical Thinking: Becoming Less Refined).

Table 4.7 How to Choose Carbohydrates Wisely

Choose more whole grains

- Substitute brown rice, wild rice, bulgur, or quinoa for white rice.
- Make sandwiches with whole wheat rather than white bread.
- Add legumes such as kidney, black, and pinto beans to casseroles and salads.
- Add barley to soups and stews.
- Choose packaged foods that contain 10% or more of the Daily Value for fiber.
- When baking at home, substitute whole-wheat flour for white or unbleached flour.
- Eat whole-grain breakfast cereals, such as Wheaties, Shredded Wheat, Grape Nuts, Kashi, muesli, and oatmeal.
- Substitute whole-grain rolls, tortillas, and crackers for those made from refined grains.
- Substitute whole-wheat pasta or pasta made from 50% whole wheat and 50% white flour for conventional pastas.

Limit added sugars

- When cooking at home, use less sugar; try adding one-fourth less sugar than called for in the recipe.
- Use less added sugar in coffee and tea and on cereals and pancakes.
- Eat fewer high-sugar prepared foods such as cookies, cakes, and candies.
- Snack on fruit. If fresh fruits are not available, choose frozen or canned fruits without added sugar.
- Read food labels to choose foods low in added sugars.

Alternative Sweeteners

America's love of sweets and the bad press surrounding sugar have driven the technological development of an increasing number of alternative or artificial sweeteners. These sugar substitutes, which provide little or no energy, are added to a host of low-kcalorie and "light" foods such as yogurts, ice creams, and soft drinks. Although many sugar substitutes are technically not carbohydrates, they were developed to replace simple sugars in food products or as an alternative for table sugar at home. Alternative sweeteners consumed in reasonable amounts are generally safe for healthy people;[49] however, to assure that they are not misused, the FDA has defined acceptable daily intakes (ADIs)—levels that should not be exceeded when using these products. The ADI is an estimate of the amount of the sweetener per kilogram of body weight that an individual can safely consume every day over a lifetime with minimal risk.

The Role of Alternative Sweeteners in the Diet The average American eats about 32 teaspoons of added sweeteners per day.[50] Replacing foods high in added sugars with foods sweetened with sugar substitutes will cut down on kcalories and decrease sugar intake, but it will not increase the intake of whole grains or fresh fruits and vegetables—key components of a healthy diet. Because foods that are high in added sugar tend to be nutrient-poor choices, replacing them with artificially sweetened alternatives does not increase the nutrient density of the diet. However, these products can be part of a healthy diet when used in moderation as part of a diet that is based on whole grains, vegetables, and fruits.

Alternative sweeteners have been shown to reduce the incidence of dental caries and can be helpful for managing blood sugar levels in diabetes, but their usefulness for weight loss has been more controversial. The rising consumption of sugared beverages has been blamed for the increasing prevalence of overweight in America.[4] If individuals trying to lose weight replace sugar and high-sugar foods, such as soft drinks, with artificially sweetened products, they will lower their kcalorie intake. Short-term studies show that this lower energy intake can promote a reduction in body weight, but it is not possible to draw conclusions about the benefits for long-term weight maintenance.[51] Although alternative sweeteners can help reduce kcalorie intake, on their own they are not the solution to the obesity epidemic.

Critical Thinking
Becoming Less Refined

(©iStockphoto)

Background

Emma thinks that a good diet is important. She is concerned that she eats too much added sugar and not enough fiber. She records her food intake for a day and calculates its nutrient content. Her fiber and sugar intake are shown below.

Diet Analysis

Emma's diet analysis indicates that her daily diet provides about 2340 kcalories, 67 grams of protein, 80 grams of fat, 350 grams of carbohydrate of which 200 grams is sugars, and 19.6 grams of fiber.

CURRENT DIET

FOOD	SERVING	FIBER (G)	SUGARS (G)
Breakfast			
White bread	2 slices	1.2	2
with jelly	1 Tbsp	0.1	6
and margarine	1 tsp	0	0
Fruit punch	8 fl oz	0	22
Lunch			
Macaroni and cheese	1 cup	1.4	8
Milk	1 cup	0	12
Apple	1 medium	3.7	18
Snack			
Soda	20 oz	0	63
3 Musketeers bar	1 regular	1	34
Dinner			
Roast beef	3 oz	0	0
Flour tortillas	1, 8-inch size	1.4	1
Pinto beans	1 cup	10	1
Snack			
Ice cream	2/3 cup	0.8	17
with cherry syrup	2 Tbsp	0	16
Total		**19.6**	**200**

(©iStockphoto)
(©iStockphoto)
(©iStockphoto)

Critical Thinking Questions

Determine whether Emma eats enough carbohydrate by calculating the percent of kcalories from carbohydrate in her diet (see Table 4.3).

▼

Now consider her fiber intake. Does it meet recommendations? If not, list specific changes she could make in her diet to increase her fiber intake to the recommended level.

▼

What about added refined sugars? Which food adds the most sugar to her diet? Identify other foods in her diet that are high in added sugar. Suggest foods she could substitute for these to reduce her added sugar intake.

 iProfile Use iProfile to find substitutions for her high sugar, low fiber snacks.

Types of Alternative Sweeteners The main competitors in the artificial sweetener market in the United States today are saccharin, aspartame, sucralose, and acesulfame K (acesulfame potassium) (**Figure 4.29**). These are used alone or in combination to sweeten a variety of foods. Rebianna, made from the stevia plant and sold as Truvia and Purevia, is the newest sweetener on the market. It is an alternative sweetener that is 300 times sweeter than sugar.[52] Cyclamate, an alternative sweetener that was popular in the 1960s, was banned by the FDA in 1969. It is still sold in Canada and some 50 other countries.

Saccharin Saccharin is a sweetener that is 200 to 700 times sweeter than sugar. In 1977, after large doses of saccharin were found to increase the incidence of bladder cancer in rats, the FDA proposed banning saccharin. However, the public and industry protested. In response to the outcry, a moratorium was imposed on the banning of saccharin, and all products containing saccharin were required to display a warning on the label informing the public that it may cause cancer. In May 2000, saccharin was dropped from the government's list of cancer-causing substances so this warning no longer appears on labels.

The intake of saccharin in the United States is estimated to be about 50 mg per person per day.[49] The ADI is set at 5 mg per kg body weight per day. For a 154-pound (70-kg) individual, this would be 350 mg per day or 115 mg per day for a 50-pound (23-kg) child.[49] A 12-ounce diet beverage sweetened with saccharin alone contains about 120 mg. A packet of sweetener contains 36 mg of saccharin.

Aspartame In 1965, James Schlatter, at the pharmaceutical company G. D. Searle, was working with a chemical made up of two amino acids aspartic acid and phenylalanine, when he spilled some of the chemical on his fingers. Shortly afterward, he licked his finger to pick up a piece of paper and discovered an intensely sweet taste. This accidental discovery led to the development of the artificial sweetener aspartame. Since aspartame is made of amino acids, the building blocks of protein, it is not a carbohydrate. Approved for some uses in the 1980s, aspartame is used in chewing gum, breakfast cereals, fruit spreads, yogurt, and beverages. Because aspartame breaks down when heated, it works best in products that are not cooked. Common trade names for this sweetener include NutraSweet, Equal, and NutriTaste. Each gram of aspartame contains 4 kcalories, but since it is about 200 times as sweet as sugar, only 1/200th as much of it needs to be used to achieve the same level of sweetness.

As with other artificial sweeteners, safety concerns have been raised about aspartame. It contains the amino acid phenylalanine and, therefore, can be dangerous to individuals with a genetic disorder called phenylketonuria (PKU). These individuals have an abnormality that affects the metabolism of phenylalanine. They must restrict their intake of this amino acid to prevent brain damage (see Chapter 6). There is also a concern that consuming aspartame might cause dangerously high blood phenylalanine levels in the general public. Phenylalanine occurs naturally in protein. A 4-ounce hamburger has 12 times more phenylalanine than a 12-ounce aspartame-sweetened soft drink. However, when phenylalanine is ingested without the other

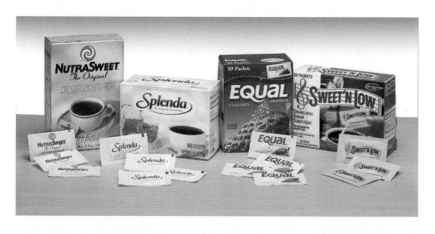

Figure 4.29
Consumers often recognize their favorite sugar substitutes by the distinctive colors of the packaging.
© Andy Washnik

Nutrition Facts

Serving Size 3 pieces (36 g)
Servings Per Container about 2.5

Amount Per Serving

Calories 110   Calories from Fat 40

	%Daily Value*
Total Fat 4.5g	**7%**
Saturated Fat 2.5g	**13%**
Trans Fat 0g	
Sodium 0mg	**0%**
Total Carbohydrate 28g	**9%**
Dietary Fiber 1g	**4%**
Sugars 0g	
Sugar Alcohols 27g	
Protein less then 1g	
Iron	**2%**

Not a significant source of cholesterol, vitamin A, vitamin C, and calcium.

*Percent Daily Values are based on a 2,000 calorie diet.

INGREDIENTS: MALTITOL; LACTITOL; (MILK); CHOCOLATE; ISOMALT; COCOA BUTTER; CONTAINS 2% OR LESS OF; SORBITOL; MILK FAT; POLYDEXTROSE; EGG WHITES; CREAM (MILK)*; SOY LECITHIN; PEPPERMINT OIL; SODIUM CASEINATE (MILK); VANILLIN; ARTIFICIAL FLAVOR; SUCRALOSE; AND PGPR (EMULSIFIER), Ⓤ D
ADDS A NEGLIGIBLE AMOUNT OF SUGAR

Figure 4.30 Sugar alcohols on food labels
The Nutrition Facts panel on a label from sugar-free candy uses the term *sugar alcohols* because the product contains more than one type of sugar alcohol. If the food contains only one type of sugar alcohol, the name of that sugar alcohol can be used.

sugar alcohols Sweeteners that are structurally related to sugars but provide less energy than monosaccharides and disaccharides because they are not well absorbed.

amino acids found in high-protein foods, blood and brain levels increase to a greater extent. Headaches, dizziness, seizures, nausea, allergic reactions, and other side effects have been reported following ingestion of aspartame; however, double-blind placebo-controlled studies have not been able to reproduce these symptoms.[49] There has also been concern that the use of aspartame might be associated with an increased risk of brain cancer in children, but controlled studies found no evidence that aspartame is a carcinogen or that there is a correlation between aspartame use and brain cancer incidence.[53] Overall, the consensus of the scientific community is that aspartame is safe for most people.

The FDA has set an ADI of 50 mg of aspartame per kg of body weight. A packet of sweetener contains about 37 mg of aspartame. A 12-ounce soft drink sweetened with aspartame contains about 225 mg. To exceed the ADI, a 70-kg adult would have to consume almost 16 cans of aspartame-sweetened soft drinks a day and a 35-kg child would have to consume almost 8 cans of soft drinks.[49]

Sucralose Sucralose (trichlorogalactosucrose) was discovered in 1976 and is the only nonkcaloric sweetener made from sugar. To make this sweetener the sugar molecule is modified so it cannot be digested and passes through the digestive tract unchanged. Approved for use in the United States in 1998, it is about 600 times sweeter than sucrose. It is sold as Splenda and can be used as a tabletop sweetener that is added directly to foods. Since it is heat stable, it can be used in baked goods.[49] It is used in beverages, chewing gum, frozen desserts, puddings, jams and jellies, syrups, and many other products. It has been extensively tested for safety and found to be safe even for children and pregnant and lactating women.[54] The ADI is 5 mg per kg of body weight, and one packet has 12 mg of sucralose.

Acesulfame K Marketed as Sunette or Sweet One, acesulfame potassium, or acesulfame K, is 200 times as sweet as sugar and provides no energy. It was approved for use in 1988 and is used in chewing gum, powdered drink mixes, gelatins, puddings, soft drinks, and nondairy creamers. It is heat stable, so it can be used in baking. The ADI has been set at 15 mg per kg body weight. A packet of sweetener contains about 50 mg of acesulfame K.[49]

Neotame Neotame is a sugar substitute that is 7000 to 13,000 times sweeter than sucrose. Like aspartame it is made from the amino acids aspartic acid and phenylalanine, but the bond between the amino acids is harder to break than the bond in aspartame so it is more stable. Since it cannot be broken down, releasing phenylalanine, it is not a problem for people with PKU. The FDA approved the use of neotame as a general-purpose sweetener in July 2002. Because it does not break down when heated it can be used in both cooking and baking applications as well as in foods and beverages that are not heated.

Sugar Alcohols Sugar alcohols, also called polyols, such as sorbitol, mannitol, lactitol, and xylitol are chemical derivatives of sugar that are used as low-kcalorie sweeteners. Because they are not digested, absorbed, or metabolized to the same extent as monosaccharides and disaccharides, they generally provide less energy than sucrose. Maltitol provides 3 kcalories per gram, lactitol 2 kcalories per gram, and erythritol only 0.2 kcalories per gram.

Sugar alcohols are not monosaccharides or disaccharides, so they can be used in products labeled "sugar free" or "no sugar added." If a product uses these descriptors, the grams of sugar alcohols in a serving must be listed in the Nutrition Facts portion of the food label under carbohydrates (**Figure 4.30**). Products sweetened with sugar alcohols, such as chewing gums, candies, ice creams, and baked goods, may carry the health claim statement that they do not promote tooth decay. These products are less likely to promote tooth decay because the bacteria in the mouth cannot metabolize sugar alcohols as rapidly as sucrose. Consumption of large amounts of sugar alcohols (more than 50 grams of sorbitol or 20 grams of mannitol per day) can cause diarrhea.

Outcome

Although Shamara lost weight when she consumed a low-carbohydrate diet, she wasn't able to stick with it for very long—a common complaint. Low-carb diet plans are based on the premise that high-carbohydrate foods cause a sharp rise in blood sugar and subsequently a rise in insulin, thereby promoting the storage of body fat. The restrictions of her diet eliminated virtually all choices from the grains and fruits food groups. She missed snacking on fruit, having sandwiches for lunch, eating pasta and rice at dinner, and enjoying cakes and cookies for dessert. She was always lightheaded and craved sweets.

When Shamara stopped her low-carb diet and went back to her old ways of eating, she began to regain weight. Fortunately, she started using MyPyramid to choose the right types and amounts of carbohydrates. She learned to limit added sugars and refined starches, which cause a sharp rise in blood sugar and promote fat deposition. One of the most useful things she found out was that unrefined carbohydrates from whole grains, fruits, and vegetables do not have this effect. The fiber in these carbohydrate sources limits the rate of glucose absorption and hence dampens the rise in blood sugar and insulin. Shamara's new diet is flavorful and varied, so she can more easily stick with it in the long term. By watching portion sizes and minimizing her refined carbohydrate intake, Shamara has lost 4 pounds over the last 2 months.

APPLICATIONS

Personal Nutrition

I. How much carbohydrate is in your diet?

a. Use iProfile and the 3-day diet record you kept in Chapter 2 to calculate your average carbohydrate and energy intake.

b. What is the percent of energy from carbohydrate in your diet?

c. How does your percent carbohydrate compare with the recommended 45% to 65% of energy from carbohydrate?

2. Look at the sources of carbohydrate in your diet?

a. Are most of your carbohydrate choices from unrefined, minimally refined, or highly refined sources?

b. Suggest some changes that would increase your intake of unrefined carbohydrates.

c. List some foods in your diet that are high in added refined sugars.

d. Suggest some changes that would reduce the amount of added sugar in your diet.

3. How much fiber is in your diet?

a. Use iProfile to calculate the grams of fiber in your original diet.

b. Does your intake meet the AI for fiber for someone of your age and gender?

c. How do the changes you suggested in question 2b affect the fiber content of your diet? If your modified diet still does not meet fiber recommendations, how might you further increase your intake?

General Nutrition Issues

I. Cheryl is trying to increase her fiber intake. For lunch she typically orders a sandwich from a local deli. Her favorite is turkey on a Kaiser roll with lettuce and mayo. Below, column A lists the types of bread available, column B lists the fillings, and column C lists the vegetables that can be added to the sandwiches. Can you suggest three different sandwiches for Cheryl that would provide more fiber than her typical sandwich?

COLUMN A	COLUMN B	COLUMN C
Kaiser roll	Sliced turkey	Lettuce
Sourdough bread	Soyburger	Tomatoes
Whole-wheat bread	Ham	Green and red peppers
Rye bread	Hummus	Onions
Sesame bagel	Falafel	Cucumber
Pumpernickel bread	Tuna salad	Olives
Pita bread	Peanut butter	Pickles
Oat bread	Grilled eggplant	Alfalfa sprouts

2. Bob weighs about 30 pounds more than he wants to weigh, so he decides to try to shed pounds quickly with a low-carbohydrate weight-loss diet. The diet allows an unlimited amount of beef, chicken, and fish as well as limited fruits and vegetables; breads, grains, and cereals are not allowed. Bob is overjoyed with his initial rapid weight loss, but after about a week his weight loss slows down and he begins to feel tired and light-headed. He is having headaches and notices a funny smell on his breath. A nutritional assessment suggests that Bob needs about 2500 kcalories a day to maintain his weight. His weight-loss diet provides about 1000 kcalories, 25 g of carbohydrate, 125 g of protein, and 44 g of fat per day. He consumes about 3 cups of fluid daily.

a. Explain why Bob is tired, light-headed, and has headaches and an unusual odor on his breath.

b. What recommendations do you have to reduce these symptoms?

3. Go to a bookstore or the library and look up a sample 1-day menu from a diet book that advocates a low-carbohydrate intake. Enter these foods into the iProfile diet analysis computer program.

a. How does this diet compare to the recommended intakes for saturated fat?

b. For calcium?

c. For fiber?

 iProfile

Summary

4.1 Carbohydrates in the Modern Diet

- Some carbohydrates in our diets are from unrefined whole foods such as whole grains, fruits, and vegetables. Others are from refined grain products like white breads and baked goods and added sugars such as those found in candies and soft drinks.

- Whole grains include the entire grain kernel, which is rich in fiber, micronutrients, and phytochemicals.

- Added refined sugars provide energy but few nutrients so they reduce the nutrient density of the diet.

4.2 Simple and Complex Carbohydrates

- Carbohydrates are chemical compounds that contain carbon, hydrogen, and oxygen.

- Simple carbohydrates include monosaccharides and disaccharides and are found in foods such as table sugar, honey, milk, and fruit.

- Complex carbohydrates include oligosaccharides and polysaccharides. Glycogen is a polysaccharide found in animals, and starch and soluble and insoluble fiber are polysaccharides found in plants.

4.3 Carbohydrates in the Digestive Tract

- Sugars and starches consumed in food are broken down in the digestive tract to monosaccharides, which can be absorbed into the blood stream.
- Lactose intolerance occurs when the enzyme lactase is not available in sufficient quantities to digest lactose. Undigested lactose passes into the colon where it draws in water and is metabolized by bacteria, producing gas and acids and causing abdominal distension, gas, cramping, and diarrhea.
- Fiber, some oligosaccharides, and resistant starch are carbohydrates that are not broken down by human digestive enzymes in the stomach and small intestine and therefore pass into the colon. These indigestible carbohydrates benefit health by increasing the amount of water and bulk in the intestine, which stimulates gastrointestinal motility; promoting the growth of a healthy microflora; and slowing nutrient absorption.

4.4 Carbohydrates in the Body

- In the body carbohydrate provides a source of energy—4 kcalories per gram—it also provides other essential roles in cell communication and as part of RNA and DNA.
- Glucose is metabolized through cellular respiration, which begins with glycolysis or anaerobic metabolism. Glycolysis breaks each 6-carbon glucose molecule into 2 3-carbon pyruvate molecules, producing ATP even when oxygen in unavailable. When oxygen is available, aerobic metabolism can proceed. Pyruvate loses a carbon as carbon dioxide to form acetyl-CoA, which is then broken down by the citric acid cycle to form 2 carbon dioxide molecules. Electrons released at each step pass to the electron transport chain where their energy is used to generate ATP and water is formed.
- Several tissues, including the brain and red blood cells, require glucose as an energy source. When glucose is not available, it can be obtained from the breakdown of glycogen or synthesized from amino acids by the process of gluconeogenesis.
- Carbohydrate is important for fatty acid metabolism because it is needed for acetyl-CoA to enter the citric acid cycle. When carbohydrate is limited acetyl-CoA is used to make ketones.

4.5 Blood Glucose Regulation

- Blood glucose levels are maintained within normal limits by the hormones insulin and glucagon. When blood glucose rises, insulin is released from the pancreas to allow body cells to take up the glucose. When blood glucose falls, glucagon is released to increase blood glucose.
- Blood glucose rises after eating. How quickly and how high blood glucose rises is referred to as glycemic response. Glycemic response can be quantified using glycemic index or glycemic load.
- Diabetes is an abnormality in blood sugar regulation resulting in high blood glucose levels, which damage tissues and cause complications including heart disease, kidney failure, blindness, and the need for amputations. This occurs either because insufficient insulin is produced or be-

cause there is a decrease in the sensitivity of body cells to insulin. Treatment to maintain glucose in the normal range includes diet, exercise, and medication.
- Hypoglycemia is a condition in which blood glucose falls to abnormally low levels, causing symptoms such as sweating, headaches, and rapid heartbeat.

4.6 Carbohydrates and Health

- When carbohydrates—particularly simple carbohydrates—remain in contact with the teeth, they increase the risk of dental caries.
- Consumption of unrefined carbohydrates can reduce glycemic response, enhance satiety, and help maintain a healthy weight. When consumed in excess of needs, carbohydrates contribute to weight gain. Low carbohydrate diets cause ketosis and have been found to cause weight loss in the short term but compliance and health risks may limit their effectiveness in the long term.
- Refined carbohydrates cause a larger glycemic response than unrefined sources and are associated with an increased risk of type 2 diabetes. Unrefined carbohydrates blunt glycemic response.
- High sugar diets can increase heart disease risk by raising blood lipids. Unrefined carbohydrate sources help lower blood lipids and provide other dietary components that help protect against heart disease.
- Indigestible carbohydrates make the stool larger and softer. This reduces the pressure needed to move material through the colon, lowering the risk of hemorrhoids and diverticular disease.
- Cancer cells differ from normal cells because they divide without restraint and are able to grow in areas reserved for other cells. Cells in the colon may be exposed to carcinogens in the colon contents. Fiber may help reduce the risk of colon cancer by decreasing the amount of contact between the cells lining the colon and these carcinogenic substances.

4.7 Meeting Carbohydrate Recommendations

- Guidelines for healthy diets recommend 45 to 65% of energy from carbohydrates and a fiber intake of 38 g/day for men and 25g/day for women. Food labels list Daily Value recommendations based on the amounts needed in a 2000 kcalorie diet; 300 grams of carbohydrate and 25 grams of fiber
- To meet carbohydrate recommendations, complex carbohydrates should be chosen from whole grains, legumes, fruits, and vegetables and simple carbohydrates from fruits, vegetables, and milk. Foods high in added sugars, such as baked goods, candy, and soft drinks should be limited.
- Alternative sweeteners can be used to reduce the amount of added sugar in the diet. They do not contribute to tooth decay and can help keep blood sugar in the normal range. They can also be used by dieters to reduce the energy content of the diet.

Review Questions

1. What foods are good sources of unrefined complex carbohydrates? Unrefined simple carbohydrates?

2. What is the basic unit of carbohydrate?

3. List three common simple carbohydrates. Where are they found in the diet or in the body?

4. Describe three types of complex carbohydrates.

5. Why is added sugar considered a source of empty kcalories?

6. How much energy is provided by a gram of carbohydrate?

7. Explain how fiber affects gastrointestinal health.

8. Describe what happens during the process of glycolysis.

9. What are the end products of cellular respiration? During which step is each produced?

10. Explain why carbohydrate is said to spare protein.

11. What is the main function of glucose in the body?

12. What is diabetes and what are the long-term complications of this disease?

13. Why is ketosis a problem only in type 1 diabetes?

14. What health benefits are associated with a diet high in unrefined carbohydrates?

15. How can you use the information on food labels to help you identify foods that are high in added sugars? In fiber?

16. What are the risks and benefits of alternative sweeteners?

References

1. Gross, L. S., Li, L., Ford, E. S., and Liu, S. Increased consumption of refined carbohydrates and the epidemic of type 2 diabetes in the United States: An ecologic assessment. *Am. J. Clin. Nutr.* 79:774–779, 2004.

2. Jensen, H. H., and Beghin, J. C. U. S. sweetener consumption trends and dietary guidelines. *Iowa Ag. Rev.* 11:10–11, 2005.

3. Institute of Medicine. Food and Nutrition Board. Dietary Reference Intakes for Energy, Carbohydrates, Fiber, Fat, Protein and Amino Acids. Washington, DC: National Academies Press, 2002.

4. Bray, G. A., Nielsen, S. J., and Popkin, B. M. Consumption of high-fructose corn syrup in beverages may play a role in the epidemic of obesity. *Am. J. Clin. Nutr.* 79:537–543, 2004.

5. Newburg, D. S., Ruiz-Palacios, G. M., Morrow, A. L. Human milk glycans protect infants against enteric pathogens. *Annu. Rev. Nutr.* 25:37–58, 2005.

6. Swallow, D. M. Genetics of lactase persistence and lactose intolerance. *Ann. Rev. Genetics.* 37:197–219, 2003.

7. The National Digestive Diseases Information Clearinghouse (NDDIC), National Institute of Diabetes and Digestive and Kidney Diseases (NIDDK), National Institutes of Health of the U.S. Department of Health and Human Services. Lactose intolerance. Available online at http://digestive.niddk.nih.gov/ddiseases/pubs/lactoseintolerance. Accessed March 18, 2008.

8. NIDDK. Lactose Intolerance. NIH Publication No. 98–2751, April 1994 e-text updated: November 1998. Available online at www.niddk.nih.gov/health/digest/pubs/lactose/lactose.htm/ Accessed October 27, 2005.

9. US Dept. of Health and Human Services, US Dept. of Agriculture. *Dietary Guidelines for Americans*, 6th ed. Washington, DC, 2005.

10. US Dept. of Agriculture. ARS Data Tables: Results from CSFII, 1996 ARS Food Surveys Research Group. Available online at www.barc.usda.bhnrc/foodsurveys/home.htm/ Accessed March 6, 2009.

11. Blaut, M. Relationship of prebiotics and food to intestinal microflora. *Eur. J. Nutr.* 41(Suppl 1):II1-II6, 2002.

12. Topping, D. L., Fukushima, M., and Bird, A. R. Resistant starch as a prebiotic and synbiotic: State of the art. *Proc. Nutr. Soc.* 62:171–176, 2003.

13. Andoh, A., Tsujikawa, T., and Fujiyama, Y. Role of dietary fiber and short-chain fatty acids in the colon. *Curr. Pharm. Des.* 9:347–358, 2003.

14. Foster-Powel, K., Holt, S .H., and Brand-Miller, J. C. International table of glycemic index and glycemic load values: 2002. *Am. J. Clin. Nutr.* 76:5–56, 2002.

15. The National Institute of Diabetes and Digestive and Kidney Diseases NIDDK National Diabetes Statistics, 2007. Available online at http://diabetes.niddk.nih.gov/dm/pubs/statistics/#allages. Accessed April 9, 2009.

16. National Diabetes Education Program. About diabetes and pre-diabetes. Available online at ndep.nih.gov/diabetes/diabetes.htm Accessed February 15, 2005.

17. National Diabetes Education Program. Overview of Diabetes in Children and Adolescents. Available online at ndep.nih.gov/diabetes/youth/youth_FS.htm#statistics/ Accessed April 9, 2009.

18. American Diabetes Association. Standards of Medical Care in Diabetes—2009. Diabetes Care 32:S13–S60, 2009.

19. Walker, C., and Reamy, B. V. Diets for cardiovascular disease prevention: What is the evidence? *Am. Fam. Physician.* 79:571–578, 2009.

20. US Dept. of Health and Human Services. US Public Health Service. *Oral Health in America: A Report of the Surgeon General*. Rockville, MD: National Institutes of Health, 2000.

21. National Institutes of Mental Health. Attention Deficit Hyperactivity Disorder. NIH Publication No. 3572. Available online at www.nimh.nih.gov/Publicat/ADHD.cfm/ Accessed January 24, 2006.

22. Jurgens, H., Haass, W., Castenada, T. R., et al. Consuming fructose beverages increases body adiposity in mice. *Obes. Res.* 13:1146–1156, 2005.

23. Office of the Surgeon General. The Surgeon General's Call to Action to Prevent and Decrease Overweight and Obesity. Rockville, MD: U.S. Dept. of Health and Human Services, 2001. Available online at www.surgeongeneral.gov/topics/obesity/ Accessed March 4, 2009.

24. Foster, G. D., Wyatt, H. R., Hill, J. O., et al. A randomized trial of a low-carbohydrate diet for obesity. *N. Engl. J. Med.* 348:2082–2090, 2003.

25. Sacks, F. M., Bray, G. A., Carey, V. J., et al. Comparison of weight-loss diets with different compositions of fat, protein, and carbohydrates. *N. Engl. J. Med.* 360:859–873, 2009.

26. Buchholz, A. C., and Schoeller, D. A. Is a calorie a calorie? *Am. J. Clin. Nutr.* 79:899S–906S, 2004.

27. Wilkinson, D. L., and McCargar, L. Is there an optimal macronutrient mix for weight loss and weight maintenance? *Best Pract. Res. Gastroenterol.* 18:1031–1047, 2004.

28. Van Dam, R. M., Rimm, E. B., Willett, W. C., et al. Dietary patterns and risk for type 2 diabetes mellitus in US men. *Ann. Intern. Med.* 136:201–109, 2002.

29. Willett, W., Manson, J., and Liu, S. Glycemic index, glycemic load, and risk of type 2 diabetes. *Am. J. Clin. Nutr.* 76:274S–280S, 2002.

30. Schulze, M. B., Liu, S., Rimm, E. B., et al. Glycemic index, glycemic load, and dietary fiber intake and incidence of type 2 diabetes in younger and middle-aged women. *Am. J. Clin. Nutr.* 80:348–356, 2004.

31. Schulze, M. B., Manson, J. E., Ludwig, D. S., et al. Sugar-sweetened beverages, weight gain, and incidence of type 2 diabetes in young and middle-aged women. *JAMA* 292:927–934, 2004.

32. Fried, S. K., and Rao, S. P. Sugars, hypertriglyceridemia, and cardiovascular disease. *Am. J. Clin. Nutr.* 78:873S–880S, 2003.

33. Jacobs, D. R., Meyer, K. A., Kushi, L. H., and Folsom, A. R. Whole-grain intake may reduce the risk of ischemic heart disease death in postmenopausal women: The Iowa Women's Health Study. *Am. J. Clin. Nutr.* 68:248–257, 1998.

34. Kushi, L. H., Meyer, K. A., and Jacobs, D. R., Jr. Cereals, legumes, and chronic disease risk reduction: Evidence from epidemiologic studies. *Am. J. Clin. Nutr.* 70(Suppl): 451S–458S, 1999.

35. Steffen, L. M., Jacobs, D. R. Jr., Stevens, J., et al. Associations of whole-grain, refined-grain, and fruit and vegetable consumption with risks of all-cause mortality and incident coronary artery disease and ischemic stroke: The Atherosclerosis Risk in Communities (ARIC) Study. *Am. J. Clin. Nutr.* 78:383–390, 2003.

36. Anderson, J. W. Whole grains protect against atherosclerotic cardiovascular disease. *Proc. Nutr. Soc.* 62:135–142, 2003.

37. Anderson, J .W., Hanna, T. J., Peng, X., and Kryscio, R. J. Whole grain foods and heart disease risk. *J. Am. Coll. Nutr.* 19(3 Suppl):291S–299S, 2000.

38. Institute of Medicine Food and Nutrition Board, Dietary Reference Intakes: Proposed Definition of Dietary Fiber. Washington, DC: National Academies Press, 2001.

39. Marlett, J. A. Sites and mechanisms for the hypocholesterolemic actions of soluble dietary fiber sources. In: Kritevsky, D., and Bonfield, C., eds. *Fiber in Human Health and Disease.* New York: Plenum Press, 1997, pp. 109–121.

40. Higgins, J. A. Resistant starch: Metabolic effects and potential health benefits. *J. AOAC Int.* 87:761–768, 2004.

41. Marlett, J. A., McBurney, M. I., and Slavin, J. L. Position of the American Dietetic Association: Health implications of dietary fiber. *J. Am. Diet. Assoc.* 102:993–1000, 2002.

42. National Digestive Diseases Information Clearinghouse. NIDDK, NIH. Diverticulosis and Diverticulitis. Available online at digestive.niddk.nih.gov/ddiseases/pubs/diverticulosis/ Accessed October 27, 2005.

43. Peters, U. N., Sinha, R., Chatterjee, N., et. al. Dietary fibre and colo-rectal adenoma in a colorectal cancer early detection programme. *Lancet.* 361: 1491–1495, 2003.

44. Bingham, S. A., Day, N. E., Luben, R., et al. Dietary fibre in food and protection against colorectal cancer in the European Prospective Investigation into Cancer and Nutrition (EPIC): An observational study. *Lancet* 361:1496–1501, 2003.

45. Alberts, D. S., Martinez, M. E., Roe, D. J., et al. Lack of effect of a high-fiber cereal supplement on the occurrence of colorectal adenomas. *N. Engl. J. Med.* 342:1156–1162, 2000.

46. Schatzkin, A., Lanza, E., Corle, D., et al. Lack of effect of a low-fat, high-fiber diet on the recurrence of colorectal adenomas. *N. Engl. J. Med.* 342:1149–1155, 2000.

47. Park, Y., Hunter, D. J., Spiegelman, D., et al. Dietary fiber intake and colorectal cancer: A pooled analysis of prospective cohort studies. JAMA 294:2849–2857, 2005.

48. WHO. Diet and Chronic Disease Prevention Report of the WHO FAO Expert Commission Geneva 2002, Available online at http://whqlibdoc.who.int/trs/WHO_TRS_916.pdf Accessed April 10, 2009.

49. American Dietetic Association. Position of the American Dietetic Association: Use of nutritive and non-nutritive sweeteners. *J. Am. Diet. Assoc.*104:255–275, 2004.

50. USDA. Profiling Food Consumption in America. The Agriculture Fact Book 2001–2002. Available online at http://www.usda.gov/factbook/chapter2.htm#sweeteners Accessed April 18, 2009.

51. Vermunt, S. H., Pasman, W. J., Schaafsma, G., and Kardinaal, A. F. Effects of sugar intake on body weight: A review. *Obes Rev.* 4:91–99, 2003.

52. Stevia sweetener gets US FDA go-ahead, December 18, 2008. Available online at http://www.foodnavigator-usa.com/Legislation/Stevia-sweetener-gets-US-FDA-go-ahead. Accessed April 12, 2009.

53. Gurney, J. G., Pogoda, J. M., Holly, E. A., et al. Aspartame consumption in relation to childhood brain tumor risk: Results from a case-control study. *J. Natl. Cancer Inst.* 89:1072–1074, 1997.

54. Calorie Control Council. Low calorie sweeteners: Sucralose. Available online at www.caloriecontrol.org/sucralos.html/ Accessed June 2, 2004.

5 Lipids

Case Study

Sam's grandfather died of a heart attack at age 50. Sam is a 20-year-old college student. He recently completed a heart disease risk assessment at a health fair and found that he was about 25 lb overweight, his percent body fat was higher than recommended, and his blood cholesterol was slightly elevated at 209 mg/100 mL. He was told that he should see a physician to evaluate his risk for a heart attack. How could a 20 year old be at risk for heart disease, and how can he lower that risk?

Sam has begun to think about changes he could make in his diet and lifestyle. He eats a lot of red meat and has only one or two servings of fruits and vegetables a day. He drinks whole milk and snacks on ice cream every night. His only exercise is a Tuesday afternoon of Frisbee with friends and lifting weights on Friday nights.

When he tells his friends and family about his health concerns, everyone is quick to offer advice. His girlfriend, who is a vegetarian, recommends that he eliminate meat from his diet. His biology lab partner tells him to cut out all fat. His sister tells him about the Mediterranean diet and recommends he eat pasta with plenty of olive oil every night. His roommate tells him to eat more fish. His mother says he should stop using margarine because of all the *trans* fat it contains. Whose advice should Sam follow?

(Karen Pearson/Getty Images, Inc.)

Rees/StockFood America)

Chapter Outline

5.1 Fat in the Modern Diet

Learning Objectives

- Name two qualities that fat adds to foods.
- Explain how the sources of fat in the U.S. diet have changed.
- Discuss how fat intake affects the risk of chronic disease.

lipids A group of organic molecules, most of which do not dissolve in water. They include fatty acids, triglycerides, phospholipids, and sterols.

Lipids, the chemical term for what we commonly call fats, contribute to the texture, flavor, and aroma of food. It's fat that gives ice cream, cheesecake, and cream cheese a smooth texture and rich taste. Sesame oil gives Chinese food its distinctive aroma and olive oil imparts a unique flavor to salads. In addition to texture, flavor, and aroma, fats add kcalories to our food and the amount and type we eat can affect our health. Fats and oils provide 9 kcalories per gram—more than twice as much as a gram of carbohydrate or protein. Because of the high-kcalorie content of fat, a high-fat diet can make it easier to consume excess energy and make it more difficult to keep weight in the healthy range.

The typical American diet today contains about 33% of its energy from fat.[1] Some of the fats in our diet are obvious—the pat of butter melting on a hot baked potato or the layer of fat around the edge of a sirloin steak. Other fats are less visible. For example, you can't see the fat in baked goods; these help make cookies and crackers crisp, muffins soft, and piecrusts flaky. It is also difficult to recognize the fats that are naturally abundant in whole milk, avocados, and nuts, or the oil that stays with your potatoes after they are removed from the fryer (**Figure 5.1**).

America's Changing Fat Intake

The amounts and sources of the fats in the typical American diet have changed over the last few decades. In the 1960s most fat came from high-fat cuts of beef, eggs, whole milk, butter, and cheese. But beginning in the 1970s, when Americans were told fat was making them fat and increasing their risk of heart disease and cancer, they replaced beef with chicken, ate fewer eggs, switched to lower fat milk, and put less butter on their toast. In the 1980s, food manufacturers offered an endless assortment of reduced-fat products such as low-fat cheese, fat-free cookies, and snack foods that were baked instead of fried. As a result, Americans reduced their fat

Figure 5.1 Potatoes absorb oil during frying. A baked potato has no fat, but a medium order of fries provides about 17 grams of fat—the equivalent of about 4 pats of butter. (Paul Poplis/ FoodPix/Jupiter Images Corp.)

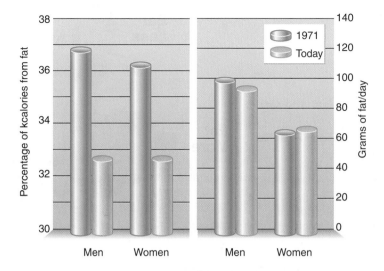

Figure 5.2 U.S. energy and fat intake: 1971 and Today Because Americans have increased their total kcalorie intake, the percentage of kcalories from fat is less today than in 1971, but the number of grams of fat we consume has not decreased.

intake as a percent of kcalories from almost 40% of energy in the 1960s and 1970s to about 33% today.[1–3] But the incidence of heart disease and cancer in the population didn't change very much and rather than getting thinner, the number of obese people doubled.

One of the reasons Americans' health didn't improve is that many of the dietary changes didn't really change fat intake. Pizza, macaroni and cheese, cheeseburgers, and burritos replaced pork chops and ribs. High-fat muffins and croissants replaced eggs for breakfast. Our intake of ice cream and cheesecake decreased, but consumption of french fries, tortilla chips, and other high-fat snacks increased.[4] Low-fat products were added to the diet but were consumed in larger servings than the higher-fat foods they were designed to replace. And instead of preparing meals at home Americans ate out more often. In 1993, Americans ate 3.8 meals per week at restaurants.[5] By 2007 this had increased to 5.9 meals per week.[6] Restaurant meals tend to be higher in energy and fat than food prepared at home. As a result of these changes our kcalorie intake increased. Between 1970 and today American men increased their energy intake by 168 kcalories a day and women by 335 kcalories a day.[1] Most of this increase was from carbohydrate, so although fat intake decreased as a percent of kcalories, the actual grams of fat we consumed each day changed very little over this time period (**Figure 5.2**).[4]

How Fat Intake Affects Health

Avoiding butter and bacon wasn't a magic bullet to solve our public health problems, but maybe it was a start. Recommendations today emphasize that the type of fat consumed may be more important than total fat when considering the risk of chronic diseases such as heart disease and cancer. Populations that have high intakes of fat from meats and dairy products, which are high in saturated fat and cholesterol, tend to have a higher incidence of heart disease and certain types of cancer. Diets high in processed fats used in shortening and margarine also increase risks. On the other hand populations where most of the fat in the diet is unsaturated fats from foods like fish, nuts, and olive oil seem to be protected from the negative effects of a high-fat diet. Many of the high-fat foods that Americans have cut back on, like red meat and high-fat dairy products are high in saturated fat and cholesterol. That is a first step toward improving our health. Now we need to recognize that the sausage and cheese on a pizza, the beef and sour cream on a burrito, and many packaged snack foods also add harmful types of fat to our diet. Eating a healthy diet doesn't necessarily mean reducing total fat, but rather eating the right kinds of fats while choosing plenty of whole grains, fruits, and vegetables (**Figure 5.3**).

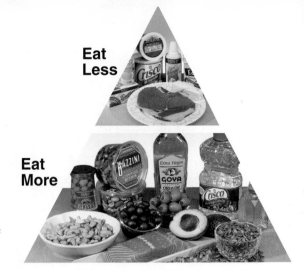

Figure 5.3 Fat recommendations for a healthy diet
Choose more fish, vegetable oils, and nuts; limit solid fats from shortening and animal products such as butter, ice cream, and fatty meats. [(top and bottom photos) Andy Washnik]

5.2 Types of Lipid Molecules

Learning Objectives

- Describe the functions of triglycerides, phospholipids, and cholesterol.
- Compare the structures of saturated, monounsaturated, polyunsaturated, omega-6, omega-3, and *trans* fatty acids.
- Name foods that are sources of saturated, monounsaturated, polyunsaturated, omega-6, omega-3, and *trans* fatty acids.

triglycerides (Triacylglycerols) The major form of lipid in food and in the body. They consist of three fatty acids attached to a glycerol molecule.

fatty acids Organic molecules made up of a chain of carbons linked to hydrogen atoms with an acid group at one end.

phospholipids Types of lipids containing phosphorous. The most common are the phosphoglycerides, which are composed of a glycerol backbone with two fatty acids and a phosphate group attached.

sterols Types of lipids with a structure composed of multiple chemical rings.

The primary type of lipid in our food and in our bodies, and what we are typically referring to when we use the word fat, is **triglycerides**. Each triglyceride includes three **fatty acids**. These fatty acids determine the physical properties and health effects of the triglycerides we consume. **Phospholipids** and **sterols** are two other types of lipid that are important in nutrition. The different structures of these lipids affect their function in the body and the properties they give to food.

Triglycerides and Fatty Acids

Triglycerides, also known as triacylglycerols, consist of a backbone of glycerol with three fatty acids attached, as shown in **Figure 5.4**. If only one fatty acid is attached to the glycerol, the molecule is called a *monoglyceride* or *monoacylglycerol* and when two fatty acids are attached, it is a *diglyceride* or *diacylglycerol*.

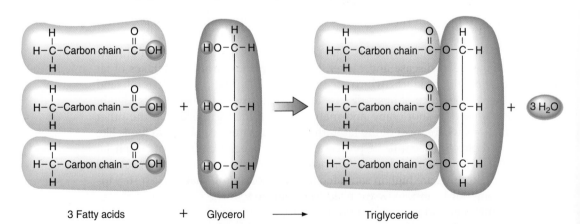

3 Fatty acids   +   Glycerol   ⟶   Triglyceride

Figure 5.4 Formation and structure of triglycerides
A triglyceride (triacylglycerol) is formed when three fatty acids bind to a molecule of glycerol. As each bond is formed, a hydrogen atom (H) from the glycerol and a hydroxyl group (OH) from the acid end of the fatty acid combine to form a molecule of water.

Structurally, a fatty acid is a chain of carbon atoms with an acid group (COOH) at one end. The other end of the carbon chain is called the *omega* or *methyl end,* and consists of a carbon atom attached to three hydrogen atoms (CH_3). Each of the carbons between is attached to its two neighboring carbons and up to two hydrogen atoms (**Figure 5.5**). The physical properties of a fatty acid depend on the length of the carbon chain and the type and location of the bonds between the carbon atoms.

Fatty Acid Chain Length The carbon chains of fatty acids vary in length from a few to 20 or more carbons. Most fatty acids in plants and animals, including humans, contain between 14 and 22 carbons. Short-chain fatty acids range from 4 to 7 carbons in length. They remain liquid at colder temperatures. For example, the short-chain fatty acids in whole milk remain liquid even in the refrigerator. Medium-chain fatty acids, such as those in coconut oil, range from 8 to 12 carbons. They solidify in the refrigerator but remain liquid at room temperature. Long-chain fatty acids (greater than 12 carbons), such as those in beef fat, usually remain solid at room temperature.

Saturated Fatty Acids Each carbon atom forms four bonds to link it to four other atoms. If a carbon is not bound to four other atoms, double bonds are formed. A fatty acid in which each carbon in the chain is bound to two hydrogens is saturated with hydrogens and is therefore called a **saturated fatty acid** (see Figure 5.5). The most common saturated fatty acids are palmitic acid, which has 16 carbons, and stearic acid, which has 18 carbons. These are found most often in animal foods such as meat and dairy products. Plant sources of saturated fatty acids include palm oil, palm kernel oil, and coconut oil. These are often called **tropical oils** because they are found in plants common in tropical climates. Tropical oils are rarely added to foods at home but, because they are more resistant to rancidity and have longer shelf lives than oils containing unsaturated fats, they have been used by the food industry in cereals, crackers, salad dressings, and cookies. However, concern about the health risks associated with saturated fats led many of the large food manufacturers to reformulate their products to avoid the use of tropical oils.

saturated fatty acid A fatty acid in which the carbon atoms are bound to as many hydrogens as possible and which therefore contains no carbon-carbon double bonds.

tropical oils A term used in the popular press to refer to the saturated oils—coconut, palm, and palm kernel oil—that are derived from plants grown in tropical regions.

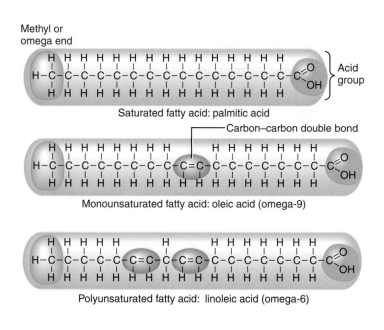

Saturated fatty acid: palmitic acid

Monounsaturated fatty acid: oleic acid (omega-9)

Polyunsaturated fatty acid: linoleic acid (omega-6)

Polyunsaturated fatty acid: alpha-linolenic acid (omega-3)

Figure 5.5 Fatty acid structure These fatty acids, commonly found in our foods, illustrate the structural differences between saturated, monounsaturated, and polyunsaturated fatty acids.

monounsaturated fatty acid A fatty acid that contains one carbon-carbon double bond.

polyunsaturated fatty acid A fatty acid that contains two or more carbon-carbon double bonds.

omega-3 (ω-3) fatty acid A fatty acid containing a carbon-carbon double bond between the third and fourth carbons from the omega end.

omega-6 (ω-6) fatty acid A fatty acid containing a carbon-carbon double bond between the sixth and seventh carbons from the omega end.

Unsaturated Fatty Acids Unsaturated fatty acids contain some carbons that are not saturated with hydrogens. The carbons within the chain that are bound to only one hydrogen form carbon-carbon double bonds (see Figure 5.5). A fatty acid containing one double bond in its carbon chain is called a **monounsaturated fatty acid**. In our diets, the most common monounsaturated fatty acid is oleic acid, which is prevalent in olive and canola oils. A fatty acid with more than one double bond in its carbon chain is said to be a **polyunsaturated fatty acid**. The most common polyunsaturated fatty acid is linoleic acid, found in corn, safflower, and soybean oils. Unsaturated fatty acids melt at cooler temperatures than saturated fatty acids of the same chain length. Therefore, the more unsaturated bonds a fatty acid contains, the more likely it is to be liquid at room temperature.

Omega-3 and Omega-6 Fatty Acids There are different categories of unsaturated fatty acids depending on the location of the first double bond in the carbon chain. If the first double bond occurs between the third and fourth carbons, counting from the omega end (CH_3) of the chain, the fat is said to be an **omega-3 (ω-3) fatty acid** (see Figure 5.5). Alpha-linolenic acid, found in vegetable oils, and eicosapentaenoic acid (EPA) and docosahexaenoic acid (DHA), found in fish oils, are omega-3 fatty acids (**Table 5.1**). If the first double bond occurs between the sixth and seventh carbons (from the omega end), the fatty acid is called an **omega-6 (ω-6) fatty acid**. Linoleic acid, found in corn and safflower oils, and arachidonic acid found in meat and fish are omega-6 fatty acids. Linoleic acid is the major omega-6 fatty acid in the North American diet. Both omega-3 and omega-6 fatty acids are used to synthesize regulatory molecules in the body and the biological effect of the molecule synthesized depends on the structure of the fatty acid from which it is made. Therefore, the ratio of omega-3 to omega-6 fatty acids in the diet is important in processes such as blood pressure regulation, blood clotting, and immune function.

Table 5.1 Sources of Omega-3 and Omega-6 Fatty Acids

Food	Portion	Omega-3 (g)	Omega-6 (g)
Swordfish, salmon, trout	3 oz cooked	1.5	0.5
Sole, cod	3 oz cooked	0.13	4.3
Shrimp	3 oz cooked	0.27	0.08
Mussels, clams	3 oz cooked	0.7	0.15
Tuna, canned	3 oz	0.23	0.04
Flax seed	1 Tbsp	2.0	0
Canola oil	1 Tbsp	1.27	2.77
Walnuts	1/4 cup	2.72	11.4
Peanuts	1/4 cup	0.09	4.01
Almonds	1/4 cup	0.13	4.3
Sunflower seeds	1/4 cup	0.02	10.5
Spinach, cooked	1/2 cup	0.08	0.01
Mustard greens, cooked	1/2 cup	0.02	0.02

***Cis* Versus *Trans* Double Bonds** The position of the hydrogen atoms around a double bond also affects the properties of unsaturated fatty acids. Most unsaturated fatty acids found in nature have both hydrogen atoms on the same side of the double bond, called the *cis* configuration. When the hydrogen atoms are on opposite sides of

Cis fatty acid	*Trans* fatty acid	Saturated fatty acid

Figure 5.6 *Cis* versus *trans* **fatty acids**
In *cis* fatty acids, the orientation of hydrogen atoms around the double bond causes a bend in the carbon chain. In *trans* fatty acids, the orientation of hydrogen atoms does not cause a bend, so the carbon chain is straighter, and resembles a saturated fatty acid.

the double bond, called the *trans* configuration, the fatty acid is a **trans fatty acid** (**Figure 5.6**). A *trans* fatty acid has a higher melting point than the same fatty acid in the *cis* configuration.

Trans fatty acids are found in small amounts in nature, but most of the *trans* fat we eat comes from products that have undergone **hydrogenation**. Hydrogenation bubbles hydrogen gas into liquid oil. This causes some of the double bonds in the oil to accept hydrogen atoms and become saturated. The resulting fat has more of the properties of a saturated fat, such as increased stability against rancidity and a higher melting point. However, during hydrogenation, only some of the bonds become saturated. Some of those that remain unsaturated are altered, converting them from the *cis* to the *trans* configuration. The resulting product therefore contains more *trans* fatty acids than the original oil. Hydrogenated or partially hydrogenated vegetable oils are a primary ingredient in margarine and vegetable shortening because they raise the melting point of the products, making them more solid at room temperature. They are also used to lengthen shelf life in other processed foods such as cookies, crackers, breakfast cereals, and potato chips. When consumed in the diet, *trans* fats raise blood cholesterol levels and increase the risk of heart disease. Because of their relationship to heart disease risk, information about *trans* fat is included on food labels and many manufacturers have reformulated their products to reduce the amounts of *trans* fatty acids.

Fatty Acids and the Properties of Triglycerides Triglycerides may contain any combination of fatty acids: long, medium, or short chain, saturated or unsaturated, *cis* or *trans* (**Figure 5.7**). The types of fatty acids in triglycerides determine their texture, taste, and physical characteristics. For example, the amounts and types of fatty acids in chocolate allow it to remain solid at room temperature, snap when bitten into, and then melt quickly and smoothly in the mouth. The triglycerides in red meat contain predominantly long-chain, saturated fatty acids so the fat on a piece of steak is solid at room temperature. The triglycerides in olive oil contain predominantly monounsaturated fatty acids, whereas those in corn oil are mostly polyunsaturated. These fats are liquid at room temperature. The triglycerides in solid margarine made from corn oil have been hydrogenated so they contain more *trans* fat than the original corn oil. The types of fatty acids in triglycerides also determine the effect they have on our health. As discussed later in the chapter, certain types of fatty acids increase the risk of heart disease and cancer, whereas others have a protective effect.

trans **fatty acid** An unsaturated fatty acid in which the hydrogen atoms are on opposite sides of the double bond.

hydrogenation The process whereby hydrogen atoms are added to the carbon-carbon double bonds of unsaturated fatty acids, making them more saturated.

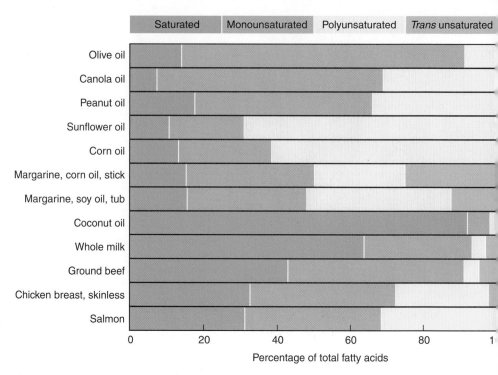

Figure 5.7 Fatty acid composition of fats and oils
The fats and oils in our diets contain combinations of saturated, monounsaturated, polyunsaturated, and *trans* fatty acids; shown here as a percentage of the total amount of fat in the item. (From USDA)

Phospholipids

Phospholipids are lipids attached to a chemical group containing phosphorus called a *phosphate group*. **Phosphoglycerides** are the major class of phospholipids. Like triglycerides, they have a backbone of glycerol. However, they have only two fatty acids attached. In place of the third fatty acid is a phosphate group, which is then attached to a variety of other molecules (**Figure 5.8**). The fatty acid end of a phosphoglyceride is soluble in fat, whereas the phosphate end is water-soluble. This allows phosphoglycerides to mix in both water and fat—a property that makes them important for many functions in foods and in the body.

In foods, the ability of phosphoglycerides to mix with both water and fat allows them to act as **emulsifiers** (**Figure 5.9a**). For example, egg yolks, which contain phosphoglycerides, function as an emulsifier in cake batter, where they allow the oil and water to mix. In the body, phosphoglycerides are an important component of cell membranes. The phosphoglycerides in membranes form a **lipid bilayer**, in which the water-soluble phosphate groups orient toward the aqueous environment inside and outside the cell, while the water-insoluble fatty acids stay in the lipid environment sandwiched in between (**Figure 5.9b**). This forms the barrier that helps regulate which substances can pass into and out of the cell.

phosphoglycerides A class of phospholipid consisting of a glycerol molecule, 2 fatty acids, and a phosphate group.

emulsifiers Substances that allow water and fat to mix by breaking large fat globules into smaller ones.

lipid bilayer Two layers of phosphoglyceride molecules oriented so that the fat-soluble fatty acid tails are sandwiched between the water-soluble phosphate-containing heads.

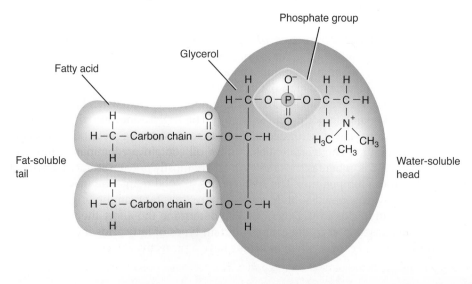

Figure 5.8 Phosphoglyceride structure
Phosphoglycerides, such as the lecithin, molecule shown here, consist of a water-soluble head containing a phosphate group and a lipid-soluble tail of fatty acids.

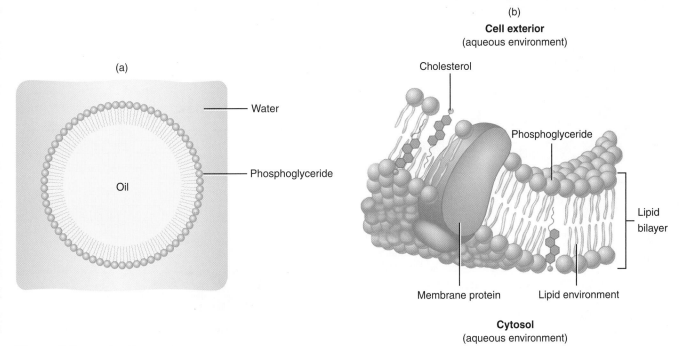

Figure 5.9 Phosphoglyceride functions
(a) Phosphoglycerides act as emulsifiers in foods because they can surround droplets of oil, allowing them to remain suspended in a watery environment. (b) In cell membranes, phosphoglycerides form a lipid bilayer by orienting the water-soluble phosphate-containing heads toward the watery environment inside and outside of the cell and the fatty acid tails toward the interior of the membrane.

The specific function of a phosphoglyceride depends on the molecule that is attached to the phosphate group. If a molecule of choline is attached, the phospholipid is called **lecithin** (see Figure 5.8). In the body, lecithin is a major constituent of cell membranes and is required for their optimal function. It is also used to synthesize the neurotransmitter acetylcholine, which is important in the memory center of the brain. Eggs and soybeans are natural sources of lecithin. Lecithin is also used by the food industry as an additive in margarine, salad dressings, chocolate, frozen desserts, and baked goods to keep the oil from separating from the other ingredients.

lecithin A phosphoglyceride composed of a glycerol backbone, two fatty acids, a phosphate group, and a molecule of choline.

Sterols

Like most other lipids, sterols do not dissolve well in water. Unlike triglycerides and phosphoglycerides their structure consists of multiple chemical rings. Sterols are found in both plants and animals. **Cholesterol**, probably the best-known sterol, is only found in animals (**Figure 5.10**). Cholesterol is necessary in the body, but because the liver manufactures it, it is not essential in the diet. More than 90% of the cholesterol in the body is found in cell membranes (see Figure 5.9). It is also part of myelin, the coating on many nerve cells. Cholesterol is needed to synthesize vitamin D in the skin; cholic acid, a component of bile; and some hormones, such as testosterone and estrogen, which promote growth and the development of sex characteristics; and cortisol, which promotes glucose synthesis in the liver.

In the diet, cholesterol is found only in foods from animal sources. Egg yolks and organ meats such as liver and kidney are high in cholesterol. One egg yolk contains about 213 mg of cholesterol. Organ meats contain about 300 mg per 3-ounce serving. Lean red meats and skinless chicken contain about 90 mg in 3 ounces, whereas fish contains 50 mg in 3 ounces. Plant foods contain other sterols, but do not contain cholesterol unless animal products are combined with them in cooking or processing. Diets high in cholesterol increase the risk of heart disease but consuming plant sterols can help reduce cholesterol levels in the body by decreasing cholesterol absorption from the diet (see: Your Choice: Eating to Lower Cholesterol Levels).

cholesterol A lipid that consists of multiple chemical rings and is made only by animal cells.

Figure 5.10 Cholesterol structure
The four colored rings indicate the backbone structure common to all sterols.

(©iStockphoto)

Eating to Lower Cholesterol Levels

Many Americans take medications to reduce their cholesterol levels and thus their heart disease risk. However, a dietary pattern that includes soluble fiber, plant sterols, soy protein, and nuts has been found to be as effective at lowering blood cholesterol levels in some people as medication.[1] Including a variety of the following is therefore a dietary prescription for heart health.

Soluble Fiber such as that in oatmeal and oat bran, lowers total and unhealthy LDL cholesterol levels.[2] The evidence is substantial enough for the FDA to allow a health claim related to the cholesterol-lowering effects of foods containing sufficient amounts of soluble fiber. The soluble fiber psyllium also lowers total and LDL cholesterol without affecting healthy HDL cholesterol.[3] So lower your cholesterol by eating oatmeal in the morning, apples at lunch, and beans and barley in your stew at dinner.

Flaxseed can lower LDL cholesterol without lowering HDL cholesterol. Bake these seeds in breads, muffins, and cookies, or grind them up and sprinkle them on cereal or yogurt. They provide soluble fiber and omega-3 fatty acids, both of which help protect against high blood lipids and cardiovascular disease.[4]

Soy Protein, when it replaces animal protein in the diet, lowers LDL cholesterol and either increases or has no effect on HDL cholesterol.[5] Although the decrease in LDL cholesterol is small, soy may also protect against heart disease because it is high in polyunsaturated fat, fiber, vitamins, and minerals, and low in saturated fat.[6] So, try tofu in your stir fry and soy milk on your cereal. Foods that are low in fat, saturated fat, and cholesterol and are a good source of soy protein can include a health claim stating that soy protein may help reduce the risk of heart disease.

Plant Sterols and Stanols resemble cholesterol chemically, making it difficult for the digestive tract to distinguish

(William Berry/iStockphoto)

them from cholesterol. They lower blood cholesterol by reducing cholesterol absorption.[7] You can get small quantities of these compounds in many fruits, vegetables, nuts, seeds, cereals, legumes, vegetable oils, and other plant foods. Larger amounts are added to margarines, salad dressings, and orange juice. Look for a health claim on the label about the relationship between plant sterols and reduced risk of heart disease.

Nuts are high in monounsaturated fat, omega-3 fatty acids, antioxidants, and fiber, all of which provide cardiovascular protection. Epidemiological studies have shown that diets rich in nuts are associated with a lower incidence of cardiovascular disease.[4] So, grab some nuts for a snack, bake them into breads, sprinkle them on salads, and mix them into stir fries.

Fish particularly fatty fish, such as mackerel, lake trout, herring, sardines, tuna, and salmon—can help reduce your risk of heart disease and protect against sudden cardiac death.[4] Eating fish positively affects blood lipids, stabilizes the heart electrically, decreases atherosclerotic plaque growth, and lowers blood pressure.[8] The American Heart Association recommends 2 servings of fatty fish a week.

[1] Jenkins, D. J. A., Kendall, C. W. C., Marchie, A. et al. Effects of a dietary portfolio of cholesterol-lowering foods vs. lovastatin on serum lipids and C-reactive protein. *JAMA* 290:502–510, 2003.

[2] Brown, L., Rosner, B., Willett, W. W., and Sacks, F. M. Cholesterol-lowering effects of dietary fiber: A meta-analysis. *Am. J. Clin. Nutr.* 69:30–42, 1999.

[3] Anderson, J. W., Allgood, L. D., Lawrence, A. et al. Cholesterol-lowering effects of psyllium intake adjunctive to diet therapy in men and women with hypercholesterolemia: Meta-analysis of 8 controlled trials. *Am. J. Clin. Nutr.* 71:472–479, 2000.

[4] Mente, A., de Koning, L., Shannon, H. S., and Anand, S. S. A systematic review of the evidence supporting a causal link between dietary factors and coronary heart disease. *Arch. Intern. Med.* 169:659–669, 2009.

[5] Anthony, M. S. Soy and cardiovascular disease: Cholesterol lowering and beyond. *J. Nutr.* 130:662S–663S, 2000.

[6] Sacks, F. M., Lichtenstein, A., Van Horn, L. et al. Soy protein, isoflavones, and cardiovascular health: An American Heart Association Science Advisory for professionals from the Nutrition Committee. *Circulation* 113:1034–1044, 2006.

[7] Law, M. Plant sterol and stanol margarines and health. *BMJ* 320:861–864, 2000.

[8] Holub, D. J., and Holub, B. J. Omega-3 fatty acids from fish oils and cardiovascular disease. *Mol. Cell. Biochem.* 263:217–225, 2004.

5.3 Lipids in the Digestive Tract

Learning Objectives

- Describe the steps involved in the digestion of triglycerides.
- Explain how micelles facilitate lipid absorption.

In healthy adults, most of the digestion of dietary fat takes place in the small intestine due to the action of lipid-digesting enzymes called *lipases*. Some triglyceride digestion also occurs in the stomach due to the action of lipases produced in the mouth and stomach. These enzymes work best on triglycerides containing short- and medium-chain fatty acids such as those in milk, and so are particularly important in infants.[7]

In the small intestine, bile from the gallbladder helps break fat into small globules. The triglycerides in these globules are digested by lipases from the pancreas, which break them down into fatty acids and monoglycerides (**Figure 5.11**). These products of triglyceride digestion, cholesterol, and other fat-soluble substances including fat-soluble vitamins mix with bile to form smaller droplets called **micelles**. Micelles have a fat-soluble center surrounded by a coating of bile acids. They facilitate the absorption of lipids into the mucosal cells of the small intestine by allowing

micelles Particles formed in the small intestine when the products of fat digestion are surrounded by bile acids. They facilitate the absorption of fat.

How it Works

View in your Wiley Plus
www.wileyplus.com

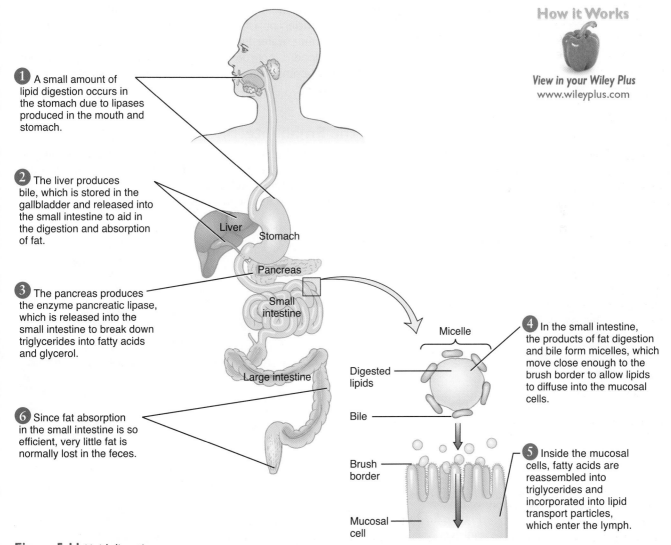

1 A small amount of lipid digestion occurs in the stomach due to lipases produced in the mouth and stomach.

2 The liver produces bile, which is stored in the gallbladder and released into the small intestine to aid in the digestion and absorption of fat.

3 The pancreas produces the enzyme pancreatic lipase, which is released into the small intestine to break down triglycerides into fatty acids and glycerol.

6 Since fat absorption in the small intestine is so efficient, very little fat is normally lost in the feces.

4 In the small intestine, the products of fat digestion and bile form micelles, which move close enough to the brush border to allow lipids to diffuse into the mucosal cells.

5 Inside the mucosal cells, fatty acids are reassembled into triglycerides and incorporated into lipid transport particles, which enter the lymph.

Liver
Stomach
Pancreas
Small intestine
Large intestine
Micelle
Digested lipids
Bile
Brush border
Mucosal cell

Figure 5.11 Lipid digestion
The bulk of our dietary lipids is triglycerides, which need to be digested before they can be absorbed. The diet also contains smaller amounts of phospholipids, which are partially digested, and cholesterol and fat-soluble vitamins, which are absorbed without digestion.

these substances to get close enough to the brush border to diffuse across into the mucosal cells. Most of the bile acids in micelles are also absorbed and returned to the liver to be reused. Because fat-soluble vitamins and other fat-soluble molecules present in foods must be incorporated into micelles to be absorbed, their absorption depends on the presence of dietary fat. Once inside the mucosal cell, long-chain fatty acids, cholesterol, and other fat-soluble substances require further processing before they can be transported in the blood.

5.4 Lipid Transport in the Body

Learning Objectives

- Describe how lipids are transported in the blood and delivered to cells.
- Compare and contrast the functions of LDLs and HDLs.

lipoproteins Particles containing a core of triglycerides and cholesterol surrounded by a shell of protein, phospholipids, and cholesterol that transport lipids in blood and lymph.

Just as water-insoluble lipids require special mechanisms to be absorbed into the body, they require special transport particles to travel throughout the body in the blood. These transport particles, called **lipoproteins**, are created by combining water-insoluble lipids with phospholipids and proteins (**Figure 5.12**). Phospholipids orient with their fat-soluble tails toward the interior and their water-soluble heads toward the outside. The resulting particle consists of a fat-soluble core surrounded by a water-soluble envelope, allowing water-insoluble lipids to be transported in the aqueous evironment of the blood. Lipoproteins help transport dietary triglycerides, cholesterol, and fat-soluble vitamins from the small intestine and stored or newly synthesized lipids from the liver.

Transport from the Small Intestine

How lipids are transported from the small intestine depends on their solubility in water. Short- and medium-chain fatty acids, which are water-soluble, can be transported from the small intestine in the blood and delivered to cells throughout the body. Lipids that are not soluble in water, such as long-chain fatty acids and choles-

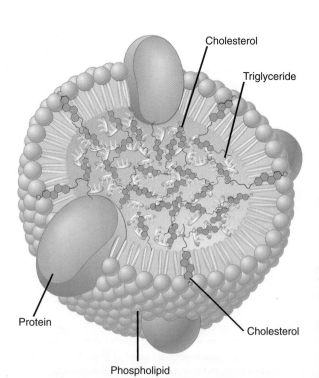

Figure 5.12 Lipoprotein structure
Lipoproteins consist of a core of triglycerides and cholesterol surrounded by a shell of proteins, phospholipids, and cholesterol.

Cholesterol

Triglyceride

Cholesterol

Protein

Phospholipid

terol, cannot enter the bloodstream directly so they must be incorporated into lipoproteins. For this to occur, long-chain fatty acids and monoglycerides are first assembled into triglycerides by the mucosal cell. These triglycerides are then combined with cholesterol, phospholipids, and a small amount of protein to form lipoproteins called **chylomicrons** (**Figure 5.13**). Chylomicrons are transferred into the lymphatic system and then enter the bloodstream without first passing through the liver.

As chylomicrons circulate in the blood, the enzyme **lipoprotein lipase**, present on the surface of the cells lining the blood vessels, breaks the triglycerides down into fatty acids and glycerol, which enter the surrounding cells. The fatty acids can be either used as fuel or resynthesized into triglycerides for storage. What remains of the chylomicron is a chylomicron remnant composed mostly of cholesterol and protein. This goes to the liver and is disassembled (see Figure 5.13).

chylomicrons Lipoproteins that transport lipids from the mucosal cells of the small intestine and deliver triglycerides to other body cells.

lipoprotein lipase An enzyme that breaks down triglycerides into fatty acids and glycerol; attached to the cell membranes of cells that line the blood vessels.

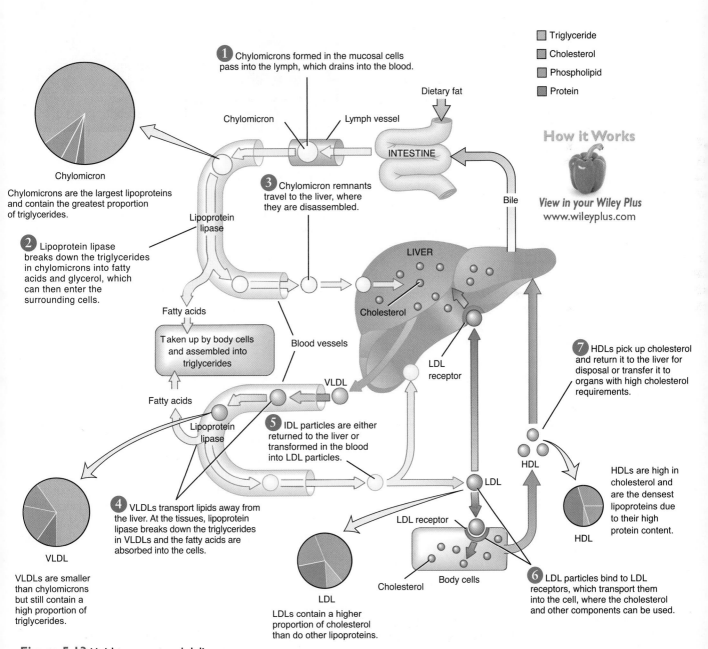

Figure 5.13 Lipid transport and delivery
Chylomicrons and very-low-density lipoproteins transport triglycerides and deliver them to body cells. Low-density lipoproteins transport and deliver cholesterol, while high-density lipoproteins help return cholesterol to the liver for reuse or elimination.

SCIENCE

ScienceAppliedScienceApplied
ScienceAppliedScienceApplied
ScienceAppliedScienceApplied

APPLIED

(DAJ/Getty Images, Inc.)   (www.victorianoizquierdo.com/Getty Images, Inc.)   (Elena Schweitzer/Shutterstock)

A Genetic Disease and Cholesterol Regulation

Children with a rare form of the inherited disease familial hypercholesterolemia have blood cholesterol levels that range from 650 to 1000 mg/100 mL—six times the normal level. Cholesterol is so high in their blood that it deposits in the tissues, forming soft, raised bumps on the skin called *xanthomas* (see figure). The elevated cholesterol damages blood vessels, leading to premature atherosclerosis. Chest pain, heart attacks, and death are common before the age of 15 and it is rare for individuals with this disease to survive past age 30.[1,2] Research into the causes of this disease led Drs. Michael Brown and Joseph Goldstein to a discovery that is key to our understanding of how blood cholesterol is regulated.

The severity of familial hypercholesterolemia depends on whether the individual inherits one or two genes for the disease. The children described above inherited two genes for this disease, causing them to have a rare and more severe form that affects only about one in a million people. About 1 in 500 persons inherits only one gene and has a less severe form of the disease. These individuals have moderately elevated blood cholesterol levels from birth and do not usually develop clinical symptoms of heart disease until after age 30. Adults with this disease have blood cholesterol levels ranging from 300 to 550 mg/100 mL. About 75% of men with this condition will have a heart attack before the age of 60, compared to only 15% of unaffected men.[3]

To study familial hypercholesterolemia, Brown and Goldstein grew cells in culture. They observed that when LDL cholesterol was added to the culture medium, the rate of cholesterol synthesis in cells from normal subjects decreased. But, in cells from individuals with familial hypercholesterolemia, the presence of LDL in the medium did not cause a decrease in cholesterol synthesis.[4] By using radioactively labeled LDL particles, Brown and Goldstein were able to demonstrate that in cells from normal individuals, LDL particles bind to the cells and are removed from the surrounding media. In cells from individuals with familial hypercholesterolemia, the LDL particles are unable to bind to the cells and therefore cholesterol cannot be removed from the surrounding media.[5] The binding

(©Visuals Unlimited)

of LDL to the cell was found to be due to a protein on the surface of the cell membrane that was named the *LDL receptor.*

The discovery of the LDL receptor led to an understanding of how the body controls the concentration of LDL cholesterol in the blood. The LDL receptor is a cell surface protein; it is synthesized by the cell and inserted into the cell membrane. The binding of an LDL particle to the receptor results in the movement of the LDL particle into the cell. Cholesterol entering the cell suppresses the synthesis of new cholesterol. An individual who inherits one gene for familial hypercholesterolemia has about half the number of LDL receptors as someone without the disease. Someone who inherits two genes has no LDL receptors. This means that LDL cholesterol is not removed from the blood and the liver continues to synthesize large amounts of cholesterol, causing LDL particles to accumulate in the blood. The elevated cholesterol leads to atherosclerosis and eventually heart attacks.

In 1985 Brown and Goldstein were awarded the Nobel Prize in Medicine for their work on cholesterol and LDL receptors. As a result of their research, scientists now understand the basis for elevated blood cholesterol and its importance in the development of heart disease. And physicians and pharmacologists have been able to develop treatments to reduce blood cholesterol levels.

[1]Fredrickson, D. S., Goldstein, J. L., and Brown, M. S. The familial hypercholesterolemias. In *The Metabolic Basis of Inherited Disease*, 4th ed. J. B. Stanbury, J. B. Wyngaarden, and D. S. Fredrickson, eds. New York: McGraw-Hill, 1974, pp. 604–655.

[2]Goldstein, J. L., and Brown, M. S. The LDL receptor locus and the genetics of familial hypercholesterolemia. *Ann. Rev. Genet.* 13:259–289, 1979.

[3]Stone, N. J., Levy, R. I., Fredrickson, D. S., and Verter, J. Coronary artery disease in 116 kindred with familial type II hyperlipoproteinemia. *Circulation* 49:476–478, 1974.

[4]Goldstein, J. L., and Brown, M. S. The low-density lipoprotein pathway and its relation to atherosclerosis. *Ann. Rev. Biochem.* 46:897–930, 1977.

[5]Brown, M. S., and Goldstein, J. L. Familial hypercholesterolemia: Defective binding of lipoproteins to cultured fibroblasts associated with impaired regulation of 3-hydroxy-3-methylglutaryl coenzyme A reductase activity. *Proc. Nat. Acad. Sci.* 71:788–792, 1974.

Transport from the Liver

The liver is the major lipid-producing organ in the body. Here excess protein, carbohydrate, or alcohol can be broken down and used to make triglycerides or cholesterol. Triglycerides made in the liver are incorporated into lipoprotein particles called **very-low-density lipoproteins (VLDLs)**. Cholesterol synthesized in the liver or delivered in chylomicron remnants can also be incorporated into VLDLs or can be used to make bile. VLDLs transport lipids out of the liver and deliver triglycerides to body cells. As with chylomicrons, the enzyme lipoprotein lipase breaks down the triglycerides in VLDLs so that the fatty acids can be taken up by surrounding cells. Once the triglycerides are removed from the VLDLs, a denser, smaller, intermediate-density lipoprotein (IDL) remains. About two-thirds of the IDLs are returned to the liver, and the rest are transformed in the blood into **low-density lipoproteins (LDLs)**. LDLs contain less triglyceride and therefore proportionally more cholesterol than VLDLs and are the primary cholesterol delivery system for cells (see Figure 5.13).

Cholesterol Delivery For LDLs to be taken up by cells, a protein on the surface of the LDL particle called *apoprotein B (apo B)* must bind to a receptor protein on the cell membrane, called an **LDL receptor**. This binding allows LDLs to be removed from the blood circulation and enter cells where their cholesterol and other components can be used (see Figure 5.13). If the amount of LDL cholesterol in the blood exceeds the amount that can be taken up by cells—due to either too much LDL cholesterol or too few LDL receptors—the result is a high level of LDL cholesterol.[8] High levels of LDL particles in the blood have been associated with an increased risk for heart disease (see Science Applied: A Genetic Disease and Cholesterol Regulation).

Reverse Cholesterol Transport

Because most body cells have no system for breaking down cholesterol, it must be returned to the liver to be eliminated from the body. This reverse cholesterol transport is accomplished by the densest of the lipoprotein particles, called **high-density lipoproteins (HDLs)** (see Figure 5.13). These particles originate from the intestinal tract and liver and circulate in the blood, picking up cholesterol from other lipoproteins and body cells. They function as a temporary storage site for lipid. Some of the cholesterol in HDLs is taken directly to the liver for disposal, and some is transferred to organs that have a high requirement for cholesterol, such as those involved in steroid hormone synthesis. High levels of HDL in the blood help prevent cholesterol from depositing in the artery walls and are associated with a reduction in heart disease risk.

5.5 Lipid Functions in the Body

Learning Objectives

- List four functions of lipids in the body.
- Discuss how fatty acids are used to generate ATP.

After lipids have been delivered to cells, they can be used to make structural and regulatory molecules, stored as an energy reserve, or be broken down via cellular respiration to produce carbon dioxide, water, and energy in the form of ATP.

Structure and Lubrication

Most of the lipids in the human body are triglycerides stored in **adipose tissue**, which lies under the skin and around internal organs. Deposits of adipose tissue help define our body shape and contours (**Figure 5.14**). In addition to providing stored energy, adipose tissue insulates the body from changes in temperature and provides a cushion to protect internal organs against shock. Lipids are also important structural

very-low-density lipoproteins (VLDLs) Lipoproteins assembled by the liver that carry lipids from the liver and deliver triglycerides to body cells.

low-density lipoproteins (LDLs) Lipoproteins that transport cholesterol to cells. Elevated LDL cholesterol increases the risk of cardiovascular disease.

LDL receptor A protein on the surface of cells that binds to LDL particles and allows their contents to be taken up for use by the cell.

high-density lipoproteins (HDLs) Lipoproteins that pick up cholesterol from cells and transport it to the liver so that it can be eliminated from the body. A high level of HDL decreases the risk of cardiovascular disease.

adipose tissue Tissue found under the skin and around body organs that is composed of fat-storing cells.

Figure 5.14 Adipose tissue cells contain large droplets of triglyceride that push the other cell components to the perimeter of the cell. (Ed Reschke/Peter Arnold, Inc.)

components at the cellular level, particularly in the brain and nervous system where they form an insulating coating around nerves. As components of all cell membranes, lipids define the boundaries of cells and partition off their organelles. Lipids are also important for lubricating body surfaces. For example, glands in the skin and mucous membranes of the eyes release oils that lubricate these tissues.

Regulation

Cholesterol and fatty acids are both used to synthesize regulatory molecules in the body. Cholesterol, either consumed in the diet or made in the liver, is used to make a number of hormones including the sex hormones estrogen and testosterone and the stress hormone cortisol. Polyunsaturated fatty acids are used to make hormone-like molecules that help regulate blood pressure, blood clotting, and other functions. However, unlike cholesterol, which is synthesized by the liver, the body cannot make all the fatty acids it needs so certain types must be consumed in the diet.

essential fatty acids Fatty acids that must be consumed in the diet because they cannot be made by the body or cannot be made in sufficient quantities to meet needs.

Essential Fatty Acids The human body is capable of synthesizing most of the fatty acids it needs from glucose or other sources of carbon, hydrogen, and oxygen. Humans, however, are not able to synthesize double bonds in the omega-6 and omega-3 positions. Therefore, the fatty acids linoleic acid (omega-6) and alpha-linolenic acid (omega-3) are **essential fatty acids**. Essential fatty acids are important for the formation of the phospholipids that give cell membranes their structure and functional properties. As such, omega-6 fatty acids are important for growth, skin integrity, fertility, and maintaining red blood cell structure. Omega-3 fatty acids are particularly important for cell membranes in the retina of the eye and the central nervous system. If the diet is low in linoleic acid or alpha-linolenic acid, the fatty acids synthesized from them become dietary essentials. Arachidonic acid is an omega-6 fatty acid synthesized from linoleic acid (**Figure 5.15**). Arachidonic acid is considered essential only when the diet is low in linoleic acid. It is found in both animal and vegetable fats. EPA and DHA are omega-3 fatty acids synthesized from alpha-linolenic acid. Arachidonic acid and DHA are necessary for normal brain development in infants and young children. Essential fatty acids also serve as regulators of glucose and fatty acid metabolism through their role in gene expression.

Figure 5.15 Essential fatty acids If the diet contains enough of the essential fatty acids linoleic acid and alpha-linolenic acid, enough of the longer chain omega-6 and omega-3 fatty acids can usually be synthesized.

Eicosanoid Synthesis and Function Both omega-6 and omega-3 fatty acids are used to make hormone-like molecules called **eicosanoids**. Eicosanoids help regulate blood clotting, blood pressure, immune function, and other body processes. The effect an eicosanoid has on these functions depends on the fatty acid from which it is made. For example, when the omega-6 fatty acid arachidonic acid is the starting material, the eicosanoid synthesized increases blood clotting; whereas when the eicosanoid is made from the omega-3 fatty acid EPA, it decreases blood clotting. Omega-3 fatty acids, particularly EPA and DHA, have anti-inflammatory properties. Some of this effect is due to the amounts and types of eicosanoids made and some is due to the effects these fatty acids have on other aspects of cell function. Since inflammation plays a role in the progression of heart disease, a nutrient with anti-inflammatory properties would protect against heart disease. Epidemiological studies and feeding trials both provide evidence for a beneficial effect of omega-3 fatty acids on the manifestations of heart disease and stroke.[9] The anti-inflammatory properties of omega-3 fatty acid have also been shown to be of benefit in other inflammatory and autoimmune diseases such as rheumatoid arthritis, inflammatory bowel disorders, and multiple sclerosis.[10]

The ratio of dietary omega-6 to omega-3 essential fatty acids affects the balance of these fatty acids in the tissues and therefore the ratio of the types of eicosanoids made from them. In order to maintain a healthy balance in the body a dietary ratio of linoleic to alpha-linolenic acid of 5:1 to 10:1 is recommended. To provide this ratio a diet that contains 20 grams of linoleic acid would need to include 2 to 4 grams of alpha-linolenic acid. However, if the diet contains plenty of arachidonic acid, EPA, and DHA, which are made from linoleic and alpha-linolenic acid, the actual ratio of linoleic to alpha-linolenic is less of a concern.[2] The American diet contains plenty of omega-6 fatty acids, so to get a healthier mix of omega-6's and omega-3's Americans should increase their intake of omega-3's from foods such as fish, walnuts, flaxseed, leafy green vegetables, and canola oil (see Table 5.1).[11]

eicosanoids Regulatory molecules, including prostaglandins and related compounds, that can be synthesized from omega-3 and omega-6 fatty acids.

ATP Production

Lipids consumed in the diet can be used as an immediate source of energy or stored in adipose tissue for future use. Throughout the day, triglycerides are continuously stored and then broken down depending on the immediate energy needs of the body. For example, after a meal some triglycerides will be stored; then, between meals some of the stored triglycerides will be broken down to provide energy. When the energy in the diet equals the body's energy requirements, the net amount of stored triglyceride in the body does not change.

Using Triglycerides to Provide Energy In muscle and other tissues, fatty acids and glycerol from triglycerides can be used to produce ATP. In the first step of this process, called **beta-oxidation**, the carbon chain of fatty acids is broken into 2-carbon units that form acetyl-CoA and release high-energy electrons (**Figure 5.16**, **Figure 5.17**).

To enter the citric acid cycle acetyl-CoA combines with oxaloacetate, a 4-carbon molecule derived from carbohydrate, to form a 6-carbon molecule called *citric acid*. The reactions of the citric acid cycle then remove one carbon at a time to produce carbon dioxide (see Figure 5.17). After two carbons have been removed in this manner, a 4-carbon oxaloacetate molecule is re-formed and the cycle can begin again. The high-energy electrons released in beta-oxidation and the citric acid cycle are shuttled to the last stage of cellular respiration, the electron transport chain. Molecules in this chain accept electrons and pass them down the chain until they are finally combined with oxygen to form water. The energy in the electrons is used to generate ATP. The glycerol from triglyceride breakdown can also be used to produce ATP or to make glucose via gluconeogenesis. Glycerol makes up only a small proportion of the carbon in a triglyceride molecule, so the amount of glucose that can result from triglyceride breakdown is small.

beta-oxidation The first step in the production of ATP from fatty acids. This pathway breaks the carbon chain of fatty acids into two-carbon units that form acetyl-CoA and releases high-energy electrons that are passed to the electron transport chain.

Figure 5.16 **Beta-oxidation**
Beta-oxidation of a molecule of palmitic acid, which contains 16 carbons, produces 8 molecules of acetyl-CoA and 8 high-energy electrons that are passed to the electron transport chain to generate ATP.

Storing Fat in Adipose Tissue When energy is ingested in excess of needs, as in when we feast, the excess can be stored in adipose tissue. Excess energy consumed as fat can be transported directly from the intestines to the adipose tissue in chylomicrons. Excess energy consumed as carbohydrate or protein must first go to the liver, where the carbohydrate and protein can be used, although inefficiently, to synthesize fatty acids; these fatty acids are then assembled into triglycerides, which are transported to the adipose tissue in VLDLs. Lipoprotein lipase at the membrane of cells lining the blood vessels breaks down the triglycerides from both chylomicrons and VLDLs so that the fatty acids can enter the cells, where they are reassembled into triglycerides for storage (**Figure 5.18**).

The ability of the body to store fat is theoretically limitless. Fat cells can increase in weight by about 50 times, and new fat cells can be synthesized when existing cells reach their maximum size (see Chapter 7). Because each gram of fat provides 9 kcalories, compared with only 4 kcalories per gram from carbohydrate or protein, a large amount of energy can be stored in the body as fat without a great increase in size or weight. Even a lean man, whose body fat is only about 10% of his weight, stores over 50,000 kcalories of energy as fat.

hormone-sensitive lipase
An enzyme present in adipose cells that responds to chemical signals by breaking down triglycerides into fatty acids and glycerol for release into the bloodstream.

Using Stored Fat When less energy is consumed than is needed, as when we fast, the body uses energy from fat stores. In this situation, the enzyme **hormone-sensitive lipase** inside the fat cells receives a hormonal signal that turns on enzyme activity so it begins breaking down stored triglycerides (see Figure 5.18). The fatty acids and glycerol are released directly into the blood, where they can be taken up by cells throughout the body to produce ATP. If there is not enough carbohydrate to allow acetyl-CoA from fat breakdown to enter the citric acid cycle (see Figure 5.17), it will be used to make ketones. Ketones can be used as an energy source by muscle and adipose tissue. During prolonged starvation, the brain can adapt to use ketones to meet about half of its energy needs. For the other half, it must use glucose. Fatty acids cannot be used to make glucose, and only a small amount of glucose can be made from glycerol.

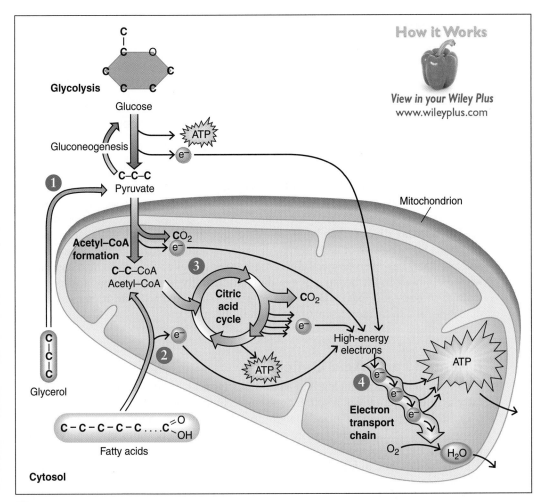

1. Glycerol molecules, which contain three carbon atoms, can be used to produce ATP or small amounts of glucose.

2. Fatty acids are transported inside the mitochondria where beta-oxidation splits the carbon chains into two-carbon units that form acetyl-CoA and produces high-energy electrons.

3. If oxygen and enough carbohydrate are available, acetyl-CoA combines with oxaloacetate to enter the citric acid cycle, producing two molecules of carbon dioxide and releasing high-energy electrons that are shuttled to the electron transport chain.

4. In the final step of aerobic metabolism, the energy in the high-energy electrons released from beta-oxidation and the citric acid cycle is trapped and used to produce ATP and water.

Figure 5.17 Triglyceride metabolism
The breakdown of triglycerides yields fatty acids and a small amount of glycerol. Fatty acids provide most of the energy stored in a triglyceride molecule.

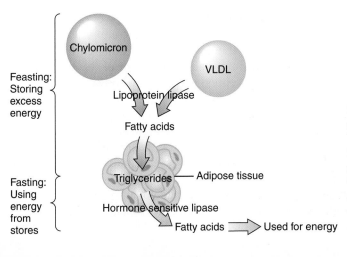

Figure 5.18 Storing and retrieving energy in fat
The enzymes lipoprotein lipase and hormone-sensitive lipase mediate the storage and removal of triglycerides in adipose tissue according to energy intake and energy needs.

5.6 Lipids and Health

Learning Objectives

- Distinguish dietary lipids that increase the risk of heart disease from those that decrease the risk.
- Discuss the relationship between dietary fat and cancer.
- Explain how dietary fat intake is related to obesity.

cardiovascular disease
Any disease affecting the heart and blood vessels.

Adequate amounts of essential fatty acids must be consumed in the diet to maintain health. However, diets high in fat, particularly certain types of fats, are associated with an increased risk for many chronic diseases. The development of **cardiovascular disease** has been linked to diets high in cholesterol, saturated fat, and *trans fat*.[2] The risk of certain types of cancer, including that of the breast, colon, and prostate, has been associated with a high-fat intake. Obesity is also associated with diets high in fat because these diets are usually high in energy and promote storage of body fat. Excess body fat in turn is associated with an increased risk of diabetes, cardiovascular disease, and high blood pressure.

Essential Fatty Acid Deficiency

essential fatty acid deficiency A condition characterized by dry scaly skin and poor growth that results when the diet does not supply sufficient amounts of the essential fatty acids.

If adequate amounts of linoleic and alpha-linolenic acid are not consumed, an **essential fatty acid deficiency** will result. Symptoms include scaly, dry skin, liver abnormalities, poor healing of wounds, growth failure in infants, and impaired vision and hearing. Essential fatty acid deficiency is rare because the requirement for essential fatty acids is well below the typical intake. Deficiencies have been seen in infants and young children fed low-fat diets and in individuals who are unable to absorb lipids.

Cardiovascular Disease

Over 80 million people in the United States suffer from some form of cardiovascular disease. It is the number one cause of death of both men and women in the United States.[12] Epidemiological studies have shown that diet and lifestyle both affect the risk of developing heart disease. The relationship between dietary fat and heart disease risk is one that has been extensively studied. In general, populations that consume high-fat diets have a higher incidence of heart disease, but this does not always hold true. Populations that consume a diet high in omega-3 fatty acids, such as the Inuits in Greenland, have a low incidence of heart disease.[13] In Mediterranean countries, where the diet is high in monounsaturated fat as well as grains and vegetables, death from heart disease is also less frequent.[14]

atherosclerosis A type of cardiovascular disease that involves the buildup of fatty material in the artery walls.

atherosclerotic plaque The cholesterol-rich material that is deposited in the arteries of individuals with atherosclerosis. It consists of cholesterol, smooth muscle cells, fibrous tissue, and eventually calcium.

How Does Atherosclerosis Develop? Atherosclerosis is a type of cardiovascular disease in which lipids and fibrous material are deposited in the artery walls, reducing their elasticity and eventually blocking the flow of blood. Although the deposition of lipids within the artery wall is an important component of the process, we now know that inflammation, which is the process whereby the body responds to injury, is what drives the formation of **atherosclerotic plaque**. An inflammatory response is initiated by an injury, such as when you cut yourself. White blood cells, which are part of the immune system, rush to the injured area, blood clots form, and new tissue grows to heal the wound. Similar inflammatory responses occur when an artery is injured, but instead of resulting in healing, they lead to the development of atherosclerotic plaque (**Figure 5.19**).

The atherosclerotic process begins as a response to an injury that causes changes in the lining of the artery wall. The exact cause of the injury is not known but may be related to elevated blood levels of LDL cholesterol, glucose, or homocysteine;

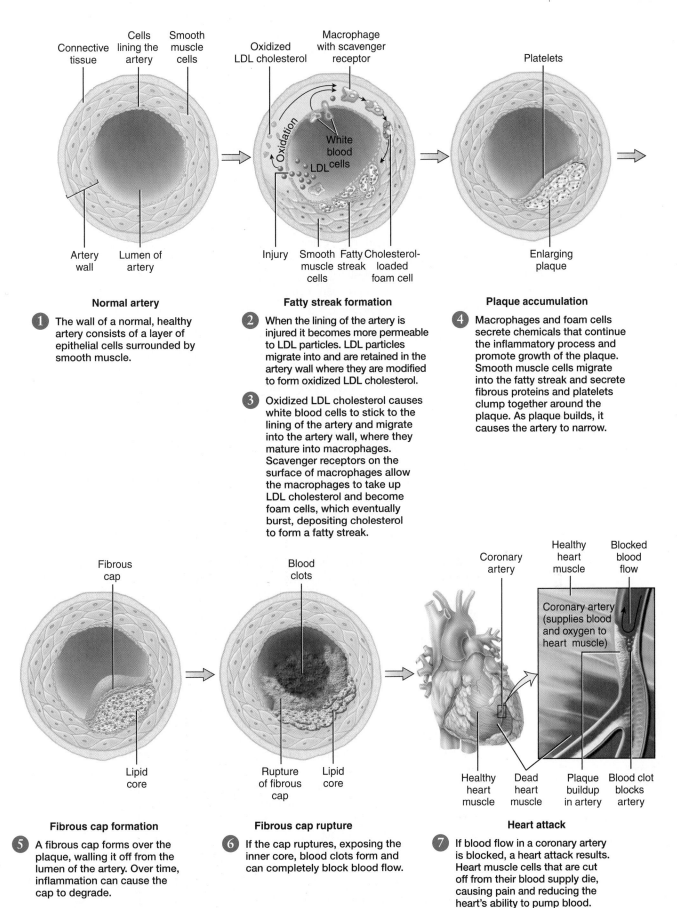

Figure 5.19 Development of atherosclerosis
The inflammation that occurs in response to an injury to the artery wall precipitates the development of atherosclerotic plaque. The build up of plaque can eventually lead to a heart attack or stroke.

high blood pressure; free radicals caused by cigarette smoking; diabetes; genetic alterations; or infectious microorganisms.[15] The specific cause may be different in different people.

Once the initial injury has occurred, the lining of the artery becomes more permeable to LDL particles, which migrate into the artery wall (see Figure 5.19). Once inside, the LDL particles are modified chemically, often by oxidation to form **oxidized LDL cholesterol**. Oxidized LDL cholesterol is harmful and its presence promotes inflammation in a number of ways. It triggers the production and release of substances that cause immune system cells to stick to the lining of the artery and then to migrate into the artery wall. Once inside, these cells become large white blood cells called *macrophages*, which have **scavenger receptors** on their surface. Just as LDL receptors bind to LDL cholesterol, scavenger receptors bind to and transport oxidized LDL cholesterol into the interior of the cell. As macrophages fill with more and more oxidized LDL cholesterol, they are transformed into cholesterol-filled foam cells (named because of their foamy appearance under a microscope). Foam cells accumulate in the artery wall and then burst, depositing cholesterol to form a fatty streak (see Figure 5.19).[15,16]

Macrophages and foam cells secrete growth factors and other chemicals that continue the inflammatory response and promote growth of the plaque. The release of growth factors signals smooth muscle cells from the wall of the artery to migrate into the fatty streak and secrete fibrous proteins. Platelets, which are cell fragments involved in blood clotting, become sticky and clump together around the lesion. As the lesion enlarges it causes the artery to narrow and lose its elasticity, hampering blood flow. As the process progresses a fibrous cap of smooth muscle cells and fibrous proteins forms over the mixture of white blood cells, lipids, and debris, walling it off from the lumen of the artery. The formation of the cap is a way of healing the injury, but if the inflammation continues substances secreted by immune system cells can degrade this cap.[16] If the cap becomes too thin and ruptures, the material leaks out and causes blood clots to form. The clots can completely block the artery at that spot, or break loose and block an artery elsewhere. If this occurs in blood vessels that supply the heart muscle, blood flow to the heart muscle is interrupted and heart cells die, resulting in a heart attack or myocardial infarction (see Figure 5.19). If the blood flow to the brain is interrupted, a stroke results.

Risk Factors for Heart Disease High blood pressure, diabetes, obesity, and high blood cholesterol levels are considered primary risk factors because they directly increase the risk of developing heart disease. Other factors that affect risk include age, gender, genetics, and lifestyle factors such as smoking, exercise, and diet. These may directly affect risk or act indirectly by altering blood cholesterol levels, blood pressure, body weight, or the risk of diabetes (**Table 5.2**).

Diabetes, High Blood Pressure, Obesity, and Blood Cholesterol Levels Individuals with diabetes have an increased risk of developing heart disease. One reason is that the high levels of blood glucose that occur with this disease cause damage to blood vessels, which initiates atherosclerotic events. Elevated blood pressure can also increase risk by damaging blood vessels. In addition, high blood pressure forces the heart to work harder, causing it to enlarge and weaken over time. Obesity both increases the amount of work required by the heart and increases blood pressure, blood cholesterol levels, and the risk of developing diabetes. High blood cholesterol levels, and, in particular, high levels of LDL cholesterol, may also injure artery walls as well as promote plaque formation.

The desirable level for total blood cholesterol in adults is below 200 mg per 100 mL of blood. In healthy adults, LDL cholesterol level should be below 100 mg per 100 mL. In those at high risk for a heart attack, an optimal level of LDL cholesterol is less than or equal to 70 mg per 100 mL. HDL cholesterol is protective against heart disease. An HDL level of less than 40 mg per 100 mL increases risk; a level of 60 mg per 100 mL or above decreases risk (see Table 5.2 and Appendix C).[17] Currently, about 45% of American adults have blood cholesterol levels of 200 mg per 100 mL or more, almost 16% have values of 240 mg per 100 mL or greater.[12]

oxidized LDL cholesterol
A substance formed when the cholesterol in LDL particles is oxidized by reactive oxygen molecules. It is key in the development of atherosclerosis because it contributes to the inflammatory process.

scavenger receptors Proteins on the surface of macrophages that bind to oxidized LDL cholesterol and allow it to be taken up by the cell.

Table 5.2 Risk Factors for Heart Disease

Heart disease risk is increased by the following:

Age:
- men ≥ 45 years
- women ≥ 55 years

Family History:
- male relative with heart disease before age 55
- female relative with heart disease before age 65

Disease Factors:
- Diabetes: fasting blood sugar ≥ 126 mg/100 mL
- High blood pressure: blood pressure ≥ 140/90 mm Hg
- Overweight: body mass index > 25 kg/m^{2}* and waist circumference > 35 inches for women and > 40 inches for men

Altered Blood Lipid Levels:
- LDL cholesterol ≥ 100 mg/100 mL
- HDL cholesterol < 40 mg/100 mL
- Total cholesterol ≥ 200 mg/100 mL
- Triglycerides ≥ 150 mg/100 mL

Lifestyle:
- Cigarette smoking
- A sedentary lifestyle
- A diet high in saturated fat, *trans* fat, and cholesterol and low in fiber, fruits, and vegetables

*See Chapter 7 for information about body mass index and how it can be calculated. See Appendix B.

Age, Gender, Genetics, and Lifestyle Factors The risk of developing heart disease increases with age; four out of five people who die of heart disease are 65 or older (**Figure 5.20**). Men and women are both at risk, but men are generally affected a decade earlier than women. This is due in part to the protective effect of the hormone estrogen in women. As women age, the effects of menopause—including the decline in estrogen level and gain in weight—increase heart disease risk. Although we tend to think of heart disease as a man's disease, cardiovascular disease has claimed the lives of more women than men in every year since 1984.[12]

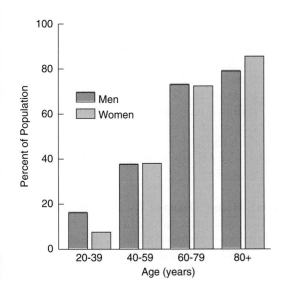

Figure 5.20 Prevalence of Cardiovascular Disease in Adults Age 20 and Older by Age and Sex The incidence of cardiovascular disease increases with age in both men and women. In 2005 454,600 women died of heart disease, compared with 409,900 men. (Source: American Heart Association. Heart Disease and Stroke Statistics: 2009 Update. Available online at http://www.americanheart.org/presenter.jhtml?identifier=3037327. Accessed May 27, 2009.)

Genetics, including ethnic background, also affect risk. Individuals with a male family member who exhibited heart disease before the age of 55 or a female family member who exhibited heart disease before the age of 65 are considered to be at greater risk. African Americans have a higher risk of heart disease than the general population because they are more likely to have high blood pressure. Mexican Americans, Native Americans, and Hawaiians have higher risk, due in part to a higher incidence of diabetes and obesity in these groups.[12]

Lifestyle factors that affect risk include activity level, smoking, and diet. An inactive lifestyle and cigarette smoking both increase the risk of heart disease. On the other hand, regular exercise decreases risk by promoting the maintenance of a healthy body weight, reducing the risk of diabetes, increasing HDL cholesterol, and reducing blood pressure. A number of dietary factors, including high intakes of saturated fat, *trans* fat, and cholesterol, increase risk. Other dietary factors, including adequate intakes of fiber, fruits and vegetables, unsaturated fats, and antioxidants, may offer a protective effect. You can't change your age, gender, or genetic background, but you can control these lifestyle factors (see Critical Thinking: Lowering the Risk of Heart Disease).

Dietary Lipids that Promote Heart Disease Excessive intake of cholesterol, saturated fat, and *trans* fatty acids can increase the risk of cardiovascular disease. Some or all of the effects of these lipids are due to their impact on blood cholesterol levels.

Dietary Cholesterol The extent to which cholesterol intake affects blood levels depends on an individual's genes. Cholesterol in the blood comes from cholesterol both consumed in the diet and made by the liver. Generally, about three to four times more cholesterol is made by the body than is consumed in the diet. In some individuals, as dietary cholesterol increases, liver cholesterol synthesis decreases so that blood levels do not change.[18] In others, however, liver synthesis does not decrease in response to an increase in dietary cholesterol, so blood cholesterol levels rise.

Saturated Fat When the diet is high in saturated fatty acids, liver production of cholesterol-carrying lipoproteins increases and the activity of LDL receptors in the liver is reduced, so that LDL cholesterol cannot be removed from the blood.[19] Therefore diets high in saturated fat increase LDL cholesterol in the blood. Increased LDL then increases the risk of atherosclerosis. When the diet is low in saturated fats, lipoprotein production decreases and the number of LDL receptors increases, allowing more cholesterol to be removed from the bloodstream. This lowers LDL cholesterol levels and the risk of heart disease. Some saturated fatty acids, such as stearic acid found in chocolate and beef, do not increase blood cholesterol levels. However, these may contribute to heart disease by lowering HDL cholesterol, and by affecting blood platelets and blood clotting, both of which are involved in the development of atherosclerosis.[20]

Trans *Fatty Acids* Both clinical and epidemiological studies provide evidence that a high *trans* fatty acid intake increases the risk of heart disease. Some of the increase in risk is due to the effect of *trans* fatty acids on blood cholesterol levels. *Trans* fatty acid intake increases LDL cholesterol levels and, at high intakes, lowers HDL cholesterol. Many studies have found that diets high in *trans* fatty acids cause a greater increase in heart disease risk than those high in saturated fatty acids.[21] This association between *trans* fatty acid intake and heart disease risk is stronger than would be predicted by changes in blood cholesterol alone. It has been hypothesized that *trans* fatty acids may increase the risk of heart disease by increasing inflammation, an important risk factor in the development of atherosclerosis.[22]

Dietary Lipids that Protect Against Heart Disease Dietary omega-6 and omega-3 polyunsaturated fatty acids as well as monounsaturated fatty acids tend to decrease the risk of heart disease. Some of this protection is due to a reduction in LDL cholesterol and an increase in HDL cholesterol, but other mechanisms also play a role.

Critical Thinking
Lowering the Risk
of Heart Disease

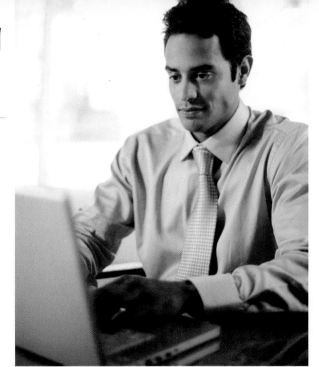

(Brand X Pictures/Getty Images, Inc.)

Background

Rafael is a financial advisor. He spends much of his day at his computer and when he does get out he is in his car or taking a client out to lunch. When he is home with his family he enjoys watching his children play soccer and basketball but rarely finds time to exercise himself. His mother died of a heart attack at age 60. Rafael is worried about his own heart disease risk, so he makes an appointment with his physician. He fills out a questionnaire about his medical history and lifestyle and has blood drawn for cholesterol analysis.

Data

The table below summarizes some of the information that may affect Rafael's risk of developing heart disease:

HEART DISEASE RISK QUESTIONNAIRE

Sex:	Male
Age:	35
Family history:	Mother had heart attack at age 60
Height/weight:	68 inches/160 lbs
Blood pressure:	120/70
Smoker:	Yes
Activity level:	Sedentary
Blood values:	
Total cholesterol	210 mg/100 mL
LDL cholesterol	170 mg/100 mL
HDL cholesterol	34 mg/100 mL
Triglycerides	120 mg/100 mL

Rafael's physician recommends he meet with a dietitian to evaluate his diet. The following information is obtained from a 24-hour diet recall and a food frequency questionnaire.

TYPICAL DAILY INTAKE

Lipids:	
Total fat	33% of kcalories
Saturated fat	18% of kcalories
Polyunsaturated fat	8% of kcalories
Monounsaturated fat	7% of kcalories
Trans fat	7% of kcalories
Cholesterol	350 mg/day
Fiber	22 g/day
Food pattern/amounts:	
Whole grains	2 oz equivalents/day
Vegetables and fruits	3 cups/day
Whole-fat dairy products	3 cups/day
Red meat	6 oz/day
Solid fats	3 tsp/day
Nuts and seeds	0
Legumes	0

Critical Thinking Questions

Is Rafael at risk for a heart attack? Review his risk factor questionnaire and list the factors that increase his risk.

▼

What about his diet? Based on the information from his typical intake, how does his fat intake compare with recommendations? Are there any other food choices he makes that increase his risk?

▼

Suggest some diet and lifestyle changes that would reduce Rafael's risk of developing heart disease.

 iProfile Use iProfile to find dinner entrées that are low in saturated fat and cholesterol.

Figure 5.21 Fish, walnuts, flaxseed, and canola oil are good sources of omega-3 fatty acids. (Andy Washnik)

Video

Omega-6 and Omega-3 Polyunsaturated Fat When saturated fat in the diet is replaced by any type of polyunsaturated fat (except *trans*), blood levels of LDL cholesterol decrease.[17] However, a high intake of omega-6 polyunsaturated fatty acids may also cause a slight decrease in HDL cholesterol, which is undesirable in terms of heart disease risk. Increasing omega-3 fatty acid intake lowers levels of LDL cholesterol but not HDL cholesterol.[17] In addition to their effects on blood lipids, omega-3 fatty acids may also reduce heart disease risk by preventing the growth of atherosclerotic plaque and by promoting the synthesis of eicosanoids that protect against heart disease. Because the beneficial effects are greater when the omega-3 fatty acids are consumed in fish as opposed to supplements, the American Heart Association recommends consuming fish two times a week to increase omega-3 intakes (**Figure 5.21**).[11]

Monounsaturated Fat Populations with diets high in monounsaturated fats, such as those in Mediterranean countries where olive oil is commonly used, have a mortality rate from heart disease that is half of that in the United States (**Figure 5.22**). This is true even when total fat intake provides 40% or more of energy intake.[23] Substituting monounsaturated fat for saturated fat reduces unhealthy LDL cholesterol without decreasing healthy HDL cholesterol and makes LDL cholesterol less susceptible to oxidation.[17] However, the type of fat in the diet is unlikely to be the only factor responsible for the difference in the incidence of heart disease between the Mediterranean countries and the United States. The typical Mediterranean diet is higher in fruits and vegetables, lower in animal products, includes more wine, and is consumed in countries where the lifestyle includes more day-to-day activity and has fewer of the stresses of modern life.

Other Dietary Factors that Affect Heart Disease Risk The amount and type of fat are not the only dietary factors that affect the risk of developing heart disease. Intakes of foods high in fiber, antioxidants, and B vitamins, as well as moderate alcohol consumption can reduce the risk of developing heart disease. On the other hand, too much added sugar and salt can increase risk by contributing to the development of high blood triglycerides or high blood pressure, respectively (see Chapters 4 and 10).

Plant Foods A number of studies have demonstrated an inverse relationship between the consumption of fruits and vegetables and the incidence of cardiovascular disease.[24] Many of the dietary components that protect you from heart disease are found in plant foods. Fruits, vegetables, whole grains, and legumes are good sources of fiber, vitamins, minerals, and phytochemicals. Soluble fibers, such as

Figure 5.22 The high proportion of monounsaturated fatty acids in olive oil, which is used liberally in the Mediterranean diet, is one factor believed to contribute to the health of the people in the Mediterranean region. (Frank Wieder/StockFood Munich/StockFoodAmerica)

those in oat bran, legumes, psyllium, pectin, and gums, have been shown to reduce blood cholesterol levels and therefore reduce heart disease risk (see Chapter 4). The vitamins, minerals, and phytochemicals in plant foods protect against heart disease because many have antioxidant functions. Antioxidants decrease the oxidation of LDL cholesterol and therefore are hypothesized to prevent development of plaque in artery walls.[24]

B Vitamins Adequate intakes of vitamin B_6, vitamin B_{12}, and folic acid can help protect against heart disease because they keep blood levels of the amino acid homocysteine low (see Chapter 8). Elevated homocysteine levels are associated with a higher incidence of heart disease.[25] Higher levels of these B vitamins in the blood are related to lower levels of homocysteine. The fortification of enriched grains with folic acid in 1998 increased folic acid intake and has resulted in a reduction in blood homocysteine levels in the American population.[26] There is not sufficient evidence supporting the relationship between intake of these vitamins and homocysteine levels to recommend supplements, but a diet high in grains, fruits, and vegetables is advised to assure adequate intake.

Niacin is another B vitamin that may affect heart disease risk. When consumed in extremely high doses the nicotinic acid form of niacin can be used to lower blood cholesterol. Nicotinic acid is inexpensive and widely available without a prescription, but at the high doses needed to lower cholesterol it is really a drug, not a nutrient. Because of the potential side effects, an individual using nicotinic acid as a drug to lower cholesterol should be monitored by a physician.

Moderate Alcohol Consumption Alcohol can be a dangerous drug, but moderate alcohol consumption has been shown to reduce stress, to raise levels of HDL cholesterol, and to reduce blood clotting and thus reduce the risk of cardiovascular disease.[27] These effects are greater when red wine is consumed, as it commonly is in France, Italy, and Greece. Red wine is high in phytochemicals called *polyphenols*, which are antioxidants that protect against LDL oxidation, and may have other effects that protect against the development of atherosclerosis.[28] The Dietary Guidelines recognize that in middle-aged and older adults moderate alcohol consumption can lower the risk of heart disease.[29] Moderate drinking means no more than one drink per day for women and two drinks per day for men. One drink is defined as 12 ounces of beer, 5 ounces of wine, or 1.5 ounces of 80-proof distilled spirits. Greater intake of alcohol increases the risk of accidental deaths, heart disease, cancer, birth defects, and drug interactions and should be avoided. Alcohol consumption is not recommended for children or adolescents, pregnant women, individuals who cannot restrict their drinking to a moderate amount, or individuals who plan to drive or perform other activities that require concentration (see Focus on Alcohol).

Life Cycle

Dietary Fat and Cancer

Cancer is the second leading cause of death in the United States. As with cardiovascular disease, epidemiology suggests that diet and lifestyle affect cancer risk. It is estimated that 30% to 40% of cancers are directly linked to dietary and lifestyle choices.[30] Populations consuming diets high in fruits and vegetables tend to have a lower cancer risk. These foods are high in fiber and provide antioxidant vitamins and phytochemicals. In contrast, populations that consume diets high in fat, particularly animal fats, have a higher cancer incidence. The mechanism whereby a high intake of dietary fat increases the incidence of various cancers is less well understood than the relationship between dietary fat and cardiovascular disease; however, dietary fat has been suggested to be both a tumor promoter and tumor initiator, depending on the type of cancer. The good news is that for the most part the same type of diet that protects you from cardiovascular disease will also protect you from certain forms of cancer.

Dietary Fat and Breast Cancer Breast cancer is the leading form of cancer in women worldwide. In the United States, over 234,000 new cases occur among women annually.[31] The incidence is similar among all ethnic groups, but the mortality is higher among minority women. Breast cancer is more common in postmenopausal women, in women who have had no children or who had children later in life, and in women with a family history of the disease.[32]

The type of fat in the diet may affect the risk of breast cancer. For example, the incidence of breast cancer in Mediterranean women who rely on olive oil, high in monounsaturated fat, as a source of dietary fat is low despite a total fat intake similar to that in the United States.[33] Epidemiology also supports a protective effect from an increased intake of omega-3 fatty acids from fish and shellfish.[34] *Trans* fatty acids on the other hand, have been suggested to increase the risk of breast cancer.[35]

The mechanism by which diet affects breast cancer has been studied in laboratory animals. Since most laboratory animals do not get breast cancer tumors, studies are conducted by implanting breast tumors and examining how diet affects their growth. These experiments demonstrate that dietary fat is a tumor promoter; the tumors are more likely to grow in mice fed a high-fat diet than in those fed a low-fat diet. The type of fat also affects tumor growth; in animals fed diets high in linoleic acid, which is found in polyunsaturated vegetable oils, the tumors grow faster than in rats fed diets high in saturated fatty acids or omega-3 fatty acids. However, these animal studies have not been supported by human trials.[36]

Dietary Fat and Colon Cancer Epidemiology has correlated the incidence of colon cancer with high-fat, low-fiber diets. Diets high in saturated fats from red meat are associated with a higher incidence of colon and prostate cancer.[37] Diets that are high in omega-3 fatty acids from fish are associated with a lower incidence of colon cancer.[38] The connection between dietary fat and colon cancer may be related to the breakdown of fat in the large intestine. Here, bacteria metabolize dietary fat and bile, producing substances that may act as tumor initiators. A high intake of fiber tends to dilute these carcinogens by increasing the volume of feces. High-fiber diets also decrease transit time. Both of these effects reduce the exposure of the intestinal mucosa to hazardous substances in the colon contents (see Chapter 4).

Dietary Fat and Obesity

In addition to affecting the risk of heart disease and cancer, dietary fat has been postulated to contribute to weight gain and obesity. One reason is that fat has 9 kcalories per gram—almost twice as much as either carbohydrate or protein. Therefore, a high-fat meal contains more kcalories in the same volume as a lower-fat meal. And, because people have a tendency to eat a certain weight or volume of food—if that food is high in fat it will contain more kcalories and contribute to weight gain.[39] High-fat diets also tend to promote overconsumption because energy from fat is less satiating than energy from carbohydrate, so when eating a high-fat meal you will eat more kcalories before you feel full.[40] The way fat is metabolized may also contribute to weight gain. It takes less energy for the body to use fat as an energy source and excess dietary fat is stored very efficiently as body fat (see Chapter 7).

Despite evidence that fat is fattening, the fat content of the American diet is unlikely to be the reason for the high rate of obesity in the United States. Short-term clinical trials show that reducing fat intake reduces energy intake, resulting in a modest reduction in body weight.[41] However, epidemiological studies do not show a relationship between fat in the diet and body weight.[42] Weight gain occurs when more energy is consumed than expended, regardless of whether the extra energy comes from fat, carbohydrate, or protein. The increasing prevalence of overweight and obesity in the United States and worldwide is likely due to increasing energy intake and decreasing energy expenditure.[43]

5.7 Meeting Recommendations for Fat Intake

Learning Objectives

- List the recommendations for fat and cholesterol intake.
- Use food labels to choose foods that provide healthy fats.
- Review a diet and suggest modifications that would help it meet current recommendations for the types and amounts of fat.

About 33% of the energy in the typical U.S. diet comes from fat.[1] This amount will easily meet the minimum requirements for essential fatty acids and is within the range of acceptable fat intakes for healthy adults. However, a healthy diet must also provide the right types of fat and include plenty of whole grains, legumes, vegetables, and fruits, which are high in fiber, micronutrients, and phytochemicals.

Types of Lipid Recommendations

Fat is needed in the diet to provide essential fatty acids, to allow the absorption of fat-soluble vitamins and phytochemicals, and to provide energy. The amounts needed for this are small but a diet that provides only the minimum amount of fat would be very high in carbohydrate, not be very palatable, and not necessarily be any healthier than diets with more fat. Therefore the DRI recommendations regarding fat include AIs for essential fatty acids as well as Acceptable Macronutrient Distribution Ranges (AMDR) for essential fatty acids and total fat intake. The DRIs also suggest that since there is no specific dietary need for saturated fats, cholesterol, or *trans* fat that these be reduced as much as possible.

Recommendations for Essential Fatty Acids The amounts of the essential fatty acids recommended by the DRIs are based on the amounts consumed by the healthy U.S. population. The AI for linoleic acid is 12 grams per day for women and 17 grams per day for men. You can meet your requirement by consuming a half cup of walnuts or 2 tablespoons of safflower oil. For alpha-linolenic acid, the AI is 1.1 grams per day for women and 1.6 grams per day for men. Your requirement can be met by eating a quarter cup of walnuts or a tablespoon of canola oil or ground flaxseeds. Consuming these amounts provides the recommended ratio of linoleic to alpha-linolenic acid of between 5:1 and 10:1.[2] AMDRs of 5% to 10% of energy for linoleic acid and 0.6% to 1.2% of energy for alpha-linolenic acid (with 10% or less of this as EPA and DHA) have been set.[2]

A Healthy Range for Fat Intake The DRIs recommend a total fat intake of 20% to 35% of kcalories for adults; this range allows for a variety of individual preferences in terms of food choices. Fat intakes above this range generally result in a higher intake of saturated fat and make it more difficult to avoid consuming excess kcalories. Intakes below 20% increase the probability that vitamin E and essential fatty acid intakes will be low and may contribute to unfavorable changes in HDL and triglyceride levels.

Because children and teens need more total fat in their diets to meet their needs for growth, the AMDRs for fat are higher for these groups: 30% to 40% of energy for ages 1 to 3 years, and 25% to 35% of energy for ages 4 to 18 years. These amounts meet the needs for growth and are unlikely to increase the risk of chronic disease.

The AMDRs for fat intake are not increased during pregnancy or lactation, but the AIs for essential fatty acids are slightly higher than those for nonpregnant women. Recommendations are not different for older adults. In this population, fat intake must be carefully balanced with other nutrients to reduce the risk of malnutrition (see Chapter 16).

Life Cycle

Table 5.3 Diets to Reduce Cancer Risks

- Choose mostly plant foods, limit red meats and processed meats
  - ○ Choose more whole grains, nuts and seeds
  - ○ Eat plenty of fruits and vegetables

- Maintain a healthy weight throughout life
  - ○ Avoid sugary drinks
  - ○ Choose energy dense foods
  - ○ Exercise portion control

- Be physically active for at least 30 minutes every day.

- If consumed at all, limit alcoholic drinks to 2 for men and 1 for women a day.

- Limit consumption of salty foods and foods processed with salt.

And always remember—do not smoke or chew tobacco.

Source: Adapted from American Institute for Cancer Research (AICR) Guidelines for Reducing Cancer Risk. Available online at www.aicr.org/ Accessed February 1, 2009.

Limit Cholesterol, Saturated, and *Trans* Fat The DRIs have not set specific guidelines for cholesterol, saturated fat, or *trans* fat, but they recommend that intake of these be kept to a minimum because the risk of heart disease increases as intakes rise. The Dietary Guidelines and Daily Values on food labels give more specific recommendations: less than 10% of energy as saturated fat and no more than 300 mg of cholesterol per day.[29] No Daily Value has been established for *trans* fat, but it is recommended that intake not increase above the current average level of 5.8 grams daily or 2.6% of energy intake.[44]

Guidelines for Prevention of Specific Diseases

In addition to these general recommendations for fat intake, some dietary recommendations target populations at risk for specific diseases. Recommendations for a diet to reduce cancer risk are included in **Table 5.3**. The American Heart Association and the National Cholesterol Education Program (NCEP) have developed recommendations to lower heart disease risk (Appendix G) (**Figure 5.23**).[17] The NCEP recommends that people with heart disease and those with risk factors for heart disease including diabetes, change their diet and lifestyle to reduce their risk (**Table 5.4**).

Figure 5.23 The National Cholesterol Education Program recommends that all adults have their blood cholesterol levels checked at least every 5 years. (Will and Deni McEntyre/Photo Researchers)

Table 5.4 Dietary Recommendations to Reduce Blood Cholesterol

Dietary Factor	Recommendation
Saturated fat	Less than 7% of kcalories
Polyunsaturated fat	Up to 10% of kcalories
Monounsaturated fat	Up to 20% of kcalories
Cholesterol	Less than 200 mg/day
Total fat	25%–35% of kcalories
Protein	Approximately 15% of kcalories
Carbohydrate	50%–60% of total kcalories
Soluble fiber	10–25 g/day
Plant stanols	2 g/day
Sodium	2400 mg/day or less
Total kcalories	Balance to maintain a desirable body weight

Source: Adapted from National Cholesterol Education Program.

The NCEP also recommends drug therapy for individuals with extremely high cholesterol levels or for those for whom lifestyle changes are not effective. The most common drugs used to treat elevated blood cholesterol are the statins; these work by blocking cholesterol synthesis in the liver and by increasing the capacity of the liver to remove cholesterol from the blood. Other cholesterol-lowering drugs act in the gastrointestinal tract by preventing cholesterol and bile absorption.

Tools for Assessing Fat Intake

How does your diet compare with the recommendation of 20% to 35% of energy from fat and less than 10% of energy as saturated fat? **Table 5.5** illustrates how to calculate fat intake as a percent of energy. This same calculation can be used to determine the percent of energy as fat or saturated fat in individual foods. To calculate the percent of energy as fat, you need to know the amount of fat in a food or in the diet. This can be estimated from the Exchange Lists or determined using values from food labels or food composition tables or data bases (see Nutrient Content of Foods Supplement or iProfile).

Table 5.5 **Calculating Percent of Energy from Fat**

Determine
- The total energy (kcalorie) intake for the day
- The grams of fat in the day's diet

Calculate Energy from Fat
- Fat provides 9 kcal/g
- Multiply grams of fat by 9 kcal/g

$$\text{Energy (kcal) from fat} = \text{grams fat} \times 9 \text{ kcal/g fat}$$

Calculate % Energy from Fat
- Divide energy from fat by total energy and multiply by 100 to express as a percent

$$\text{Percent of energy from fat} = \frac{\text{kcal from fat}}{\text{Total kcal}} \times 100$$

For example:

A diet contains 2000 kcal and 75 g of fat

$$75 \text{ g of fat} \times 9 \text{ kcal/g} = 675 \text{ kcal from fat}$$

$$\frac{675 \text{ kcal from fat}}{2000 \text{ kcal}} \times 100 = 34\% \text{ of energy (kcals) from fat}$$

Fat Exchange Lists Exchange Lists can be used to give a quick estimate of the total amount of fat in a food or in the diet (**Table 5.6**; Appendix I). An exchange from the fat list contains 5 grams of fat. An exchange of fruits, vegetables, or breads contains 1 gram or less. An exchange of dairy products provides 0 to 8 grams depending on what items you choose to consume. A serving of nonfat milk provides less than a gram of fat, but a serving of whole milk contains 8 grams. Likewise, the amount of fat in a meat exchange depends on your choice; an ounce of very lean meat such as turkey breast contains 1 gram of fat or less, whereas an ounce of bologna contains 8 grams.

Fats on Food Labels Food labels provide an accessible source of information on the fat content of packaged foods. Understanding how to use this information can help you make more informed choices about the foods you include in your diet. Unfortunately, food labels are not always available on fresh meats, which are one of the main contributors of fat in our diets (see Off the Label: Choosing Lean Meat).

Table 5.6 Using Exchange Lists to Estimate Fat Content

Exchange Groups/Lists	Serving Size	Fat (g)
Carbohydrate Group		
Starch	1/2 cup pasta, cereal, potatoes; 1 slice bread	0–1
Fruit	1 small apple, peach, pear; 1/2 banana; 1/2 cup canned fruit (in juice)	0
Milk	1 cup milk or yogurt	
Nonfat		0
Low-fat		2–3
Reduced-fat		5
Whole		8
Other carbohydrates	Serving sizes vary	Varies
Vegetables	1/2 cup cooked vegetables, 1 cup raw	0
Meat/Meat Substitute Group	1 oz meat or cheese, 1/2 cup legumes	
Very lean		0–1
Lean		3
Medium fat		5
High fat		8
Fat Group	1 tsp butter, margarine, or oil; 1 Tbsp salad dressing	5

The Nutrition Facts section provides the number of kcalories from fat, the number of grams of total fat, saturated fat, and *trans* fat, and the number of milligrams of cholesterol in a serving.[44] With the exception of *trans* fat, these are also presented as a percent of the Daily Value (**Figure 5.24**). This information allows consumers to tell at a glance how one food will fit into the recommendations for fat intake for the day. For example, if a serving provides 50% of the Daily Value for fat—that is, half the recommended maximum daily intake for a 2000-kcalorie diet—the rest of the day's

Cheese Crackers

Nutrition Facts

Serving Size 1 Package (43g)
Servings Per Container 12

Amount/Serving

Calories 230	Calories from Fat 120

	% Daily Value*
Total Fat 14g	**22%**
Saturated Fat 3.5g	**18%**
Trans Fat 4g	
Cholesterol 5mg	**2%**
Sodium 410mg	**17%**
Total Carbohydrate 23g	**8%**
Dietary Fiber Less than 1g	**2%**
Sugars 6g	
Protein 3g	

Vitamin A 0%	●	Vitamin C 0%
Calcium 6%	●	Iron 6%

*Percent Daily Values are based on a 2,000 calorie diet. Your daily values may be higher or lower depending on your calorie needs:

	Calories:	2,000	2,500
Total Fat	Less than	65g	80g
Sat Fat	Less than	20g	25g
Cholesterol	Less than	300mg	300mg
Sodium	Less than	2,400mg	2,400mg
Total Carbohydrate		300g	375g
Dietary Fiber		25g	30g

INGREDIENTS: ENRICHED FLOUR (WHEAT FLOUR, NIACIN, REDUCED IRON, THIAMINE MONONITRATE {VITAMIN B1}, RIBOFLAVIN {VITAMIN B2}, FOLIC ACID), PARTIALLY HYDROGENATED SOYBEAN OIL, WHEY (FROM MILK), SUGAR, HIGH FRUCTOSE CORN SYRUP, BUTTER (PASTEURIZED CREAM, SALT, ANNATTO COLOR), CHEDDAR CHEESE (CULTURED MILK, SALT, ENZYMES, AND ANNATTO EXTRACT COLOR), BUTTERMILK SOLIDS, SALT, LEAVENING (BAKING SODA, CALCIUM PHOSPHATE), DISODIUM PHOSPHATE (STABILIZER), NATURAL FLAVOR, SOY LECITHIN (EMULSIFIER), COLOR ADDED (INCLUDES YELLOW 6), MALTED BARLEY FLOUR, PEANUTS.

Figure 5.24 Fat and cholesterol on food labels
This label from cheese crackers tells us that they are low in cholesterol but high in total fat, and they add saturated and *trans* fat to the diet. (iStockphoto)

Off the Label
Choosing Lean Meat

(©iStockphoto)

Looking for lean meat? Although fresh meats are not required to carry a Nutrition Facts label, they often do carry information about fat content. Understanding the terminology can help you choose meats that will fit into your diet plan.

The terms "lean" and "extra lean" describe the fat content of packaged meats such as hot dogs and lunch meat, as well as fresh meats such as pork chops and steaks. "Lean" means the meat contains less than 10% fat by weight, and "extra lean" means it contains no more than 5% fat by weight. Ground beef is an exception to these labeling rules. The USDA allows ground beef to be labeled "lean" even if as much as 22.5% of its weight is fat. To further complicate your shopping, the amount of fat in ground beef labeled "lean" and "extra lean" can vary from store to store.

You can still figure out how much fat is in lean ground beef, because ground meats labeled "lean" or "extra lean" must indicate the actual percentage of fat versus lean by stating that it

is a certain "% lean" (see figure). But, "% lean" claims can be misleading. A food that is 85% lean has only 15% fat, which might not sound like much. However, "% lean" refers to the weight of the meat that is lean. So when the label says the meat is 85% lean, it means that 15% of the weight of the meat is fat, or that there are 15 grams of fat in 100 grams (3.5 ounces) of raw hamburger. There are 215 kcalories in 100 grams of raw 85% lean meat, so almost 63% of the kcalories are from fat.

So, if even lean ground beef is high in fat, should you stop eating ground beef altogether? Not necessarily. Purchase ground beef that fits the definition of a lean meat—it contains no more than 10% of its weight from fat—by choosing packages labeled as 90% lean or greater. If you do add some not-so-lean ground beef to your burgers, tacos, meatloaf, or lasagna from time to time, balance this higher fat choice by eating foods that are low in fat and saturated fat at other times during the day.

(Andy Washnik)

foods will have to be carefully selected to not exceed the recommended maximum. To choose foods low in saturated fat and cholesterol use the general rule that 5% of the Daily Value or less of these in a serving is low and 20% or more is high.

The amount of monounsaturated and polyunsaturated fat is voluntarily included on the labels of some products. For example, in addition to listing the 2 grams of saturated fat, the label on a bottle of olive oil may indicate that it contains 2 grams of polyunsaturated fat and 10 grams of monounsaturated fat per tablespoon. There are no Daily Values for polyunsaturated and monounsaturated fat.

If you want to know the source of fat in a packaged food, you can check the ingredient list. This will show you, for example, if a food contains corn oil, soybean oil, coconut oil, or partially hydrogenated vegetable oil (see Figure 5.24). Labels may also include terms such as "low-fat," "fat-free," and "low cholesterol" that describe their fat content. Food labeling regulations have developed standard definitions for these terms and they can be used only in ways that do not confuse consumers (**Table 5.7**). For instance, a food that contains no cholesterol but is high in saturated fat, such as crackers containing coconut oil, cannot be labeled "cholesterol free" because saturated fat in the diet raises blood cholesterol. Food labels may also include health claims related to their fat content. For example, foods low in saturated fat and cholesterol may state that they help to reduce the risk of coronary heart disease (see Appendix J).

Table 5.7 Fat and Cholesterol on Food Labels

Fat-free	Contains less than 0.5 g of fat per serving.
Low-fat	Contains 3 g or less of fat per serving.
Percent fat free	May be used only to describe foods that meet the definition of fat-free or low-fat.
Reduced or less fat	Contains at least 25% less fat per serving than the regular or reference product.
Saturated fat-free	Contains less than 0.5 g of saturated fat per serving and less than 0.5 g *trans* fatty acids per serving.
Low saturated fat	Contains 1 g or less of saturated fat and not more than 15% of kcalories from saturated fat per serving.
Reduced or less saturated fat	Contains at least 25% less saturated fat than the regular or reference product.
Cholesterol-free	Contains less than 2 mg of cholesterol and 2 g or less of saturated fat per serving.
Low cholesterol	Contains 20 mg or less of cholesterol and 2 g or less of saturated fat per serving.
Reduced or less cholesterol	Contains at least 25% less cholesterol than the regular or reference product and 2 g or less of saturated fat per serving.
Lean	Contains less than 10 g of fat, 4.5 g or less of saturated fat, and less than 95 mg of cholesterol per serving and per 100 g.
Extra lean	Contains less than 5 g of fat, less than 2 g of saturated fat, and less than 95 mg of cholesterol per serving and per 100 g.

Source: FDA, Center for Food Safety and Applied Nutrition. Available online at www.cfsan.fda.gov/ Accessed February 1, 2009.

Translating Recommendations Into Healthy Diets

The typical North American diet meets some but not all of the recommendations for fat intake. Typical intake of total fat is within the recommended 20% to 35% of kcalories and cholesterol intake is below 300 mg, but intakes of saturated and *trans* fats exceed recommendations. In order to improve their diets Americans need to get more of their fats from foods like fish, nuts, and vegetable oils, which are sources of polyunsaturated and monounsaturated fatty acids. Using the recommendations of MyPyramid can help consumers choose healthy diets. **Table 5.8** gives some suggestions on how to make healthy fat choices.

Choose Added Fats Carefully The most concentrated sources of fat—oils, butter, margarine, sauces, and salad dressings—should be chosen carefully to keep the amount and type of fat in the diet healthy (**Figure 5.25**). Limiting the amount of fat added to food at the table and in cooking will reduce total fat consumption. Avoiding solid fats like butter and cream cheese will reduce saturated fat intake. The Dietary Guidelines and MyPyramid consider the energy from solid fats (because they are high in saturated or *trans* fatty acids) discretionary kcalories—those kcalories left over once nutrient needs have been met with nutrient-dense foods from each of the food groups. A 2000-kcalorie diet should include only about 270 discretionary kcalories. Spreading a tablespoon of butter on your morning toast uses up 100 of these discretionary kcalories. Oils are not considered discretionary kcalories. Using vegetable oils such as canola and olive oil that are high in monounsaturated fat, or corn and soybean oils that are high in polyunsaturated fat instead of butter will increase the proportion of unsaturated fats. Soybean oil and canola oil are also good plant sources of omega-3 unsaturated fatty acids. Choosing margarines and other spreads that are low in *trans* fat can reduce *trans* fat intake (see Critical Thinking: Eating Healthier Fats).

Table 5.8 How to Choose Fats Wisely

Limit cholesterol, *trans* fat, and saturated fat

- Choose lower-fat cuts of meat
- Opt for chicken and fish—don't eat the skin
- Try a vegetarian meal once a week—beans and other vegetarian sources of protein are low in *trans* and saturated fat and don't contain cholesterol
- Use low-fat milk, yogurt, and cheese
- Choose a margarine with no *trans* fat
- Cut down on packaged foods that contain *trans* fats

Increase mono- and polyunsaturated fats

- Choose olive, peanut, or canola oil (high in monounsaturated fat) for cooking and salad dressing
- Use corn, sunflower, or safflower oil (high in polyunsaturated fat) for baking
- Snack on nuts and seeds
- Add olives, avocados, nuts, and seeds to your salad

Get enough omega-3's

- Sprinkle flaxseed on your cereal or yogurt or bake it into muffins
- Add another serving of fish to your weekly menu
- Have a leafy green vegetable with dinner
- Put walnuts in your salad

Watch your total fat

- Instead of frying, bake, broil, barbecue, roast, steam, or microwave
- Have a smaller serving of ice cream
- Try oven-fried rather than deep-fried potatoes
- Use half your usual amount of butter

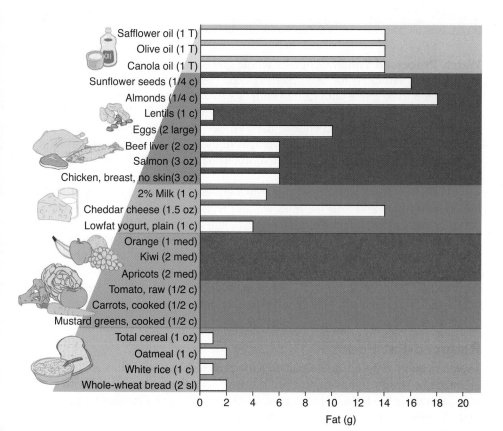

Figure 5.25 The fat content of MyPyramid food groups
Oils, nuts, and seeds are high in fat, but the fat they provide is rich in mono- and polyunsaturated fat. Animal products contain saturated fat and cholesterol.

Choose Protein Sources Wisely Meats and dairy products are the major sources of saturated fat and the only sources of cholesterol in our diets. Trimming the fat from meat, choosing leaner cuts, and removing the skin from poultry can reduce the amount of total fat and saturated fat (**Table 5.9**). Likewise, using nonfat or low-fat milk and milk products will cut both total and saturated fat as well as cholesterol. Choosing fish and shellfish will provide a meal with less saturated fat and more heart-protective long-chain omega-3 fatty acids. Levels of omega-3 fatty acids are higher in oilier fish such as salmon, trout, and herring (see Table 5.1). Using vegetable sources of protein such as legumes will limit total fat, saturated fat, and cholesterol and choosing nuts and seeds will add a source of omega-3 and monounsaturated fat.

Table 5.9 Making Choices that Lower Saturated Fat Intake

Higher-Fat Food	Saturated Fat (g)	Total Fat (g)	Energy (kcal)	Lower-Fat Equivalent	Saturated Fat (g)	Total Fat (g)	Energy (kcal)
Steak, fat not trimmed, 3 oz cooked	4.8	12.7	211	Steak, fat trimmed, 3 oz cooked	1.4	4.2	153
Regular ground beef (25% fat), 3 oz cooked	7.5	19	260	Extra lean ground beef (4% fat), 3 oz cooked	1.9	3.3	122
Fried-chicken breast (with skin), 3 oz	3.2	12	240	Broiled-chicken breast (no skin), 3 oz	1	3.9	149
Fish (fried), 3 oz	1.3	5.5	149	Fish (baked), 3 oz	0.3	1.4	118
Whole milk, 1 cup	4.6	8	146	Low-fat milk, 1 cup	1.5	4	102
Butter, 1 tsp	2.4	3.8	34	Soft margarine with zero *trans* fat, 1 tsp	0.5	3.8	34
Regular ice cream, 1/2 cup	4.5	7.3	133	Low-fat frozen yogurt, 1/2 cup	0.7	1	98
Potato, baked with sour cream, 1 medium	3.5	5.6	169	Potato, baked plain, 1 medium	0	0.2	113
Doughnut, glazed, 1 large	8.4	22	412	Bagel, 1 large	0.2	1	195
Frozen broccoli with cheese sauce, 1 cup	10.8	17.3	256	Fresh broccoli, 1 cup	0	0.1	27
Ramen noodles, 1 cup	4.4	15.6	426	Egg noodles, 1 cup	0.5	2.4	213
Spaghetti with Alfredo sauce, 1 cup	4.5	20	368	Spaghetti with tomato sauce, 1 cup	0.7	5	250

Watch Processed Foods Generally whole grains, fruits, and vegetables are low in total fat and saturated fat and have no cholesterol. However, choices from these groups need to be made with care to limit fats that are added in processing or preparation. Processed foods are a major source of fat in the diet. From the grains group, frozen pizzas, macaroni and cheese, flavored rice dishes, and baked goods such as doughnuts, cookies, and muffins are sources of dietary fat. In fact, most baked goods are so high in added fats and sugars that about half of their kcalories are considered discretionary kcalories.

Within the fruits group, fresh fruits are a low-fat choice while fruits that are baked into pies and tarts add total fat, *trans* fat, and refined sugar. Olives and avocados are naturally high in fat, but provide monounsaturated fats. Most fresh vegetables have little or no fat. However, fats are often added to vegetables in cooking and processing; french fries and breaded fried vegetables, such as onion rings and mushrooms, are high in fat and energy, and depending on the fat used for frying, can be a source of saturated fat or *trans* fat (see Table 5.8). Careful selection from these food groups can help keep the amount and type of fat in the diet in the recommended range.

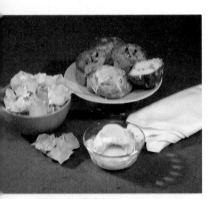

Figure 5.26 The carbohydrate-based fat replacers used in the muffins and ice cream shown here add kcalories because they are made from carbohydrate. The Olestra, which replaces the fat in these chips is not absorbed so it adds no kcalories to the diet. (Andy Washnik)

Reduced-Fat Foods

There are many reduced-fat and fat-free foods available. Some, such as low-fat milk, are made by simply removing the fat. In other foods the fat is replaced with ingredients that mimic the taste and texture of fat. Some of these fat substitutes are lower in kcalories because they are carbohydrate- or protein-based. Others are lipids, but contribute fewer kcalories because they are poorly digested and absorbed (**Figure 5.26**).

Critical Thinking
Eating Healthier Fats

(Hola Images/Getty Images, Inc.)

Background

Isabel has a busy schedule—working full-time and attending college—and has little time to cook meals at home. Currently, for breakfast and lunch she relies on things she can pick up on the way to school or between classes. She makes a quick dinner when she gets home in the evening. She is concerned about the fat in her diet and wants to know how to make healthier choices.

Data

Isabel analyzes her original diet and then modifies it to try to meet the recommendations for a healthy mix of fats (see table).

FOOD	SERVING	FAT (G)	SAT (G)	*TRANS* (G)	CHOLESTEROL (MG)	FOOD	SERVING	FAT (G)	SAT (G)	*TRANS* (G)	CHOLESTEROL (MG)
ORIGINAL DIET						**MODIFIED DIET**					
Breakfast						**Breakfast**					
Bran muffin	I large	6	2.6	0.5	24	Bran muffin	I large	6	2.6	0.5	24
Margarine	2 tsp	8	1.3	2	0	Orange	I medium	0.2	0	0	0
Coffee	I cup	0	0	0	0	Coffee	I cup	0	0	0	0
Whole milk	I cup	8	5	0.2	33	Low-fat milk	I cup	2.6	1.6	0	10
Lunch						**Lunch**					
Big Mac	I	31	12.5	I	80	Rice noodles	I cup	0	0	0	0
French fries	medium order	22	5	5	0	Stir-fry vegetables	I cup	0.3	0	0	0
						in peanut oil	I tsp	5	0.8	0	0
Water	I bottle	0	0	0	0	Water	I bottle	0	0	0	0
Snack						**Snack**					
Apple	I	0	0	0	0	Apple	I medium	0	0	0	0
						Pretzels	I oz	I	0	0	0
Dinner						**Dinner**					
Fish sticks	5	17	2.4	2	33	Trout	3 oz	12	1.2	0	63
Tater tots	10	8	6	4	0	Baked potato w/sour cream	I medium / I Tbsp	0.2 / 3	0 / 1.7	0 / 0	0 / 10
						Green beans	1/2 cup	0	0	0	0
						Salad w/oil & vinegar	I cup	10	1.2	0	0
						Melon	I cup	0	0	0	0
Tea	I cup	0	0	0	0	Tea	I cup	0	0	0	0
Coconut cookies	2	13	3.4	3.3	0	Frozen yogurt	2/3 cup	1.8	1.2	0	5
Totals		113	38.2	18	170	**Totals**		42.1	10.3	0.5	112

Critical Thinking Questions

Assuming Isabel is eating 2250 kcalories per day, calculate the percent of energy from fat and saturated fat (sat) in her original diet. How do these percentages compare to recommendations? What foods are the biggest contributors to her saturated fat intake? To her *trans* fat intake? To her cholesterol intake?

▼

Now look at the changes she has made. Assuming her kcalorie intake stayed the same calculate the percent of energy from fat and saturated fat in her modified diet.

▼

Fat is not the only concern in choosing a healthy diet. How does her modified diet stack up to the MyPyramid recommendations in terms of grains, fruits, and vegetables?

 iProfile   Use iProfile to find fast food choices that are low in saturated fat.

The Role of Reduced-Fat Foods in a Healthy Diet To reduce fat intake people often choose foods that have been modified to reduce their fat content. Some of these foods can make an important contribution to a healthy diet. For example, low-fat dairy products are recommended because they provide all the essential nutrients contained in the full-fat versions but have fewer kcalories and less saturated fat and cholesterol. Using these products increases the nutrient density of the diet as a whole. However, not all reduced-fat foods are nutrient dense and using them does not necessarily transform a poor diet into a healthy one or improve overall diet quality. Some reduced-fat foods are lower-fat versions of nutrient-poor choices such as baked goods and chips. If these reduced-fat desserts and snack foods replace whole grains, fruits, and vegetables, the resulting diet could be low in fat but also low in fiber, vitamins, minerals, and phytochemicals—a dietary pattern that could increase the risk of chronic disease. However, if used appropriately, fat-modified foods can be part of a healthy diet. For example, if a low-fat salad dressing replaces a full-fat version it allows consumers to enhance the appeal of a nutrient-rich salad without the added fat and kcalories from the dressing. Replacing regular potato chips with fat-free ones, will not add any other nutrients to the diet, but will reduce fat and energy intake. If the extra kcalories are consumed as fruits, vegetables, or whole grains the overall diet has been improved. If the extra kcalories are not replaced this substitution could be helpful for weight loss. However, those using low-fat products to aid weight loss should be aware that these foods are not kcalorie-free and cannot be consumed liberally without adding kcalories to the diet and contributing to weight gain. If you are using low-fat products to reduce your kcalorie intake, check the label—don't assume they are low in kcalories.

Fat Substitutes One way to replicate the texture of fat in foods is to replace some of the fat with carbohydrates such as cellulose, dextrins, pectins, gums, or modified starch. These thicken foods and mimic the slippery texture that fat provides. Since they are carbohydrates they can provide up to 4 kcalories per gram, but because they are often mixed with water they typically provide only 1 to 2 kcalories per gram.[45] Some of these products, such as Oatrim, made from oats, and Nutrim, made from oats and barley, also add soluble fiber. These carbohydrate-based fat replacers are used in baked goods, salad dressings, sauces, and ice cream.

Protein has also been used to simulate fat. The fat replacer Simplesse is made from egg white and milk proteins that are modified by heating, filtering, and high-speed mixing. The resulting protein consists of millions of microscopic balls that slip and slide over each other to give it the creamy texture of fat. Because the protein is mixed with water, Simplesse contains only 1.3 kcalories per gram. It is used in frozen desserts, cheese foods, and other products, but it cannot be used for cooking because heat causes it to break down.

Some fat substitutes are made from fats that have been modified to reduce how well they can be digested or absorbed. One way to do this is to use triglycerides made up of poorly absorbed fatty acids. These are digested like other triglycerides, but the fatty acids are only partially absorbed, so they provide fewer kcalories per gram. The artificial fat Olestra (sucrose polyester) provides no kcalories because it is not digested by either the human enzymes or the bacterial enzymes in the gastrointestinal tract. It is, therefore, excreted in the feces without being absorbed. It is made by attaching fatty acids to a molecule of sucrose. One of the problems with Olestra is that it reduces the absorption of other fat-soluble substances, including the fat-soluble vitamins A, D, E, and K. To avoid depleting these vitamins, Olestra has been fortified with them. However, it is not fortified with beta-carotene and other fat-soluble substances that may be important for health. Another potential problem with Olestra is that it can cause gastrointestinal irritation, bloating, and diarrhea in some individuals because it passes into the colon without being digested. Olestra has been approved by the FDA for use in snack foods such as chips and crackers.

Another modification that changes the health impact of a fat is to increase the proportion of diglycerides. Only about 10% of the glycerides naturally present in plant oils are diglycerides. However, food manufacturers are able to modify these oils to created oils that contain 70% diglycerides. These high-diglycerides oils (marketed as ENOVA oil) are not lower in kcalories, but when they replace similar oils containing triglycerides, blood lipid levels are lower after eating and body weight and fat accumulation in the abdominal region is reduced.[45]

Outcome

Sam's friends and relatives all offered advice about how to reduce his risk of heart disease, but their solutions weren't things that he could or should follow to the letter. The best approach is for Sam to make a number of small changes in his diet and lifestyle that he can stick with for the long term. To eat a heart-healthy diet he doesn't need to become a vegetarian, as his girlfriend recommended, but he should eat more fruits and vegetables and not make meat the focus of every meal. Despite his lab partner's suggestions, it is not necessary—or even healthy—to eliminate all fat from the diet. Instead, Sam should change the types of foods he eats to reduce his intake of saturated fat, cholesterol, and *trans* fat and increase his monounsaturated and polyunsaturated fat intake. Cutting out margarine, as his mother advised, will lower his *trans* fat intake, but he can still enjoy margarine by using food labels to select a *trans*-free brand. Adding fish to his diet, as his roommate recommended, will increase his intake of heart-healthy omega-3 fatty acids. And using olive oil, which is plentiful in the Mediterranean diet his sister proposed, will boost his intake of monounsaturated fatty acids.

With the help of the information in this chapter, Sam incorporated many of the suggestions from his friends and relatives. He eats more fruits, vegetables, and fish; chooses healthy fats; and has started exercising regularly. Over the past 6 months he has lost 10 pounds and lowered his total cholesterol to 185 mg/dL.

APPLICATIONS

Personal Nutrition

I. How do the fats in your diet compare to the recommendations?

a. Use iProfile to calculate your average fat, saturated fat, and cholesterol intake using the 3-day food record you kept in Chapter 2.

b. How does your fat intake compare with the recommendation of 20% to 35% of energy from total fat?

c. How does your percent of energy from saturated fat compare to the Daily Value recommendation of less than 10% of kcalories?

d. What foods do you typically consume that are high in saturated fat? Suggest food substitutions that will decrease the amount of saturated fat in your diet.

e. How does your cholesterol intake compare to the Daily Value recommendation of less than 300 mg per day? If it is greater than 300 mg suggest some substitutions that will decrease your cholesterol intake.

f. List some foods in your diet that are high in *trans* fat. What substitutions could you make to decrease your *trans* fat intake?

2. Do you make healthy choices from all the food groups?

a. List the dairy products in your diet and indicate if they are full fat or reduced fat.

b. List the grain products you typically consume. How many of them are baked goods with added fats? How many of them are eaten with an added high-fat spread or sauce? Suggest changes you could make to reduce the fats added to your carbohydrates.

c. List the vegetables in your diet. Underline those that are cooked or prepared in a way that increases their fat intake. For example, are they fried or topped with butter or salad dressing?

d. List the high-protein foods in your diet. Which ones are naturally high in fat? What types of fats do these provide? Which, if any, are high in fat because fat is added in cooking or as sauces or gravies? Which are low in fat?

3. Are you getting your omega-3's?

a. Review all 3 days of the food record you kept in Chapter 2 and list foods you eat that are good sources of omega-3 fatty acids.

b. If your diet does not contain good sources of omega-3 fatty acids suggest some substitutions that would boost your omega-3 intake.

4. How much fat is in your packaged foods?

a. Select four packaged foods that you routinely consume.

b. Examine the food labels. If you consumed only this food for an entire day, how many servings could you eat before exceeding the Daily Value for:

   I. Total fat?

   2. Saturated fat?

   3. Cholesterol?

General Nutrition Issues

I. The percent of kcalories from fat in the typical American diet has decreased over the last 30 years. There are thousands of reduced-fat products on the market and millions of dollars have been spent teaching Americans about the benefits of a low-fat diet. Nevertheless, there has been an increase in the incidence of obesity in the United States over this same period. Discuss how it is possible that people are cutting down on the percent fat in their diet and still gaining weight.

2. Ka Ming is 54 years old and has lived in the United States since 1964. An annual physical reveals that his total blood cholesterol is 280 mg/100 mL and his HDL cholesterol is 25 mg/100 mL. He is of normal weight and does not smoke. He works as a laboratory technician and so spends part of the day on his feet but gets little other exercise. A medical history reveals that none of Ka Ming's relatives in China have had cardiovascular disease.

a. Is Ka Ming at risk for developing cardiovascular disease?

b. Why might the lack of cardiovascular disease in his family history not be a true indication of Ka Ming's risk?

c. A diet analysis reveals that Ka Ming consumes a mixture of American foods and traditional Chinese foods. He likes a cooked breakfast and typically buys fast food for lunch. Dinner is often Chinese-style food that he cooks himself at home or buys from a family-owned Chinese-American restaurant near his home. His diet contains approximately 40% of its energy from fat, and 15% is from saturated fat. It contains about 350 mg of cholesterol a day. Below is a list of foods that Ka Ming routinely consumes. What modifications, selection suggestions, or cooking tips would decrease his intake of saturated fat and cholesterol?

Breakfast foods	*Lunch foods*
Scrambled eggs	Ham and cheese sub
Pancakes	Meatball sandwich
Cheese omelet	Fried chicken
Sausages	Pepperoni pizza

Dinner foods

Crispy fried beef over white rice

Sweet and sour pork over white rice

Chicken and broccoli stir-fry over white rice

Pork fried rice

Egg rolls

iProfile

Summary

5.1 Fat in the Modern Diet

- Lipids add kcalories, texture, and flavor to our foods. Some of the fats we eat are visible, but others are less obvious. Over the past 40 years Americans have reduced their intake of some of the more visible sources of fat, such as red meat, whole milk, and butter but have increased the amount of fat they consume from baked goods, snack foods, and mixed dishes.

- Changes in the types of fats in the American diet can help reduce the risk of chronic disease.

5.2 Types of Lipid Molecules

- Lipids are a diverse group of organic compounds, most of which do not dissolve in water. Triglycerides, commonly referred to as fat, are the most abundant lipid in our diet and our bodies. They consist of a backbone of glycerol with three fatty acids attached. The physical properties and health effects of triglycerides depend on the fatty acids they contain.

- Fatty acids consist of a carbon chain with an acid group at one end. Fatty acids that are saturated with hydrogen atoms are saturated fatty acids and those that contain carbon-carbon double bonds are unsaturated. The length of the carbon chain and the number and position of the carbon-carbon double bonds as well as the configuration of the double bonds determine the physical properties and health effects of fatty acids.

- Phosphoglycerides are a type of phospholipid that consist of a backbone of glycerol, two fatty acids, and a phosphate group. Phosphoglycerides allow water and oil to mix. They are used as emulsifiers in the food industry and are an important component of cell membranes and lipoproteins.

- Sterols, of which cholesterol is the best known, are made up of multiple chemical rings. Cholesterol is made by the body and consumed in animal foods in the diet. In the body, it is a component of cell membranes and is used to synthesize vitamin D, bile acids, and a number of hormones.

5.3 Lipids in the Digestive Tract

- In the small intestine, muscular churning mixes chyme with bile from the gallbladder to break fat into small globules. This allows pancreatic lipase to access these fats for digestion.

- The products of fat digestion (primarily fatty acids and monoglycerides), cholesterol, phospholipids, and other fat-soluble substances combine with bile to form micelles, which facilitate the absorption of these materials into the cells of the small intestine.

5.4 Lipid Transport in the Body

- In body fluids, water-insoluble lipids are transported as lipoproteins. Lipids absorbed from the intestine are incorporated into chylomicrons, which enter the lymphatic system before entering the blood. The triglycerides in chylomicrons are broken down by lipoprotein lipase on the surface of cells lining the blood vessels. The fatty acids released are taken up by surrounding cells and the chylomicron remnants that remain are taken up by the liver.

- Very-low-density lipoproteins (VLDLs) are synthesized by the liver. With the help of lipoprotein lipase, they deliver triglycerides to body cells. Once the triglycerides have been removed, intermediate-density lipoproteins (IDLs) remain. These are transformed in the blood into low-density lipoproteins (LDLs). LDLs deliver cholesterol to tissues by binding to LDL receptors on the cell surface.

- High-density lipoproteins (HDLs) are made by the liver and small intestine. They help remove cholesterol from cells and transport it to the liver for disposal.

5.5 Lipid Functions in the Body

- Triglycerides provide a concentrated source of energy. After eating, chylomicrons and VLDLs deliver triglycerides to cells for energy or storage. During fasting, triglycerides stored in adipose cells are broken down by hormone-sensitive lipase, and the fatty acids and glycerol are released into the blood. To generate ATP from fatty acids, beta-oxidation first breaks fatty acids into two carbon units that form acetyl-CoA, which can then be broken down by the citric acid cycle.

- Lipids in adipose tissue insulate against shock and temperature changes. Oils lubricate body surfaces and phosphoglycerides and cholesterol contribute structure to cell membranes.

- Hormones synthesized from cholesterol and eicosanoids synthesized from fatty acids have important regulatory roles.

5.6 Lipids and Health

Video

Go to WileyPLUS to view a video clip on the Mediterranean Diet.

- Linoleic acid (omega-6) and alpha-linolenic acid (omega-3) are considered essential fatty acids because they cannot be synthesized by the body. The proper ratio of omega-6 to omega-3 fatty acids is essential for optimal health.

- Atherosclerosis is a disease characterized by deposits of lipids and fibrous material in the artery wall. It is begun by an injury to the artery wall that triggers an inflammatory response that leads to plaque formation. A key event in plaque formation is the oxidation of LDL cholesterol in the artery wall. Oxidized LDL cholesterol is taken up by macrophages and deposited in the artery wall. Oxidized LDL cholesterol also contributes to plaque formation by promoting inflammation and sending signals that lead to fibrous deposits and blood clot formation.

- High blood levels of total and LDL cholesterol are a risk factor for heart disease. High blood HDL cholesterol protects against heart disease. The risk of heart disease is also increased by diabetes, high blood pressure, and obesity.

- Diets high in saturated fat, *trans* fatty acids, and cholesterol increase the risk of heart disease. Diets high in omega-6 and omega-3 polyunsaturated fatty acids, monounsaturated fatty acids, certain B vitamins, and plant foods containing fiber, antioxidants, and phytochemicals reduce the risk of heart disease. The total dietary and lifestyle pattern is more important than any individual dietary factor in reducing heart disease risk.

- Diets high in fat are associated with an increased incidence of certain types of cancer. In some types of cancer, such as breast cancer, fat may act as a tumor promoter, increasing the rate of tumor growth. In the case of colon cancer, dietary fat in the colon may act as a tumor initiator by forming compounds that cause mutations.

- Fat contains 9 kcalories per gram. A high-fat diet therefore increases the likelihood of weight gain, but it is not the primary cause of obesity. Consuming more energy than expended leads to weight gain regardless of whether the energy is from fat, carbohydrate, or protein.

5.7 Meeting Recommendations for Fat Intake

- The DRI recommendations regarding fat include AIs and AMDRs for essential fatty acids and an AMDR for total fat intake of 20% to 35% of energy for adults. The DRIs also advise keeping *trans* fats, saturated fats, and cholesterol to a minimum to reduce the risk of heart disease. The Daily Values recommend that total fat account for no more than 30% of energy, that saturated fat account for no more than 10% of energy, and that dietary cholesterol be no more than 300 mg per day.

- To keep the amount and type of fat in the diet healthy added fats, protein sources, and processed foods must be chosen carefully. Limiting animal fats from meat and dairy products reduces saturated fat intake. Choosing fish increases intake of omega-3 fatty acids. Eating nuts and seeds increase both monounsaturated fats and of omega-3 fatty acids. Processed foods can be high in saturated and *trans* fat. A diet based on whole grains, fruits, vegetables, and lean meats and low-fat dairy products will meet the recommendations for fat intake.

- Fat substitutes are used to create reduced-fat products with taste and texture similar to the original. Some low-fat products are made by using mixtures of carbohydrates or proteins to simulate the properties of fat, and some use lipids that are modified to reduce absorption. Products containing fat substitutes can help reduce fat and energy intake when used in moderation as part of a balanced diet.

Review Questions

1. How has the amount of fat in the American diet changed over the past 40 years?

2. Name two functions of fat in foods.

3. What is a lipid?

4. Name the types of lipids found in the body.

5. What distinguishes a saturated fat from a monounsaturated fat? From a polyunsaturated fat?

6. What type of processing increases the amounts of *trans* fatty acids?

7. List three functions of fat in the body.

8. What is the advantage of storing energy as body fat rather than as carbohydrate?

9. What is the function of bile in fat digestion and absorption?

10. How do HDLs differ from LDLs?

11. How are blood levels of LDLs and HDLs related to the risk of cardiovascular disease?

12. Is essential fatty-acid deficiency common in developed countries? Why or why not?

13. What types of foods contain cholesterol?

14. How does an atherosclerotic plaque form?

15. What is the AMDR for total dietary fat intake?

16. What information about dietary fat is included on food labels?

17. List two foods that are sources of monounsaturated fatty acids, two that are sources of omega-3 fatty acids, and two that are souces of cholesterol.

References

1. Wright, J. D., Kennedy-Stephenson, J., Wang, C.Y., et al. Trends in intake of energy and macronutrients—United States, 1971–2000. *Morb. Mortal. Wkly. Rep.* 6:80–82, 2004. Available online at www.cdc.gov/mmwr/preview/mmwrhtml/mm5304a3.htm/ Accessed May 26, 2009.

2. Institute of Medicine, Food and Nutrition Board. *Dietary Reference Intakes for Energy, Carbohydrates, Fiber, Fat, Protein and Amino Acids.* Washington, DC: National Academies Press, 2002.

3. Centers for Disease Control and Prevention. Trends in intake of energy and macronutrients—United States, 1971–2000. *MMWR Morb. Mortal. Wkly. Rep.* 53:80–82, 2004.

4. Popkin, B. M., Siega-Riz, A. M., Haines, P. S., and Jahns, L. Where's the fat? Trends in U.S. diets 1965–1996. *Prev. Med.* 32:245–254, 2001.

5. Warshaw, H. S. America eats out: Nutrition in the chain and family restaurant industry. *J. Am. Diet. Assn.* 93: 17–20, 1993.

6. Campbell, J. B. New insights on the away-from-home eating patterns and nutritional preferences of Americans. *J. Am. Diet. Assn.* 107: A68S, 2007.

7. Hamosh, M., Iverson, S. J., Kirk, C. L., and Hamosh, P. Milk lipids and neonatal fat digestion: Relationship between fatty acid composition, endogenous and exogenous digestive enzymes and digestion of milk fat. *World Rev. Nutr. Diet.* 75:86–91, 1994.

8. Brown, M. S., and Goldstein, J. L. How LDL receptors influence cholesterol and atherosclerosis. *Sci. Am.* 251:58–66, 1984.

9. Mori, T. A., and Beilin, L. J. Omega-3 fatty acids and inflammation. *Curr. Atheroscler. Rep.* 6:461–467, 2004.

10. Simopoulos, A. P. Omega-3 fatty acids in inflammation and autoimmune diseases. *J. Am. Coll. Nutr.* 21:495–505, 2002.

11. American Heart Association. Diet and Lifestyle Recommendations. Available online at www.americanheart.org/presenter.jhtml?identifier=851. Accessed February 16, 2009.

12. Heart Disease and Stroke Statistics—2009 Update. American Heart Association. Available online at http://www.americanheart. org/downloadable/heart/123783441267009Heart%20and%20Stroke%20Update.pdf Accessed May 29, 2009.

13. Ascherio, A., Rimm, E. B., Stampfer, M. J. et al. Marine ω-3 fatty acids, fish intake, and the risk of coronary disease among men. *N. Engl. J. Med.* 332:977–982, 1995.

14. American Heart Association. Mediterranean Diet. Available online at 216.185.112.5/presenter.jhtml?identifier/4644/ Accessed May 21, 2009.

15. Libby, P. Inflammation and cardiovascular disease mechanisms. *Am J Clin Nutr* 83:456S–460S, 2006.

16. Kher, N., and Marsh, J. D. Pathobiology of atherosclerosis—A brief review. *Semin Thromb Hemost* 30:665–672, 2004.

17. National Cholesterol Education Program. Adult Treatment Panel III Report, 2001, 2004. Available online at www.nhlbi.nih.gov/ guidelines/cholesterol/atp3udp04.htm/ Accessed May 26, 2009.

18. Denke, M. A. Review of human studies evaluating individual dietary responsiveness in patients with hypercholesterolemia. *Am. J. Clin. Nutr.* 62(suppl):471S–477S, 1995.

19. Ginsberg, H. N., and Karmally, W. Nutrition, lipids, and cardiovascular disease. In *Biochemical and Physiological Aspects of Human Nutrition.* M. H. Stipanuk, ed. Philadelphia: W. B. Saunders Company, 2000, pp. 917–944.

20. Connor, W. E. Harbingers of coronary heart disease: Dietary saturated fatty acids and cholesterol. Is chocolate benign because of its stearic acid content? *Am. J. Clin. Nutr.* 70:951–952, 1999.

21. Van Horn, L., McCoin, M., Kris-Etherton, P. M. et al. The evidence for dietary prevention and treatment of cardiovascular disease. *J Am Diet Assoc* 108:287–331, 2008.

22. Lopez-Garcia, E., Schulze, M. B., Meigs, J. B. et al. Consumption of *trans* fatty acids is related to plasma biomarkers of inflammation and endothelial dysfunction. *J Nutr.* 135:562–566, 2005.

23. Willett, W. C., Sacks, F., Trichopouluo, A., et al. Mediterranean diet pyramid: A cultural model for healthy eating. *Am. J. Clin. Nutr.* 61(suppl):1402S–1406S, 1995.

24. Keaney, J. F., and Vita, J. A. Vascular oxidative stress and antioxidant protection in atherosclerosis. *J. Cardiopulmonary Rehabil.* 22:225–233, 2002.

25. Humphrey, L. L., Fu, R., Rogers, K. et al. Homocysteine level and coronary heart disease incidence: A systematic review and meta-analysis. *Mayo Clin Proc* 83:1203–1212, 2008.

26. Selhub, J., Jacques P. F., Bostom A. G. et al. Relationship between plasma homocysteine and vitamin status in the Framingham study population. Impact of folic acid fortification. *Public Health Rev.* 28:117–1145, 2000.

27. Lucas, D. L., Brown, R. A., Wassef, M., and Giles, T. D. Alcohol and the cardiovascular system: Research challenges and opportunities. *J. Am. Coll. Cardiol.* 45:1916–1924, 2005.

28. Zern, T. L., and Fernandez, M. L. Cardioprotective effects of dietary polyphenols. *J. Nutr.* 135:2291–2294, 2005.

29. US Dept. of Health and Human Services, US Dept. of Agriculture. *Dietary Guidelines for Americans*, 6th ed. Washington, DC, 2005.

30. American Institute for Cancer Research. The Diet and Cancer Link: Dietary Choices Play an Important Role in Reducing Cancer. Available online at www.aicr.org/diet.html/ Accessed June 28, 2004.

31. American Cancer Society. Breast Cancer Facts and Figures 2007–2008. Available online at http://www.cancer.org/downloads/STT/BCFF-final.pdf. Accessed May 27, 2009.

32. Nation Cancer Institute. Breast Cancer Prevention. Available online at http://www.cancer.gov/cancertopics/pdq/prevention/breast/HealthProfessional/page2 Accessed August 16, 2009.

33. Schultz, M., Hoffmann, K., Weikert, C. et al. Identification of a dietary pattern characterized by high-fat food choices associated with increased risk of breast cancer: The European Prospective Investigation into Cancer and Nutrition (EPIC)-Potsdam Study, *Br J Nutr* 100:942–946, 2008.

34. Gago-Dominguez, M., Yuan, J. M., Sun, C. L. et al. Opposing effects of dietary ω-3 and ω-6 fatty acids on mammary carcinogenesis: The Singapore Chinese Health Study. *Br. J. Cancer* 89:1686–1692, 2003.

35. Voorrips. L. E., Brants, H. A., Kardinaal, A. F. et al. Intake of conjugated linoleic acid, fat and other fatty acids in relation to post menopausal breast cancer: The Netherlands Study on Diet and Cancer. *Am. J. Clin. Nutr.* 76:873–882, 2002.

36. Zock, P. L., and Katan, M. B. Linoleic acid intake and cancer risk: A review and meta-analysis. *Am. J. Clin. Nutr.* 68:142–153, 1998.

37. Kushi, L., and Giovannucci, E. Dietary fat and cancer. *Am. J. Med.* 113(suppl 9B):63S–70S, 2002.

38. Hall, M. N., Chavarro, J. E., Lee, I. M. et al. A 22-year prospective study of fish, n-3 fatty acid intake, and colorectal cancer risk in men. *Cancer Epidemiol Biomarkers Prev.* 17:1136–1143, 2008.

39. Devitt, A. A., and Mattes, R. D. Effects of food unit size and energy density on intake in humans. *Appetite* 42:213–220, 2004.

40. Ledikwe, J. H., Blanck, H. M., Kettel Khan, L. et al. Dietary energy density is associated with energy intake and weight status in US adults. *Am J Clin Nutr* 83:1362–1368, 2006.

41. Astrup, A., Astrup, A., Buemann, B. et al. Low-fat diets ands energy balance: How does the evidence stand in 2002? *Proc. Nutr. Soc.* 61:299–309, 2002.

42. Willett, W. C., and Leibel, R. L. Dietary fat is not a major determinant of body fat. *Am. J. Med.* 113:47S–59S, 2002.

43. Hill, J.O. Understanding and addressing the epidemic of obesity: An energy balance perspective. *Endocr Rev* 27:750–761, 2006.

44. Revealing *trans* fats. FDA Consumer 37:20–26, Sept./Oct. 2003.

45. American Dietetic Association. Position of the American Dietetic Association: Fat replacers. *J. Am. Diet. Assoc.* 105:266–275, 2005.

46. Tada, N., and Yoshida, H. Diacylglycerol on lipid metabolism. *Curr. Opin. Lipidol.* 14:29–33, 2003.

(©iStockphoto)

FOCUS ON
Alcohol

Outline

Almost every human culture since the dawn of civilization has produced and consumed some type of alcoholic beverage. These intoxicating beverages are part of religious ceremonies, social traditions, and even medical prescriptions. Sumerian clay tablets dating back to 2100 B.C.E. record physicians' prescriptions for beer, and in ancient Egypt, both beer and wine were prescribed as part of medical treatment.

Depending on the times and the culture, alcohol use has been touted, casually accepted, denounced, and even outlawed. Today, some people refrain from its use for religious, cultural, personal, and medical reasons while others enjoy the relaxing effects afforded by drinking these beverages. Whether alcohol consumption represents a risk or provides some benefits depends on who is drinking and how much is consumed. In some groups moderate alcohol consumption provides health advantages, but excessive alcohol consumption always has medical and social consequences that negatively impact drinkers and their families. It can reduce nutrient intake and affect the storage, mobilization, activation, and metabolism of nutrients. Its breakdown produces toxic compounds that damage tissues, particularly the liver.

F1.1 What's in Alcoholic Beverages?

Learning Objective

- Explain the difference between alcohol and ethanol.

Chemically, any molecule that contains a hydroxyl group (—OH) is an alcohol. Although there are many molecules present in our diet and our bodies that can be classified as alcohols, the term alcohol refers almost always to **ethanol**, also known as grain alcohol, and often to any beverage that contains ethanol (**Figure F1.1**). Alcoholic beverages, whether beer, wine, or distilled liquor, consist primarily of water, ethanol, and varying amounts of sugars. The amounts of other nutrients such as protein, vitamins, and minerals are almost negligible. Carbohydrate and alcohol provide the kcalories in these beverages. An average drink, defined as about 5 fl oz of wine,

ethanol The type of alcohol in alcoholic beverages. It is produced by yeast fermentation of sugar.

Figure F1.1 Ethanol, the type of alcohol in all alcoholic beverages, is a small water-soluble molecule. (Andy Washnik)

12 fl oz of beer, or 1.5 fl oz of distilled spirits, contains about 12 to 14 grams (about 0.5 oz) of alcohol, which contributes about 90 kcalories (7 kcals per gram). The amount of energy contributed by carbohydrate depends on the type of beverage (**Table F1.1**).

Table F1.1 Energy, Carbohydrate, and Alcohol Content of Alcoholic Beverages

Beverage	Typical Serving (fluid oz)	Energy (kcals)	Carbohydrate (g)	Alcohol (g)
Long Island iced tea	7	170	24.3	17.8
Gin and tonic	10	114	10.5	10.7
Wine cooler	12	170	20.2	13.2
Beer	12	146	13.2	12.8
Light beer	12	100	4.6	11.3
White wine	5	100	1.2	13.7
Red wine	5	106	2.5	13.7
Bourbon	1.5	96	0	13.9
Whiskey	1.5	96	0	13.9
Vodka	1.5	96	0	13.9

F1.2 Absorption, Transport, and Excretion of Alcohol

Learning Objectives

- Explain how food in the stomach affects alcohol absorption.
- Discuss how alcohol is eliminated from the body.

Ingested alcohol is absorbed by simple diffusion along the entire gastrointestinal tract. Only a small amount is absorbed in the mouth and esophagus. Larger amounts are absorbed in the stomach, and the majority of absorption occurs in the duodenum and jejunum of the small intestine. Because alcohol is absorbed rapidly and significant amounts can be absorbed directly from the stomach, the effects of alcohol consumption are almost immediate, especially if it is consumed on an empty stomach. If there is food in the stomach, absorption is slowed because the stomach contents dilute the alcohol, reducing the amount in direct contact with the stomach wall. Food in the stomach also slows absorption because it slows stomach emptying and therefore decreases the rate at which alcohol enters the small intestine, where absorption is the most rapid.

Figure F1.2 Blood alcohol concentrations in men and women
Consuming an equivalent amount of alcohol (0.5 g per kg of body weight) causes higher blood alcohol concentrations in women than in men.

Once absorbed, alcohol enters the bloodstream. It is a small water-soluble molecule, and therefore is rapidly distributed throughout all body water compartments. It crosses cell membranes by diffusion so the amount that enters a cell depends on the concentration gradient across the cell membrane. Blood alcohol level therefore reflects the amount of alcohol in the body and is dependent on the difference between the rates of alcohol absorption and elimination. Peak blood concentrations are attained approximately 1 hour after ingestion (**Figure F1.2**). Many variables, including the kind and quantity of alcoholic beverage consumed, the speed at which the beverage is drunk, the food consumed with it, the weight and gender of the consumer, and the activity of alcohol-metabolizing enzymes in the body, determine blood alcohol level (**Table F1.2**).

Table F1.2 Factors Affecting Blood Alcohol Level

Factor	Effect
Weight	The more people weigh, the more body water they have, so the more dilute the alcohol in their blood is after consuming a given amount.
Gender	Men have more body water and more stomach alcohol dehydrogenase (ADH) activity and thus have a lower blood alcohol level after consuming a standard amount of alcohol than women of the same size.
Food	Food in the stomach slows alcohol absorption so the more food people eat before drinking, the lower their blood alcohol level will be.
Drinking Rate	The body metabolizes alcohol slowly. As the number of drinks per hour increases, blood alcohol level steadily rises.
The Type of Drink	The amount of alcohol in the drink affects how fast the blood alcohol level rises. When carbonated mixers (such as tonic water or club soda) are used, the body absorbs alcohol more quickly.

Because alcohol is a toxin and cannot be stored in the body, it must be eliminated quickly. Absorbed alcohol travels to the liver via the portal circulation. In the liver it is given metabolic priority and is therefore broken down before carbohydrate, protein, and fat. About 90% of the alcohol consumed is metabolized by the liver, about 5% is excreted into the urine, and the remainder is eliminated via the lungs during exhalation. The alcohol that reaches the kidney acts as a di-

Figure F1.3 The amount of alcohol lost in exhaled breath is proportional to the amount of alcohol in the blood. Therefore a measurment of breath alcohol can be used to estimate blood alcohol level and determine if an individual is driving under the influence of alcohol. (Science Photo Library/Photo Researchers, Inc.)

uretic, increasing water excretion. Therefore, excessive alcohol intake can cause dehydration. The amount lost through the lungs is predictable and reliable enough to be used to estimate blood alcohol level from a measure of breath alcohol (**Figure F1.3**).

F1.3 Alcohol Metabolism

Learning Objectives

- Compare the two enzyme pathways that metabolize alcohol.
- Explain why alcohol intake increases fatty acid synthesis.

There are two primary pathways for alcohol metabolism: the **alcohol dehydrogenase (ADH)** pathway located in the cytosol of the cell and the **microsomal ethanol-oxidizing system (MEOS)** located in small vesicles called microsomes that form in the cell when they split off from an organelle called the *smooth endoplasmic reticulum*.[1]

alcohol dehydrogenase (ADH) An enzyme found primarily in the liver and stomach that helps break down alcohol into acetaldehyde, which is then converted to acetyl-CoA.

microsomal ethanol-oxidizing system (MEOS) A liver enzyme system located in microsomes that converts alcohol to acetaldehyde. Activity increases with increases in alcohol consumption.

Alcohol Dehydrogenase

In people who consume moderate amounts of alcohol and/or only consume alcohol occasionally, most of the alcohol is broken down via the ADH pathway. Although liver cells have the highest levels of ADH activity, this enzyme has also been found in all parts of the gastrointestinal tract with the greatest amounts in the stomach.[2] The amount of alcohol broken down in the stomach may be significant when small amounts of alcohol are consumed. One hypothesis as to why women become intoxicated after consuming less alcohol than men is that women have lower activities of this stomach enzyme.[3,4] Another explanation for why women have higher blood alcohol concentrations than men following a standard amount of alcohol is the fact that they have a higher proportion of body fat and thus less body water than men. The alcohol they do consume therefore is distributed in a smaller amount of body water (see Figure F1.2).

ADH converts alcohol to acetaldehyde. Acetaldehyde is a toxic compound that is further degraded by the mitochondrial enzyme aldehyde dehydrogenase to a 2-carbon molecule called acetate that forms acetyl-CoA (**Figure F1.4**). These reactions release electrons and hydrogen ions. Although these processes produce ATP, they also slow the citric acid cycle, preventing acetyl-CoA from being further broken down. Instead, the acetyl-CoA generated by alcohol breakdown, as well as acetyl-CoA from carbohydrate or fat metabolism, is used to synthesize fatty acids that accumulate in the liver. Fat accumulation can be seen in the liver after only a single bout of heavy drinking.

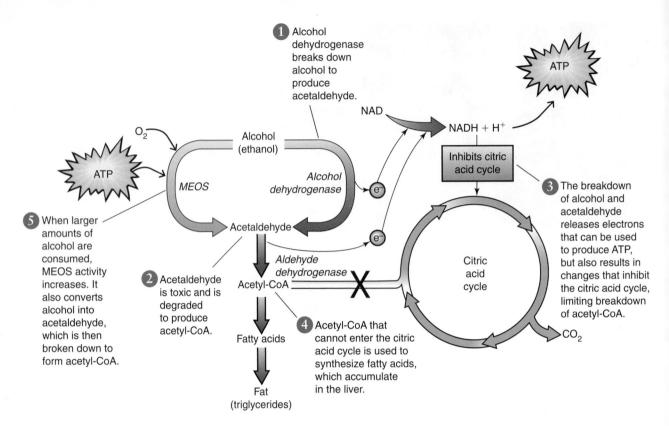

Figure F1.4 Alcohol metabolism

Alcohol can be metabolized by two pathways. The alcohol dehydrogenase pathway predominates when small amounts of alcohol are consumed and the MEOS pathway becomes important when larger amounts are consumed.

Microsomal Ethanol-Oxidizing System

Alcohol can also be metabolized in the liver by a second pathway called the microsomal ethanol-oxidizing system (MEOS). This system is particularly important when greater amounts of alcohol are consumed. MEOS converts alcohol to acetaldehyde, which is then broken down by aldehyde dehydrogenase in the mitochondria (see Figure F1.4). The MEOS system requires oxygen and the input of energy to break down alcohol. In addition to forming acetaldehyde and water, reactive oxygen molecules are generated. These reactive molecules can contribute to liver disease. The rate that ADH breaks down alcohol is fairly constant but MEOS activity increases when more alcohol is consumed. The MEOS also metabolizes other drugs, so as activity increases in response to high alcohol intake the metabolism of other drugs may be altered.

Alcohol Metabolism in the Colon

Although alcohol does not reach the colon through the digestive tract, alcohol is transported from the blood into the lumen of the colon. The alcohol that enters the large intestine is then metabolized by bacterial ADH to yield acetaldehyde. The capacity to metabolize alcohol to acetaldehyde by bacteria is greater than the ability to convert acetaldehyde to acetate. Therefore toxic acetaldehyde accumulates in the colon where it may contribute to mucosal injury and colon cancer. Acetaldehyde absorbed back into the blood contributes to liver damage.

F1.4 Adverse Effects of Alcohol Consumption

Learning Objectives

- Describe the short-term symptoms of alcohol intoxication.
- Explain why chronic excessive alcohol consumption can lead to malnutrition.
- Describe the long-term effects of alcoholism on the liver.

The consumption of alcohol has short-term effects that interfere with organ function for several hours after ingestion. It also has long-term effects that result from chronic alcohol consumption. Chronic alcohol consumption can cause disease both because it interferes with nutritional status and because it produces toxic compounds during its breakdown.

The effects of alcohol vary with life stage. When consumed during pregnancy, alcohol can cause abnormal brain development and other birth defects in the fetus (see Chapter 14). When consumed during childhood and adolescence, when the brain is still developing and changing, alcohol can cause permanent reductions in learning and memory.[5] In everyone, alcohol either directly or indirectly affects every organ in the body and increases the risk of malnutrition and many chronic diseases (**Table F1.3**).

Table F1.3 **Health Effects of Chronic Alcohol Use**

Health Effect	Role of Alcohol
Birth defects	Increases the risk of fetal alcohol syndrome and alcohol-related birth defects and neurodevelopmental disorders when consumed during pregnancy.
Gastrointestinal problems	Damages the lining of the stomach and small intestine, and contributes to the development of pancreatitis.
Liver disease	Causes fatty liver, alcoholic hepatitis, and cirrhosis.
Malnutrition	Decreases nutrient absorption and alters the storage, metabolism, and excretion of some vitamins and minerals. Associated with a poor diet because alcohol replaces more nutrient-dense energy sources in the diet.
Neurological disorders	Contributes to impaired memory, dementia, and peripheral neuropathy.
Cardiovascular disorders	Associated with cardiovascular diseases such as cardiomyopathy, hypertension, arrhythmias, and stroke.
Blood disorders	Increases the risk of anemia and infection.
Immune function	Depresses the immune system and results in a predisposition to infectious diseases, including respiratory infections, pneumonia, and tuberculosis.
Cancer	Increases the risk for cancer, particularly of the upper digestive tract—including the esophagus, mouth, pharynx, and larynx—and of the liver, pancreas, breast, and colon.
Sexual dysfunction	Can lead to inadequate functioning of the testes and ovaries, resulting in hormonal deficiencies, sexual dysfunction, and infertility. It is also related to a higher rate of early menopause and a higher frequency of menstrual irregularities (duration, flow, or both).
Psychological disturbances	Causes depression, anxiety, and insomnia, and is associated with a higher incidence of suicide.
Mortality	About 75,000 deaths per year in the United States are alcohol-related.

Acute Effects of Alcohol Consumption

Depending on body size, amount of previous drinking, food intake, and general health, the liver can break down about 0.5 oz of alcohol per hour. This is the amount of alcohol in one drink (5 fl oz of wine, 12 fl oz of beer, or 1.5 fl oz of distilled liquor). When alcohol intake exceeds the ability of the liver to break it down, the excess accumulates in the bloodstream until the liver enzymes can metabolize it. The circulating alcohol affects the brain resulting in impaired mental and physical abilities. In the brain, alcohol acts as a depressant, slowing the rate that neurological signals are received. First, it affects reasoning; if drinking continues, the vision and speech centers of the brain are affected. Next, large-muscle control becomes impaired, causing lack of coordination. Finally, if alcohol consumption continues, it can result in **alcohol poisoning**, a serious condition that can slow breathing, heart rate, and the gag reflex, leading to loss of consciousness, choking, coma, and even death (**Table F1.4**). This occurs most frequently with **binge drinking**. Binge drinking is a problem on college campuses that causes about 50 deaths and hundreds of cases of alcohol poisoning annually. It is estimated that about 40% of college students "binge" on alcohol at least once during a 2-week period.[6]

alcohol poisoning When the quantity of alcohol consumed exceeds an individual's tolerance for alcohol and impairs mental and physical abilities.

binge drinking When five or more drinks are consumed at one time by a man or 4 or more by a woman.

Table F1.4 Effects of Alcohol on the Central Nervous System

Number of Drinks[a]	Blood Alcohol[b] (%)	Effect on Central Nervous System
2	0.05	Impaired judgment, altered mood, relaxed inhibitions and tensions, increased heart rate
4	0.10	Impaired coordination, delayed reaction time, impaired peripheral vision
6	0.15	Unrestrained behavior, slurred speech, blurred vision, staggered gait
8	0.20	Double vision, inability to walk, lethargy
12	0.30	Stupor, confusion, coma
≥ 14	0.35–0.60	Unconsciousness, shock, coma, death

[a]Each drink contains 0.5 oz of ethanol and is equivalent to 5 fl oz of wine, 12 fl oz of beer, or 1.5 fl oz of distilled liquor.

[b]Values represent blood alcohol within approximately 1 hour after consumption for a 150-lb individual. Actual blood alcohol values depend on the amount of alcohol in the beverage, the rate of consumption, foods consumed with the alcohol, gender, and body weight.

The effects of alcohol on the central nervous system are what make driving while under the influence of alcohol so dangerous. Alcohol affects reaction time, eye-hand coordination, accuracy, and balance. Not only does alcohol impair one's ability to operate a motor vehicle, but it also impairs one's judgment in the decision to drive. The abuse of alcohol also contributes to domestic violence and leads to about 75,000 deaths per year, including approximately 40% of all traffic fatalities.[7]

Even if the individual does not lose consciousness, excess drinking may still result in memory loss. Drinking enough alcohol to cause amnesia is called **blackout drinking**. Blackout drinking puts people at risk because they have no memory of events that occurred during the blackout. During blackouts, individuals may engage in risky behaviors such as unprotected sexual intercourse, property vandalism, or driving a car—and have no memory of it afterward.

blackout drinking Amnesia following a period of excess alcohol consumption.

Alcoholism: Chronic Effects of Alcohol Use

One risk associated with regular alcohol consumption is the possibility of addiction. Alcohol addiction is referred to as **alcoholism**. The risk of addiction is increased in individuals who begin drinking at a younger age.[6] Alcohol addiction, like any other drug

alcoholism A chronic disorder characterized by dependence on alcohol and development of withdrawal symptoms when alcohol intake is reduced.

addiction, is a physiological problem that needs treatment. Alcoholism is believed to have a genetic component that makes some people more likely to become addicted, but environment also plays a significant role.[8] Thus, someone with a genetic predisposition toward alcoholism whose family and peers do not consume alcohol is much less likely to become addicted than someone with the same genes who drinks regularly with friends.

Alcohol and Malnutrition One of the complications of long-term excessive alcohol consumption is malnutrition. Alcoholic beverages contributes energy but few nutrients; they may replace more nutrient-dense energy sources in the diet, thereby reducing overall nutrient intake. As the percent of kcalories from alcohol increases, the risk of nutrient deficiencies rises. With more moderate alcohol intakes the drinker typically substitutes alcohol for carbohydrate in the diet and total energy intake increases slightly. When intake of alcohol exceeds 30% of kcalories, protein and fat intake as well as carbohydrate intake decrease and consumption of essential micronutrients such as thiamin and vitamins A and C may fall below recommended amounts.[1] Therefore a diet that is high in alcohol causes primary malnutrition because nutrient-dense energy sources in the diet are replaced by alcoholic beverages, decreasing overall nutrient intake.

In addition to decreasing nutrient intake, alcohol can contribute to a secondary malnutrition by interfering with nutrient absorption, even when adequate amounts of nutrients are consumed. Alcohol causes inflammation of the stomach, pancreas, and intestine, which impairs the digestion of food and absorption of nutrients into the blood. Alcohol damage to the lining of the small intestine decreases the absorption of several B vitamins and vitamin C.[2] Deficiency of the B vitamin thiamin is a particular concern with chronic alcohol consumption (see Chapter 8). The mucosal damage caused by alcohol also increases the ability of large molecules to cross the mucosa. This allows toxins from the gut lumen to enter the portal blood, increasing the liver's exposure to these toxins and, consequently, the risk of liver injury. Alcohol also contributes to malnutrition by altering the storage, metabolism, and excretion of other vitamins and some minerals.

In addition to contributing to undernutrition alcohol consumption may be related to obesity. Kcalories consumed as alcohol are more likely to be deposited as fat in the abdominal region; excess abdominal fat increases the risk of high blood pressure, heart disease, and diabetes. An analysis of alcohol consumption patterns and body weight showed that individuals who consumed a small amount of alcohol frequently (one drink per day, 3 to 7 days per week) had the lowest BMI while those who consumed large amounts infrequently had the highest BMI.[9] Alcohol may contribute to weight gain because liquids are less satiating than solid food and drinking may stimulate appetite, promoting consumption of additional energy sources.

Toxic Effects of Alcohol Chronic alcohol consumption is associated with hypertension, heart disease, and stroke, but the most significant physiological effects occur in the liver. In addition to causing liver damage from malnutrition, alcohol causes liver damage through its toxic effects. Metabolism via ADH produces excess amounts of the election carrier NADH. NADH inhibits the citric acid cycle and affects the metabolism of lipids, carbohydrates, and proteins. High NADH favors fat synthesis and inhibits fatty acid breakdown, leading to fat accumulation in the liver (**Figure F1.5**). Metabolism by MEOS generates free radicals resulting in oxidative stress, which causes oxidation of lipids, membrane damage, and altered enzyme activities. Whether broken down by ADH or MEOS, toxic acetaldehyde is formed. Acetaldehyde exerts its toxic effects by binding to proteins and by inhibiting reactions and functions of the mitochondria. This decreases the metabolism of acetaldehyde to acetic acid allowing more acetaldehyde to accumulate causing further liver damage.

Alcoholic liver disease progresses in a number of phases. The first phase is **fatty liver**, a condition that occurs when alcohol consumption increases the synthesis and deposition of fat in the liver. The second phase, **alcoholic hepatitis**, is an inflammation of the liver. Both of these conditions are reversible if alcohol consumption is

fatty liver The accumulation of fat in the liver.

alcoholic hepatitis Inflammation of the liver caused by alcohol consumption.

Normal liver

Normal liver

Cirrhotic liver

Figure F1.5 Chronic alcohol consumption can cause permanent liver damage. (Martin/Custom Medical Stock Photo, Inc.; Science Heritage/Custom Medical Stock Photo, Inc.)

cirrhosis Chronic liver disease characterized by the loss of functioning liver cells and the accumulation of fibrous connective tissue.

stopped and good nutritional and health practices are followed. If alcohol consumption continues, **cirrhosis** may develop. This is an irreversible condition in which fibrous deposits scar the liver and interfere with its function (see Figure F1.5). Because the liver is the primary site of many metabolic reactions, cirrhosis is often fatal.

Alcohol and Cancer In addition to causing liver disease, heavy drinking is associated with certain types of cancer. A meta-analysis of alcohol consumption and cancer risk found an association between alcohol consumption and cancer of the oral cavity, pharynx, esophagus, larynx, breast, liver, colon, rectum, and stomach.[10] Epidemiology shows that alcohol consumption is associated with an increased risk of breast cancer and that risk is directly related to the amount of alcohol consumed. How alcohol promotes breast cancer is still unclear but it has been hypothesized to affect cancer risk by altering estrogen metabolism through the mutagenic effects of acetaldehyde, by causing oxidative damage, or by interfering with folate metabolism.[11] There is some evidence that adequate dietary folate protects against the increased risk of breast cancer associated with alcohol consumption.[12]

F1.5 Benefits of Alcohol Consumption and Safe Drinking

Learning Objectives

- Describe how moderate alcohol intake reduces the risk of cardiovascular disease.
- List three things you could do to reduce the chances of becoming intoxicated while drinking alcoholic beverages.

For some people, moderate alcohol consumption (defined by the Dietary Guidelines as no more than one drink per day for women and two drinks per day for men) may be beneficial. Consuming alcoholic beverages before or with meals can stimulate appetite and improve mood. It can be relaxing, producing a euphoria that can enhance social interactions. It can also reduce the risk of heart disease.

Epidemiological and clinical studies have shown that light to moderate drinking reduces the risk for heart disease and stroke when compared to not consuming alcohol at all.[13] This reduction in heart disease risk results in a reduced mortality in middle-aged and older adults who consume moderate amounts of alcohol.[14] However, at high levels of consumption the mortality from heart disease is increased[15] (**Figure F1.6**). Wine consumption has been suggested as a reason for the lower incidence of heart disease in certain cultures. The Mediterranean diet (see Chapter 1), which has been associated with a reduced risk of heart disease, includes daily consumption of wine in moderation. And one explanation for the French paradox—the fact that the French eat a diet that is as high or higher in fat than the American diet but suffer from far less heart disease—is the glass of wine

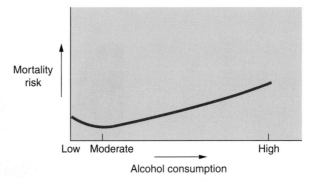

Figure F1.6 Alcohol consumption and mortality The risk of mortality plotted against the amount of alcohol consumed generally results in a J-shaped curve with lowest mortality at the level that corresponds to moderate alcohol consumption. The actual shape of the curve varies with age and gender. (Stock 4B/Getty Images, Inc.)

they drink with meals. The particular benefit of red wine is likely due not only to the alcohol, but also to the phytochemicals (phenols) it contains[16,17] (**Figure F1.7**).

There are a number of ways that moderate alcohol consumption reduces the risk of heart disease[15,18] (**Figure F1.8**). The most significant is its effect on HDL cholesterol. Moderate alcohol consumption can increase HDL cholesterol by 30% and is believed to account for about half of alcohol's protective effect. Alcohol also reduces the risk of heart disease by reducing levels of the blood-clotting protein fibrinogen. These lower levels reduce blood clots that can block blood flow to the heart resulting in a heart attack. Smaller beneficial effects have been attributed to alcohol's effect on insulin sensitivity, inflammatory molecules, and platelets.[18] Although all of these effects have been documented, the benefit any one individual will gain from moderate alcohol consumption depends on their genetic background, health status, and overall lifestyle.

Alcohol, like other drugs, has risks as well as benefits. The risks posed by alcohol depend on the consumer and the amount consumed. Some people should not consume any alcohol. For instance, women who are pregnant or trying to conceive should not consume alcohol because it can damage the fetus (see Chapter 14). Children and adolescents should not consume alcohol because they are more likely to suffer its toxic effects—drunkenness and poisoning leading to seizures, coma, and death.[5] Individuals who plan to drive or operate machinery should not consume alcohol because it can impair coordination and reflexes. Alcoholics should avoid alcohol because they cannot restrict their drinking to moderate levels. Finally, individuals taking medications that can interact with alcohol should avoid alcohol. For everyone, the risks of excess alcohol consumption outweigh the benefits.

Figure F1.7 Alcohol has a number of effects that reduce the risk of heart disease. The phytochemicals in red wine may add to this beneficial effect. (©Rayes/Digital Vision/Age Fotostock America, Inc.)

Life Cycle

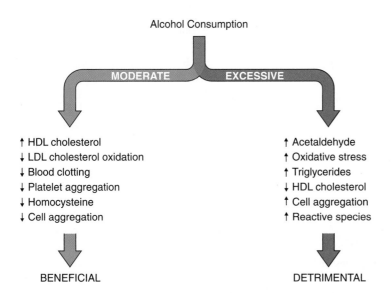

Alcohol Consumption

MODERATE   EXCESSIVE

↑ HDL cholesterol
↓ LDL cholesterol oxidation
↓ Blood clotting
↓ Platelet aggregation
↓ Homocysteine
↓ Cell aggregation

↑ Acetaldehyde
↑ Oxidative stress
↑ Triglycerides
↓ HDL cholesterol
↑ Cell aggregation
↑ Reactive species

BENEFICIAL

DETRIMENTAL

Figure F1.8 Benefits and risks of alcohol consumption Moderate alcohol consumption may reduce the risk of heart disease, but greater intakes contribute to cardiovascular disease risk.

Figure F1.9 When a moderate amount of alcohol is consumed with food, the risk of intoxication is reduced and the potential benefits are enhanced. (Thomas Tolstrup/Getty Images, Inc.)

Whether the benefits of alcohol consumption outweigh the risks, drinking is a personal decision that must take into account medical and social considerations. But those who choose to drink should do so in moderation. Alcohol should be consumed slowly; no more than one drink every 1.5 hours. Sipping, not gulping, allows the liver time to break down the alcohol that has already been consumed. Alternating nonalcoholic and alcoholic drinks will also slow down the rate of alcohol intake and prevent dehydration. Alcohol absorption is most rapid on an empty stomach. Consuming alcohol with meals slows its absorption and may also enhance its protective effects on the cardiovascular system (**Figure F1.9**). Also, the effect of alcohol on HDL is believed to be greater when the liver is processing nutrients from a meal.

References

1. Lieber, C. S. Relationships between nutrition, alcohol use, and liver disease. *Alcohol Res. Health* 27:220–231, 2003.

2. Bode, C., and Bode, J. C. Effect of alcohol consumption on the gut. *Best Pract. Res. Clin. Gastroenterol.* 17:575–592, 2003.

3. Baraona, E., Abittan, C. S., Dohmen, K. et al. Gender differences in pharmacokinetics of alcohol. *Alcohol Clin. Exp. Res.* 25:502–507, 2001.

4. Lai, C. L., Chao, Y. C., Chen, Y. C. et al. No sex and age influence on the expression pattern and activities of human gastric alcohol and aldehyde dehydrogenases. *Alcohol Clin. Exp. Res.* 24:1625–1632, 2000.

5. American Medical Association. Harmful Consequences of Alcohol Use on the Brains of Children, Adolescents and College Students, 2002. Fact Sheet. Available online at www.ama-assn.org/ama1/pub/upload/mm/388/harmful_consequences.pdf Accessed September 11, 2009.

6. National Council on Alcoholism and Drug Dependence (NCAAD). Youth, Alcohol and Other Drugs. Available online at www.ncadd.org/facts/youthalc.html/ Accessed September 11, 2009.

7. National Institutes of Health. Traffic crashes, traffic crash fatalities, and alcohol-related traffic crash fatalities, United States, 1982–2004. Available online at www.niaaa.nih.gov/Resources/DatabaseResources/QuickFacts/TrafficCrashes/crash01.htm. Accessed September 11, 2009.

8. Whitfield, J. B. Alcohol and gene interactions. *Clin. Chem. Lab. Med.* 43:480–487, 2005.

9. Breslow, R. A., and Smothers, B. A. Drinking patterns and body mass index in never smokers: National Health Interview Survey, 1997–2001. *Am. J. Epidemiol.* 161:368–376, 2005.

10. Bagnardi, V., Blangiardo, M., La Vecchia, C, and Corrao, G. A meta-analysis of alcohol drinking and cancer risk. *Br. J. Cancer* 85:1700–1705, 2001.

11. Dumitrescu, R. G., and Shields, P. G. The etiology of alcohol-induced breast cancer. *Alcohol* 35:213–225, 2005.

12. Baglietto, L., English, D. R., Gertig, D. M. et al. Does dietary folate intake modify effect of alcohol consumption on breast cancer risk? Prospective cohort study. *BMJ* 331:807, 2005.

13. Djousse, L., Ellison, R. C., Beiser, A. et al. Alcohol consumption and the risk of ischemic stroke: The Framingham Study. *Stroke* 4:907–912, 2002.

14. Meister, K. A., Whelan, E. M., and Kava, R. The health effects of moderate alcohol intake in humans: An epidemiologic review. *Crit. Rev. Clin. Lab. Sci.* 37:261–296, 2000.

15. Lucas, D. L., Brown, R. A., Wassef, M., and Giles, T. D. Alcohol and the cardiovascular system: Research challenges and opportunities. *J. Am. Coll. Cardiol.* 45:1916–1924, 2005.

16. Gronbaek, M., Becker, U., Johansen, D. et al. Type of alcohol consumed and mortality from all causes, coronary heart disease, and cancer. *Ann. Intern. Med.* 133:411–419, 2000.

17. Goldfinger, T. M. Beyond the French paradox: The impact of moderate beverage alcohol and wine consumption in the prevention of cardiovascular disease. *Cardiol. Clin.* 21:449–457, 2003.

18. Klatsky, A. L. Alcohol and cardiovascular disease. *Expert Rev. Cardiovasc. Ther.* 7:499–506, 2009.

6 Proteins and Amino Acids

Case Study

Teresa, a Peace Corps volunteer, recently arrived in Somalia to help care for children in a rural health clinic. A small 2-year-old boy named Songe catches her eye. His hair is an odd color, his legs are scrawny, and his belly is so large he looks pregnant. Songe and his new baby brother live with their mother and three other siblings in a refugee camp. His mother says that his symptoms began shortly after his younger brother was born. His gaunt look suggests that he isn't getting enough to eat, but why is his belly so large?

The clinic nurse explains to Teresa that Songe is suffering from protein-energy malnutrition. When his brother was born, Songe stopped nursing at his mother's breast and started eating the camp diet, which is high in starch and fiber. He no longer consumes enough protein to support the needs of his growing body. His belly is bloated because his abdomen is filling with fluid and his liver is filling with fat. There is not enough protein in his blood to hold the fluid there, so it seeps into his abdomen; nor is there enough protein to transport fat, so it accumulates in his liver. Songe is also experiencing health problems that are less visible. Without adequate protein, his immune system cannot function normally, increasing his susceptibility to infections and making the immunizations provided in the camp less effective.

Teresa asks the nurse why Songe's older siblings, who consume the same high-carbohydrate diet, don't have large bellies too. The nurse explains that because Songe's siblings are older, they can eat a larger volume of food. Also, their protein needs per kcalorie are less than Songe's, so they are able to eat enough of the camp diet to meet their protein needs. To treat his malnutrition, the clinic provides Songe with a special high-protein drink to consume along with his regular diet.

(Digital Vision/Getty Images, Inc.)

(©iStockphoto)

(iStockphoto)

Chapter Outline

6.1 Protein in the Modern Diet

Learning Objectives

- Indicate which types of foods provide the most concentrated sources of protein.
- Describe how the protein source affects the other nutrients it provides.

Protein deficiency is rare in the United States because the food supply is plentiful and varied; typical protein intake is about 90 g/day and has changed little over the past 30 years.[1,2] Most people in the United States and other developed countries have access to meats, eggs, and dairy products, which provide animal protein, and to legumes, grains, and vegetables, which provide plant sources of protein. Even those who choose a vegetarian diet can easily meet their protein needs. Yet, people still worry about getting enough protein. Protein drinks, pills, and powders fill the shelves of health-food stores. Consumers often choose high-protein foods and supplements because protein is associated with good health. They think it will make their mind sharp and their hair shine and help them lose weight. Unlike carbohydrate and fat, the popular press associates protein only with positive effects. It has not been accused of being fattening, causing tooth decay, or increasing the risk of heart disease.

Sources of Dietary Protein

Most of the world relies on plant proteins from grains and vegetables to meet their needs. These foods tend to be more available and less expensive than animal sources of protein. For example, in rural Mexico, most of the protein in the diet comes from beans, rice, and tortillas; in India protein comes from lentils and rice; in China rice with small amounts of meat and soy provides the protein. As the economic prosperity of a population grows, the proportion of animal foods in its diet typically increases.

In the United States, about two-thirds of the dietary protein comes from meat, poultry, fish, eggs, dairy products, and other animal sources.[3] These animal products are the most concentrated sources of protein. One egg contains about 7 grams of protein, a cup of milk contains 8 grams, and a 3-ounce serving of meat provides over 20 grams. But, plant foods such as grains and legumes are also important sources of protein. Legumes, such as lentils, soybeans, peanuts, black-eyed peas, chickpeas, and dried beans provide about 6 to 10 grams of protein per half-cup serving. Nuts and seeds provide about 5 to 10 grams per quarter cup. Even bread, rice, and pasta provide protein—about 2 to 3 grams per slice or half cup (**Figure 6.1**). Although most plant sources of protein are not used as efficiently by the human body as animal sources, they can still easily meet most people's needs.

Figure 6.1 Both plant and animal foods provide good sources of protein in the American diet. (Amy Etra/PhotoEdit)

Nutrients Supplied by Animal and Plant Foods

The source of the protein in the diet determines what other nutrients are consumed along with it. Animal products provide an excellent source of B vitamins and minerals such as iron, zinc, and calcium. But animal products are low in fiber and are often high in saturated fat and cholesterol—a nutrient mix that increases the risk of heart disease. Plant sources of protein are a good source of most, but not all, B vitamins and they also supply iron, zinc, and calcium but in less absorbable forms. But foods that provide good sources of plant proteins also contain fiber, phytochemicals, and unsaturated fats—dietary components that should be increased to promote health. Recommendations for a healthy diet suggest that our diets be based on whole-grain products, vegetables, and fruits and provide smaller amounts of lean meats and low-fat dairy products. Following these guidelines will provide plenty of protein but without an over-reliance on animal protein.

6.2 Protein Molecules

Learning Objectives

- Describe the general structure of an amino acid, a polypeptide, and a protein.
- Distinguish between essential and nonessential amino acids.
- Discuss how the order of amino acids in a polypeptide chain affects protein structure and function.

A protein molecule, whether found in a steak, a kidney bean, or a part of the human body, is constructed of one or more folded, chainlike strands of **amino acids**. The amino acid chain of each type of protein molecule contains a characteristic number and proportion of amino acids that are bound together in a precise order. This chain folds into a specific orientation, giving each protein a unique three-dimensional shape that is essential to its particular function. Variations in the number, proportion, and order of amino acids allow for an infinite number of different protein structures.

Like carbohydrates and lipids, protein molecules contain the elements carbon, hydrogen, and oxygen, but proteins are distinguished from the other energy-yielding nutrients by the presence of the element nitrogen in their structure.

amino acids The building blocks of proteins. Each contains a central carbon atom bound to a hydrogen atom, an amino group, an acid group, and a side chain.

Amino Acid Structure

Approximately 20 amino acids are commonly found in proteins. Each amino acid consists of a carbon atom bound to four chemical groups: a hydrogen atom; an amino group, which contains nitrogen; an acid group; and a fourth group or side chain that varies in length and structure (**Figure 6.2**). Different side chains give specific properties to individual amino acids.

Of the 20 amino acids commonly found in protein, 9 cannot be made by the adult human body. These amino acids, called **essential** or **indispensable amino acids**, must be consumed in the diet (**Table 6.1**). If the diet is deficient in one or more of these amino acids, new proteins containing them cannot be made without breaking down other body proteins to provide them. The 11 **nonessential** or **dispensable amino acids** can be made by the human body and are not required in the diet.

essential or **indispensable amino acids** Amino acids that cannot be synthesized by the human body in sufficient amounts to meet needs and therefore must be included in the diet.

nonessential or **dispensable amino acids** Amino acids that can be synthesized by the human body in sufficient amounts to meet needs.

Table 6.1 Essential and Nonessential Amino Acids

Essential Amino Acids	Nonessential Amino Acids
Histidine	Alanine
Isoleucine	Arginine*
Leucine	Asparagine
Lysine	Aspartic acid (aspartate)
Methionine	Cysteine (cystine)*
Phenylalanine	Glutamic acid (glutamate)
Threonine	Glutamine*
Tryptophan	Glycine*
Valine	Proline*
	Serine
	Tyrosine*

*These amino acids are considered conditionally essential by the Institute of Medicine, Food and Nutrition Board (*Dietary Reference Intakes for Energy Carbohydrates, Fiber, Fat, Protein and Amino Acids*, Washington, DC: National Academies Press, 2002).

Figure 6.2 Amino acid structure
All amino acids have a similar structure, but each has a different side chain.

Figure 6.3 Transamination
In this example, transamination transfers the amino group from the nonessential amino acid alanine to the carbon compound alpha-ketoglutarate to form the 3-carbon compound pyruvate and the essential amino acid glutamate.

Alanine + alpha-Ketoglutarate ⟶ Pyruvate + Glutamate

transamination The process by which an amino group from one amino acid is transferred to a carbon compound to form a new amino acid.

conditionally essential amino acids Amino acids that are essential in the diet only under certain conditions or at certain times of life.

When a nonessential amino acid needed for protein synthesis is not available from the diet, it can be made in the body. Most of the nonessential amino acids can be made by the process of **transamination**, in which an amino group from one amino acid is transferred to a carbon-containing molecule to form a different amino acid (**Figure 6.3**).

Some amino acids are **conditionally essential**. These are essential only under certain conditions. For example, the conditionally essential amino acid tyrosine can be made in the body from the essential amino acid phenylalanine. If phenylalanine is in short supply, tyrosine cannot be made and becomes essential in the diet. Likewise, the amino acid cysteine is only essential when the essential amino acid methionine is in short supply or cannot be converted to cysteine. Other amino acids may be essential at certain times of life, such as premature infancy, or due to certain conditions, such as metabolic abnormalities or physical stress.

Protein Structure

To form proteins, amino acids are linked together by a unique type of chemical bond called a *peptide bond*. This bond is formed between the acid group of one amino acid and the nitrogen atom of the next amino acid (**Figure 6.4**). When two amino acids are linked with a peptide bond, it is called a **dipeptide**; when three amino acids are linked, they form a **tripeptide**. Many amino acids bonded together constitute a **polypeptide**.

A protein is made of one or more polypeptide chains folded into a complex three-dimensional shape (see Figure 6.4). The order and chemical properties of the amino acids in a polypeptide chain determine the three-dimensional shape of the protein. Folds and bends in the chain occur when some of the amino acids attract each other and other amino acids repel each other. For example, amino acids at various places along the chain that are attracted to each other may cause segments of the chain to coil like a telephone cord. Amino acids that are attracted to water will orient to the outside of the structure to be in contact with body fluids, whereas amino acids that repel water will fold to the inside to be away from body fluids. After polypeptide chains have folded, several chains may bind together to form the final protein.

dipeptide Two amino acids linked by a peptide bond. A **tripeptide** is three amino acids linked by peptide bonds, and a **polypeptide** is a chain of three or more amino acids linked by peptide bonds.

It is the shape of the final protein that determines its function. For example, the elongated shape of the connective tissue proteins, collagen and alpha-keratin, allows them to give strength to fingernails and ligaments. The oxygen-carrying protein hemoglobin has a spherical shape, which allows proper functioning of the red blood cells. If the shape of a protein is altered, its function may be disrupted. For example in the genetic disease sickle cell anemia, a single amino acid in the hemoglobin molecule is altered, causing the protein molecules to bind together in long chains. Thus, rather than having the disc-shape characteristic of normal red blood cells, red blood cells containing these rope-like strands of sickle cell hemoglobin have a distorted shape that resembles a crescent or sickle (**Figure 6.5**). Sickle-shaped red blood cells can block capillaries, causing inflammation and pain. They also rupture easily, leading to anemia from a shortage of red blood cells.

denaturation The alteration of a protein's three-dimensional structure.

Changes in protein structure can also be caused by changes in the physical environment of the protein such as an increase in temperature or a change in pH. Such changes cause protein **denaturation**. In food, the heat of cooking denatures protein,

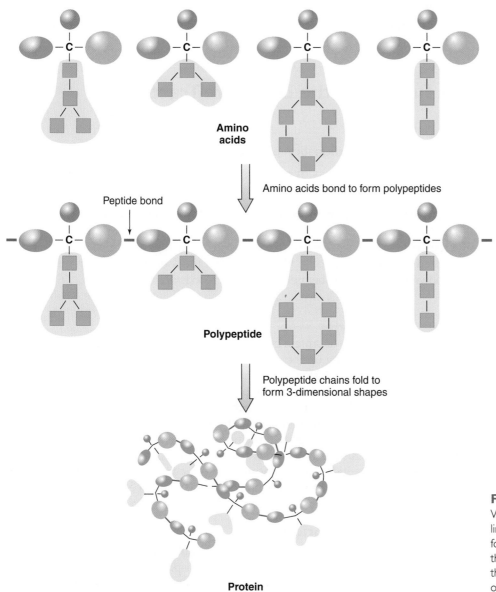

Amino acids

Amino acids bond to form polypeptides

Peptide bond

Polypeptide

Polypeptide chains fold to form 3-dimensional shapes

Protein

Figure 6.4 Protein structure
When many amino acids are linked by peptide bonds they form a polypeptide. Folding of the polypeptide chains creates the three-dimensional structure of the protein.

Polypeptide shape	Hemoglobin shape	Hemoglobin arrangement	Red blood cell shape
Normal	Normal	Individual molecules	Disc-shaped
Altered	Altered	Long chains of molecules	Sickle-shaped

Figure 6.5 Sickle cell anemia
In sickle cell anemia, a change in the sequence of amino acids in hemoglobin alters the shape and function of the protein molecule. Sickle cell hemoglobin forms long chains that distort the shape of red blood cells. (Stan Fleger/Visuals Unlimited)

Figure 6.6 Why does the protein in egg white change from clear and liquid to white and firm when it is cooked? (Charles D. Winters)

thereby changing its shape and physical properties. For example, a raw egg white is clear and liquid, but once it has been denatured by cooking, it becomes white and firm (**Figure 6.6**).

6.3 Protein in the Digestive Tract

Learning Objectives

- Describe protein digestion and amino acid absorption.
- Explain why an excess of one amino acid could cause a deficiency of another amino acid.
- Discuss how protein digestion is related to food allergies.

Protein enters the digestive tract from food, from digestive secretions, and from sloughed gastrointestinal cells. No matter what the source, the protein must be broken down to amino acids before entering the bloodstream.

Protein Digestion

The chemical digestion of protein begins in the stomach, where hydrochloric acid denatures proteins, opening up their folded structure to make them more accessible to enzyme attack (**Figure 6.7**). The acid also activates the protein-digesting enzyme pepsin, which breaks proteins into polypeptides and amino acids. When the polypeptides enter the small intestine, they are broken into smaller polypeptides, tripeptides, dipeptides, and amino acids by pancreatic protein-digesting enzymes such as trypsin and chymotrypsin. Protein-digesting enzymes in the brush border of the small intestine further break down the small polypeptides. Single amino acids, dipeptides, and tripeptides can be absorbed into the mucosal cells of the small intestine. Once inside they are broken into single amino acids (see Figure 6.7).

Amino Acid Absorption

Amino acids and di- and tripeptides enter the mucosal cells of the small intestine using one of several energy-requiring active transport systems. Amino acids with similar structures share the same transport system and therefore compete for absorption. For instance, the amino acids leucine, isoleucine, and valine, referred to as branched-chain amino acids because their carbon side chains have a branching structure (see Appendix L), share the same transport system. If there is an excess of any one of the amino acids sharing a transport system, more of it will be absorbed, slowing the absorption of the other competing amino acids. This is generally not a problem when amino acids are consumed in foods because they contain a variety of amino acids without disproportionately large amounts of any one. However, taking a supplement of one amino acid can provide enough of it to impair absorption of other amino acids that share the same transport system (see Figure 6.7). For example, weight lifters often take supplements of the amino acid arginine, which shares the same transport system as lysine. When large doses of arginine are ingested, the absorption of lysine will be reduced.

Protein Digestion and Food Allergies

Food allergies are triggered when a protein from the diet is absorbed without being completely digested. The proteins from milk, eggs, peanuts, tree nuts, wheat, soy, fish, and shellfish are common causes of food allergies. The first time the protein is consumed and a piece of it is absorbed intact, the immune system is stimulated (see Chapter 3). When the protein is consumed again, the immune system sees it as a foreign substance and mounts an attack, causing an allergic reaction. Allergic reactions

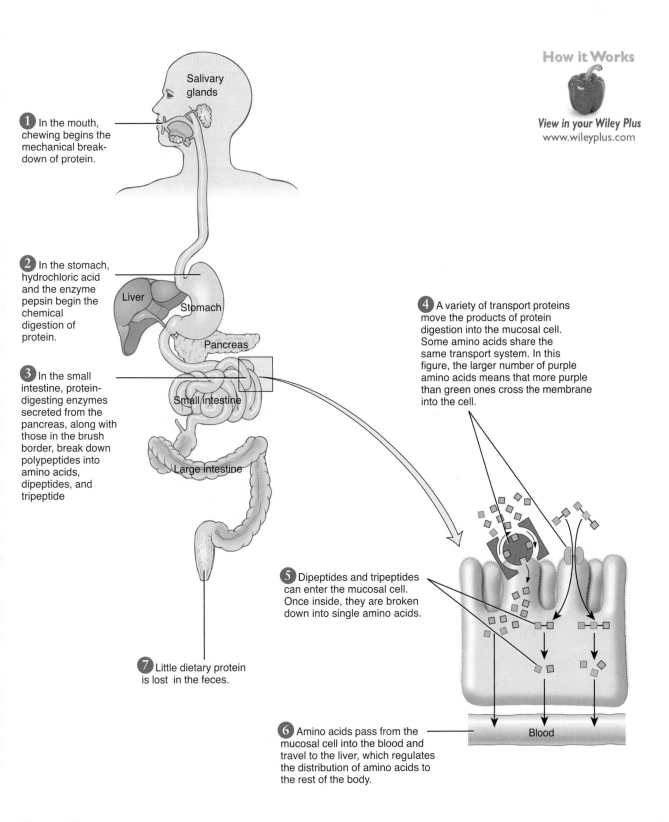

1 In the mouth, chewing begins the mechanical breakdown of protein.

2 In the stomach, hydrochloric acid and the enzyme pepsin begin the chemical digestion of protein.

3 In the small intestine, protein-digesting enzymes secreted from the pancreas, along with those in the brush border, break down polypeptides into amino acids, dipeptides, and tripeptide

7 Little dietary protein is lost in the feces.

Salivary glands

Liver

Stomach

Pancreas

Small intestine

Large intestine

How it Works

View in your Wiley Plus
www.wileyplus.com

4 A variety of transport proteins move the products of protein digestion into the mucosal cell. Some amino acids share the same transport system. In this figure, the larger number of purple amino acids means that more purple than green ones cross the membrane into the cell.

5 Dipeptides and tripeptides can enter the mucosal cell. Once inside, they are broken down into single amino acids.

6 Amino acids pass from the mucosal cell into the blood and travel to the liver, which regulates the distribution of amino acids to the rest of the body.

Blood

Figure 6.7 Protein digestion and absorption
Protein must be broken down into small peptides and amino acids before it can be absorbed into the mucosal cells.

anaphalaxis An immediate and severe allergic reaction to a substance (e.g., food or drugs). Symptoms include breathing difficulty, loss of consciousness, and a drop in blood pressure and can be fatal.

Life Cycle

to food can cause symptoms throughout the body. These can involve the digestive system causing vomiting or diarrhea; the skin, causing a rash or hives; the respiratory tract, causing difficulty breathing; or the cardiovascular system, causing a drop in blood pressure. A rapid, severe allergic reaction that involves more than one part of the body is called **anaphylaxis**. A severe anaphylactic reaction can cause breathing difficulty or a dangerous drop in blood pressure and can be fatal.

Allergies are common in people with gastrointestinal disease, because their damaged intestine allows the absorption of incompletely digested proteins. Allergies are also common in infants, because their immature gastrointestinal tracts are more likely to allow larger polypeptides to be absorbed. Once an infant's intestinal mucosa matures, absorption of incompletely digested proteins is less likely and some food allergies disappear. The absorption of whole proteins by very young infants, however, can also be of benefit since antibody proteins absorbed from breast milk can provide temporary protection against certain diseases (see Chapter 14).

6.4 Protein in the Body

Learning Objectives

- List the sources of amino acids entering the "amino acid pool" and the uses for amino acids drawn out of the pool.
- Discuss the steps involved in synthesizing proteins.
- Name four functions of body proteins.
- Describe the conditions under which the body uses protein to provide energy.

amino acid pool All of the amino acids in body tissues and fluids that are available for use by the body.

Once dietary proteins have been digested and absorbed, their constituent amino acids become available to the body. The amino acids in body tissues and fluids are referred to collectively as the **amino acid pool** (**Figure 6.8**). Amino acids in this pool can be metabolized to provide energy—4 kcalories per gram. This occurs both when the diet contains protein in excess of needs and when the diet is low in energy. When dietary intake of protein and energy are adequate but not excessive, most amino acids in the amino acid pool are used to synthesize body proteins and other nitrogen-containing compounds.

Protein Turnover

protein turnover The continuous synthesis and breakdown of body proteins.

Body proteins are not static but rather are continuously broken down and resynthesized. This process, referred to as **protein turnover**, is necessary for normal growth and maintenance of body tissues and for adaptation to changing situa-

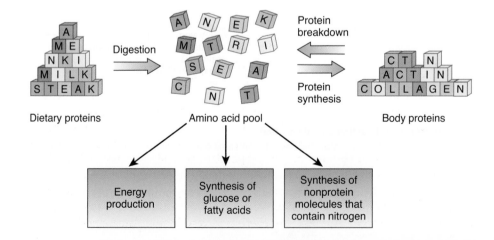

Figure 6.8 Amino acid pool Amino acids in the available pool come from the diet and from the breakdown of body proteins. They are used to synthesize body proteins and nonprotein molecules, and to generate ATP, or to synthesize glucose or fatty acids.

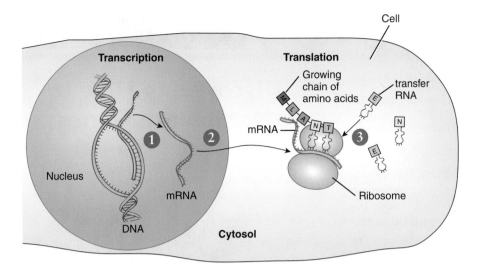

1. In the nucleus the blueprint, or code, for the protein is copied or transcribed from the DNA gene into a molecule of messenger RNA (mRNA).

2. The mRNA takes the genetic information from the nucleus to structures called ribosomes in the cytosol, where proteins are made.

3. In the cytosol, transfer RNA (tRNA) reads the genetic code and delivers the needed amino acids to the ribosome to form a polypeptide chain.

Figure 6.9 Transcription and translation
DNA in cell nuclei provides the information needed to assemble proteins (transcription and translation).

tions. The rate at which proteins are made and degraded varies with the protein and is related to its function. Proteins whose concentration must be regulated and proteins that act as chemical signals in the body tend to have high rates of turnover—that is, synthesis and degradation. For example, the level of insulin in the blood can be rapidly increased by increasing its synthesis and decreasing the rate at which it is degraded. To decrease insulin levels, breakdown can be increased and synthesis slowed. Altering levels of synthesis and degradation allows protein levels to quickly change to maintain homeostasis as body conditions change. Structural proteins, such as collagen in connective tissue, have slower rates of turnover. The total amount of body protein broken down each day is large; twice as many of the amino acids in the amino acid pool come from recycled proteins as from dietary proteins.

Protein Synthesis

The amino acids used to synthesize body proteins come from the amino acid pool. The instructions that dictate which amino acids are needed, and in what order they should be combined, are contained in stretches of DNA called **genes**. When a protein is needed, the process of protein synthesis is turned on.

The first step in protein synthesis involves copying, or transcribing, the DNA code from the gene into a molecule of *messenger RNA (mRNA)*. This process is called **transcription** (**Figure 6.9**). The mRNA then takes this information from the nucleus of the cell to ribosomes in the cytosol where proteins are made. Here the information in mRNA is translated through another type of RNA, called *transfer RNA (tRNA)*. Transfer RNA reads the code and delivers the needed amino acids to form a polypeptide chain. This process is called **translation**. After translation polypeptides typically undergo further chemical modifications before achieving their final protein structure and function (see Science Applied: Discovering How to Manipulate Genes).

gene A length of DNA containing the information needed to synthesize RNA or a polypeptide chain.

transcription The process of copying the information in DNA to a molecule of mRNA.

translation The process of translating the mRNA code into the amino acid sequence of a polypeptide chain.

SCIENCE

ScienceAppliedScienceApplied
Science**AppliedScience**Applied
ScienceAppliedScienceApplied

APPLIED

(DAJ/Getty Images, Inc.)   (www.victorianoizquierdo.com/Getty Images, Inc.)   (Elena Schweitzer/Shutterstock)

Discovering How to Manipulate Genes

Genetic engineering is the process of manipulating the genetic makeup of plants, animals, and microorganisms. By modifying DNA, scientists can change the proteins that a cell or organism can make. This technology, developed over the past 30 years, has allowed researchers to create bacteria that make medicines for humans, plants that are disease-resistant, and foods that provide a healthier mix of nutrients.

To alter the genetic composition of a cell, a specific piece of DNA, or gene, from one type of cell must be clipped out and pasted into the DNA in another cell. The new DNA, called *recombinant DNA*, can then provide the blueprint for new proteins. For example, if scientists take a piece of human DNA containing the gene for the hormone insulin and paste it into the DNA of a bacterium, the bacterium can then make human insulin. Today, more than 80% of people with diabetes who require insulin use genetically engineered insulin. Before genetically engineered insulin was available the only source of insulin was the pancreases of slaughtered animals such as pigs and sheep.

Before 1970, genetic engineering was not possible because there was no way to cut DNA. The ability to cut DNA emerged from basic laboratory research that studied bacteria. In the 1950s it was recognized that some strains of bacteria were able to slice viral DNA into pieces.[1] This ability was found to be due to bacterial enzymes, called *restriction enzymes*, which cut DNA in specific places. By the late 1960s and early 1970s, restriction enzymes were being isolated and characterized.[2,3] At the same time, bacterial enzymes that repair breaks in DNA, called *DNA ligases*, were also being studied. DNA ligases had the ability to paste together two strands of DNA. At the time of their discovery restriction enzymes and DNA ligases were recognized as interesting in the field of microbiology but it was impossible to predict the impact they would have on the fields of biology and medicine. These seemingly obscure bacterial enzymes changed the course of technology and will continue to impact many fields of science for years to come.

Restriction enzymes are present in bacteria as a form of protection. If a virus invades the bacterium, it can defend itself by cutting the viral DNA into little pieces before the virus can cause harm. In the laboratory these enzymes act like precision scissors that can clip out a gene that produces a specific protein. Because DNA in all forms of life is made of the same building blocks, an enzyme from a bacterium can cut the DNA from a cow, a soybean plant, and a human cell with equal efficiency. When DNA from one cell is combined with

The insulin used to treat diabetics today is made by genetic engineering. In the past insulin had to be extracted from the pancreases of slaughtered animals.

that of another, the resulting cells can produce new proteins and provide new functions to the host. For example, a corn plant can be given a gene that makes a protein that is toxic to the corn borer, an insect that attacks corn plants. The corn plant is then resistant to that insect pest.

The discovery of restriction enzymes and DNA ligases provided the tools needed for the techniques of molecular biology. Today scientists can purchase these enzymes from scientific suppliers, and use them to locate, isolate, prepare, and study small segments of DNA. Obscure experiments done 30 years ago with oddball enzymes have created an endless supply of human insulin for diabetics and blood clotting proteins for hemophiliacs. They have led to new, more powerful cancer therapies and vaccines to prevent disease. Genetic engineering is also changing the foods we eat. It has created insect-resistant corn, virus-resistant papaya, grains with higher protein quality, and fruits and vegetables with longer shelf life. However, despite the potential and realized benefits, this technology has raised new questions and concerns, both ethical and scientific (see Focus on Biotechnology).

[1]Old, R. W., and Primrose, S. B. *Principles of Gene Manipulation: An Introduction to Genetic Engineering*, 5th ed. London: Blackwell Science, Ltd., 1994.

[2]Meselson, M., and Yuan, R. DNA restriction enzyme from *E. coli. Nature* 217:1110–1114, 1968.

[3]Smith, H. O., and Wilcox, K. W. A restriction enzyme from *Hemophilus influenzae*. I. Purification and general properties. *J. Molecular Biol.* 51:379–391, 1970.

Regulation of Gene Expression Gene expression refers to the process whereby the information coded in a gene is used to produce a product that functions in the body. This means that when a gene is expressed the product for which it codes is synthesized. Sometimes the final product is a molecule of RNA and sometimes it is a protein. Which gene products are made and when they are made is important to the health of the cell and the organism, therefore gene expression is carefully regulated. Not all genes are expressed in all cells or at all times. For example, the hormone glucagon is a protein that is made in pancreatic cells. Glucagon is not made by other body cells because the gene is not expressed in cells other than those in the pancreas. The expression of some genes changes depending on the need for the proteins for which they code. For example, when zinc intake is high, the expression of a gene that codes for metallothioneine, a metal-binding protein, is turned on. This allows more of this protein to be synthesized, increasing the capacity to bind zinc and other metal ions. The levels of nutrients in the body also affect the expression of other genes. For example, vitamin A levels affect the expression of genes involved in the maturation and specialization of cells and vitamin D affects the expression of genes that code for calcium transport proteins (see Chapter 9).

Limiting Amino Acids During the synthesis of a protein, a shortage of one needed amino acid can stop the process. Just as on an assembly line, if one part is missing, the line stops—a different part cannot be substituted. If the missing amino acid is a nonessential amino acid, it can be synthesized in the body and protein synthesis can continue. If the missing amino acid is an essential amino acid, the body can break down some of its own proteins to obtain this amino acid. If an amino acid cannot be supplied, protein synthesis will stop. The essential amino acid present in shortest supply relative to need is called the **limiting amino acid**, because lack of this amino acid limits the ability to make protein (**Figure 6.10**). If all amino acids are present in adequate amounts at the time of synthesis, proteins will be completed and released for further processing by the cell. Animal foods are generally better sources of protein because animal proteins provide enough of all of the amino acids needed to build human proteins. Plant sources of protein are generally low in one or more of the essential amino acids so are used less efficiently to synthesize body protein. An exception is soy protein, which is as good as animal protein when it comes to supplying essential amino acids (see Your Choice: Should You Increase Your Soy Intake?).

Synthesis of Nonprotein Molecules

Amino acids are needed for the synthesis of a variety of nonprotein molecules that contain nitrogen. For example, the amino acid tryptophan is used to synthesize the neurotransmitter serotonin, which acts in the relaxation center of the brain. Amino acids are needed for the synthesis of the nitrogen-containing compounds that are the building blocks of DNA and RNA. Other molecules synthesized from amino acids include the skin pigment melanin, the vitamin niacin, creatine needed for muscle contraction, and histamine, which causes blood vessels to dilate.

gene expression The events of protein synthesis in which the information coded in a gene is used to synthesize a product; either a protein or a molecule of RNA.

limiting amino acid The essential amino acid that is available in the lowest concentration in relation to the body's needs.

A shortage of the amino acid represented by the orange blocks limits the ability to synthesize a protein that is high in this amino acid.

Amino acid pool

Protein

Figure 6.10 Limiting amino acids The amino acids needed for protein synthesis come from the amino acid pool. If the protein to be made contains more of a particular amino acid than is available, that amino acid limits protein synthesis and is said to be the limiting amino acid.

Should You Increase Your Soy Intake?

(©iStockphoto)

Soy products have long been a major protein source in Japan and China, countries where heart disease is less prevalent than it is in the United States. Both soy protein and *isoflavones*, phytochemicals found in soy, have been hypothesized to be responsible for the lower incidence of heart disease in these Asian countries. Isoflavones are estrogen-like compounds. Their estrogen-like effects has led some to speculate that in addition to affecting heart disease risk, they may reduce the symptoms of menopause (including hot flashes) and prevent bone loss. Soy has also been suggested to have beneficial effects in preventing and treating certain forms of cancer.

Some of the excitement about the health benefits of soy may have been premature. A review of the effect of soy on the risk of heart disease concluded that soy has only a small LDL cholesterol-lowering effect and this occurs only when large amounts were consumed.[1] Soy has not been found to affect HDL cholesterol, triglyceride levels, or blood pressure. Research has not shown soy to reduce the symptoms of menopause and results are mixed with regard to its effect on postmenopausal bone loss. Little evidence has been found to support the effectiveness of soy in the prevention or treatment of cancers of the breast, uterus, and prostate.[1]

Despite the disappointing news with regard to blood lipid levels, soy may still be good for your heart and overall health. Soybeans and products made from them provide plant protein equivalent in quality to animal proteins, so choosing soy can help you meet your protein needs by adding high quality protein to your diet. Soy products are also high in polyunsaturated fat, fiber, vitamins, and minerals, and low in saturated fat.

Therefore, replacing foods high in animal protein, like hamburgers, with soy products, like soy burgers, is likely to benefit your health.

Soy-based foods are available in many forms. Soybeans can be eaten boiled or roasted. Soybean sprouts can be added to salads. Soy butter, which is similar to peanut butter, can be spread on crackers and sandwiches. Tofu, also known as bean curd, is often consumed raw in soups or salads or cooked in stir fries. Miso and tempeh, which are fermented soybean products, are used in soups and mixed dishes. Soy flour can be incorporated into baked goods; made into the texturized soy protein (TSP) used to make meat substitutes for vegetarian burgers, hot dogs, meatballs, and chicken; or added to animal protein as an extender or filler.

Remember, though, that simply including soy-based foods—or any single food, for that matter—in your diet is not the answer to good health. Replacing some of the animal sources of protein with soy protein may help protect your health, but other dietary and lifestyle factors also influence your overall risk of developing heart disease.

Tofu, also known as bean curd, is a soft, cheese-like product made by curdling fresh hot soymilk. (Daniel Bendjy/iStockphoto)

[1]Sacks, F. M., Lichtenstein, A., Van Horn, L., et al. Soy protein, isoflavones, and cardiovascular health: An American Heart Association Science Advisory for professionals from the Nutrition Committee. *Circulation* 113:1034–1044, 2006.

ATP Production

Although carbohydrate and fat are more efficient energy sources, amino acids from the diet and from body proteins are also used to provide energy. Before this can occur, the nitrogen-containing amino group must be removed from the amino acids in a process called **deamination** (**Figure 6.11**). The carbon compounds remaining after the amino group is removed can be used in a number of ways, depending on the needs of the body. If glucose is in short supply, amino acids that break down to form 3-carbon compounds can be used by the liver to synthesize glucose via gluconeogenesis. If

deamination The removal of the amino group from an amino acid.

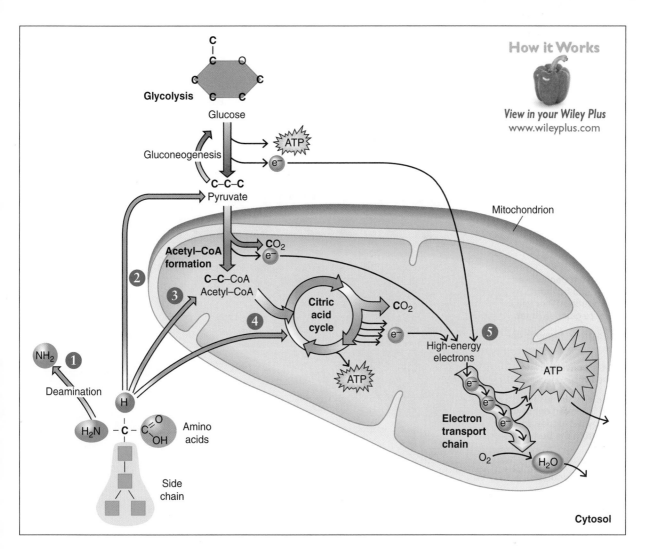

1. The amino group is removed by deamination.

2. Deamination of some amino acids produces three-carbon molecules that can be used to synthesize glucose, via gluconeogenesis.

3. Deamination of some amino acids results in two-carbon molecules that form acetyl-CoA, which can enter the citric acid cycle or be used to synthesize fatty acids.

4. Deamination of some amino acids forms molecules that are intermediates in the citric acid cycle.

5. High-energy electrons from the breakdown of amino acids are transferred to the electron transport chain where the energy is trapped and used to produce ATP and water.

Figure 6.11 Amino acid metabolism

In order for the body to use amino acids as an energy source, the nitrogen-containing amino group must be removed. The compounds remaining after the amino group has been removed are composed of carbon, hydrogen, and oxygen and can be broken down to produce ATP or used to make glucose or fatty acids.

energy is needed, the carbon structure of the amino acids can be converted into acetyl-CoA or compounds that directly enter the citric acid cycle to produce ATP (see Figure 6.11). The use of amino acids as an energy source increases both when the diet does not provide enough total energy to meet needs, as in starvation, and when protein is consumed in excess of needs. When both protein and energy are plentiful, amino acids can be converted into acetyl-CoA and used to synthesize fat for storage. The nitrogen released from amino acids by deamination forms ammonia, a toxic waste product. High levels of ammonia in the blood can be fatal. To protect the body,

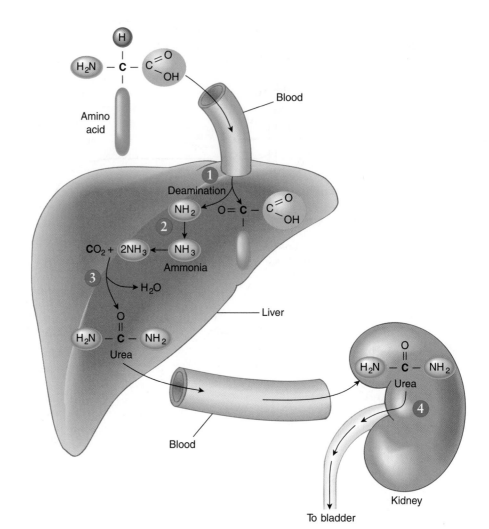

1 Amino acids are deaminated before they can be metabolized to produce ATP or used to synthesize glucose or fat.

2 The amino group forms toxic ammonia

3 Ammonia is converted into urea in the liver.

4 Urea can safely travel in the blood and is filtered out of the blood by the kidney and eliminated from the body in the urine.

Figure 6.12 Urea Synthesis
The nitrogen from amino acid breakdown is eliminated from the body as urea.

urea A nitrogen-containing waste product formed from the breakdown of amino acids that is excreted in the urine.

the liver combines ammonia with carbon dioxide to form a less toxic waste product called **urea** (**Figure 6.12**). Urea can be eliminated from the body by the kidneys.

When Energy Intake Is Low When energy is deficient, body proteins, such as enzymes and muscle proteins, are broken down into amino acids that can then be used to generate ATP or synthesize glucose. This provides energy in times of need, but it also robs the body of functional proteins. The most dispensable proteins are broken down first, conserving others for the numerous critical roles they play, but if the energy deficit continues, more critical proteins, such as those that make up the heart and other internal organs, will also be degraded. A loss of more than 30% of the body's protein reduces the strength of the muscles required for breathing and heart function, depresses immune function, and causes a general loss of organ function that is great enough to cause death.

When Protein Intake Exceeds Needs Amino acids are used for energy when protein intake exceeds protein needs. If the diet is adequate in energy and high in protein, the amino acids from the excess protein are deaminated and used to produce ATP. If both energy and protein exceed needs, the extra amino acids are converted into fatty acids, stored as triglycerides in adipose tissue, and can contribute to weight gain.

Protein Functions

About 15% of body weight is protein. Much of this is due to muscle proteins but there are also many other body proteins, each with a unique function. Some have important structural roles and others help regulate body processes.

Structural Proteins Proteins provide structure to individual cells and to the body as a whole. In cells, proteins are an integral part of the cell membrane, the cytosol, and the organelles. Skin, hair, and muscle are body structures that are composed largely of protein. The most abundant protein in the body is collagen; it holds cells together and forms the protein framework of bones and teeth. It also forms tendons and ligaments, strengthens artery walls, and is a major constituent of scar tissue. When the diet is deficient in protein, these structures break down. The muscles shrink, the skin loses its elasticity, and the hair becomes thin and can easily be pulled out by the roots. These outward signs of protein deficiency have become marketing strategies for cosmetic companies. Shampoo and hand lotion manufacturers add protein to their products, suggesting that protein applied to the hair or skin will improve its structure. However, the proteins that make up hair and skin can only be made inside the body, so a healthy diet will do more for hair and skin quality than expensive protein shampoos or lotions.

Enzyme Proteins Enzymes are protein molecules that speed up metabolic reactions but are not used up or destroyed in the process. Without the help of enzymes the metabolic reactions that break down molecules to provide energy and build molecules needed by the body would occur too slowly to support life. Each of the reactions involved in the production of ATP and the synthesis and breakdown of carbohydrates, lipids, and proteins requires a specific enzyme with a specific structure. If the structure of the enzyme molecule is changed, it can no longer function in the reaction it is designed to accelerate.

Enzymes that function in the body are made by the body and therefore do not need to be consumed in the diet. Enzymes present in raw foods are denatured by the cooking process and are no longer functional when the cooked food is eaten. When foods are eaten raw, the enzymes present are broken down during digestion and are absorbed from the gastrointestinal tract as amino acids. Purified enzymes sold as dietary supplements are also broken down in the gut. Some of these may provide function while in the gut; for example, lactase, taken by individuals with lactose intolerance, remains functional long enough to break down lactose consumed at the same time. Eventually, these enzymes are also digested and absorbed as amino acids.

Transport Proteins Proteins transport substances into and out of individual cells and throughout the body. At the cellular level, transport proteins present in cell membranes help move substances such as glucose and amino acids across the cell membrane into and out of cells. For example, transport proteins in the intestinal mucosa are necessary to absorb amino acids from the intestinal lumen into the mucosal cells. Transport proteins in the blood carry substances from one organ to another. For example, hemoglobin, the protein in red blood cells, picks up oxygen in the lungs and transports it to other organs of the body (**Figure 6.13**). The proteins in lipoproteins are needed to transport lipids from the intestines and liver to body cells. Some nutrients must be bound to a specific protein to be transported in the blood. When protein is deficient, the nutrients that require specific proteins for transport cannot travel to the cells. For this reason, a protein deficiency can cause a vitamin A deficiency; even if vitamin A is consumed in the diet, without protein it cannot be transported to the cells where it is needed.

Figure 6.13 The protein hemoglobin, which gives red blood cells their red color, shuttles oxygen to body cells and carries away carbon dioxide. (David Phillips/Visuals Unlimited)

Proteins that Provide Protection Proteins play an important role in protecting the body from injury and invasion by foreign substances. Skin, which is made up primarily of protein, is the first barrier against infection and injury. Foreign particles such as dirt or bacteria that are on the skin cannot enter the body and can be washed away. If the skin is broken and blood vessels are injured, blood-clotting proteins, including fibrin and thrombin, help prevent too much blood from being lost. If a foreign particle such as a virus or bacterium enters the body, the immune system fights it off by synthesizing proteins called **antibodies**. Each antibody has a unique structure that allows it to attach to a specific invader. When an antibody binds to an invading substance, the production of more antibodies is stimulated, and other parts

antibodies Proteins produced by the body's immune system that recognize foreign substances in the body and help destroy them.

Figure 6.14 How will this immunization prevent the child from contracting measles or mumps? (Picture Partners/Age Fotostock America, Inc.)

Figure 6.15 Proteins in muscle contraction
During muscle contraction the proteins actin and myosin slide past each other, causing the muscle fibers to shorten.

pH A measure of acidity.

of the immune system are signaled to help destroy the invading substance. The next time the same type of invading bacterium or virus enters the body, the immune system is already primed to produce specific antibodies to fight off that particular invader. Immunizations against diseases, such as measles, work in a similar way. A small amount of dead or inactivated virus is injected into the body; the injected material does not cause disease, but it does stimulate the immune system to produce antibodies to the virus (**Figure 6.14**). When the body comes in contact with the live virus, the immune system is already primed so a large-scale immune system attack is mounted and the infection is prevented. When the immune system malfunctions as a result of protein deficiency, human immunodeficiency virus (HIV) infection, or other causes, the ability to protect the body from infection is compromised.

Contractile Proteins The proteins in muscles allow us to move. When you climb a flight of stairs, walk across the room, or run around the block, you are relying on the muscle proteins actin and myosin, which cause the contraction of muscles. Contraction occurs when these two proteins slide past each other, shortening the muscle. For example, when you do a biceps curl, the muscles in your biceps shorten as the alternating actin and myosin protein fibers slide past one another (**Figure 6.15**). A similar process causes contraction in the heart muscle and in the muscles that cause constriction in the digestive tract, blood vessels, and glands. Actin and myosin can also cause contraction in nonmuscle cells. For example, this contraction helps white blood cells change shape and move so they can reach infected tissues in the body. The energy for contraction comes from ATP, which is derived primarily from the metabolism of carbohydrate and fat.

Protein Hormones Hormones are chemical messengers that are secreted into the blood by one tissue or organ and act on target cells in other parts of the body. Hormones made from amino acids are classified as protein or peptide hormones. For instance, insulin and glucagon are peptide hormones involved in maintaining a steady level of blood glucose. Unlike steroid hormones, which are made from cholesterol and can diffuse across the cell membrane and enter the cell, peptide hormones act by binding to protein receptors on the surface of the cell membrane.

Proteins that Regulate Fluid Balance The distribution of fluid among body cells, the bloodstream, and the spaces between cells is important for homeostasis. Fluid moves back and forth across membranes to maintain appropriate concentrations of particles and fluids inside and outside cells and tissues (see Chapter 10). Proteins help regulate this fluid balance in two ways. First, protein pumps located in cell membranes transport substances from one side of a membrane to the other. Second, large protein molecules present in the blood hold fluid in the blood by contributing to the osmotic load in the bloodstream. In cases of protein malnutrition, the concentration of these large proteins in the blood decreases, so fluid is no longer held in the blood, and it accumulates in tissues and in the abdomen.

Proteins that Regulate Acid-Base Balance The chemical reactions of metabolism require a specific level of acidity, or **pH**, to function properly. In the gastrointestinal tract, acidity levels vary widely. The digestive enzyme pepsin works best in the acid environment of the stomach, whereas the pancreatic enzymes operate best in the more neutral environment of the small intestine. Inside the body, the range of optimal pH is much tighter. The acids and bases produced by metabolic reactions must be neutralized in order to prevent changes in pH, which in turn can prevent life-sustaining metabolic reactions from proceeding normally. The lungs and kidneys help maintain a normal pH by eliminating some of these waste products. Proteins both in the blood and within the cells act as buffers to prevent changes in pH. They function by attracting or releasing hydrogen ions. For instance, the protein hemoglobin in red blood cells helps neutralize acid produced when carbon dioxide reacts with water. Untreated type 1 diabetes is an example of what happens when the amount of acid produced exceeds the ability of the body's proteins and other systems to neutralize it. In type 1 diabetes the inability to get glucose into cells results in the breakdown of fats and the buildup of ketones, which are acidic. As ketones accumulate, they cause a drop in pH called ketoacidosis (see Chapter 4). The acidic pH denatures proteins and they are unable to perform their functions, resulting in coma and eventually, if not treated, death.

6.5 Protein, Amino Acids, and Health

Learning Objectives

- Compare kwashiorkor with marasmus.
- Explain why protein-energy malnutrition develops more rapidly in young children than in adults.
- Discuss the potential risks associated with a high protein diet.

A diet adequate in protein is essential to health. Dietary protein is needed for growth and to replace body protein that is broken down and lost each day. If too little protein is consumed, the consequences can be dramatic and devastating. Too much protein, particularly if it is derived primarily from animal sources, may also have negative health effects. In addition some people are sensitive to specific proteins and amino acids.

Protein Deficiency

Because of the availability and variety of foods in developed countries, protein deficiency is uncommon. However, in developing nations, concerns about inadequate protein are very real. Diets deficient in protein are most often deficient in energy as well, but a pure protein deficiency can occur when food choices are extremely limited and the staple food of a population is very low in protein. The term **protein-energy malnutrition (PEM)** is used to refer to the continuum of protein deficiency conditions ranging from pure protein deficiency, called **kwashiorkor**, to overall energy deficiency, called **marasmus**. Most protein-energy malnutrition is a combination of the two.

Kwashiorkor Kwashiorkor is typically a disease of children. The word "kwashiorkor" comes from the Ga tribe of the African Gold Coast. It means the disease that the first child gets when a second child is born.[4] When the new baby is born, the older child is no longer breast-fed. Rather than receiving protein-rich breast milk, the young child is fed a watered-down version of the diet eaten by the rest of the family. This diet is low in protein and is often high in fiber and difficult to digest. The child, even if able to get adequate energy, is not able to eat a large enough quantity to get adequate protein. Because children are growing, their protein needs per unit of body weight are higher than those of adults, and the effects of a deficiency become evident much more quickly.

The symptoms of kwashiorkor can be explained by examining the roles that proteins play in the body. Because protein is needed for the synthesis of new tissue, growth in height and weight is hampered in children. Because proteins are important in immune function, there is an increased susceptibility to infection. There are changes in hair color because the skin pigment melanin is not made; the skin flakes because structural proteins are not available to provide elasticity and support. Cells lining the digestive tract die and cannot be replaced, so nutrient absorption is impaired. The bloated belly typical of this condition is a result of both fat accumulating in the liver, because there is not enough protein to transport it to other tisues, and fluid accumulating in the abdomen, because there is not enough protein in the blood to keep water from diffusing out of the blood vessels (**Figure 6.16a**).

Kwashiorkor occurs most commonly in Africa, South and Central America, the Near East, and the Far East. It has also been reported in poverty-stricken areas in the United States. Although kwashiorkor is thought of as a disease of children, it is seen in hospitalized adults who have high-protein needs due to infection or trauma and a low-protein intake because they are unable to eat.

protein-energy malnutrition (PEM) A condition characterized by wasting and an increased susceptibility to infection that results from the long-term consumption of insufficient amounts of energy and protein to meet needs.

Life Cycle

kwashiorkor A form of protein-energy malnutrition in which only protein is deficient.

marasmus A form of protein-energy malnutrition in which a deficiency of energy in the diet causes severe body wasting.

(a)   (b)

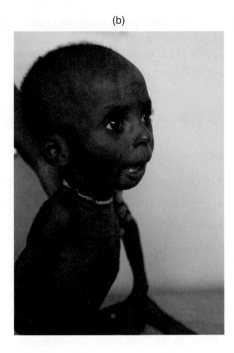

Figure 6.16 (a) Kwashiorkor is characterized by a bloated belly, whereas (b) marasmus presents as severe wasting. (Courtesy Food and Agriculture Organization; ©AP/Wide World Photos)

Marasmus At the other end of the continuum of protein-energy malnutrition is marasmus, meaning to waste away. Marasmus is due to a deficiency of energy, but protein and other nutrients are usually also insufficient to meet needs. Marasmus may have some of the same symptoms as kwashiorkor, but there are also differences. In kwashiorkor, some fat stores are retained, since energy intake is adequate. In contrast marasmic individuals appear emaciated because their body fat stores have been used to provide energy (**Figure 6.16b**). Since fat is a major energy source and carbohydrate is limited, ketosis may occur in marasmus. This is not so in kwashiorkor because carbohydrate intake is adequate—only protein is deficient.

Life Cycle

Marasmus occurs in individuals of all ages but is most devastating in infants and children because adequate energy is essential for growth. Most brain growth takes place in the first year of life, so malnutrition early in life causes a decrease in intelligence and learning ability that persists throughout life. Marasmus often occurs in children who are fed diluted infant formula prepared by caregivers trying to stretch limited supplies. Marasmus occurs less often in breast-fed infants. Marasmus is the form of malnutrition that occurs with eating disorders.

Protein Excess

Adequate protein intake is absolutely essential to life, but too much protein has been hypothesized to affect the health of the kidneys and bones, and to impact on the healthfulness of the overall diet. For a healthy person there are no short-term problems associated with consuming a diet very high in protein but we are still investigating whether the same is true in the long term.

Life Cycle

Hydration and Kidney Function As protein intake increases above the amount needed, so does the production of protein breakdown products, such as urea, which must be eliminated from the body by the kidneys. To do this, more water must be excreted in the urine, increasing water losses. Although not a concern for most people, this can be a problem if the kidneys are not able to concentrate urine. For example, the immature kidneys of newborn infants are not able to concentrate urine and therefore they need to excrete more water than adults to eliminate the same amount of urea. Feeding a newborn infant formula that is too high in protein can increase fluid losses and lead to dehydration. High-protein diets are also a risk for people with kidney disease. The increased wastes produced on a high-protein diet may speed the progression of renal failure in these individuals.[5] Despite this, there is little evidence that a high-protein diet increases the risk of kidney disease in healthy people.[6]

Bone Health It has been suggested that the amount and source of protein in the diet affect calcium status and bone health.[7] For healthy bone, intakes of both calcium and protein must be adequate. There is general agreement that diets that are moderate in protein (1.0 to 1.5 g/kg/day) are associated with normal calcium metabolism and do not alter bone metabolism.[7,8] However, a high protein intake may increase the amount of calcium lost in the urine. Some studies suggest that the amount of calcium lost in the urine is greater when protein comes from animal rather than vegetable sources.[9] These findings have contributed to a widely held belief that high-protein diets (especially diets that are high in animal protein) result in bone loss. However, clinical studies do not support the idea that animal protein has a detrimental effect on bone health or that vegetable-based proteins are better for bone health.[8] In fact, when calcium intake is adequate, higher-protein diets are associated with greater bone mass and fewer fractures.[7] This is likely the case because in healthy adults, a high protein intake increases intestinal calcium absorption as well as urinary excretion, so the increase in the amount of calcium lost in the urine does not cause an overall loss of body calcium.

Kidney Stones The increase in urinary calcium excretion associated with high-protein diets has led to speculation that a high protein intake may increase the risk of kidney stones. Kidney stones are deposits of calcium and other substances in the kidneys and urinary tract. Higher concentrations of calcium and acid in the urine increase the likelihood that the calcium will be deposited, forming these stones. Epidemiological studies suggest that diets that are rich in animal protein and low in fluid contribute to the formation of kidney stones.[10]

Heart Disease and Cancer Risk Another concern with high-protein diets is related more to the dietary components that accompany animal versus plant proteins. Typically, high protein diets are also high in animal products; this dietary pattern is high in saturated fat and cholesterol and low in fiber and therefore increases the risk of heart disease. These diets are also typically low in grains, vegetables, and fruits, a pattern associated with a greater risk of cancer.[11] Such diets are also usually high in energy and total fat, which may promote excess weight gain.

Proteins and Amino Acids that May Cause Harm

Unlike lipids and carbohydrates, people don't think of protein as contributing to health problems, but for some people, the wrong protein can be harmful. In some cases, this is because a protein in food is recognized and targeted by the immune system causing an allergic reaction. There are no cures for food allergies so, to avoid symptoms, allergic individuals need to avoid eating foods that contain proteins that cause an allergic reaction (see Off the Label: Is it Safe for You?). Not all adverse reactions to proteins and amino acids are due to allergies; some are due to food intolerances. These reactions do not involve the immune system. The symptoms of a food intolerance can range from minor discomfort, such as the abdominal distress some people feel after eating raw onions, to more severe reactions.

Aspartame and Phenylketonuria Aspartame is a sugar substitute composed of two amino acids, aspartic acid and phenylalanine. Aspartame is used in a wide variety of foods, including carbonated beverages, gelatin desserts, and chewing gum. Digestion breaks aspartame into aspartic acid, phenylalanine, and an alcohol called methanol. Because the phenylalanine released from aspartame digestion is absorbed into the blood, food products containing this alternative sweetener must be avoided by individuals with a genetic disorder called **phenylketonuria (PKU)**.

Individuals with PKU inherit a defective gene for an enzyme called *phenylalanine hydroxylase* which is needed to metabolize phenylalanine. In those with this faulty gene the enzyme does not function properly, and they are unable to convert the essential amino acid phenylalanine to the semiessential amino acid tyrosine. Instead, phenylalanine is converted to compounds called *phenylketones*, which build

phenylketonuria (PKU)
An inherited disease in which the body cannot metabolize the amino acid phenylalanine. If the disease is untreated, toxic by-products called *phenylketones* accumulate in the blood and interfere with brain development.

Life Cycle

Off the Label
Is it Safe for you?

"What is food to one, is to others bitter poison," said the Roman philosopher and scientist Lucretius. Today, fortunately, the information in ingredient lists can help those with food allergies tell the difference. Food manufacturers are required to clearly state if a product contains any of the eight major food allergens: milk, eggs, peanuts, tree nuts, fish, shellfish, soy, and wheat.[1] Products that contain tree nuts also must list the type of nut on the label, and foods containing fish or shellfish must give the species. This information helps quickly identify foods that contain these allergens so they can be avoided.

The information about allergens can be presented on the label in one of three ways. One is to simply list it clearly in the ingredient list. For example, **MILK** can be listed with other ingredients. A second way is to use a parenthetical statement. Sometimes this is helpful when listing the actual ingredient is not clear to the consumer. For example, someone who is allergic to milk might be allergic to the milk protein casein. They must not only avoid milk and other dairy products, but also foods to which casein has been added. Casein, often listed as sodium-caseinate, is used in coffee whiteners and frozen dessert toppings. Foods containing casein can identify it as a milk-derived allergen by using a parenthetical statement, such as **CASEIN (MILK)**.

A third way food labels may indicate the presence of one or more of these eight common allergens is to use the word "Contains" followed by the name of the major food allergen, printed at the end of the ingredient list or next to it. For example: **CONTAINS WHEAT AND SOY INGREDIENTS**. This is helpful because some foods are unexpected sources of allergens. For example, isolated soy protein may be added to canned soups or gravies to aid in emulsification or add texture. A person trying to avoid soy would not necessarily think of soup as a soy product, but the statement at the end of the ingredients warns them that this product **CONTAINS SOY INGREDIENTS** (see figure).

Keep in mind that even a food whose Nutrition Facts lists zero grams of protein may include protein sources in the ingredient list. The amounts may be too small to add a significant amount of protein, but can be enough to cause an allergic reaction. For example, small amounts of *protein hydrolysates* or *hydrolyzed proteins*—proteins that have been treated with acid or enzymes to break them down into amino acids and small peptides—are often added as flavorings, flavor enhancers, stabilizers, or thickening agents in foods such as soups and packaged rice and potato products. To help individuals avoid specific proteins, foods containing protein hydrolysates are required to list the source of the hydrolysate—**HYDROLYZED CORN PROTEIN** in the soup example.

Finally, products that do not intentionally contain proteins that cause allergies may provide a special warning if there is a potential for cross-contamination from equipment or foods processed in the same facility. For example, you may see products declaring that they were **MANUFACTURED IN A FACILITY THAT PROCESSES PEANUTS**—a potentially life-saving warning for individuals with peanut allergy, who can have a severe reaction from minute amounts of peanut protein.

INGREDIENTS: CHICKEN BROTH, CARROTS, COOKED WHITE CHICKEN MEAT (WHITE CHICKEN MEAT, WATER, SALT, SODIUM PHOSPHATE, ISOLATED SOY PROTEIN, MODIFIED CORN STARCH, CORN STARCH, CARRAGEENAN), TOMATOES, WILD RICE, RICE, CELERY. LESS THAN 2% OF: SALT, MONOSODIUM GLUTAMATE, HYDROLYZED CORN PROTEIN, CHICKEN FAT, ONION POWDER, AUTOLYZED YEAST EXTRACT, PARSLEY FLAKES, NATURAL FLAVOR. **CONTAINS SOY INGREDIENTS.**

Nutrition Facts

Serving Size 1 cup (239g)
Servings Per Container about 2

Amount Per Serving	
Calories 100	Calories from Fat 30

	% Daily Value*
Total Fat 1.5g	**2%**
Saturated Fat 2g	**10%**
Trans Fat 0g	
Cholesterol 15mg	**5%**
Sodium 850mg	**35%**
Total Carbohydrate 15g	**5%**
Dietary Fiber 1g	**4%**
Sugars 1g	
Protein 7g	

Vitamin A 25%	•	Vitamin C 0%
Calcium 0%	•	Iron 2%

*Percent Daily Values (DV) are based on a 2,000 calorie diet.

CHICKEN & RICE

The Nutrition Facts panel lists the grams of protein in a serving, but the ingredient list tells you which amino acids or protein-containing ingredients have been added to the product.

---

[1]FDA, CFSAN. Food Allergen Labeling and Consumer Protection Act of 2004. Available online at www.cfsan.fda.gov/~dms/alrgact.html/. Accessed June 8, 2009.

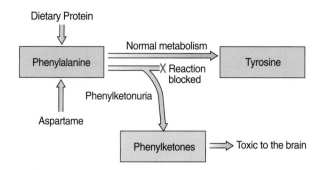

Figure 6.17 Phenylketonuria
In individuals with phenylketonuria, phenylalanine accumulates and is converted to phenylketones, which can interfere with brain development.

up in the blood (**Figure 6.17**). In infants and children high phenylketone levels can interfere with brain development, causing intellectual disability. Pregnant women with PKU must be especially careful to consume a low-phenylalanine diet in order to protect their unborn children from high phenylketone levels, which can cause brain abnormalities and other birth defects.[12]

PKU afflicts about 1 in 12,000 newborn infants.[13] Infants are tested for this disorder at birth because brain damage can be avoided by a special low-phenylalanine diet. The diet must provide just enough phenylalanine to meet the body's need for protein synthesis but not so much that the buildup of phenylketones occurs. The diet must also provide sufficient tyrosine, because the disease prevents conversion of phenylalanine to tyrosine, causing it to become an essential amino acid. All proteins naturally contain phenylalanine so a low-phenylalanine diet must carefully regulate overall protein intake. Special low-phenylalanine or phenylalanine-free formulas are manufactured for infants with this disease. Because foods like diet soda and other artificially sweetened beverages do not contain protein, individuals with this disease might not expect them to contain phenylalanine. Therefore, warnings for individuals with PKU are included on the labels of all products containing aspartame, though few of them specify the actual amount of the sweetener contained in the product (**Figure 6.18**).

Life Cycle

Celiac Disease Gluten intolerance, also called **celiac disease**, celiac sprue, or gluten-sensitive enteropathy, is another form of food intolerance. Individuals with celiac disease cannot tolerate gluten, a protein found in wheat, rye, barley and other grains. Celiac disease is an autoimmune disease in which gluten causes the body to attack the villi in the small intestine, causing symptoms such as diarrhea, abdominal bloating and cramps, weight loss, and anemia. Once thought to be a rare childhood disease, it is now known to affect more than 2 million people in the United States.[14] The only treatment is to avoid gluten by eliminating all products containing gluten from the diet.

celiac disease A disorder that causes damage to the intestines when the protein gluten is eaten.

Monosodium Glutamate Sensitivity Monosodium glutamate (MSG) is a flavor enhancer best known for its use in Chinese cooking. It is added to a variety of packaged foods such as potato chips, canned soups, cured meats, and packaged entrees. It is also sold as a seasoning. Seasonings that contain MSG include Accent, Ajinomoto, Zest, Vestin, Gourmet Powder, Subu, Chinese seasoning, Glutavene, Glutacyl, RL-50 Kombu

Phenylketonurics: Contains phenylalanine

Figure 6.18 Diet sodas that are sweetened with aspartame carry a warning to alert individuals with PKU that the soda is a source of phenylalanine. (Urbano Delvalle/Time Life Pictures/Getty Images, Inc.)

extract, and Meijing or Wei-jing. MSG consists of the amino acid glutamic acid (or glutamate) bound to sodium. Some people report adverse reactions including a flushed face, tingling or burning sensations, headache, rapid heartbeat, chest pain, and general weakness after consuming MSG.[15] These symptoms are referred to as *MSG symptom complex*, commonly termed *Chinese restaurant syndrome*, and are most likely to occur within an hour after eating about 3 grams or more of MSG on an empty stomach. However, a typical serving of foods containing MSG includes only about 0.5 mg of MSG. Controlled studies have not been able to consistently document reactions to MSG.[16]

Because glutamate is a neurotransmitter, some brain researchers have expressed concern that very high dietary intakes of glutamate could be toxic to nerves in humans. However, a review of scientific data has found no evidence that dietary MSG causes brain lesions or damages nerve cells in humans. The FDA has therefore maintained glutamate on the list of substances generally recognized as safe (see Chapter 17).[17] However, individuals who are sensitive to this additive can avoid it by checking the ingredient list on food labels for monosodium glutamate or potassium glutamate. If the label states that the product contains "no MSG" or "no added MSG" then neither MSG nor hydrolyzed protein containing glutamate has been added to the food. When eating out you can avoid this additive by asking the restaurant to prepare your food without added MSG.

6.6 Meeting Protein Needs

Learning Objectives

- Discuss how protein needs are determined.
- Explain what is meant by protein quality.
- Review a diet and substitute complementary plant proteins for the animal proteins it contains.

Protein consumed in the diet must supply amino acids to replace losses that occur during protein turnover, to repair damaged tissues, and to synthesize new body proteins for growth. In a typical U.S. diet, protein provides about 20% of the energy.[18] This is equal to approximately 90 grams of protein—which is about twice the RDA.[2] Current recommendations do not suggest a reduction in protein intake, but do recommend increasing the amount of plant protein and decreasing the amount of animal protein. The recommended dietary pattern is based on whole grains, legumes, fruits, and vegetables, with smaller amounts of lean meats and low-fat milk products.

Determining Protein Requirements

Historically, recommendations for protein intake were estimated from the amount of protein consumed by healthy workingmen in the general population. These protein levels were often as high as 150 grams per day. Current recommendations are generally lower than this and are based on **nitrogen balance** studies (**Figure 6.19**). Since protein is the only macronutrient that contains nitrogen, the amount of protein used by the body can be estimated by comparing nitrogen intake with nitrogen loss. Nitrogen intake is calculated from dietary protein intake. Nitrogen loss or output is measured by totaling the amounts of nitrogen excreted in urine and feces and that lost from skin, sweat, hair, and nails. The majority of the nitrogen lost is excreted in the urine as urea. Comparing the amount of nitrogen consumed with the amount lost provides information about the amount of protein being synthesized and broken down within the body. An individual who is consuming enough protein to meet body needs is in protein or nitrogen balance. This means the individual is consuming enough nitrogen or protein to replace the amount that is lost from the body. The protein requirement is the smallest amount of dietary protein that will maintain balance when energy needs are met by carbohydrate and fat.

nitrogen balance
The amount of nitrogen consumed in the diet compared with the amount excreted by the body over a given period.

Nitrogen intake

Nitrogen intake

Nitrogen intake

Nitrogen output

Nitrogen output

Nitrogen output

Nitrogen balance
Nitrogen intake = nitrogen output
Total body protein does not change

Negative nitrogen balance
Nitrogen intake < nitrogen output
Total body protein decreases

Positive nitrogen balance
Nitrogen intake > nitrogen output
Total body protein increases

Figure 6.19 Nitrogen balance
Nitrogen balance indicates whether the amount of protein in the body is remaining constant, decreasing, or increasing. (Cameron Lawson/NG Image Collection; Brian Yarvin/Photo Researchers; Roy Toft/NG Image Collection)

If the body breaks down more protein than it synthesizes then nitrogen balance is negative; this means more nitrogen is lost than ingested (see Figure 6.19). This indicates that body protein is being lost. Negative nitrogen balance can occur when intake is too low or when the amount of protein breakdown has been increased by a stress such as injury, illness, or surgery.

If the body is synthesizing more protein than it breaks down, nitrogen balance is positive; this indicates that the body is using dietary protein for the synthesis of new body proteins (see Figure 6.19). Positive nitrogen balance occurs when new tissue is synthesized, such as during growth, pregnancy, wound healing, or muscle building (see Critical Thinking: What Does Nitrogen Balance Tell Us?).

The protein requirement of a specific individual can be determined by doing a nitrogen balance study for that individual. Because this procedure cannot be done for everyone, the protein needs of populations must be estimated from balance study data. Recommendations for protein intake for the general public are actually higher than the requirements determined by nitrogen balance studies for individuals. This is to allow a margin of safety that will ensure that the needs of the majority of the population are met.

The RDA for Protein

The RDA for protein for adults is 0.8 gram of protein per kilogram of body weight per day.[6] For a person weighing 70 kg (154 lb), the recommended intake would be 56 grams of protein per day (**Table 6.2**). Protein needs are increased if protein is being deposited in the body as it is during growth, or when protein losses are increased, such as during lactation or when the body is injured.

RDAs have also been established for each of the essential amino acids (see Appendix A); these are not a concern in a typical diet but are important when developing for intravenous feeding solutions.

Infants and Children For an individual to grow, new body proteins must be synthesized. During the first year of life, a large amount of protein is required to support the rapid growth rate. Thus, an AI for the first 6 months of life has been set at

Life Cycle

Critical Thinking
What Does Nitrogen Balance Tell Us?

Background

The Amecht Company wants to include nitrogen balance studies in the assays it performs in its clinical laboratory. To test their methodology, they analyze nitrogen balance in three individuals. The technicians are given information about the daily nitrogen intake of these subjects and analyze samples of urine and feces to determine daily nitrogen losses. Nitrogen balance is equal to nitrogen intake minus nitrogen output.

Data

Subject A consumed 6.4 grams of nitrogen. The laboratory determines that she lost 8.0 grams of nitrogen in her urine and feces. The nitrogen balance equation for subject A is

$$6.4 \text{ g} - 8.0 \text{ g} = -1.6 \text{ g}$$

Subject B is a healthy 29-year-old man who weighs 82 kg and consumes an adequate diet providing 2700 kcalories and 70 grams of protein a day. His nitrogen values are:

	Nitrogen In	Nitrogen Out
Subject B	11.2	11.2

Subject C is a 31-year-old pregnant woman of average prepregnancy weight who is consuming 2500 kcalories and 80 grams of protein a day. Her nitrogen values are:

	Nitrogen In	Nitrogen Out
Subject C	12.8	10.4

(©Kari Pearson, Photodisc/Getty Images, Inc.)

Critical Thinking Questions

Subject A is in negative nitrogen balance. List some possible reasons that would explain this.

▼

Calculate Subject B's nitrogen balance. What can you determine about subject B based on your answer?

▼

What would you predict about Subject C's nitrogen balance based on the fact that she is pregnant? Calculate her nitrogen balance. Explain whether it supports your prediction.

iProfile Use iProfile to find a snack that provides the additional 25 g of protein needed during pregnancy.

Table 6.2 Calculating Protein Needs

To determine protein requirement:

- Determine body weight. If weight is measured in pounds, convert it to kilograms by dividing by 2.2;

$$\frac{\text{weight in lbs}}{2.2 \text{ lbs/kg}} = \text{weight in kg}$$

For example:

$$\frac{150 \text{ lbs}}{2.2 \text{ lbs/kg}} = 68 \text{ kg}$$

- Determine the grams of protein required per day. Multiply weight in kilograms by the grams of protein per kilogram recommended for the specific gender and life-stage group (see below).

For example:

A 23-year-old woman weighing 68 kg would require 0.8 g/kg/day $\times$ 68 kg = 54.4 grams of protein/day.

Group	Age (yrs)	RDA (g/kg/day)
Infants	0–0.5	1.52*
	0.5–1	1.5
Children	1–3	1.1
	4–8	0.95
Adolescents	9–13	0.95
	14–18	0.85
Adults	19 and older	0.8
Pregnancy		Nonpregnant RDA + 25 g/day
Lactation	First 6 months	Nonlactation RDA + 25 g/day

*This value is an AI.

1.52 grams per kilogram of body weight per day; for the second 6 months, the RDA is 1.5 grams per kilogram.[6] As the growth rate slows, requirements per unit of body weight decrease but continue to be greater than adult requirements until 19 years of age (**Figure 6.20**).

Pregnancy and Lactation During pregnancy both the mother and the unborn baby are growing. The mother's diet must supply enough protein to provide for the expansion of her blood volume, enlargement of her uterus and breasts, development of the placenta, and growth and development of the fetus. The RDA for pregnant women is 25 grams of protein per day above the nonpregnant recommendation. Most women in North America already consume this much protein in their typical diets.

Protein needs are also increased during lactation, but not because protein is being deposited in the body. Lactation increases protein needs because a lactating woman is producing and secreting breast milk, which is very high in protein. The quantity of milk produced and the protein content of the milk determine the additional protein needs of lactation. The RDA during lactation is 25 grams of protein per day greater than the RDA for nonlactating women.

Illness and Injury Extreme stresses on the body such as infections, fevers, burns, or surgery increase protein breakdown. These losses must be replaced by dietary protein. Requirements for these types of stresses must be assessed on an individual basis, depending on the extent of the losses. For example, a severe infection increases requirements by about one-third. Burns can increase requirements to two to four times the normal level.

Exercise The marketing of protein powders and amino acid supplements to athletes might lead people to believe that protein is in short supply in the athlete's diet. In fact, athletes can obtain plenty of protein in their diets without supplements.

Life Cycle

Figure 6.20 Young children have high protein needs because of their rapid rate of growth. (Cheryl Maeder/Taxi/Getty Images)

Most athletes can meet their protein needs by consuming the RDA of 0.8 gram per kg of body weight per day. Only endurance athletes and strength athletes, such as triathletes and body builders, require more than the RDA. The reason endurance athletes need more is that some protein is used for energy and to maintain blood glucose during endurance events, such as ultramarathons and long-distance cycling. Athletes participating in endurance events such as these may benefit from 1.2 to 1.4 grams of protein per kilogram per day. Strength athletes, such as body builders, need extra protein because it provides the raw materials needed for building their large muscles; 1.2 to 1.7 grams per kilogram per day is recommended.[19] The higher protein needs of endurance and strength athletes can be met without protein supplements as long as the diet provides adequate kcalories. For example, if a 200-lb (91-kg) man consumes 3600 kcalories per day, 15% of which is from protein (approximately the amount contained in a typical North American diet), he will consume 135 grams of protein. This equals about 1.5 grams of protein per kilogram of body weight. Consuming additional protein as food or supplements will not enhance performance. The protein needs of athletes are also discussed in Chapter 13.

A Range of Healthy Protein Intakes

In addition to the RDA, the DRIs give a recommendation for protein intake as a percentage of kcalories; the Acceptable Macronutrient Distribution Range (AMDR) is 10% to 35% of kcalories from protein. This range allows for different food preferences and eating patterns. A protein intake in this range will meet needs, balance with carbohydrate and fat kcalories, and not increase health risks. A diet that provides 10% of kcalories from protein will meet the RDA but is a relatively low-protein diet based on typical eating patterns in the United States.[6] Most people consume about 20% of their kcalories from protein.[18] Very few people consume more protein than the upper end of the healthy range—35% of kcalories. If the proportion of protein goes higher than this, the diet will likely be higher in fat and lower in carbohydrate than is recommended. As discussed previously, the health concerns associated with high-protein diets relate more to the relative amounts of energy-yielding nutrients included in these diets. For a certain level of energy intake, as the protein content of the diet increases, fat also increases because most of the high-protein foods in our diets are animal products that contain fat along with the protein. Therefore, a diet that contains 35% protein would tend to have more fat, saturated fat, and cholesterol and less carbohydrate than a diet with the same number of kcalories that has only 10% protein.

Estimating Protein Intake

To determine how much protein is in your diet, you can use food composition tables or databases to look up the number of grams of protein in individual foods. To get a quick estimate you can also use the Exchange Lists (**Table 6.3** and Appendix I). According to the exchanges, 1 ounce of meat provides 7 grams of protein, 1 cup of milk provides 8 grams, and a serving of grains or vegetables provides 2 to 3 grams. Food labels provide a ready source of information about the protein content of packaged foods; however, since the labeling of raw meats and fish is voluntary, many of the greatest sources of protein in the diet do not carry food labels. The Nutrition Facts section lists the number of grams of protein per serving, but the % Daily Value is generally not included. It is required only on labels that carry a claim related to the food's protein content, such as "high protein." The ingredient list provides information on the protein and amino acid-containing ingredients in the food. This information can be important for people with allergies and those trying to avoid certain additives (see Off the Label: Is it Safe for You?).

Table 6.3 Using Exchange Lists to Estimate Protein Content

Exchange Groups/List	Serving Size	Protein (g)
Carbohydrate Group		
Starch	1/2 cup pasta, cereal, potatoes; 1 slice bread	3
Fruit	1 small apple, peach, pear; 1/2 banana;	
	1/2 cup canned fruit (in juice)	0
Milk	1 cup milk or yogurt	
Nonfat		8
Low-fat		8
Reduced-fat		8
Whole		8
Other carbohydrates	Serving sizes vary	Varies
Vegetables	1/2 cup cooked vegetables, 1 cup raw	2
Meat/Meat Substitute Group	1 oz meat or cheese, 1/2 cup legumes	
Very lean		7
Lean		7
Medium-fat		7
High-fat		7
Fat Group	1 tsp butter, margarine, or oil;	
	1 Tbsp salad dressing	0

Considering Protein Quality

Most Americans eat plenty of protein, but to evaluate protein intake it is important to consider both the amount and the quality of the protein. **Protein quality** is a measure of how good the protein in a food is at providing the essential amino acids needed by the body. The RDA for protein is calculated assuming that the diet contains a mixture of plant and animal proteins and therefore is of mixed quality. Protein needs can be met with lower quality proteins, but more protein is needed to supply enough of all the essential amino acids. Choosing a diet that includes a variety of protein-containing foods will provide enough protein and enough of each of the essential amino acids to meet needs.

Complete and Incomplete Protein Because we are animals, it makes sense that animal proteins generally contain mixtures of amino acids more similar to those we need. This is why animal proteins are considered higher quality than proteins from plant sources. Animal proteins also tend to be digested more easily than plant proteins; only protein that is digested can contribute amino acids to meet requirements.[20] Because they are easily digested and supply essential amino acids in the proper proportions for human use, foods of animal origin are sources of **complete dietary protein**. Plant proteins are usually more difficult to digest and are low in one or more of the essential amino acids and are therefore referred to as **incomplete dietary protein**. As mentioned earlier soy protein, which is a high-quality plant protein, is an exception to this generalization.

Measuring Protein Quality Being able to evaluate the protein quality of a food or a diet is valuable when assessing the adequacy of human diets throughout the world. For example, knowing the quality of the protein in cassava is extremely important in determining the adequacy of the diet in countries where it is a staple and both food and protein are scarce.

Protein quality is evaluated experimentally in a number of ways (see **Table 6.4**). One way is to compare the amino acid pattern of the food protein of interest with that found in a reference protein known to be of high quality, such as egg protein. A **chemical** or **amino acid score** is calculated by comparing the amount of the limiting amino acid in the test protein with the amount of that amino acid in egg protein. In this analysis, proteins with the most desirable proportions of amino acids will have the

protein quality A measure of how efficiently a protein in the diet can be used to make body proteins.

complete dietary protein
Protein that provides essential amino acids in the proportions needed to support protein synthesis.

incomplete dietary protein
Protein that is deficient in one or more essential amino acids relative to body needs.

chemical or **amino acid score** A measure of protein quality determined by comparing the essential amino acid content of the protein in a food with that in a reference protein. The lowest amino acid ratio calculated is the chemical score.

Table 6.4 Measures of Protein Quality

Chemical or Amino Acid Score =	$\dfrac{\text{mg of limiting amino acid per g of test protein}}{\text{mg of limiting amino acid per g of reference protein}} \times 100$
Protein Digestibility–Corrected Amino Acid Score (PDCAAS) =	amino acid score $\times$ digestibility factor
Protein Efficiency Ratio (PER) =	$\dfrac{\text{wt gain when fed test protein}}{\text{wt gain when fed reference protein}}$
Net Protein Utilization (NPU) =	$\dfrac{\text{nitrogen retained}}{\text{nitrogen consumed}} \times 100$
Biological Value (BV) =	$\dfrac{\text{nitrogen retained}}{\text{nitrogen absorbed}} \times 100$

protein digestibility-corrected amino acid score (PDCAAS) A measure of protein quality that reflects a protein's digestibility as well as the proportions of amino acids it provides.

protein efficiency ratio A measure of protein quality determined by comparing the weight gain of a laboratory animal fed a test protein with the weight gain of an animal fed a reference protein.

net protein utilization A measure of protein quality determined by comparing the amount of nitrogen retained in the body with the amount eaten in the diet.

biological value A measure of protein quality determined by comparing the amount of nitrogen retained in the body with the amount absorbed from the diet.

highest scores. Amino acid score is a useful measure, but it does not consider digestibility. A measure that considers both amino acid composition and digestibility is the **protein digestibility-corrected amino acid score (PDCAAS)** (**Figure 6.21**). PDCAAS measures the quality of a protein by comparing its amino acid composition to the amino acid requirements of a 2- to 5-year-old child (the age group with the highest needs relative to size), and then adjusting this for digestibility. A higher PDCAAS means that less of the protein is needed to provide all the needed amino acids. This method is currently used to assess the protein quality of foods for humans and is the standard used by the FDA to determine the % Daily Value for protein for food labels on products intended for people over 1 year of age.

Other methods of evaluating protein quality include the **protein efficiency ratio**, which measures how well a protein promotes growth in animals, and **net protein utilization** and **biological value**, which measure how well a protein is used by the body for growth and maintenance.

Protein Complementation Assessing protein quality is important in planning diets for regions of the world where protein is scarce. It is less important in industrialized countries, where high-quality protein is readily available to most people. A more appropriate way of evaluating protein quality in an individual diet is to look at the sources of the protein. As discussed previously, foods of animal origin are sources of complete dietary protein, whereas most plant foods contain proteins that are incomplete. If the protein in a diet comes from both animal and plant sources, it most likely contains adequate amounts of all the essential amino acids needed for protein synthesis. If the protein in a diet comes only from incomplete plant sources, a technique, called **protein complementation**, can be used to meet protein needs.

Figure 6.21 Protein digestibility-corrected amino acid score (PDCAAS)
The PDCAAS of plant proteins is generally lower than that of animal proteins. An exception is soy protein. (Source: Protein Quality Evaluation, Report of the Joint FAO/WHO Expert Consultation, FAO/WHO, 1989.)

Figure 6.22 Protein complementation
A meal that contains both rice and beans contains enough methionine (met), cysteine (csy), and lysine (lys) to meet the body's need for essential amino acids. (StockFood/Getty Images, Inc.)

Protein complementation combines foods containing proteins with different limiting amino acids in order to improve the protein quality of the diet as a whole. By eating plant proteins with complementary amino acid patterns, essential amino acid requirements can be met without consuming any animal proteins. The amino acids that are most often limited in plant proteins are lysine, methionine, cysteine, and tryptophan. As a general rule, legumes are deficient in methionine and cysteine but high in lysine. Grains, nuts, and seeds are deficient in lysine but high in methionine and cysteine. Corn is deficient in lysine and tryptophan but is a good source of methionine. Combining foods with complementary proteins provides all of the essential amino acids. For example, consuming rice, which is limited in the amino acid lysine but high in methionine and cysteine, with beans, which are high in lysine but limited in methionine and cysteine, provides enough of all of the amino acids needed by the body (**Figure 6.22**).

Common combinations of grains and legumes that have become cultural staples include beans and rice or beans and wheat or corn tortillas in Central and South America; rice and tofu in China and Japan; rice and lentils in India; rice and black-eyed peas in the southern United States; and peanut butter (peanuts are legumes) and bread throughout the United States. Plant proteins can also be complemented with animal proteins in order to meet the need for essential amino acids. For example, in Asia rice is often flavored with a small amount of spiced beef, chicken, or fish. Although it is not necessary to consume complementary proteins at each meal, the entire day's diet should include proteins from complementary sources in order to satisfy the daily need for amino acids.[21]

Translating Recommendations into Healthy Diets

Following the recommendations of MyPyramid will result in a diet that includes both animal and plant sources of protein. A cup of milk provides about 8 grams of protein and an ounce-equivalent from the meat and beans group can add another 7 to 10 grams. These two food groups contain the foods that are the highest in protein, and most choices provide high-quality animal protein (**Figure 6.23**). Each serving of grains and vegetables provides another 1 to 3 grams. But just getting enough protein does not ensure a healthy diet. The sources of dietary protein also affect the healthfulness of the diet, particularly how well it meets the recommendations for fat and fiber intake.

Choose Fish, Lean Meats, and Low-Fat Dairy Animal foods high in protein are the major source of saturated fat and the only source of cholesterol in the diet. This doesn't mean you need to become a vegetarian. Choosing wisely can keep your

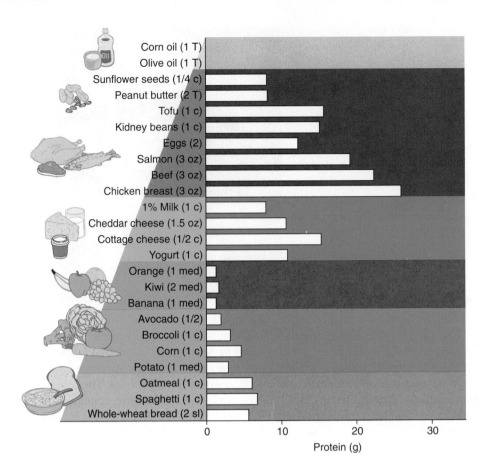

Figure 6.23 Protein content of MyPyramid food groups Meats, legumes, eggs, and dairy products contain the most protein per serving.

diet healthy. For example, to benefit from the iron, zinc, and B vitamins in meats without adding too much saturated fat, select lean cuts of meat and remove the skin from poultry. Choosing fish adds iron and zinc and also contributes heart-healthy omega-3 fatty acids. Nonfat or low-fat milk and milk products provide high-quality protein and calcium without as much saturated fat as whole milk.

Get More of Your Protein From Plants Plant sources of protein bring with them poly- and monounsaturated fats and dietary fiber. Legumes for example, provide about 15 grams of fiber per cup. Much of this is soluble fiber, which helps lower blood cholesterol. Choosing nuts and seeds increases intake of heart-healthy monounsaturated fats as well as fiber. Whole grains and vegetables add fiber, phytochemicals, vitamins and minerals, and because we eat a larger number of servings from these groups, they make an important contribution to our protein intake. Depending on how they are processed and prepared, grains and vegetables are generally low in saturated fat and contribute no cholesterol.

Protein and Amino-Acid Supplements Even though protein is plentiful in the American diet, protein and amino acid supplements remain popular among some segments of the population. Protein is needed for proper immune function, healthy hair, and muscle growth, but supplements will impact these only if the diet is deficient in protein in the first place. Increasing protein intake above the requirement does not protect you from disease, make your hair shine, or stimulate muscle growth. Although protein supplements are not harmful for most people, they are an expensive and unnecessary way to increase protein intake. A typical protein drink provides 10 to 35 g of protein per serving, or 20% to 70% of the Daily Value (**Figure 6.24**). It can add about 100 to 250 kcalories to the diet and thus can contribute to weight gain. If consumed consistently, a high intake of protein from supplements or from foods increases water loss in the urine and may contribute to dehydration.

Figure 6.24 Supplements marketed to increase the intake of protein or specific amino acids are expensive and usually unnecessary. (Charles D. Winters/Photo Researchers, Inc.)

Amino acid supplements are also an unnecessary and expensive addition to a healthy diet. They are popular among athletes and dieters. For instance, the amino acids arginine and ornithine stimulate the release of growth hormone, which promotes muscle growth. These amino acids are therefore marketed to those who want to build muscle and lose fat. However, the amounts of these amino acids contained in supplements are too small to affect growth-hormone release and supplements have not been shown to increase muscle growth or strength.[22] Branched-chain amino acids (leucine, isoleucine, and valine), arginine, and alanine are also taken to enhance exercise performance. Studies have not shown any of these amino acid supplements to provide a consistent benefit (see Chapter 13). Because some amino acids are absorbed using the same transport systems, supplementing one amino acid can cause a deficiency of others that share the same transport system (see Figure 6.8).

6.7 Meeting Needs with a Vegetarian Diet

Learning Objectives

- Describe the benefits associated with vegetarian diets.
- Discuss the nutrients at risk of deficiency in vegetarian diets.

Animal foods are not necessary for health. Combining plant proteins containing different limiting amino acids can provide the right combinations of amino acids to meet protein needs (**Figure 6.25**). And, making wise food choices and, in some cases, using fortified foods or supplements can meet the need for other nutrients. In many parts of the world plant protein-based or vegetarian diets have evolved mostly out of necessity because animal sources of protein are unavailable physically or economically. In affluent societies, vegetarian diets are followed for a variety of reasons other than economics, such as health, religion, personal ethics, or environmental awareness. About 2.3% of the adult U.S. population consistently consumes a diet that does not include meat, fish, or poultry and about 1.4% consumes a **vegan** diet.[21]

vegan A pattern of food intake that eliminates all animal products.

Rice & beans
Rice and lentils
Bread with peanut butter
Tofu and cashew stirfry
Bean burrito in corn tortilla
Hummus (chick peas & sesame seeds)
Black-eyed peas and corn bread
Tahini (sesame seeds) and
peanut sauce
Trail mix (soy beans
and nuts)
Rice and tofu

Grains, Nuts, and Seeds

Legumes

Figure 6.25 Combining Plant Proteins
Combining complementary sources of incomplete plant proteins can provide a diet containing enough of all the essential amino acids. (Jean Paul Chassenet/Photo Researchers; Corbis Images; George Semple)

Types of Vegetarian Diets

vegetarianism A pattern of food intake that eliminates some or all animal products.

Traditionally, **vegetarianism** is defined as abstinence from meat, fish, and fowl. Vegans consume the most restrictive vegetarian diets, however the term vegetarian has come to include a wide variety of eating patterns depending on the degree of abstinence from animal products. Semivegetarians are those who avoid only certain types of red meat, fish, or poultry—for example, individuals who avoid all red meat but continue to consume poultry and fish. Lacto-ovo vegetarians are those who eat no animal flesh but do eat eggs and dairy products such as milk and cheese; lacto vegetarians are those who avoid animal flesh and eggs but do consume dairy products. Pescetarians exclude all animal flesh except for fish.

Benefits of Vegetarian Diets

A vegetarian diet can be a healthy, low-cost alternative to the traditional American meat-and-potatoes diet. Vegetarians have been shown to have lower body weight and a reduced incidence of obesity and of other chronic diseases, such as diabetes, cardiovascular disease, high blood pressure, and some types of cancer.[21,23] The lower body weight of vegetarians is a result of lower energy intake, primarily due to higher intake of fiber, which makes the diet more filling. The reductions in the risk of other chronic diseases may be due to lower body weight and to the fact that these diets are typically lower in saturated fat and cholesterol, which increase disease risk. Or it could be that vegetarian diets are higher in grains, legumes, vegetables, and fruits, which add fiber, vitamins, minerals, antioxidants, and phytochemicals—substances that have been shown to lower disease risk. It is likely that the total dietary pattern, rather than a single factor alone, is responsible for the health-promoting effects of vegetarian diets.

In addition to reducing disease risks, diets that rely more heavily on plant protein than on animal protein are more economical. For example, a vegetarian stir-fry over rice costs about half as much as a meal of steak and potatoes. Yet both meals provide a significant portion of the day's protein requirement.

Nutrients at Risk in Vegetarian Diets

Despite the health and economic benefits, nutrient deficiencies can be a problem for people consuming unsupplemented vegetarian diets, particularly vegan diets. Most people can easily meet their protein needs with lacto and lacto-ovo vegetarian diets.

These diets contain high-quality animal proteins from eggs or milk, which complement the limiting amino acids in the plant proteins. Protein deficiency is a potential risk when vegan diets, which contain little high-quality protein, are consumed by small children and adults with increased protein needs, such as pregnant women and those recovering from illness or injury. These individuals must consume carefully planned diets to meet their protein needs.

Life Cycle

Deficiencies of particular vitamins and minerals are a greater risk for vegetarians than protein deficiency. Of primary concern to vegans is vitamin B_{12}. Because this B vitamin is found almost exclusively in animal products, to meet needs people following vegan diets must consume vitamin B_{12} supplements or foods fortified with vitamin B_{12}. Another nutrient of concern is calcium. Dairy products are the major source of calcium in the North American diet, so diets that eliminate these foods must contain plant sources of calcium or calcium fortified foods to meet needs. Likewise, since most dietary vitamin D comes from fortified dairy products, this vitamin must be obtained from sunlight (see Chapter 9) or consumed in other sources, such as fortified soy milk. Iron and zinc may be deficient in vegetarian diets because the best sources of these minerals are red meats and the iron and zinc present in plant foods is poorly absorbed. Since iron and zinc are low in dairy products, lacto-ovo and lacto vegetarians as well as vegans are at risk for deficiencies. Low intakes of omega-3 fatty acids including EPA and DHA (see Chapter 5) are also a concern in vegan diets.[21] Diets that do not include fish, eggs, or large amounts of sea vegetables will not provide preformed EPA and DHA and therefore higher levels of alpha-linolenic acid are needed. By including flaxseed or flax and canola oil, which are good sources of alpha-linolenic acid, vegetarians can have a healthy ratio of omega-3 to omega-6 fatty acids and be able to synthesize enough of the longer-chain length omega-3 fatty acids, EPA and DHA, without consuming animal products.[21] Vegetarian sources of these nutrients are listed in **Table 6.5** (see Critical Thinking: Choosing a Healthy Vegetarian Diet).

Table 6.5 Meeting Nutrient Needs with a Vegan Diet

Nutrient at Risk	Sources in Vegan Diets
Protein	Soy-based products, legumes, seeds, nuts, grains, and vegetables
Vitamin B_{12}	Products fortified with B_{12} such as soy beverages and cereals, nutritional yeast, vitamin supplements
Calcium	Tofu processed with calcium, broccoli, kale, bok choy, legumes, and products fortified with calcium such as soy beverages, grain products, and orange juice
Vitamin D	Sunshine, products fortified with vitamin D such as soy beverages, cereals, and margarine
Iron	Legumes, tofu, dark green leafy vegetables, dried fruit, whole grains, iron-fortified cereals and breads (absorption is improved by vitamin C, found in citrus fruit, tomatoes, strawberries, and dark green vegetables)
Zinc	Whole grains, wheat germ, legumes, nuts, tofu, and fortified cereals
Omega-3 fatty acids	Canola oil, flaxseed and flaxseed oil, soybean oil, walnuts, sea vegetables (seaweed), and DHA-rich microalgae

Vegetarian Food Groups

Life Cycle

Well-planned vegetarian diets, including vegan diets, are appropriate for all stages of the life cycle, including pregnancy, lactation, infancy, childhood, and adolescence.[21] One way to plan a healthy vegetarian diet is to modify the selections from MyPyramid

Critical Thinking
Choosing a Healthy Vegetarian Diet

(©iStockphoto)

Background

A year ago Ajay decided to stop eating meat. Now that he is studying protein in his nutrition class, he has become concerned that his vegetarian diet isn't meeting his needs.

Data

Ajay is 26 years old and weighs 154 lbs. He records his food intake for one day and then uses iProfile to calculate his protein intake.

FOOD	SERVING	PROTEIN (G)
Breakfast		
Grape Nuts	1/2 cup	7.2
Milk, low-fat	1/2 cup	4
Orange juice	3/4 cup	0.8
Toast, wheat	2 slices	5
Peanut butter	1 Tbsp	4
Coffee	1 cup	0
Lunch		
Dahl (lentil soup)	1 cup	9
Rice	1 cup	6
Banana	1 medium	1
Apple juice	1 cup	0
Dinner		
Green salad	1 cup	1
with dressing	1 Tbsp	0
Rice	1 cup	6
Curried potatoes	1/2 cup	1.5
and chickpeas	1/2 cup	5
Yogurt, plain	1 cup	13
Poori (fried bread)	2 pieces	5
Ice cream	1/2 cup	2
Total		**70.5**

Critical Thinking Questions

Does Ajay get enough protein? Compare his intake with the RDA for someone his age and size.

▼

Does his diet contain complementary proteins? List the protein sources in his diet and explain how they complement each other.

▼

If Ajay decided to become a vegan, what could he substitute for his dairy foods in order to meet his protein needs?

▼

How could he make sure his vegan diet meets his need for calcium and vitamin D (see Table 6.5)?

 iProfile Use iProfile to find the protein content of your favorite vegetarian entrée.

(**Figure 6.26**). The food choices and recommended amounts from the grains, vegetables, and fruits should stay the same for vegetarians. Including 1 cup of dark green leafy vegetables daily will help meet iron and calcium needs. The foods in the milk and the meat and beans groups include foods of animal origin. Vegetarians who consume eggs and milk can still choose these foods. Those who avoid all animal foods can choose dry beans, nuts, and seeds from the meat and beans group. Fortified soy milk can be substituted for the dairy foods. To obtain adequate vitamin B_{12}, vegans must take supplements or use products fortified with vitamin B_{12}.

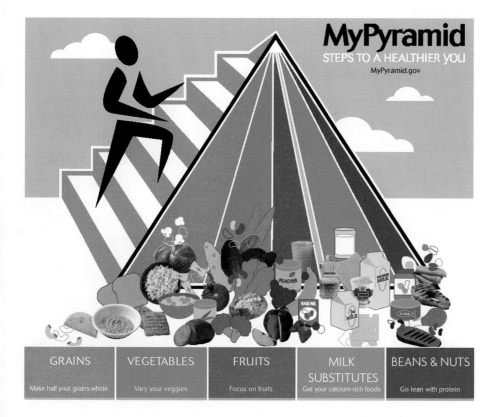

Figure 6.26 My Vegetarian Pyramid
MyPyramid food groups and recommendations can be modified to select a diet that meets nutrient needs without including animal foods.

Outcome

When Teresa joined the Peace Corps she quickly learned the huge effect malnutrition has on the health of children around the world. Songe introduced her to the impact of protein-energy malnutrition (PEM). When his mother stopped nursing him and he no longer consumed adequate protein, Songe developed Kwashiorkor; his belly became bloated because fat and fluid accumulated there. After a few months of consuming the high-protein supplement he was given at the clinic, his belly had shrunk and his arms and legs began filling out with muscle. Songe is now 3 years old, and although small for his age, he is a healthy, playful child.

At the clinic, Teresa helps educate families about the right combinations of foods needed to prevent PEM. She is learning all she can about the locally available foods so she can recommend meals that will provide the complementary proteins needed to meet amino acid needs. Teresa knows that with the scarcity of certain types of food in the typical local diet, she will likely see many other young children with symptoms similar to Songe's. Those who don't get early intervention will not be as fortunate as he was. Many children who have PEM die from infections because their immune systems cannot function optimally. Others suffer from permanent mental or physical ailments.

APPLICATIONS

Personal Nutrition

1. **How much protein do you eat?**

   a. Use iProfile to calculate your average daily protein intake using the 3-day food record you kept in Chapter 2.

   b. How does your protein intake compare to the RDA for protein for someone of your weight, age, and life stage? How does your protein intake compare to the recommended percent of kcalories from protein of between 10% and 35%? If you consumed just the RDA for protein, what percent of kcalories would this represent?

   c. Is your protein intake greater than the RDA? If so, do you think you should decrease your protein intake? Why or why not?

   d. Is your protein less than the RDA? If so, modify 1 day of your diet to meet your protein needs.

2. Are high-protein foods also high in saturated fat?

    a. Using the 3-day record you kept in Chapter 2, record your total protein and saturated fat intake for each day in the table below.

	PROTEIN (G)	SATURATED FAT (G)
Day 1	_____	_____
Day 2	_____	_____
Day 3	_____	_____

    b. What is the relationship between the amount of saturated fat and protein in your diet?

    c. For each day list the three foods that contribute the most protein to your diet. Are they animal or plant foods?

    d. What percentage of your total saturated fat for that day do these three foods provide?

3. What changes would make your diet vegetarian?

    a. Make a list of the nondairy animal foods in your diet and then list plant foods you could substitute for these.

    b. If you made these substitutions how much protein would the diet provide? Would it meet your RDA for protein?

    c. Convert this lacto-vegetarian diet into a vegan diet by substituting plant sources of protein for dairy products. Use protein complementation (see Figure 6.25) to be sure that you meet your need for essential amino acids. Make sure the diet includes at least 8 servings of calcium-rich foods.

General Nutrition Issues

1. A friend of yours is a weight lifter. He has read that if he eats a high-protein diet he will build muscle more quickly. He is 5' 8" tall and weighs 160 lbs. He drinks 2 or 3 protein shakes daily and always has 2 eggs for breakfast, a 4-ounce hamburger for lunch, and a 6-ounce steak for dinner.

    a. Use iProfile to determine how much protein the eggs, hamburger, and steak contribute to his diet?

    b. Use the internet to determine how much protein a typical "protein shake" contains.

    c. How does the protein he consumes from these sources compare to his requirement? (Remember that protein needs may be slightly higher for weight lifters.)

    d. Does he need the protein shakes to meet his protein needs?

2. What food proteins complement each other? For each food in column A, select one or more in column B that could be combined with it to provide a meal of high-quality protein.

COLUMN A	COLUMN B
Rice	Tofu
Wheat bread	Peanut butter
Corn tortilla	Cheese
Pasta	Kidney beans
Tofu	Cashews
Peanut butter	Corn tortilla
Corn bread	Wheat bread
Soybeans	Chickpeas
Black-eyed peas	Chicken

3. One of the most common examples of protein complementation is a peanut butter sandwich. The table here gives the grams of each essential amino acid in 100 grams of peanut butter protein and 100 grams of wheat bread protein and in a reference amino acid pattern.

AMINO ACID	PEANUT BUTTER	WHEAT BREAD	REFERENCE AMINO ACID PATTERN
Isoleucine	4.0	3.4	5.9
Leucine	7.7	6.2	9.0
Lysine	3.9	1.7	7.2
Methionine + Cysteine	2.4	3.6	6.3
Phenylalanine + Tyrosine	10.8	6.4	10.3
Threonine	3.0	2.4	5.0
Tryptophan	1.2	1.0	1.3
Valine	4.6	3.8	6.7

    a. For both peanut butter and wheat bread calculate the percentage of each amino acid supplied relative to the amino acid reference pattern.

    b. Which is the limiting amino acid in peanut butter (the amino acid present in the smallest amount relative to the reference pattern)? Which is the limiting amino acid in wheat bread? Which of the two food proteins has the higher amino acid score?

Summary

6.1 Protein in the Modern Diet

- Most of the protein in the American diet comes from animal foods, but protein comes from both animal and plant sources. In developing countries most dietary protein comes from plant sources.

- Whether protein is from a plant or animal source affects the amounts of fiber, saturated and unsaturated fat, cholesterol, and micronutrients in the diet.

6.2 Protein Molecules

- Amino acids consist of a carbon atom with a hydrogen atom, a nitrogen-containing group, an acid group, and a unique side chain attached. The amino acids that the body is unable to make in sufficient amounts are essential amino acids and must be consumed in the diet.

- Proteins are made of amino acid chains that fold over on themselves to create unique three-dimensional structures. The shape of a protein determines its function.

6.3 Protein in the Digestive Tract

- Digestion breaks dietary protein into small peptides and amino acids, which are absorbed into the mucosal cell using one of several active transport systems.

- Undigested protein fragments that are absorbed can trigger a food allergy.

6.4 Protein in the Body

- The amino acids in body tissues and fluids that are available for the synthesis of protein and other nitrogen-containing molecules or ATP production are known as the amino acid pool; they come from both dietary protein and the degradation of body proteins. The continuous breakdown and resynthesis of body proteins is referred to as protein turnover and is necessary for growth, maintenance, and regulation.

- DNA in the nucleus of cells contains the information needed to make body proteins. In transcription this information is copied into a molecule of mRNA, which carries it to the cytosol. In translation, tRNA translates the mRNA code into a sequence of amino acids. Which genes are expressed determines which proteins are made.

- Amino acids are used to make nonprotein molecules that contain nitrogen.

- Amino acids can be used to provide energy when the diet doesn't meet energy needs or when protein intake exceeds needs. Amino acids that are used for energy are first deaminated. The amino groups are converted into urea, which can safely be excreted. The carbon compounds that remain can be broken down to generate ATP, or be used to synthesize glucose or fatty acids, depending on the needs of the body.

- In the body proteins provide structure, regulate body functions as enzymes and hormones, transport molecules in the blood and into and out of cells, function in the immune system, and aid in muscle contraction, fluid balance, and acid balance.

6.5 Protein, Amino Acids, and Health

- Protein-energy malnutrition (PEM) is a concern, primarily in developing countries. Kwashiorkor is a form of PEM that occurs when the protein content of the diet is deficient but energy intake is adequate. It is most common in children. Marasmus is a form of PEM that occurs when total energy intake is deficient.

- High-protein diets increase the production of urea and other waste products that must be excreted in the urine and therefore can increase water losses. High protein intakes increase urinary calcium losses, but when calcium intake is adequate, high-protein diets are associated with greater bone mass and fewer fractures. Diets high in animal proteins and low in fluid are associated with an increased risk of kidney stones. High-protein diets can be high in saturated fat and cholesterol

- People with food allergies must avoid certain protein sources. Some proteins and amino acids trigger food intolerances. Those with the genetic disease phenylketonuria and sensitivities to gluten or monosodium glutamate (MSG) must avoid specific foods.

6.6 Meeting Protein Needs

- Nitrogen balance compares the amount of nitrogen consumed in the diet with the amount excreted.

- Nitrogen balance studies have been used to determine an RDA for protein for healthy adults of 0.8 gram per kilogram of body weight per day.

- Healthy diets can include 10% to 35% of energy from protein. Growth, pregnancy, lactation, illness, and injury can increase requirements. Certain types of physical activity may also increase protein needs.

- Animal proteins contain a pattern of amino acids that matches the needs of the human body more closely than the pattern of amino acids in plant proteins. Animal proteins are therefore said to be of higher quality than plant proteins. Diets that include little or no animal protein can provide adequate protein if the sources of protein are complemented to supply enough of all the essential amino acids.

- Recommendations for a healthy diet suggest that we get more of our protein from plant sources. These foods are low in saturated fat and cholesterol and are good sources of monounsaturated and polyunsaturated fats, fiber, micronutrients, and phytochemicals.

6.7 Meeting Needs with a Vegetarian Diet

- Many vegetarian diets include some animal products. Vegan diets exclude all foods of animal origin.

- Vegetarian diets are associated with a lower risk for obesity, diabetes, cardiovascular disease, high blood pressure, and some types of cancer.

- Vegetarian diets can easily meet protein needs, but care must be taken to include enough iron and zinc in lacto-ovo vegetarian diets. Vegan diets must be well planned to meet the needs for calcium, vitamin D, iron, zinc, and omega-3 fatty acids and must include supplements or fortified foods that provide vitamin B_{12}.

- MyPyramid can be used to plan vegetarian diets by choosing plant sources of protein from the meat and beans group and substituting fortified soymilk for dairy products.

R e v i e w Q u e s t i o n s

1. List some plant sources of protein.

2. What are amino acids?

3. Describe the general structure of a protein.

4. What is an essential amino acid?

5. What is the "amino acid pool" and where do these amino acids come from?

6. List six functions of proteins in the body.

7. Explain how proteins are synthesized.

8. Why is protein deficiency most common in infants and children?

9. Compare and contrast the causes and symptoms of kwashiorkor and marasmus.

10. How does the typical protein intake in the United States compare to recommendations?

11. What health problems are associated with a diet high in animal proteins?

12. What effect does moderate exercise have on protein needs?

13. What does nitrogen balance suggest about the balance between protein synthesis and protein breakdown in the body?

14. What is protein quality?

15. What is protein complementation?

16. What nutrients are at risk of deficiency in vegan diets?

References

1. Wright, J. D., Kennedy-Stephenson, J., Wang, C.Y. et al. Trends in intake of energy and macronutrients—United States, 1971–2000. *Morb. Mortal. Wkly. Rep.* 6:80–82, 2004. Available online at www.cdc.gov/mmwr/preview/ mmwrhtml/mm5304a3.htm/. Accessed June 6, 2009.

2. Fulgoni, V. L. Current protein intake in America: Analysis of the National Health and Nutrition Examination Survey, 2003–2004. *Am. J. Clin. Nutr.* 87:1554S–1557S, 2008.

3. Smit, E., Nieto, F. J., Crespo, C. J., and Mitchell, P. Estimates of animal and plant protein intake in U.S. adults: Results from the Third National Health and Nutrition Examination Survey, 1988–1991. *J. Am. Diet. Assoc.* 99:813–820, 1999.

4. Williams, C. D. Kwashiorkor: Nutritional disease of children associated with maize diet. *Lancet* 2:1151–1154, 1935.

5. Alebiosu, C. O. An update on 'progression promoters' in renal diseases. *J. Natl. Med. Assoc.* 95:30–42, 2003.

6. Institute of Medicine, Food and Nutrition Board. Dietary Reference Intakes for Energy, Carbohydrates, Fiber, Fat, Protein and Amino Acids. Washington, DC: National Academies Press, 2002.

7. Heaney, R. P., and Layman, D. K. Amount and type of protein influences bone health. *Am. J. Clin. Nutr.* 87:1567S–1570S, 2008.

8. Kerstetter, J., O'Brien, K., and Insogna, K. Dietary protein, calcium metabolism, and skeletal homeostasis revisited. *Am. J. Clin. Nutr.* 78(Suppl):S584–S592, 2003.

9. Weikert, C., Walter, D., Hoffmann, K. et al. The relation between dietary protein, calcium and bone health in women: Results from the EPIC-Potsdam cohort. *Ann. Nutr. Metab.* 49:312–318, 2005.

10. Siener, R. Impact of dietary habits on stone incidence. *Urol. Res.* 34:131–133, 2006.

11. van't Veer, P., Jansen, M. C., Klerk, M., and Kok, F. J. Fruits and vegetables in the prevention of cancer and cardiovascular disease. *Public Health Nutr.* 3:103–107, 2000.

12. Brown, A. S., Fernhoff, P. M., Waisbren, S. E. et al. Barriers to successful dietary control among pregnant women with phenylketonuria. *Genet. Med.* 4:84–89, 2002.

13. Seymour, C. A., Cockburn, F., Thomason, M. J. et al. Newborn screening for inborn errors of metabolism: A systematic review. *Health Technol. Assess.* I:1–95, 1997.

14. Fasano, A., Berti, I., Gerarduzzi, T. et al. Prevalence of celiac disease in at-risk and not-at-risk groups in the United States. *Arch. Intern. Med.* 163:268–292, 2003.

15. Walker, R., and Lupien, J. R. The safety evaluation of monosodium glutamate. *J. Nutr.* 130:1049S–1052S, 2000.

16. Geha, R. S., Beiser, A., Ren, C. et al. Review of alleged reaction to monosodium glutamate and outcome of a multicenter double-blind placebo-controlled study. *J. Nutr.* 130:1058S–1062S, 2000.

17. U.S. Department of Health and Human Services, U.S. Food and Drug Administration. FDA and Monosodium Glutamate (MSG) FDA Backgrounder, August 31, 1995. Available online at http://vm.cfsan.fda.gov/~lrd/msg.html. Accessed February 16, 2009.

18. Moshfegh, A., Goldman, J., Cleveland, L. What we eat in America, NHANES 2001–2002. Usual nutrient intake from foods as compared to dietary reference intakes. US Department of Agriculture, Agricultural Research Service. 2005. Available online at http://www.ars.usda.gov/ SP2UserFiles/Place/12355000/pdf/usualintaketables2001– 02.pdf. Accessed June 6, 2009.

19. American Dietetic Association. Position of the American Dietetic Association, Dietitians of Canada, and the American College of Sports Medicine: Nutrition and athletic performance. *J. Am. Diet. Assoc.* 109:509–527, 2009.

20. Stipanuk, M. H. Protein and amino requirements. In *Biochemical and Physiological Aspects of Human Nutrition.* M. H. Stipanik, ed. St. Louis: Saunders Elsevier, 2006, pp. 419–448.

21. American Dietetic Association. Position of the American Dietetic Association: Vegetarian diets. *J. Am. Diet. Assoc.* 109:1266–1282, 2009.

22. Williams, M. H. Facts and fallacies of purported ergogenic amino acid supplements. *Clin. Sports Med.* 18:633–649, 1999.

23. Leitzmann, C. Vegetarian diets: What are the advantages? *Forum Nutr.* 57:147–156, 2005.

7

Energy Balance and Weight Management

Case Study

Erin had always been "the fat one" in her family. She and her sister, Sara, had the same parents and were only 3 years apart in age, yet they were very different. Sara had brown hair, long legs, and a slender build. Why had Erin ended up with freckles, red hair, and chunky thighs? She was always the one who could stand to lose a few pounds. She would rather read than ride her bike and often spent the afternoon munching chips while she studied.

Then one day, when she was a college freshman, Erin decided she didn't want to be "the fat one" any more. She changed her diet and started to exercise. At first it was just a walk after dinner, but soon exercise became part of her daily routine. She covered a few miles every day whether at the gym, on her bike, or jogging. The extra pounds disappeared.

Sara, in contrast, spent the fall finishing law school and snacking as she studied for the bar exam. She passed the bar 30 pounds heavier than she had ever been. At the family reunion that summer, Sara heard a relative say to her sister, "Didn't you used to be the fat one?" What happened? How could two women with the same parents have such different builds? And how could they change so much in one year?

Sara and Erin inherited different combinations of genes from their parents. These genes determine their body builds, but, lifestyle factors also affect how much body fat they accumulate. Sara inherited her slender build, but eating too much and exercising too little while she studied for the bar exam added pounds. Erin, in contrast, may never have thin thighs, but when she exercises regularly and watches what she eats, she can keep her weight in a healthy range.

(Photodisc/Getty Images, Inc.)

(©iStockphoto)

(...rt Daily/Getty Images, Inc.)

Chapter Outline

7.1 The Obesity Epidemic

Learning Objective

• Discuss how the incidence of obesity has changed in the United States and around the world.

overweight Being too heavy for one's height. It is defined as having a body mass index (a ratio of weight to height squared) of 25 to 29.9 kg/m².

obesity A condition characterized by excess body fat. It is defined as a body mass index (a ratio of weight to height squared) of 30 kg/m² or greater.

In the United States today, a staggering 66% of adults are **overweight** or **obese**.[1] The numbers have increased dramatically over the past 40 to 50 years. In 1960 only 13.4% of American adults were obese. By 1991, 23% were obese; and today, 32% are obese (**Figure 7.1**). Overweight and obesity are a problem in both men and women and in all racial and ethnic groups. Obesity rates for minorities often exceed those in the general population: Among African Americans, 34% of men and 54% of women are obese; among Mexican Americans, about 32% of men and over 42% of women are obese.[1] The problem is not limited to adults. Sixteen percent of U.S. children and adolescents ages 2 through 19 are obese.[2] As with adults, the problem is even greater in certain ethnic groups. Between 1986 and 1998 the prevalence of overweight rose by more than 120% among African-American and Hispanic children, compared to about 50% among white children.[3]

The reason Americans are getting fatter is that changes in the nation's food supply and lifestyle have created an energy imbalance; we are eating more and exercising less, leading to weight gain. The repercussions of this rise in obesity have led public health officials to call it an epidemic. Carrying excess body fat increases the risk of a host of chronic health problems including high blood pressure, heart disease, high blood cholesterol, diabetes, stroke, gallbladder disease, arthritis, sleep disorders, respiratory problems, and cancers of the breast, uterus, prostate, and colon.

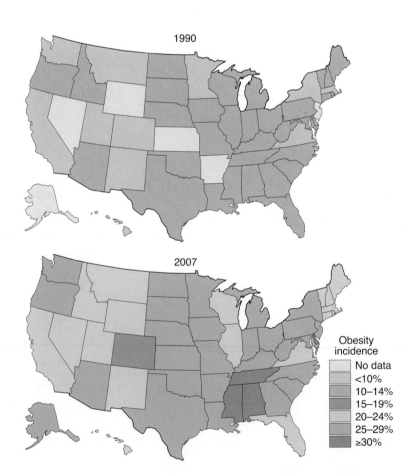

Figure 7.1 Incidence of obesity by state
In 1990 the percentage of the adult population that was obese was less than 20% in all 50 states. By 2007 only Colorado had an adult obesity rate less than 20%. (Source: Behavior Risk Factor Surveillance System, CDC.)

Obesity incidence
- No data
- <10%
- 10–14%
- 15–19%
- 20–24%
- 25–29%
- ≥30%

Lifestyle transitions similar to those in the United States are occurring worldwide and the incidence of obesity is following suit. It is such an important trend that the word *globesity* has been coined to reflect the escalation of global obesity and overweight. Around the world, approximately 1.6 billion adults are overweight, and 400 million are obese. The World Health Organization projects that by 2015, approximately 2.3 billion adults will be overweight and more than 700 million will be obese.[4] Once considered a problem only in high-income countries, overweight and obesity are now on the rise in low- and middle-income countries, particularly in urban settings.

7.2 Exploring Energy Balance

Learning Objectives

- Explain the principle of energy balance.
- Describe the processes involved in generating ATP from food.
- Describe the components of energy expenditure.
- Indicate how excess dietary energy is stored in the body.

The principle of **energy balance** states that when energy consumption equals energy expenditure, body weight remains constant. Energy balance can be achieved at any weight—fat, thin, or in between (**Figure 7.2**); it simply means that body weight is not changing. If, however, less energy is taken in than expended, energy balance is negative and weight will be lost. On the other hand, if the amount of energy taken in exceeds the amount expended, energy balance is positive and the extra energy will be stored in the body causing weight to increase.

Energy is defined as the ability to do work. In nutrition, energy is measured in kilocalories (kcalories, kcal), which are units of heat or kilojoules (kjoules, kJ), which are units of work. In the United States, kcalories are the standard measure of energy in food and the body. In Europe, kjoules are the measure most commonly used. Technically, a kcalorie is the amount of heat required to raise the temperature of 1 kilogram of water 1 degree Celsius. In practical terms, a kcalorie is a measure of the amount of energy that is supplied to or expended by the body.

energy balance The amount of energy consumed in the diet compared with the amount expended by the body over a given period.

Energy In: Kcalories Taken in as Food

The energy taken into the body comes from the energy-yielding nutrients (carbohydrates, lipids, and proteins) and alcohol consumed in food and beverages. Individuals who struggle with weight loss often think of the kcalories in food as an enemy—something to be avoided. However, food and the energy it provides are essential for

Figure 7.2 Energy balance
What you weigh is a balance between how much energy you consume and how much energy you expend.

life. Just as gasoline is necessary to run an engine, kcalories are necessary to run the body. The amount of energy (number of kcalories) taken in depends on the total amount of food consumed and the nutrient composition of that food. The energy content of food can be measured precisely in the laboratory or estimated from its nutrient composition.

Determining the Amount of Energy in Food The amount of energy in a food or a mixture of foods can be determined in the laboratory using a **bomb calorimeter**. A bomb calorimeter consists of a chamber surrounded by a jacket of water (**Figure 7.3**). Food is dried, placed in the chamber, and burned. As the food combusts, heat is released, raising the temperature of the water. The increase in water temperature can be used to calculate the amount of energy in the food based on the fact that 1 kcalorie is the amount of heat needed to increase the temperature of 1 kilogram of water by 1 degree Celsius.

Combusting a food in a bomb calorimeter determines the total amount of energy contained in that food. However, because the body cannot completely digest, absorb, and utilize all of the substances in a food, bomb calorimeter values are slightly higher than the amount of energy the body can obtain from that food. To correct for this difference, feeding experiments have been done to measure the amount of energy that is not available to the body, such as that lost in urine and feces. Subtracting this unavailable energy from the values determined by the bomb calorimeter gives a more accurate estimate of the energy obtained from food. These types of experiments were used to determine the amount of energy provided by the carbohydrate (4 kcalories per gram), fat (9 kcalories per gram), protein (4 kcalories per gram), and alcohol (7 kcalories per gram) in a mixed diet.

When the nutrient composition of a food is known, totaling the energy from the carbohydrate, fat, and protein in the food can approximate the energy content (**Table 7.1**). Vitamins, minerals, and water, though essential nutrients, do not provide energy to the body. Carbohydrate and protein provide about 4 kcalories per gram, so 5 grams of sugar, which is almost pure carbohydrate, contains about 20 kcalories (5 g × 4 kcal/g) and 5 grams of dried egg white, which is almost pure protein, also provides about 20 kcalories. Fat, the most concentrated source of energy, provides 9 kcalories per gram. Five grams of corn oil, which is almost pure fat, contains about 45 kcalories (5 g × 9 kcal/g). Alcohol provides 7 kcalories per gram. Most foods are of mixed composition; for instance, a slice of pizza contains about 15 grams of protein,

bomb calorimeter
An instrument used to determine the energy content of food. It measures the heat energy released when a dried food is combusted.

Figure 7.3 Bomb calorimeter
When dried food is combusted inside the chamber of a bomb calorimeter, the rise in temperature of the surrounding water can be used to determine the energy content of the food.

Table 7.1 **Estimating the Energy Content of Food**

Determine:

• The number of grams of carbohydrate, protein, fat, and alcohol in a food or meal

Calculate the energy provided by each:

grams of carbohydrate × 4 kcal/g = kcalories from carbohydrate
grams of protein   × 4 kcal/g = kcalories from protein
grams of fat   × 9 kcal/g = kcalories from fat
grams of alcohol   × 7 kcal/g = kcalories from alcohol

Calculate the total energy:

• Total energy (kcal) = (kcal from carbohydrate) + (kcal from protein) + (kcal from fat) + (kcal from alcohol)

For example:

• A half-cup (100 g) serving of macaroni and cheese contains 8 grams of protein, 20 grams of carbohydrate, and 11 grams of fat:

20 grams of carbohydrate × 4 kcal/g = 80 kcalories
8 grams of protein   × 4 kcal/g = 32 kcalories
11 grams of fat   × 9 kcal/g = 99 kcalories
Total energy = 80 kcal + 32 kcal + 99 kcal = 211 kcalories

50 grams of carbohydrate, and 10 grams of fat (**Figure 7.4**). Its energy content is therefore: (4 kcal/g × 15 g protein) + (4 kcal/g × 50 g carbohydrate) + (9 kcal/g × 10 g fat) = 350 kcal

Information on the energy content of foods can be found on food labels and in food composition tables and databases such as iProfile. The Nutrition Facts portion of food labels lists the total kcalories in a serving of food (see Off the Label: How Many Kcalories in that Bowl, Box, or Bottle?). The energy content of foods in a diet can also be estimated from the Exchange Lists shown in **Table 7.2**. For example, one starch exchange, whether a slice of bread, 1/2 cup (100 g) of cereal, or 6 saltines, provides about 80 kcalories.

Figure 7.4 You can calculate the kcalories in a slice of pizza if you know how much carbohydrate, protein, and fat it provides. (Glenn Peterson/StockFood America)

 iProfile

Table 7.2 **Using Exchange Lists to Estimate Energy Content**

Exchange Groups/Lists	Serving Size	Energy (kcal)
Carbohydrate Group		
Starch	1/2 cup pasta, cereal, potatoes; 1 slice bread	80
Fruit	1 small apple, peach, pear; 1/2 banana; 1/2 cup canned fruit (in juice)	60
Milk	1 cup milk or yogurt	
Nonfat		90
Low-fat		110
Reduced-fat		120
Whole		150
Other carbohydrates	Serving sizes vary	Varies
Vegetables	1/2 cup cooked vegetables, 1 cup raw	25
Meat/Meat Substitute Group	1 oz meat or cheese; 1/2 cup legumes	
Very lean		35
Lean		55
Medium-fat		75
High-fat		100
Fat group	1 tsp butter, margarine, or oil; 1 Tbsp salad dressing	45

Off the Label

How Many Kcalories in That Box, Bowl or Bottle?

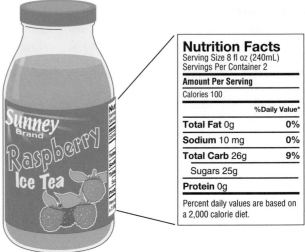

(©)iStockphoto)

Are you watching your kcalorie intake? The Nutrition Facts portion of a food label can help, if you read it carefully. It provides information about kcalories per serving and serving size. Make sure you check both.

People tend to eat in units—one bottle of juice, one can of iced tea, one bag of potato chips—but the serving size on the label doesn't always reflect the kcalorie count for those units. For example, the label on the fruit juice bottle shown here says that a serving has only 100 kcalories. But, the serving size is 8 ounces, and the bottle holds 20 ounces. So if you finish the bottle you will be getting 250 kcalories, mostly from added sugars.

The discrepancy between the "serving sizes" listed on packages and the "portion sizes" we consume is one of the reasons Americans are getting fatter. We choose portions that are generally larger than recommended. For example, the label on your ice cream shows that it provides about 140 kcalories per serving and that a serving is only 1/2 cup, a portion the size of half a tennis ball. If you scoop a cup of ice cream onto your cone or into your bowl you will be consuming about 280 kcalories. Likewise, if you

pour yourself a cup of granola for breakfast, you are probably having about 4 servings, for a total of over 400 kcalories.

Knowing what a serving is can help you keep your kcalories under control. But it isn't always easy. Pasta portions are particularly tricky. The serving size is usually given as dry pasta. What does 2 ounces of dry spaghetti—for 200 kcalories—look like once it is cooked?

The answer is about a cup, so if you pile 2 cups onto your plate, you are getting 400 rather than 200 kcalories. Some product labels list nutritional information both before and after the product is prepared; this can help you figure out what you are choosing. So read carefully, and use all the information on the label to determine how many kcalories are in your portions.

Nutrition Facts
Serving Size 8 fl oz (240mL)
Servings Per Container 2

Amount Per Serving

Calories 100

	%Daily Value*
Total Fat 0g	**0%**
Sodium 10 mg	**0%**
Total Carb 26g	**9%**
Sugars 25g	
Protein 0g	

Percent daily values are based on a 2,000 calorie diet.

Converting Food Energy into ATP Just as the energy in flowing water can be converted into electrical energy, which can then be converted into the light energy emitted by a lightbulb, the energy stored in the chemical bonds of carbohydrates, fats, and proteins can be converted into ATP, which can be used to keep you alive and moving. To generate ATP, metabolic reactions break down or oxidize carbohydrate, fat, and protein (**Figure 7.5** and Chapters 4 through 6). All three can be converted into the common intermediate acetyl-CoA. Glycolysis converts glucose from carbohydrate into pyruvate, which then loses a carbon to form acetyl-CoA. Triglycerides are broken into fatty acids and glycerol. Beta-oxidation breaks fatty acids into 2-carbon units that form acetyl-CoA. Amino acids from protein are deaminated and their carbon skeletons used to make acetyl-CoA or other intermediates. Acetyl-CoA can then enter the citric acid cycle. The high-energy electrons released at various metabolic steps are passed to the electron transport chain where their energy is trapped and used to generate ATP. The ATP is then used to fuel metabolic reactions that build and maintain body components and to power other cellular and body activities. Much of the energy consumed in food is also converted to and lost from the body as heat.

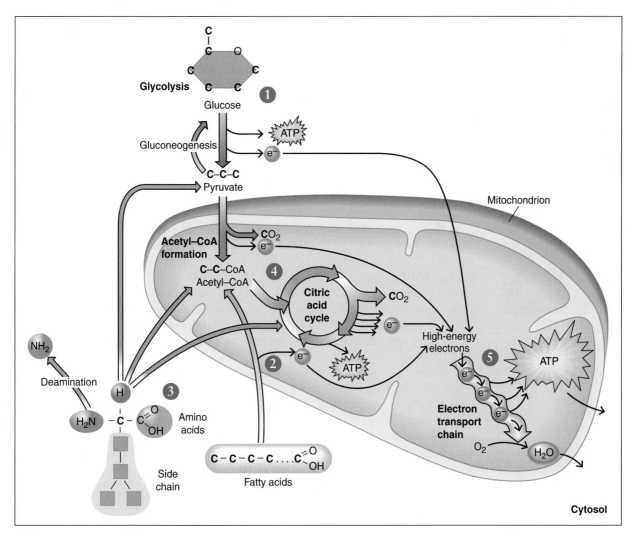

1. Glycolysis breaks glucose in half to yield pyruvate, which is then converted to acetyl CoA.

2. Beta-oxidation breaks fatty acids into 2-carbon units that form acetyl-CoA.

3. Amino acids are deaminated and can break down to form acetyl-CoA, pyruvate, or other intermediates.

4. The acetyl-CoA from glucose, fatty acid, and amino acid breakdown can enter the citric acid cycle.

5. The electrons released are passed to the electron transport chain and their energy is used to make ATP.

Figure 7.5 Producing ATP from glucose, fatty acids, and amino acids
Glucose, fatty acids, and amino acids can be broken down by the reactions of cellular respiration to yield carbon dioxide, water, and energy in the form of ATP.

Energy Out: Kcalories Used by the Body

The total amount of energy used by the body each day or **total energy expenditure (TEE)** includes the energy needed to maintain basic bodily functions such as the beating of your heart, as well as that needed to fuel activity and process food. In individuals who are growing or pregnant, total energy expenditure also includes the energy used to deposit new tissues. In women who are lactating, it includes the energy used to produce milk. A small amount of energy is also used to maintain body temperature in a cold environment.

total energy expenditure (TEE) The sum of the energy used for basal metabolism, activity, processing food, deposition of new tissue, and production of milk.

Figure 7.6 To assess BMR, expired gases can be collected and measured by having the subject breathe into a hood. (St. Bartholomew's Hospital/ Science/Custom Medical Stock Photo)

basal energy expenditure (BEE) The energy expended to maintain an awake resting body that is not digesting food.

basal metabolic rate (BMR) The rate of energy expenditure under resting conditions. BMR measurements are performed in a warm room in the morning before the subject rises, and at least 12 hours after the last food or activity.

resting energy expenditure (REE) or resting metabolic rate (RMR) Terms used when an estimate of basal metabolism is determined by measuring energy utilization after 5 to 6 hours without food or exercise.

lean body mass Body mass attributed to nonfat body components such as bone, muscle, and internal organs. It is also called *fat-free mass.*

Basal Metabolism For most people, about 60% to 75% of the body's total energy expenditure is used for basal metabolism. **Basal energy expenditure (BEE)** includes all of the involuntary things your body does to stay alive such as breathing, circulating blood, regulating body temperature, synthesizing tissues, removing waste products, and sending nerve signals. The rate at which energy is used for these basic functions is called **basal metabolic rate (BMR)** and is often expressed in kcalories per hour. Basal needs include the energy necessary for essential metabolic reactions and life-sustaining functions but do not include the energy needed for physical activity or for the digestion of food and the absorption of nutrients. Therefore, to minimize residual energy expenditure for activity or processing food, BMR is measured in the morning, in a warm room before the subject rises, and at least 12 hours after food intake or activity (**Figure 7.6**). Because of the difficulty of achieving these conditions, measures are often made after about 5 to 6 hours without food or exercise. When done under these conditions it is reported as **resting energy expenditure (REE) or resting metabolic rate (RMR)**. RMR values are about 10% to 20% higher than BMR values.[5]

Basal needs are affected by factors such as body weight, gender, growth rate, and age. BMR increases with increasing body weight, so it is higher in heavier individuals. It also rises with increasing **lean body mass**; thus, BMR is generally higher in men than in women because men have more lean tissue. BMR increases during periods of rapid growth because energy is required to produce new body tissue. It decreases with age, partly due to the decrease in lean body mass that usually occurs in older adults.

Basal needs can be altered by certain abnormal conditions. An elevation in body temperature, increases BMR. It is estimated that for every 1 degree Fahrenheit above normal body temperature, there is a 7% increase in BMR. This extra energy use explains why a fever can cause weight loss. Abnormal levels of thyroid hormones can also affect BMR. Individuals who overproduce these hormones burn more energy; in fact, a symptom used to diagnose thyroid hormone excess is unexplained weight loss. Individuals with an underproduction of thyroid hormones require less energy. The fact that hormones produced by the thyroid gland affect energy expenditure is the reason that obesity was once explained as a glandular problem. It is now known that obesity due to a thyroid hormone deficiency is rare.

Metabolic rate may also be affected by low-energy diets. Energy intake below needs may depress resting metabolic rate by 10% to 20%, or the equivalent of 100 to 400 kcalories per day.[6] This drop in basal needs decreases the amount of energy needed to maintain weight. It is a beneficial adaptation in starvation, but it makes intentional weight loss more difficult.

Physical Activity Physical activity is the second major component of energy expenditure. It represents the metabolic cost of external work, which includes the energy needed for planned exercise as well as for the activities of daily life, such as cooking, gardening, and, house cleaning.

Figure 7.7 Activity as a percentage of total energy requirement
The percentage of energy expended in physical activity increases from only about 15% in a sedentary person to 30% or more in an active individual. Increasing activity increases total energy expenditure.

| Activity | Basal metabolism | Thermic effect of food (TEF) |

Sedentary person (1800 kcal/day)

Physically active person (2200 kcal/day)

Figure 7.8 A carpenter may burn about twice as many kcalories in a workday as someone with a desk job. (Ryan McVay/Getty Images, Inc./Photodisk; Rubberball Productions/Getty)

The energy expended for unintentional exercise is called **nonexercise activity thermogenesis (NEAT)**. NEAT accounts for the majority of the energy expended for activity and varies enormously, depending on an individual's occupation and daily movements.[7] For most people, physical activity accounts for 15% to 30% of energy requirements, but this varies greatly (**Figure 7.7**). An endurance athlete who trains 5 or 6 hours a day may expend more energy in activity than for basal metabolism. A person's occupation can also have a great affect on the energy expended for activity. For example, a construction worker who spends 8 hours a day doing physical labor uses a great deal more energy in his daily activities than does an office worker who spends most of his day sitting at a desk (**Figure 7.8**).

The energy required for an activity depends on how strenuous the activity is and the length of time it is performed. For example, walking at a speed of 3 to 4 miles per hour requires a moderate degree of exertion and uses about 300 kcal/hr for a 70-kg man. The energy required increases progressively as the walking speed and length of time the activity continues increase, and as the body weight of the exerciser rises. In addition to the energy expended during exercise, there is a small increase in energy expenditure for a period of time after exercise has been completed. The energy expended for activity is the one component of our total energy needs over which we have control. To maintain health, people today need to consciously increase their physical activity. This does not mean they have to run marathons. Choosing to take the stairs rather than the elevator, walking rather than taking the bus, and riding a bike rather than driving to the store all increase activity. The energy costs of specific activities are listed in Appendix K.

Thermic Effect of Food Our energy comes from food, but we also need energy to digest food and to absorb, metabolize, and store the nutrients from this food. The energy used for these processes is called the **thermic effect of food (TEF)** or **diet-induced thermogenesis**. This increase in energy expenditure causes body temperature to rise slightly for several hours after eating. The energy required for TEF is estimated to be about 10% of energy intake but can vary depending on the amounts and types of nutrients consumed. Because it takes energy to store nutrients, TEF increases with the size of the meal. A meal that is high in fat has a lower TEF than a meal high in carbohydrate or protein, because dietary fat can be used or stored more efficiently than either protein or carbohydrate. The metabolic cost of either oxidizing or storing dietary fat is only 2% to 3% of the energy consumed, whereas the cost of using amino acids by either oxidizing them or incorporating them into proteins is 15% to 30% of the energy consumed, and the cost of breaking down carbohydrate or storing it as glycogen is 6% to 8%.[8] The difference in the cost of storing different nutrients as fat means that a diet high in fat may produce more body fat than a diet high in carbohydrate.[9]

Energy Stores

Energy is stored in the body as glycogen and triglycerides. Stored energy can be used when intake is less than needs, whether this occurs between meals or over a longer period such as during starvation, fasting, or dieting for weight-loss.

nonexercise activity thermogenesis (NEAT) The energy expended for everything we do other than sleeping, eating, or sports-like exercise.

thermic effect of food (TEF) or **diet-induced thermogenesis** The energy required for the digestion of food and the absorption, metabolism, and storage of nutrients. It is equal to approximately 10% of daily energy intake.

adipocytes Fat-storing cells.

Glycogen stores are located in the liver and muscle and fill when dietary carbohydrate is adequate. The body generally stores only about 200 to 500 grams of glycogen—enough to provide glucose for about 24 hours (**Table 7.3**). Triglycerides are stored in adipose tissue, which is made up of fat-storing cells called **adipocytes**. Adipocytes grow in size as they accumulate more triglycerides and shrink as triglycerides are removed from them. The greater the number of adipocytes an individual has, the greater the ability to store fat. Although most adipocytes are formed between infancy and adolescence, excessive weight gain can cause the production of new fat-storing cells in adults.

Table 7.3 Sources of Stored Energy in the Body

Energy Source	Primary Location	Energy (kcal)[a]
Glycogen	Liver and muscle	1,400
Glucose or lipid	Body fluids	100
Triglyceride	Adipose tissue	115,000
Protein	Muscle	25,000

[a]Values represent the approximate amounts in a 70-kg male.
Source: Cahill, G. F. Starvation in man. *N. Engl. J. Med.* 282:668–675, 1970; and Frayn, K. *Metabolic Regulation: A Human Perspective.* London: Portland Press, 1996, pp. 78–102.

Using Body Energy Stores: Weight Loss To function normally, the body needs a steady supply of energy. Some of this energy must come from glucose, which is needed to fuel the brain and several other types of body cells. After eating, energy is supplied by absorbed nutrients. Between meals the breakdown of glycogen provides glucose, and the breakdown of stored fat meets other energy needs. Typically, these stores are then replaced by energy consumed in the next meal so that there is no net change in the amount of stored energy. However, if energy stores are not replenished, the amount of stored energy—and hence, body weight—will decrease (**Figure 7.9**).

If no food is eaten for more than several hours the body must shift the way it uses energy to ensure that glucose continues to be available to cells that need it. Glycogen stores can provide glucose, but are limited, so glucose is also supplied by the breakdown of small amounts of body protein, primarily muscle protein, to yield

Figure 7.9 Feasting and fasting
When you eat more than you need at that time, some energy is put into body stores. When you haven't eaten in a while, you retrieve energy from these stores. A small amount of body protein is also broken down to amino acids to make glucose and provide energy.

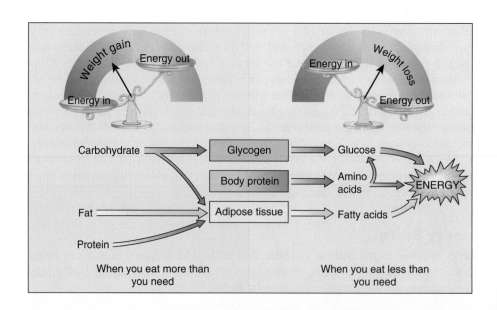

amino acids. Amino acids can then be used to synthesize glucose via gluconeogenesis (see Chapters 4 and 6). Once glycogen stores are depleted all of the glucose must come from gluconeogenesis. Because protein is not stored in the body, the breakdown of protein to provide energy and glucose results in the loss of functional body proteins.

Energy for tissues that don't require glucose is provided by the breakdown of stored fat. If the supply of glucose is limited, such as during starvation, fatty acids delivered to the liver cannot be completely oxidized, so ketones are produced (see Chapter 4). Ketones can be used as an energy source by many tissues. After about 3 days of starvation, even the brain adapts to meet some of its energy needs from ketones (see Chapter 5). This reduces the amount of glucose needed and thus slows the rate of protein breakdown.

If energy intake is restricted for a prolonged period (fasting), substantial amounts of fat are used to provide energy and protein is degraded to provide glucose. This results in weight loss (see Figure 7.9). The magnitude of the weight loss depends on the degree of energy deficit and the length of time over which it occurs. It is estimated that an energy deficit of about 3500 kcalories will result in the loss of a pound of adipose tissue.

Building Body Stores: Weight Gain People typically eat three to six times during the day. For weight to remain stable, the sum of the energy in all of these meals and snacks must equal daily energy expenditure, but at each meal or snack more energy is likely to be consumed than is needed at that moment in time. When excess energy is consumed (feasting), we generally say this excess is stored as fat. This is an oversimplification of a complex situation. After eating, the body prioritizes how nutrients are used based on body needs, which nutrients can be stored, and how efficiently they can be stored. Nonetheless, regardless of the composition of the diet, when excess energy is consumed over the long term, fat stores will enlarge and weight will increase (see Figure 7.9).

Hierarchy of Nutrient Use There is a metabolic hierarchy of how fuels are used by the body. Alcohol, although not a nutrient, does supply energy. Because it is toxic and cannot be stored in the body, it is rapidly oxidized. Amino acids from dietary protein are next in the hierarchy. They are first used to synthesize needed body proteins and non-protein molecules; any excess is then broken down because there is no mechanism for storing them as amino acids or proteins. Carbohydrate is used to maintain blood glucose and to build glycogen stores. Once glycogen stores are full, the remaining carbohydrate is oxidized for energy. Fat, unlike the other energy-yielding nutrients, is not needed as a fuel for a particular tissue or to build tissues, and can be stored in the body in virtually unlimited amounts. Therefore, if the energy consumed is in excess of immediate needs, dietary fat is preferentially stored. For example, after a meal the body's energy needs are met by first breaking down protein and carbohydrate that is not needed for essential functions. To meet any remaining energy needs dietary fat is oxidized and any dietary fat that is left is stored as triglycerides, primarily in adipose tissue (**Figure 7.10**). Therefore, most of the fat that is stored in the body comes from dietary fat.

Synthesizing Fat from Carbohydrate and Protein The body is capable of converting glucose and amino acids into triglycerides for storage. However, under normal dietary circumstances, this rarely occurs because these conversions are energetically costly.[10] Making fat from glucose involves converting glucose to acetyl Co-A and then assembling fatty acids from the 2-carbon acetyl-CoA units. The fatty acids must then be joined to a molecule of glycerol to make triglycerides for storage. To convert amino acids to fat the amino group must first be removed and then the carbon skeleton must be broken down to yield acetyl-CoA that can be used for fatty acid synthesis. In contrast, the conversion of dietary fat to body fat requires only the removal and reattachment of fatty acids from the glycerol backbone (see Chapter 5); it takes only 2% to 3%

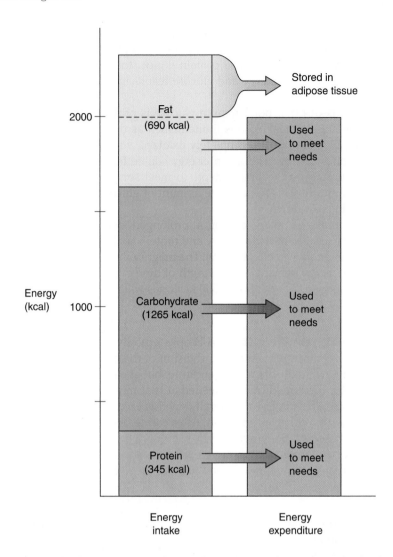

Figure 7.10 Nutrient usage
If energy intake exceeds expenditure dietary fat is stored in adipose tissue. In this example, all the kcalories from carbohydrate and protein are used to meet body needs, but only some of the kcalories from fat are used. The remaining kcalories are stored in adipose tissue.

of the energy in the fat to store the fat in adipose tissue (**Figure 7.11**). The low metabolic cost of converting dietary fat to stored body fat makes it more efficient for the body to use dietary fat to make body fat and to oxidize carbohydrate and protein to meet immediate energy needs rather than convert it to fat. The conversion of carbohydrate to fat becomes important only when the diet is composed primarily of carbohydrate and energy intake exceeds expenditure.[10]

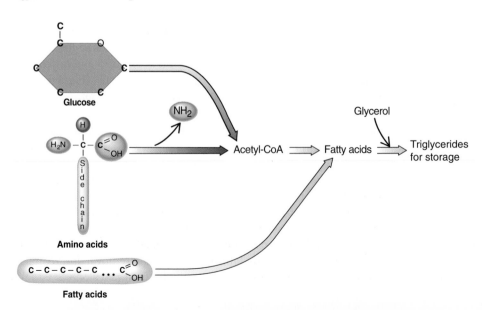

Figure 7.11 Storing kcalories as fat
It is metabolically much simpler and less costly to convert dietary fatty acids to triglycerides for storage than to convert glucose or amino acids to triglycerides.

7.3 Estimating Energy Needs

Learning Objectives

- Distinguish indirect and direct calorimetry.
- Calculate your EER at various levels of activity.

The amount of energy expended by the body, and hence the energy needed to maintain body weight, can be measured using a variety of techniques. Data from these measurements can then be used to estimate energy needs for a variety of people under a variety of circumstances. Calculations of energy needs have been used to generate recommendations about how much energy should be consumed in order to keep body weight stable.

Measuring Energy Expenditure

Energy expenditure can be measured by calorimetry, which is the science of measuring heat flow. Calorimetry can determine energy expenditure directly or indirectly. The use of doubly-labeled water is a newer technique for measuring energy expenditure that can be used over prolonged periods.

Direct Calorimetry Measuring the amount of heat produced when a food is combusted in a bomb calorimeter is a type of **direct calorimetry**. In humans, direct calorimetry measures the amount of heat given off by the body; the heat produced is proportional to the amount of energy used. This heat is generated by metabolic reactions that both convert food energy into ATP and use ATP for body processes. Direct calorimetry is an accurate method for measuring energy expenditure, but it is expensive and impractical because it requires that the individual being assessed remain in an insulated chamber throughout the procedure in order to measure the heat produced.

Indirect Calorimetry Indirect calorimetry, which estimates energy use by assessing oxygen utilization, is somewhat less cumbersome than direct calorimetry. To obtain a measurement the subject must breathe into a mouthpiece, mask, or ventilated hood (**Figure 7.12**). Oxygen use and carbon dioxide production is measured by analyzing the difference between the composition of inhaled and exhaled air. The body's energy use can be calculated from these values because the burning of fuels by the body in cellular respiration uses oxygen and produces carbon dioxide. This method can measure the energy used for individual components of expenditure, such as physical activity or BMR. It can also be used to estimate total energy needs, but it is not practical in free-living individuals because the equipment is too cumbersome for long-term use.

Doubly-Labeled Water A more practical method for measuring energy needs is the **doubly-labeled water technique**. This involves having the individual ingest or be injected with water labeled with **isotopes** of oxygen and hydrogen. The labeled oxygen and hydrogen are used by the body in metabolism. The labeled hydrogen leaves the body as part of water and the labeled oxygen leaves the body as part of both water and carbon dioxide. The difference in the rates of disappearance of these two isotopes can be used to calculate the amount of carbon dioxide produced by reactions in the body.

The doubly-labeled water method does not require the individual to carry any equipment and can be used to measure energy expenditure in free-living subjects for periods up to 2 weeks. It is now the preferred method for determining the total daily energy expenditures of both healthy and clinical populations.[5,11] However, it is not helpful in determining the proportion of energy used for BMR, physical activity, or TEF.

direct calorimetry A method of determining energy use that measures the amount of heat produced.

indirect calorimetry A method of estimating energy use that compares the amount of oxygen consumed to the amount of carbon dioxide expired.

doubly-labeled water technique A method for measuring energy expenditure based on measuring the disappearance of isotopes of hydrogen and oxygen in body fluids after consumption of a defined amount of water labeled with both isotopes.

isotopes Alternative forms of an element that have different atomic masses, which may or may not be radioactive.

Figure 7.12 Indirect calorimetry can be used to assess the energy expended for specific activities. Subjects breathe into a mouthpiece or through a mask that is placed over their nose and mouth. The amount of O_2 and CO_2 in the inhaled and exhaled air is measured. (Stockbyte/Getty Images, Inc.)

estimated energy requirements (EER) The amount of energy recommended by the DRIs to maintain body weight in a healthy person based on age, gender, size, and activity level.

Recommendations for Energy Intake

Measurements of energy expenditure using doubly-labeled water have been used to develop formulas for estimating individuals' energy needs. These **Estimated Energy Requirements (EER)**, established by the DRIs, are the current recommendations for energy intake in the United States.[5] An EER is the amount of energy predicted to maintain energy balance in a healthy person of a defined age, gender, weight, height, and level of physical activity. EERs predict energy expenditure in normal-weight individuals. Equations that predict the amount of energy needed for weight maintenance for overweight and obese individuals are given in Appendix A. No specific RDAs or ULs for energy have been established.

Determining Physical Activity Level In order to calculate an individual's energy needs using the EER equations, his or her activity level must be estimated. The DRIs have defined four physical activity levels: sedentary, low active, active, and very active.[5] A "sedentary" individual is one who does not participate in any activity beyond that required for daily independent living, such as housework, homework, yard work, and gardening. To be in the "low active" category, an adult weighing 70 kg would need to expend an amount of energy equivalent to walking 2.2 miles at a rate of 3 to 4 miles per hour in addition to the activities of daily living. To be "active," an individual would need to perform daily exercise equivalent to walking 7 miles at a rate of 3 to 4 miles per hour, and to be "very active," an individual would need to perform the equivalent of walking 17 miles at this rate in addition to the activities of daily living. In order to maintain a healthy weight and reduce the risk of chronic disease, physical activity at the "active" level is recommended. Not everyone has the time to walk for an hour and three-quarters every day, but if you engage in more vigorous activities you will expend the same number of kcalories in less time and still be in the active activity category.

Activity level can be estimated by keeping a daily log of your activities and recording the amount of time spent in each. Activities can then be categorized as activities of daily living, moderate, or vigorous (**Table 7.4**). As seen in **Table 7.5**,

Table 7.4 Categorizing Activities

Activities of Daily Living[a]	Moderate Activities[b]	Vigorous Activities[c]
Gardening (no lifting)	Bicycling (leisurely, < 10 mph)	Aerobics (moderate to heavy)
Watering plants	Calisthenics (light, no weights)	Basketball (vigorous)
Raking leaves	Dancing	Bicycling (> 10 mph)
Mowing the lawn	Gardening/yard work (light)	Climbing (hills or mountains)
Household tasks	Golf (walking and carrying clubs)	Jogging (5 mph or faster)
Mopping	Hiking	Rope jumping
Vacuuming	Skating leisurely	Skating vigorous
Doing laundry	Swimming (slow)	Skiing (water, downhill, or cross-country)
Washing dishes	Walking (3.5 mph, 15–20 min/mile)	Swimming (freestyle laps)
Walking from the house to car or bus	Water aerobics	Tennis
Loading/unloading the car	Weight lifting (light workout)	Walking (4.5 mph)
Walking the dog	Yoga	Weight lifting (vigorous effort)
		Yard work (heavy, chopping wood)

[a]It is assumed that we spend about 2.5 hours per day in these types of activities.
[b]Activities that expend about 210 to 420 kcal/hr for a 154-lb (70 kg) individual.
[c]Activities that expend more than 420 kcal/hr for a 154-lb (70 kg) individual.

Table 7.5 Determining Physical Activity (PA) Values

	PA values			
	3–18 years		≥ 19 years	
Physical Activity Level	Boys	Girls	Men	Women
Sedentary: Engages in only the activities of daily living and no moderate or vigorous activities.	1.00	1.00	1.00	1.00
Low active: Daily activity equivalent to at least 30 minutes of moderate activity and a minimum of 15 to 30 minutes of vigorous activity depending on the intensity of the activity.	1.13	1.16	1.11	1.12
Active: Engages in at least 60 minutes of moderate activities or a minimum of 30 to 60 minutes of vigorous activity depending on the intensity of the activity.	1.26	1.31	1.25	1.27
Very active: Engages in at least 2.5 hours of moderate activity or a minimum of 1.0 to 1.75 hours of vigorous activity depending on the intensity of the activity.	1.42	1.56	1.48	1.45

your physical activity level is determined based on the time you spend in each category of activity. Each physical activity level is assigned a numerical **PA (physical activity) value** that can then be used in the EER calculation. It is important to carefully estimate activity level because it has a significant effect on energy needs. For example, a 30-year-old woman who is 5' 5" tall and weighs 130 lbs needs about 1900 kcals/day if she is at the sedentary activity level. If she increases her activity to "active," the level recommended by the DRIs, her energy needs increase to 2370 kcals/day.

PA (physical activity) value A numeric value associated with activity level that is a variable in the EER equations used to calculate energy needs.

Other Factors Affecting Energy Needs Energy needs are affected by gender, height, weight, life stage, and age as well as level of physical activity. These factors are all taken into consideration in the EER equations (**Table 7.6**, or inside cover). Separate equations for men and women reflect gender differences in energy requirements. Height and weight are variables in the equations and when larger numbers are entered, calculated results reflect the higher energy needs of taller, heavier individuals. For example, an active 25-year-old man who is 5' 11" tall and weighs 170 lbs, requires 3175 kcalories to maintain his weight. If the same man weighed 220 lbs, he would need about 400 kcalories per day more to maintain his weight.

The EER values for infants, children, and adolescents include the energy used to deposit tissues associated with growth. Beginning at age 3, there are separate EER equations for boys and girls because of differences in growth and physical activity. The EER for pregnancy is determined as the sum of the total energy expenditure of a nonpregnant woman plus the energy needed to maintain pregnancy and deposit maternal and fetal tissue. During lactation, EER is the sum of the total energy expenditure of nonlactating women and the energy in the milk produced, minus the energy mobilized from maternal tissue stores.

The impact of age on the energy needs of adults can be striking. As people get older, their EER declines. So, the 25-year-old man described above who needs 3175 kcalories to maintain his weight when he is 25 years old, will need only 2935 kcalories when he turns 50. If he decreases his level of activity, as many people do when they age, the number of kcalories he can eat without gaining weight drops even more—he will only require 2385 kcalories to maintain his 170-lb weight at age 50 if he is sedentary. If people do not decrease their kcalorie intake to compensate for getting older and becoming less active, body weight will increase.

Life Cycle

Table 7.6 Calculating Your EER

- **Find your weight in kilograms (kg) and your height in meters (m):**

  Weight in kilograms = weight in pounds ÷ 2.2 lbs/kg

  Height in meters = height in inches × 0.0254 in/m

  For example: 160 pounds = 160 lbs ÷ 2.2 lbs/kg = 72.7 kg

  5' 9" = 69 in × 0.0254 in/m = 1.75 m

- **Estimate the amount of physical activity you get per day and use Table 7.5 to find the PA value for someone your age, gender, and activity level.**

  For example, if you are a 19-year-old male who performs 40 minutes of vigorous activity a day you are in the active category and have a PA of 1.25.

- **Choose the appropriate EER prediction equation below and calculate your EER:**

  For example: if you are an active 19-year-old male:

  EER = 662 − (9.53 × Age in yrs) + PA [(15.91 × Weight in kg) + (539.6 × Height in m)]

  Where age = 19 yrs, weight = 72.7 kg, height = 1.75 m, Active PA value = 1.25

  EER = 662 − (9.53 × 19) × 1.25([15.91 × 72.7] + [539.6 × 1.75]) = 3107 kcal/ day

Life Stage	EER Prediction Equation[a]
Boys 9–18 yrs	EER = 88.5 − (61.9 × Age in yrs) + PA [(26.7 × Weight in kg) + (903 × Height in m)] + 25
Girls 9–18 yrs	EER = 135.3 − (30.8 × Age in yrs) × PA [(10.0 × Weight in kg) + (934 × Height in m)] + 25
Men ≥ 19 yrs	EER = 662 − (9.53 × Age in yrs) + PA [(15.91 × Weight in kg) + (539.6 × Height in m)]
Women ≥ 19 yrs	EER = 354 − (6.91 × Age in yrs) + PA [(9.36 × Weight in kg) + (726 × Height in m)]

[a]These equations are appropriate for determining EERs in normal-weight individuals. Equations that predict the amount of energy needed for weight maintenance in overweight and obese individuals are also available (see Appendix A).

7.4 Body Weight and Health

Learning Objectives

- Define "healthy weight."
- Name some health problems that are more common in overweight than in normal-weight individuals.

Some body fat is essential for health; it provides an energy store, cushions internal organs, and insulates against changes in temperature, but too much body fat can increase the risk of disease and create psychological and social problems. Individuals who have little stored fat also have a greater risk for early death than individuals whose body fat is within the normal range.[12]

Excess Body Fat and Disease Risk

Heart disease, high blood cholesterol, high blood pressure, stroke, diabetes, gallbladder disease, sleep apnea, respiratory problems, arthritis, gout, and cancers of the breast, uterus, prostate, and colon all occur more frequently in obese individuals (**Table 7.7**). In addition, the presence of these diseases increases the risk of illness and premature death that is associated with being obese. Obesity also increases the incidence and severity of infectious disease and has been linked to poor wound healing and surgical complications.[13] The magnitude of the health risks increases as the amount of excess fat rises (**Figure 7.13**).

Life Cycle

Being overweight causes problems throughout life. During pregnancy, carrying excess body fat increases risks both for the mother and her baby (see Chapter 14).[14] In children and adolescents, being overweight contributes to the development of high blood cholesterol levels, high blood pressure, and elevated blood glucose (see Chapter 15). The high rate of childhood obesity is a major threat to this generation because the longer a person is overweight the greater the risks; those who gain excess weight at a young age and remain overweight throughout life have the greatest health risks.

Table 7.7 Health Risks Associated with Excess Body Weight

Cardiovascular disease is more likely when body weight is elevated.
- Blood pressure increases as body weight increases.
- Triglyceride levels increase as body weight increases.
- LDL cholesterol increases as body weight increases.
- HDL cholesterol falls as body weight increases.

Type 2 diabetes risk increases with body weight.
- Fasting blood sugar increases with increasing body weight.
- 80% of people with type 2 diabetes are obese.
- Incidence increases as much as 30-fold with a BMI >35.

Respiratory problems are more common in overweight people.
- Sleep apnea is more common in overweight people.
- The workload of muscles used for breathing increases.
- Asthma is worse.

Gall bladder disease is more common in overweight people.

Osteoarthritis and degenerative joint disease increase with increasing weight.

Menstrual irregularities are increased in overweight women.

Cancer risk is higher in overweight people.
- Obese women are at increased risk for cancers of the endometrium, breast, cervix, and ovaries.
- Obese men are at increased risk for colorectal and prostate cancer.

A sedentary lifestyle further increases risk.
- Obese individuals who are inactive have higher risks of illness and death.
- Inactivity increases the likelihood of developing diabetes and heart disease.

Heart Disease, Stroke, and Diabetes Obesity is considered a primary risk factor for cardiovascular disease. Carrying excess body fat increases the amount of work required by the heart and the risk of developing high blood pressure and abnormal blood lipid levels. When body weight and fat are reduced blood cholesterol levels improve, blood pressure decreases, and the risk of heart disease is lowered.[15,16] Being overweight also contributes to angina (chest pain caused by decreased oxygen to the

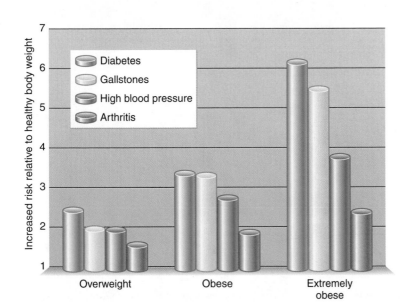

Figure 7.13 Excess body fat and disease risk
The more excess body fat an individual carries, the greater their risk of a number of chronic diseases. A value of 1.0 represents the risk of having these disorders if your weight is in the healthy range; a value of 2 indicates that the risk is doubled.

heart) and sudden death from heart disease or stroke without any signs or symptoms. Obesity increases the risk of developing diabetes; more than 85% of people with type 2 diabetes are overweight.[17] Having diabetes, in turn, increases the risks of heart disease and stroke.[16] This is also a concern in children. Among white children born in the United States in 2000, 31% of girls and 27% of boys are predicted to develop diabetes sometime during their lives. These percentages are higher for African Americans—49% of girls and 40% of boys—and even higher for Hispanics—53% of girls and 45% of boys.[18] Atherosclerosis is the most common long-term complication of diabetes, and cardiovascular risk factors including hypertension, which predisposes to stroke, are more frequent in diabetics. In overweight individuals who have diabetes, weight loss can help maintain blood glucose levels in the normal range.[17]

Gallbladder Disease Obesity is associated with an increase in gallstone formation (**Figure 7.14**). Gallstones are typically composed mostly of cholesterol and may form as a single large stone or many small ones. They often cause no symptoms, but if they lodge in the bile ducts gallstones can cause pain and cramps. If the passage of bile is blocked lipid absorption in the small intestine is impaired and the gallbladder can become inflamed.

The more obese a person is, the greater his or her risk is of developing gallstones. Women who are obese have about three to seven times the risk of developing gallstones as women at a healthy body weight.[19] The reason that obesity increases the risk of gallstones is unclear, but researchers believe that in obese people, the liver produces too much cholesterol, which deposits in the gallbladder and forms stones. Although the risk of gallstones decreases with a lower body weight, weight loss, in particular rapid weight loss, increases the risk of gallbladder disease because as lipids are released from body stores, cholesterol synthesis increases, increasing the tendency for cholesterol stone formation. Gallstones are one of the most medically important complications of voluntary weight loss.[19]

Sleep Apnea Sleep apnea is a serious, potentially life-threatening condition characterized by brief interruptions of breathing during sleep. These short stops in breathing can happen up to 400 times every night and therefore patients with sleep apnea sleep very poorly and wake up in the morning still feeling tired. Sufferers remain tired throughout the day. Sleep apnea has also been associated with cardiovascular

Figure 7.14 Gallstones, visible in this image of the abdomen, are depostis of cholesterol, bile pigments, and calcium in the gallbladder or bile duct. They may form as a single large stone or many small ones. (Simon Fraser/ Photo Researchers, Inc.)

conditions such as high blood pressure, heart attack, stroke, impotence, and irregular heartbeat.[20] It is common in obesity because fatty tissue in the pharynx and neck compress the airway and block airflow. In obese individuals, weight loss may decrease both the frequency and severity of sleep apnea symptoms.[17]

Cancer Excess body weight and fat affect the risks of certain forms of cancer. In obese men, cancers of the prostate and colon are increased. In women, being overweight seems to protect against the form of breast cancer that occurs in the child-bearing years but it increases the risks of postmenopausal breast cancer.[21] Adipose tissue produces estrogen. It has been hypothesized that obese women are at greater risk of postmenopausal breast cancer because of the elevated estrogen levels associated with their excess body fat.[22]

Joint Disorders Excess weight and fat can also increase the risk of developing osteoarthritis. This is a type of arthritis that occurs when the cartilage cushioning the joints breaks down and gradually becomes rougher and thinner. As the process continues, a substantial amount of cartilage wears away so the bones in the joint rub against each other causing pain and reducing movement. Being overweight is the most common cause of excess pressure on the joints and it can speed the rate at which the cartilage wears down. Losing weight reduces the pressure and strain on the joints and slows the wear and tear of cartilage.[17] In individuals suffering from osteoarthritis, weight loss can help reduce pain and stiffness in the affected joints, especially those in the hips, knees, back, and feet.[23]

Gout is a joint disease caused by high levels of uric acid in the blood. Uric acid is a nitrogenous waste product resulting from the breakdown of DNA and similar types of molecules. It sometimes forms into solid stones or crystal masses that become deposited in the joints, causing pain. Gout is more common in overweight people and the risk of developing the disorder increases with higher body weight.

Psychological and Social Consequences of Obesity

Carrying excess body fat has psychological and social consequences. Our society puts a high value on physical appearance. Being thin is considered attractive and being fat is not. Those who do not conform to standards may pay a high psychological and social price. For example, overweight children are often teased and ostracized. This teasing about body weight is associated with low body satisfaction, low self-esteem, depression, social isolation, and thinking about and attempting suicide.[24,25] If obese children grow into obese adolescents and adults, and most of them do, they may be discriminated against in college admissions, in the job market, in the workplace, and even on public transportation. Obese individuals of every age are more likely to experience depression, a negative self-image, and feelings of inadequacy.[26] The physical health consequences of obesity may not manifest themselves as disease for years, but the psychological and social problems experienced by the obese are felt every day.

Health Implications of Being Underweight

Some people are naturally lean and this reduces their health risks. Research has suggested that having a low level of body fat may reduce the risk of diabetes and other chronic diseases and may even increase longevity[27] (see Chapter 16, Science Applied: Eat Less—Live Longer?). But it is not good to be too thin. Body fat is needed for cushioning, as an insulator, and as a reserve for periods of illness. People with little energy reserves have a disadvantage during a famine or when battling a medical condition such as cancer that causes wasting and malnutrition. Therefore, despite the lower incidence of certain chronic diseases in people with low body weights, when compared to normal weight, being too lean is associated with an increased risk of early death.[12]

Life Cycle

When leanness is due to intentional or forced restriction of food intake rather than a genetic tendency to be lean it can create severe health problems. Substantial reductions in body weight due to starvation or eating disorders reduce body fat and muscle mass, affect electrolyte balance, and decrease the ability of the immune system to fight disease. Too little body fat can cause problems at all stages of life. During adolescence it can delay sexual development. During pregnancy too little weight gain increases the risk that the baby will have health complications, and in the elderly, too little body fat increases the risk of malnutrition. In developed countries, socioeconomic conditions may create isolated pockets of undernutrition, but severe cases of wasting are usually a result either of self-starvation due to an eating disorder, such as anorexia nervosa (see Focus on Eating Disorders), or of a disease process, such as AIDS or cancer.

7.5 Guidelines for a Healthy Body Weight

Learning Objectives

- Describe three methods used to estimate percent body fat.
- Calculate your BMI and determine if it is in the healthy range.
- Compare the health implications of excess visceral versus subcutaneous fat.

Guidelines for a healthy body weight are based on the weight at which the risk of illness and death are lowest. These risks are associated not only with body weight, but also with the amount and location of body fat, therefore assessment of a healthy body weight must consider body composition. Despite this, body composition measures are generally not used clinically to assess health. Instead, **body mass index (BMI)**, which is calculated from body weight and height, is the most common measure used to assess the healthfulness of body weight.

body mass index (BMI) A measure of body weight in relation to height that is used to compare body size with a standard.

Lean Versus Fat Tissue

The human body is composed of lean tissue and body fat. Lean tissue, referred to as lean body mass or fat-free mass, includes bones, muscles, and all tissue except fat tissue. Body fat, or adipose tissue, lies under the skin and around internal organs. The amount of fat an individual carries and where that fat is deposited are affected by age, gender, and genetics as well as by energy balance.

Life Cycle

At birth, about 12% of a baby's weight is fat. This percentage increases in the first year of life and then, during childhood, as muscle mass increases, the percentage of body fat decreases. During adolescence, girls gain proportionately more fat and boys gain more muscle mass. As adults, women have more stored body fat than men so the level that is healthy for women is somewhat higher. A healthy level of body fat for young adult women is between 21% and 32% of total weight; for young adult men, it is between 8% and 19%.[28] There is an increase in body fat during pregnancy to provide energy stores for the mother and fetus. With aging, lean body mass decreases; between the ages of 20 and 60, body fat typically doubles even if body weight remains the same. This occurs regardless of energy intake. Some of this loss of lean body mass can be prevented by strength training.[29]

Assessing Body Composition

A number of techniques are available for assessing body composition. Many require expensive equipment and must be performed in a research setting by trained technicians. Others are more portable, so they are more appropriate for use in a clinic, office, or health club.

Bioelectric Impedance Analysis Bioelectric impedance analysis is the most popular way to measure body composition. It estimates body fat by directing a painless, low-energy electrical current through the body. The difference between the current applied to the first electrode and the current that reaches the second electrode is used to determine the resistance, or the amount of current a substance will stop. Because fat is a poor conductor of electricity, it offers resistance to the current. Thus, the amount of resistance to current flow is proportional to the amount of body fat. The equipment needed for impedance measurements is inexpensive and the process is quick and painless (**Figure 7.15**). However, because impedance is affected by the amount of water in the body, measurements must be performed when the gastrointestinal tract and bladder are empty and body hydration is normal. Measurements performed within 24 hours of strenuous exercise are not accurate because body water is low due to losses in sweat.

bioelectric impedance analysis A technique for estimating body composition that measures body fat by directing a low-energy electric current through the body and calculating resistance to flow.

Skinfold Thickness Measurements of **skinfold thickness** at various locations on the body can also be used to assess body composition. Skinfold thickness is measured with calipers and is used to assess the amount of **subcutaneous fat** (**Figure 7.16**). Measurements are taken from one or more standard locations. The most common sites are the triceps (the area over the muscles on the back of the upper arm) and the subscapular area (just below the shoulder blade). Either a nomogram or mathematical equations are then used to estimate percent body fat from these measurements. Skinfold measurements are noninvasive and, when performed by a trained individual, can accurately predict body fat in normal-weight individuals. These measures are more difficult to perform and less accurate in obese and elderly subjects.

skinfold thickness A measurement of subcutaneous fat used to estimate total body fat.

subcutaneous fat Adipose tissue that is located under the skin.

Underwater Weighing An accurate noninvasive technique for assessing body composition is **underwater weighing**, which involves weighing an individual both on land and in the water. The difference between these two weights can be used to determine body volume and body density, which is proportional to fat-free mass. The percentage of body fat can then be determined using standardized equations. To measure underwater weight, subjects must sit on a scale, expel the air from their

underwater weighing A technique that uses the difference between body weight underwater and body weight on land to estimate body density and calculate body composition.

Figure 7.15 Hand-held bioelectric impedance devices such as this one are available for home use. (Yoav Levy/Phototake/Alamy)

Figure 7.16 The triceps skinfold is measured at the midpoint of the back of the arm. This measure of the thickness of the fat layer under the skin can be used to estimate body fat. (David Young-Wolff/PhotoEdit)

Figure 7.17 Underwater weighing is an accurate technique for determining body composition that relies on measurements of body weight on land and underwater. (W. Jim Olive/Peter Arnold, Inc.)

lungs, and be lowered into a tank of water (**Figure 7.17**). Although this method is accurate, it requires special equipment and cannot be used for some groups such as small children or frail adults. A newer method for estimating body composition measures air displacement rather than water displacement to determine body volume. The individual is placed in an air-filled chamber (known as the BOD POD) rather than in water. It is accurate and more convenient than underwater weighing.[30]

Dilution Methods Body fat can also be assessed by using the principle of dilution. Because water is present primarily in lean tissue and not in fat, a water-soluble isotope can be ingested or injected into the bloodstream and allowed to mix with the water throughout the body. The concentration of the isotope in a sample of body fluid, such as blood, can then be measured. The extent to which the isotope has been diluted can be used to calculate the amount of lean tissue in the body, and body fat can then be calculated by subtracting lean weight from total body weight. Another technique measures a naturally occurring isotope of potassium. Because potassium is found primarily in lean tissue, a measure of the amount of this isotope in the body can be used to determine the total amount of body potassium, which can then be used to estimate the amount of lean tissue. Dilution techniques are expensive and invasive, usually requiring injections. They are used primarily for research purposes.

Radiologic Methods A variety of radiologic technologies have been used to assess body composition. These are less invasive but more expensive than dilution methods. Computerized tomography (CT), generally employed as a diagnostic technique, can be used to visualize fat and lean tissue. CT is more accurate than underwater weighing, skinfold measures, and total body potassium for evaluation of body composition, and is particularly useful for measuring the amount of **visceral fat** (**Figure 7.18**).[31] Dual-energy X-ray absorptiometry (DXA) is another method that uses low-energy X-rays for assessing body composition. A single investigation can accurately determine total body mass, bone mineral mass, and the amount and percentage of body fat. Another method, magnetic resonance imaging (MRI), uses magnetic fields to create an internal body image. MRI can be used to accurately estimate the amount of abdominal fat, which is associated with the risk of heart disease and other chronic diseases.

visceral fat Adipose tissue that is located in the abdomen around the body's internal organs.

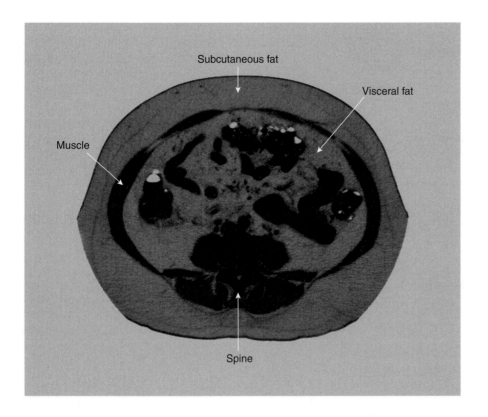

Figure 7.18 A CT scan taken at waist level in an overweight female shows that fat in the abdominal region is located both under the skin (subcutaneous) and around the internal organs (visceral). (Courtesy Michael F. Smolin)

Body Mass Index

The current standard for evaluating body weight is body mass index (BMI). Although BMI does not directly assess percent body fat, BMI values correlate well with body fat in most people.[32,33] BMI is calculated from a ratio of weight to height according to either of the following equation:

$$BMI = \text{weight in kg}/(\text{height in m})^2$$

or,

$$BMI = \text{weight in lbs}/(\text{height in inches})^2 \times 703^*$$

For example, someone who is 6 feet (72 in or 1.83 m) tall and weighs 180 lb (81.8 kg) has a BMI of 24.5 kg/m².

Figure 7.19 Although wrestler/actor Hulk Hogan has a BMI of 30.3 kg/m², which falls into the category of obese, it probably does not indicate that he has excess body fat or an increased risk of disease. (Hubert Boesl/dpa/Landov)

---

*The multiplier 703 is used by the Center for Disease Control in developing growth charts, 704.5 is used by the National Institutes of Health, and 700 is used by the American Dietetic Association. The variation in outcome is insignificant.

What Is a Healthy BMI? A healthy body weight is defined as a BMI of 18.5 to 24.9 kg/m^2. In general, people with a BMI within this range have the lowest health risks. Underweight is defined as a BMI of less than 18.5 kg/m^2, overweight is identified as a BMI of 25 to 29.9 kg/m^2, and obese as a BMI of 30 kg/m^2 or greater.[33] A BMI of 40 or over is classified as extreme or morbid obesity. **Table 7.8** can be used to find your BMI and determine whether it is in the healthy range.

Limitations of BMI Even though BMI correlates well with the amount of body fat; it is not a perfect tool for evaluating the health risks associated with obesity. This is particularly true in athletes who have highly developed muscles; their BMI may be high because they have an unusually large amount of lean body mass. In these individuals BMI is high, but body fat and hence disease risk is low (**Figure 7.19**). BMI is also not suitable for evaluating weight in pregnant and lactating women because of their rap-

Table 7.8 Is Your BMI in the healthy range.*

Height (feet/inches)	UNDER-WEIGHT Body Weight (pounds)		NORMAL						OVERWEIGHT					OBESE										EXTREME OBESITY		
BMI	17	18	19	20	21	22	23	24	25	26	27	28	29	30	31	32	33	34	35	36	37	38	39	40	41	42
4' 10"	81	86	91	96	100	105	110	115	119	124	129	134	138	143	148	153	158	162	167	172	177	181	186	191	198	201
4' 11"	84	89	94	99	104	109	114	119	124	128	133	138	143	148	153	158	163	168	173	178	183	188	193	198	203	208
5' 0"	87	92	97	102	107	112	118	123	128	133	138	143	148	153	158	163	168	174	179	184	189	194	199	204	209	215
5' 1"	90	95	100	106	111	116	122	127	132	137	143	148	153	158	164	169	174	180	185	190	195	201	206	211	217	222
5' 2"	93	98	104	109	115	120	126	131	136	142	147	153	158	164	169	175	180	186	191	196	202	207	213	218	224	229
5' 3"	96	102	107	113	118	124	130	135	141	146	152	158	163	169	175	180	186	191	197	203	208	214	220	225	231	237
5' 4"	99	105	110	116	122	128	134	140	145	151	157	163	169	174	180	186	192	197	204	209	215	221	227	232	238	244
5' 5"	102	108	114	120	126	132	138	144	150	156	162	168	174	180	186	192	198	204	210	216	222	228	234	240	246	252
5' 6"	105	112	118	124	130	136	142	148	155	161	167	173	179	186	192	198	204	210	216	223	229	235	241	247	253	260
5' 7"	108	115	121	127	134	140	146	153	159	166	172	178	185	191	198	204	211	217	223	230	236	242	249	255	261	268
5' 8"	112	119	125	131	138	144	151	158	164	171	177	184	190	197	203	210	216	223	230	236	243	249	256	262	269	276
5' 9"	115	122	128	135	142	149	155	162	169	176	182	189	196	203	209	216	223	230	236	243	250	257	263	270	277	284
5' 10"	119	126	132	139	146	153	160	167	174	181	188	195	202	209	216	222	229	236	243	250	257	264	271	278	285	292
5' 11"	122	129	136	143	150	157	165	172	179	186	193	200	208	215	222	229	236	243	250	257	265	272	279	286	293	301
6' 0"	125	133	140	147	154	162	169	177	184	191	199	206	213	221	228	235	242	250	258	265	272	279	287	294	302	309
6' 1"	129	137	144	151	159	166	174	182	189	197	204	212	219	227	235	242	250	257	265	272	280	288	295	302	310	318
6' 2"	132	140	148	155	163	171	179	186	194	202	210	218	225	233	241	249	256	264	272	280	287	295	303	311	319	326
6' 3"	136	144	152	160	168	176	184	192	200	208	216	224	232	240	248	256	264	272	279	287	295	303	311	319	327	335
6' 4"	140	148	156	164	172	180	189	197	205	213	221	230	238	246	254	263	271	279	287	295	304	312	320	328	336	344

*Locate your height in the left most column and read across to your weight. Follow the column containing your weight up to the top line to find your BMI.

idly changing weight and body composition (see Chapter 14). It is also less accurate in individuals who have lost muscle, such as many older adults. Because of these limitations BMI should not be the only measure used to determine nutritional health and fitness. For example, someone who is in the overweight category based on BMI but consumes a healthy diet and exercises regularly may be more fit and have a lower risk of chronic disease than someone with a BMI in the healthy range who is sedentary and eats a poor diet.

Life Cycle

Location of Body Fat

Where body fat is stored affects the health risks associated with having too much. Subcutaneous fat carries less risk than visceral fat, which is deposited around the organs in the abdomen. An increase in visceral fat is associated with a higher incidence of heart disease, high blood pressure, stroke, and diabetes.[16,34,35] Generally, fat in the hips and lower body is subcutaneous, whereas fat deposited around the waist in the abdominal region is primarily visceral fat. Therefore, people who carry their excess fat around and above the waist have more visceral fat. Those who carry their extra fat below the waist in the hips and thighs have more subcutaneous fat. In the popular literature these body types have been dubbed apples and pears, respectively (**Figure 7.20**).

Where your extra fat is deposited is determined primarily by your genes.[36] Visceral fat storage is more common in men than women. African-American men store less visceral fat than white men of the same age and level of total body fat.[37] After menopause, visceral fat increases in women. Other factors that affect the amount of visceral fat include stress, tobacco use, and alcohol consumption, all of which predispose people to visceral fat deposition, and physical activity, which reduces it.

Distinguishing the relative amounts of visceral and subcutaneous fat requires sophisticated imaging techniques. However, the risk associated with visceral fat deposition can be estimated by measuring waist circumference. For men whose BMI is greater than 25, a waist circumference greater than 40 inches is associated with an increased risk. For women in this BMI range, a waist circumference of greater than 35 inches increases risks[33] (**Table 7.9**). In individuals under 5 feet in height or with a BMI greater than or equal to 35 kg/m^2 these cutoff points are not helpful in predicting health risks.

Figure 7.20 Visceral and subcutaneous body fat
Overweight individuals with apple-shaped body types deposit more fat in the abdominal region. They are at greater risk of developing heart disease and diabetes than are those with pear-shaped body types who deposit more fat in the hips and thighs where it is primarily subcutaneous. (©Corbis; Tom McHugh/Photo Researchers, Inc.)

Table 7.9 **BMI, Waist Circumference, and Disease Risk**

	BMI (kg/m²)ᵃ	Men, waist ≤ 40 Inches, and women, waist ≤ 35 inches	Men, waist > 40 inches, and women, waist > 35 inches
		Disease Riskᵇ	
Underweight	<18.5		
Normal weight	18.5–24.9		
Overweight	25.0–29.9	Increased	High
Obesity (class I)	30.0–34.9	High	Very high
Obesity (class II)	35.0–39.9	Very high	Very high
Extreme or morbid obesity (class III)	≥ 40	Extremely high	Extremely high

ᵃBMI = body weight (kg)/height squared (m²)
ᵇDisease risk for type 2 diabetes, hypertension, and cardiovascular disease relative to individuals with a normal weight and normal waist circumference.
Source: National Institutes of Health, National Heart, Lung, and Blood Institute. The Practical Guide to the Identification, Evaluation, and Treatment of Overweight and Obesity in Adults, 2002.

7.6 Regulation of Energy Balance

Learning Objectives

- Describe what is meant by a set point for body weight.
- List four physiological signals that determine whether you feel hungry or full.
- Explain why leptin levels might be higher in an obese than in a lean individual.
- Discuss how genes contribute to obesity.

We inherit our body shape and characteristics from our parents. Some of us inherit tall, slender bodies with long, thin bones. Others inherit stocky bodies with short, wide bones. Some people have broad hips and others broad shoulders (**Figure 7.21**). Some people naturally carry a larger amount of body fat than others. These inherited characteristics don't change much over time. Even body weight tends to remain relatively constant for long periods despite short-term fluctuations in the amount of exercise we get and the amount of food we consume. This can be explained by the **set-point theory**, which suggests that body weight is genetically determined and that there are internal mechanisms that defend against weight change.[38] Studies that under- or overfeed experimental subjects provide support for the set-point theory. The subjects lose or gain weight in response to changes in intake, but when they are allowed to return to their normal diet, their weight returns to its original "set" level.[39] Likewise, as anyone who has dieted can attest, it is difficult to decrease body weight, and most people who lose weight eventually regain all they have lost.

If body weight is regulated at a particular set-point, then why are so many of us getting fatter? Despite experimental support for the existence of a set-point, it appears that the mechanisms that defend body weight are not absolute. Changes in physiological, psychological, and environmental circumstances do cause the level at which body weight is regulated to change, usually increasing it over time. For example, body weight increases in most adults between the ages of 30 and 60 years, and after childbearing, most women return to a weight that is 1 to 2 lbs higher than their

set-point theory The theory that when people finish growing, their weight remains relatively stable for long periods despite periodic changes in energy intake or output.

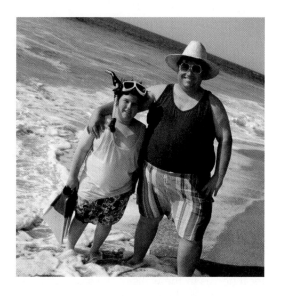

Figure 7.21 The genes we inherit from our parents are important determinants of our body size and shape. (Courtesy Lori Smolin; Bruce Ayres/Stone/Getty Images, Inc.)

prepregnancy weight. This suggests that the mechanisms that defend against weight loss are stronger than those that prevent weight gain.

Obesity Genes

Genes involved in regulating body fatness have been called **obesity genes** because an abnormality in one or more of these could result in obesity. More than 300 genes and regions of human chromosomes have been linked to body weight regulation and, hence, obesity.[40] These genes are responsible for the production of proteins that affect how much food people eat, how much energy they expend, and how efficiently their body fat is stored. The combined effects of all these genes help to determine and regulate what people weigh and how much fat they carry. The influence of genes on body weight was demonstrated dramatically by a study done with identical twins. During the study the pairs of identical twins were overfed to the same extent. Each set of twins tended to gain the same amount of weight and to deposit fat in the same parts of their bodies. In contrast, large differences were seen between sets of twins— some of the twin sets gained only 9 lbs, whereas others gained as much as 29 lbs[36] (**Figure 7.22**).

obesity genes Genes that code for proteins involved in the regulation of food intake, energy expenditure, or the deposition of body fat. When they are abnormal, the result is abnormal amounts of body fat.

Figure 7.22 Identical twins inherit the same genes and thus tend to gain the same amount of weight and deposit fat in the same locations. (Dennis MacDonald/Age Fotostock America, Inc.)

Mechanisms for Regulating Body Weight

To regulate weight and fatness at a constant level the body must be able to respond both to changes in food intake that occur over a short time frame as well as to more long-term changes in the amount of stored body fat. Signals related to food intake affect **hunger** and **satiety** over a short period of time—from meal to meal—whereas signals from the adipose tissue trigger the brain to adjust both food intake and energy expenditure for long-term regulation.

hunger Internal signals that stimulate one to acquire and consume food.

satiety The feeling of fullness and satisfaction, caused by food consumption, that eliminates the desire to eat.

Short-Term: Regulating Food Intake from Meal-to-Meal How do you know how much to eat for breakfast, or when it is time to eat lunch? To some extent, your level of hunger or satiety determines how much you eat at each meal. These physical sensations that tell people to eat or stop eating are triggered by signals from the GI tract, levels of circulating nutrients, and messages from the brain.[41] Some signals are sent before food is eaten, some are sent while food is in the GI tract, and some occur once nutrients are circulating in the bloodstream.

The simplest type of signal about how much food has been eaten comes from local nerves in the walls of the stomach and small intestine that sense the volume or pressure of food and send a message to the brain to either start or stop eating. Once food is consumed, the presence of nutrients in the GI tract sends information directly to the brain and triggers the release of gastrointestinal hormones that signal eating to stop. Once nutrients have been absorbed, circulating levels of nutrients, including glucose, amino acids, ketones, and fatty acids, are monitored by the brain and may trigger signals to eat or not to eat.[42] Nutrients that are taken up by the brain may affect neurotransmitter concentrations, which then affect the amount and type of nutrients consumed. For example, some studies suggest that when brain levels of the neurotransmitter serotonin are low, carbohydrate is craved, but when it is high, protein is preferred.[42] Absorbed nutrients also affect metabolism in the liver because absorbed water-soluble nutrients go there directly. Changes in liver metabolism, in particular the amount of ATP, are believed to be involved in regulating food intake.

There are many different hormonal signals that regulate different aspects of food intake. For instance, the hormone insulin is released by the pancreas in response to the intake of carbohydrate. Insulin allows glucose to be taken up by cells, thereby reducing circulating levels of glucose and increasing hunger. The hormone **ghrelin** may be the reason people typically feel hungry around lunchtime regardless of when and how much they had for breakfast. It is produced by the stomach and is believed to stimulate the desire to eat meals at usual times. Levels rise an hour or two before a meal and drop very low after a meal. Levels have been found to rise in people who have lost weight, increasing their desire to eat more.[43] Overproduction of ghrelin could contribute to obesity. Cholecystokinin, released when chyme enters the small intestine, causes us to stop eating by inducing satiety. Another hormone that causes a reduction in appetite is peptide PYY. It is released from the GI tract after a meal and the amount released is proportional to the kcalorie content of a meal.[44]

ghrelin A hormone produced by the stomach that stimulates food intake.

Psychological factors can also affect hunger and satiety. For example, some people eat for comfort and to relieve stress. Others may lose their appetite when these same emotions are felt. Psychological distress can alter the mechanisms that regulate food intake.

Long-Term: Regulating the Amount of Body Fat Short-term regulators of energy balance affect the size and timing of individual meals, but if a change in input is sustained over a long period it can affect long-term energy balance and, hence, body weight and fatness. To regulate the amount of fat at a set level, the body must be able to monitor how much fat is present. This information is believed to come from hormones, such as insulin and **leptin**, which are secreted in proportion to the amount of body fat.[45] Insulin is secreted from the pancreas when blood glucose levels rise; its circulating concentration is proportional to the amount of body fat. Insulin interacts with the hypothalamus to reduce food intake and body weight, and insulin levels are believed to affect the amount of leptin produced and secreted. Leptin is a hormone

leptin A protein hormone produced by adipocytes that signals information about the amount of body fat.

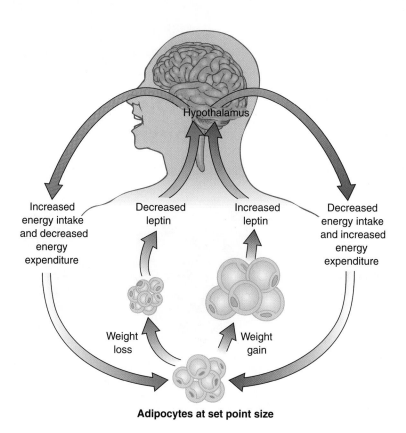

Figure 7.23 Leptin regulation of body fat
Changes in the size of the adipocytes affect the amount of leptin released. The amount of leptin reaching the hypothalamus determines the response and helps return body fat stores to a set level.

that is produced by the adipocytes and acts in the hypothalamus. The amount of leptin produced is proportional to the size of adipocytes—more leptin is released as fat stores increase. Leptin exerts its effect on food intake and energy expenditure by binding to leptin receptors present in the hypothalamus. This triggers mechanisms that affect energy intake and expenditure. When leptin levels are high, mechanisms that increase energy expenditure and decrease food intake are stimulated, and pathways that promote food intake and hence weight gain are inhibited. When fat stores shrink, less leptin is released. Low leptin levels in the brain allow pathways that decrease energy expenditure and increase food intake to become active.[45] Unfortunately, leptin regulation, like other regulatory mechanisms, is much better at preventing weight loss than at defending against weight gain. Obese individuals generally have high levels of leptin, but these levels are not effective at reducing calorie intake and increasing energy expenditure[46] (**Figure 7.23**; see Science Applied: Leptin: Discovery of an Obesity Gene).

Hormonal signals involved in the long-term regulation of body weight act in the brain not only to favor shifts in energy balance, but also to affect the sensitivity of the brain to short-term signals of energy balance. For example, during weight loss, low levels of these hormones are hypothesized to decrease the efficacy of satiety signals, suppress pathways that cause weight loss, and activate pathways that contribute to weight gain.[47]

How Genes Contribute to Obesity

When a gene is defective, the protein it codes for is not made or is made incorrectly. When an obesity gene, such as the gene for leptin, is defective, the signals to decrease food intake and/or increase energy expenditure are not received, and weight gain results. A few cases of human obesity have been linked directly to defects in the genes for leptin and leptin receptors,[48] but mutations in single genes such as these are not responsible for most human obesity. Rather, variations in many genes interact with one another and affect metabolic rate, food intake, fat storage, and activity level. These in turn affect overall body shape and size.

SCIENCE

ScienceAppliedScienceApplied
Science**AppliedScience**Applied
ScienceAppliedScienceApplied
APPLIED

Leptin: Discovery of an Obesity Gene

A mouse with a defect in the leptin gene (*ob*) may weigh three times as much as a normal mouse. Both of these mice have defective *ob* genes but the one on the right was treated with leptin injections. (© AP/Wide World Photos)

A discovery made by Dr. Jeffrey Friedman and colleagues in 1994 brought hope to millions of people. Perhaps the cause of obesity had been found and a cure might be close behind. Was relief in sight for those who suffer from the physical and social consequences of obesity?

Dr. Friedman's work began with a strain of mice called *ob* for obese. *Ob* mice become grossly obese, gaining up to three times the normal body weight. The *ob* strain arose spontaneously in 1950 in the mouse colony at the Jackson Laboratory in Bar Harbor, Maine. Friedman and colleagues unraveled the cause for the obesity in this strain of mice when they identified and cloned the gene that was responsible.[1]

Researchers used a series of breeding experiments to localize the gene to a particular stretch of DNA. They then looked to see if any of the genes in this stretch of DNA were expressed in adipose tissue. The search yielded a single gene. Evidence that this gene was involved in the regulation of body weight was obtained by examining the gene and the protein it codes for in the *ob* mice. Researchers found that this protein, which they named leptin, was either not produced or produced in an inactive form in the obese mice. Soon afterward a similar gene was identified in humans.

Optimism about the role of the protein hormone leptin in human obesity was so great that a biotechnology firm (Amgen) paid $25 million for the commercial rights to leptin in the hope that it could be used to treat human obesity. Those hopes grew even higher when Friedman and colleagues were able to demonstrate that injections of the hormone could restore the genetically obese mice to normal weight (see figure).[2,3] Unfortunately, the role of leptin in human obesity has not lived up to expectations. Mutations in this gene are not responsible for most human obesity.[4] In fact, obese humans generally have high blood leptin levels.[5] High doses of leptin administered to obese humans produces only modest weight loss.[6]

The leptin receptor—a protein in the brain to which leptin must bind to produce weight reduction—was also identified.[7] The fact that obese humans have high levels of leptin suggested that the cause of human obesity might involve an abnormality in leptin receptors. If leptin receptors were defective, the leptin produced would have no place to bind and would not be able to signal mechanisms to promote weight reduction. Thus far, however, defective leptin receptors have not been found to be an important cause of human obesity.[8]

Continued study of the role of leptin in obesity has confirmed that it is an important signal involved in the long-term regulation of body fat, but it does not act alone. There are many steps, involving many genes, that occur between the production of leptin and alterations in food intake and energy expenditure. Researchers have discovered about a dozen molecules that interact with leptin in the brain to control appetite.[9] For example, neuropeptide Y and melanin-concentrating hormone boost appetite, whereas alpha-melanocyte stimulating hormone blunts appetite, and a protein called SOCS3 reduces the sensitivity of leptin receptors.

Despite the fact that the identification of leptin has not produced a cure for human obesity, its discovery lit up the field. This research was an important advance in our understanding of the genetics of body weight regulation. Continued work will someday answer the questions that remain about why some of us are obese and some of us are lean.

[1]Zhang, Y., Proenca, R., Maffei, M. et al. Positional cloning of the mouse obese gene and its human homologue. *Nature* 372:425–432, 1994.

[2]Halaas, J. L., Gajiwala, K. S., Maffei, M. et al. Weight-reducing effects of the plasma protein encoded by the obese gene. *Science* 269:543–546, 1995.

[3]Pelleymounter, M.A., Cullen, M. J., Baker, M. B. et al. Effects of the obese gene product on body weight regulation in *ob/ob* mice. *Science* 269:540–543, 1995.

[4]Montague, C.T., Farooqi, I. S., Whitehead, J. P. et al. Congenital leptin deficiency is associated with severe early onset obesity in children. *Nature* 387:903–908, 1997.

[5]Considine, R.V., Sinha, M. K., Heiman, M. L. et al. Serum immunoreactive-leptin concentrations in normal weight and obese humans. *N. Engl. J. Med.* 334:292–295, 1996.

[6]Gura, T. Obesity research: Leptin not impressive in clinical trial. *Science* 286:881–882, 1999.

[7]Tartaglia, L.A., Dembski, M., Weng X. et al. Identification and expression cloning of a leptin receptor, OB-R. *Cell* 83:1263–1271, 1995.

[8]Tsigos, C., Kyrou, I., and Raptis, S. A. Monogenic forms of obesity and diabetes mellitus. *J. Pediatr. Endocrinol. Metab.* 15:241–253, 2002.

[9]Gura, T. Tracing leptin's partners in regulating body weight. *Science* 287:1738–1741, 2000.

Thrifty Metabolism Many overweight people contend that they eat very few kcalories and yet continue to gain weight. This would imply that their energy expenditure is less than in normal-weight individuals. One possible explanation for this is that overweight individuals inherited a thrifty metabolism. An individual with a thrifty metabolism theoretically uses energy very efficiently so that more of the energy they consume is converted into ATP or deposited in energy stores than in someone with a less efficient metabolism. They would therefore need to eat less to maintain their body weight. Throughout human history, starvation has threatened survival. Over time, the human body has evolved ways to conserve body fat stores and prevent weight loss. Individuals with the "thriftiest" metabolism would have been more likely to survive. In the United States today, however, food is abundant, so people who inherited these "thrifty genes" are more likely to be obese.

Adaptive Thermogenesis The body has mechanisms that help keep weight at a specific set-point. When people overeat occasionally, their metabolism speeds up to burn the extra energy and prevent weight gain.[49,50,52] Conversely, when body weight is reduced by restricting food intake, energy expenditure decreases to conserve energy.[39] These changes in the amount of energy expended in response to changes in circumstance, such as over- or undereating, changes in environmental temperature, or trauma, are referred to as **adaptive thermogenesis**. Some studies found the drop in BMR seen with weight reduction was greater in obese than in lean subjects, and the increase in BMR seen with weight gain was less in obese than in lean subjects.[39] It has been proposed that these differences in the adaptive responses of lean versus obese subjects may help explain why some people gain weight more easily.

adaptive thermogenesis The change in energy expenditure induced by factors such as changes in ambient temperature and food intake.

Futile Cycling Several biochemical mechanisms have been proposed to explain adaptive thermogenesis. The first is substrate cycling or futile cycling, which wastes energy by allowing opposing biochemical reactions to occur simultaneously. For example, a molecule is formed, consuming ATP, and then is quickly broken down again. Energy is consumed but there is no net change in the number of molecules in the body, and therefore no storage of energy as fat.

Brown Adipose Tissue A second way that excess energy might be dissipated is by separating or uncoupling the electron transport chain from the production of ATP. When this occurs, energy is lost as heat rather than being used to produce ATP. For example, the increase in energy expenditure that occurs when mice are injected with leptin is believed to be due to the stimulation of receptors on a specialized type of adipose tissue called **brown adipose tissue**. Brown adipose tissue can waste energy as heat. This tissue contains many more mitochondria than regular white adipose tissue, and these mitochondria can be uncoupled from the electron transport chain allowing the energy in food to be released as heat. In rats, brown adipose tissue generates heat to prevent weight gain during overfeeding and to provide warmth when the ambient temperature is low. Significant amounts of brown adipose tissue are present in human infants, but until recently it was believed that adults did not have enough brown adipose tissue for it to be relevant physiologically. Newer technology now allows researchers to measure the amount of brown adipose tissue in adults. In a study of young men brown adipose tissue activity was found to be lower in overweight and obese men, suggesting that it may play a role in human obesity.[51]

brown adipose tissue A type of fat tissue that has a greater number of mitochondria than the more common white adipose tissue. It can waste energy by producing heat.

Level of Activity Activity burns kcalories; this is true whether the activity is planned exercise, or NEAT activities such as housework, walking between classes, fidgeting, and moving to maintain posture. How active you are is affected by your genes and your personal choices. Some people may gain weight more easily because they inherit a tendency to expend less energy on activity.[52] Even if they spend the same amount of time exercising as a lean person, their total energy expenditure may be lower because they expend less energy for NEAT activities (**Figure 7.24**). The impact of NEAT on weight gain was demonstrated by a study that overfed normal-weight

Figure 7.24 NEAT in obese versus lean individuals
Sedentary obese individuals were found to stand and walk less than sedentary lean individuals and therefore expended about 350 kcalories per day fewer than their lean counterparts. (Source: Levine, J.A., Lanningham-Foster L.M, McCrady S.K., et al. Interindividual variation in posture allocation: Possible role in human obesity. Science 307:584–586, 2005.)

individuals. There was a 10-fold variation in the amount of fat they gained. Some subjects were able to increase energy expenditure to a greater extent and so gained less fat. About two-thirds of the increase in energy expenditure that occurred with overfeeding was found to be due to an increase in unplanned exercise.[53] Those who gained the least weight had the greatest levels of involuntary exercise. The mechanisms that cause some people to respond to excess energy intake by becoming restless and increasing NEAT activity while others remain lethargic are still not understood.

7.7 Why Are Americans Getting Fatter?: Genes Versus Lifestyle

Learning Objectives

- Compare the impact of genetics and lifestyle on the "obesity epidemic."
- Discuss strategies to reduce the incidence of obesity.

The genes you inherit are an important determinant of what you weigh. If one or both of your parents is obese, your risk of becoming obese is increased. Individuals with a family history of obesity are two to three times more likely to be obese, and the risk increases with the magnitude of the obesity.[54] But even if you inherit genes that predispose you to being overweight, your weight is determined by the balance between the genes you inherit and the lifestyle choices you make. By studying identical twins, researchers have been able to determine that about 75% of the variation in BMI between individuals can be attributed to genes.[55] This means that the remaining 25% is determined by the environment in which you live and the lifestyle choices you make. Someone with a genetic predisposition to obesity who carefully monitors his or her diet and exercises regularly may never be obese, but someone with no genetic tendency toward obesity who consumes a high-energy diet and gets little exercise may end up overweight. When genetically susceptible individuals find themselves in an environment where food is appealing and plentiful and physical activity is easily avoided, obesity is a likely outcome.

An example of human obesity that clearly demonstrates the interaction of a genetic predisposition and an environment that is conducive to obesity is the Pima Indian tribe living in Arizona. The incidence of obesity in this population is much higher than in the general U.S. population. Studies have identified a number of genes that may be responsible for this group's tendency to store more body fat. Their current lifestyle demands little physical activity and includes many high-kcalorie foods. The outcome is the strikingly high incidence of obesity. In contrast, there is a genetically similar group of Pima Indians living in Mexico, but they are farmers who work in the fields and consume the food they grow. They still have higher rates of obesity than would be predicted from their diet and exercise patterns, suggesting genes that favor high body weight. However, they are significantly less obese than the Arizona Pima Indians.[56]

Lifestyle and Rising Obesity Rates

Although genes are an important determinant in what people weigh, they are not the reason more Americans are obese today than 30 years ago. The frequency of genes in a population takes many generations to change, but environmental conditions can change quickly. Significant environmental and social changes that have occurred in the United States over the past 50 years have caused lifestyle changes that affect what Americans eat, how much they eat, and how much exercise they get. Simply put, more Americans are overweight than ever before because they are eating more and burning fewer kcalories than they did in the past. Food is plentiful and continuously available and little activity is required in our daily lives.[57]

Americans are Eating More Part of the reason Americans are eating more is the increase in the availability of tempting food choices. Palatable, affordable, convenient food is readily available to the majority of the population 24 hours a day in supermarkets, fast-food restaurants, and convenience marts. The accessibility of enticing treats stimulates **appetite**. Appetite is the desire to eat that is not related to physiological hunger. It is triggered or inhibited by external factors such as the sight, taste, and smell of food, as well as the time of day, emotions, and cultural and social conventions. It is usually appetite and not hunger that makes us stop for an ice cream cone on a summer afternoon or buy chocolate chip cookies and cinnamon rolls while strolling through the mall. Americans today are constantly bombarded with cues to eat—we see and hear about tasty, inexpensive foods in TV ads and we see and smell tempting food in convenience stores, food courts, and vending machines.

appetite The desire to consume specific foods that is independent of hunger.

Not only have the variety, visibility, and convenience of tempting foods increased in the past 50 years, but so have the portion sizes.[58] Studies of how much people eat demonstrate that when more food is put in front of people, they eat more.[59] So if you increase the amount of pasta on your plate or cereal in your bowl you will most likely consume more kcalories. People tend to eat in units, such as one cookie, one sandwich, or one bag of chips, regardless of the size of the unit. So, when presented with larger units, such as bigger muffins, burgers, or bottles of soda, people still eat or drink the whole thing. As the portions offered have increased so has the amount Americans consume. As carbonated beverage standards went from a 12-ounce can to a 20-ounce bottle, beverage intake increased; energy intake from sweetened beverages alone increased 135% between 1977 and 2001.[60] One of the best examples of how portion size has increased is the food served at fast-food restaurants; the hamburger and french fries served today is two to five times bigger than it was when fast food was first introduced[61] (**Figure 7.25**). You probably wouldn't order an extra hamburger but you will finish the one you order even if it is twice as big.

Americans are also super-sizing at home but are not aware that they are. According to a survey by the American Dietetic Association, Americans overestimate the recommended serving size for many foods; fewer than half of respondents accurately estimated the recommended serving sizes for pasta, meat, and vegetables.[62] The serving size is listed on food labels, but people often assume that the kcalories

Figure 7.25 Larger portion sizes
The relative size of these two fast-food meals clearly illustrates the dramatic increase in portion sizes since the 1970s. (Source: Adapted from Nielsen, S. J. and Popkin, B. M. Patterns and trends in food portion sizes, 1977–1998. JAMA 289:450–453, 2003.) (Andy Washnik)

listed are for the entire container, even when the package contains 2 or more servings (see Off the Label: How Many Kcalories in that Bowl, Box, or Bottle?).

Social changes that have occurred over the last few decades have also contributed to the increase in the number of kcalories Americans consume. The increasing number of single-parent households and households with two working parents means that the time families have to prepare meals at home is limited. Fifty years ago hours of time and effort were invested in preparing meals. The main course might cook all afternoon and dessert was baked and served at the conclusion of the family meal. Today a fast-food meal can be in hand in a matter of minutes and getting a snack just involves opening a package. As a result of our fast-paced lifestyles, prepackaged, convenience, and fast food have become mainstays. These foods are typically higher in energy than meals prepared at home. The consequence of all these factors has been an increase in the average number of kcalories in the American diet.[63]

Americans are Exercising Less Along with the increase in energy intake, there has been a decrease in the amount of energy Americans expend, both at work and play. Fewer American adults today work in jobs that require physical labor. People drive to work, rather than walk or bike, take elevators instead of stairs, use dryers rather than hang clothes outside, and cut the lawn with riding rather than push mowers. All of these simple changes reduce the amount of energy expended to perform the tasks of daily living. A typical office worker today walks only about 3000 to 5000 steps in his or her daily activities. In contrast, in the Amish community where driving automobiles and using electrical appliances and other modern conveniences are not allowed, a typical adult takes 14,000 to 18,000 steps a day. The overall incidence of obesity in this group is only 4%.[64]

In addition to less-active jobs, busy schedules and long days at work and commuting make people feel they have no time for active recreation. Instead, at the end of the day Americans sit in front of televisions, electronic games, and computers—all sedentary ways to spend leisure time.

The reduction in physical activity is not restricted to adults. Many schools have reduced or even eliminated physical education programs to save money and find more time for academics. Social changes have increased crime, forcing children to stay inside after school. In the 1960s children spent their after school hours outdoors with bikes, balls, and friends. Today they are more likely to spend it indoors with video games and computers. The end result is that they burn fewer kcalories and have more opportunities to snack, and consequently they gain weight.

Life Cycle

Strategies to Reduce the Incidence of Obesity

To become a thinner nation, we need strategies that can help all Americans improve their food choices, reduce serving sizes, and increase their physical activity.[65] Although successful weight management ultimately depends on an individual's choices, food manufacturers and restaurants can help us cut kcalories by offering healthier foods and packaging or serving foods in smaller portions. Communities can help increase activity by providing parks, bike paths, and other recreational facilities for people of all ages. Businesses and schools can contribute by offering more opportunities for physical activity at the workplace and during the school day.

Even small changes, if they are consistent, can arrest the increase in obesity in the population. It has been estimated that a population-wide shift in energy balance of only 100 kcalories a day, the equivalent of walking a mile or cutting out a scoop of ice cream, would prevent further weight gain in the majority of the population[57] (see Critical Thinking: Balancing Energy: Genetics and Lifestyle).

7.8 Achieving and Maintaining a Healthy Body Weight

Learning Objectives

- Evaluate an individual's weight and medical history to determine whether weight loss is recommended.
- Discuss the recommendations for the rate and amount of weight loss.
- Name the three components of an ideal weight management plan.

Managing body weight to keep it within the healthy range involves a series of lifestyle choices. It requires maintaining a balance between kcalorie intake and exercise. For some people, this means making healthy food choices, controlling portion sizes, and maintaining an active lifestyle to avoid weight gain as they age. For many others, it may mean developing a meal and exercise plan that will allow their weight to decrease. And for some it may mean working to increase weight and then keep it in the healthy range. The goal for everyone is to achieve a healthy weight and stay there.

Who Should Lose Weight?

Not everyone who is a few pounds overweight will benefit from weight loss. The risks associated with overweight and obesity are related to the degree of excess weight or fat, the distribution of the excess body fat, the presence of other diseases or risk factors

Critical Thinking
Balancing Energy: Genetics and Lifestyle

Background

Aysha was a chubby child. As an adolescent she continued to be a little heavy. No one was surprised because her parents are both obese. At home her mother served healthy meals, but the family never missed dessert and the house was always stocked with plenty of high-kcalorie snack foods. Her mother spent her spare time sewing or knitting and her dad was more inclined to watch sports on TV than to participate in them. During her freshman year at college, Aysha gained 10 lbs and became resigned to the inevitability that she would be fat like her parents. Then she noticed that many of her thin friends made different dietary choices than she did and spent more of their free time being active. Since she was now in charge of all her lifestyle choices, she decided to make some changes.

(©iStockphoto)

Data

- Aysha is 5′4″ tall, 23 years old, and currently weighs 155 lbs.
- Aysha snacks while studying. She estimates that this adds about 350 kcalories a day to her intake.
- By keeping an activity log, Aysha estimates that a typical day includes 30 minutes of moderate-intensity activity. This puts her activity level in the "low-active" category. By recording and analyzing her food intake for 3 days, she determines that she eats about 2450 kcalories per day.

Critical Thinking Questions

Is Aysha overweight? Calculate her BMI.

▼

Is she in energy balance? Calculate her EER. How do her energy needs compare with her typical intake?

▼

If Aysha's weight does not change, but she increases her activity to 60 minutes per day, what will her new EER be?

▼

If she maintains the higher activity level, but doesn't change her intake, how long will it take her to lose 10 pounds (assume 3500 kcalories per pound)?

▼

Is she destined to be overweight based on her family history? Why or why not?

(Tim Mantoani/Masterfile)

iProfile   Use iProfile to find snacks that provide less than 100 kcalories.

that often accompany obesity, and the age and life stage of the individual (**Figure 7.26**). To determine if someone should lose weight the first step is to evaluate the person's current weight and weight history and review their medical conditions. If a person's BMI is above the healthy range it generally means that weight loss would improve long-term health, but this is not always the case. Some people with a high BMI, such as weight lifters, may have a large amount of muscle mass but not more body fat than is recommended. If, however, the high BMI is accompanied by an elevation in the proportion of body fat or an increase in waist circumference, weight loss is usually recommended.

Medical Risk Factors A key factor in whether or not weight loss is recommended is the presence of diseases and abnormalities associated with excess body fat (see Table 7.7). For example, blood pressure, blood glucose, and blood cholesterol levels all increase with body weight and, with these conditions, the risk of heart disease and diabetes increase as well. A person who's BMI is above the healthy range, and has two or more of these risk factors, will probably benefit from weight loss. A family history of these conditions is also a consideration in determining whether or not weight loss is recommended. Based on these criteria, not everyone who is a few pounds over ideal body weight needs to lose the extra weight. People who have a BMI in the overweight range (25 to 29.9 kg/m^2) but have none of the health conditions associated with excess body fat and have a healthy lifestyle may not benefit from the weight loss. For example, a person with a BMI of 28 kg/m^2 whose blood pressure and cholesterol levels are normal and who exercises regularly would not reduce his or her health risks by losing weight. For this individual weight management may mean simply preventing further weight gain. For others, this risk assessment may indicate that the excess body weight is a health risk and a weight-loss plan should be developed. For example, weight loss would be recommended for a person with a BMI of 28 kg/m^2 who has high blood pressure and high blood cholesterol levels.

Weight Loss and Life Stage Age and life stage are also important in determining the health risks associated with body weight and fat; at certain times of life weight loss is not recommended. For example, obesity and overweight is a growing problem among children. However, strict weight-loss diets are generally not recommended for children or adolescents because a reduction in intake can interfere with growth. A better approach is to encourage an increase in physical activity, along with

Life Cycle

Figure 7.26 Weight loss decisions
This simple flow chart illustrates some of the factors to consider when deciding if an individual will benefit from weight loss.

Life Cycle

a moderate restriction in energy intake. This will allow the child to grow in height with little additional weight gain (see Chapter 15). In addition, an increase in body weight in a growing child or teen may be followed by a growth spurt that puts BMI back in the healthy range without any intervention.

Weight-loss diets are also not recommended during pregnancy. Even women who are overweight or obese at the start of pregnancy should gain at a slow, steady rate over the course of pregnancy.[14] A weight-loss program can be initiated after the baby is born and the mother has recovered (see Chapter 14). Slow weight loss is appropriate during lactation, but rapid weight loss can decrease milk production.

In older adults a few extra pounds may provide a reserve that is beneficial in the event of a long-term illness. In addition, the risks associated with excess body fat are lower for older adults than they are for younger adults.[66] However, the decision to treat obesity should not be based on age alone. Weight loss can enhance day-to-day functioning and improve cardiovascular disease risk factors at all ages.[34] Older people tend to lose muscle and replace it with fat; therefore, weight-training activities are an important part of a weight-loss program in the elderly (see Chapter 16).

Weight-Loss Goals and Guidelines

The medical goal for weight loss in an overweight person is to reduce the health risks associated with being overweight. For most people, a loss of 5% to 15% of body weight will significantly reduce disease risk. The initial goal of weight loss should therefore be to reduce body weight by about 10% over a period of about 6 months.[33] A slow loss of 10% of body weight is considered achievable for most people. After this initial weight loss, the person's health risks can be reassessed to determine if additional weight loss would be beneficial. To ensure that most of what is lost is fat and not lean tissue, the weight should be lost slowly at a rate of between 0.5 and 2 lbs per week. If weight is lost more rapidly, the loss is less likely to be maintained, and the additional loss will be from fluid, glycogen, and muscle protein. Most people who lose large amounts of weight or lose weight rapidly eventually regain all that they have lost. Repeated cycles of weight loss and regain, referred to as **weight cycling** or **yo-yo dieting**, decrease the likelihood that future attempts at weight loss will be successful (**Figure 7.27**).[67]

Losing weight requires tipping the energy balance scale: eating less or exercising more. A pound of body fat provides about 3500 kcalories. Therefore, to lose a pound of fat, you need to decrease your intake or increase your expenditure by this amount. To lose a pound in a week, you would need to tip your energy balance by

weight cycling or **yo-yo dieting** The repeated loss and regain of body weight.

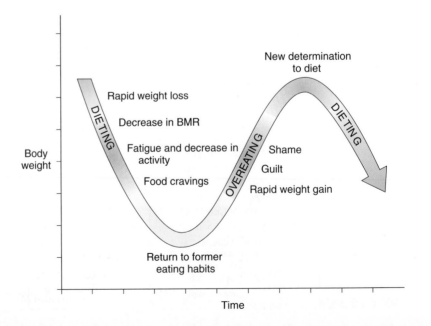

Figure 7.27 Weight cycling
Weight cycling, the repeated loss and regain of body weight, makes future attempts at weight loss less likely to succeed.

about 500 kcalories per day. This could mean adding 500 kcalories of exercise, subtracting 500 kcalories from your food intake, or some combination of the two. The arithmetic is simple, but achieving and maintaining weight loss is not easy. As discussed previously, there are regulatory mechanisms at work to keep body weight stable and there are environmental and emotional motivators to increase food intake and reduce the inclination to exercise. Nonetheless, reductions in intake, increases in activity, and changes in behavior can promote weight loss and long-term weight management (**Table 7.10**).

Table 7.10 Tips for Shifting Energy Balance Toward Weight Loss

Watch your serving size
- Pour one serving of chips into a bowl rather than eating right from the big bag
- Fill your plate once, skip the seconds
- Check labels to see if your serving size matches the label
- Don't super size—choose a small drink and a small order of fries
- Have a plain old burger, not one with a special sauce or extra large patty
- Don't overeat when you eat out—share an entrée with a friend or take it home for lunch the next day

Cut down on high-kcalorie foods
- Have one scoop of ice cream rather than two
- Use less butter or margarine on your toast
- Bake, roast, or grill, rather than fry your food
- Skip the baked goods and have fruit for dessert
- Bring your own lunch instead of buying lunch in the cafeteria
- Have an apple with lunch instead of a candy bar
- Have water instead of soda
- Switch to low-fat milk

Don't get too hungry
- Eat breakfast, you'll eat less later in the day
- Fill up on high-fiber foods
- Increase your vegetable servings
- Plan nutrient-dense snacks
- Keep cut up veggies and fruit available for snacks
- Cut down on high-fat and high-sugar choices

If you want to eat more—exercise more
- Go for a bike ride
- Try bowling instead of watching TV on Friday night
- Take a walk during your lunch break or after dinner
- Play tennis, you don't have to be good to get plenty of exercise
- Shoot some hoops
- Get off the bus one stop early

Decreasing Energy Intake In order to promote weight loss without compromising nutrient intake, an individual's diet must be low in energy but provide for all the body's nutrient needs. Nutrient density becomes more important as energy intake is reduced. The Dietary Guidelines suggest reducing kcalories from added sugars, solid fats, and alcohol, which provide kcalories but few essential nutrients.[32] Even when choosing nutrient-dense foods, it is difficult to meet nutrient needs with intakes of less than 1200 kcalories per day, therefore dieters consuming less than this should take a multivitamin and mineral supplement. Medical supervision is recommended if intake is 800 kcalories per day or less.

Increasing Physical Activity Physical activity is an important component of any weight-management program. Exercise promotes fat loss and weight maintenance. It increases energy expenditure, so if intake remains the same, energy stored as fat is used for fuel. An increase in activity of 200 kcalories five times a week will result in the loss of 1 lb in about 3½ weeks. In addition to increasing energy expenditure, exercise also promotes muscle development. This is important for promoting weight loss because muscle is metabolically active tissue. Increasing muscle mass helps to prevent the drop in metabolic rate that occurs as body weight decreases. Weight loss is better maintained when physical activity is included. In addition, physical activity improves overall fitness and relieves boredom and stress.

To promote health and prevent gradual weight gain in adulthood an hour of moderate to vigorous activity is recommended on most days.[32,68] For those who need to lose weight or have lost weight and want to keep it off, more than 60 minutes of moderate exercise per day may be necessary. The benefits of exercise are discussed further in Chapter 13.

Modifying Behavior People tend to think of weight loss as something they can accomplish by going on a diet. When the weight is lost they go off the diet. The problem is that when their eating patterns return to what they were previously they regain the weight. This "on a diet, off a diet" pattern may allow you to look good for the prom but it isn't what is needed for long-term weight management. To mange your weight at a healthy level, you need to establish a pattern of food intake and exercise that allows you to enjoy foods and activities you like without your weight climbing. It should be a pattern that you can comfortably adapt for life.

behavior modification
A process used to gradually and permanently change habitual behaviors.

Changing food consumption and exercise patterns requires identifying the old patterns that led to weight gain and replacing them with new ones to promote and maintain weight loss. This can be accomplished through a process called **behavior modification**, which is based on the theory that behaviors involve (1) Antecedents or cues that lead to the behavior, (2) the Behavior itself, and (3) Consequences of the behavior. These are referred to as the ABCs of behavior modification.

The first step in a behavior modification program is to identify cues that lead to eating. You can do this by keeping a log of everything you eat or drink, where you were when you ate, what else you were doing at the time, and what motivated you to eat at that time. Then by analyzing this log, you can see what prompted you to eat excessive amounts or high-kcalorie foods. For instance, sitting in front of the television and mindlessly demolishing a bag of potato chips may cause you to overeat and then feel bad because you consumed the extra kcalories (**Figure 7.28**). In this case, the antecedent is watching TV, the behavior is mindlessly eating the chips, and the consequence is feeling remorse and gaining weight. The key to modifying this behavior is to recognize the antecedent, change the behavior, and replace the negative consequence with a positive one. In this example, not taking food with you to the television, or taking only the portion of food you want to consume, eliminates the antecedent and the behavior. The consequence is that you have consumed only the food you planned, you do not gain weight, and you feel a sense of accomplishment. Applying behavior modification techniques to change eating behaviors has been shown to improve long-term weight maintenance.

Suggestions for Weight Gain

As difficult as weight loss is for some people, weight gain can be equally elusive for underweight individuals. The first step toward weight gain is a clinical evaluation to rule out medical reasons for low body weight. This is particularly important when weight loss occurs unexpectedly. If the low body weight is due to low intake or high expenditure, gradually increasing consumption of energy-dense foods is suggested. More frequent meals and high-kcalorie snacks such as nuts, peanut butter, or milkshakes between meals can help increase energy intake. Replacing low-kcalorie fluids like water and diet beverages with fruit juices and milk may also help. To encourage a gain in muscle rather than fat, strength-training exercise should be a component of

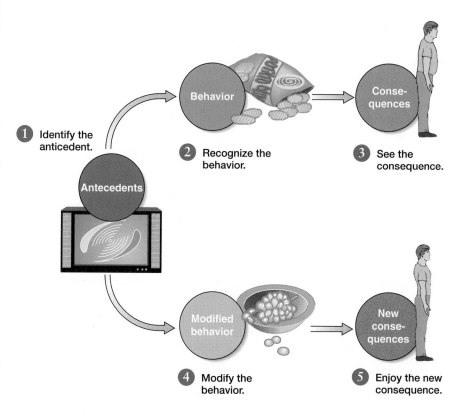

1. Identify the anticedent.

Antecedents

2. Recognize the behavior.

Behavior

3. See the consequence.

Conse-quences

4. Modify the behavior.

Modified behavior

5. Enjoy the new consequence.

New conse-quences

Figure 7.28 Behavior modification
Behavior modification can be used to identify and change undesirable behaviors.

any weight-gain program. This approach requires extra kcalories to fuel the activity needed to build muscles. These recommendations apply to individuals who are naturally thin and have trouble gaining weight on the recommended energy intake. This dietary approach may not promote weight gain for those who limit intake because of an eating disorder (see Focus on Eating Disorders).

7.9 Diets, Diets, Everywhere

Learning Objectives

- Distinguish between a healthy weight management program and a fad diet.
- Discuss the importance of the proportions of carbohydrate, protein, and fat in a weight loss plan.

Want to lose ten pounds in just 5 days? What dieter wouldn't? People desperate to lose weight are prey to all sorts of diets that promise quick fixes. They willingly eat a single-food for days at a time, select foods based on special fat-burning qualities, and consume odd combinations at specific times of the day. Most diets, no matter how outlandish, will promote weight loss because they reduce energy intake. Even diets that focus on modifying fat or carbohydrate intake or promise to allow unlimited amounts of certain foods work because intake is reduced. The true test of the effectiveness of a weight-loss diet is whether those who follow it maintain their weight loss over the long term.

An ideal diet is one that is part of a weight-management program that promotes weight loss and then maintenance of that loss over the long term. To be successful the program needs to encourage changes in the lifestyle patterns that led to weight gain. When selecting a program look for one that is based on sound nutrition and exercise principles, suits your individual food preferences, promotes long-term lifestyle changes, and meets your needs in terms of cost, convenience, and time commitment (**Table 7.11**). While quick fixes are tempting, if the program's approach is not one that can be followed for a lifetime, it is unlikely to promote successful weight management.

Table 7.11 Distinguishing Between Healthy Diets and Fad Diets

A healthy diet ...	A fad diet ...
Promotes a healthy dietary pattern that meets nutrient needs, includes a variety of foods, suits food preferences, and can be maintained throughout life.	Limits food selections to a few food groups or promotes rituals such as eating only specific food combinations. As a result, it may be limited in certain nutrients and in variety.
Promotes a reasonable weight loss of 0.5 to 2 pounds per week and does not restrict Calories to under 1200 a day.	Promotes rapid weight loss of much more than 2 pounds per week.
Promotes or includes physical activity.	Advertises weight loss without the need to exercise.
Is flexible enough to be followed when eating out and includes foods that are easily obtained.	May require a rigid menu or avoidance of certain foods or may include "magic" foods that promise to burn fat or speed up metabolism.
Does not require costly supplements.	May require the purchase of special foods, weight-loss patches, expensive supplements, creams, or other products.
Promotes a change in behavior. Teaches new eating habits. Provides social support.	Does not recommend changes in activity and eating habits, recommends an eating pattern that is difficult to follow for life, provides little social support.
Is based on sound scientific principles and may include monitoring by qualified health professionals.	Makes outlandish and unscientific claims, does not support claims that it is clinically tested or scientifically proven, claims that it is new and improved or based on some new scientific discovery, or relies on testimonials from celebrities or connects the diet to trendy places such as Beverly Hills.

Video

The following sections discuss some of the more common methods for reducing kcalorie intake. The advantages and disadvantages of a number of popular diets and commercial weight-management programs are given in **Table 7.12**.

Food Exchanges

Diets that are based on exchanges instruct the dieter to select a certain number of servings from specific food groups in order to limit kcalorie intake while providing an adequate balance of nutrients. For example, for breakfast the dieter might be instructed to choose one food from group A, one from group B, and two from group C. The foods in these groups or exchanges are similar in their energy and nutrient content so they can be exchanged for one another. Some diet plans use the Exchange Lists established by the American Diabetes Association and American Dietetic Association (see Table 7.2 and Appendix I). Others, such as Weight Watchers, have developed their own "systems" by which to limit kcalorie intake. These programs offer variety from meal to meal and from day to day and if carefully planned are likely to meet nutrient needs. In addition, they teach meal-planning skills that are easy to apply away from home and can be used over the long term.

Prepared Meals and Drinks

It is easier to eat less when someone else decides what you're having and puts appropriate portions of that food in front of you (**Figure 7.29**). This is the idea behind diet plans that sell prepackaged meals designed to replace some or all of your usual meals. These diets are easy to follow as long as you are not traveling or eating out, but they can be expensive and are not practical in the long term. Because all meals are provided, they do not teach the food selection skills needed to make a long-term lifestyle change.

Table 7.12 Pros and Cons of Some Commercial Weight Loss Diets

Diet	Approach	Pros	Cons
Weight Watchers	Low energy, social support	Safe, inexpensive, flexible	Requires group participation for optimal results
Jenny Craig	Low energy	Safe, convenient	Expensive; relies on purchase of special foods
SlimFast	Low energy	Safe	Does not promote long-term behavior change
The New Beverly Hills Diet	Specific timing and combinations of foods	Inexpensive	Based on unusual principles; does not promote long-term behavior change; nutritionally unsound
Optifast	Very-low-kcalorie formula	Rapid weight loss	Expensive; dangerous if does not include medical supervision
Fit or Fat	Increased exercise	Safe, inexpensive	No social support
The Zone (and Mastering the Zone) Diet	Low carbohydrate (40% of energy)	Inexpensive, flexible	Based on questionable principles; no social support
Eating Thin for Life	Moderation—written as weight-loss success stories, recipes, and menu ideas	Inexpensive	No social support
Dieting with the Duchess	Simple nutrition and exercise tips	Inexpensive, flexible	No social support
Cabbage soup diet	Unlimited amounts of cabbage soup, fruit, coffee, and tea	Rapid weight loss	No social support; does not promote long-term behavior change; lacks variety
Grapefruit diet	Some foods have special qualities that burn fat	Inexpensive	Based on unsound principles
Sugar Busters	Eliminates sugar; low kcalorie— 1200 kcal per day	Inexpensive	No social support; based on unsound principles; insufficient carbohydrate
Volumetrics Weight Control Plan	Emphasizes foods high in water, fiber, and air to promote fullness with few kcalories	Safe, inexpensive	No social support or exercise component
Atkins' Diet	Very low carbohydrate	Inexpensive; rapid initial weight loss	Difficult to follow in the long term; no social support
South Beach Diet	Initially very low carbohydrate, then more healthy carbohydrates are allowed	Safe, inexpensive, heart-healthy	Initial weight loss is mostly water; no social support

Figure 7.29 Frozen prepared meals are popular with dieters because the food is preportioned and no decisions or measuring are required. (David Young Wolff/PhotoEdit)

Over-the-Counter Diet Drinks Rather than a prepackaged meal, many diet plans replace some or all meals with special beverages. They can make reducing intake easy because they eliminate the problem of choosing appropriate portions of low-kcalorie foods. Many of the liquid weight-loss diets that are available over-the-counter recommend a combination of food and the liquid formula to provide about 800 to 1200 kcalories per day. These formula plans promote weight loss as long as the foods eaten with them are low in kcalories. They are easy to use and relatively inexpensive, but they do little to change eating habits for life. Most diet programs that rely exclusively on liquid formulas have high dropout rates and poor long-term weight-maintenance results. These are not recommended without medical supervision.

very-low-kcalorie diet
A weight-loss diet that provides fewer than 800 kcalories per day.

protein-sparing modified fast A very-low-kcalorie diet with a high proportion of protein, designed to maximize the loss of fat and minimize the loss of protein from the body.

Very-Low-Kcalorie Diets A **very-low-kcalorie diet** is defined as one with fewer than 800 kcalories per day. These diets are generally a variation of the **protein-sparing modified fast**, which is a diet providing a high proportion of protein, but little energy. The concept behind this is that the protein in the diet will be used to meet the body's protein needs and will, therefore, prevent excessive loss of body protein. Frequently, very-low-kcalorie diets are offered as a liquid formula. These formulas provide from 300 to 800 kcalories and 50 to 100 grams of protein per day and meet all other nutrient needs.

These diets will cause rapid weight loss; initial weight loss is 3 to 5 lbs per week. This can provide a psychological boost and motivate the dieter to continue losing weight; however, in most cases, much of this initial weight loss is from water loss. Once the initial water loss ends, weight loss slows. The dieter's basal metabolism slows to conserve energy, and physical activity decreases because the dieter often does not have the energy to continue his or her typical level of activity.

Very-low-kcalorie diets are no more effective than other methods of weight loss in the long term and carry more risks. At these low-energy intakes, body protein is broken down and potassium is excreted. Depletion of potassium can result in an irregular heartbeat and is potentially deadly. Other side effects include gallstones, fatigue, nausea, cold-intolerance, light-headedness, nervousness, constipation or diarrhea, anemia, hair loss, dry skin, and menstrual irregularities. These diets are not recommended for people with a BMI < 30 kg/m^2, for children, adolescents, pregnant or breast-feeding women, or for those with severe medical problems.[69] Since 1984, the FDA has required that all very-low-kcalorie diet formulas carry a warning that they can cause serious illness and should be used only under medical supervision.

Low-Fat Diets

Low-fat weight-loss diets have been popular for decades. Fat is high in energy: 9 kcalories per gram—almost twice as much as either carbohydrate or protein. Low-fat diets therefore tend to provide a greater volume of food for less energy than a diet with more fat. Because people have a tendency to eat a certain weight or volume of food—if that food is low in fat it will contribute fewer kcalories.[70] Low-fat diets also satisfy hunger after less energy is consumed. Differences in the way dietary fat and dietary carbohydrate are used by the body also explain why low-fat diets are more effective for weight loss. Excess kcalories from dietary fat are stored more efficiently than excess kcalories from carbohydrate, so consuming excess energy from fat leads to a greater accumulation of body fat than consuming excess energy as carbohydrate. Short-term clinical trials demonstrate that a reduction in fat without intentional energy restriction leads to a decrease in energy intake and a modest reduction in body weight.[71,72] Although there are no long-term clinical trials on the effect of a low-fat diet on body weight, they are believed to be as effective as other diets for long-term weight loss.

Problems with low-fat diets occur when people eat large quantities of low-fat foods without considering that these foods are not necessarily low in kcalories. Even a diet low in fat will result in weight gain if energy intake exceeds energy output. In the 1990s the food industry flooded the market with reduced-fat cookies and cakes. These foods were low in fat, but not in energy, so when consumed in large amounts they caused weight gain, not weight loss.

Low-Carbohydrate Diets

If you cut out the pasta and potatoes you will lose weight, right? The Atkins' Diet, South Beach Diet, Sugar-Busters, Calories Don't Count, the Scarsdale Diet, and the Zone are just a few of the low-carbohydrate weight-loss diets that have been promoted over the past 50 years. In addition to promising weight loss, these diets claim to improve athletic performance and promote overall health. Low-carbohydrate diets are all based on the premise that a high-carbohydrate intake causes an increase in insulin levels, which promotes the storage of body fat. Restricting carbohydrate intake is hypothesized to reduce insulin, thereby reducing fat storage and promoting fat loss. Unfortunately, the relationship between carbohydrate intake, insulin levels, and body fat is not that simple. Some of these diets severely limit carbohydrate intake while others are less restrictive and are more concerned with the type of carbohydrate.

Very-Low-Carbohydrate Diets Very restrictive low-carbohydrate diets prohibit foods such as breads, grains, and fruits, and limit vegetable intake while allowing unlimited quantities of meat and high-fat foods that are low in carbohydrate. These diets cause a rapid initial weight loss, most of which is water. This occurs because when carbohydrate intake is low, glycogen stores, along with the water they hold, are lost quickly. Ketones are produced because fat is not completely broken down in the absence of carbohydrate. Excretion of these ketones causes further water loss.

Weight loss continues on low-carbohydrate diets because total energy intake is reduced. Elevated blood ketones and reduced insulin levels suppress appetite, making it easier to reduce food intake. In addition, these diets limit food choices to such an extent that the monotony results in a spontaneous reduction in energy intake.[73] The availability of carbohydrate-modified products such as low-carbohydrate bread and pasta makes these diets more palatable, but may also make them less effective. As with special low-fat products, low-carbohydrate foods are not necessarily low in kcalories and cannot be eaten liberally without affecting energy balance (see Critical Thinking: Choosing a Weight Loss Plan that Works for You).

Although these diets do promote weight loss, more research is needed to determine the health consequences of consuming very low-carbohydrate diets for long periods. These diets are higher in fat and protein than is recommended. High intakes of saturated fat and cholesterol increase the risk of high blood cholesterol and gallbladder disease. They are also lower in fruits, vegetables, whole grains, and milk than is recommended. Low intakes of these foods will reduce intakes of essential nutrients, phytochemicals, and fiber.

Including Unrefined Carbohydrate Not all low-carbohydrate diets severely restrict carbohydrate and most allow the dieter to increase carbohydrate intake over time. The carbohydrates that are included come from unrefined sources such as vegetables and whole grains. These foods are high in fiber and do not increase blood glucose and insulin levels nearly as much as refined carbohydrates such as white flour and sugar. Including whole grains and vegetables in the diet increases the intake of fiber, phytochemicals, and micronutrients and has only a modest effect on insulin levels.

Critical Thinking
Choosing a Weight Loss Plan that Works for You

Background

Rose has gained 40 lbs over the past few years. She wants to lose weight. She researches her options and narrows her choice of weight loss programs to three. To decide which weight-loss program is best for her, Rose considers the advantages and disadvantages of each plan in terms of the nutritional soundness of the diet, variety, ease, expense, and how it will affect her activity level.

(©iStockphoto)

Data

Rose's Information

BMI: 31 kg/m^2
Waist circumference: 36 inches
Blood pressure: 160/92
Total cholesterol: 235 mg/100 mL
LDL cholesterol: 165 mg/100 mL
Activity: plays golf once a month using a golf cart

Weight-loss Options

Low-carbohydrate plan This plan limits carbohydrate intake to 30 g per day—this means she cannot eat any grains, milk, or fruit. Many of her friends have used this to shed pounds and say they were never hungry.
Liquid formula plan This plan uses cans of formula to replace 2 meals a day. A one week supply costs $10.00. It is easy because she doesn't need to do much meal planning and she can still eat dinner with her family.
Exchange plan This plan is run through her community center. It includes a walking group that meets 5 days a week and weekly meetings for weigh-ins and nutrition lectures. The cost is $25.00 per week.

Critical Thinking Questions

Would Rose benefit from weight loss based on the data given about her in the table?

▼

Evaluate the programs she is considering: are the diets nutritionally sound? Do they recommend activity and include social support? What about cost?

▼

Which plan do you think would benefit Rose most in the long term?

 iProfile   Use iProfile to look up the kcalorie content of a liquid weight loss product.

7.10 Weight-Loss Drugs and Surgery

Learning Objectives

* Explain how surgery can promote weight loss.
* Discuss when weight-loss drugs or surgery might be considered appropriate.

Anyone who has battled a weight problem has probably dreamed of a solution that would melt away the pounds without having to measure every morsel that passes their lips. Unfortunately, there is no magic weight-loss cure but prescription medications and surgery can be acceptable weight-management tools for obese individuals when diet and exercise alone are not enough. However, such drastic measures are not for everyone.

Drugs and Supplements

A few drug therapies are available to promote weight loss. Some are well studied and offer legitimate aids to weight loss; others offer little more than water loss. An ideal drug for the treatment of obesity would permit an individual to lose weight and maintain the loss, be safe when used for long periods of time, have no side effects, and not be addictive. Many attempts have been made to develop such a drug, but weight-loss drugs still carry risks. For example, in 1996, approximately 18 million prescriptions were written for a drug combination called *fen-phen* (fenfluramine and phentermine) that was being used to reduce food intake. The following year, it was linked to serious heart valve damage. As a result, fenfluramine and the related drug dexfenfluramine were withdrawn from the market.[74]

Prescription and Nonprescription Drugs Prescription drugs available for the treatment of obesity include those that decrease food intake by affecting the activity of brain neurotransmitters (sibutramine, brand name Meridia) and those that decrease energy intake by reducing fat absorption (orlistat, brand name Xenical). Prescription drugs such as these are recommended only for those whose health is seriously compromised by their body weight: those with a BMI greater than 30 kg/m^2 and those with a BMI greater than or equal to 27 kg/m^2 who have obesity-related risk factors or diseases.[33] One of the major disadvantages of drug treatment is that even if the drug promotes weight loss in the short term, the weight is regained when the drugs are discontinued.

Like prescription drugs, nonprescription medications sold over-the-counter to promote weight loss are regulated by the FDA and must adhere to strict guidelines regarding the dose per pill and the effectiveness of the ingredients. Only a limited number of substances have been approved by the FDA for sale as nonprescription weight-loss medications. One of these is a nonprescription version of orlistat, called Alli® (**Figure 7.30**). It acts by disabling the enzyme lipase, preventing triglycerides from being digested into fatty acids and glycerol. The undigested triglycerides continue through the intestines and are eliminated in the feces. This cuts the number of kcalories available to the body, but the fat in the stool may cause gas, diarrhea, and more frequent and hard-to-control bowel movements. As with prescription medications, any weight loss that occurs with over-the-counter weight-loss medications is usually regained when the product is no longer consumed.

Dietary Supplements The FDA does not regulate dietary supplements, including those for weight loss, unless they claim to be a substitute for a drug or to perform a drug action or therapy (see Chapter 2). As with other dietary supplements, the manufacturers of weight-loss supplements are not required to provide proof of their products' safety and efficacy before they are marketed.

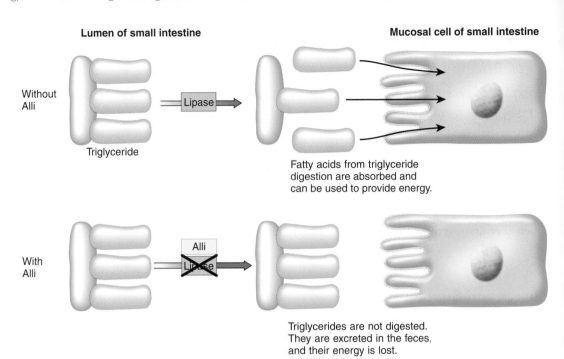

Lumen of small intestine

Mucosal cell of small intestine

Without Alli

Lipase

Triglyceride

Fatty acids from triglyceride digestion are absorbed and can be used to provide energy.

With Alli

Alli
~~Lipase~~

Triglycerides are not digested. They are excreted in the feces, and their energy is lost.

Figure 7.30 Alli and fat digestion
Alli is an over-the-counter weight loss aid that acts by preventing triglyceride digestion.

Over 100 individual dietary supplements and proprietary products are commonly used for weight loss.[75] Overweight patients are attracted to these supplements for a number of reasons. Some see them as an alternative to conventional approaches that have failed them in the past. Many believe that since they are natural they are safer than prescription drugs. Unfortunately, it cannot be assumed that a product is safe simply because it is labeled "herbal" or "all natural" (**Table 7.13**). Some of these are powerful drugs with dangerous side effects. These products are also popular because of their cost and accessibility (see Your Choice: Can a Weight-Loss Supplement Help You Trim Pounds?).

Bariatric Surgery

There are a number of surgical weight-loss procedures available. These bariatric surgeries cause weight loss because they alter the GI tract to reduce food intake and nutrient absorption. Such surgical approaches are only recommended for individuals in whom the risk of dying from obesity and its complications is great. Generally this includes those with a BMI greater than or equal to 40 kg/m^2 (extreme obesity) and those with a BMI between 35 and 40 kg/m^2 who have other life-threatening conditions that could be remedied by weight loss. Each case must be evaluated individually to assess the potential risks and benefits of the surgery, but it is usually recommended only for those who have tried other methods and failed and whose weight severely limits their quality of life and ability to perform daily activities. To be successful, the individual must understand the procedure and its risks and be aware of how his or her life may change after the operation. Even after surgery, success requires a lifelong behavioral commitment that includes well-balanced eating and physical activity.

gastric banding A surgical procedure in which an adjustable band is placed around the upper portion of the stomach to limit the volume that the stomach can hold and the rate of stomach emptying.

Types of Surgical Procedures Weight-loss surgery may restrict the amount of food that can be consumed, limit the amount that can be absorbed, or both. **Gastric banding** is a procedure that just restricts food intake. It uses an adjustable band to create a small

Table 7.13 Common Weight-Loss Supplements

Supplement	Proposed Action	Effectiveness and Safety
Apple cider vinegar	Increases energy expenditure, reduces hunger and food cravings	Safe, but no evidence that it has any affect on body weight.
Bitter orange	Increases energy expenditure	Does promote weight loss. May increase the risk of hypertension, arrhythmias, heart attacks, strokes, and seizure.
Cascara, senna, aloe, buckthorn, rhubarb root, and castor oil	Increase water loss	Do not cause fat loss and overuse can cause diarrhea, vomiting, stomach cramps, chronic constipation, fainting, and severe electrolyte imbalances.
Chitosan	Blocks fat absorption	Has not been shown to enhance weight loss. Short-term human trials have not reported any severe adverse effect. No long-term studies have been done.
Chromium	Affects carbohydrate metabolism	Human trials have not demonstrated an effect on body composition or body weight. No reports of adverse effects in humans.
Conjugated linoleic acid (CLA)	Increases fat oxidation or reduces fat synthesis	No evidence that it is effective for weight loss in humans. It causes gastrointestinal symptoms.
Country mallow	Increases energy expenditure	Does promote weight loss. May increase the risk of hypertension, arrhythmias, heart attacks, strokes, and seizure.
Dandelion	Increases water loss	Does not cause fat loss. No side effects other than rare allergic reactions.
Ginseng	Affects carbohydrate metabolism	No evidence that it enhances weight loss. Side effects include diarrhea, headache, insomnia, changes in blood pressure, and altered bleeding time.
Glucomannan	Increases satiety	Safe, but has not been shown to promote weight loss.
Green tea	Increases fat oxidation or reduces fat synthesis	Safe, but no evidence from controlled clinical trials that tea or tea extracts promote weight loss.
Guar gum	Increases satiety	Safe, but has not been shown to promote weight loss.
Guggul	Boosts metabolism by stimulating thyroid activity	No human studies support the claim that it boosts thyroid activity. Side effects include gastrointestinal upset, headache, nausea, and hiccups.
Guarana	Suppresses appetite	It contains caffeine (about twice as much as coffee beans) and has been shown to be effective for short-term weight loss when used in combination with ephedra. Side effects include anxiety, nervousness, and difficulty sleeping.
Hydroxycitric acid (extract from *Garcinia cambogia*)	Increases fat oxidation or reduces fat synthesis	Not found to be effective. Side effects include a laxative effect, abdominal pain, and vomiting.
L-carnitine	Increases fat oxidation	Not found to significantly affect total body mass or fat mass. Side effects include nausea, vomiting, abdominal cramps, diarrhea, and body odor.
Licorice	Increases fat oxidation or reduces fat synthesis	Has been shown to reduce body fat in normal-weight subjects but causes high blood pressure and low blood potassium.
Psyllium	Increases satiety	Safe, but has not been shown to promote weight loss.
Pyruvate	Increases fat oxidation or reduces fat synthesis	Some studies have shown a weight-loss benefit in individuals on weight-loss diets, but the dosage used in the studies was very high. No known side effects
Spirulina (blue-green algae)	Suppresses appetite	Safe, but no evidence that it aids weight loss.
St. John's wort	Enhances mood	No evidence it promotes weight loss. Contains similar ingredients to the antidepressant drug fluoxetine (Prozac) and should not be used by people taking antidepressants.
Yerba maté	Increases energy expenditure	No studies supporting its benefit for weight loss. Side effects include nervousness, dehydration, and nausea.
Yohimbine	Suppresses appetite and the body's ability to store fat	No evidence that it aids weight loss. Potential side effects include anxiety, elevated blood pressure, a feeling of queasiness, insomnia, rapid heartbeat, tremors, and vomiting.

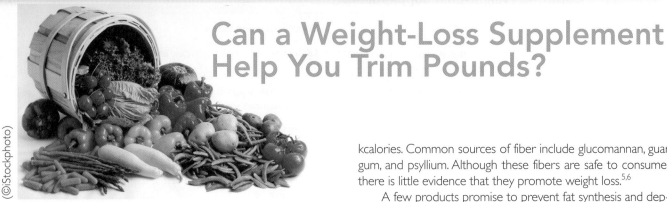

Can a Weight-Loss Supplement Help You Trim Pounds?

(©iStockphoto)

Losing weight is not easy, and keeping it off is even harder. Wouldn't it be nice if there were a pill that you could take to help lose the weight and keep it off? A walk through any supermarket, pharmacy, or supplement store will reveal an assortment of supplements that advertise to do just this. But are they safe and do they work?

Some weight-loss supplements claim to increase metabolism. These "fat burners" promise not only to boost metabolism, but also to prevent the loss of lean muscle tissue, suppress appetite, and increase the burning of stored fat. Although they are probably the most effective over-the-counter weight-loss supplements, they are also the most dangerous. One of the most popular and controversial herbal fat burners is ephedra, a stimulant that increases blood pressure and heart rate and constricts blood vessels. Use of ephedra-containing products has been associated with an increased risk of psychiatric, nervous, and gastrointestinal symptoms, heart palpitations, hypertension, arrhythmias, heart attacks, strokes, and seizure.[1] Due to these safety concerns, ephedra was banned by the FDA in 2004. Despite legal challenges the sale of ephedra-containing dietary supplements remains illegal in the United States.[2]

After ephedra was removed from the market supplement manufacturers substituted other herbal products, such as bitter orange that contain similar stimulants and therefore may have similar side effects.[3] Fat burners also typically contain guarana, an herbal source of caffeine. Green tea extract is another popular supplement used to boost metabolism and aid weight loss. It appears to be safe if used in appropriate amounts, but studies have not shown it to enhance weight loss.[4]

Some weight loss supplements contain soluble fiber, which absorbs water so your stomach fills up after consuming fewer kcalories. Common sources of fiber include glucomannan, guar gum, and psyllium. Although these fibers are safe to consume, there is little evidence that they promote weight loss.[5,6]

A few products promise to prevent fat synthesis and deposition. Hydroxycitric acid supplements are marketed to block fat synthesis. Although few side effects have been reported, evidence for its effectiveness for weight loss is inconsistent.[6] Conjugated linoleic acid has been shown to reduce body weight and/or fat deposition in animal models.[7] However, there is no evidence that it is effective for weight loss in humans, and it causes gastrointestinal symptoms. Chromium picolinate is marketed to decrease body fat and increase the proportion of lean tissue. Human trials, however, have not supported these claims. There are no reports of adverse effects in humans, but laboratory studies show that the picolinate form may cause oxidative damage to DNA and lipids.[8]

Supplements containing chitosan, which is derived from a molecule found in the shells of crustaceans, claim to block fat absorption. Results of most clinical trials have not shown any increase in weight loss, however, and healthy people taking chitosan do not show increased fecal fat excretion.[9]

Several supplements cause weight loss by increasing the amount of water lost from the body. Water loss decreases body weight but does not cause a decrease in body fat. Dandelion is a diuretic, so it increases water excretion by the kidneys. Other herbal products induce diarrhea, which causes water loss through the GI tract. Herbal laxatives found in weight-loss teas and supplements include senna, aloe, buckthorn, rhubarb root, cascara, and castor oil. Overuse of these substances can have serious side effects, including nausea, diarrhea, vomiting, and electrolyte imbalances, leading to cardiac arrhythmia and death.[10]

In short, if a secret pill could safely help people eat less or burn more kcalories without effort, it would not be a secret for long. The best and safest way to lose weight is to eat less and exercise more.

[1]Shekelle, P. G., Hardy, M. L., Morton, S. C. et al. Efficacy and safety of ephedra and ephedrine for weight loss and athletic performance: A meta-analysis. *JAMA* 289: 1537–1545, 2003.

[2] U.S. Food and Drug Administration. *Sales of Supplements Containing Ephedrine Alkaloids (Ephedra) Prohibited.* Available online at www.fda.gov/oc/initiatives/ephedra/february2004/. Accessed January 11, 2009.

[3]Hess, A. M., and Sullivan, D. L. Potential for toxicity with use of bitter orange extract and guarana for weight loss. *Ann. Pharmacother.* 39:574–575, 2005.

[4]Sarma D. N., Barrett, M. L., Chavez, M. L. et al. Safety of green tea extracts: A systematic review by the U.S. Pharmacopeia. *Drug Saf.* 31:469–484, 2008.

[5]Pittler, M. H., and Ernst, E. Dietary supplements for body-weight reduction: A systematic review. *Am. J. Clin. Nutr.* 79:529–536, 2004.

[6]Saper, R. B., Eisenberg, D. M., and Phillips, R. S. Common dietary supplements for weight loss. *Am. Fam. Physician* 70:1731–1738, 2004.

[7]Li, J. J., Huang, C. J., and Xie, D. Anti-obesity effects of conjugated linoleic acid, docosahexaenoic acid, and eicosapentaenoic acid. *Mol. Nutr. Food Res.* 52:631–645, 2008.

[8]Vincent, J. B. The potential value and toxicity of chromium picolinate as a nutritional supplement, weight loss agent and muscle development agent. *Sports Med.* 33:213–230, 2003.

[9]Gades, M. D., and Stern, J. S. Chitosan supplementation and fecal fat excretion in men. *Obes. Res.* 11:683–688, 2003.

[10]Kurtzweil, P. Dieter's brews make tea time a dangerous affair. *FDA Consumer* 31: July–August, 1997. Available online at www.fda.gov/fdac/features/1997/597_tea.html/. Accessed February 18, 2001.

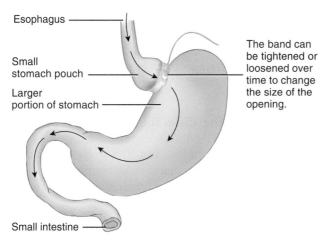

Figure 7.31 Gastric banding
Gastric banding involves surgically placing an adjustable band around the upper part of the stomach, creating a small pouch.

pouch at the upper end of the stomach (**Figure 7.31**). This new smaller stomach, which typically holds about one ounce, limits the amount of food that can be comfortably consumed at one time and slows the rate at which food leaves the stomach. Another procedure, called **gastric bypass**, bypasses part of the stomach and small intestine. It is currently the most common and most successful type of bariatric surgery. Gastric bypass connects the intestine to the upper, smaller portion of the stomach. The smaller stomach limits intake and the shorter intestine reduces absorption (**Figure 7.32**). Individuals who have any of these procedures must make permanent changes in their eating habits and experience permanent changes in their bowel habits. Some weight regain is common after 2 to 5 years.

Liposuction is another surgical procedure, but it is primarily a cosmetic one. It involves inserting a large hollow needle under the skin into a localized fat deposit and literally vacuuming out the fat. It is often advertised as a way to remove cellulite, which is just fat that has a lumpy appearance because of the presence of connections to the tissue layers below. The risks of liposuction include those associated

gastric bypass A surgical procedure to treat morbid obesity that both reduces the size of the stomach and bypasses a portion of the small intestine.

liposuction A procedure that suctions out adipose tissue from under the skin; used to decrease the size of local fat deposits such as on the abdomen or hips.

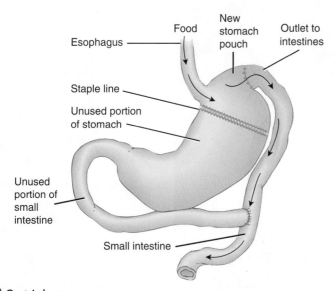

Figure 7.32 Gastric bypass surgery
Gastric bypass surgery reduces the size of the stomach by placing staples across the top of the stomach. It reduces absorption by attaching the stomach pouch to the small intestine, bypassing a portion of the intestine.

with general anesthesia and the possibility of infection. The procedure can reduce the amount of fat in a specific location, but will not significantly reduce overall body weight. Liposuction has not been found to affect obesity-related metabolic abnormalities, and therefore, unlike overall weight loss, it does not reduce the risk of heart disease and diabetes that is associated with excess body fat.[76]

Weighing the Benefits and the Risks The most obvious benefit of bariatric surgery is weight loss (**Figure 7.33**). Ninety percent of individuals have a significant (20% to 25% of body weight) weight loss and 50% to 80% maintain this loss for at least 5 years.[69] The weight loss occurs quickly and continues for about 2 years after surgery. With this weight loss comes a reduction in the presence and risk of diseases related to obesity such as diabetes, high blood pressure, and heart disease. Other benefits commonly reported include improved mobility and stamina, better mood, and increased self-esteem and interpersonal effectiveness. These benefits, however, do not come without a price.

Gastric banding and gastric bypass have short-term surgical risks and complications. Complications that require follow-up surgeries include abdominal hernias, the breakdown of the staple line, and stretched stomach outlets. More than one-third of obese patients who have weight-loss surgery develop gallstones; the risk is increased during rapid or substantial weight loss. Many patients develop "dumping syndrome"—a condition in which food moves too rapidly into the small intestine, causing nausea, weakness, sweating, faintness, and diarrhea after eating. To avoid dumping syndrome patients must eat small, frequent meals and avoid foods that cause problems. Another risk of bariatric surgery is nutrient deficiencies, particularly of vitamin B_{12}, folate, calcium, and iron.[77] Almost 30% of patients experience deficiency symptoms such as anemia, osteoporosis, and metabolic bone disease. To prevent these deficiencies, patients who have these surgeries must take nutritional supplements. Because rapid weight loss and nutritional deficiencies can harm a developing fetus, women who have weight-loss surgery should not become pregnant until their weight is stable.

Figure 7.33 NBC's Today Show weather anchor Al Roker lost 100 lbs after undergoing gastric bypass surgery. (Nick Elgar/Getty Images, Inc.; Evan Agostini/Getty Images, Inc.)

Outcome

Many factors interact to determine how much a person weighs. The genes Sara and Erin inherited from their parents determined their body shape and how easily they put on pounds. But what they actually weigh is determined by how much they eat and how much they exercise. Erin, who had been heavy all her life, has learned to control her tendency to gain weight by eating a healthy diet and exercising regularly. What started as a plan to lose weight has now become part of her lifestyle. She monitors her weight and food intake and enjoys daily activity. Sara, who never needed to think about her weight, experienced lifestyle changes that promoted weight gain. But she is inspired by the changes her sister has made and has reevaluated her own lifestyle. After starting a job with a law firm, Sara has begun watching what she eats and has started riding her bike after work to reduce stress and keep her weight under control. In the past 6 months she has lost about 15 of the pounds that she had gained. At this year's family picnic, both sisters have a BMI in the healthy range.

APPLICATIONS

1. **Are you in the healthy weight range?**

   a. Use Table 7.8 to determine if your BMI falls in the healthy range.

   b. If your BMI is greater than 25, measure your waist circumference. Does it indicate you are at increased risk due to visceral fat storage?

   c. Even if you are not overweight, answer the following questions to see how many factors you have that may increase your risk of obesity-related complications if you become overweight.

      1. Do you have a personal or family history of heart disease?

      2. Are you a male older than 45 years?

      3. Are you a postmenopausal female?

      4. Do you smoke cigarettes?

      5. Do you have a sedentary lifestyle?

      6. Do you have high blood pressure?

      7. Do you have high LDL cholesterol, low HDL cholesterol, or high triglycerides?

      8. Do you have diabetes?

2. **Are you in energy balance?**

   a. Use iProfile to calculate your average daily energy intake from the 3-day food record you kept in Chapter 2.

   b. Keep an activity log for several days. Use Table 7.4 and 7.5 to determine your physical activity level and PA value. Calculate your EER (see Table 7.6).

   c. How does your EER compare with your energy intake?

   d. If you consumed and expended this amount of energy every day, would your weight increase, decrease, or stay the same?

   e. If your intake does not equal your EER, how much would you gain or lose in a month? (Assume that 1 lb of fat is equal to 3500 kcalories.)

   f. If your energy intake does not equal your EER, list some specific changes you could make in your diet or the amount of activity you get to make the two balance.

3. **Are genetic or environmental factors a larger influence on your energy balance? Answer the following questions to help you decide.**

   a. How has your weight changed over the past year?

   b. How much have your parents' weights changed since they were 21?

   c. Do you eat more servings of snack foods such as chips and candy bars, or of fruits and vegetables daily? Has this changed over the past year?

   d. How has your activity changed over the past year?

   e. What patterns do you see emerging that can predict if your weight will change over the next year? The next 10 years? The next 20 years? What are your predictions?

4. **What are the goals and guidelines for weight loss?**

   a. Imagine you have a BMI of 30 kg/m^2. Use your own height and the equation for BMI on page 279 to determine about how many pounds you would need to lose to get your BMI into the healthy range.

   b. How much weight should you lose per week?

   c. Choose a weight-loss plan that best suits your individual needs and explain why you chose this plan.

   d. Review the criteria for recognizing a healthy weight-loss diet listed in Table 7.11. Does your plan meet each of these guidelines?

   e. Should you consider surgery or drugs? Why or why not?

1. **What weight patterns and influences are present in your class?**

   a. Do a class survey by collecting everyone's answers to question 3 above. Tabulate the patterns that you see.

   b. Is weight generally increasing or decreasing?

   c. Is exercise increasing or decreasing?

   d. Which are the more popular snacks—prepackaged snack foods or fruits and vegetables?

   e. What percentage of your classmates has one parent whose weight increased by 20 lbs or more since they were 21?

   f. What percentage of your classmates has two parents whose weight increased by 20 lbs or more since they were 21?

2. **How useful are low-kcalorie products?**

   a. Go to the grocery store and select 5 to 10 products labeled "light," "reduced calorie," "low calorie," or "calorie free." Record the number of kcalories per serving.

   b. Would any of these products be useful for someone on a weight-loss diet?

   c. Can they be consumed in unlimited amounts without significantly increasing energy intake?

   d. Rate these foods in terms of their nutrient density.

3. **Several strains of mice with mutations in genes that regulate body weight have been identified. For each of the following, predict whether the mouse will be over- or underweight and explain why.**

   a. A mouse that makes excess leptin.

   b. A mouse that makes leptin normally, but the leptin receptor in the brain is defective, so it always acts as if large amounts of leptin are bound to it.

   c. A mouse that makes more leptin than normal, but the leptin molecule made is defective and cannot bind to receptors in the brain.

   d. A mouse that makes too much ghrelin.

4. **Roger just celebrated his 40th birthday. He is about 40 lbs heavier than he was on his 30th birthday. At his current rate of weight gain he will be 80 lbs overweight when he reaches age 50. Roger is 5' 8" tall and weighs 190 lbs. He has three young children at home and works full-time as a salesperson. His day starts at about 6 A.M. when he gets up and has breakfast with his wife and**

iProfile

children. He spends most of the morning in his car traveling to visit his clients. He usually has at least one doughnut-and-coffee break. Lunch is fast food if he is alone or a restaurant meal if he is with clients. Most evenings he is home for dinner. By the time his children are in bed it is about 8 P.M. He sits down with his wife for a glass of wine or a bowl of ice cream.

a. Design a weight-loss and exercise regimen for Roger. Assume that his wife and children are supportive regarding dietary changes at home.
b. Does the program you designed fit in with Roger's schedule? Why or why not?
c. If he follows your suggestions, how long will it take him to lose 40 lbs?

Summary

7.1 The Obesity Epidemic

- The rapid rise in the incidence of overweight and obesity in the United States over the past 50 years has been called epidemic. It is also a growing problem around the world.

7.2 Exploring Energy Balance

- The principle of energy balance states that if energy intake equals energy needs, body weight will remain constant. A kcalorie is the amount of heat needed to raise the temperature of 1 kilogram of water 1 degree Celsius.

- Energy is provided to the body by carbohydrate (4 kcalories per gram), fat (9 kcalories per gram), protein (4 kcalories per gram), and alcohol (7 kcalories per gram). To power the body these need to be broken down and their energy converted into ATP. The ATP then fuels metabolic reactions that build and maintain body components and provides energy for other cellular and body activities.

- Total energy expenditure (TEE) includes the energy required for basal metabolism, physical activity, the thermic effect of food, growth, milk production in lactating women, and maintenance of body temperature in a cold environment. The largest component of energy expenditure in most people is basal energy expenditure (BEE), which varies depending on body size, body composition, age, and gender. The energy needed for activity, which includes planned exercise and nonexercise activity thermogenesis (NEAT), typically accounts for 15% to 30% of energy expenditure but varies greatly depending on the individual. The thermic effect of food (TEF) is the energy required for the digestion of food and the absorption, metabolism, and storage of nutrients. It is equal to about 10% of energy consumed.

- When the diet does not meet needs, body stores are used. Glucose is provided by glycogen stores or synthesized from amino acids by gluconeogenesis. Energy for tissues that don't require glucose is provided by the breakdown of stored fat. When the diet contains excess energy, the extra energy is stored for later use, primarily as fat.

7.3 Estimating Energy Needs

- The amount of energy expended by the body can be determined by direct calorimetry, which measures the heat produced by the body and indirect calorimetry, which measures oxygen utilization. The doubly-labeled water method estimates energy expenditure by using water labeled with isotopes of hydrogen and oxygen to calculate carbon dioxide production. Current recommendations for energy needs were determined using the doubly labeled water method.

- An individual's energy needs can be predicted by calculating estimated energy requirements (EER). EER calculations take into account age, gender, life stage, height, weight, and activity level. As physical activity increases, more kcalories need to be consumed to maintain body weight.

7.4 Body Weight and Health

- Some body fat is essential for health but too much increases the risk of developing chronic diseases such as diabetes, heart disease, high blood pressure, gallbladder disease, sleep apnea, arthritis, and certain types of cancer.

- Excess body fat can create psychological and social problems.

- Being naturally lean decreases health risks, but if low body weight is due to starvation or eating disorders it can affect electrolyte balance and immune function and increase the risk of early death.

7.5 Guidelines for a Healthy Body Weight

- A healthy body weight is a weight at which the risk of illness and death are lowest. Health risks increase when too little or too much body fat is stored, and when the excess fat is visceral—stored around the internal organs.

- The amount of body fat can be assessed using techniques such as bioelectric impedance, skinfold thickness, underwater weighing, isotope dilution techniques, and imaging.

- The most common way to evaluate the healthfulness of body weight is body mass index (BMI), which is calculated from a ratio of weight to height.

- An increase in visceral fat is associated with a greater incidence of heart disease, high blood pressure, stroke, and diabetes. Waist measurement can be used to assess the presence of too much visceral fat.

7.6 Regulation of Energy Balance

- The genes people inherit determine their body shape and characteristics. Genes involved in regulating body fatness are referred to as obesity genes.

- Signals from the GI tract, hormones, and levels of circulating nutrients regulate body weight in the short term by affecting hunger and satiety. Signals that relay information about the size of body fat stores, such as the release of leptin from adipocytes, regulate long-term energy intake and expenditure. Although body weight appears to be regulated around a set-point, changes in physiological, psychological, and environmental circumstances do cause the level at which body weight is regulated to change, usually increasing it over time.

• Defects in one or more of the genes that regulate body weight could lead to the storage of too much body fat. Variations in the genes that regulate metabolic rate, the ability to dissipate excess kcalories, and levels of NEAT have been hypothesized to contribute to obesity.

7.7 Why Are Americans Getting Fatter?: Genes Versus Environment

• More Americans are obese today because, as a population, we are taking in more kcalories and expending fewer. We eat more today because we are exposed to large portions of a wide variety of tasty, convenient foods that stimulate our appetite. We move less due to modern conveniences, busy lifestyles, and the availability of sedentary ways to spend our leisure time.

• To reduce the incidence of obesity Americans need to move more and eat less. Even a shift in energy balance of 100 kcalories a day would prevent further weight gain in most people.

7.8 Achieving and Maintaining a Healthy Body Weight

• Whether a person needs to lose weight depends on how much body fat they have, where the fat is located, and what their health risks are.

• Weight management involves adjusting energy intake and expenditure and modifying long-term behaviors. To lose a pound of fat, expenditure must exceed intake by approximately 3500 kcalories. A slow, steady weight loss

of 0.5 to 2 lb per week is more likely to be maintained than rapid weight loss.

• If underweight is not due to a medical condition, weight gain can be accomplished by increasing energy intake and lifting weights to increase muscle mass.

7.9 Diets, Diets, Everywhere

• There are thousands of diets that promise weight loss. All cause short-term weight loss because they decrease energy intake. Common methods for reducing kcalorie intake include the use of food exchanges, prepared meals or meal-replacement drinks, and decreasing the fat or carbohydrate content of the diet.

• A good weight-loss diet is one that allows a wide range of food choices, does not require the purchase and consumption of special foods or combinations of foods, and can be followed for life.

• *Go to WileyPLUS to view a video clip on evaluating diets.*

7.10 Weight-Loss Drugs and Surgery

• Prescription weight-loss drugs are only recommended for individuals who are significantly overweight or have accompanying health risks. Those currently available act by suppressing appetite or blocking fat absorption. Nonprescription weight-loss medications and dietary supplements are also available. Some herbal weight-loss supplements may cause serious side effects.

• The use of surgery to promote weight loss is a drastic measure that is considered only for those whose health is seriously at risk because of their obesity. It causes permanent changes in the GI tract that affect the amount of food that can be consumed and the absorption of nutrients. Even after surgery, weight loss requires changes in eating patterns and behavior.

Review Questions

1. What is a kcalorie?

2. Explain how energy balance is related to body weight.

3. Which nutrients provide energy? How much does each provide?

4. What is basal metabolic rate?

5. What is NEAT? How does it affect energy balance?

6. What is the thermic effect of food?

7. Explain why the energy in dietary fat is stored in body fat more efficiently than the energy in dietary carbohydrate.

8. Describe three methods for measuring energy expenditure.

9. What is EER and what variables are used in its calculation?

10. Explain what is meant by a healthy body weight.

11. List five health problems that are associated with excess body fat.

12. How does the distribution of body fat affect the risks of excess body fat?

13. List some methods for determining the amount of body fat.

14. How is BMI calculated and why is it commonly used to assess body weight?

15. Explain three mechanisms that make you stop eating when you have eaten enough at a meal.

16. Discuss the role of leptin in regulating body weight.

17. List some social and environmental factors that affect energy balance and discuss how these might interact with an individual's genetic predisposition to a particular body weight.

18. Explain why weight loss might be recommended for one overweight individual, but not for another of the same BMI.

19. How many kcalories must be expended to lose a pound of fat?

20. What is the best approach to weight management? Why?

21. List some risks and benefits of weight-loss drugs.

22. How does weight-loss surgery cause negative energy balance?

References

1. Ogden, C. L., Carroll, M. D., Curtin, L. R. et al. Prevalence of overweight and obesity in the United States 1999–2004, *JAMA* 295:1549–1555, 2006.

2. Ogden, C. L., Carroll, M. D., Flegal, K. M. High Body Mass Index for Age Among US Children and Adolescents, 2003–2006. *JAMA*.;299:2401–2405, 2008.

3. Strauss, R. S., and Pollack, H. A. Epidemic increase in childhood overweight. *JAMA* 286:2845–2848, 2001.

4. World Health Organization. *Obesity and Overweight,* September 2006. Fact sheet no. 311. Available online at www.who.int/mediacentre/factsheets/fs311/en/print.html. Accessed July 2, 2008.

5. Institute of Medicine, Food and Nutrition Board. *Dietary Reference Intakes for Energy, Carbohydrate, Fiber, Fat, Protein and Amino Acids.* Washington, DC: National Academies Press, 2002.

6. Weinsier, R. L., Nagy, T. R., Hunter, G. R. et al. Do adaptive changes in metabolic rate favor weight regain in weight-reduced individuals? An examination of the set-point theory. *Am. J. Clin. Nutr.* 72:1088–1094, 2000.

7. J. A. Levine, C. M. Kotz, NEAT—non-exercise activity thermogenesis—egocentric & geocentric environmental factors vs. biological regulation. *Acta. Physiologica. Scandinavica* 184: 309–318, 2005.

8. Kriketos, A. D., Peters, J. C., and Hill, J. O. Cellular and whole-animal energetics. In: *Biochemical and Physiological Aspects of Human Nutrition*. M. H. Stipanuk, ed. Philadelphia: W.B. Saunders Company, 2000, pp. 411–424.

9. Horton, T. S., Drougas, H., Brachey, A. et al. Fat and carbohydrate overfeeding in humans: Different effects on energy storage. *Am. J. Clin. Nutr.* 62:19–29, 1995.

10. Hellerstein, M. K. De novo lipogenesis in humans: Metabolic and regulatory aspects. *Eur. J. Clin. Nutr.* 53(suppl 1):S53–S65, 2000.

11. Schoeller, D. A. Recent advances from application of doubly-labeled water to measurement of human energy expenditure. *J. Nutr.* 129:1765–1768, 1999.

12. Flegal, K. M., Graubard, B. I., Williamson, D. F., and Gail, M. H. Excess deaths associated with underweight, overweight, and obesity. *JAMA.* 293:1861–1867, 2005.

13. Marti, A., Marcos, A., and Martínez, J. A. Obesity and immune function relationships. *Obes. Rev.* 2:131–140, 2001.

14. Committee to Reexamine IOM Pregnancy Weight Guidelines, Institute of Medicine, National Research Council *Weight Gain During Pregnancy: Reexamining the Guidelines,* Washington, DC: National Academies Press, 2009.

15. NIDDK Weight Control Information Network. Understanding Adult Obesity. Available online at http://win.niddk.nih.gov/publications/understanding.htm. Accessed June 11, 2009.

16. National Cholesterol Education Program. Adult Treatment Panel III Report, 2001, 2004. Available online at www.nhlbi.nih.gov/guidelines/cholesterol/atp3udp04.htm/. Accessed June 11, 2009.

17. NIDDK Weight Control Information Network. Do You Know the Risks of Being Overweight? Available online at win.niddk.nih.gov/publications/health_risks.htm#sleep/. Accessed June 11, 2009.

18. Narayan, K. M.V., Boyle, J. P., Thompson, T. J. et al. Lifetime risk for diabetes mellitus in the United States. *JAMA* 290:1884–1890, 2003.

19. NIDDK Weight Control Information Network. Dieting and Gallstones. Available online at win.niddk.nih.gov/publications/gallstones.htm/.Accessed June 11, 2009.

20. Phillips, B. Sleep-disordered breathing and cardiovascular disease. *Sleep Med. Rev.* 9:131–140, 2005.

21. McTiernam, A. Associations between energy balance and body mass index and the risk of breast carcinoma in women from diverse racial and ethnic backgrounds in the U.S. *Cancer* 88:1248–1255, 2000.

22. Key, T. J., Appleby, P. N., Reeves, G. K. et al. Body mass index, serum sex hormones, and breast cancer risk in postmenopausal women. *J. Natl. Cancer Inst.* 95:1218–1226, 2003.

23. Lementowski, P. W., and Zelicof, S. B. Obesity and osteoarthritis. *Am. J. Orthop.* 37:148–151, 2008.

24. Eisenberg, M. E., Neumark-Sztainer, D., and Story, M. Associations of weight-based teasing and emotional well-being among adolescents. *Arch. Pediatr. Adolesc. Med.* 157:733–738, 2003.

25. Strauss, R. S., and Pollack, H. A. Social marginalization of overweight children. *Arch. Pediatr. Adolesc. Med.* 157:746–752, 2003.

26. Onyike, C. U., Crum, R. M., Lee, H. B. et. al. Is obesity associated with major depression? Results from the Third NHANES. *Am. J. Epidemiol.* 158:1139–1147, 2003.

27. Allison, D. B., Zhu, S. K., Plankey, M. et al. Differential associations of body mass index and adiposity with all-cause mortality among men in the first and second National Health and Nutrition Examination Surveys (NHANES I and NHANES II) follow-up studies. *Int. J. Obes. Relat. Metab. Disord.* 26:410–416, 2002.

28. Gallagher, D., Heymsfield, S., Heo, M. et al. Healthy percentage body fat ranges: An approach for developing guidelines based on body mass index. *Am. J. Clin. Nutr.* 72:694–701, 2000.

29. Evans, W. J. Protein nutrition, exercise and aging. *J. Am. Coll. Nutr.* 23:601S–609S, 2004.

30. Fields, D. A., Hunter, G. R., and Goran. M. I. Validation of the BOD POD with hydrostatic weighing: Influence of body clothing. *Int. J. Obes. Relat. Metab. Disord.* 24:200–205, 2000.

31. Goodpaster, B.H. Measuring body fat distribution and content in humans. *Curr. Opin. Clin. Nutr. Metab. Care*:481–487, 2002.

32. U.S. Department of Health and Human Services, U.S. Department of Agriculture. *Dietary Guidelines for Americans,* 6th ed. Washington, DC, 2005.

33. National Institutes of Health. NHLBI. The Practical Guide to Identification, Evaluation and Treatment of Overweight and Obesity in Adults. NIH Publication No. 02-4084. Bethesda, MD: National Institutes of Health, 2002. Available online at http://www.nhlbi.nih.gov/guidelines/obesity/practgde.htm. Accessed June 11, 2009.

34. Nicklas, B. J., Penninx, B. W., Cesari M. et al. Association of visceral adipose tissue with incident myocardial infarction in older men and women: The Health, Aging and Body Composition Study. *Obstet. Gynecol. Surv.* 60:173–175, 2005.

35. Redinger, R. N. The physiology of adiposity. *J. Ky. Med. Assoc.* 106:53–62, 2008.

36. Bouchard, C., Tremblay, A., Després, J.-P. et al. The response to long term feeding in identical twins. *N. Engl. J. Med.* 322:1477–1482, 1990.

37. Hoffman, D. J., Wang, Z., Gallagher, D., and Heymsfield, S. B. Comparison of visceral adipose tissue mass in adult African Americans and whites. *Obes. Res.* 13:66–74, 2005.

38. Major, G. C., Doucet, E., Trayhurn, P. et al. Clinical significance of adaptive thermogenesis. *Int. J. Obes. (Lond.)* 31:204–212, 2007.

39. Leibel, R. L., Rosenbaum, M., and Hirsch, J. Changes in energy expenditure resulting from altered body weight. *N. Engl. J. Med.* 332:622–628, 1995.

40. Chagnon, Y. C., Rankinen, T., Snyder, E. E., et al. The human obesity gene map: The 2002 update. *Obes. Res.* 11:313–367, 2003.

41. Wynne, K., Stanley, S., McGowan, B., and Bloom, S. Appetite control. *J. Endocrinol.* 184:291–318, 2005.

42. Smith, G. P. Controls of food intake. In: *Modern Nutrition in Health and Disease*, 10th ed. M. E. Shils, Shike, M., A. C. Ross et al., eds. Philadelphia: Lippincott Williams & Wilkins, 2006, pp. 751–770.

43. Cummings, D. E., Weigle, D. S., Frayo, R. S. et al. Plasma ghrelin levels after diet-induced weight loss or gastric bypass surgery. *N. Engl. J. Med.* 346:1623–1630, 2002.

44. Batterham, R. L., Cowley, M. A., Small, C. J. et al. Gut hormone PYY(3-36) physiologically inhibits food intake. *Nature* 418(6898):650–654, 2002.

45. Friedman, J. M. The alphabet of weight control. *Nature* 385:119–120, 1997.

46. Enriori, P. J., Evans, A. E., Sinnayah, P., and Cowley, M. A. Leptin resistance and obesity. *Obesity* 14:254S–258S, 2006.

47. Peters, J. C. Control of energy balance. In Stipanuk, M. H. (ed.). *Biochemical and Physiological Aspects of Human Nutrition*, 2nd ed. Philadelphia: W.B. Saunders, 2006, pp. 618–639.

48. Tsigos, C., Kyrou, I., and Raptis, S. A. Monogenic forms of obesity and diabetes mellitus. *J. Pediatr. Endocrinol. Metab.* 15:241–253, 2002.

49. Tremblay, A., Després, J-P., Thriault, G. et al. Overfeeding and energy expenditure in humans. *Am. J. Clin. Nutr.* 56:857–862, 1992.

50. Diaz, E. O., Prentice, A. M., Goldberg, G. R. et al. Metabolic response to experimental overfeeding in lean and overweight healthy volunteers. *Am. J. Clin. Nutr.* 56:641–655, 1992.

51. van Marken Lichtenbelt, W. D., Vanhommerig, J. W., Smulders, N. M. et al. Cold-activated brown adipose tissue in healthy men. *N. Engl. J. Med.* 360:1500–1508, 2009.

52. Levine, J. A., Lanningham-Foster L. M, McCrady S. K. et al. Interindividual variation in posture allocation: Possible role in human obesity. *Science* 307:584–586, 2005.

53. Levine, J. A., Eberhardt, N. L., and Jensen, M. D. Role of nonexercise activity thermogenesis in resistance to fat gain in humans. *Science* 283:212–214, 1999.

54. Bouchard, C. Genetics of human obesity: Recent results from linkage studies. *J. Nutr.* 127:1887S–1890S, 1997.

55. Wardle, J., Carnell, S., Haworth, C. M., and Plomin, R. Evidence for a strong genetic influence on childhood adiposity despite the force of the obesogenic environment. *Am. J. Clin. Nutr.* 87:398–404, 2008.

56. Schultz, L. O., Bennett, P. H., Ravussin, E. et al. Effects of traditional and western environments on prevalence of type 2 diabetes in Pima Indians in Mexico and the U.S. *Diabetes Care* 29:1866–1871, 2006.

57. Hill, J. O. Can a small-changes approach help address the obesity epidemic? A report of the Joint Task Force of the American Society for Nutrition, Institute of Food Technologists, and International Food Information Council. *J. Clin. Nutr.* 89:477–484, 2009.

58. Young, L. R., and Nestle, M. The contribution of expanding portion size to the obesity epidemic. *Am. J. Public Health* 92:246–249, 2002.

59. Rolls, B. J., Morris, E. L., and Roe, L. S. Portion size of food affects energy intake in normal-weight and overweight men and women. *Am. J. Clin. Nutr.* 76:1207–1213, 2002.

60. Nielsen, S. J,. and Popkin, B. M. Changes in beverage intake between 1977 and 2001. *Am. J. Prev. Med.* 27:205–210, 2004.

61. Nielsen, S. J., and Popkin, B. M. Patterns and trends in food portion sizes, 1977–1998. *JAMA.* 289:450–453, 2003.

62. American Dietetic Association. Nutrition and You: Trends 2002. Available online at www.eatright.org/ada/files/trends02findings.pdf/Accessed March 23, 2009.

63. Wright, J. D., Kennedy-Stephenson, J., Wang, C. Y. et al. Trends in intake of energy and macronutrients—United States, 1971–2000. *Morb. Mortal. Wkly. Rep.* 6:80–82, 2004. Available online at www.cdc.gov/mmwr/preview/mmwrhtml/mm5304a3.htm/ Accessed March 7, 2009.

64. Bassett, D. R., Schneider, P. L., and Huntington, G. E. Physical activity in an Old Order Amish community. *Med. Sci. Sports Exerc.* 36:79–85, 2004.

65. Office of the Surgeon General. The Surgeon General's Call to Action to Prevent and Decrease Overweight and Obesity. U.S. Department of Health and Human Services. Rockville, MD, 2001. Available online at www.surgeongeneral.gov/topics/obesity/ Accessed March 4, 2004.

66. Stevens, J., Cai, J., Pamuk, E. R. et al. The effect of age on the association between body mass index and mortality. *N. Engl. J. Med.* 338:1–7, 1998.

67. Kroke, A., Liese, A. D., Schulz, M. et al. Recent weight changes and weight cycling as predictors of subsequent two year weight change in a middle-aged cohort. *Int. J. Obes. Relat. Metab. Disord.* 26:403–409, 2002.

68. United States Department of Health and Human Services. *2008 Physical Activity Guidelines for Americans.* Available online at www.health.gov/paguidelines. Accessed June 19, 2009.

69. American Dietetic Association. Position of the American Dietetic Association: Weight management. *J. Am. Diet. Assoc.* 109:330–346, 2009.

70. American Dietetic Association. Position of the American Dietetic Association: Fat replacers. *J. Am. Diet. Assoc.* 105:266–275, 2005.

71. Hill, J. O., Melanson, E. L., and Wyatt, H. T. Dietary fat intake and regulation of energy balance: Implications for obesity. *J. Nutr.* 130:284S–288S, 2000.

72. Astrup, A., Astrup, A., Buemann, B. et al. Low-fat diets and energy balance: How does the evidence stand in 2002? *Proc. Nutr. Soc.* 61:299–309, 2002.

73. Westman, E. C., Feinman, R. D., Mavropoulos, J. C., et al. Low-carbohydrate nutrition and metabolism. *Am. J. Clin. Nutr.* 86:276–284, 2007.

74. Frackelmann, K. Diet drug debacle: How two federally approved weight-loss drugs crashed. *Science News* 152:252–253, 1997.

75. Saper, R. B., Eisenberg, D. M., and Phillips, R. S. Common dietary supplements for weight loss. *Am. Fam. Physician* 70:1731–1738, 2004.

76. Klein, S., Fontana, L., Young, V. L. et al. Absence of an effect of liposuction on insulin action and risk factors for coronary heart disease. *N. Engl. J. Med.* 350:2549–2557, 2004.

77. WIN, National Institutes of Health. NIDDK. Gastrointestinal Surgery for Severe Obesity. Available online at win.niddk.nih.gov/publications/gastric.htm/ Accessed September 17, 2009.

(©iStockphoto)

Focus On

Eating Disorders

Chapter Outline

Normal eating patterns are flexible. One day you may eat twice as much as on another. On some days your food choices are varied and nutritious, while on others you may survive on snacks and fast food. Lunch one day may include an appetizer, entrée, and dessert and on the next it may be a carton of yogurt grabbed on the run. Normal eating patterns include eating more than we need at a party or other special occasion and less than we need when we are busy or stressed. Normal eating may also involve limiting intake in order to manage weight and meet recommendations for a healthy diet. What and how much people eat varies in response to social occasions, emotions, time limitations, hunger, and the availability of food, but generally people eat when they are hungry, choose foods they enjoy, and stop eating when they are satisfied. Abnormal eating occurs when a person is overly concerned with food, eating, and body size and shape. When the emotional aspects of food and eating overpower the role of food as nourishment an **eating disorder** may develop.

eating disorder A persistent disturbance in eating behavior or other behaviors intended to control weight that affects physical health and psychosocial functioning.

F2.1 What Are Eating Disorders?

Learning Objective

• Name the three categories of eating disorders.

Eating disorders are psychological disorders that involve a persistent disturbance in eating patterns or other behaviors intended to control weight. They affect physical and nutritional health and psychosocial functioning. If untreated, eating disorders can be fatal.

316

According to mental health guidelines, there are three categories of eating disorders. The first, **anorexia nervosa**, is characterized by self-starvation to reduce weight or prevent weight gain. **Bulimia nervosa**, the second category, involves frequent episodes of **bingeing** or **binge eating** during which extremely large amounts of high-kcalorie foods are consumed. These episodes are almost always followed by depression, guilt, and **purging** behaviors, such as self-induced vomiting, to rid the body of the extra energy. The final category is **eating disorders not otherwise specified (EDNOS)**, which includes abnormal eating behaviors that don't fit into the other two categories. Over 50% of all people who seek treatment for an eating disorder are categorized as EDNOS. For example, someone who has a body weight that is very low but not low enough to be classified as anorexia would fit into the EDNOS category. Someone who binges and purges, but not often enough to be considered bulimic, would also fit the EDNOS category. **Binge-eating disorder**, which involves bingeing without purging, is also included in the EDNOS category[1] (**Table F2.1**).

anorexia nervosa An eating disorder characterized by self-starvation, a distorted body image, and below normal body weight.

bulimia nervosa An eating disorder characterized by the consumption of large amounts of food at one time (binge eating), followed by purging behaviors such as vomiting or the use of laxatives to eliminate kcalories from the body.

bingeing or **binge eating** The rapid consumption of a large amount of food in a discrete period of time associated with a feeling that eating is out of control.

purging Behaviors such as self-induced vomiting and misuse of laxatives, diuretics, or enemas to rid the body of kcalories.

eating disorders not otherwise specified (EDNOS) A category of eating disorders that includes abnormal eating behaviors that don't fit into the anorexia or bulimia nervosa categories.

binge-eating disorder An eating disorder characterized by recurrent episodes of binge eating in the absence of purging behavior.

Table F2.1 Diagnostic Criteria for Eating Disorders

Anorexia nervosa
- Refusal to maintain body weight at or above 85% of normal weight for age and height.
- Intense fear of gaining weight or becoming fat, even though underweight.
- Disturbance in the way body weight or shape is experienced, or denial of the seriousness of the current low body weight.
- Absence of at least three consecutive menstrual cycles without other known cause.

  Restricting Type: During the current episode of anorexia nervosa, the person does not regularly engage in binge-eating or purging behavior (i.e., self-induced vomiting or the misuse of laxatives, diuretics, or enemas).

  Binge-Eating Type or **Purging Type:** During the current episode of anorexia nervosa, the person regularly engages in binge-eating or purging behavior (i.e., self-induced vomiting or the misuse of laxatives, diuretics, or enemas).

Bulimia nervosa
- Recurrent episodes of binge eating.
- Recurrent inappropriate compensatory behavior to prevent weight gain, such as self-induced vomiting; misuse of laxatives, diuretics, enemas, or other medications; fasting; or excessive exercise.
- Occurrence, on average, of binge eating and inappropriate compensatory behaviors at least twice a week for 3 months.
- Undue influence by body shape and weight on self-evaluation.
- Disturbance does not occur exclusively during episodes of anorexia nervosa.

  Purging Type: During the current episode of bulimia nervosa, the person regularly engages in self-induced vomiting or the misuse of laxatives, diuretics, or enemas.

  Nonpurging Type: During the current episode of bulimia nervosa, the person uses other inappropriate compensatory behaviors, such as fasting or excessive exercise, but does not regularly engage in self-induced vomiting or the misuse of laxatives, diuretics, or enemas.

Eating disorders not otherwise specified (EDNOS)
- Criteria for anorexia nervosa are met except the individual menstruates regularly.
- Criteria for anorexia nervosa are met except that, despite substantial weight loss, the individual's current weight is in the normal range.
- Criteria for bulimia nervosa are met except binges occur at a frequency of less than twice a week and for a duration of less than 3 months.
- Inappropriate compensatory behavior after eating small amounts of food in individuals of normal body weight.
- Regularly chewing and spitting out, without swallowing, large amounts of food.
- Recurrent episodes of binge eating in the absence of regular use of inappropriate compensatory behaviors characteristic of bulimia (binge eating disorder).

Source: From the *DSM-IV, Diagnostic and Statistical Manual of Mental Disorders*, 4th ed., TR, Washington DC: American Psychiatric Association, 2000.

F2.2 What Causes Eating Disorders?

Learning Objectives

- Discuss the genetic, psychological, and sociocultural factors that influence the development of eating disorders.
- Describe how a societies' body ideal affects the incidence of eating disorders.

Genetic, psychological, and sociocultural factors all contribute to the development of eating disorders (**Figure F2.1**). Eating disorders typically begin in adolescence when physical, psychological, and social development is occurring rapidly but they occur in people of all ages, races, and socioeconomic backgrounds. They are more common in women than men. Although typically associated with white middle-class females, eating disorders are also a growing problem among African-American and Hispanic women. They also occur in other minority groups, but the data concerning eating disorders in minority populations remain very limited.[2] In the United States, anorexia, bulimia, and binge-eating disorder affect about 3% of girls and women between the ages of 18 and 30 years.[3]

Eating disorders occur in the greatest frequency in groups that are concerned about maintaining a low body weight, such as professional dancers and models.[3] They are on the rise among athletes, especially those involved in sports that require the athlete to be thin, such as gymnastics and figure skating, or to fit into a particular weight class, such as wrestling.

The Role of Genetics

Eating disorders are not necessarily passed from parent to child, but the genes you inherit contribute to personality traits and other biological characteristics that might predispose you to developing an eating disorder. For example, inherited abnormalities in the levels of neurotransmitters such as serotonin, which affects food intake, have been hypothesized to contribute to the behaviors typical of anorexia and bulimia.[4] Binge-eating disorder may be linked to a defect in a gene called the melanocortin 4 receptor gene. The protein made by this gene helps control hunger and satiety. If this gene is abnormal and makes too little protein, the body feels too much hunger. In one

Figure F2.1 Causes of eating disorders
Medical professionals must address genetic, psychological, and sociocultural factors if treatment for eating disorders is to be effective.

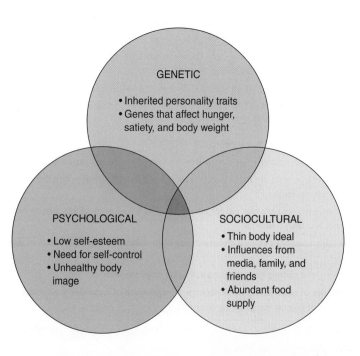

study, all carriers of the mutant gene were binge eaters and mutations were found in 5% of obese subjects.[5] Genes such as this contribute to eating disorders but a single gene is not likely to be the sole cause. These are complex diseases that are the result of the interaction of multiple genes with the environment. Each gene may have a small effect, but when taken together, they can increase risk severalfold. When placed in an environment conducive to eating disorders, individuals who carry such genes will be more likely to develop one.

Psychological Characteristics

Certain personality characteristics and psychological problems are common among individuals with eating disorders.[3] For example, people with eating disorders often have low **self-esteem**. Self-esteem refers to the judgments people make and maintain about themselves—a general attitude of approval or disapproval that indicates if the person thinks they are worthy and capable. Eating disorders are also rooted in the need for self-control. Those with eating disorders are often perfectionists who set very high standards for themselves and others. In order to be perfect they strive to be in control of their bodies and their lives. They view everything as either a success or a failure. Being fat is seen as failure, thin as success, and thinner as even more successful. In spite of their many achievements, those with eating disorders feel inadequate, defective, and worthless.

self-esteem The general attitude of approval or disapproval that people make and maintain about themselves.

    People with eating disorders often try to use their relationship with food to gain control over their lives and boost their self-esteem. They believe that controlling their food intake and weight demonstrates their ability to control other aspects of their lives and solve other problems. Their fixation with food and weight loss and their ability to control their intake and weight help them to feel better about themselves. Even if they feel insecure, helpless, or dissatisfied in other aspects of life, if they are in control of their food intake, weight, and body size they can associate this control with success. This feeling of being in control can become addictive.

Sociocultural Messages About the Ideal Body

While genetic and psychological issues may predispose individuals to eating disorders, sociocultural and economic factors are important triggers for the onset of these disorders. An important sociocultural factor is body ideal. What is viewed as an ideal body differs across cultures and has changed throughout history. Ancient drawings and figurines show women with large breasts and swollen abdomens. This plump body ideal is still prevalent today in cultures where food is not readily available. Young women in these cultures may struggle to gain weight to achieve what is viewed as the ideal female body (**Figure F2.2**). In contrast, women in the United States strive to achieve a thin, lean body. The sociocultural ideals about body size are linked to **body image** and the incidence of eating disorders.[6] Eating disorders occur in societies where food is abundant and the body ideal is thin. They do not occur where food is scarce and people must worry about where their next meal is coming from.

body image The way a person perceives and imagines their body.

Figure F2.2 A fuller figure is still desirable in many cultures, such as the Zulu of South Africa. As television images of very thin western women become more accessible, the Zulu cultural view of plumpness as desirable may be changing. (SCPhotos/Alamy)

Body Ideal in Modern America From television and movies to magazines and advertisements and even toys, the culture in America today is a culture of thinness. Messages about what society views as a perfect body—the ideal we should strive for— are constantly delivered by the mass media. The perfect body is long, lean, and muscled. The tall dark muscular man gets the girl; the thin athletic woman gets her man. Thin fashion models adorn billboards and magazine covers to show off the latest clothes (**Figure F2.3**). Being thin is associated with beauty, success, intelligence, and vitality. Being plump, on the other hand, is associated with failure, stupidity, and clumsiness. What young woman would want to be plump when exposed to these negative associations? Although men are also affected by these messages, American culture still places much more emphasis on the appearance of women's bodies. A young woman facing a future where she must be independent, have a prestigious job, maintain a

Figure F2.3 The fashion models whom women want to emulate are thinner than 98% of women in the United States. (Andy Washink)

successful love relationship, bear and nurture children, manage a household, and stay in fashion can become overwhelmed. Unable to master all these roles, she may look for some aspect of her life that she can control. Food intake and body weight are natural choices, since being thin brings the societal associations of success. These messages about how we should look are difficult to ignore and can create pressure to achieve this ideal body. But it is a standard that is very hard to meet—a standard that is contributing to disturbances in body image and eating behavior. This is illustrated by the fact that as the body dimensions of female models, actresses, and other cultural icons have become thinner over the last several decades, the incidence of eating disorders has increased (**Figure F2.4**).

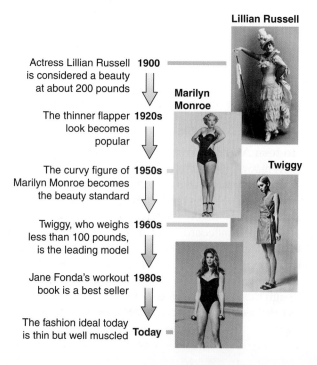

Lillian Russell

Actress Lillian Russell is considered a beauty at about 200 pounds — **1900**

The thinner flapper look becomes popular — **1920s**

Marilyn Monroe

The curvy figure of Marilyn Monroe becomes the beauty standard — **1950s**

Twiggy

Twiggy, who weighs less than 100 pounds, is the leading model — **1960s**

Jane Fonda's workout book is a best seller — **1980s**

The fashion ideal today is thin but well muscled — **Today**

Figure F2.4 The changing female body ideal
As this timeline shows, extreme thinness has not always been the beauty standard in the United States. (Bettmann/© Corbis; Bettmann/© Corbis; Bettmann/© Corbis; © rein/Corbis)

Body Image and Eating Disorders What an individual thinks they should look like or wishes they would look like is affected by the ideals of their culture and society. Many women and girls, particularly teenage girls, are dissatisfied with their bodies because they look different than what they and their culture see as ideal. The average American woman is 5'4" and weighs 140 lbs. The average fashion model is 5'11" and weighs 117 lbs. The difference between models and average women has been increasing over the years. Forty years ago the average weight of a model was 8% lower than that of an average woman; today the difference is over 25%.[7] Almost everyone has something that they would like to change about their bodies, but for some this becomes a pathological concern with body weight and shape and as a result body image may become distorted. A distorted body image means that an individual is unable to judge the size of his or her own body and does not see themselves as they really are (**Figure F2.5**). Body image distortion is common with eating disorders so even if the person achieves a body weight comparable to that of a fashion model, they may continue to see themselves as fat and strive to lose more weight (**Table F2.2**).

Figure F2.5 When someone with a distorted body looks in the mirror they see themselves as fat even when they are normal or underweight. (David Young Wolff/ PhotoEdit)

Table F2.2 **To Maintain a Healthy Body Image**

Try to . . .
- Accept that healthy bodies come in many shapes and sizes.
- Recognize your positive qualities.
- Remember that you can be your worst critic.
- Explore your internal self, as well as your external appearance.
- Spend your time and energy enjoying the positive things in your life.
- Be aware of your own weight prejudice. Explore how your feelings may affect your self-esteem.

And try not to . . .
- Let your body define who or what you are.
- Judge others on the basis of appearance, body size, or shape.
- Forget that society changes its ideals of beauty over the years.
- Forget that you are not alone in your pursuit of self-acceptance.
- Be afraid to enjoy life.

F2.3 Anorexia Nervosa

Learning Objectives

- Describe the features of anorexia nervosa.
- Explain how anorexia is treated.

"Anorexia" means lack of appetite, but in the case of the eating disorder anorexia nervosa it is a desire to be thin, rather than a lack of appetite, that causes individuals to decrease their food intake. Anorexia nervosa was first recognized by physicians in the second half of the nineteenth century and the characteristics they described are still true of the syndrome today: severe weight loss, **amenorrhea**, constipation, and restlessness. Anorexia nervosa affects 1% of female adolescents in the United States.[8] The average age of onset is 17 years. There is a 5% death rate in the first 2 years, and this can reach 20% in untreated individuals.[3]

amenorrhea Delayed onset of menstruation or the absence of three or more consecutive menstrual cycles.

Psychological Issues

The psychological component of anorexia nervosa revolves around an overwhelming fear of gaining weight, even in those who are already underweight (**Figure F2.6**). It is not uncommon for individuals with anorexia to feel that they would rather be dead

Dear Diary,
    For breakfast today I had a cup of tea. For lunch I ate some lettuce and a slice of tomato, but no dressing. I cooked dinner for my family. I love to cook, but it is hard not to taste. I tried a new chicken recipe and served it with rice and asparagus. I even made a chocolate cake for dessert but I didn't even lick the bowl from the frosting. When it came time to eat, I only took a little. I told my mom I nibbled while cooking. I pushed the food around on my plate so no one would notice that I only ate a few bites. I was good today - I kept my food intake under control. The scale says I have lost 20 pounds but I still look fat.

Figure F2.6 A day in the life of an anorexic
People with anorexia nervosa carefully regulate what they eat to maintain a very low body weight. (David Young Wolff/PhotoEdit)

than fat. Anorexia is also characterized by disturbances in body image or perception of body size that prevent those affected from seeing themselves as underweight even when they are dangerously thin. Those with this disorder may use body weight and shape as a means of self-evaluation: "If I weren't so fat then everyone would like and respect me and I wouldn't have other problems." However, no matter how much weight they lose individuals with anorexia nervosa do not gain self-respect, inner assurance, or the happiness they seek. Therefore, they continue to restrict their intake and use other behaviors in order to lose weight.

Anorexic Behaviors

The most obvious behaviors associated with anorexia are those that contribute to the maintenance of a body weight that is 15% or more below normal body weight. These behaviors include restriction of food intake, binge eating and purging episodes, strange eating rituals, and excessive exercise. Based on these behaviors, anorexia is subdivided into two subtypes. Those with the *Restricting Type* maintain their low body weight solely by restricting their food intake and increasing their activity. Those with the *Binge-Eating/Purging Type* also typically restrict their food intake but, in addition, regularly engage in binge-eating and/or purging behaviors (see Table F2.1). It is estimated that about half of people with anorexia use purging as a means of weight control.[9]

For individuals with anorexia food and eating become an obsession. In addition to restricting the total amount of food consumed, anorexics develop personal diet rituals, limiting certain foods and eating them in specific ways. Although they do not consume very much food they are preoccupied with food and spend an enormous amount of time thinking about food, talking about food, and preparing food for others. Instead of eating, they move the food around the plate and cut it into tiny pieces.

Both hyperactivity and overactivity are behaviors that are also typical of anorexia. This is in contrast to the decrease in activity and fatigue characteristic of other starvation states associated with weight loss. Many anorexics exercise excessively to burn kcalories. For some the activity is surreptitious, such as going up and down stairs repeatedly or getting off the bus a few stops too early. For others the activity takes the form of strenuous physical exercise. They may become fanatical athletes and feel guilty if they cannot exercise. The exercise is typically done alone and is performed as a regular rigid routine. They may link exercise and eating, so a certain amount of exercise earns them the right to eat and if they eat too much they must pay the price by adding extra exercise. Those who use exercise to increase energy expenditure do not stop when they are tired; instead, they train compulsively beyond reasonable endurance (**Figure F2.7**).

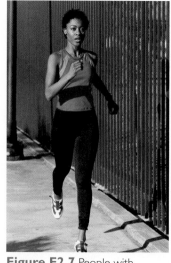

Figure F2.7 People with anorexia nervosa often use exercise as well as food restriction to achieve and maintain a very low body weight. (Stockbyte/Getty Images, Inc.)

Physical Symptoms of Anorexia

The first obvious physical manifestation of anorexia is weight loss. As weight loss becomes severe, symptoms of starvation begin to appear. Starvation affects mental function, causing those with anorexia to become apathetic, dull, exhausted, and depressed. Physical symptoms include depletion of fat stores; wasting of muscles; inflammation and swelling of the lips; flaking and peeling of skin; growth of fine hair, called lanugo hair, on the body, and dry, thin, brittle hair on the head that may fall out. In females, estrogen levels drop, and menstruation becomes irregular or stops. This can delay sexual maturation and can have long-term effects on bone density. In males, testosterone levels decrease. In the final stages of starvation, there are abnormalities in electrolyte and fluid balance and cardiac irregularities. Ketones are typically absent because fat-stores are depleted. Immune function is suppressed leading to infections which further increase nutritional needs.

Treatment

The goal of treatment for anorexia nervosa is to help resolve the psychological and behavioral problems while providing for physical and nutritional rehabilitation. Early treatment of anorexia is important because starvation may cause irreversible damage. The goal of nutrition intervention is to promote weight gain by increasing energy intake and expanding dietary choices.[2] Nutritional rehabilitation in mild cases involves learning about nutrition and meal planning in order to develop healthy eating patterns. In more severe cases, hospitalization is required so food intake and exercise behaviors can be carefully controlled. Intravenous nutrition may be necessary to keep these individuals alive. Although some people recover fully from anorexia about half have poor long-term outcomes—remaining irrationally concerned about weight gain and never achieving normal body weight. Some patients with anorexia also transition to bulimia nervosa.[10]

F2.4 Bulimia Nervosa

Learning Objectives

- Explain what is meant by the binge/purge cycle.
- Discuss the complications and treatment of bulimia nervosa.

"Bulimia" is from the Greek *bous* (ox) and *limos* (hunger), denoting hunger of such intensity that a person could eat an entire ox. The modern concept of bulimia nervosa as an eating disorder arose in the early 1970s, when a set of symptoms was identified and distinguished from anorexia and obesity. Many different names were used for this disorder, including dysorexia, bulimarexia, thin-fat syndrome, binge/purge syndrome, and dietary chaos syndrome. The term bulimia nervosa was coined in 1979 by a British psychiatrist who suggested that bulimia consisted of powerful urges to overeat in combination with a morbid fear of becoming fat and the avoidance of the fattening effects of food by inducing vomiting or abusing purgatives or both.[11] Today, an estimated 2% to 5% of the female population will have bulimia nervosa in their lifetime.[3] A diagnosis of bulimia is based on the frequency with which episodes of binge eating and inappropriate compensatory behaviors occur.

Psychological Issues

As with anorexia, people with bulimia have an intense fear of becoming fat. They have a negative body image accompanied by a distorted perception of their body size. Since their self-esteem is highly tied to their impressions of their body shape and weight, they blame all of their problems on their appearance; this allows them to not face the real problems in their life. People with bulimia are preoccupied with the fear that once they start eating they will not be able to stop. They may engage in continuous dieting, which leads to a preoccupation with food. They also think they are the only person in the world with this problem. As a result they are often socially isolated. In addition, they may avoid situations that will expose them to food, such as going to parties or out to dinner, further isolating themselves.

Bulimic Behaviors

Bulimia typically begins with food restriction motivated by the desire to be thin. Overwhelming hunger may finally cause the dieting to be interrupted by a period of overeating. Eventually a pattern develops involving semi-starvation interrupted by periods of gorging. During a food binge, a person with bulimia experiences a sense of lack of control. The amount of food consumed during a binge varies, but is typically on the order of 3400 kcalories, while a normal teenager may consume 2000 to 3000 kcalories in an entire day. One study found that bulimics consumed an average of about 7000 kcalories in a 24-hour period.[12] Binges usually last less than 2 hours and occur in secrecy. They stop when the food runs out, or when pain, fatigue, or an interruption intervenes. The amount of food consumed in a binge may not always be enormous but it is perceived by the bulimic individual as a binge episode. Binging and purging are then followed by intense feelings of guilt and shame (**Figure F2.8**).

After binge episodes, individuals with bulimia use various inappropriate compensatory behaviors to eliminate the extra kcalories and prevent weight gain. Bulimia is subdivided into two types based on the type of compensatory behavior used. *Nonpurging bulimia* involves behaviors such as fasting or excessive exercise to prevent weight gain, whereas *purging bulimia* involves regularly engaging in behaviors that may include self-induced vomiting and misuse of enemas, laxatives and diuretics, or other medications (see Table F2.1). Self-induced vomiting is the most common purging behavior. It is used at the end of a binge but also after normal eating to eliminate food before it is absorbed and the energy it provides can cause weight gain. At first a physical maneuver such as sticking a finger down the throat is needed to induce vomiting but patients eventually learn to vomit at will. Vomiting does not purge all kcalories consumed in a binge. After a binge containing 3530 kcalories, on average 1209 kcalories were retained. Interestingly, after a smaller binge of only 1549 kcalories, almost the same amount of energy remained in the stomach, 1128 kcalories.[13] Some bulimic individuals take laxatives to induce diarrhea. Although the patients believe the diarrhea prevents kcalories from being absorbed, in fact, nutrient absorption is almost complete before food enters the colon where laxatives have their effect. The weight loss associated with laxative abuse is due to dehydration. Diuretics also cause water loss, but via

Figure F2.8 A day in the life of a bulimic
Bulimia is characterized by binge eating followed by purging. (David Young Wolff/PhotoEdit)

Dear Diary,
Today started well. I stuck to my diet through breakfast, lunch, and dinner, but by 8 PM I was feeling depressed and bored. I thought food would make me feel better. Before I knew it I was at the convenience store buying two pints of ice cream, a large bag of chips, a one pound package of cookies, a half dozen candy bars, and a quart of milk. I told the clerk I was having a party. But it was a party of one. Alone in my dorm room I started by eating the chips, then polished off the cookies and the candy bars, washing them down with milk and finishing with the ice cream. Luckily no one was around so I was able to vomit without anyone hearing. I feel weak and guilty but also relieved that I got rid of all those calories. Tomorrow, I will start a new diet.

the kidney rather than the GI tract. They do not cause fat loss. Some bulimia sufferers use a combination of purging and nonpurging methods to eliminate excess kcalories.

Physical Complications of Bulimia

It is the purging portion of the binge-purge cycle that is most hazardous to health in bulimia nervosa. Purging by vomiting brings stomach acid into the mouth. Frequent vomiting affects the GI tract by causing tooth decay, sores in the mouth and on the lips, swelling of the jaw and salivary glands, irritation of the throat, inflammation of the esophagus, and changes in stomach capacity and stomach emptying.[3] It also causes broken blood vessels in the face from the force of vomiting, electrolyte imbalance, dehydration, muscle weakness, and menstrual irregularities. Laxative and diuretic abuse can also cause dehydration and electrolyte imbalance. Rectal bleeding may occur from laxative overuse.

Treatment

The overall goal of therapy for people with bulimia nervosa is to separate eating from their emotions and from their perceptions of success and to promote eating in response to hunger and satiety. Psychological counseling is needed to address issues related to body image and a sense of lack of control over eating. Nutritional therapy addresses physiological imbalances caused by purging episodes as well as provides education on nutrient needs and how to meet them. Antidepressant medications may be beneficial in reducing the frequency of binge episodes. Treatment has been found to speed recovery, especially if it is provided soon after symptoms begin, but for some individuals this disorder may remain a chronic problem throughout life.[14]

F2.5 Binge-Eating Disorder

Learning Objective

• Distinguish binge-eating disorder from anorexia and bulimia.

Binge-eating disorder, which is in the EDNOS category, is probably the most common eating disorder. It affects at least 1% of the total population.[15] Unlike anorexia and bulimia, binge-eating disorder is not uncommon in men who account for about 40% of cases.[16] It is more common in overweight individuals (**Figure F2.9**). Individuals

Dear Diary,
   I got on the scale today. What a mistake! My weight is up to 250 pounds. I hate myself for being so fat. Just seeing that I gained more weight made me feel ashamed - all I wanted to do was bury my feelings in a box of cookies or a carton of ice cream. Why do I always think the food will help? Once I started eating I couldn't stop. When I finally did I felt even more disgusted, depressed, and guilty. I am always on a diet but it is never long before I lose control and pig out. I know my eating and my weight are not healthy but I just can't seem to stop.

Figure F2.9 A day in the life of a binge eater
Individuals with binge eating disorder binge but do not purge and are typically overweight. (Ken Ross/Getty Images, Inc.)

with binge-eating disorder engage in recurrent episodes of binge eating but do not regularly engage in purging and other inappropriate compensatory behaviors such as vomiting, fasting, or excessive exercise (**Table F2.3**). The major complications of binge-eating disorder are the conditions that accompany obesity, which include diabetes, high blood pressure, high cholesterol levels, gallbladder disease, heart disease, and certain types of cancer.[16] Treatment of binge-eating disorder involves counseling to improve body image and self-acceptance, a healthy nutritious diet, and increased exercise to promote weight loss along with behavior therapy to reduce bingeing.

Table F2.3 Diagnostic Criteria for Binge Eating Disorder

Recurrent episodes of binge eating. An episode is characterized by:
- Eating a larger amount of food than normal during a short period of time (within any 2 hour period).
- Lack of control over eating during the binge episode (i.e., the feeling that one cannot stop eating).

Binge eating episodes are associated with three or more of the following:
- Eating until feeling uncomfortably full.
- Eating large amounts of food when not physically hungry.
- Eating much more rapidly than normal.
- Eating alone because you are embarrassed by how much you're eating.
- Feeling disgusted, depressed, or guilty after overeating.

Marked distress regarding binge eating is present.

Binge eating occurs, on average, at least 2 days a week for 6 months.

The binge eating is not associated with the regular use of inappropriate compensatory behavior (i.e., purging, excessive exercise, etc.) and does not occur exclusively during the course of bulimia nervosa or anorexia nervosa.

Source: From the *DSM-IV, Diagnostic and Statistical Manual of Mental Disorders*, 4th ed. Washington DC: American Psychiatric Association, 2000.

F2.6 Eating Disorders in Special Groups

Learning Objectives

- Describe how eating disorders are different in men and women.
- List some eating disorders that occur in children, pregnant women, and athletes.

Although anorexia, bulimia, and binge-eating disorder are most common in women in their teens and twenties, eating disorders occur in both genders and all age groups. They can be a complication in pregnant women and a problem for athletes and young children. They also occur in individuals with diseases that have a nutrition component such as diabetes. In addition, there are a number of less common eating disorders that appear in special groups and in the general population. These are listed in **Table F2.4**.

Eating Disorders in Men

The incidence of anorexia, bulimia, and binge-eating disorder is much lower among men than women. One reason for the lower incidence is that the cultural pressure for males to be thin is less intense. Women are encouraged to be thin to attract friends and romantic partners and to be successful at school and work, whereas men are encouraged to be strong and powerful. The male ideal is a V-shaped upper body that is muscular, moderate in weight, and low in body fat. This difference in societal expectations is reflected in the BMI of men and women when they first "feel fat" and begin dieting. Women who develop eating disorders generally feel fat and

Table F2.4 Other Eating Disorders

Eating Disorder	Characteristics	Who Is Affected	Consequences
Anorexia athletica	Engaging in compulsive exercise to lose weight or maintain a very low body weight.	Athletes	Can lead to more serious eating disorders and serious health problems including kidney failure, heart attack, and death.
Avoidance emotional disorder	Similar to anorexia nervosa in that the child avoids eating and experiences weight loss and the physical symptoms of anorexia. However, there is no distorted body image or fear of weight gain.	Children	Weight loss, reduced body fat, malnutrition.
Bigorexia (muscle dysmorphia or reverse anorexia)	Obsession with being small and underdeveloped. Individuals believe their muscles are inadequate even when they have a good muscle mass.	Bodybuilders and avid gym-goers, more common in men than women	Sufferers are at risk if they take steroids or other muscle-enhancing drugs.
Body dysmorphic disorder	An obsession with a perceived defect in the sufferer's body or appearance.	Affects males and females equally	Increased risk for depression and suicide.
Chewing and spitting	The person puts food in his/her mouth, tastes it, chews it, and then spits it out.	Those with other eating disorders	Since the food is not swallowed it can result in the same symptoms as starvation dieting.
Female athlete triad	A triad of disordered eating, amenorrhea, and osteoporosis.	Female athletes in weight-dependent sports	Low estrogen levels, which interfere with calcium balance, eventually causing reductions in bone mass and an increased risk of bone fractures.
Insulin misuse (diabulimia)	Withholding insulin to cause weight loss or prevent weight gain.	People with type 1 diabetes	Uncontrolled blood sugar, which can lead to blindness, kidney disease, heart disease, nerve damage, and amputations.
Night-eating syndrome	Most of the day's kcalories are eaten late in the day or at night. A similar disorder, in which a person may eat while asleep and have no memory of the events, is called nocturnal sleep-related eating disorder. It is considered a sleep disorder, not an eating disorder.	Obese adults and those experiencing stress	Obesity
Orthorexia nervosa	Obsession with eating food considered to be healthy or beneficial. Focus on the quality of the food, not the quantity.	No particular group	Harmful to interpersonal relationships.
Pica	Craving and eating nonfood items such as dirt, clay, paint chips, plaster, chalk, laundry starch, coffee grounds, and ashes.	Pregnant women, children, people whose family or ethnic customs include eating certain nonfood substances.	Mineral deficiencies, perforated intestines, intestinal infections.
Rumination syndrome	Eating, swallowing, and then regurgitating food back into the mouth where it is chewed and swallowed again.	Infants and adults with mental and emotional impairment	Bad breath, indigestion, chapped lips, damage to dental enamel and tissues in the mouth, aspiration of food leading to pneumonia, weight loss and failure to grow (children), electrolyte imbalance, and dehydration.
Selective eating disorder	Eating only a few foods, mostly carbohydrate.	Children	Malnutrition

Figure F2.10 The ideal male body is as difficult for most men to achieve as the thin athletic ideal is for women. (Jim Cummins/Getty Images, Inc.)

Life Cycle

pica An abnormal craving for and ingestion of nonfood items.

Life Cycle

begin dieting when their BMI is in the healthy range, whereas men who develop eating disorders usually do not start dieting until they have a BMI in the overweight range.[17] Men also often acquire an eating disorder at an older age than women.

Although men currently represent a small percentage of those with eating disorders, the numbers seem to be on the rise.[18] This is likely due to increasing pressure to achieve an ideal male body. Advertisements directed at men today are showing more and more exposed skin with a focus on well-defined abdominal and chest muscles (**Figure F2.10**). Just as the Barbie doll set an unrealistic standard for young women, male action figures, super-hero cartoons, and media ideals set a standard that is impossible for young men to achieve.

The physical consequences of eating disorders are similar in men and women. Both lose bone but men are more severely affected by disorders related to bone loss and tend to have lower bone mineral density than women with the same disorder.[19] Rather than amenorrhea, men experience a gradual drop in testosterone levels. This causes a loss of sexual desire. Men with eating disorders have psychiatric conditions that are similar to those affecting women, including mood and personality disorders. Like women, men with eating disorders require professional help in order to recover and the outcome of treatment is similar in men and women. Men, however, are less likely to seek treatment because they do not want to be perceived as having a "woman's disease."

Eating Disorders During Pregnancy

Eating disorders are common in women in their twenties, an age when many people choose to start a family. If the eating disorder interrupts the menstrual cycle it will cause infertility.

Some women with eating disorders are able to conceive. What and how much they eat during pregnancy influences their health and the health of the baby before and after birth. Pregnancy can also make other medical problems related to the eating disorder worse, such as liver, heart, and kidney damage. Pregnant women with eating disorders are at increased risk of caesarean delivery and have a higher rate of miscarriages, premature birth, babies who are small for their age, and congenital malformations.[20] Babies born to women with eating disorders are more likely to be slower to grow and develop and they may lag behind intellectually and emotionally and remain dependent. They may also have difficulty developing social skills and relationships with other people.

An eating disorder that is more common in pregnancy is **pica** (see Chapters 12 and 14). This is an abnormal craving for and ingestion of nonfood substances having little or no nutritional value. Commonly consumed substances include dirt, clay, chalk, paint chips, laundry starch, ice and freezer frost, baking soda, cornstarch, coffee grounds, and ashes. Pica during pregnancy is potentially dangerous. The consumption of large amounts of nonfood substances may cause micronutrient deficiencies by reducing the intake of nutrient-dense foods and by interfering with the absorption of certain minerals from food. Substances consumed could also cause intestinal obstruction or perforation and could contain toxins or harmful bacteria. The cause of pica is unknown but there is some evidence that it results from cultural beliefs related to pregnancy, along with changes in food preferences that occur during pregnancy.

Eating Disorders in Children

Eating disorders also occur in children. These can be difficult to diagnose because most children are finicky eaters at some point in their development. But, when being finicky becomes extreme and growth is impaired, an eating disorder may be the cause. Disorders may involve consumption of a very limited number of foods or a general restriction of food intake (see Table F.2.4). Anorexia may also begin in children under the age of 13, but the incidence is much lower than it is in late adolescence and early adulthood. There is concern however that its prevalence is increasing in younger children in the United States as they are exposed to our cultural values about food and body weight. Forty-two percent of girls in first through third grades want to be thinner. Eighty-one percent of 10-year-olds are afraid of being fat, and

46% of 9- to 11-year-olds are "sometimes" or "very often" on diets.[21] More girls than boys are affected but the proportion of boys is greater than the proportion of men in the older age groups.[22] Diagnosing anorexia in girls under 13 is more challenging than in older girls because many have not started menstruating and it is difficult to calculate expected weight because growth may have slowed. Despite these problems there is little doubt that childhood-onset anorexia does occur and is a serious illness.

Children with anorexia, like older patients, are perfectionists, conscientious, and hardworking. They also exhibit similar symptoms including weight loss, food avoidance, preoccupation with food and kcalories, fear of fatness, excessive exercise, self-induced vomiting, and laxative abuse. Other physical changes that may accompany the weight loss include growth of lanugo hair, low blood pressure, slow heart rate, poor peripheral circulation, cold peripheries, and delayed or arrested growth. Bone density may be reduced and bone age delayed. Vitamin and mineral deficiencies are common.

As with older patients, the prognosis for children with anorexia is variable.[22] If treatment is not effective, the resulting undernutrition is even more likely to cause physical complications such as heart and circulatory failure in children than in older patients. Growth is affected, but the long-term consequences depend on the outcome of treatment. If treatment restores normal eating, these children will catch up in growth. Complications that may persist include amenorrhea, delayed growth, impaired fertility, and osteoporosis.

Eating Disorders in Athletes

The relationship between body weight and performance in certain sports contributes to the higher prevalence of eating disorders in athletes than in the general population.[23] It is higher in female athletes than in male athletes, and more common among those competing in leanness-dependent and weight-dependent sports such as ballet and other dance, figure skating, gymnastics, track and field, swimming, cycling, crew, wrestling, and horse racing[23] (**Figure F2.11**). The most problematic women's sports are cross-country, gymnastics, swimming, and track and field. The male sports with the highest number of participants with eating disorders are wrestling and cross-country.[24]

Both anorexia nervosa and bulimia occur in athletes. The regimented schedule of an athlete makes it easy for them to use training diets and schedules, travel, or competition as an excuse to not eat normally and hide the eating disorder. Over time the continued starvation characteristic of anorexia leads to serious health problems as well as a decline in athletic performance. Starvation can lead to abnormal heart rhythms, low blood pressure, and atrophy of the heart muscle. The lack of food means that there is not adequate energy and nutrients to support activity and growth. Bulimia nervosa is more common in athletes than anorexia. It may begin because an athlete is unable to stick with a restrictive diet or the hunger associated with a very-low-kcalorie diet leads to bingeing. As in nonathletes, most of the health complications associated with bulimia are the result of purging. It causes fluid loss and low-potassium levels, which can result in extreme weakness, as well as dangerous and sometimes lethal heart rhythms.

Anorexia Athletica Compulsive exercise, which has been termed *anorexia athletica*, is a type of eating disorder that is a particular problem in athletes. People with this disorder focus on exercise rather than food but anorexia athletica is considered an eating disorder because the goal of the behavior is to expend kcalories to control weight. Extreme training is easy to justify because it is a common belief that serious athletes can never work too hard or too long and pain is accepted as an indicator of achievement. Compulsive exercisers will force themselves to exercise even when they don't feel well and may miss social events in order to fulfill their exercise quota. They often calculate exercise goals based on how much they eat. They believe that any break in the training schedule will cause them to gain weight and performance will suffer. Compulsive exercise can lead to more serious eating disorders such as anorexia and bulimia as well as serious health problems including kidney failure, heart attack, and death.

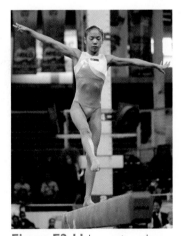

Figure F2.11 In sports such as gymnastics, the advantages offered by a small, light body can motivate athletes to diet to stay thin and can potentially contribute to the development of an eating disorder. (Pornchai Kittiwongsakul/AFP/Getty Images, Inc.)

Low estrogen affects calcium homeostasis in the bone and reduces calcium absorption in the intestines, leading to low peak bone mass, premature bone loss, and increased risk of stress fractures.

Osteoporosis

Amenorrhea

Disordered Eating

Energy restriction combined with exercise contributes to a drop in estrogen levels, which causes amenorrhea.

Figure F2.12 Female athlete Triad
Women with female athlete triad typically have low body fat, do not menstruate regularly, and may experience multiple or recurrent stress fractures.

female athlete triad The combination of disordered eating, amenorrhea, and osteoporosis that occurs in some female athletes, particularly those involved in sports in which low body weight and appearance are important.

osteoporosis A bone disorder characterized by a decrease in bone mass, an increase in bone fragility, and an increased risk of fractures.

Female Athlete Triad Female athletes with eating disorders are at risk for a syndrome of interrelated disorders referred to as the **female athlete triad** (see Chapter 13) (**Figure F2.12**). This syndrome includes disordered eating, amenorrhea, and **osteoporosis**. The three are linked because the extreme energy restriction that occurs in eating disorders creates a physiological condition similar to starvation, which leads to menstrual irregularities. High levels of exercise can also affect the menstrual cycle by increasing energy demands and causing hormonal changes.[25] When combined, energy restriction and excessive exercise contribute to amenorrhea. The low-estrogen levels associated with amenorrhea then interfere with calcium balance, leading to reductions in bone mass and bone-mineral density. Low-estrogen levels also reduce calcium absorption and, when combined with poor calcium intake (common in female athletes and females in general), lead to premature bone loss, failure to reach maximal peak bone mass, and an increased risk of stress fractures.

Eating Disorders and Diabetes

Diabetes does not cause eating disorders but it may set the stage for them both physically and emotionally and can be used to hide them. Diabetes is a disease characterized by a chronic elevation in blood glucose that is due to abnormalities in the production or effectiveness of the hormone insulin (see Chapter 4). Treatment involves paying careful attention to diet, exercise, body weight, and blood glucose levels. The timing of exercise and timing and composition of meals are crucial to good glucose control. This regimentation, which is part of routine diabetes management, may contribute to the development of eating disorders because it places attention on food portions and body weight; a focus similar to that seen in women with eating disorders who do not have diabetes.[26]

Control is a central issue in diabetes as it is in eating disorders. A person with diabetes may feel guilty or out of control if their blood sugar is too high. Anorexics feel the same way if their weight increases. People with diabetes become consumed with strategies to control blood sugar and those with an eating disorder become consumed with ways to control weight. Both are preoccupied with weight, food, and diet. Because this is expected in diabetes, people with this disease can use their diabetes to hide anorexia or bulimia. They are supposed to watch what they eat and the diabetes can be blamed for weight loss.

Those who take insulin to control their diabetes are at particular risk because they can misuse it to control their weight, a condition that has been termed *diabulimia*. Insulin is responsible for allowing glucose to enter cells. If patients cut back on the amount of insulin they take, the sugar in their blood cannot enter cells and it is excreted in the urine. This causes weight loss, but at a very high cost. The long-term complications of having high levels of blood glucose include blindness, kidney disease, cardiovascular disease, impaired circulation, and nerve death that can lead to limb amputations. Once a person with diabetes starts to control their weight by withholding insulin they are reluctant to stop and may also begin using other inappropriate behaviors to control weight. Sometimes the weight loss seems to improve the diabetes, at least temporarily, by reducing the need for insulin, but if the weight loss continues it can lead to organ failure and death.

F2.7 Preventing and Getting Treatment for Eating Disorders

Learning Objectives

- Describe factors that predispose people to eating disorders.
- List the steps you could take if you had a friend with an eating disorder.

Reducing the incidence of and morbidity from eating disorders involves action on a number of levels. The first step is to recognize individuals who are at risk. Early intervention can help prevent those who are at risk from developing serious eating disorders, and the actions of family and friends can help those who are affected get help before their health is impaired. To reduce the overall incidence of eating disorders changes in social attitudes that contribute to their development need to occur.

Recognizing the Risks

To prevent eating disorders it is important to first recognize factors that increase risk. Excessive concerns about body weight, having friends who are preoccupied with weight, being teased by peers about weight, and problems with one's family all predispose people to eating disorders. There is an association between parental criticism and children's weight preoccupation. Dieting also increases risk. Girls and women who diet are more likely to develop an eating disorder than those who don't diet.[2] Those who have a mother, sister, or friend who diets are also at increased risk. Exposure to media pressure to be thin is also associated with the development of eating disorders.

Getting Help for a Friend or Family Member

Those who are at risk for eating disorders can be targeted for intervention. For teens, parents play an important role. Arranging an evaluation with a physician and a mental health specialist when the first symptoms are discovered may help prevent the disorder.

Once an eating disorder has developed people usually do not get better by themselves. Helping them to get medical and psychological treatment can avoid severe physical consequences. But getting a friend or relative with an eating disorder to agree to seek help is not always easy. People with eating disorders are good at hiding their behaviors and denying the problem and often do not want help.

If you suspect a friend has an eating disorder you can alert a parent, teacher, coach, religious leader, school nurse, or other trusted adult about your concerns or confront your friend or relative yourself and express your concern. If you approach the person yourself, you need to be firm but supportive and caring. The goal in discussing a person's eating disorder is to encourage them to seek help. But, help is only effective if it is desired. People with eating disorders are likely to refuse help initially.

When approaching someone about an eating disorder it is therefore important to make it clear that you are not trying to force them to do anything they don't want to do. Continued encouragement can help some people to seek professional help. The first reaction of someone confronted about an eating disorder is often to deny that they have a problem. Support your suspicions with examples of things you have seen that make you believe your friend has a problem. You should be prepared for all possible reactions. People with eating disorders usually try to hide their behaviors so it is traumatic for them when someone has discovered their secret. One person may be relieved that you are concerned and willing to help, whereas another may be angry and defensive (**Table F2.5**).

Table F2.5 Eating Disorders: How to Help

- Get the person to a doctor; the sooner the illness is treated the more likely there will be a successful outcome.

- Talk to the parents, spouse, or other family members.

- Explain your concerns and the potential hazards of the disease.

- Do not expect the person to cooperate; denial is common.

- If you work with the person, contact your employee assistance program.

Reducing the Prevalence of Eating Disorders

Eating disorders are easier to prevent than to cure. The biggest impact on prevention can be made by social interventions that target the elimination of weight-related teasing and criticism from peers and family members. Another important target for reducing the incidence of eating disorders is the media. If the unrealistically thin body ideal presented by the media could be altered the incidence of eating disorders would likely decrease. Even with these interventions however, eating disorders are unlikely to go away, but education through schools and communities about the symptoms and complications of eating disorders can help people identify friends and family members at risk and persuade those with early symptoms to seek help.

References

1. American Psychiatric Association. *Diagnostic and Statistical Manual of Mental Disorders*, 4th ed., TR, Washington, DC: American Psychiatric Association, 2000.

2. Fitzgibbon, M., and Stolley, M. Minority Women: The Untold Story. NOVA Online: Dying to Be Thin. Available online at www.pbs.org/wgbh/nova/thin/minorities.html/. Accessed December 21, 2005.

3. American Dietetic Association. Position of the American Dietetic Association: Nutrition intervention in the treatment of anorexia nervosa, bulimia nervosa, and other eating disorders. *J Am Diet Assoc* 106:2073–2082, 2006.

4. Milano, W., Petrella, C., Sabatino, C., and Capasso, A. Treatment of bulimia nervosa with sertraline: A randomized controlled trial. *Adv. Ther.* 21:232–237, 2004.

5. Branson, R., Potoczna, N., Kral, J. G. et al. Binge eating as a major phenotype of melanocortin 4 receptor gene mutations. *N. Engl. J. Med.* 348:1096–1103, 2003.

6. Stice, E. Sociocultural influences on body weight and eating disturbance. In: *Eating Disorders and Obesity: A Comprehensive Handbook*, 2nd ed., C. G. Fairburn, and K. D. Brownell, eds. New York: The Guilford Press 2002, pp. 103–107.

7. Mediascope. Body Image and Advertising. Available online at www.mediascope.org/pubs/ibriefs/bia.htm/. Accessed April 20, 2005.

8. ANRED. Anorexia Nervosa and Related Eating Disorders, Inc. Statistics: How Many People Have Eating Disorders? Available online at www.anred.com/stats.html/. Accessed April 2, 2002.

9. Peat, C., Mitchell, J. E., Hoek, H. W., and Wonderlich, S. Validity and utility of subtyping anorexia nervosa. *Int. J. Eat. Disord.* 42:1–7, 2009.

10. Tozzi, F., Thornton, L. M., Klump, K. L. et al. Symptom fluctuation in eating disorders: Correlates of diagnostic crossover. *Am. J. Psychiatry* 162:732–740, 2005.

11. Vandereycken, W. History of anorexia nervosa and bulimia nervosa. In: *Eating Disorders and Obesity: A Comprehensive Handbook,* 2nd ed., C. G. Fairburn, and K. D. Brownell, eds. New York: The Guilford Press, 2002, pp. 151–154.

12. Kaye, W. H., Weltzin, T. E., McKee, M. et al. Laboratory assessment of feeding behavior in bulimia nervosa and healthy women. Methods of developing a human feeding laboratory. *Am. J. Clin. Nutr.* 55:372–380, 1992.

13. Kaye, W. H., Weltzin, T. E., Hsu, L. K. et al. Amount of calories retained after binge eating and vomiting. *Am. J. Psychiatry* 150:969–971, 1993.

14. Ebeling, H., Tapanainen, P., and Joutsenoja, A. A practice guideline for treatment of eating disorders in children and adolescents. *Ann. Med.* 35:488–501, 2003.

15. Hoek H. W., van Hoeken, D. Review of the prevalence and incidence of eating disorders. *Int. J. Eat Disord.* 34:383–396, 2003.

16. National Eating Disorders Association. Binge Eating Disorder. Available online at http://www.nationaleatingdisorders.org/nedaDir/files/documents/handouts/BED.pdf Accessed June 13, 2009.

17. Andersen, A. E., and Holman, J. E. Males with eating disorders: Challenges for treatment and research. *Psychopharmacol. Bull.* 33:391–397, 1997.

18. Woodside, D. B., Garfinkel, P. E., Lin, E. et al. Comparisons of men with full or partial eating disorders, men without eating disorders, and women with eating disorders in the community. *Am. J. Psychiatry* 158:570–574, 2001.

19. Andersen, A. E., Watson, T., and Schlechte, J. Osteoporosis and osteopenia in men with eating disorders. *Lancet* 355:1967–1968, 2000.

20. Mitchell-Gieleghem, A., Mittelstaedt, M. E., and Bulik, C. M. Eating disorders and childbearing: Concealment and consequences. *Birth* 29:182–191, 2002.

21. University of Nebraska Medical Center, Department of Obstetrics and Gynocology. Don't Weigh Your Self Esteem—Every Body Counts. Available online at www.unmc.edu/olson/education/ed.htm/. Accessed June 12, 2009.

22. Casper, R. C. Eating disturbances and eating disorders in childhood. Psychopharmacology—The Fourth Generation of Progress. The American College of Neuropsychopharmacology, 2000, Available online at www.acnp.org/g4/GN401000162/Default.htm/. Accessed April 15, 2005.

23. Sundgot-Borgen, J., and Torstveit, M. K. Prevalence of eating disorders in elite athletes is higher than in the general population. *Clin. J. Sports Med.* 14:25–32, 2004.

24. National Eating Disorders Information Center. Available online at www.nedic.ca/glossary.html/. Accessed June 12, 2009.

25. Warren, M. P., and Goodman, L. R. Exercise-induced endocrine pathologies. *J. Endocrinol. Invest.* 26:873–878, 2003.

26. Goebel-Fabbri, A. E., Fikkan, J., Connell, A. et al. Identification and treatment of eating disorders in women with type 1 diabetes mellitus. *Treat. Endocrinol.* 1:155–162, 2002.

8

The Water-Soluble Vitamins

Case Study

Chen is 65 years old and has always been healthy. He and his wife exercise regularly, watch their weight, and eat a healthy diet. Recently Chen experienced a few episodes of forgetfulness, but he laughed it off as old age. Then he began feeling tired and having tingling in his hands and feet, difficulty walking, and diarrhea. Fearing the worst, he made an appointment to see his doctor.

Laboratory tests showed that Chen had low levels of vitamin B_{12}. A diet history revealed that his diet didn't provide much of the vitamin. He eats lots of grains, fruits, and vegetables, which do not provide vitamin B_{12} and very little meat, which is a source of this vitamin. The doctor explained that Chen's symptoms were due to a vitamin B_{12} deficiency. The deficiency was likely caused by an inflammation of his stomach that reduced his ability to absorb the small amounts of vitamin B_{12} provided by his diet. Chen's doctor gave him an injection of vitamin B_{12} and recommended that he start taking a daily supplement containing the vitamin.

Because of our plentiful food supply and the availability of vitamin supplements, Americans tend to think of vitamin deficiencies as a thing of the past, or perhaps as conditions that afflict people only in the developing world. For the most part that is true. But, as Chen's case illustrates, some segments of the U.S. population still don't get enough of some vitamins due to low intakes, increased needs, or conditions that interfere with absorption or utilization.

(Hiroshi Yagi/Getty Images, Inc.)

(©iStockphoto)

(...obertson/FoodPix/Jupiter Images)

Chapter Outline

8.1 What Are Vitamins?

Learning Objectives

- Name the sources of vitamins in the U.S. diet.
- Describe how bioavailability affects vitamin requirements.
- Explain the role of coenzymes.

vitamins Organic compounds needed in the diet in small amounts to promote and regulate the chemical reactions and processes needed for growth, reproduction, and maintenance of health.

water-soluble vitamins Vitamins that dissolve in water.

fat-soluble vitamins Vitamins that dissolve in fat.

Vitamins are organic compounds that are essential in the diet in small amounts to promote and regulate the processes necessary for growth, reproduction, and the maintenance of health. When a vitamin is lacking in the diet, deficiency symptoms occur. When the vitamin is restored to the diet the symptoms resolve. Vitamins have traditionally been grouped based on their solubility in water or fat. This chemical characteristic allows generalizations to be made about how they are absorbed, transported, excreted, and stored in the body. The **water-soluble vitamins** include the B vitamins and vitamin C. The **fat-soluble vitamins** include vitamins A, D, E, and K (**Table 8.1**). The vitamins were initially named alphabetically in approximately the order in which they were identified: A, B, C, D, and E. The B vitamins were first thought to be one chemical substance but were later found to be many different substances, so the alphabetical name was broken down by numbers; thiamin, riboflavin, and niacin were originally referred to as vitamin B_1, B_2, and B_3, respectively. Vitamins B_6 and B_{12} are the only ones that are still commonly referred to by their numbers.

Table 8.1 The Vitamins

Water-Soluble Vitamins	Fat-Soluble Vitamins
B vitamins	Vitamin A
Thiamin (B_1)	Vitamin D
Riboflavin (B_2)	Vitamin E
Niacin (B_3)	Vitamin K
Biotin	
Pantothenic acid	
Vitamin B_6	
Folate	
Vitamin B_{12}	
Vitamin C	

Vitamins in the Modern Diet

The last of the 13 compounds recognized as vitamins today was characterized in 1948. The ability to isolate and purify vitamins has allowed them to be added to the food supply and incorporated into pills. As a result, the modern diet includes not only vitamins that are naturally present in food but also those that have been added to foods and those consumed as dietary supplements. Despite the variety of options for obtaining vitamins, it is still possible to consume too little of some vitamins and the likelihood of consuming too much of others is increasing.

Natural Sources of Vitamins Almost all foods contain some vitamins (**Figure 8.1**). Grains are good sources of most of the B vitamins. Leafy green vegetables provide folate, vitamin A, vitamin E, and vitamin K; citrus fruit provides vitamin C. Meat and fish are good sources of all of the B vitamins and milk provides riboflavin and vitamins A and D. Even oils provide vitamins; vegetable oils are high in vitamin E. How much of each of these vitamins remains in a food when it reaches the table depends on how the food is handled. Cooking and storage methods can cause vitamin

GRAINS	VEGETABLES	FRUITS	OILS	MILK	MEAT & BEANS
Thiamin	Riboflavin	Folate	Vitamin E	Riboflavin	Thiamin
Riboflavin	Niacin	Vitamin C		Vitamin A	Riboflavin
Niacin	Vitamin B$_6$	Vitamin A		Vitamin D	Niacin
Pantothenic acid	Folate			Vitamin B$_{12}$	Biotin
Vitamin B$_6$	Vitamin C				Pantothenic acid
Folate	Vitamin A				Folate
	Vitamin E				Vitamin B$_{12}$
	Vitamin K				Vitamin A
					Vitamin D
					Vitamin K

Figure 8.1 Vitamins in MyPyramid food groups
Vitamins are found in foods from all groups, as well as oils, but some groups are lacking in specific vitamins.

losses. Processing can cause vitamin losses but can also add vitamins and other nutrients to food.

Fortified Foods The addition of nutrients to foods is called **fortification**. Consuming fortified foods increases nutrient intake. This can be beneficial if the added nutrients are deficient in the diet but it can also increase the risk of toxicity.

Government-mandated fortification programs have been used to increase nutrient intake and reduce deficiency diseases in populations. Adding nutrients to food is an effective way to supplement nutrients that are deficient in the population's diet without having to rely on consumers to alter their food choices or to take nutrient supplements. Which foods are fortified, which nutrients are added, and how much of a nutrient is added depends on the food supply, the needs of the population, and public health policies. In the United States, iodine was added to salt in the 1920s and vitamin D was first added to cow's milk in the early 1930s. By 1943 most refined grain products were **enriched** with thiamin, riboflavin, niacin, and iron. Today, fortification programs are used throughout the world to increase the intake of nutrients likely to be deficient (see Chapter 18). The levels of nutrients added are based on an amount that is high enough to benefit those who need to increase their intake but not so high as to increase the risk of excessive intakes in others.

Fortification today extends beyond government-mandated programs. Manufacturers are now fortifying their products with a variety of nutrients. Much of this discretionary fortification involves nutrients that are of public health concern. For example, because many Americans do not consume enough calcium, the food industry has supplied us with calcium-fortified orange juice, breakfast cereal, and cheese. Other nutrients that are commonly added are those that are easy and inexpensive to add to a food and may promote sales of the product. When fortification goes beyond applications defined by the FDA, the level of fortification may be arbitrary. Consuming large amounts of these fortified foods, particularly along with nutrient supplements, has the potential to cause nutrient imbalances and toxicities. For example, almost all breakfast cereals are fortified with iron and calcium and a complement of vitamins, many of which are not deficient in the U.S. diet. A breakfast that includes a few servings of fortified cereal and a multivitamin, could easily provide

fortification A term used generally to describe the process of adding nutrients to foods, such as the addition of vitamin D to milk.

enriched Refers to a food that has had nutrients added to restore those lost in processing to a level equal to or higher than originally present.

Fortified Breakfast Cereal

Nutrition Facts

Serving Size 1 Cup (50g/1.8 oz.)
Servings per Container About 10

Amount Per Serving	Cereal	Cereal with 1/2 Cup Vitamins A&D Fat Free Milk
Calories	180	220
Calories from Fat	5	5

	% Daily Value**	
Total Fat 0.5g*	1%	1%
Saturated Fat 0g	0%	0%
Trans Fat 0g		
Cholesterol 0mg	0%	0%
Sodium 280mg	12%	14%
Potassium 100mg	3%	9%
Total Carbohydrate 35g	12%	14%
Dietary Fiber 2g	9%	9%
Sugars 7g		
Other Carbohydrate 26g		
Protein 3g		

Vitamin A	15%	20%
Vitamin C	25%	25%
Calcium	0%	15%
Iron	100%	100%
Vitamin D	10%	25%
Vitamin E	100%	100%
Thiamin	100%	100%
Riboflavin	100%	110%
Niacin	100%	100%
Vitamin B₆	100%	100%
Folic Acid	100%	100%
Vitamin B₁₂	100%	110%
Pantothenate	100%	100%
Phosphorus	10%	20%
Magnesium	8%	10%
Zinc	100%	100%
Copper	4%	6%

Figure 8.2 Nutrients in fortified breakfast cereal
The amounts and variety of nutrients added to some fortified breakfast cereals are so great that they resemble multivitamin/mineral supplements.

more than the recommended amounts for some vitamins (**Figure 8.2**). Thirty-six percent of children now have zinc intakes that exceed the UL, primarily due to an increase in the amount of zinc from zinc-fortified breakfast cereals.[1] The percent of children at risk for toxicity would be even greater if zinc from supplements were included in the analysis. Extensive fortification in the breakfast cereal industry has also made it difficult for those who must limit iron intake to find breakfast cereals that are not fortified with iron.

Fortification may also cause people to believe a food is a more nutritious choice than it really is. For example a Fruit Roll-Up fortified with vitamin C looks like a healthy choice. But, this food is still high in added sugars and low in most of the nutrients that would be provided by a piece of fruit. Because of the potential for over- and underfortification and nutrient imbalances, the FDA cautions against the indiscriminant addition of nutrients to foods and the fortification of snack foods and candy[2] (see Your Choice: Are They Foods? Should You Choose Them?).

Dietary Supplements Supplements are another source of vitamins in the modern diet. Dietary supplements are products intended to supplement the diet that contain one or more of the following dietary ingredients: vitamins; minerals; herbs, botanicals, or other plant-derived substances; amino acids; enzymes; concentrates or extracts. They are taken to increase nutrient intake, as well as to enhance athletic performance, promote weight loss, alleviate existing symptoms and conditions, extend life, and prevent chronic disease. They come as pills, tablets, liquids, and powders. While supplements provide specific nutrients, and can help some people meet their nutrient needs, they do not provide all the benefits of a diet containing a wide variety of foods[3] (see Chapter 9, Off the Label: Think Before You Supplement). A varied diet provides phytochemicals and other substances that are not nutrients but that have health-promoting properties. A pill that meets vitamin needs does not provide the energy, water, protein, minerals, fiber, or phytochemicals that would have been supplied by food sources of these vitamins (**Figure 8.3**). Epidemiological studies show that people who eat more fruits and vegetables have a lower incidence of a host of chronic diseases. These same benefits are not duplicated by taking supplements of nutrients found in these foods. Scientists have not yet identified all the substances contained in foods, nor have they determined all of their effects on human health. What is clear is that a wholesome, varied diet is important for optimal health. If chosen with care supplements

Figure 8.3 Vitamin supplements cannot take the place of a balanced diet. (©Charles D. Winters)

(©iStockphoto)

Are They Foods? Should You Choose Them?

An energy bar that contains soy protein and 23 vitamins and minerals; a canned soft drink with echinacea and 100% of the Daily Value for most of the B vitamins; a fruit juice designed for women that provides 600% of the Daily Value for thiamin, riboflavin, vitamin B_6, and vitamin B_{12} along with guarana and Dong Quai; bottled water with 100% of the Daily Value for vitamin C—are these foods? As food manufacturers cash in on the concept that "health sells," the line between what is a supplement and what is a food has become blurred. Should these foods be part of your diet? Are they safe?

One of the first things to consider when selecting a fortified product is what nutrients it provides. These products must all carry either a Nutrition Facts or Supplement Facts label. If you are looking for a way to ensure that you get enough vitamins, you may choose a fortified breakfast cereal. Vitamin-fortified foods, such as breakfast cereals, can help ensure your vitamin needs are met and serve as an alternative to a multivitamin pill, but if you are looking for a source of added phytochemicals or herbs, these may disappoint you. A close look at the label will probably reveal that the amounts of these substances added are almost insignificant.

Once you have found a product that provides the nutrients you want to add to your diet, it is important to consider whether it also contains things you don't want. For example, an energy bar with added soy may help you increase your intake of soy protein. But if it also includes more energy, fat, and added vitamins than you want, you may do better getting your soy protein from tofu. Likewise, fortified fruit juice may seem like a good way to get your vitamin C, but if the juice also includes one or more herbs that you don't want, a glass of orange juice might be a better choice.

Finally, evaluate any risks associated with consuming the product. If this food becomes a regular part of your diet, will you exceed the recommended intakes for any nutrients? It is almost impossible to consume harmful amounts of nutrients in unfortified foods, but doing so is easy with fortified foods. For example, if the water you drink is fortified with vitamin C,

niacin, vitamin E, and vitamins B_6 and B_{12}, on a hot day you may drink enough to consume these nutrients well in excess of your needs and increase your risk of a toxic dose. There are no Daily Values or ULs for herbs, so if you consume products containing herbs you may not be able to tell whether you're getting enough to have any effect or getting a dose high enough to cause an adverse reaction. As consumers today, we enjoy a great variety of choices, but we need to choose wisely to be sure we are getting health benefits, not health risks.

(Andy Washnik)

are unlikely to be harmful, but consumers should not rely heavily on these to meet their needs.

Despite their healthful intentions, many of the people taking supplements may still not be getting the nutrients they need the most. When the types of products people take are compared to the nutrients at risk for deficiency in the American diet, the two don't match. An analysis of the current U.S. diet has shown that average intakes of thiamin, riboflavin, niacin, and vitamin C from food meet or exceed recommendations. However, the average calcium intake in the American diet is only 700 to 800 mg per day—well below the recommended intake for anyone over the age of 8 years. The multivitamin/mineral pills that most people take provide plenty of B vitamins and vitamin C, but little calcium. Additional information on micronutrient supplements is included in the discussion of each vitamin and mineral in this chapter and Chapters 9 through 12.

Understanding Vitamin Needs

Today, in the United States and other industrialized countries, an understanding of the sources and functions of the vitamins, a varied food supply, and the ability to fortify foods and supplement nutrients has helped to eliminate severe vitamin deficiencies as a public health problem. For example, niacin deficiency, which was common in the southern United States in the early 1900s, is now almost unheard of; vitamin C deficiency, which killed countless sailors and soldiers throughout history, is now a rarity; and vitamin A deficiency, which remains a major public health concern worldwide, rarely occurs in developed countries. However, despite all of our knowledge, our varied diet, and shelves of vitamin supplements, not everyone gets enough of every vitamin all the time. Certain segments of the population, such as children, pregnant women, and the elderly are at particular risk for deficiency. Some vitamin deficiencies are on the rise because of changes in dietary patterns. In addition, marginal deficiencies, which may have been present in the population for a long time, are now being recognized and their detrimental effects better understood. In order to make recommendations about how much of each vitamin is needed to optimize health it is important to understand how vitamins are absorbed, transported, used, stored, and excreted.

Video

bioavailability A general term that refers to how well a nutrient can be absorbed and used by the body.

Bioavailability of Vitamins Whether vitamins come from foods, fortified foods, or supplements, they must be absorbed into the body to perform their functions. About 40% to 90% of the vitamins in food are absorbed, primarily in the small intestine (**Figure 8.4**). The composition of the diet and conditions in the body, however, may influence how much of a vitamin is available in the body. **Bioavailability** considers the amount of a nutrient that can be absorbed and utilized by the body.

One of the key factors affecting bioavailability is whether the vitamin is soluble in fat or water. Fat-soluble vitamins require fat in the diet for absorption and are poorly absorbed when the diet is very low in fat. The water-soluble vitamins do not require fat for absorption but many depend on energy-requiring transport systems or must be bound to specific molecules in the gastrointestinal tract in order to be absorbed. For example, thiamin and vitamin C are absorbed by energy-requiring transport systems, riboflavin and niacin require carrier proteins for absorption, and vitamin B_{12} must be bound to a protein produced in the stomach before it can be absorbed in the intestine.

Once absorbed into the blood, vitamins must be transported to the cells. Most of the water-soluble vitamins are bound to blood proteins for transport. Fat-soluble vitamins must be incorporated into lipoproteins or bound to transport proteins in order to be transported in the aqueous environment of the blood. For example, vitamins A, D, E, and K are all incorporated into chylomicrons for transport from the intestine. Vitamin A is stored in the liver, but it must be bound to a specific transport protein to be transported in the blood to other tissues; therefore,

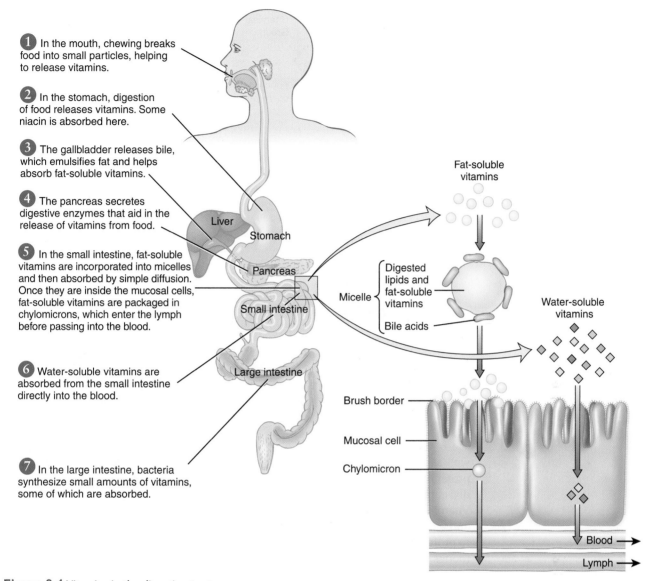

1 In the mouth, chewing breaks food into small particles, helping to release vitamins.

2 In the stomach, digestion of food releases vitamins. Some niacin is absorbed here.

3 The gallbladder releases bile, which emulsifies fat and helps absorb fat-soluble vitamins.

4 The pancreas secretes digestive enzymes that aid in the release of vitamins from food.

5 In the small intestine, fat-soluble vitamins are incorporated into micelles and then absorbed by simple diffusion. Once they are inside the mucosal cells, fat-soluble vitamins are packaged in chylomicrons, which enter the lymph before passing into the blood.

6 Water-soluble vitamins are absorbed from the small intestine directly into the blood.

7 In the large intestine, bacteria synthesize small amounts of vitamins, some of which are absorbed.

Liver
Stomach
Pancreas
Small intestine
Large intestine

Fat-soluble vitamins

Digested lipids and fat-soluble vitamins
Micelle
Bile acids

Water-soluble vitamins

Brush border
Mucosal cell
Chylomicron

Blood →
Lymph →

Figure 8.4 Vitamins in the digestive tract
Most vitamin absorption takes place in the small intestine. The mechanism by which vitamins are absorbed and transported affects their bioavailability.

the amount delivered to the tissues depends on the availability of the transport protein.

Some vitamins are absorbed in inactive **provitamin** or **vitamin precursor** forms that must be converted into active vitamin forms once inside the body. How much of each provitamin can be converted into the active vitamin and the rate at which this occurs affect the amount of a vitamin available to function in the body.

Vitamin Functions Vitamins promote and regulate body activities. Each provides a unique role, but some of their functions have similarities or work toward a common goal in the body. The B vitamins are all **coenzymes**, which are organic nonprotein substances that bind to enzymes to promote their activity (**Figure 8.5**). Although vitamins do not provide energy, many of the B vitamins are coenzymes essential for the proper functioning of numerous enzymes involved in the metabolism of the energy-yielding nutrients. Thiamin, riboflavin, niacin, pantothenic acid, and biotin all serve as coenzymes for reactions that release energy from carbohydrate, fat, and protein as

provitamin or **vitamin precursor** A compound that can be converted into the active form of a vitamin in the body.

coenzymes Small nonprotein organic molecules that act as carriers of electrons or atoms in metabolic reactions and are necessary for the proper functioning of many enzymes.

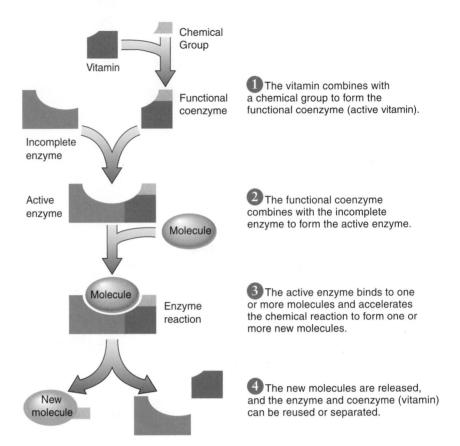

① The vitamin combines with a chemical group to form the functional coenzyme (active vitamin).

② The functional coenzyme combines with the incomplete enzyme to form the active enzyme.

③ The active enzyme binds to one or more molecules and accelerates the chemical reaction to form one or more new molecules.

④ The new molecules are released, and the enzyme and coenzyme (vitamin) can be reused or separated.

Figure 8.5 **Coenzymes**
The active coenzyme form of a vitamin is necessary for enzyme activity and acts as a carrier of chemical groups or electrons in the reaction.

well as alcohol (**Figure 8.6**). Vitamin B_6 plays an important role in amino acid and protein metabolism and folate and vitamin B_{12} work together to ensure normal cell division. Vitamin K is a fat-soluble coenzyme needed for proper blood clotting. Vitamin C is a coenzyme essential for the synthesis of neurotransmitters, hormones, and a protein vital to the structure of connective tissue. It also works with vitamin E to protect the body from oxidative damage. Vitamins A and D function more like hormones by affecting the proteins synthesized by the cell.

Storage and Excretion The ability to store and excrete vitamins helps to regulate the amount present in the body. With the exception of vitamin B_{12}, the water-soluble vitamins are easily excreted from the body in the urine. Because they are not stored to any great extent, supplies of water-soluble vitamins are rapidly depleted and they must be consumed regularly in the diet. Nevertheless, it takes more than a few days to develop deficiency symptoms, even when these vitamins are completely absent from the diet. Fat-soluble vitamins, on the other hand, are stored in the liver and fatty tissues and cannot be excreted in the urine. In general, because they are stored to a larger extent, it takes longer to develop a deficiency of fat-soluble vitamins when they are no longer provided by the diet.

Recommended Intakes Recommendations for vitamin intake for healthy populations in the United States and Canada are made by the DRIs (see Chapter 2). The DRIs provide either an RDA value, when sufficient information is available to establish an EAR, or an AI, when a recommendation is estimated from population data. These values are used as a goal for dietary intake by individuals. The DRIs also establish Tolerable Upper Intake Levels (ULs) as a guide to the maximum amount of a nutrient that is unlikely to cause adverse health effects (see inside cover). Meeting vitamin needs without exceeding a safe level of intake requires careful attention to the kinds of foods chosen as well as knowledge of the nutrients added to foods and those consumed in supplements.

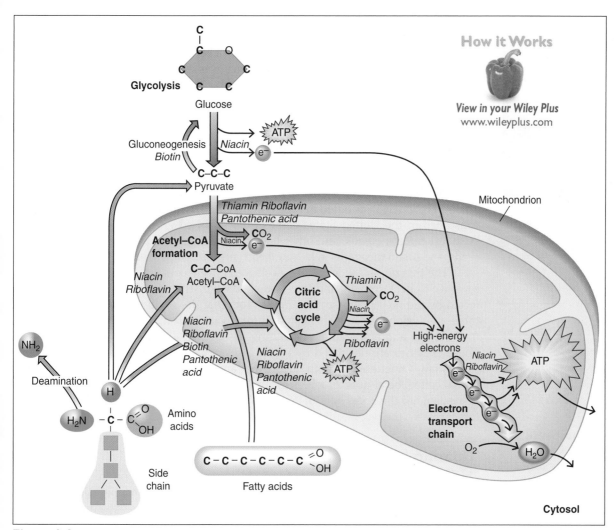

Figure 8.6 B Vitamins and energy metabolism
Reactions that require thiamin, riboflavin, niacin, biotin, or pantothenic acid as coenzymes are particularly important in the production of ATP from glucose, fatty acids, and amino acids.

8.2 Thiamin

Learning Objectives

- Discuss the role of thiamin in providing energy.
- Explain why a thiamin deficiency causes neurological symptoms.

Thiamin was the first of the B vitamins to be identified and is therefore sometimes called vitamin B$_1$. The disease that results from a deficiency of this vitamin, **beriberi**, has been present in East Asia for over 1000 years and came to the attention of Western medicine in colonial Asia in the nineteenth century. Beriberi became such a problem that the Dutch East India Company sent a team of scientists to find its cause. What they were expecting to find was a microorganism like those that caused cholera and rabies. What they found for a long time was nothing. For over 10 years, a young physician named Christian Eijkman tried to induce beriberi in chickens. His success came as a twist of fate. He ran out of food for his experimental chickens and instead of the usual brown rice, he fed them white rice. Shortly thereafter, the chickens came down with beriberi-like symptoms. When he fed them brown rice again,

beriberi The disease resulting from a deficiency of thiamin.

Figure 8.7 Why might thiamin deficiency be more common in cultures where unenriched white rice is a dietary staple? (Charles D. Winters)

they got well. This provided evidence that the cause of beriberi was not a poison or a microorganism, but rather something missing from the chickens' diet.

Just as a diet of white rice was the cause of beriberi in Eijkman's chickens, a diet consisting primarily of white or polished rice was also the reason the incidence of beriberi in East Asia increased dramatically in the 1800s. Polished or white rice is produced by polishing off the bran layer of brown rice creating a more uniform product. However, polishing off the bran also removes the thiamin-rich portion of the grain (**Figure 8.7**). Therefore, in populations where white rice was the staple of the diet, beriberi, became a common health problem.

Thiamin in the Diet

Thiamin is widely distributed in foods (**Figure 8.8**). A large proportion of the thiamin consumed in the United States comes from enriched grains used in foods such as breakfast cereals, breads, and other baked goods. Pork, whole grains, legumes, nuts, seeds, and organ meats (liver, kidney, heart) are also good sources.

The thiamin in foods may be destroyed during cooking or storage because it is sensitive to heat, oxygen, and low-acid conditions. Thiamin bioavailability is also affected by the presence of antithiamin factors that destroy the vitamin. For instance, there are enzymes in raw shellfish and freshwater fish that degrade thiamin during food storage and preparation and during passage through the gastrointestinal tract. These enzymes are destroyed by cooking so they are only a concern in foods consumed raw. Other anti-thiamin factors that are not inactivated by cooking are found in tea, coffee, betel nuts, blueberries, and red cabbage. Because these make thiamin unavailable to the body, habitual consumption of foods containing anti-thiamin factors increases the risk of thiamin deficiency.[4]

Thiamin in the Body

Thiamin is a vitamin so it does not provide energy, but it is important in the energy-yielding reactions in the body. The active form, **thiamin pyrophosphate**, is a coenzyme for reactions in which carbon dioxide is lost from larger molecules (see Appendix L). For

thiamin pyrophosphate
The active coenzyme form of thiamin. It is the predominant form found inside cells, where it aids reactions in which a carbon-containing group is lost as CO_2.

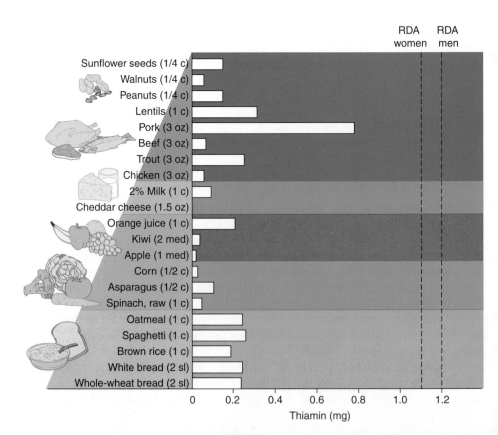

Figure 8.8 Thiamin content of MyPyramid food groups
A combination of grains and foods from the meats and beans group can easily supply the RDA of thiamin (dashed lines).

instance, the reaction that forms acetyl-CoA from pyruvate and one of the reactions of the citric acid cycle require thiamin pyrophosphate (see Figure 8.6). Thiamin is therefore essential to the production of ATP from glucose.

Thiamin is also needed for the metabolism of other sugars and certain amino acids; the synthesis of the neurotransmitter acetylcholine; and the production of the sugar ribose, which is needed to synthesize RNA (ribonucleic acid).

Some, but not all, of the symptoms of beriberi can be explained by the roles of thiamin in glucose metabolism and in the synthesis of the neurotransmitter acetylcholine. The earliest symptoms, depression and weakness, which occur after only about 10 days on a thiamin-free diet, are probably related to the inability to completely use glucose. Since brain and nerve tissue rely on glucose for energy, the inability to form acetyl-CoA rapidly affects nervous system activity. Poor coordination, tingling in the arms and legs, and paralysis may also be caused by the lack of acetylcholine. The reason thiamin deficiency causes cardiovascular symptoms is not well understood.

Recommended Thiamin Intake

The RDA for thiamin for adult men age 19 and older is set at 1.2 mg per day and for adult women 19 and older, at 1.1 mg per day. The RDA is based on the amount of thiamin needed to achieve and maintain normal activity of a thiamin-dependent enzyme found in red blood cells and normal urinary thiamin excretion.[5] For an average adult, half of the RDA can be obtained from 4 ounces of pork or 1/4 cup of shelled sunflower seeds.

The requirement for thiamin is increased during pregnancy to accommodate the needs of growth and energy utilization, and during lactation to meet the need for increased energy for milk production and to replace the thiamin secreted in milk. There is not enough information to establish an RDA for infants, so an AI has been set based on the thiamin intake of infants fed human milk. A summary of the sources, recommended intakes, functions, deficiencies, and toxicities of thiamin and other water-soluble vitamins is provided in **Table 8.2**.

Life Cycle

Thiamin Deficiency

Thiamin deficiency results in the disease beriberi. Beriberi causes lethargy, fatigue and other neurological symptoms (**Figure 8.9**). It can also cause cardiovascular problems such as rapid heartbeat, enlargement of the heart, and congestive heart failure.

Figure 8.9 In Sri Lanka, the word *beriberi* means "I cannot," referring to the extreme weakness and depression that are the earliest symptoms of the disease. (U.S. Library of Medicine/ Photo Researchers, Inc.)

Table 8.2 A Summary of the Water-Soluble Vitamins and Choline

Vitamin	Sources	Recommended Intake for Adults	Major Functions	Deficiency Diseases and Symptoms	Groups at Risk of Deficiency	Toxicity	UL
Thiamin (vitamin B_1, thiamin mononitrate)	Pork, whole and enriched grains, seeds, nuts, legumes	1.1–1.2 mg/d	Coenzyme in acetyl-CoA formation and citric acid cycle; acetylcholine synthesis; nerve function	Beriberi: weakness, apathy, irritability, nerve tingling, poor coordination, paralysis, heart changes	Alcoholics, those living in poverty	None reported	ND
Riboflavin (vitamin B_2)	Dairy products, whole and enriched grains, leafy green vegetables, meats	1.1–1.3 mg/d	Coenzyme in citric acid cycle, lipid metabolism, and electron transport chain	Ariboflavinosis: inflammation of mouth and tongue, cracks at corners of the mouth	None	None reported	ND
Niacin (nicotinamide, nicotinic acid, vitamin B_3)	Beef, chicken, fish, peanuts, legumes, whole and enriched grains. Can be made from tryptophan.	14–16 mg NE/d	Coenzyme in glycolysis, citric acid cycle, electron transport chain, and lipid synthesis and breakdown	Pellagra: diarrhea, dermatitis on areas exposed to sun, dementia	Those consuming a limited diet based on corn, alcoholics	Flushing, nausea, rash, tingling extremities	35 mg/d from fortified foods and supplements
Biotin	Liver, egg yolks, synthesized by bacteria in the gut	30 μg/d[a]	Coenzyme in glucose and fatty acid synthesis and amino acid metabolism	Dermatitis, nausea, depression, hallucinations	Those consuming large amounts of raw egg whites, alcoholics	None reported	ND
Pantothenic acid (calcium pantothenate)	Meat, legumes, whole grains, widespread in foods	5 mg/d[a]	Coenzyme in citric acid cycle and lipid synthesis and breakdown	Fatigue, rash	Alcoholics	None reported	ND
Vitamin B_6 (Pyridoxine, pyridoxal phosphate, pyridoxamine)	Meat, fish, poultry, liver, legumes, whole grains, nuts and seeds	1.3–1.7 mg/d	Coenzyme in protein and amino acid metabolism, neurotransmitter and hemoglobin synthesis	Headache, convulsions, other neurological symptoms, decreased immune function, poor growth, anemia	Alcoholics	Numbness, nerve damage	100 mg/d
Folate (folic acid, folacin, pteroyglutamic acid)	Leafy green vegetables, legumes, nuts, seeds, enriched grains, oranges, liver	400 μg DFE/d	Coenzyme in DNA synthesis and amino acid metabolism	Macrocytic anemia, inflammation of tongue, diarrhea, poor growth, neural tube defects	Pregnant women, premature infants, alcoholics	Masks B_{12} deficiency	1000 μg/d from fortified food and supplements
Vitamin B_{12} (Cobalamin, cyanocobalamin)	Animal products	2.4 μg/d	Coenzyme in folate and fatty acid metabolism; nerve function	Pernicious anemia, macrocytic anemia, nerve damage	Vegans, elderly, those with stomach or intestinal disease	None reported	ND
Vitamin C (ascorbic acid, ascorbate)	Citrus fruits, broccoli, strawberries, greens, peppers, potatoes	75–90 mg/d	Coenzyme in collagen synthesis, hormone and neurotransmitter synthesis; antioxidant	Scurvy: poor wound healing, bleeding gums, loose teeth, bone fragility, joint pain, pinpoint hemorrhages	Alcoholics, elderly people	GI distress, diarrhea	2000 mg/d
Choline[b]	Egg yolks, organ meats, leafy greens, nuts, body synthesis	425–550 mg/d[a]	Synthesis of cell membranes and neurotransmitters	Liver dysfunction	None	Sweating, low blood pressure, liver damage	3500 mg/d

[a]Adequate Intake (AI).
[b]Choline is technically not a vitamin but recommendations have been made for its intake.
UL, Tolerable Upper Intake Level; NE, niacin equivalent; DFE, dietary folate equivalent; ND, insufficient data to determine a UL

Overt beriberi is rare in North America today, but thiamin deficiency does occur in alcoholics. They are particularly vulnerable because thiamin absorption is decreased due to the effect of alcohol on the GI tract. In addition, the liver damage that occurs with chronic alcohol consumption reduces conversion of thiamin to active coenzyme forms; thiamin intake also may be low due to a diet high in alcohol and low in nutrient-dense foods. Thiamin-deficient alcoholics may develop a neurological condition known as the **Wernicke-Korsakoff syndrome**. It is characterized by mental confusion, psychosis, memory disturbances, and coma.

Wernicke-Korsakoff syndrome A form of thiamin deficiency associated with alcohol abuse that is characterized by mental confusion, disorientation, loss of memory, and a staggering gait.

Thiamin Toxicity

Since no toxicity has been reported when excess thiamin is consumed from either food or supplements, a UL for thiamin intake has not been established.[5] This does not mean that high intakes are necessarily safe. Intakes of thiamin above the RDA have not been shown to provide health benefits.

Thiamin Supplements

Thiamin supplements containing up to 50 mg per day are widely available and are marketed with the promise that they will provide "more energy." Although thiamin is needed to produce ATP, it does not increase "energy levels." Unless thiamin is deficient, increasing thiamin intake does not increase the ability to produce ATP. Because thiamin deficiency causes mental confusion and damages the heart, supplements often promise to improve mental function and prevent heart disease. However, in the absence of a deficiency, supplements do not have these effects. Thiamin is also included in supplements referred to as B-complex supplements (**Table 8.3**).

Table 8.3 Benefits and Risks of Water-Soluble-Vitamin Supplements

Supplement	Claim	Actual Benefits or Risks
B complex (thiamin, riboflavin, niacin, pantothenic acid, biotin, vitamin B_6, vitamin B_{12})	Increases energy, needed during stress	Needed for energy metabolism but does not provide energy. Low risk of toxicity except for vitamin B_6.
Niacin (nicotinic acid form)	Lowers cholesterol	Medicinal doses may reduce cholesterol levels. Causes flushing, tingling and potentially liver damage. Doses above 35 mg should only be taken under medical supervision.
Vitamin B_6	Prevents heart disease; relieves carpal tunnel syndrome (CTS), autism, and PMS; enhances immune function	Adequate amounts needed to maintain immune function and normal homocysteine levels, which reduces heart disease risk—excess provides no additional benefit; higher doses may have a slight benefit in some people with CTS or PMS. Levels above the UL may cause tingling, numbness, and muscle weakness.
Folate (folic acid)	Prevents birth defects, protects against heart disease and cancer	Adequate amounts needed to keep homocysteine levels normal, which reduces heart disease risk. Low folate may increase cancer risk. Supplemental sources reduce the risk of birth defects and are recommended for women of childbearing age. May mask a vitamin B_{12} deficiency at high intakes.
Vitamin B_{12}	Prevents heart disease, prevents dementia, reduces fatigue	Adequate amounts needed for nerve function, red blood cell synthesis, and to keep homocysteine levels low, which reduces heart disease risk. Supplemental sources recommended for older adults and vegans. No benefit of excess. Low risk of toxicity.
Vitamin C	Prevents colds, reduces cold symptoms, enhances immunity, protects against heart disease and cancer, enhances antioxidant protection	May reduce duration of colds. Important antioxidant but extra as supplements has not been shown to provide additional benefits. Too much can cause GI distress, damage teeth, promote kidney stone formation, and interfere with anticoagulant medications.

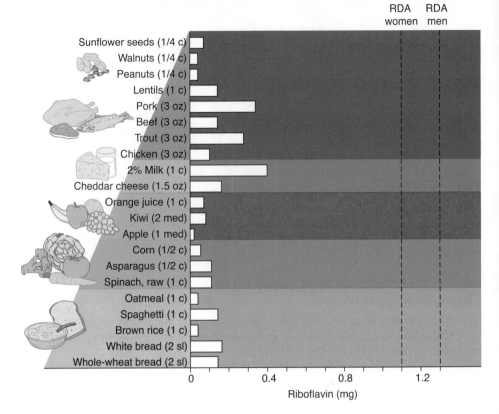

Figure 8.10 Riboflavin content of MyPyramid food groups
Milk and fortified cereals are exceptionally good sources of riboflavin, but a combination of foods are needed to supply the RDA (dashed lines).

Figure 8.11 Why is milk often supplied in opaque or cardboard containers? (©Charles D. Winters)

flavin adenine dinucleotide (FAD) and **flavin mononucleotide (FMN)** The active coenzyme forms of riboflavin. The structure of these molecules allows them to pick up and donate hydrogens and electrons in chemical reactions.

8.3 Riboflavin

Learning Objectives

- Describe the function shared by thiamin and riboflavin.
- Explain why milk sold in clear bottles might be low in riboflavin.

While searching for a cure for beriberi, scientists isolated riboflavin and several other B vitamins in addition to thiamin. This occurred because the extracts they made from vegetables and grains could be separated into two components: one contained thiamin, the antiberiberi factor they sought, and cured beriberi; the other was a mix of B vitamins that was later determined to contain riboflavin along with vitamin B_6, niacin, and pantothenic acid.

Riboflavin in the Diet

Milk is the best source of riboflavin in the North American diet. Other important sources include liver, red meat, poultry, fish, and whole and enriched grain products. Vegetable sources include asparagus, broccoli, mushrooms, and leafy green vegetables such as spinach (**Figure 8.10**). Because riboflavin is destroyed by exposure to light, poor handling decreases a food's riboflavin content. This is a problem when milk is stored in clear containers and exposed to light. Cloudy plastic milk bottles block some light, partially protecting the riboflavin, but cardboard or opaque plastic milk containers are even better at preventing losses[6] (**Figure 8.11**).

Riboflavin in the Body

Riboflavin forms the active coenzymes **flavin adenine dinucleotide (FAD)** and **flavin mononucleotide (FMN)** (see Appendix L). FAD functions in the citric acid cycle and is important for the breakdown of fatty acids. Both FMN and FAD function as electron carriers in the electron transport chain (see Figure 8.6). Therefore, adequate riboflavin is crucial in providing energy from carbohydrate, fat, and protein. Riboflavin is also involved directly or indirectly in converting a number of other vitamins, including folate, niacin, vitamin B_6, and vitamin K, into their active forms.

Recommended Riboflavin Intake

The RDA for riboflavin for adult men age 19 and older is 1.3 mg per day and for adult women 19 and older, 1.1 mg per day. This recommendation is based on the amount of riboflavin needed to maintain normal activity of a riboflavin-dependent enzyme in red blood cells and normal riboflavin excretion in the urine.[5] Two cups of milk provide about half the amount of riboflavin recommended for a typical adult. The recommended intake can be met without milk if the daily diet includes 2 to 3 servings of meat and 4 to 5 servings of enriched grain products and high-riboflavin vegetables, such as spinach.

Additional riboflavin is recommended during pregnancy to support growth and increased energy utilization, and during lactation to allow for the riboflavin secreted in milk. There is not enough information to establish an RDA for infants, so an AI has been set based on the amount of riboflavin consumed by infants fed human milk.

Life Cycle

Riboflavin Deficiency

When riboflavin is deficient, injuries heal poorly because new cells cannot grow to replace the damaged ones. Tissues that grow most rapidly, such as the skin and the linings of the eyes, mouth, and tongue, are the first to be affected by a deficiency. Symptoms of riboflavin deficiency, called **ariboflavinosis**, include inflammation of the eyes, lips, mouth, and tongue; scaly, greasy skin eruptions; cracking of the tissue at the corners of the mouth; and confusion. Deficiency symptoms may develop after approximately 2 months on a riboflavin-poor diet.

A deficiency of riboflavin is rarely seen alone. It usually occurs in conjunction with deficiencies of other B vitamins. One reason is that the food sources of B vitamins are similar (see Table 8.2). Therefore, a deficiency of riboflavin due to poor diet will likely lead to multiple vitamin deficiencies. Because riboflavin is needed to convert other vitamins into their active forms, some of the symptoms seen with riboflavin deficiency are actually due to deficiencies of these other nutrients.

ariboflavinosis The condition resulting from a deficiency of riboflavin.

Riboflavin Toxicity

No adverse effects have been reported from overconsumption of riboflavin from foods or supplements, and there are not sufficient data to establish a UL for this vitamin. Large doses of riboflavin are not well absorbed, and it is readily excreted in the urine. A harmless side effect of high riboflavin intake, such as may be obtained from over-the-counter supplements, is bright yellow urine.

Riboflavin Supplements

As with thiamin, the role of riboflavin in energy metabolism has led to claims that supplements containing riboflavin, such as B complex supplements, will provide an energy boost (see Table 8.3). Although riboflavin is needed for energy metabolism, it does not provide energy. Since a deficiency causes skin and eye symptoms, riboflavin has also been suggested as a cure for eye diseases and skin disorders. However, in the absence of a deficiency, supplementation does not affect the eyes or skin.

8.4 Niacin

Learning Objectives

- Discuss why a niacin deficiency is more likely in someone consuming a diet that is based on corn.
- List the 3 D's of pellagra.

A deficiency of niacin results in a disease called **pellagra**, which causes progressive physical and mental deterioration. It was first observed in Europe in the eighteenth century, and in the early twentieth century it became endemic in the southeastern

pellagra The disease resulting from a deficiency of niacin.

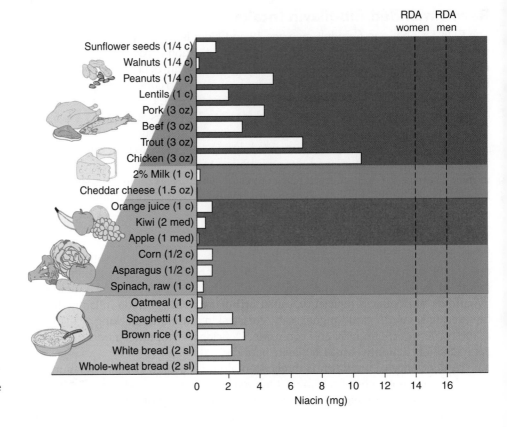

Figure 8.12 Niacin content of MyPyramid food groups
Meat, legumes, and whole and enriched grains are good sources of niacin; the dashed lines represent the RDAs for adult men and women.

United States (see Science Applied: Pellagra: Infectious Disease or Dietary Deficiency?). The emergence of pellagra can be traced to the cultivation of corn as a dietary staple.[7] It primarily affects the poor who cannot afford a varied diet.

Niacin in the Diet

Meat and fish are good sources of niacin (**Figure 8.12**). Other sources include legumes, mushrooms, wheat bran, asparagus, and peanuts. Niacin added to enriched flours used in baked goods provides much of the usable niacin in the North American diet. Niacin can also be synthesized in the body from the essential amino acid tryptophan (**Figure 8.13**). In a diet that contains high-protein foods such as milk and eggs, which are poor sources of niacin but good sources of tryptophan, much of the need for niacin can be met by tryptophan. Tryptophan, however, is only used to make niacin if enough is available to first meet the needs of protein synthesis. When the diet is low in tryptophan, it is not used to synthesize niacin. Food composition tables and databases list only preformed niacin in a food, not the amount of niacin that can be made from tryptophan contained within the food.

Figure 8.13 Structure of tryptophan, nicotinic acid, and nicotinamide
The amino acid tryptophan can be used to synthesize the two forms of niacin, nicotinic acid, and nicotinamide. These can be converted into the active coenzyme forms of niacin.

Tryptophan   Nicotinic acid   Nicotinamide

(DAJ/Getty Images, Inc.)   (www.victorianoizquierdo.com/Getty Images, Inc.)   (Elena Schweitzer/Shutterstock)

Pellagra: Infectious Disease or Dietary Deficiency?

In the early 1900s, psychiatric hospitals in the southeastern United States were filled with patients with dementia due to a disease called pellagra. Although we now know pellagra is due to niacin deficiency, at the time it was thought to be caused by an infectious agent or toxin. As many as 100,000 people were affected by pellagra and upward of 10,000 deaths resulted per year. In response to this epidemic, the government set up the Thompson-McFadden Pellagra Commission and the U.S. Public Health Service sent Dr. Joseph Goldberger to investigate.

Between 1912 and 1916 investigators with the Pellagra Commission conducted epidemiological and bacteriological studies. Monkeys and baboons were injected with blood, urine, and other extracts from patients with pellagra; they were fed feces and skin scrapings. None of the animals developed the disease. Although these results supported the view that pellagra was not due to an infectious agent, many questioned whether animal studies could be applied to humans. Perhaps monkeys and baboons were not susceptible to pellagra? The commission still believed that pellagra could be transmitted in some way from a pellagrous to a nonpellagrous person.[1]

Goldberger spent 2 years studying the communities and institutions where pellagra was common. He noticed that pellagra was prevalent among people in institutions but that the attendants and nurses never contracted the disease—a fact that did not support an infectious nature. While looking for factors that distinguished the patients from the staff, Goldberger noted that the patients were fed a diet typical of the Southern poor; it consisted primarily of corn meal, molasses, and fatback or salt pork. The staff ate a more varied diet. So, Goldberger began experimenting with diet. In an orphanage and a state hospital, he was able to cure pellagra and prevent recurrences by adding milk, eggs, and more meat to the diet. The next experimental step needed to support his hypothesis was to produce pellagra in healthy people by feeding them a diet similar to the institutional diet. In 1915, at a work farm affiliated with the Mississippi State Penitentiary, 12 convicts volunteered to participate in the experiment in exchange for pardons. They were fed a diet consisting of corn meal, grits, cornstarch, white wheat flour, white rice, cane syrup, sugar, sweet potatoes, small amounts of turnip greens, cabbage, and collards, and a liberal amount of pork fat. After about 6 months, 6 men had developed pellagra. Goldberger concluded that the cause was a deficiency of an amino acid, a mineral, a fat-soluble vitamin, or some as yet unknown vitamin factor.

During the summer of 1919, a young artist named John Carroll was assigned to work with Joseph Goldberger's pellagra study. He produced 41 drawings of pellagra patients. The drawing shown here depicts a femal pellagra patient in the Georgia State Sanitarium in 1919. (Eskind Biomedical Library, Vanderbilt University Medical Center.)

To provide the final proof that pellagra was not due to an infectious agent, Goldberger and 15 of his colleagues voluntarily injected themselves with blood, swabbed their throats with nasal secretions, and swallowed urine, feces, and skin cells from patients who were severely ill with pellagra (later in the experiment they put the feces and other materials in capsules). After 6 months, none had become ill. Goldberger had proven that pellagra was not an infectious disease but he continued to search for the dietary cause.

In 1922, a diet comparable to that used to produce pellagra in Goldberger's experiment caused a similar disease in dogs, called black tongue. Subsequent food experiments found that yeast and liver contained a pellagra-preventative factor. These foods could be used to prevent pellagra and cure mild cases. However, despite Goldberger's efforts, the epidemic raged on. Even though it had been demonstrated that yeast and liver could cure pellagra, nothing had been done to change the Southern diet that produced the disease. And, in serious cases of the disease, providing food sources of niacin was often ineffective because inflammation of the GI tract, lack of appetite,

(Continued on next page)

and vomiting made it difficult for patients to ingest and absorb enough of the pellagra-preventative factor to cure the deficiency. Joseph Goldberger died in 1929, the year the epidemic reached its peak.

In 1937, another research team identified the pellagra-preventative factor as nicotinic acid. With this form of the vitamin isolated, it could be given intravenously, bypassing the digestive tract, and saving the lives of those suffering with pellagra. Despite this advance in treatment, pellagra remained a problem among the Southern poor. Poor dietary habits, poverty, and chronic malnutrition made it a difficult problem to address.[2] Finally, the economic boom created by World War II, combined with a federally sponsored enrichment program, added enough niacin to the diet to end the pellagra epidemic in the United States.

---

[1]Roe, D.A. *A Plague of Corn: The Social History of Pellagra.* Ithaca, NY: Cornell University Press, 1973.
[2]Syndenstricker, V. P. The history of pellagra, its recognition as a disorder of nutrition and its conquest. *Am. J. Clin. Nutr.* 6:409–441, 1958.

Figure 8.14 The treatment of corn with lime water during the preparation of tortillas improves niacin bioavailability and has helped prevent pellagra in Mexico and other Latin American countries. (Jeff Greenberg/Photo Researchers, Inc.)

nicotinamide adenine dinucleotide (NAD) and **nicotinamide adenine dinucleotide phosphate (NADP)** The active coenzyme forms of niacin that are able to pick up and donate hydrogens and electrons. They are important in the transfer of electrons to oxygen in cellular respiration and in many synthetic reactions.

niacin equivalents (NEs) The measure used to express the amount of niacin present in food, including that which can be made from its precursor, tryptophan. One NE is equal to 1 mg of niacin or 60 mg of tryptophan.

Life Cycle

The association between niacin deficiency and a limited diet based on corn and low in animal products has been attributed to the low-tryptophan content of corn and the fact that the niacin found naturally in corn (and to a lesser extent in other cereal grains) is bound to other molecules and therefore not well absorbed. The treatment of corn with lime water (water and calcium hydroxide), as is done in Mexico and Central America during the making of tortillas, enhances the availability of niacin (**Figure 8.14**). The diet in these regions also contains legumes, which provide both niacin and a source of tryptophan for the synthesis of niacin. As a result, despite their corn-based diet, populations in these regions have not suffered from pellagra. Today, pellagra remains common in India and parts of China and Africa.[8] Efforts to eradicate this deficiency include the development of new varieties of corn that provide more available niacin and more tryptophan than traditional varieties.

Niacin in the Body

Niacin is important in the production of ATP from the energy-yielding nutrients as well as in reactions that synthesize other molecules. There are two forms of niacin: nicotinic acid and nicotinamide (see Figure 8.13). Either form can be used by the body to make the two active coenzymes **nicotinamide adenine dinucleotide (NAD)** and **nicotinamide adenine dinucleotide phosphate (NADP)**. NAD functions in glycolysis and the citric acid cycle, accepting released electrons and passing them on to the electron transport chain where ATP is formed (see Figure 8.6). NADP acts as an electron carrier in reactions that synthesize fatty acids and cholesterol. The need for niacin is so widespread in metabolism that a deficiency causes damage throughout the body.

Recommended Niacin Intake

The RDA for niacin is expressed as **niacin equivalents (NEs)**. One NE is equal to 1 mg of niacin or 60 mg of tryptophan. This allows for the fact that some of the requirement for niacin can be met by the synthesis of niacin from tryptophan. Approximately 60 mg of tryptophan is needed to make 1 mg of niacin. To estimate the niacin contributed by high-protein foods, protein is assumed to be about 1% tryptophan. The criterion used to estimate the average niacin requirement is urinary excretion of niacin metabolites. The RDA for adult men and women of all ages is 16 and 14 mg NE per day, respectively.[5] A meal containing a medium chicken breast and a cup of steamed asparagus provides this amount.

Niacin needs are increased during pregnancy to account for the increase in energy expenditure, and during lactation to account for both the increase in energy expenditure and the niacin secreted in milk. There is not enough information to establish an RDA for infants, so an AI has been set based on the amount of niacin found in human milk.

Niacin Deficiency

The early symptoms of pellagra include fatigue, decreased appetite, and indigestion, followed by the three D's: dermatitis, diarrhea, and dementia. If left untreated, niacin deficiency results in a fourth D—death. The dermatitis resembles sunburn and strikes parts of the body exposed to sunlight, heat, or injury (**Figure 8.15**). Gastrointestinal symptoms include a bright-red tongue and may include vomiting, constipation, or diarrhea. Mental symptoms begin with irritability, headaches, loss of memory, insomnia, and emotional instability and progress to psychosis and acute delirium.

Niacin Toxicity

There is no evidence of any adverse effects from consumption of niacin naturally occurring in foods, but supplements can be toxic. The adverse effects of high intakes of niacin include flushing of the skin, a tingling sensation in the hands and feet, a red skin rash, nausea, vomiting, diarrhea, high blood sugar levels, abnormalities in liver function, and blurred vision. Since flushing is the first toxicity symptom to appear as the dose is increased, the UL for adults has been set at 35 mg, the highest level that is unlikely to cause flushing in the majority of healthy people. This value applies to the forms of niacin contained in supplements and fortified foods, but does not include niacin naturally occurring in foods.

Niacin Supplements

Niacin deficiency is no longer of public health concern in the United States. Despite this, niacin is a commonly used vitamin supplement. It is included in multivitamins as well as in B-complex vitamin supplements marketed to give you more energy. High-dose supplements of this vitamin are also used to treat elevated blood cholesterol (see Table 8.3). When vitamin supplements are taken in large doses to treat or prevent diseases that are not due to vitamin deficiencies, they are really being used as drugs rather than vitamins. Doses of 50 mg per day or greater of the nicotinic acid form of niacin have been found to decrease blood levels of LDL cholesterol and triglycerides and increase HDL cholesterol. These high-dose niacin supplements are also associated with a reduction in recurrent heart attacks and deaths in individuals with cardiovascular disease.[9] Since the UL for niacin is only 35 mg, many people are unable to take niacin as a cholesterol-lowering drug because they experience side effects due to niacin toxicity. Because niacin supplements are available over-the-counter people may try to treat themselves for high cholesterol, but high doses of vitamins are as dangerous as drugs and should be used only with medical supervision. Supplements of the nicotinamide form of niacin have been investigated for their benefit in the prevention of another disease—type 1 diabetes. A recent intervention trial has not found it to be effective for this purpose.[10]

Figure 8.15 The cracked, inflamed skin characteristic of pellagra most commonly appears on areas exposed to sunlight or other stresses. (Dr. M. A. Ansary/ SPL/Photo Researchers, Inc.)

8.5 Biotin

Learning Objective

- Explain why consuming raw eggs might cause a biotin deficiency.

Biotin was discovered when rats fed protein derived from raw egg white developed a syndrome of hair loss, dermatitis, and neuromuscular dysfunction. The symptoms were due to a deficiency of biotin. The deficiency was caused by a protein in raw egg white, called avidin, which tightly binds biotin and prevents its absorption.

Biotin in the Diet

Good dietary sources of biotin include liver, egg yolks, yogurt, and nuts. Fruit and meat are poor sources. Foods containing raw egg whites should be avoided not only because avidin binds biotin and prevents its absorption, but because raw eggs also

Figure 8.16 Why is the consumption of raw eggs not the best way to meet your biotin needs? (©Charles D. Winters)

may be contaminated with bacteria that can cause food-borne illness (**Figure 8.16**). Thoroughly cooking eggs destroys bacteria and denatures avidin so that it cannot bind biotin.

Biotin in the Body

Biotin is a coenzyme for a group of enzymes that add the acid group COOH to molecules. It functions in energy metabolism because it is needed to make a 4-carbon molecule necessary in the citric acid cycle and in glucose synthesis. It is also important in the metabolism of fatty acids and amino acids (see Figure 8.6).

Recommended Biotin Intake

A dietary requirement for biotin has been difficult to estimate because some biotin is produced by bacteria in the gastrointestinal tract and absorbed into the body. Therefore no RDA could be determined but an AI of 30 μg per day has been established for adult men and women based on the amount of biotin found in a typical North American diet.[5]

Life Cycle

No additional biotin is recommended for pregnancy, but the AI is increased during lactation to account for the amount secreted in milk. The AI for infants is based on the amount of biotin consumed by infants fed human milk.

Biotin Deficiency and Toxicity

Although biotin deficiency is uncommon, it has been observed in people with malabsorption or protein-energy malnutrition, those receiving tube feedings or total parenteral nutrition without biotin, those taking anticonvulsant drugs for long periods, and those frequently consuming raw egg whites.[5] When biotin intake is deficient, symptoms including nausea, thinning hair, loss of hair color, a red skin rash, depression, lethargy, hallucinations, and tingling of the extremities gradually appear.

No toxicity has been reported in patients given 200 mg per day of biotin to treat various disease states, and sufficient data are not available to establish a UL.

8.6 Pantothenic Acid

Learning Objective

• Discuss why pantothenic acid deficiency is rare.

Pantothenic acid, which gets its name from the Greek word *pantothen* (meaning "from everywhere"), is widely distributed in foods.

Pantothenic Acid in the Diet

Pantothenic acid is particularly abundant in meat, eggs, whole grains, and legumes. It is found in lesser amounts in milk, vegetables, and fruits (**Figure 8.17**). Pantothenic acid is susceptible to damage by exposure to heat and low- or high-acid conditions.

Pantothenic Acid in the Body

In the body pantothenic acid is part of the coenzyme A (CoA) molecule, which is part of acetyl-CoA, a molecule formed during the breakdown of carbohydrates, fatty acids, and amino acids (see Appendix L). Pantothenic acid is also needed to produce acyl carrier protein needed for the synthesis of cholesterol and fatty acids (see Figure 8.6).

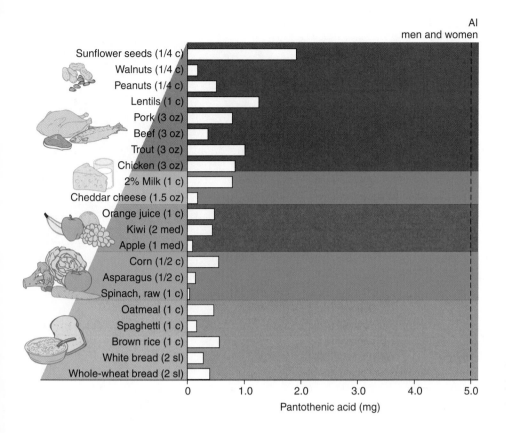

AI
men and women

Sunflower seeds (1/4 c)
Walnuts (1/4 c)
Peanuts (1/4 c)
Lentils (1 c)
Pork (3 oz)
Beef (3 oz)
Trout (3 oz)
Chicken (3 oz)
2% Milk (1 c)
Cheddar cheese (1.5 oz)
Orange juice (1 c)
Kiwi (2 med)
Apple (1 med)
Corn (1/2 c)
Asparagus (1/2 c)
Spinach, raw (1 c)
Oatmeal (1 c)
Spaghetti (1 c)
Brown rice (1 c)
White bread (2 sl)
Whole-wheat bread (2 sl)

0   1.0   2.0   3.0   4.0   5.0
Pantothenic acid (mg)

Figure 8.17 **Pantothenic acid content of MyPyramid food groups**
All groups in MyPyramid contain good sources of pantothenic acid; the dashed line represents the AI for adult men and women.

Recommended Pantothenic Acid Intake

There is no RDA for pantothenic acid, but an AI of 5 mg per day has been recommended for adult men and women.[5] This value is based on the intake of pantothenic acid sufficient to replace urinary losses. The AI is increased to 6 and 7 mg per day to meet the needs of pregnancy and lactation, respectively.

Pantothenic Acid Deficiency and Toxicity

The wide distribution of pantothenic acid in foods makes deficiency rare in humans. A deficiency of this vitamin alone has not been reported, but it may occur as part of a multiple B vitamin deficiency resulting from malnutrition or chronic alcoholism.

Pantothenic acid is relatively nontoxic. No toxic symptoms were reported in a study that fed young men 10 grams of pantothenic acid per day for 6 weeks. Another study found that doses of 10 to 20 grams per day may result in diarrhea and water retention.[5] Data are not sufficient to establish a UL for pantothenic acid.

Life Cycle

8.7 Vitamin B$_6$

Learning Objectives

- Explain the role of vitamin B$_6$ in amino acid metabolism.
- Describe the relationship between vitamin B$_6$ and heart disease.

Vitamin B$_6$ was identified only when a deficiency syndrome was discovered that did not respond to thiamin or riboflavin supplementation. The important role of vitamin B$_6$ in amino acid metabolism distinguishes it from the other B vitamins.

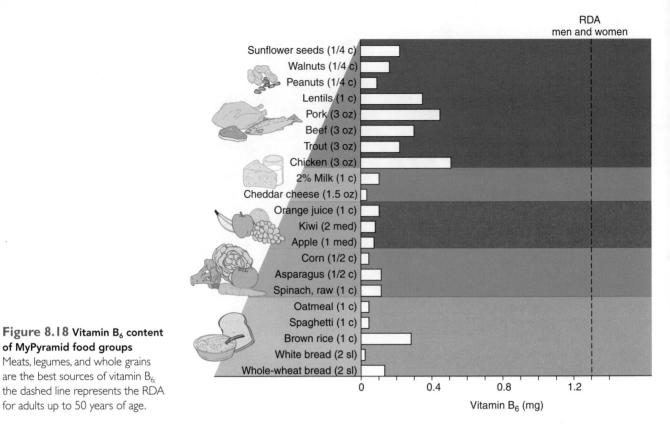

Figure 8.18 Vitamin B$_6$ content of MyPyramid food groups
Meats, legumes, and whole grains are the best sources of vitamin B$_6$; the dashed line represents the RDA for adults up to 50 years of age.

Vitamin B$_6$ in the Diet

Vitamin B$_6$ is found in both animal and plant foods. Animal sources include chicken, fish, pork, and organ meats. Good plant sources include whole-wheat products, brown rice, soybeans, sunflower seeds, and some fruits and vegetables such as bananas, broccoli, and spinach (**Figure 8.18**). Vitamin B$_6$ is easily destroyed by exposure to heat and light and is easily lost in processing. It is not added back in the enrichment of grain products, but fortified breakfast cereals make an important contribution to vitamin B$_6$ intake.[11]

Vitamin B$_6$ in the Body

Vitamin B$_6$, also known as **pyridoxine**, comprises a group of compounds including pyridoxal, pyridoxine, and pyridoxamine. All three forms can be converted into the active coenzyme form, **pyridoxal phosphate** (see Appendix L). Pyridoxal phosphate is needed for the activity of more than 100 enzymes involved in the metabolism of carbohydrate, fat, and protein. It is particularly important for protein and amino acid metabolism (**Figure 8.19**). Without pyridoxal phosphate, the nonessential amino acids cannot be synthesized and the conditionally essential amino acid cysteine cannot be synthesized from methionine. Pyridoxal phosphate is needed to synthesize hemoglobin, the oxygen-carrying protein in red blood cells. Pyridoxal phosphate is important for the immune system because it is needed to form white blood cells. It is also needed for the conversion of tryptophan to niacin, the metabolism of glycogen, the synthesis of certain neurotransmitters, and the synthesis of the lipids that are part of the myelin coating on nerves (**Figure 8.20**).

pyridoxine The chemical term for vitamin B$_6$.

pyridoxal phosphate The major coenzyme form of vitamin B$_6$ that functions in more than 100 enzymatic reactions, many of which involve amino acid metabolism.

Recommended Vitamin B$_6$ Intake

The RDA for vitamin B$_6$ is 1.3 mg per day for both adult men and women 19 to 50 years of age.[5] This is the amount needed to maintain adequate blood concentrations of the active coenzyme pyridoxal phosphate. In adults 51 years and older, the RDA is

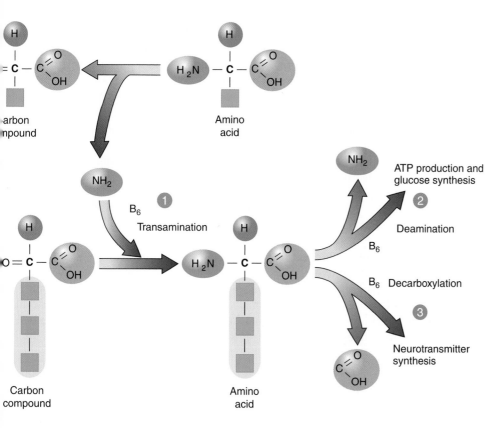

1 Vitamin B$_6$ is needed to synthesize nonessential amino acids by transamination

2 Vitamin B$_6$ is needed for deamination so amino acids can be used to produce ATP or to synthesize glucose

3 Vitamin B$_6$ is needed for decarboxylation, which removes the COOH group from amino acids so they can be used to synthesize neurotransmitters

Figure 8.19 Functions of vitamin B$_6$
Vitamin B$_6$ is needed for a number of reactions that are essential to amino acid synthesis and breakdown.

increased to 1.7 mg per day in men and 1.5 mg per day in women to maintain normal blood levels of pyridoxal phosphate. A 3-ounce (85-g) serving of chicken, fish, or pork, or half a baked potato, provides about a quarter of the RDA for an average adult; a banana provides about a third.

The RDA for vitamin B$_6$ is increased during pregnancy to provide for metabolic needs and growth of the mother and fetus. Because the vitamin B$_6$ concentration in breast milk is dependent on the mother's intake, the RDA is increased during lactation to assure adequate levels are supplied to the infant. There is no RDA for infants, but an AI has been established based on the vitamin B$_6$ content of human milk.

Life Cycle

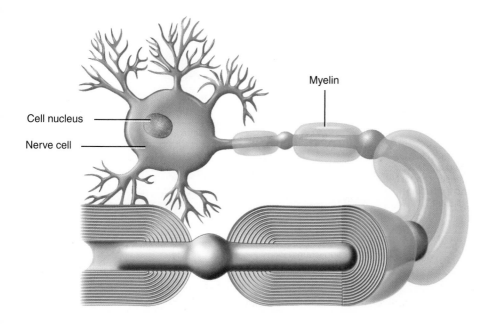

Figure 8.20 Myelin
Both vitamin B$_6$ and vitamin B$_{12}$ are needed to synthesize and maintain the mylein coating on nerve cells, which is essential for normal nerve transmission.

Vitamin B₆ Deficiency

A vitamin B₆ deficiency syndrome was defined in 1954 when an infant formula was overheated in the manufacturing process, destroying the vitamin B₆. The infants who consumed only this formula developed abdominal distress, convulsions, and other neurological symptoms.[12] The neurological symptoms associated with vitamin B₆ deficiency include depression, headaches, confusion, numbness and tingling in the extremities, and seizures. These may be related to the role of vitamin B₆ in neurotransmitter synthesis and myelin formation. Anemia also occurs in vitamin B₆ deficiency due to impaired hemoglobin synthesis; red blood cells are small (microcytic) and pale due to the lack of hemoglobin. Other deficiency symptoms such as poor growth, skin lesions, and decreased antibody formation may occur because vitamin B₆ is important in protein and energy metabolism. Since vitamin B₆ is needed for amino acid metabolism, the onset of a deficiency can be hastened by a diet that is low in vitamin B₆ but high in protein.

Vitamin B₆ status in the body can be affected by a number of drugs, including alcohol and oral contraceptives. Alcohol decreases the formation of the active coenzyme pyridoxal phosphate and makes it more susceptible to breakdown. Oral contraceptive use has been associated with small decreases in blood levels of pyridoxal phosphate, but vitamin B₆ supplements are not routinely recommended for women taking oral contraceptives.[5]

Vitamin B₆, Homocysteine, and Cardiovascular Disease

It has been hypothesized that vitamin B₆ affects the risk of heart disease through its role in the breakdown of the amino acid homocysteine, an intermediate in methionine metabolism (**Figure 8.21**). Individuals with homocystinuria, a rare genetic disorder that causes chronically high blood levels of homocysteine, develop atherosclerosis at an early age. Large doses of vitamin B₆ (100 to 1000 mg/day) have been successfully used to reduce elevated homocysteine and the risk of atherosclerosis in patients with this disease but these doses are not recommended for the general public.

Among healthy individuals, a mild elevation in blood homocysteine has been shown to be a risk factor for cardiovascular disease.[13] It has been proposed that a

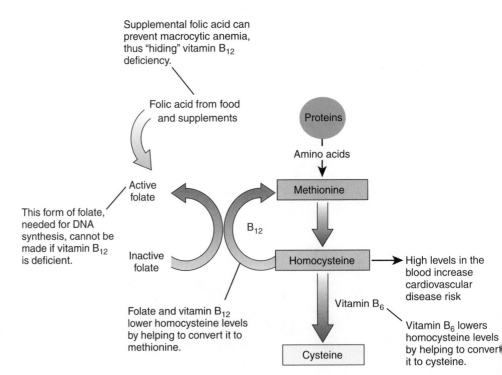

Figure 8.21 Role of B vitamins in cardiovascular disease risk
A deficiency of vitamin B₆, vitamin B₁₂, or folate, can lead to the accumulation of homocysteine and thus an increased risk of cardiovascular disease.

deficiency of vitamin B$_6$, vitamin B$_{12}$, or folate, the latter two of which are also involved in homocysteine metabolism, may cause homocysteine accumulation and eventually lead to atherosclerosis. A study that examined the relationship between plasma levels of vitamin B$_6$ in women found that those with the highest levels of vitamin B$_6$ in their plasma had the lowest risk of having a heart attack.[14] Supplements of all three of these vitamins have been used to reduce homocysteine levels in individuals with mild homocysteine elevation.[15] At this time, however, the DRI panel believes that it is premature to conclude that increased intakes of vitamin B$_6$, vitamin B$_{12}$, or folate could decrease the risk of cardiovascular disease.[5]

Vitamin B$_6$ Supplements and Toxicity

No adverse effects have been associated with high intakes of vitamin B$_6$ from foods, but large doses found in supplements can cause serious toxicity symptoms. This was first recognized in the 1980s when severe nerve impairment was reported in individuals taking 2 to 6 grams of supplemental pyridoxine per day.[16] Symptoms were serious enough in some subjects that they were unable to walk. These symptoms improved when the pyridoxine supplements were stopped. To avoid toxicity when taking supplements containing vitamin B$_6$, it is important that intake not exceed the UL of 100 mg per day from food and supplements.[5] The UL is based on an amount that will not cause nerve damage in the majority of healthy people. Since high-dose supplements of vitamin B$_6$ containing 100 mg per dose (5000% of the Daily Value) are available over the counter, it is easy to obtain a dose that exceeds the UL.

Despite the potential for toxicity, vitamin B$_6$ supplements are marketed to help a wide variety of ailments. These marketing claims are usually founded in science, but may be exaggerated to sell products (see Table 8.3).

Can Vitamin B$_6$ Treat Carpal Tunnel Syndrome? Vitamin B$_6$ has been suggested to be useful in treating carpal tunnel syndrome, in which pressure on the nerves in the hand causes pain and weakness. Vitamin B$_6$ may act by directly alleviating the symptoms, by altering pain perception and increasing pain threshold, or by alleviating an unrecognized peripheral neuropathy. Although the evidence to support its use is inconclusive, some patients will improve when treated with doses of up to 100 mg, often used in conjunction with other treatments for this condition.[17]

Does Vitamin B$_6$ Prevent Premenstrual Syndrome? Premenstrual syndrome (PMS) is a collection of physical and emotional symptoms that some women experience prior to menstruation. It causes mood swings, food cravings, bloating, tension, depression, headaches, acne, breast tenderness, anxiety, temper outbursts, and over 100 other symptoms. The proposed connection between these symptoms and vitamin B$_6$ is the fact that the vitamin is needed for the synthesis of the neurotransmitters serotonin and dopamine. Insufficient vitamin B$_6$ has been suggested to reduce levels of these neurotransmitters and cause the anxiety, irritability, and depression associated with PMS. However, there is little evidence that supplementing vitamin B$_6$ will provide significant benefit for women with PMS.[18]

Will Vitamin B$_6$ Boost Immunity? Immune function can be impaired by a deficiency of any nutrient that hinders cell growth and division. Therefore, one of the most common claims for vitamin supplements in general is that they improve immune function. Vitamin B$_6$ is no exception and there is data to support the claim. Vitamin B$_6$ supplements have been found to improve immune function in older adults.[5] However, since elderly individuals frequently have low intakes of vitamin B$_6$, it is unclear whether the beneficial effects of supplements are due to an improvement in vitamin B$_6$ status or immune system stimulation.

8.8 Folate or Folic Acid

Learning Objectives

- Explain how folate deficiency causes anemia.
- Discuss why folic acid supplementation is recommended for women of child-bearing age.

It has been known for over 100 years that anemia often occurs during pregnancy. In 1937, anemia in a pregnant woman was successfully treated with a yeast preparation named *Wills Factor*, after Dr. Lucy Wills, who treated this patient. The Wills Factor was later isolated from spinach and named *folate*, after the Latin word for foliage. **Folate** and **folacin** are general terms for compounds that have chemical structures and nutritional properties similar to those of **folic acid** (**Figure 8.22**). The chemical name for folate is pteroylglutamic acid.

folate and **folacin** General terms for the many forms of this vitamin.

folic acid The monoglutamate form of folate, which is present in the diet in fortified foods and supplements.

Folate in the Diet and the Digestive Tract

Excellent dietary sources of folate include liver, yeast, asparagus, oranges, legumes, and fortified grain products. Fair sources include vegetables such as corn, snap beans, mustard greens, and broccoli, as well as some nuts and seeds. Small amounts are found in meats, cheese, and milk (**Figure 8.23**). Most folate found naturally in food contains a string of glutamate molecules (see Figure 8.22). Glutamate is an amino acid, and folate bound to many glutamates is referred to as folate polyglutamate. Before this form can be absorbed, all but one of the glutamate molecules must be removed by enzymes in the brush border of the small intestine to yield folic acid, the monoglutamate form. It is estimated that about 50% of the folate in food is absorbed.[5] The folic acid form rarely occurs naturally in food but is used in supplements and fortified foods. It is more easily absorbed because it does not require the enzymatic removal of a string of glutamate molecules. The bioavailability of the synthetic folic acid added to grain products and used in supplements is about twice that of the folate naturally found in food. Since 1998, enriched grain products, including breads, flours, corn meal, pasta, grits, and rice, have been fortified with folic acid.

Folate in the Body

A number of different active coenzyme forms of folate are involved in reactions that transfer chemical groups containing a single carbon atom. Folate coenzymes are needed for the synthesis of DNA and the metabolism of some amino acids. Before a cell divides, its DNA must replicate. Therefore, the role of folate in DNA synthesis makes it particularly important in tissues where cells are rapidly dividing, such as

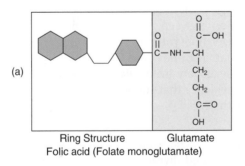

(a) Ring Structure   Glutamate
Folic acid (Folate monoglutamate)

(b) Glutamate — Glutamate — Glutamate — Glutamate — Glutamate

Folate polyglutamate

Figure 8.22 Structure of folate (a) Folic acid is the monoglutamate form of folate. It is the form found in fortified foods and supplements. (b) Folate polyglutamate is the form found naturally in foods; it includes many glutamate molecules attached to form a chain.

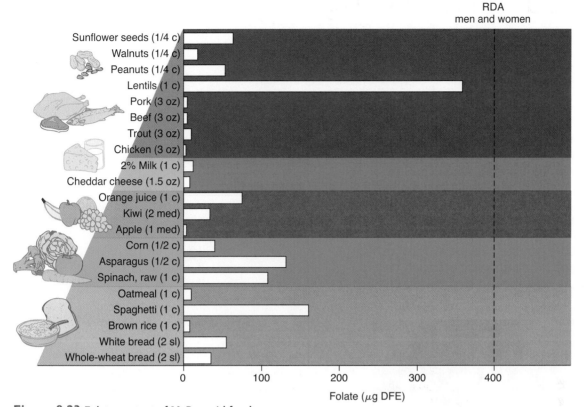

RDA
men and women

Folate (μg DFE)

Figure 8.23 Folate content of MyPyramid food groups
Adults can obtain the RDA for folate (dashed line) by eating legumes, fortified foods, and fruits and vegetables.

bone marrow, where red blood cells are made; intestines; and skin; and during periods of rapid growth, such as early in embryonic life. Low folate intake in early pregnancy is associated with an increased risk of **neural tube defects**.

Recommended Folate Intake

The RDA for folate is set at 400 μg **dietary folate equivalents (DFEs)** per day for adult men and women. One DFE is equal to 1 μg of food folate, 0.6 μg of synthetic folic acid from fortified food or supplements consumed with food, or 0.5 μg of synthetic folic acid consumed on an empty stomach. In order to reduce the risk of neural tube defects, a special recommendation is made for women capable of becoming pregnant.[5] A daily intake of 400 μg of synthetic folic acid from fortified foods and/or supplements is recommended in addition to the food folate consumed in a varied diet. Therefore, the total folate intake of this group should exceed the RDA (see Critical Thinking: Meeting Folate Recommendations).

The RDA for folate during pregnancy is increased to 600 μg per day to provide for the increase in cell division. Although this level can be met by a carefully selected diet, folate is typically supplemented during pregnancy. The RDA is increased during lactation to account for folate secretion in milk. Needs per unit of body weight are higher for infants and children than for adults because of their rapid growth. Human and cow milk provide enough folate to meet infant needs, but goat milk does not. Infants and children given goat milk may not receive adequate folate unless it is provided from other sources.

Meeting Folate Needs

Women of childbearing age can meet folate recommendations by taking a multivitamin containing folic acid or by including fortified foods in their diet. To get the recommended 400 μg DFE of synthetic folic acid from fortified foods would require eating about 1 to 4 servings of fortified breakfast cereal or 4 to 6 servings of other fortified grain products each day. If it is not possible to meet recommendations from fortified foods, supplements should be used.

neural tube defects
Abnormalities in the brain or spinal cord that result from errors that occur during prenatal development.

dietary folate equivalents (DFEs) The unit used to express the amount of folate present in food. One DFE is equivalent to 1 μg of folate naturally occurring in food, 0.6 μg of synthetic folic acid from fortified food or supplements consumed with food, or 0.5 μg of synthetic folic acid consumed on an empty stomach.

Life Cycle

Critical Thinking
Meeting Folate
Recommendations

Background

Mercedes would like to have a baby but before she tries to conceive, she wants to be sure she is in the best possible health. She consults her physician who gives her a clean bill of health but suggests she make sure she is getting enough folic acid. Her doctor told her that women who are capable of becoming pregnant should consume 400 µg of folic acid from fortified foods or supplements each day in addition to the folate found in a varied diet.

(©iStockphoto)

Data:

Mercedes records her food intake for 1 day to determine her folate intake:

CURRENT DIET

FOOD	AMOUNT	TOTAL FOLATE (µG)
Breakfast		
Oatmeal, regular	1 cup	2
Milk	1 cup	12
Banana	1 medium	22
Orange juice	1 cup	75
Coffee	1 cup	0
Lunch		
Hamburger	3 oz	11
Hamburger bun	1	32
French fries	20 pieces	24
Coke	12 oz	0
Apple	1 medium	4
Dinner		
Chicken	3 oz	4
Refried beans	1/2 cup	106
White rice	1 cup	80
Flour tortilla	1	60
Salad	1 cup	64
Salad dressing	1 Tbsp	1
Milk	1 cup	12
White cake	1 piece	32
Total		**541**

Critical Thinking Questions

Why is folate a concern for Mercedes when planning a pregnancy?

▼

Look at Mercedes' diet. Which foods are highest in folate? Of these, which are fortified with folic acid?

▼

Mercedes has oatmeal for breakfast because it is a whole grain, but why is it low in folate? If she replaced her white rice with brown rice and her tortilla and hamburger bun with whole wheat products, how would this affect her total folate intake?

▼

Would you recommend Mercedes take a folic acid supplement?

 iProfile   Use iProfile to find out how much folate is in the folate-fortified grain products you consume each day.

The Daily Values on food labels and values in some food composition tables are listed as µg total folate, not as µg DFE. DFEs correct for differences in the bioavailability of different forms of folate. For foods that are natural sources of folate, the folate content can be determined by multiplying the Daily Value (400 µg) by the % Daily Value listed on the label (see Off the Label: How Much Vitamin C Is in Your Orange Juice?). So, to calculate the folate in a package of frozen spinach that provides 25% of the Daily Value, multiply 400 µg folate × 25% = 100 µg DFE. In foods fortified with folic acid, the amount of folate indicated by the % Daily Value must be multiplied by 1.7 to account for the greater bioavailability of folic acid (**Table 8.4**).

Table 8.4 **Calculating Dietary Folate Equivalents in Fortified Foods**

The folate listed on labels of fortified foods is primarily folic acid, which is more available than natural forms of folate. In order to compare the folate content of these foods to recommendations, the amount of folic acid must be converted to dietary folate equivalents, expressed as µg DFE. This calculation assumes that all of the folate in these foods is from added folic acid.

Determine the amount of folic acid in the fortified food:
- Multiply the Daily Value for folate by the % Daily Values listed on the label.

  Daily Value is 400 µg

Convert the µg folic acid into µg DFE:
- Multiply the µg folic acid by 1.7.

  Folic acid added to a food in fortification provides 1.7 times more available folate per µg than folate naturally present in foods.

For example:
- A serving of English muffins provides 6% of the Daily Value for folate:

  To find the µg folic acid: 400 µg × 6% = 24 µg folic acid

  To convert to µg DFE: 24 µg folic acid × 1.7 = 40 µg DFE

Folate Deficiency

A deficiency of folate leads to a drop in blood folate levels and a rise in blood homocysteine followed by changes that affect rapidly dividing cells. Deficiency symptoms include poor growth, problems in nerve development and function, diarrhea, inflammation of the tongue, and anemia. Anemia results when folate is deficient because cells in the bone marrow that develop into red blood cells cannot duplicate their DNA and so cannot divide. Instead, they just grow bigger. These large immature cells are known as **megaloblasts** and can be converted into large red blood cells called **macrocytes**. The result is that fewer mature red blood cells are produced, and the oxygen-carrying capacity of the blood is reduced. This condition is called **megaloblastic** or **macrocytic anemia** (**Figure 8.24**). Groups at risk of folate deficiency include

megaloblasts Large, immature red blood cells that are formed when developing red blood cells are unable to divide normally.

macrocytes Larger-than-normal mature red blood cells that have a shortened life span.

megaloblastic or **macrocytic anemia** A condition in which there are abnormally large immature and mature red blood cells in the bloodstream and a reduction in the total number of red blood cells and the oxygen-carrying capacity of the blood.

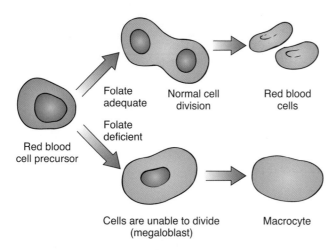

Folate adequate — Normal cell division — Red blood cells

Red blood cell precursor

Folate deficient

Cells are unable to divide (megaloblast) — Macrocyte

Figure 8.24 Role of folate in macrocytic anemia
Macrocytic anemia occurs when red blood cell precursors are unable to divide, resulting in the formation of abnormally large red blood cells (macrocytes).

Off the Label
How Much Vitamin C Is in Your Orange Juice?

(©iStockphoto)

How much vitamin C is in your orange juice? How much folate is in your breakfast cereal? And how much iron is in a box of raisins? It can be difficult to tell from the Nutrition Facts section of a food label exactly how much of a micronutrient is in a food. Food labels are required to provide the % Daily Values for vitamin A, vitamin C, iron, and calcium, but not the actual amount. To determine the amount of one of these nutrients in a serving of food, you need to know its Daily Value (see Table 2.7 and Appendix J). Once you know the Daily Value, you can multiply it by the % Daily Value on the label to determine the amount in a serving of the food. So, follow these steps to find out how much vitamin C is in a cup of orange juice:

1. Look up the Daily Value:

VITAMIN	DAILY VALUE
Vitamin A	5000 IU[a]
Vitamin D	400 IU[a]
Vitamin E	30 IU[a]
Vitamin K	80 mg
Biotin	300 mg
Pantothenic acid	10 mg
Vitamin C	60 mg
Thiamin	1.5 mg
Riboflavin	1.7 mg
Niacin	20 mg
Vitamin B$_6$	2.0 mg
Folic acid	400 mg
Vitamin B$_{12}$	6 mg

[a]The Daily Values for some fat-soluble vitamins are expressed in International Units (IU). The DRIs use a newer system of measurement.

2. Find the % Daily Value (%DV) on the food label (see figure): % DV for vitamin C in orange juice = 120%.
3. Multiply the % Daily Value by the Daily Value to find out how much is in a serving: 60 mg × 120% DV = 60 × 1.2 = 72 mg vitamin C.

Even if you don't look up the Daily Value and calculate the exact amount of vitamin C or some other vitamin or mineral in a food, the % Daily Value on the food label helps you judge how much the food contains. As a general guideline, if the % Daily Value of a nutrient is 5% or less, the food is a poor source; if it is 10 to 19%, the food is a good source; and if it is 20% or more, the food is an excellent source. Whether you are converting a Daily Value into the amount of a vitamin or are just looking at the Daily Value, be sure to consider how many servings you plan to eat. Remember that doubling the serving doubles the nutrients and kcalories.

Orange Juice

Nutrition Facts
Serving Size 8 fl oz (250 mL)
Servings Per Container 8

Amount Per Serving

Calories 110	Calories from Fat 0

	%Daily Value**
Total Fat 0g	**2%**
Sodium 0mg	**0%**
Potassium 450mg	**13%**
Total Carbohydrate 26g	**9%**
Sugars 7g	
Protein 2g	

Vitamin C 120%	•	Calcium	2%
Thiamin 10%	•	Riboflavin	4%
Niacin 4%	•	Vitamin B$_6$	6%
Folate 15%	•	Magnesium	6%

Not a significant source or saturated fat, cholesterol, dietary fiber, vitamin A and iron.

*Percent Daily Values are based on a 2,000 calorie diet.

(Foodcollection/Getty Images, Inc.)

pregnant women and premature infants because of their rapid rate of cell division and growth; the elderly because of their limited intake of foods high in folate; alcoholics because alcohol inhibits folate absorption; and tobacco smokers because smoke inactivates folate in the cells lining the lungs.[5]

Folate and the Risk of Neural Tube Defects

Neural tube defects, such as **spina bifida**, **anencephaly**, and other birth defects that affect the brain and spinal cord, are not true folate-deficiency symptoms because not every pregnant woman with inadequate folate levels will give birth to a child with a neural tube defect. Instead, neural tube defects are probably due to a combination of factors that include low folate levels and a genetic predisposition. The exact role of folate in neural tube development is not known, but it is necessary for a critical step called *neural tube closure*. When neural tube closure does not occur normally portions of the brain or spinal cord are not adequately protected (**Figure 8.25**). Neural tube closure is complete by 28 days after conception; therefore, folate status should be adequate even before a pregnancy begins to assure an adequate supply during early development (see Chapter 14). Studies in which supplemental folic acid was given to women before and during early pregnancy showed that 360 to 800 μg per day of synthetic folic acid in addition to food folate was associated with a reduced incidence of neural tube defects.[5] Because it is not known whether a diet naturally rich in folate offers the same protection as folic acid, supplemental folic acid from supplements or fortified foods is recommended. To be effective, folate must be adequate before most women are aware that they are pregnant, therefore, supplemental folic acid is recommended for all women of childbearing age. The fortification of grain products in 1998 made it easier for women to meet this recommendation. Although other factors may also have played a role, the incidence of neural tube defects decreased by 25% in the United States since the fortification of grains with folic acid.[19] A similar enrichment program in Canada has resulted in a decrease of almost 50%.[20]

Folate and Heart Disease

Low intakes of folate have been associated with an increased risk of heart disease. Its effect on heart disease is related to its role in the metabolism of the amino acid homocysteine (see Figure 8.21). Folate is needed to convert homocysteine to methionine. When folate is deficient homocysteine levels rise because less is converted to methionine. The risk of cardiovascular disease increases with elevated homocysteine (see preceding discussion of vitamin B_6 and cardiovascular disease). Homocysteine levels, and therefore the risk of cardiovascular disease, are reduced by increasing intakes of folate.[14,15]

Life Cycle

spina bifida A birth defect resulting from the incorrect development of the spinal cord that can leave the spinal cord exposed.

anencephaly A birth defect due to failure of the neural tube to close that results in the absence of a major portion of the brain, skull, and scalp.

Normal spine

Spine with mild spina bifida

Spine with severe spina bifida

Figure 8.25 Spina bifida
The neural tube develops into the brain and spinal cord. If folate is inadequate during neural tube closure, neural tube defects such as spina bifida occur more frequently. (Wellcome Trust/Custom Medical Stock Photo, Inc.)

Folate and Cancer

Low folate status increases the risk of developing cancer of the ovary, breast, pancreas, and colon.[21–23] Although folate deficiency does not cause cancer, it has been hypothesized that low folate intake enhances an underlying predisposition to cancer. Epidemiological data have shown that higher plasma levels of folate are associated with a reduced risk of developing breast cancer, particularly in women at high risk due to alcohol consumption.[24] Alcohol consumption greatly increases the cancer risk associated with a low folate diet.[25] Epidemiological and clinical studies indicate that higher dietary folate intake and blood folate levels are associated with a lower risk of colorectal cancer. Studies suggest an approximately 40% reduction in the risk of colorectal cancer in individuals with the highest dietary folate intake compared with those with the lowest intake.[26]

Folate Toxicity

Although there is no known folate toxicity, a high intake may mask the early symptoms of vitamin B_{12} deficiency, allowing it to go untreated and resulting in irreversible nerve damage. The UL for folic acid for adults is set at 1000 μg per day from supplements and/or fortified foods. This value was determined based on the progression of neurological symptoms seen in patients who are deficient in vitamin B_{12} and taking folic acid supplements.

8.9 Vitamin B_{12}

Learning Objectives

- Name foods that are good sources and poor sources of vitamin B_{12}.
- List the steps involved in vitamin B_{12} absorption.
- Compare the functions of folate and vitamin B_{12}.

pernicious anemia An anemia resulting from vitamin B_{12} deficiency that occurs when dietary vitamin B_{12} cannot be absorbed due to a lack of intrinsic factor.

Pernicious anemia is a form of anemia that does not respond to iron supplementation. At the time it was first described in 1820, it could not be treated and was fatal. Pernicious anemia is caused by an inability to absorb sufficient vitamin B_{12}. In 1926,

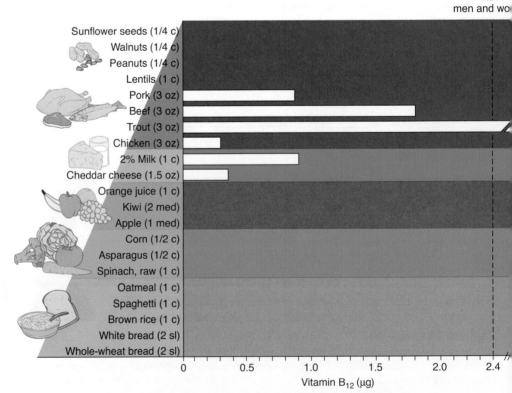

Figure 8.26 Vitamin B_{12} content of MyPyramid food groups
Vitamin B_{12} is found only in foods of animal origin or foods that have been fortified with the vitamin; the dashed line represents the RDA for adult men and women.

Drs. Minot and Murphy were awarded the Nobel Prize for curing the disease with a diet containing large quantities of liver, which is a good source of vitamin B$_{12}$. Today, concern focuses on the effects of marginal deficiencies of this vitamin and the potential masking of B$_{12}$ deficiency by high intakes of folic acid.

Vitamin B$_{12}$ in the Diet

Vitamin B$_{12}$ is found almost exclusively in animal products (**Figure 8.26**). It can be made by bacteria, fungi, and algae but not by plants and animals. It accumulates in animal tissue from the diet or from synthesis by bacterial microflora. Bacteria in the human colon produce vitamin B$_{12}$, but it cannot be absorbed. Vitamin B$_{12}$ is not found in plant products unless they have been contaminated with bacteria, soil, insects, or other sources of vitamin B$_{12}$, or have been fortified with it. Diets that do not include animal products must include supplements or foods fortified with vitamin B$_{12}$ in order to meet needs.[27]

Vitamin B$_{12}$ in the Digestive Tract

Naturally occurring vitamin B$_{12}$ is bound to proteins in food and must be released before it can be absorbed. It is released in the stomach by acid and the protein-digesting enzyme pepsin. In the small intestine, vitamin B$_{12}$ binds to **intrinsic factor**. Intrinsic factor is a protein secreted by the **parietal cells** in the lining of the stomach. The intrinsic factor-vitamin B$_{12}$ complex binds to receptor proteins in the ileum of the small intestine, allowing the vitamin to be absorbed (**Figure 8.27**). Only a small amount of

intrinsic factor A protein produced in the stomach that is needed for the absorption of adequate amounts of vitamin B$_{12}$.

parietal cells Large cells in the stomach lining that produce and secrete intrinsic factor and hydrochloric acid.

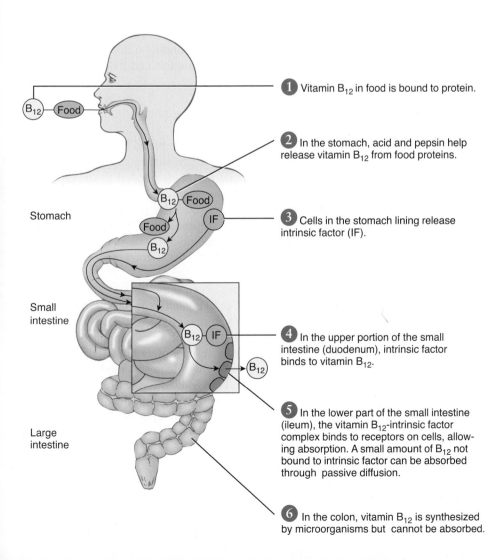

1 Vitamin B$_{12}$ in food is bound to protein.

2 In the stomach, acid and pepsin help release vitamin B$_{12}$ from food proteins.

3 Cells in the stomach lining release intrinsic factor (IF).

4 In the upper portion of the small intestine (duodenum), intrinsic factor binds to vitamin B$_{12}$.

5 In the lower part of the small intestine (ileum), the vitamin B$_{12}$-intrinsic factor complex binds to receptors on cells, allowing absorption. A small amount of B$_{12}$ not bound to intrinsic factor can be absorbed through passive diffusion.

6 In the colon, vitamin B$_{12}$ is synthesized by microorganisms but cannot be absorbed.

Stomach

Small intestine

Large intestine

Figure 8.27 Absorption of vitamin B$_{12}$
Normal absorption of vitamin B$_{12}$ requires a healthy stomach, pancreas, and small intestine.

vitamin B_{12} can be absorbed when intrinsic factor is absent. Vitamin B_{12} absorption is also reduced by low stomach acid and insufficient pancreatic secretions.

Vitamin B_{12} is secreted in bile, but most of this is reabsorbed, rather than being lost in the feces. Because of this efficient recycling, it can take many years of a deficient diet before the symptoms of vitamin B_{12} deficiency appear.

Vitamin B_{12} in the Body

cobalamin The chemical term for vitamin B_{12}.

The terms vitamin B_{12} and **cobalamin** refer to members of a group of cobalt-containing compounds. Vitamin B_{12} is necessary for the maintenance of myelin, which insulates nerves and is essential for normal nerve transmission (see Figure 8.20). Vitamin B_{12} can be converted into either of two active cobalamin coenzyme forms, methylcobalamin and adenosylcobalamin (see Appendix L). These coenzymes function in 2 important metabolic reactions. One rearranges carbon atoms so that the breakdown products of fatty acids with an odd number of carbons in the chain can enter the citric acid cycle and be used to provide energy. A second reaction synthesizes the amino acid methionine from homocysteine. This reaction also regenerates the active coenzyme form of folate that functions in DNA synthesis (see Figure 8.21).

Recommended Vitamin B_{12} Intake

The RDA for adults of all ages for vitamin B_{12} is 2.4 μg per day.[5] This is the amount needed to maintain normal red blood cell parameters and normal blood concentrations of vitamin B_{12}. Average intake in the U.S. population exceeds the RDA for both adult men and women.

Life Cycle

The RDA for vitamin B_{12} is increased during pregnancy, even though absorption is increased. The RDA during lactation is increased to account for the amount secreted in milk. Pregnant and lactating vegans, like anyone who does not eat animal products, are advised to take a supplement or consume fortified foods to obtain the recommended intake for vitamin B_{12}.[27]

Vitamin B_{12} Deficiency

Symptoms of vitamin B_{12} deficiency include an increase in blood homocysteine levels and a macrocytic, megaloblastic anemia that is indistinguishable from that seen in folate deficiency. This anemia occurs because vitamin B_{12} is needed to convert folate into the form that is active for DNA synthesis (see Figure 8.21). Lack of vitamin B_{12} causes a secondary folate deficiency and, consequently, megaloblastic anemia. Vitamin B_{12} deficiency also causes neurological symptoms, which include numbness and tingling, abnormalities in gait, memory loss, and disorientation. These are due to degeneration of the myelin that coats the nerves, spinal cord, and brain. If not treated, this eventually causes paralysis and death.

Blatant deficiencies of vitamin B_{12} are rare because the body stores and reuses it. However, marginal vitamin B_{12} status is of public health concern, particularly for older adults and vegetarians who consume no animal products. Because of the efficient recycling of vitamin B_{12}, it can take many years of a deficient diet before the symptoms of deficiency appear. However, when absorption is impaired, neither dietary vitamin B_{12} nor the vitamin B_{12} secreted in the bile is absorbed, so deficiency symptoms appear more rapidly. This occurs in both individuals with pernicious anemia, an autoimmune disease in which the parietal cells that produce intrinsic factor are destroyed, and in those with **atrophic gastritis**, an inflammation of the stomach lining that results in a reduction in stomach acid and bacterial overgrowth.

atrophic gastritis An inflammation of the stomach lining that results in reduced secretion stomach acid and bacterial overgrowth.

Pernicious Anemia Pernicious anemia is the major cause of severe vitamin B_{12} deficiency. Without intrinsic factor, vitamin B_{12} cannot be absorbed normally. This anemia can be treated with injections of the vitamin, with a B_{12}-containing nasal gel, or with oral megadoses. The injections, which deliver vitamin B_{12} to the subcutaneous fat or muscle, and the nasal gel, which allows the vitamin to enter the bloodstream through the nasal mucosa, bypass the gastrointestinal tract, and thus the need for intrinsic factor. Megadoses can treat pernicious anemia because they allow adequate amounts of vitamin B_{12} to be absorbed by passive diffusion, which does not require intrinsic factor.

Atrophic Gastritis About 10% to 30% of individuals over 50 years of age are unable to absorb food-bound vitamin B_{12} normally because they have atrophic gastritis. When stomach acid is reduced, the enzymes that release protein-bound vitamin B_{12} cannot function properly and the bound vitamin B_{12} cannot be released and absorbed. Atrophic gastritis also causes microbial overgrowth in the intestine. These microbes reduce vitamin B_{12} absorption by competing for available vitamin B_{12}. In severe cases of atrophic gastritis the production of intrinsic factor is also reduced, further impairing vitamin B_{12} absorption. It is recommended that individuals over the age of 50 meet their RDA by consuming foods fortified with vitamin B_{12} such as breakfast cereals or soy-based products or by taking a vitamin B_{12}-containing supplement. Because the vitamin B_{12} in these products is not bound to proteins, it is absorbed even when stomach acid is low.

Vegan Diets Vitamin B_{12} deficiency is also a concern among vegans since vitamin B_{12} is only found in foods of animal origin. Severe deficiency has been observed in breast-fed infants of vegan women, but marginal deficiency is a concern for all vegans if supplements or fortified foods are not included in the diet.

Vitamin B_{12} Deficiency and Supplemental Folate If individuals with vitamin B_{12} deficiency consume enough folate, they will not develop anemia, which is an easily identified and reversible symptom of vitamin B_{12} deficiency. Without this symptom, diagnosis can be delayed, allowing more serious and irreversible symptoms, such as nerve damage, to progress. Although the fortification of grain products with folic acid has raised concern that additional folate in the food supply could delay diagnosis of vitamin B_{12} deficiency, the amount consumed from a typical diet is unlikely to be high enough to cause problems.

Vitamin B_{12} Toxicity and Supplements

No toxic effects have been reported with excess vitamin B_{12} intakes of up to 100 μg per day from food or supplements. There are not sufficient data to establish a UL for vitamin B_{12}.

Supplements of vitamin B_{12} are available as cyanocobalamin in both oral and injectable forms. Because vitamin B_{12} deficiency causes anemia, supplements of the vitamin, particularly as injections, have been promoted as a pick-me-up for tired, run-down individuals. However, there are no proven benefits of vitamin B_{12} supplementation in individuals who are not vitamin B_{12} deficient. Oral supplements may be of benefit for those at risk for vitamin B_{12} deficiency, such as vegans and individuals over 50 years of age.[5]

8.10 Vitamin C

Learning Objectives

- Name foods that are good sources and poor sources of vitamin C.
- Relate the role of vitamin C in the body to the symptoms of scurvy.
- Explain how vitamin C prevents oxidative damage.

Scurvy has been the scourge of armies, navies, and explorers throughout history. This vitamin C deficiency disease was described by ancient Greeks, Egyptians, and Romans. The reason obtaining enough vitamin C, also known as **ascorbic acid** or **ascorbate**, has been a particular problem for armies and explorers is that fresh fruits and vegetables are its main sources; these foods spoil quickly and don't transport well on long voyages. In the mid-1500s, the Indians of eastern Canada knew that an extract from white cedar needles would cure the disease. In 1594, after a voyage to

Life Cycle

scurvy The vitamin C deficiency disease.

ascorbic acid or **ascorbate** The chemical term for vitamin C.

the South Seas, Sir Richard Hawkins recommended that this sickness be treated by including citrus fruit in the diet. Despite his recommendation, 10,000 British sailors died of scurvy that same year. Over 100 years later, James Lind, a Scottish physician serving in the British navy, tested various agents for their effectiveness at curing scurvy and reported that two patients given citrus fruits recovered within six days. However, it was another 48 years before it was required that lime or lemon juice be included in the rations of the mercantile service, earning British sailors the name *limeys*. Unfortunately, the rest of the world did not heed the lesson of the limeys. In the mid-nineteenth century, during the U.S. Civil War, scurvy was rampant.

Vitamin C in the Diet

Citrus fruits, such as oranges, lemons, and limes, are an excellent source of vitamin C. Other fruits that are high in vitamin C include strawberries and cantaloupe. Vegetables in the cabbage family, such as broccoli, cauliflower, bok choy, and brussels sprouts, as well as green leafy vegetables, green and red peppers, okra, tomatoes, and potatoes, are also good sources (**Figure 8.28**). Meat, fish, poultry, eggs, dairy products, and grains are poor sources. The amount of vitamin C in packaged foods must be listed on food labels as a percentage of the Daily Value. This information can be used to identify packaged foods, such as frozen strawberries and orange juice, that are good sources of vitamin C. Fresh fruits and vegetables, which are the best sources of vitamin C, do not carry food labels.

Vitamin C is unstable and is destroyed by oxygen, light, and heat, so it is readily lost in cooking. This loss is accelerated by contact with copper or iron cooking utensils and by low-acid conditions.

Vitamin C in the Body

Vitamin C is a water-soluble vitamin that donates electrons in biochemical reactions, including those needed for the synthesis and maintenance of connective tissue. Because it can donate electrons, vitamin C also has a more general role as an antioxi-

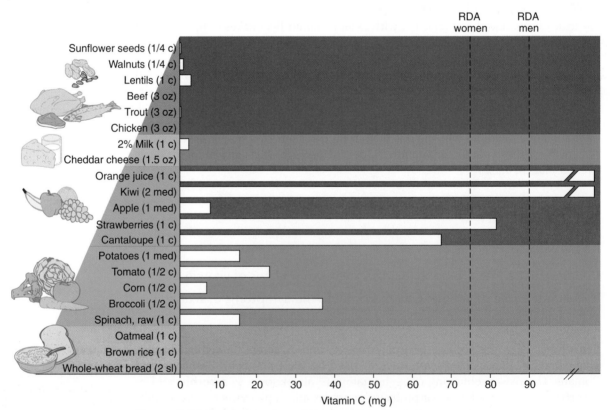

Figure 8.28 Vitamin C content of MyPyramid food groups
Fruits and vegetables are the best sources of vitamin C; the dashed lines represent the RDAs for adult men and women.

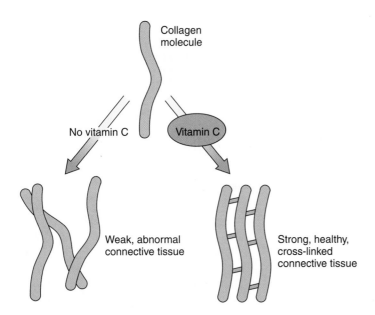

H—C—OH
HO—C—H O
C — C=O
H
C = C
OH   OH
Ascorbic acid

e⁻ → H⁺

H⁺ ← e⁻

H—C—OH
HO—C—H O
C — C=O
H
C — C
O   O
Dehydroascorbic acid

Figure 8.29 Oxidation and reduction of vitamin C When ascorbic acid donates electrons and hydrogens in chemical reactions, the structure changes to form a molecule of dehydroascorbic acid. This reaction is reversible and vitamin C can be restored when electrons and hydrogens are provided by other antioxidants such as glutathione.

dant that, along with other antioxidants, protects the body from reactive oxygen molecules (**Figure 8.29**). It also helps maintain the immune system and aids in the absorption of iron.

Vitamin C as a Coenzyme Many of the biochemical reactions requiring vitamin C add a hydroxyl group (OH) to other molecules. Two such reactions are essential for the formation of **collagen**, the protein that forms the base of all connective tissue in the body. Vitamin C is needed for activity of the enzymes that add the hydroxyl groups to the amino acids proline and lysine to form hydroxyproline and hydroxylysine, respectively. These hydroxyl groups are necessary for the formation of chemical bonds that cross-link the polypeptide strands of collagen to give it strength (**Figure 8.30**). Vitamin C also serves as a coenzyme in reactions needed for the synthesis of other cell compounds, including neurotransmitters, hormones such as the thyroid and steroid hormones, bile acids, and carnitine needed for fatty acid breakdown.

Vitamin C as an Antioxidant Vitamin C also functions as an **antioxidant**. Antioxidants are substances that protect against **oxidative damage**, which is damage caused by reactive oxygen molecules. **Oxidative stress** refers to a serious imbalance between the amounts of reactive oxygen molecules and the availability of antioxidant defenses. Oxidative stress has been related to the aging process as well as to the development of cancer and heart disease. Agents that can induce oxidative stress by causing an increase in reactive oxygen molecules, a decrease in antioxidant defenses, or an increase in oxidative damage are called **pro-oxidants**.

How Do Antioxidants Work? Reactive oxygen molecules such as **free radicals** come from environmental sources such as air pollution or cigarette smoke as well as from normal oxygen-requiring reactions inside the body. Free radicals cause damage

collagen The major protein in connective tissue.

antioxidant A substance that is able to neutralize reactive oxygen molecules and thereby reduce oxidative damage.

oxidative damage Damage caused by highly reactive oxygen molecules that steal electrons from other compounds, causing changes in structure and function.

oxidative stress A condition that occurs when there are more reactive oxygen molecules than can be neutralized by available antioxidant defenses. It occurs either because excessive amounts of reactive oxygen molecules are generated or because antioxidant defenses are deficient.

pro-oxidant A substance that promotes oxidative damage.

free radical One type of highly reactive molecule that causes oxidative damage.

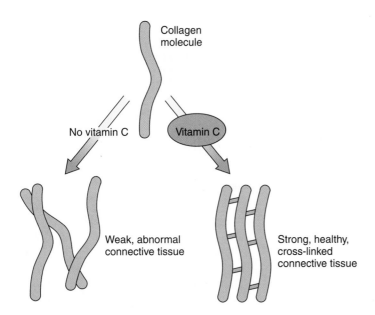

Collagen molecule

No vitamin C   Vitamin C

Weak, abnormal connective tissue

Strong, healthy, cross-linked connective tissue

Figure 8.30 Role of vitamin C in collagen synthesis Vitamin C is needed for the formation of chemical bonds that link collagen molecules together to give connective tissue strength and stability.

by snatching electrons from DNA, proteins, carbohydrates, or unsaturated fatty acids. This results in changes in the structure and function of these molecules. DNA damage is hypothesized to be a major reason for the increase in cancer incidence that occurs with age. Free radical damage to lipoproteins and lipids in membranes is implicated in the development of atherosclerosis.[28]

Antioxidants act by destroying reactive oxygen molecules before they can do damage. Some directly destroy free radicals, while others neutralize superoxide radicals or hydrogen peroxide, which are other reactive molecules, before they can form free radicals. Some antioxidants are produced in the body; others are consumed in the diet. Vitamin C, vitamin E, and the mineral selenium have been classified as **dietary antioxidants** (see Chapter 12, Your Choice: Are Antioxidant Supplements Beneficial?).[29]

dietary antioxidant
A substance in food that significantly decreases the adverse effects of reactive species on normal physiological function in humans.

The Role of Vitamin C Vitamin C acts as an antioxidant in the blood and other body fluids. It can neutralize superoxide radicals and free radicals before they can damage lipids and DNA (**Figure 8.31**). Vitamin C has also been shown to scavenge reactive oxygen molecules in white blood cells, the lungs, and the stomach mucosa.[29] The antioxidant properties of vitamin C are also important for the functioning of other nutrients. Vitamin C regenerates the active antioxidant form of vitamin E and enhances iron absorption by keeping iron in its more readily absorbed reduced form (Fe^{+2}). When about 50 mg of vitamin C—the amount contained in a small glass of orange juice—is consumed in a meal containing iron, iron absorption is enhanced sixfold (see Chapter 12).

Vitamin C may also act as a pro-oxidant by converting iron and copper to reduced forms that can then generate free radicals. There is some evidence that vitamin C supplements could lead to oxidative damage to DNA. However, studies of the pro-oxidant effects of vitamin C are inconsistent.[30] More research is needed to determine what factors influence whether the antioxidant or pro-oxidant properties of vitamin C predominate.

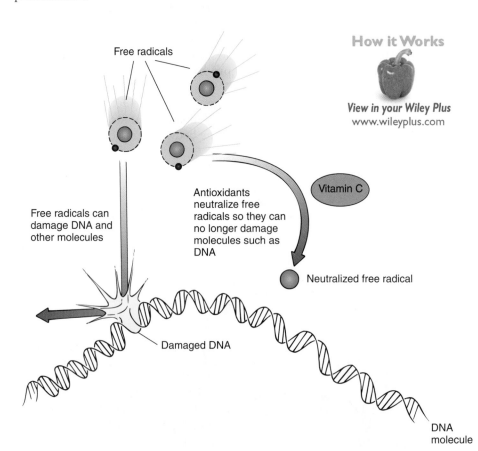

Free radicals

How it Works

View in your Wiley Plus
www.wileyplus.com

Vitamin C

Antioxidants neutralize free radicals so they can no longer damage molecules such as DNA

Free radicals can damage DNA and other molecules

Neutralized free radical

Damaged DNA

DNA molecule

Figure 8.31 Antioxidant role of vitamin C
Vitamin C functions as an antioxidant that donates electrons to neutralize free radicals so that they are no longer damaging.

Recommended Vitamin C Intake

Humans are one of only a few animal species that require vitamin C in the diet. Most animals can synthesize vitamin C in their bodies. For example, a pig makes 8 grams of the vitamin each day. The recommendations for vitamin C intake are based on the amount needed to maximize concentrations in neutrophils, a type of white blood cell, with minimal excretion of the vitamin in the urine. The RDA is 90 mg per day for men and 75 mg per day for women. This amount is easily obtained by drinking an 8-ounce glass of orange juice.

The RDA for vitamin C is increased during pregnancy and lactation. The recommendation for infants is based on the vitamin C content of human milk. Cigarette smoking increases the requirement for vitamin C because vitamin C is used to break down compounds in cigarette smoke. It is recommended that cigarette smokers consume an extra 35 mg of vitamin C daily[29]—the amount in one half-cup of broccoli. Exercise and mental and emotional stress have not been found to affect the need for vitamin C.

Life Cycle

Vitamin C Deficiency

When vitamin C intake is below 10 mg per day, the symptoms of scurvy may appear. These symptoms reflect the role of vitamin C in the maintenance of collagen. Without vitamin C, the bonds holding adjacent collagen molecules together cannot be formed so healthy collagen cannot be synthesized and maintained, resulting in symptoms such as poor wound healing, the reopening of previously healed wounds, bone and joint aches, bone fractures, and improperly formed and loose teeth. Connective tissue is also important for blood vessel integrity. A vitamin C deficiency therefore causes weakened blood vessels and ruptured capillaries, which leads to symptoms such as tiny bleeds around the hair follicles, bleeding gums, and easy bruising (**Figure 8.32**). Iron absorption is reduced when vitamin C is deficient so anemia may also occur. The psychological manifestations of scurvy include depression and hysteria.

Throughout history a lack of fruits and vegetables containing vitamin C has caused the death of thousands of sailors, soldiers, and explorers. Today, severe vitamin C deficiency leading to scurvy is rare, but marginal vitamin C deficiency is a concern for individuals who consume few fruits and vegetables. Scurvy has been reported in infants fed diets consisting exclusively of cow's milk and in alcoholics and elderly individuals consuming nutrient-poor diets.

Vitamin C Toxicity

Vitamin C is generally considered nontoxic. Large increases in intake do not cause large increases in the amount of vitamin C in body fluids. This is because the percentage of the dose absorbed decreases as the size of the dose increases and vitamin C absorbed in excess of need is excreted by the kidney. The most common symptoms that occur with consumption of vitamin C doses of 1 gram or more are diarrhea, nausea, and abdominal cramps. These are caused when unabsorbed vitamin C draws water into the intestine. The UL for vitamin C is based on an amount that is unlikely to cause gastrointestinal symptoms in healthy individuals and has been set at 2000 mg/day from food and supplements.

A high intake of vitamin C should be avoided by individuals prone to kidney stones because it can increase stone formation, by individuals who are unable to regulate iron absorption because it increases absorption, and by those with sickle cell anemia because it can worsen symptoms. Other potential problems associated with vitamin C intakes greater than 3 grams per day include interference with drugs prescribed to slow blood clotting and, because the structure of vitamin C is similar to that of glucose, interference with urine tests used to monitor glucose levels.

Figure 8.32 When vitamin C is deficient, the symptoms of scurvy begin to appear. The gums become inflamed, swell, and bleed. The teeth loosen and eventually fall out. (Science Photo Library/Photo Researchers, Inc.)

Another concern with high doses of vitamin C taken as supplements is damage to tooth enamel. Vitamin C is an acid that is strong enough to dissolve tooth enamel when vitamin C tablets are chewed.

Vitamin C Supplements

One-third of the population of the United States takes supplements of vitamin C in the hope that they will prevent or reduce symptoms of the common cold. More recently, however, the role of vitamin C as an antioxidant has been used to promote vitamin C supplements as protection against cardiovascular disease and cancer.

How it Works

View in your Wiley Plus
www.wileyplus.com

Vitamin C and the Common Cold Studies examining the relationship between vitamin C and the common cold date back to the 1930s. A review of placebo-controlled trials that supplemented diets with vitamin C failed to find that routine vitamin C supplementation reduced the incidence of colds in the healthy population.[31] The incidence of respiratory infections was reduced somewhat in those exposed to periods of severe physical exercise and/or cold environments.[31,32] Regular supplementation with vitamin C did however reduce the duration and severity of colds (**Figure 8.33**). To have this effect the supplements needed to be introduced before the onset of the cold symptoms. The effect of vitamin C on cold symptoms may be due to its direct antiviral effect, its antioxidant effect, its role in stimulating various aspects of immune function, its ability to increase the breakdown of histamine (a molecule that causes inflammation), or a combination of these.[33,34]

Figure 8.33
Vitamin C supplements won't prevent you from catching a cold, but they may help you recover faster.

Critical Thinking
Supplemental Choices

Background:

Hazel is suffering through her third cold of the winter. She is tired of being sick! When she complains at a local health food store, the clerk recommends several supplements to keep her healthy. These include a vitamin C supplement, a stress formula B vitamin supplement called B$_{50}$, a supplement called Prevention Plus, and the herbal supplement echinacea. When she gets home with her new supplements, her friend who is a nutrition student questions whether Hazel needs all of these products.

Data

Hazel is a generally healthy 22-year-old. Her Body Mass Index (BMI) is in the healthy range and she exercises a couple of days each week. She checks the labels of the supplements she has purchased. The information is summarized in the table below:

(©Jason/Alamy)

SUPPLEMENT	INGREDIENTS	DOSE	%DV/DOSE	FREQUENCY	TOTAL AMOUNT (% DV)
Vitamin C	Vitamin C	500 mg	833%	3/day	1500 mg (2500%)
B$_{50}$	Thiamin	50 mg	3333%	3/day	150 mg (10,000%)
	Niacin	50 mg	250%		150 mg (750%)
	Vitamin B$_6$	60 mg	2500%		180 mg (7500%)
	Riboflavin	50 mg	2941%		150 mg (8823%)
	Biotin	50 mg	16.66%		150 mg (50%)
	Pantothenic Acid	50 mg	500%		150 mg (1500%)
	Folic Acid	50 mg	12.5%		150 mg (38%)
	Vitamin B$_{12}$	50 mg	833%		150 mg (2500%)
Prevention Plus	Vitamin C	1000 mg	1667%	1/day	1000 mg (1667%)
	Zinc	15 mg	100%		15 mg (100%)
Echinacea	Echinacea	125 mg	-	6/day	750 mg

Critical Thinking Questions

Review the ingredients in Hazel's supplements. If she takes all these products at the frequency recommended in the table, will she be exceeding the UL for any nutrients? List them.

▼

Did you find a UL for echinacea? Why not?

▼

Would you recommend that Hazel take these supplements? Why or why not?

 iProfile Use iProfile to compare the vitamin C content of an orange and a multivitamin supplement.

Vitamin C and Cardiovascular Disease Vitamin C supplements have been suggested to reduce the risk of cardiovascular disease by lowering blood pressure, preventing the oxidation of LDL cholesterol, and reducing blood cholesterol levels. Several studies have suggested that blood pressure is inversely related to vitamin C status; however, the data are not conclusive.[35] Vitamin C is suggested to prevent LDL oxidation because of its antioxidant function. Vitamin C may reduce blood cholesterol because it is involved in the synthesis of bile acids from cholesterol in the liver. Adequate vitamin C allows cholesterol to be used for bile synthesis and therefore may reduce the amount of cholesterol in the blood. Despite these roles of vitamin C in protecting LDL cholesterol from oxidation and modulating blood cholesterol levels, data thus far from epidemiology and human intervention trials have provided little evidence to support the use of vitamin C supplements in preventing atherosclerosis in humans.[36]

Vitamin C and Cancer It has been suggested that high doses of vitamin C both treat and prevent cancer. Although controlled trials have not found any benefits of vitamin C in the treatment of patients with advanced cancer,[37] there is evidence supporting a role for vitamin C in cancer prevention. Epidemiological studies have found inverse relationships between the intake of fruits and vegetables, foods high in vitamin C, and cancer incidence.[38] Higher plasma vitamin C levels are associated with a lower cancer mortality in men.[39] As an antioxidant, vitamin C may protect against cancers caused by oxidative damage. In the case of gastrointestinal cancers, vitamin C may prevent cancer by inhibiting the formation of carcinogenic nitrosamines in the gut (see Chapter 17). Despite the association between higher intakes of vitamin C and a lower incidence of various cancers, a low risk of cancer is more closely linked to a dietary pattern that is rich in whole-food sources of antioxidants than to any individual antioxidant. Factors other than vitamin C found in fruits and vegetables are likely to contribute to the overall protective effect[38] (see Critical Thinking: Supplemental Choices).

8.11 Choline: Is It a Vitamin?

Learning Objective

- Explain why choline is not considered a vitamin.

Choline is needed to synthesize a number of important molecules, including a phospholipid found in cell membranes, the neurotransmitter acetylcholine, and the methyl donor betaine. It is also an important source of carbon atoms in biochemical reactions. Choline can be synthesized to a limited extent by humans and is not currently classified as a vitamin. However, there is evidence that it is essential in healthy men and women, but it is not yet clear whether it is also essential in the diets of infants and children.[5,40]

Choline is widely distributed in foods. Particularly good sources include egg yolks, organ meats, spinach, nuts, and wheat germ. Average daily choline intake is estimated to be about 600 to 1000 mg per day. An AI of 550 mg per day for men and 425 mg per day for women has been established based on the amount needed to prevent liver damage. There are few data to assess whether dietary choline is needed at all stages of life. At some stages, requirements may be met by synthesis in the body. Choline deficiency causes liver abnormalities. Deficiency is unlikely in healthy humans, but it has been observed in individuals fed a choline-deficient diet and in those receiving total parenteral nutrition without choline.[5] Choline is required by human cells grown in culture and prolonged deficiency in animals leads to fat accumulation in the liver and may contribute to liver cancer.

Intakes of choline that are much higher than can be obtained from foods can cause body odor, sweating, reduced growth rate, low blood pressure, and liver damage. A UL for adults of 3.5 g per day has been set based on the occurrence of low blood pressure.

Outcome

Chen and his wife work hard to maintain a healthy diet and lifestyle. They were shocked, then, to find that the fruits, vegetables, and whole grains in their diet were not providing all of the nutrients Chen needs. Because of Chen's low-meat diet, he was consuming little vitamin B_{12}. In addition, he had developed a condition common in older adults called atrophic gastritis, which reduces the amount of stomach acid. Stomach acid is essential for releasing vitamin B_{12} from the proteins it is bound to in food and allowing it to be absorbed. Without sufficient vitamin B_{12}, the myelin coating on nerves cannot be maintained, and nerve function is disrupted. To boost Chen's vitamin B_{12} status, his doctor gave him an injection and then instructed him to start taking a supplement containing vitamin B_{12}. The vitamin B_{12} in supplements is not bound to proteins, so it is more easily absorbed when stomach acid is low. Chen is now back to his old self. He continues his healthy diet and lifestyle, but has added a supplement to increase his vitamin B_{12} intake. He is grateful he discovered his condition early, because an untreated vitamin B_{12} deficiency might have resulted in permanent neurological damage.

APPLICATIONS

Personal Nutrition

1. **Do you get enough folate?**
   a. Use iProfile and your food intake record from Chapter 2 to determine how much folate your diet contains.
   b. How does your intake compare with the RDA?
   c. If your diet doesn't meet recommendations, suggest some dietary modifications that will help you meet the RDA for folate.
   d. List several natural sources of folate in your diet and several foods that are fortified with folic acid.

2. **Do you get enough vitamin B_{12}?**
   a. Use iProfile and your food intake record from Chapter 2 to determine how much vitamin B_{12} your diet contains.
   b. How does your intake compare with the RDA?
   c. If your diet doesn't meet recommendations, suggest some dietary modifications that will help you meet the RDA for vitamin B_{12}.
   d. If you eliminated meat, fish, poultry, and eggs from your diet would you be getting enough vitamin B_{12}? List the foods remaining in your diet that contribute vitamin B_{12}.
   e. If you were 60 years old, would your diet meet the recommendation for vitamin B_{12} intake?

3. **How much vitamin C is in your fast-food favorites?**
   a. Use iProfile or information from company Web sites to determine the amount of vitamin C in five items you commonly order from fast-food restaurants.

b. What percentage of your RDA for vitamin C does each provide? How does this compare with the percentage of your daily energy needs that each provides?

c. What fast-food items are highest in vitamin C? Why?

General Nutrition Issues

1. Evaluate each of the following supplements:

SUPPLEMENT	INGREDIENTS	DOSE
Pyridoxine	100 mg pyridoxine	2 tablets daily
Stress tab	35 mg pyridoxine 1 mg thiamin 1.1 mg riboflavin 30 mg niacin 500 mg choline	3 times daily
Folic acid	800 μg folic acid	Once daily

a. Do any of these supplements create a risk for toxicity when taken at the recommended dosage? Which ones and why?

b. Would you recommend them for everyone? For a specific lifestage group? Why or why not?

2. **Take a look at the Nutrition Facts label on a box of breakfast cereal.**

a. What percent of the Daily Value is included in a serving for each of the water-soluble vitamins?

b. What percent of the Daily Value would you consume for each water-soluble vitamin if you consumed the portion of cereal you typically have for breakfast?

c. Does the amount in your portion exceed the UL for any of these vitamins? Which ones?

iProfile

Summary

8.1 What Are Vitamins?

- Vitamins are essential organic nutrients that do not provide energy and are required in small quantities in the diet. Americans consume vitamins that are naturally present in foods, added to foods by fortification, and supplied by supplements. Some foods are fortified with nutrients according to government guidelines to promote public health. Others are fortified according to manufacturer's perceptions of what will sell in the marketplace.

- Vitamins are needed to promote and regulate body processes needed for growth, reproduction, and tissue maintenance. Vitamin deficiencies remain a major health problem worldwide. The amount of a vitamin that is available to the body is regulated by vitamin absorption, transport, activation, storage, and excretion. Recommended intakes for vitamins are expressed as RDAs or AIs. UL values estimate the highest dose that is unlikely to cause toxicity.

  Go to WileyPLUS to view a video clip on vitamin supplements.

8.2 Thiamin

- The best food sources of thiamin are lean pork, legumes, and whole or enriched grains.

- Thiamin is required for the formation of acetyl-CoA from pyruvate and for a reaction in the citric acid cycle and is therefore particularly important for the production of ATP from glucose. It is also needed for the synthesis of the neurotransmitter acetylcholine.

- Thiamin deficiency, or beriberi, causes nervous system abnormalities. Deficiencies are common in alcoholics. No toxicity has been identified.

8.3 Riboflavin

- Milk, meat, and enriched grain products are the best food sources of riboflavin.

- Riboflavin coenzymes are needed for the generation of ATP from carbohydrate, fat, and protein.

- Riboflavin deficiency is rarely seen alone because food sources of riboflavin are also sources of other B vitamins and because riboflavin is needed for the utilization of several other vitamins. No toxicity has been identified.

8.4 Niacin

- Beef, chicken, turkey, fish, and enriched grain products are the best food sources of niacin. The amino acid tryptophan can be converted into niacin, so tryptophan from dietary protein can meet some of the niacin requirement.

- Niacin coenzymes are important in the breakdown of carbohydrate, fat, and protein to provide energy and in the synthesis of fatty acids and sterols.

- Niacin deficiency results in pellagra, which is characterized by dermatitis, diarrhea, dementia, and finally, if untreated, death.

- Supplements of the nicotinic acid form of niacin can lower elevated blood cholesterol but frequently cause toxicity symptoms such as flushing, tingling sensations, nausea, and a red skin rash.

8.5 Biotin

- Liver and egg yolks are good sources of biotin.
- Biotin is needed for the synthesis of glucose and fatty acids, and the metabolism of certain amino acids.
- An RDA has not been established because some of our biotin need is met by bacterial synthesis in the GI tract. However, an AI has been set. Toxicity has not been reported.

8.6 Pantothenic Acid

- Pantothenic acid is abundant in the food supply and deficiency is rare.
- Pantothenic acid is part of coenzyme A (CoA), which is required for the production of ATP from carbohydrate, fat, and protein and the synthesis of cholesterol and fatty acids. There is no RDA, but an AI has been established.

8.7 Vitamin B$_6$

- Food sources of vitamin B$_6$ include chicken, fish, liver, and whole grains.
- Pyridoxal phosphate, the coenzyme form of vitamin B$_6$, is needed for the activity of more than 100 enzymes involved in the metabolism of carbohydrate, fat, and protein. Vitamin B$_6$ is a coenzyme for transamination and deamination reactions and is therefore particularly important for amino acid metabolism.
- Vitamin B$_6$ deficiency causes neurological symptoms, anemia due to impaired hemoglobin synthesis, poor immune function, and elevated levels of homocysteine, which can increase the risk of heart disease. High intakes from supplements can cause nervous system abnormalities.

8.8 Folate or Folic Acid

- Food sources of folate include liver, legumes, oranges, leafy green vegetables, and fortified grains.
- Folate is necessary for the synthesis of DNA, so it is especially important for rapidly dividing cells.
- It is recommended that women of childbearing age consume 400 μg of folic acid from fortified foods and supplements in addition to the folate found in a varied diet.
- Folate deficiency results in macrocytic anemia and can cause an increase in homocysteine levels. Low levels of folate before and during early pregnancy are associated with an increased incidence of neural tube defects in the off-

spring. A high intake of folate can mask the early symptoms of vitamin B$_{12}$ deficiency.

8.9 Vitamin B$_{12}$

- Vitamin B$_{12}$ is found almost exclusively in animal products.
- The absorption of vitamin B$_{12}$ from food requires adequate levels of stomach acid, intrinsic factor, and pancreatic secretions.
- Vitamin B$_{12}$ is needed for the metabolism of folate and fatty acids and to maintain the insulating layer of myelin surrounding nerves.
- Vitamin B$_{12}$ deficiency causes homocysteine levels to increase and can result in anemia and permanent nerve damage. In pernicious anemia severe deficiency occurs due to an absence of intrinsic factor. Vitamin B$_{12}$ deficiency may also occur in vegans, who consume no animal products, and in older individuals with low stomach acid due to atrophic gastritis.

8.10 Vitamin C

- The best food sources of vitamin C are citrus fruits.
- Vitamin C is necessary for the synthesis and maintenance of connective tissue and for the synthesis of hormones and neurotransmitters. Vitamin C is also a water-soluble antioxidant. Antioxidants protect the body from reactive oxygen molecules such as free radicals. These molecules are generated from normal body reactions and come from the environment. They cause damage by stealing electrons from DNA, proteins, carbohydrates, and unsaturated fatty acids.
- Vitamin C deficiency, called scurvy, is characterized by poor wound healing, bleeding, and other symptoms related to the improper formation and maintenance of collagen.
- Vitamin C supplements are the most commonly taken vitamin supplements and are usually used to reduce the symptoms of the common cold.

8.11 Choline

- Choline is a substance necessary for metabolism and is not currently classified as a vitamin. It may be required in the diet at certain stages of life, so an AI has been established.

Review Questions

1. What is a vitamin?

2. List four factors that affect how much of a vitamin is available to the body.

3. Define coenzyme and describe the coenzyme functions of five vitamins.

4. Why is thiamin deficiency common in alcoholics?

5. Why should milk be packaged in opaque containers?

6. What is pellagra?

7. How is vitamin B$_6$ involved in amino acid and protein metabolism?

8. Why is low folate intake of particular concern for women of childbearing age?

9. Why would someone who has had his stomach removed (or had gastric bypass surgery) need to receive injections of vitamin B_{12} to meet his needs?

10. Why are vegans at risk for vitamin B_{12} deficiency? The elderly?

11. Explain why a deficiency of vitamin B_6, folate, or vitamin B_{12} can all cause an increase in homocysteine levels.

12. Why does vitamin C deficiency cause poor wound healing?

13. What are reactive oxygen molecules and how do they cause damage?

14. What is the role of antioxidants and pro-oxidants in oxidative stress?

15. Does choline fit the definition of a vitamin? Why or why not?

References

1. Arsenault, J. E., and Brown, K. H. Zinc intake of US preschool children exceeds new dietary reference intakes. *Am. J. Clin. Nutr.* 78:1011–1017, 2003.

2. Food and Drug Administration, Health and Human Services. Fortification Policy, 21 CFR, Chapter 1, 104.20, 172, 2000.

3. American Dietetic Association. Position of the American Dietetic Association: Fortification and nutritional supplements. *J. Am. Diet. Assoc.* 105:1300–1311, 2005.

4. Butterworth, R. F. In: *Modern Nutrition in Health and Disease*, 10th ed. M. E. Shils, M. Shike, A. C. Ross et al., eds. Philadelphia: Lippincott Williams & Wilkins, 2006, pp. 426–433.

5. Institute of Medicine, Food and Nutrition Board. *Dietary Reference Intakes for Thiamin, Riboflavin, Niacin, Vitamin B-6, Folate, Vitamin B-12, Pantothenic Acid, Biotin, and Choline.* Washington, DC: National Academies Press, 1998.

6. Saffert, A., Pieper, G., and Jetten, J. Effect of package light transmittance on vitamin content of milk. *Technology and Science* 21:47–55, 2008.

7. Roe, D. A. *A Plague of Corn: The Social History of Pellagra.* Ithaca, NY: Cornell University Press, 1973.

8. Seal, A. J., Creeke, P. I., Dibari, F. et al. Low and deficient niacin status and pellagra are endemic in postwar Angola. *Am. J. Clin. Nutr.* 85:218–242, 2007.

9. Guyton, J. R., Blazing, M. A., Hagar, J. et al. Extended-release niacin vs. gemfibrozil for the treatment of low levels of high-density lipoprotein cholesterol. Niaspan-Gemfibrozil Study Group. *Arch. Intern. Med.* 160:1177–1184, 2000.

10. Gale, E. A., Bingley, P. J., Emmett, C. L., and Collier, T. European Nicotinamide Diabetes Intervention Trial (ENDIT) Group. European Nicotinamide Diabetes Intervention Trial (ENDIT): A randomized controlled trial of intervention before the onset of type 1 diabetes. *Lancet* 363:925–931, 2004.

11. Galvin, M. A., Kiely, M., and Flynn, A. Impact of ready-to-eat breakfast cereal (RTEBC) consumption on adequacy of micronutrient intakes and compliance with dietary recommendations in Irish adults. *Public Health Nutr.* 6:351–363, 2003.

12. Bessey, O. A., Adam, D. J., and Hansen, A. E. Intake of vitamin B_6 and infantile convulsions: A first approximation of requirements of pyridoxine in infants. *Pediatrics* 20:33–44, 1957.

13. Selhub, J. Public health significance of elevated homocysteine. *Food Nutr. Bull.* 29:S116–S125, 2008.

14. Page, J. H., Ma, J., Chiuve, S. E. et al. Plasma vitamin B(6) and risk of myocardial infarction in women. *Circulation* 120:649–655, 2009.

15. McNulty, H., Pentieva, K., Hoey, L., and Ward, M. Homocysteine, B-vitamins and CVD. *Proc. Nutr. Soc.* 67:232–237, 2008.

16. Schaumburg, H., Kaplan, J., Windebank, A. et al. Sensory neuropathy from pyridoxine abuse. *N. Engl. J. Med.* 309:445–448, 1983.

17. Aufiero, E., Stitik, T. P., Foye, P. M., and Chen, B. Pyridoxine hydrochloride treatment of carpal tunnel syndrome: A review. *Nutr. Rev.* 62:96–104, 2004.

18. Bendich, A. The potential for dietary supplements to reduce premenstrual syndrome (PMS) symptoms. *J. Am. Coll. Nutr.* 19:3–12, 2000.

19. Centers for Disease Control and Prevention. Spina bifida and anencephaly before and after folic acid mandate—United States, 1995–1996 and 1999–2000. *MMWR Morb. Mortal Wkly. Rep.* 17:362–365, 2004. Available online at www.cdc.gov/MMWR/preview/mmwrhtml/mm5317a3.htm. Accessed April 17, 2009.

20. De Wals, P., Tiarou, F., Van Allen, M. I. et al. Reduction in neural-tube defects after folic acid fortification in Canada. *N. Engl. J. Med.* 357:135–142, 2007.

21. Hubner, R. A., and Houlston, R. S. Folate and colorectal cancer prevention. *Br. J. Cancer* 100:233–239, 2009.

22. Larsson, S. C., Bergkvist, L., and Wolk, A. Folate intake and risk of breast cancer by estrogen and progesterone receptor status in a Swedish cohort. *Cancer Epidemiol. Biomarkers. Prev.* 17:3444–3449, 2008.

23. Larsson, S. C., Håkansson, N., Giovannucci, E., and Wolk, A. Folate intake and pancreatic cancer incidence: A prospective study of Swedish women and men. *J. Natl. Cancer. Inst.* 98:407–413, 2006.

24. Zhang, S. M., Willett, W. C., Selhub, J. et al. Plasma folate, vitamin B_6, vitamin B_{12}, homocysteine, and risk of breast cancer. *J. Natl. Cancer Inst.* 95:373–380, 2003.

25. Su, L. J., and Arab, L. Nutritional status of folate and colon cancer risk: Evidence from NHANES I epidemiologic follow-up study. *Ann. Epidemiol.* 11:65–72, 2001.

26. Kim, Y. I. Role of folate in colon cancer development and progression. *J. Nutr.* 133:3731S–3739S, 2003.

27. American Dietetic Association. Position of the American Dietetic Association and Dietitians of Canada: Vegetarian diets. *J. Am. Diet. Assoc.* 103:748–765, 2003.

28. Stocker, R., and Keaney, J. F., Jr. Role of oxidative modifications in atherosclerosis. *Physiol. Rev.* 84:1381–1478, 2004.

29. Food and Nutrition Board, Institute of Medicine. *Dietary Reference Intakes for Vitamin C, Vitamin E, Selenium, and Carotenoids.* Washington, DC: National Academies Press, 2000.

30. Carr, A., and Frei, B. Does vitamin C act as a pro-oxidant under physiological conditions? *FASEB J.* 13:1007–1024, 1999.

31. Douglas, R. M., Hemila, H., D'Souza, R. et al. Vitamin C for preventing and treating the common cold. *Cochrane Database System Review* 18:CD000980, 2004.

32. Hemila, H. Vitamin C supplementation and respiratory infections: A systematic review. *Mil. Med.* 169:920–925, 2004.

33. Jari, R. J., and Harakeh, S. Antiviral and immunomodulatory activities of ascorbic acid. In: *Subcellular Biochemistry,* Vol. 25: Ascorbic Acid: Biochemistry and Biomedical Cell Biology. J. R. Harris, ed. New York: Plenum Press, 1996, pp. 215–231.

34. Johnston, C. S. The antihistamine action of ascorbic acid. In *Subcellular Biochemistry,* Vol. 25: Ascorbic Acid: Biochemistry and Biomedical Cell Biology. J. R. Harris, ed. New York: Plenum Press, 1996, pp. 189–213.

35. Wilburn, A. J., King, D. S., Glisson, J. et al. The natural treatment of hypertension. *J. Clin. Hypertens. (Greenwich)* 6:242–248, 2004.

36. Blomhoff, R. Dietary antioxidants and cardiovascular disease. *Curr. Opin. Lipidol.* 16:47–54, 2005.

37. Shekelle, P., Hardy, M. L., Coulter, I. et al. Effect of the supplemental use of antioxidants vitamin C, vitamin E, and coenzyme Q10 for the prevention and treatment of cancer. *Evid. Rep. Technol. Assess.* (Summ). 75:1–3, 2003.

38. Lee, K. W., Lee, H. J., Surh, Y. J., and Lee, C. Y. Vitamin C and cancer chemoprevention: reappraisal. *Am. J. Clin. Nutr.* 78:1074–1078, 2003.

39. Khaw, K. T., Bingham, S., Welch, A. et al. Relation between plasma ascorbic acid and mortality in men and women in EPIC-Norfolk prospective study: A prospective population study. European Prospective Investigation into Cancer and Nutrition. *Lancet* 357:657–663, 2001.

40. Fischer, L. M., daCasta, K. A., Kwack, L. et al. Sex and menopausal status influence human dietary requirements for the nutrient choline. *Am. J. Clin. Nutr.* 85:1275–1285, 2007.

9 The Fat-Soluble Vitamins

Case Study

Ana's pediatrician is concerned because she has just one tooth. Ana was adopted from an orphanage in central China when she was 9 months old, and she'll be a year old next week. After noting her one tooth and examining her ribs and legs, the doctor tells Ana's parents that she wants to draw a blood sample to help confirm her suspicion that Ana has a vitamin D deficiency disease called rickets. The pediatrician explains that this deficiency is relatively common in children adopted from China because children in orphanages there consume a diet low in the vitamin and often are not exposed to enough sunlight to synthesize adequate amounts of vitamin D.

Vitamin D is needed for proper formation and maintenance of bones and teeth. Without sufficient vitamin D, a child's legs bow under the weight of standing, and bony bumps appear on each of the ribs. The poorly formed bones can break easily. The teeth erupt late and are very prone to decay. Ana is beginning to show these symptoms. A blood test can detect rickets by measuring levels of calcium and phosphorus, as well as levels of an enzyme produced by cells that break down bone.

Like Ana's parents, most people in the United States are not familiar with rickets. Recent evidence, however, suggests that rickets due to vitamin D deficiency may be reemerging as a problem in the U.S. population.[1,2]

(Peter Griffith/Masterfile)

(©iStockphoto)

(aas Studio/StockFood America)

Chapter Outline

9.1 Fat-Soluble Vitamins in the Modern Diet

Learning Objectives

- Name the fat-soluble vitamins.
- Discuss factors that impact fat-soluble vitamin status in the United States.

Vitamins A, D, E, and K are grouped together due to their solublity in fat (see Chapter 8). Because of this, they require special handling for absorption into and transport through the body. Fat-soluble vitamins require bile and dietary fat for absorption. Once absorbed, they are transported with fats through the lymphatic system in chylomicrons before entering the blood. Since excesses of these vitamins can be stored in the body and retrieved as needed, intakes can vary without a risk of deficiency as long as average intake over a period of weeks or months meets needs. Solubility in fat, however, limits their routes of excretion and therefore increases the risk of toxicity.

Despite the body's ability to store the fat-soluble vitamins, deficiencies of vitamin A and D are common in the developing world. Elimination of these deficiencies through supplementation and fortification is a focus of public health programs. In the United States and other developed countries, severe deficiencies of these nutrients are rare, but trends in the modern diet have affected the amounts of fat-soluble vitamins people consume. Our rising reliance on fast food has reduced our intake of fruits and vegetables, particularly leafy greens, reducing our intake of vitamins A, E, and K (**Figure 9.1**). We work at indoor jobs, exercise at indoor gyms, and protect ourselves from the sun by using sunscreens when we go out, all of which limit our ability to get adequate vitamin D from sunshine. We limit our fat intake to reduce our waistlines and risk of chronic disease. But animal fats are good sources of vitamin D and preformed vitamin A, and vegetable fats provide much of our vitamin E, as well as fat-soluble phytochemicals, some of which serve as precursors to vitamin A. Medications that limit fat absorption also limit fat-soluble vitamin absorption. Even the low-carbohydrate diet craze has had an impact on the amounts of fat-soluble vitamins consumed from whole foods because eliminating grains, fruits, and many vegetables can reduce intake of vitamin E and vitamin A precursors, as well as vitamin K. To avoid the risks of limited intakes, we take supplements of these vitamins and fortify our food with them. This then increases the risks of consuming toxic amounts. It is unclear whether these new patterns will have a long-term impact on our fat-soluble vitamin status.

Figure 9.1 Even though vitamins A, E, and K are soluble in fat, leafy green vegetables such as this Swiss chard, which are very low in fat, are good sources of vitamin A precursors, as well as vitamin E and vitamin K. (Maximillian Stock/StockFood America)

9.2 Vitamin A

Learning Objectives

- Compare the sources, functions, and potential toxicity of preformed vitamin A and provitamin A.
- Describe the role of vitamin A in night vision.
- Discuss how vitamin A affects gene expression.
- Explain why a vitamin A deficiency can cause eye infections and blindness.

Are carrots really good for your eyes? Carrots are high in provitamin A, and vitamin A is important for vision. This connection between vision and foods that we now know are high in vitamin A has been recognized for centuries. In ancient times, the Egyptians knew that eating liver could improve night vision in those who had difficulty in adjusting from bright light to dim light. In 1968, George Wald earned the Nobel Prize in medicine for identifying the mechanism by which vitamin A is involved in vision. Although this is a key function of vitamin A, attention today is focused more on how vitamin A interacts with genes to regulate growth and **cell differentiation**. Despite our expanding understanding of the functions of vitamin A, deficiency remains a world health problem.

cell differentiation Structural and functional changes that cause cells to mature into specialized cells.

Vitamin A in the Diet

Vitamin A is found preformed and in precursor or provitamin forms in our diet. Preformed vitamin A is found primarily in animal foods, and the provitamin A forms are found in plants (**Figure 9.2**). Both sources can be used to meet vitamin A needs in the body.

Preformed vitamin A compounds are known as **retinoids**. The retinoids include retinol, retinal, and retinoic acid. Animal foods such as liver, fish, egg yolks, and dairy products provide preformed vitamin A, primarily as retinol, or retinol attached to a fatty

retinoids The chemical forms of preformed vitamin A: retinol, retinal, and retinoic acid.

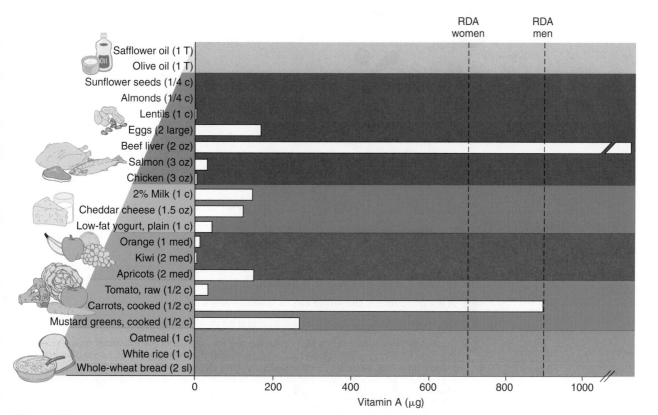

Figure 9.2 Vitamin A content of MyPyramid food groups
Both plant and animal foods are good sources of vitamin A; the dashed lines show the RDAs for men and women.

carotenoids Natural pigments synthesized by plants and many microorganisms. They give yellow and red-orange fruits and vegetables their color.

beta-carotene (β-carotene) A carotenoid that has more provitamin A activity than other carotenoids. It also acts as an antioxidant.

acid. Margarine and nonfat and reduced-fat milk are fortified with retinol because they are often consumed in place of butter and whole milk, which are good sources of this vitamin. Retinal and retinoic acid can be formed in the body from retinol (**Figure 9.3**).

Plants contain provitamin A compounds called **carotenoids**. Carotenoids are yellow, orange, and red pigments that give these colors to fruits and vegetables. About 50 of the 600 carotenoids that have been isolated provide vitamin A activity. **Beta-carotene (β-carotene)**, the most potent precursor, is plentiful in dark orange fruits and vegetables such as mangos, apricots, cantaloupe, carrots, red peppers, pumpkins, and sweet potatoes as well as in leafy greens where the orange color is masked by the green color of chlorophyll. Other carotenoids that provide some provitamin A activity include alpha-carotene (α-carotene) found in carrots, leafy green vegetables, and winter squash, and beta-cryptoxanthin (β-cryptoxanthin) found in mangos, papayas, winter squash, and sweet red peppers.[3] Lutein, lycopene, and zeaxanthin are carotenoids with no vitamin A activity (see Focus on Phytochemicals).

To help consumers identify food sources of vitamin A, labels on packaged foods must list the vitamin A content as a percentage of the Daily Value. All forms of vitamin A in the diet are fairly stable when heated but may be destroyed by exposure to light and oxygen (see Your Choice: Fresh, Frozen, or Canned—Does It Matter?).

Retinol-fatty acid (animal foods)

β-Carotene (plant foods)

Retinol

Retinal

Retinoic acid

1. In the diet, preformed vitamin A is present primarily as retinol bound to fatty acids.

2. In the body, retinol and retinal can be interconverted.

3. Once retinoic acid has been formed, it cannot be converted back to retinal or retinol.

4. β-carotene from plant foods can be converted into retinal in the intestinal mucosa and in the liver. Cleaving a molecule of β-carotene in half theoretically yields two molecules of retinal; however, because β-carotene is not as well absorbed as preformed vitamin A and may not be efficiently converted to retinal, it takes about 12 mg of dietary β-carotene to yield 1 mg of retinol.

Figure 9.3 Forms of Vitamin A
Both preformed and provitamin A from the diet can be used to obtain retinol, retinal, and retinoic acid.

Fresh, Frozen, or Canned—Does It Matter?

(©iStockphoto)

Fresh fruits and vegetables seem healthiest. Frozen are handy, but canned are the least expensive. Does it matter which you choose?

Heat, light, air, and time cause the loss of nutrients from food. Therefore, how a food has been handled is an important consideration when trying to make the most nutritious choice. Fresh produce would seem to be the best, but if the "fresh" vegetable has actually spent a week in a truck traveling to your store, several days on the shelf, and then another week in your refrigerator, it may not be the most nutritious choice. A frozen version may actually supply more vitamins. Although freezing, itself, can cause some losses, much produce is frozen right in the field, so nutrients are not lost due to time and exposure after picking.

What about canned vegetables or fruits? The canning process uses high temperatures, which reduce the vitamin content. In addition, canned fruit is often high in added sugar, and canned vegetables are high in salt. Despite these disadvantages, canned foods keep a long time, do not require refrigeration, and are typically less expensive than fresh or frozen.

How you handle your produce at home can also affect its nutrient content. Remembering that exposure to oxygen, light, and heat can destroy vitamins can help you store, prepare, and cook foods to minimize losses. Store food away from heat and light, and begin preparation as close to serving time as possible. Cutting vegetables and fruits increases the surface area exposed to light and oxygen, so don't cut up the fruit for your salad or chop the vegetables for your stir fry until the last minute. Cooking at higher temperatures and for longer periods causes greater vitamin losses, so use pressure cookers and microwaves, which cook foods quickly,

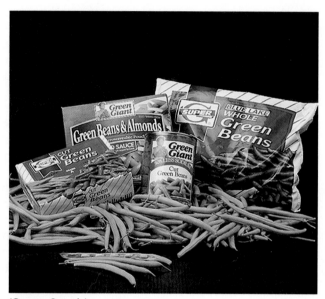

(George Semple)

to reduce nutrient losses. Water-soluble vitamins can be washed away in cooking water, so roast, grill, stir-fry, or bake when possible. When foods are cooked in water, use the cooking water to make soups and sauces so you retrieve some of the nutrients.

So, which should you choose? The answer is whichever helps you get the recommended amounts of vegetables and fruits daily. Choose what works for your lifestyle—even a vegetable that has lost some of its vitamins is still a good source of nutrients as well as fiber and phytochemicals.

Vitamin A in the Digestive Tract

Both preformed vitamin A and carotenoids are bound to proteins in foods. To be absorbed, they must be released from the protein by pepsin and other protein-digesting enzymes. In the small intestine, the released retinol and carotenoids combine with bile acids and other fat-soluble food components to form micelles, which facilitate their diffusion into mucosal cells. Absorption of preformed vitamin A is efficient—70 to 90% of what is consumed. The provitamin carotenoids are less well absorbed, and absorption decreases as intake increases, so large amounts are not well absorbed.[4] Once inside the mucosal cells, much of the β-carotene is converted to retinoids (see Figure 9.3).

The fat content of the diet and the ability to absorb fat can affect the amount of vitamin A that is absorbed. A diet that is very low in fat (less than 10 g/day) can reduce vitamin A absorption. This is rarely a problem in industrialized countries, where typical fat intake ranges from 50 to 100 grams per day. However, in populations with low dietary fat intakes, vitamin A deficiency may occur due to poor absorption. Diseases that cause fat malabsorption, as well as some medications, can also interfere with vitamin A absorption and cause a deficiency.

Vitamin A in the Body

Preformed vitamin A and carotenoids absorbed from the diet are transported from the intestine in chylomicrons. These lipoproteins deliver the preformed vitamin A and carotenoids to body tissues such as bone marrow, blood cells, spleen, muscles, kidney, and liver. In the liver, some carotenoids can be converted into retinol. To move from liver stores to the tissues, retinol must be bound to **retinol-binding protein**. There is no specific blood transport protein for carotenoids, but since they are fat soluble, they are incorporated into lipoproteins to travel in the bloodstream.

retinol-binding protein A protein that is necessary to transport vitamin A from the liver to other tissues.

The different forms of vitamin A have different functions. The body can make the retinal and retinoic acid forms from the retinol and carotenoids in the diet (see Figure 9.3). Retinol is the form that circulates in the blood. Retinal is the form that is important for vision. Retinol and retinal can be interconverted from one to the other. Retinoic acid, which is made from retinol or retinal, cannot be used in the visual cycle (see the following section) but is the form that affects gene expression and is responsible for vitamin A's role in cell differentiation, growth, and reproduction.[5] Carotenoids that are not converted to retinoids may act as antioxidants or provide other biological functions.

The Visual Cycle Vitamin A is involved in the perception of light (**Figure 9.4**). In the eye, the retinal form of the vitamin combines with the protein opsin to form the visual pigment **rhodopsin**. Rhodopsin helps transform the energy from light into a nerve impulse that is sent to the brain. This nerve impulse allows us to see.

rhodopsin A light-absorbing compound found in the retina of the eye that is composed of the protein opsin loosely bound to retinal.

The visual cycle begins when light passes into the eye and strikes rhodopsin. The light changes the retinal in rhodopsin from a curved molecule to a straight one by converting a *cis* double bond in retinal to a *trans* double bond. This change in shape initiates a series of events causing a nerve signal to be sent to the brain and retinal to be released from opsin. After the light stimulus has passed, the *trans* retinal is converted back to its original *cis* form and recombined with opsin to regenerate rhodopsin. Each time this cycle occurs, some retinal is lost and must be replaced by retinol from the blood. The retinol is converted into retinal in the eye. When vitamin A is deficient, there is a delay in the regeneration of rhodopsin, which causes difficulty seeing in dim light, particularly after exposure to a bright light—a condition called **night blindness**. Night blindness is one of the first and more easily reversible symptoms of vitamin A deficiency.

night blindness The inability of the eye to adapt to reduced light causing poor vision in dim light.

Regulating Gene Expression: Cell Differentiation Cell differentiation is the process whereby cells change in structure and function to become specialized. For instance, in the bone marrow, some cells differentiate into various white blood cells, whereas others differentiate to form red blood cells. Vitamin A affects cell differentiation through its effect on gene expression. This means that it can turn on or turn off the production of certain proteins that regulate functions within cells and throughout

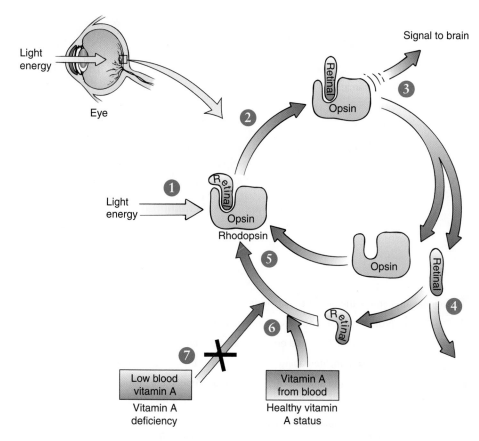

① Light strikes the visual pigment rhodopsin, which is formed by combining retinal with the protein opsin.

② The retinal molecule changes from a bent (*cis*) to a straight (*trans*) configuration.

③ A nerve signal is sent to the brain, telling us that there is light, and retinal is released from opsin.

④ Some retinal is lost from the cycle.

⑤ Some retinal returns to its original *cis* configuration and binds opsin to begin the cycle again.

⑥ When vitamin A status is normal, vitamin A from the blood replaces any retinal lost from the cycle.

⑦ When vitamin A is deficient, little vitamin A is available in the blood, and the regeneration of rhodopsin is delayed. Until it is reformed, light cannot be perceived.

Figure 9.4 The visual cycle
Looking into the bright headlights of an approaching car at night is temporarily blinding for all of us, but for someone with vitamin A deficiency, the blindness lasts much longer.

the body. By affecting gene expression, vitamin A can also determine what type of cell an undifferentiated cell will become.

In order to affect gene expression, the retinoic acid form of vitamin A enters the nucleus of specific target cells, where it binds to protein receptors; this retinoic acid–protein receptor complex then binds to a regulatory region of DNA (**Figure 9.5**). This binding changes the amount of messenger RNA (mRNA) that is made by the gene. The change in mRNA changes the amount of the protein that is produced. This turning on (or turning off) of the gene increases (or decreases) the production of proteins and thereby affects various cellular functions. For example, vitamin A turns on a gene that makes an enzyme in liver cells. This enzyme enables the liver to make glucose through the process of glyconeogenesis.

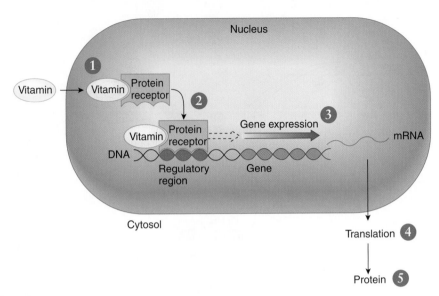

1. Retinoic acid enters the nucleus and binds to a protein receptor.

2. The vitamin-protein receptor complex binds to a regulatory region of DNA.

3. Transcription of the gene is turned on, increasing the amount of mRNA made.

4. mRNA directs translation, increasing the synthesis of the protein coded by this gene.

5. There is an increase in the amount of the protein and hence the cellular functions and body processes affected by this protein.

Figure 9.5 Vitamin A and gene expression
The retinoic acid form of vitamin A (shown as the yellow vitamin) affects cell function by changing gene expression. The steps illustrate what happens when vitamin A turns on gene expression.

Maintenance of Epithelial Tissue Vitamin A's role in cell differentiation is necessary for the maintenance of epithelial tissue. This type of tissue covers external body surfaces and lines internal cavities and tubes. It includes the skin and the linings of the eyes, intestines, lungs, vagina, and bladder. When vitamin A is deficient, epithelial cells do not differentiate normally because vitamin A is not there to turn on or turn off the production of particular proteins. For example, the epithelial tissue on many body surfaces contains cells that produce mucus for lubrication. When mucus-secreting cells die, new cells differentiate into mucus-secreting cells to replace them. When vitamin A is deficient, the new cells do not differentiate properly and instead become cells that produce a protein called **keratin** (**Figure 9.6a**). Keratin is the hard protein that makes up hair and fingernails. As the mucus-secreting cells die and are replaced by keratin-producing cells, the epithelial surface becomes hard and dry. This process is known as *keratinization*. The hard, dry surface does not have the protective capabilities of normal epithelium and so the likelihood of infection is increased. The risk of infection is compounded by the fact that vitamin A deficiency also decreases immune function.

All epithelial tissues are affected by vitamin A deficiency, but the eye is particularly susceptible to damage. The mucus in the eye normally provides lubrication, washes away dirt and other particles, and also contains a protein that helps destroy bacteria. When vitamin A is deficient, the lack of mucus and the buildup of keratin cause the cornea to dry and leave the eye open to infection. A spectrum of eye disorders, known as **xerophthalmia**, is associated with vitamin A deficiency. Xerophthalmia begins as night blindness and extreme dryness and progresses to wrinkling, cloudiness, and softening of the cornea, called **keratomalacia**. If left untreated, it can result in rupture of the cornea, infection, degenerative tissue changes, and permanent blindness (**Figure 9.6b**).

keratin A hard protein that makes up hair and nails.

xerophthalmia A spectrum of eye conditions resulting from vitamin A deficiency that may lead to blindness. An early symptom is night blindness, and as deficiency worsens, lack of mucus leaves the eye dry and vulnerable to cracking and infection.

keratomalacia Softening and drying and ulceration of the cornea resulting from vitamin A deficiency.

Figure 9.6 Vitamin A deficiency
(a) When vitamin A is deficient immature cells can't differentiate normally, and instead of mucus-secreting cells, they become cells that produce keratin.
(b) As xerophthalmia progresses, the drying of the cornea results in ulceration, infection, and ultimately blindness. (ISM/Phototake)

Reproduction, Growth, and Immunity The ability of vitamin A to regulate the growth and differentiation of cells makes it essential throughout life for normal reproduction, growth, and immune function. In reproduction, vitamin A is important for the formation of the heart and circulatory system, the nervous system, respiratory system, and skeleton.[6] Lack of vitamin A during embryonic development results in abnormalities and death. Poor overall growth is an early sign of vitamin A deficiency in children. Vitamin A affects the activity of cells that form and break down bone, and a deficiency early in life can cause abnormal jawbone growth, resulting in crooked teeth and poor dental health.

In the immune system, vitamin A is needed for the differentiation that produces the different types of immune cells. Vitamin A deficiency also reduces the function of specific immune cells and hinders the normal regeneration of mucosal barriers damaged by infection.[7] This impaired immune function increases the risk of illness and infection due to defective epithelial tissue barriers (see Chapter 18: Science Applied: Vitamin A: The Anti-Infective Vitamin).

Beta-Carotene: A Vitamin A Precursor and an Antioxidant Some carotenoids, particularly β-carotene, can be converted to vitamin A in the intestinal mucosa and liver. Unconverted carotenoids also circulate in the blood and reach tissues where they may function as antioxidants, a role independent of any conversion to vitamin A. Beta-carotene and other carotenoids are fat-soluble antioxidants that may play a role in protecting cell membranes from damage by free radicals. The antioxidant properties of carotenoids have stimulated interest in their ability to protect against diseases in which oxidative processes play a role, such as cancer, heart disease, and impaired vision due to macular degeneration and cataracts.

Recommended Vitamin A Intake

Life Cycle

The recommended intake for vitamin A is based on the amount needed to maintain normal body stores. The RDA is set at 900 μg of vitamin A per day for men and 700 μg per day for women[4] (**Table 9.1**). The RDA is increased in pregnancy to account for the vitamin A that is transferred to the fetus and during lactation to account for the vitamin A lost in milk. The RDA for children is set lower than that for adults based on their smaller body size. For infants, an AI has been set based on the amount of vitamin A consumed by an average healthy breast-fed infant.

Table 9.1 A Summary of the Fat-Soluble Vitamins

Vitamin	Sources	Recommended Intake for Adults	Major Functions	Deficiency Diseases and Symptoms	Groups at Risk of Deficiency	Toxicity	UL
Vitamin A (retinol, retinal, retinoic acid, vitamin A acetate, vitamin A palmitate, retinyl palmitate, provitamin A, carotene, β-carotene, carotenoids)	Retinol: liver, fish, fortified milk and margarine, butter, eggs Carotenoids: carrots, leafy greens, sweet potatoes, broccoli, apricots, cantaloupe	700–900 μg/d	Vision, health of cornea and other epithelial tissue, cell differentiation, reproduction, immune function	Night blindness, xerophthalmia, poor growth, dry skin, impaired immunity	Those with a limited diet (particularly children and pregnant women), those consuming very low-fat or low-protein diets	Headache, vomiting, hair loss, liver damage, skin changes, bone and muscle pain, fractures, birth defects	3000 μg/d of preformed vitamin A
Vitamin D (calciferol, cholecalciferol, ergocalciferol, dihydroxy vitamin D)	Egg yolk, liver, fish oils, tuna, salmon, fortified milk, synthesis from sunlight	5–15 μg/d[a]	Absorption of calcium and phosphorus, maintenance of bone	Rickets in children: abnormal growth, misshaped bones, bowed legs, soft bones; Osteomalacia in adults: weak bones and bone and muscle pain	Some breast-fed infants, children and elderly (especially those with dark skin and little sun exposure), people with kidney disease	Calcium deposits in soft tissues, growth retardation, kidney damage	50 μg/d
Vitamin E (tocopherol, α-tocopherol)	Vegetable oils, leafy greens, seeds, nuts, peanuts	15 mg/d	Antioxidant, protects cell membranes	Broken red blood cells, nerve damage	Those with poor fat absorption, premature infants	Inhibition of vitamin K activity	1000 mg/d from supplemental sources
Vitamin K (phylloquinones, menaquinone)	Vegetable oils, leafy greens, synthesis by intestinal bacteria	90–120 μg/d[a]	Coenzyme for synthesis of blood clotting proteins and proteins in bone	Hemorrhage	Newborns (especially premature), people on long-term antibiotics	Anemia and brain damage in infants	ND

[a]Adequate Intake (AI).

UL, Tolerable Upper Intake Level; ND, insufficient evidence to set a UL.

retinol activity equivalent (RAE) The amount of retinol, β-carotene, α-carotene, or β-cryptoxanthin that provides vitamin A activity equal to 1 μg of retinol.

Recommendations for vitamin A intake are expressed in micrograms (μg) of retinol. Retinol can be supplied by both preformed vitamin A and carotenoids in the diet. No quantitative recommendations have been made for intakes of β-carotene or other carotenoids. Their intake is considered only with regard to the amount of retinol they provide. Because carotenoids are less well absorbed and not completely converted to vitamin A, a correction factor, referred to as **retinol activity equivalents (RAE)**, must be applied to carotenoids to determine the amount of usable vitamin A they provide. Twelve micrograms of β-carotene provide 1 RAE of vitamin A, and 24 μg of α-carotene or β-cryptoxanthin provide 1 RAE.[4]

As our understanding of vitamin A has increased, the units in which recommended intakes have been expressed have changed. Prior to 1980, vitamin A was expressed in international units (IUs). The 1989 RDAs used values called retinol equivalents (REs) to account for differences in absorption between preformed vitamin A and carotenoids. These older units are still found in some food composition databases and tables. Values for converting REs and IUs to micrograms of retinol are given in **Table 9.2**.

Table 9.2 **Converting Vitamin A Units**

Form and Source	Amount Equal to 1 μg Retinol
Preformed vitamin A in food or supplements	1 μg 1 RAE 1 μg RE 3.3 IU
β-carotene in food[a]	12 μg 1 RAE 2 μg RE 20 IU
α-carotene or β-cryptoxanthin in food	24 μg 1 RAE 2 μg RE 40 IU

[a]Beta-carotene in supplements may be better absorbed than β-carotene in food and so provides more vitamin A activity. It is estimated that 2 μg of β-carotene dissolved in oil provides 1 μg of vitamin A activity.

Vitamin A Deficiency: A World Health Problem

Vitamin A deficiency is a threat to the health, sight, and lives of millions of children in the developing world. Children deficient in vitamin A have poor appetites, are anemic, have an increased susceptibility to infections, including measles, and are more likely to die in childhood. It is estimated that more than 250 million children worldwide are vitamin A deficient and that 250,000 to 500,000 children go blind annually due to vitamin A deficiency.[8] It is most common in India, Africa, Latin America, and the Caribbean.

Vitamin A deficiency can be caused by insufficient intakes of vitamin A, fat, protein, or the mineral zinc. As discussed, without fat, vitamin A cannot be absorbed, so a diet very low in fat can cause a deficiency by reducing vitamin A absorption. Protein deficiency can cause vitamin A deficiency because the retinol-binding protein needed to transport vitamin A from the liver cannot be made in sufficient quantities. The importance of zinc for vitamin A utilization is believed to be due to its role in protein synthesis. When zinc is deficient, the proteins needed for vitamin A transport and metabolism are lacking.

Vitamin A deficiency is not common in developed countries, but dietary intake surveys in the United States indicate that many Americans do not meet the recommendations for this vitamin.[4] Intakes below the RDA can be caused by poor food choices even when the food supply is plentiful. In the United States the intake of fruits and vegetables, many of which are excellent sources of provitamin A, does not meet recommendations. A typical fast-food meal of a hamburger and french fries provides almost no vitamin A (see Critical Thinking: How Much Vitamin A Is in Your Fast-Food Meal?).

Life Cycle

Critical Thinking

How Much Vitamin A Is in Your Fast-Food Meal?

(©TNT Magazine/Alamy)

Background

John lives on his own, goes to school, and works part-time. He eats Frosted Flakes and milk for breakfast at home and usually brings a ham and cheese sandwich with potato chips and a cola for lunch; dinner is always a fast-food meal. He recently heard a report indicating that fast-food was low in some vitamins, particularly vitamin A. To explore this issue, John uses iProfile to look up the nutrient composition of his favorite fast-food meals.

Data

FOOD		VITAMIN A (μG)	% DAILY VALUE
McDonalds	Big Mac	89	10
	Fries	2	0.2
Pizza Hut	Pepperoni pizza	358	40
KFC	Chicken leg and breast	24	2.6
	Mashed potatoes and gravy	14	1.5

Critical Thinking Exercises

Looking at his fast food options, John notices that pizza has lots of vitamin A. What ingredients in pizza make it higher in vitamin A than the other choices?

▼

Should John be concerned about his vitamin A intake? Use iProfile to estimate how much vitamin A he is getting in his breakfast and lunch. How much vitamin C is provided by these meals?

▼

How could John's breakfast and lunch be modified to increase his intake of vitamin A and vitamin C?

 iProfile Use iProfile to find out how much vitamin A is in your favorite fast food meal.

Vitamin A Toxicity and Supplements

Preformed vitamin A can be toxic. Acute toxicity has been reported in Arctic explorers who consumed polar bear liver, which contains about 100,000 μg of vitamin A in just 3 ounces. Although polar bear liver is not a common dish at most dinner tables, supplements of preformed vitamin A also have the potential to deliver a toxic dose. Signs of acute toxicity include nausea, vomiting, headache, dizziness, blurred vision, and a lack of muscle coordination. Chronic toxicity occurs when preformed vitamin A doses as low as 10 times the RDA are consumed for a period of months to years. The symptoms of chronic toxicity include weight loss, muscle and joint pain, liver damage, bone abnormalities, visual defects, dry scaling lips, and skin rashes. Excess vitamin A is a particular concern for pregnant women because it may contribute to birth defects.[4,9] High intakes of vitamin A have also been found to increase the incidence of bone fractures.[10,11] The UL is set at 2800 μg per day of preformed vitamin A for 14- to 18-year-olds and 3000 μg/day for adults.

Vitamin A as a Drug Derivatives of vitamin A are currently used as drugs. One derivative of retinoic acid, marketed as Retin A, is used topically to treat acne and to reduce wrinkles due to sun damage. It acts by increasing the turnover of cells. In patients with acne, new cells replace the cells of existing pimples and the rapid turnover of cells prevents new pimples from forming. By a similar mechanism, Retin A can reduce wrinkles and diminish areas of darkened skin and rough skin. Another vitamin A derivative, 13-*cis*-retinoic acid, marketed as Accutane, is taken orally to treat acne. This medication can have serious side effects including dry, itchy skin and chapped lips, irritated eyes, joint and muscle pain, decreased night vision, depression, and increases in blood lipid levels. In pregnant women it can cause severe birth defects, including brain damage and physical malformations. Although Retin A and Accutane are derivatives of vitamin A, they are drugs. Vitamin A supplements cannot be substituted as a treatment for acne, and large doses will cause toxicity symptoms.

Carotenoid Toxicity Because of the toxicity of preformed vitamin A, most supplements provide some or all of their vitamin A as carotenoids (**Table 9.3**). Carotenoids are not toxic because their absorption from the diet decreases at high doses, and once in the body, their conversion to retinoids is limited. Large daily intakes of carotenoids—usually from carrot juice or β-carotene supplements—do, however, lead to a condition known as **hypercarotenemia**. In this condition, large amounts of carotenoids stored in the adipose tissue give the skin a yellow-orange color (**Figure 9.7**). This is particularly apparent on the palms of the hands and the soles of the feet. It is not known to be dangerous, and when intake decreases, the skin returns to its normal color.

Life Cycle

hypercarotenemia
A condition in which carotenoids accumulate in the adipose tissue, causing the skin to appear yellow-orange.

Table 9.3 Benefits and Risks of Fat-Soluble Vitamin Supplements

Supplement	Marketing Claim	Actual Benefits or Risks
Vitamin A (retinoids)	Improves vision, prevents skin disorders, enhances immunity	Needed for vision and eye health, growth, reproduction, and immunity but extra as supplements does not provide additional benefits. Toxic at high doses, can cause birth defects and bone loss.
Carotenoids	Needed for vision, prevents skin disorders, antioxidant	Can provide all functions of vitamin A and is an antioxidant but supplements do not provide additional benefits. High doses can cause orange-colored skin and increase lung cancer risk in smokers.
Vitamin D	Bone health, prevents multiple sclerosis	Needed for calcium absorption and bone maintenance. There is evidence that supplements reduce the risk of autoimmune diseases and cancer. High doses cause heart and kidney damage.
Vitamin E	Prevents heart disease, improves symptoms of fibrocystic breast disease, promotes immune function, reduces scar formation	Antioxidant, protects cell membranes, little evidence that oral supplements reduce risk of heart disease or that topical application reduces scar formation. High doses interfere with anticoagulant medications.

Figure 9.7 This photo compares normal hand color (right) with more orange color seen on the hand of a patient with hypercarotenemia (left). (James Stevenson/SPL/Photo Researchers)

Although not considered toxic, carotenoid supplements may be harmful to cigarette smokers. Two clinical research trials found an increased incidence of lung cancer in cigarette smokers who took β-carotene supplements.[12,13] Even though other trials have not shown this effect, until more information is available, smokers are advised to avoid β-carotene supplements and to rely on food sources to obtain carotenoids in their diet. The small amounts found in standard strength multivitamin supplements are not likely to be harmful for any group. No UL has been determined for carotenoid intake.

9.3 Vitamin D

Learning Objectives

- Explain why vitamin D is known as the sunshine vitamin.
- Relate the functions of vitamin D to the symptoms that occur when it is deficient.
- Discuss why vitamin D deficiency is on the rise.

Vitamin D is known as the "sunshine vitamin" because it can be produced in the skin by exposure to ultraviolet light. Because vitamin D can be made in the body, there is a long-standing debate as to whether vitamin D is a vitamin or a hormone. By definition, vitamins are dietary essentials. However, vitamin D can be formed in the skin, so it is only essential in the diet when exposure to sunlight is limited or the body's ability to synthesize the vitamin is reduced. Vitamin D acts like a hormone because it is produced in one organ, the skin, and affects other organs, primarily the intestine, bone, and kidney.

Vitamin D in the Diet

cholecalciferol The chemical name for vitamin D$_3$. It can be formed in the skin of animals by the action of sunlight on a form of cholesterol called 7-dehydrocholesterol.

The major source of vitamin D for most humans is exposure to sunlight.[14] Only a few foods are natural sources of vitamin D. These include liver; fatty fish such as salmon, mackerel, and sardines; cod liver oil; and egg yolks (**Figure 9.8**). These foods contain **cholecalciferol**, also known as vitamin D$_3$. Cholecalciferol is the form of vitamin D that is made in the skin of animals by the action of sunlight on a compound made from cholesterol, called 7-dehydrocholesterol (**Figure 9.9**). Fortified milk and fortified breakfast cereals are important sources of vitamin D in the United States. These may contain vitamin D$_3$ or another active form of the vitamin called vitamin D$_2$.

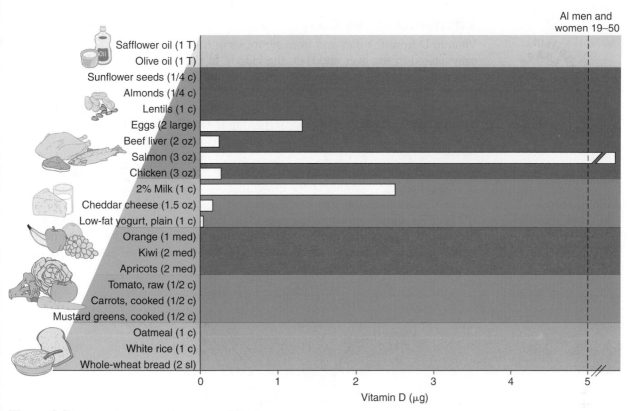

Figure 9.8 **Vitamin D content of MyPyramid food groups**
Only a few foods are natural sources of vitamin D; the dashed line shows the AI for adults 19 through 50 years of age.

Figure 9.9 **Vitamin D synthesis**
In the body, 7-dehydrocholesterol can be made from cholesterol. Vitamin D_3 (cholecalciferol) can then be formed by the action of sunlight on 7-dehydrocholesterol in the skin.

Vitamin D in the Body

Vitamin D from the diet and from synthesis in the skin is inactive until it is chemically altered in the liver and then the kidney. In the liver, a hydroxyl group (OH) is added to vitamin D to form 25-hydroxy vitamin D_3. This is the form of the vitamin that circulates in the blood and is monitored in the blood to indicate the vitamin D status of patients. However, 25-hydroxy vitamin D_3 is inactive and must be modified by the kidney where another hydroxyl group is added to make the active form of vitamin D: 1,25-dihydroxy vitamin D_3 (**Figure 9.10**).

Vitamin D and Bone Health The principal function of vitamin D is to maintain levels of calcium and phosphorus in the blood that favor bone mineralization. When blood calcium levels drop too low the parathyroid gland releases **parathyroid hormone (PTH)**. PTH release stimulates enzymes in the kidney to convert 25-hydroxy vitamin D_3 to the active form of the vitamin. Active vitamin D functions by binding to vitamin D receptor proteins at target tissues and affecting gene expression (see Figure 9.5). Its affect

parathyroid hormone (PTH) A hormone released by the parathyroid gland that acts to increase blood calcium levels.

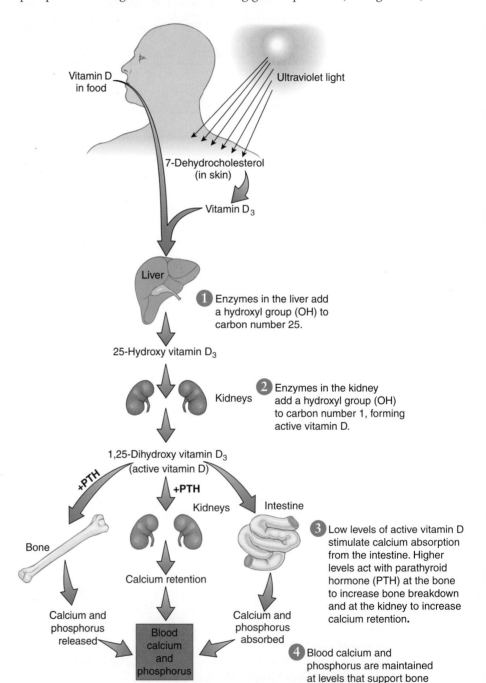

Figure 9.10 Vitamin D activation and functions
In order to function, vitamin D from food and from synthesis in the skin, must be activated.

at three different target tissues helps to increase blood calcium levels.[15] One target is intestinal cells, where vitamin D increases the expression of genes that code for the production of intestinal calcium transport proteins. This enhances the active transport of dietary calcium from the intestinal lumen into the body. This action requires only very low levels of the active vitamin. If dietary calcium is unavailable, higher levels of vitamin D act at the bone and kidney in conjunction with PTH to return blood calcium to normal. At the bone, vitamin D causes precursor cells to differentiate into cells that break down bone. Bone breakdown releases calcium and phosphorus into the blood. At the kidney vitamin D acts with PTH to increase the amount of calcium retained by the kidneys.[15]

Other Functions of Vitamin D In addition to bone, intestine, and kidney, receptors for active vitamin D have been found in cells of the colon, parathyroid gland, pituitary gland, immune system, reproductive organs, and skin.[15] Vitamin D is needed to maintain normal functioning of the parathyroid gland and is an important immune system regulator.

Vitamin D also plays a role in preventing cells from being transformed into cancerous cells.[16] It has been recognized for many years that the risk of certain cancers is increased in people who live at higher latitudes, where less vitamin D can be synthesized in the skin. Studies now support the hypothesis that vitamin D deficiency increases the risk of developing and dying from colon, breast, ovarian, and prostate cancers.[17] There is also evidence that vitamin D may play a role in the increased risk of type 1 diabetes, multiple sclerosis, and high blood pressure in people who live at higher latitudes.[18]

Recommended Vitamin D Intake

The recommended intake of vitamin D is based on the amount needed in the diet to maintain normal blood levels of 25-hydroxy vitamin D_3. The AI for adult men and women is set at 5 μg per day.[19] The AI is expressed in micrograms, but the vitamin D content of foods and supplements may also be given as International Units (IUs); one IU is equal to 0.025 μg of vitamin D_3 (40 IU = 1 μg of vitamin D). The AI for vitamin D for adults is contained in about 2 cups of vitamin D-fortified milk (see Table 9.1).

Video

Despite the smaller body size of infants and children, the AI for vitamin D for this age is the same as that for adults. This is to allow sufficient vitamin D for bone development during periods of rapid growth. Although breast milk is low in vitamin D, infants who are exposed to sunlight for about half an hour per day do not require supplemental vitamin D. The AI for adults 50 to 70 years of age is 10 μg per day to prevent bone loss during periods of low sun exposure. In adults 70 and older, the AI is 15 μg per day to maintain blood levels of vitamin D and prevent skeletal fractures. The AI for pregnancy and lactation is not increased above young adult levels.

Life Cycle

The AI is based on the assumption that no vitamin D is synthesized in the skin. This assumption is made because of the variation in the extent to which synthesis from sunlight meets the requirement. If there is sufficient sun exposure, dietary vitamin D is not needed, but the amount synthesized in the skin is affected by many factors. Climate, season, and latitude all affect the amount of sunlight that reaches the earth (**Figure 9.11**). Clothing and the presence of pollution and tall buildings block sunlight, preventing it from reaching the skin, and sunscreens and dark skin pigmentation prevent the ultraviolet (UV) light rays from penetrating into the dermis of the skin, thereby reducing the formation of vitamin D. Properly applied sunscreen can reduce the amount of vitamin D synthesized by more than 95%.[18] Because the amount of vitamin D synthesized in the skin is affected by so many variables it is not possible to make a single recommendation regarding the amount of time a person needs to spend in the sun to meet their vitamin needs. For example, during the spring, summer, and fall light-skinned individuals may need to spend only 5 to 10 minutes, 2 to 3 times a week, outdoors with their faces, hands, arms, and legs exposed to meet their vitamin D requirement, whereas very dark-skinned (never sunburn) individuals may need 10 to 50 times more sun exposure to produce the same amount of vitamin D.[20,21] In the summer, children and active adults usually spend enough time outdoors without sunscreens to provide for their vitamin D requirement. It has been estimated that

Figure 9.11 Effect of latitude on sun exposure
During the winter at latitudes greater than about 40 degrees north or south, there is not enough UV radiation to synthesize adequate amounts of vitamin D.

rickets A vitamin D deficiency disease in children that is characterized by poor bone development because of inadequate calcium absorption.

osteomalacia A vitamin D deficiency disease in adults characterized by a loss of minerals from bones. It causes bone pain, muscle aches, and an increase in bone fractures.

Life Cycle

Figure 9.12 Bowed legs are characteristic of rickets. (Biophoto Associates/Photo Researchers)

more than 90% of the vitamin D requirement for most people comes from casual exposure to sunlight.[22] In the absence of adequate exposure to sunlight, many vitamin D experts now agree that 20 to 25 μg of vitamin D may be needed per day for all adults and children.[18]

Vitamin D Deficiency

When vitamin D is deficient only about 10 to 15% of the calcium in the diet can be absorbed. As a result, calcium is not available for proper bone mineralization and abnormalities in bone structure occur.

In children who are deficient in vitamin D, bones are weak because they do not contain enough calcium and phosphorus. This syndrome, called **rickets**, is characterized by bone deformities such as narrow rib cages, known as pigeon breasts, and bowed legs (**Figure 9.12**). The legs bow because the bones are too weak to support the weight of the body. Vitamin D deficiency also prevents children from reaching their genetically programmed height and reduces bone mass and causes muscle weakness. Rickets, first recognized in the 1600s, was common during the Industrial Revolution when large numbers of poorly nourished children lived under a layer of smog in the newly industrialized cities. Tall buildings and smog-filled air reduced children's exposure to sunlight. The fortification of milk with vitamin D has helped to greatly reduce rickets in most developed countries, but it is still a problem in infants and young children with dark skin and those who are breast-fed.[2] Rickets is also seen in children with disorders that affect fat absorption and in children, who for any variety of reasons, do not drink milk.

In adults, the vitamin D deficiency disease comparable to rickets is called **osteomalacia**. Because bone growth is complete in adults, osteomalacia does not cause bone deformities, but bones are weakened because not enough calcium is available to form the mineral deposits needed to maintain healthy bone. Insufficient bone mineralization leads to fractures of the weight-bearing bones such as those in the hips and spine. It can precipitate or exacerbate osteoporosis, which is a loss of total bone mass, not just minerals (see Chapter 10). Osteomalacia also causes bone pain and muscle aches and weakness. It is estimated that over half of African Americans in the United States are at risk of vitamin D deficiency either chronically or during the winter months.[22] This group is at particular risk because vitamin D synthesis is low due to dark pigmentation and consumption of milk fortified with vitamin D is low due to the high frequency of lactose intolerance. Vitamin D deficiency is also common in adults with kidney failure because the conversion of vitamin D from the inactive to active form is reduced. The elderly are at risk because the ability to synthesize vitamin D in the skin decreases with age and older adults typically cover more of their skin with clothing and spend less time in the sun than their younger counterparts.[22] In addition, the elderly tend to have a lower intake of dairy products.

Vitamin D Supplements

Vitamin D supplements are recommended to a number of groups. Because breast milk is low in vitamin D the American Academy of Pediatrics recommends that all breast-fed infants be given 10 μg per day of supplemental vitamin D by 2 months of age and that the supplement be continued until they are consuming this amount of dietary vitamin D from other sources.[23] Supplemental vitamin D is also recommended for all non-breast-fed infants who are ingesting less than 2 cups per day of vitamin D-fortified formula or milk and for children and adolescents who do not get regular sunlight exposure and do not ingest at least 500 mL per day of vitamin D-fortified milk. Other groups that might benefit from vitamin D supplements include people who do not drink milk or consume dairy products (see Chapter 6), older adults (see Chapter 16), individuals with dark skin pigmentation, individuals who do not absorb fat normally, and individuals with limited sun exposure because they are homebound, wear robes and head coverings for religious reasons, or work in occupations that prevent sun exposure.[24]

Life Cycle

Vitamin D Toxicity

Too much vitamin D in the body can cause high calcium concentrations in the blood and urine, deposition of calcium in soft tissues such as the blood vessels and kidneys, and cardiovascular damage. However, consumption of unfortified foods does not cause vitamin D toxicity, nor does synthesis of vitamin D from exposure to sunlight. Oversupplementation and overfortification can pose a risk. One case of accidental overfortification of milk resulted in the hospitalization of 56 individuals and the death of 2.[25] A UL for adults for vitamin D has been set at 50 μg (2000 IU) per day.[19] However, based on the fact that sunshine can provide an adult with vitamin D in an amount equivalent to daily oral consumption of 250 μg (10,000 IU) per day, it is now believed that intakes this high will not cause adverse reactions in the majority of healthy people.[26]

9.4 Vitamin E

Learning Objectives

- List two food sources of vitamin E.
- Discuss the function of vitamin E.

Vitamin E is a fat-soluble vitamin with an antioxidant function. It was first identified as a fat-soluble component of grains that was necessary for fertility in laboratory rats. It took almost 30 years to isolate this vitamin and to determine that it is also necessary for reproduction in humans. The chemical name for vitamin E, **tocopherol**, is from the Greek *tos*, meaning childbirth, and *phero*, meaning to bring forth. Although vitamin E has been promoted to slow aging, cure infertility, reduce scarring, and protect against air pollution, research has not shown it to be useful for these purposes. Today we continue to explore the role of this antioxidant in protecting us from chronic disease (see Chapter 12: Your Choice: Are Antioxidant Supplements Beneficial?).

tocopherol The chemical name for vitamin E.

Vitamin E in the Diet

alpha-tocopherol (α-tocopherol) The form of tocopherol that provides vitamin E activity in humans.

isomers Molecules with the same molecular formula but a different arrangement of the atoms.

Several naturally occurring forms of vitamin E are found in foods, but only the **alpha-tocopherol (α-tocopherol)** form can meet vitamin E requirements in humans. The other forms do not meet vitamin E needs because they are not converted to α-tocopherol in humans and cannot be transported by the α-tocopherol transfer protein, a liver protein that helps distribute vitamin E to body tissues.

Dietary sources of vitamin E include nuts and peanuts; plant oils, such as soybean, corn, and sunflower oils; leafy green vegetables; and wheat germ (**Figure 9.13**). Vitamin E is also consumed in fortified foods and supplements; however, the vitamin E from these sources may not be as efficient at meeting needs. The synthetic form of α-tocopherol found in dietary supplements and fortified foods is composed of eight different **isomers**. Only half of these are active in the body. Therefore, synthetic α-tocopherol provides half of the biological activity of natural α-tocopherol; 10 mg of synthetic α-tocopherol provides the function of 5 mg of natural α-tocopherol.

Because the discovery that only the alpha-tocopherol form of vitamin E provides activity is relatively recent, most nutrient databases and nutrition labels overrepresent the amount of functional vitamin E in foods. Previously, all forms of tocopherol were included when calculating vitamin E content. Vitamin E content was expressed as either International Units (IUs), defined as 1 mg of synthetic α-tocopherol, or α-tocopherol equivalents (α-TEs), which considered other tocopherols as fractions of α-tocopherol. To correct for this, formulas have been developed to convert IUs and α-TEs into milligrams of α-tocopherol (**Table 9.4**).

Because vitamin E is sensitive to destruction by oxygen, metals, light, and heat, some is lost during food processing, cooking, and storage. Although it is relatively stable at normal cooking temperatures, the vitamin E in cooking oils may be destroyed if the oil is repeatedly heated to the high temperatures used for deep-fat frying.

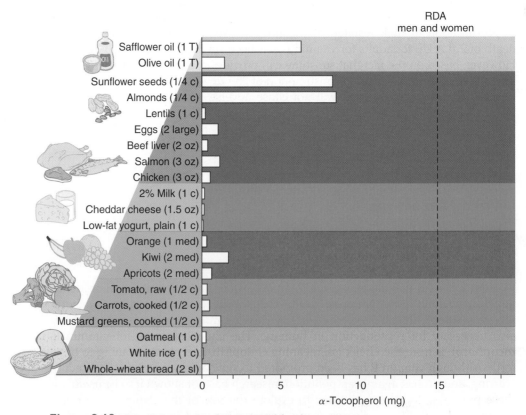

Figure 9.13 Vitamin E content of MyPyramid food groups
Adults can obtain their RDA for vitamin E (dashed line) by consuming plant oils, nuts and seeds, and leafy green vegetables.

Table 9.4 Converting Vitamin E Units

To estimate the α-tocopherol intake from foods:

- If values are given as mg α-TEs:

  mg α-TE $\times$ 0.8 = mg α-tocopherol

- If values are given as IUs:

  First, determine if the source of the α-tocopherol is natural or synthetic.

- For natural α-tocopherol:

  IU of natural α-tocopherol $\times$ 0.67 = mg α-tocopherol

- For synthetic α-tocopherol (dl-α-tocopherol):

  IU of synthetic α-tocopherol $\times$ 0.45 = mg α-tocopherol

Vitamin E in the Body

Vitamin E absorption depends on normal fat absorption. Once absorbed, vitamin E is incorporated into chylomicrons. As chylomicrons are broken down, some vitamin E is distributed to other lipoproteins and delivered to tissues, but most is taken to the liver where, with the help of α-tocopherol transfer protein, the α-tocopherol form is incorporated into very-low-density lipoproteins (VLDLs).[27] The α-tocopherol in VLDLs is distributed to other plasma lipoproteins and delivered to cells.

Vitamin E functions primarily as a fat-soluble antioxidant. It neutralizes reactive oxygen compounds before they damage unsaturated fatty acids in cell membranes. After vitamin E is used to eliminate free radicals, its antioxidant function can be restored by vitamin C (**Figure 9.14**). Because polyunsaturated fats are

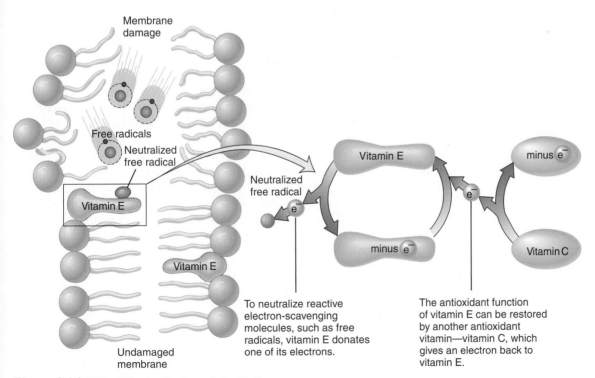

Figure 9.14 Antioxidant mechanism of vitamin E
By neutralizing free radicals, vitamin E guards not only cell membranes, as shown here, but also body proteins, DNA, and cholesterol. Vitamin E must be regenerated by vitamin C to restore it to the form that can act as an antioxidant.

particularly susceptible to oxidative damage, vitamin E needs increase as polyunsaturated fat intake increases.

By protecting cell membranes, vitamin E is important in maintaining the integrity of red blood cells, cells in nervous tissue, cells of the immune system, and lung cells, where it is particularly important because oxygen concentrations in those cells are high.[28] Vitamin E can also defend cells from damage by heavy metals, such as lead and mercury, and toxins, such as carbon tetrachloride, benzene, and a variety of drugs. It also protects against some environmental pollutants such as ozone. A number of vitamin E's roles are hypothesized to reduce the risk of heart disease. As an antioxidant, it helps protect low-density lipoprotein (LDL) cholesterol from oxidation. Studies done in the laboratory indicate that it also inhibits a number of events critical to the development of atherosclerosis.[29]

Recommended Vitamin E Intake

The recommendation for vitamin E intake is based on the amount needed to maintain plasma concentrations of α-tocopherol that protect red blood cell membranes from rupturing. The RDA for adult men and women is set at 15 mg/day of α-tocopherol.[29]

Life Cycle

For infants, an AI for vitamin E has been set based on the amount consumed by infants fed principally with human milk. EARs and RDAs for children and adolescents have been estimated from adult values. The RDA for pregnancy is not increased above nonpregnant levels. To estimate the requirement for lactation, the amount secreted in human milk is added to the requirement for nonlactating women.[29]

Vitamin E Deficiency

Vitamin E protects membranes; therefore a deficiency can cause membrane changes. Nerve tissue and red blood cells are particularly susceptible. Vitamin E deficiency is usually characterized by neurological problems associated with nerve degeneration. Symptoms observed in humans include poor muscle coordination, weakness, and impaired vision. Because vitamin E is plentiful in the food supply and is stored in many of the body's tissues vitamin E deficiency is rare, occurring only in those unable to absorb the vitamin due to fat malabsorption, those with inherited abnormalities in vitamin E metabolism, those with protein-energy malnutrition, and premature infants. For example, in individuals with cystic fibrosis, an inherited condition that reduces fat absorption, deficiency can develop rapidly, causing serious neurological problems, which, if untreated, can become permanent.

Life Cycle

All newborn infants have low blood tocopherol levels because there is little transfer of vitamin E from mother to fetus until the last weeks of pregnancy. The levels are lower in premature infants, who are born before much vitamin E is transferred from the mother. In these infants, red blood cell membranes may be damaged by oxidation causing them to rupture. This results in a type of anemia called **hemolytic anemia**. Infant formula for premature newborns is supplemented with higher amounts of vitamin E than formula for full-term infants.

hemolytic anemia Anemia that results when red blood cells break open.

Vitamin E Supplements and Toxicity

Although vitamin E deficiency is uncommon, supplements are promoted to grow hair; restore, maintain, or increase sexual potency and fertility; alleviate fatigue; maintain immune function; enhance athletic performance; reduce the symptoms of premenstrual syndrome (PMS) and menopause; slow aging; and treat a host of other medical problems. There is little conclusive evidence that supplemental vitamin E provides any of these benefits.

The antioxidant role of vitamin E suggests that it may help reduce the risk of heart disease, cancer, Alzheimer's disease, macular degeneration, and a variety of other chronic diseases associated with oxidative damage. Particular attention has been paid to its potential benefits in guarding against heart disease.

In epidemiological studies, intakes of vitamin E greater than 100 IU per day were associated with a reduced risk of heart disease in both men and women.[30,31] This led to the hypothesis that the risk of heart disease could be reduced by increasing vitamin E intake with supplements. Although studies on the biological effects of vitamin E supplements indicate that they decrease LDL oxidation, decrease platelet stickiness, and have an anti-inflammatory effect[32] and individuals with the highest vitamin E levels in their blood have been found to have the lowest risk of death,[33] studies examining the effects of vitamin E supplements have not found them to be beneficial in preventing heart disease or other chronic diseases, and some studies have shown an increase in the risk of death.[33,34] Therefore, there is not sufficient evidence to recommend supplemental vitamin E to protect against heart disease. The FDA has also concluded that the evidence concerning the relationship between supplemental vitamin E and heart disease is not strong enough to allow a health claim on food labels.

Like other antioxidants, supplements of vitamin E have been suggested to prevent oxidative damage that could lead to cancer development. Vitamin E supplements have also been hypothesized to prevent cancer by boosting immune function and preventing the formation of carcinogenic nitrosamines in the digestive tract. Currently the evidence supporting a benefit of vitamin E supplements for cancer prevention is inconsistent and limited so supplements are not recommended for this purpose.

Vitamin E is relatively nontoxic. There is no evidence of adverse effects from consuming large amounts from food. The UL is 1000 mg per day from supplemental sources. Vitamin E supplements should not be taken by individuals taking blood-thinning medications because it reduces blood clotting and interferes with the action of vitamin K (see Your Choice: Think Before You Supplement).

9.5 Vitamin K

Learning Objective

- Describe how vitamin K is involved in blood clotting.
- Explain why newborns and people taking antibiotics are at risk for vitamin K deficiency.

Vitamin K is one of the few vitamins about which extravagant claims are not made. Like the other fat-soluble vitamins, it was discovered inadvertently by feeding animals a fat-free diet. In this case, researchers in Denmark noted that chicks fed this diet developed a bleeding disorder that was cured by feeding them a fat-soluble extract from green plants. Vitamin K was named for *koagulation*, the Danish word for **coagulation**, or blood clotting.

coagulation The process of blood clotting.

Vitamin K in the Diet

As with other fat-soluble vitamins, vitamin K is found in several forms. **Phylloquinone** is the form found in plants and the primary form in the diet. A group of vitamin K compounds, called **menaquinones**, are found in fish oils and meats and are synthesized by bacteria, including those in the human intestine. Menaquinones are the form found in supplements. Only a small number of foods provide significant amounts of vitamin K, however typical intakes in the U.S. meet recommendations.[4] The best dietary sources are liver and leafy green vegetables such as spinach, broccoli, brussels sprouts, kale, and turnip greens. These leafy greens provide about half of the vitamin K in a typical North American diet.[35] Some vegetable oils are also good

phylloquinone The form of vitamin K found in plants.

menaquinones The forms of vitamin K synthesized by bacteria and found in animals.

Off the Label

Think Before You Supplement

About half of the adults in the United States use dietary supplements.[1] People take them to energize themselves, to protect themselves from disease, to cure their illnesses, to enhance what they get in food, and simply to ensure against deficiencies. You can purchase almost any nutrient as an individual supplement or you can choose from a surfeit of combinations of nutrients, herbs, and other components. Some claim to be "all natural;" others entice you with terms like "mega," "advanced formula," "high potency," and "ultra." Do you need a supplement? How can you decide which is best?

Eating a variety of foods is the best way to meet nutrient needs, and most healthy adults who consume a reasonably good diet do not need supplements. For some people, however, supplements may be the only way to meet needs because they have low intakes, increased needs, or excess losses. Groups for whom vitamin and mineral supplements are typically recommended include the following:[2]

- **Dieters**—People who consume fewer than 1600 kcalories/day should take a multivitamin-mineral supplement.[2]
- **Vegans and those who eliminate all dairy foods**—To obtain adequate vitamin B$_{12}$, those who do not eat animal products need to take supplements or consume B$_{12}$-fortified foods. Because dairy products are an important source of calcium and vitamin D, those who do not consume dairy products due to lactose intolerance, milk allergies, or other reasons may benefit from a supplement providing calcium and vitamin D.
- **Infants and children**—Supplemental fluoride, vitamin D, and iron are recommended under certain circumstances.
- **Young women and pregnant women**—Women of childbearing age should consume 400 µg of folic acid daily from either fortified foods or supplements (see Chapter 8 and 14). Supplements of iron and folic acid are recommended for pregnant women, and multivitamin and mineral supplements are usually prescribed.
- **Older adults**—Because of the high incidence of atrophic gastritis in adults over 50, vitamin B$_{12}$ supplements or fortified foods are recommended. Meeting the AI for vitamin D and calcium may also be difficult for older adults so supplements of these nutrients are often recommended.
- **Individuals with dark skin pigmentation**—Those with dark skin may not be able to synthesize enough vitamin D to meet needs and may therefore benefit from supplementation.[2]
- **Individuals with restricted diets**—Individuals with health conditions that affect what foods they can eat or how nutrients are used may require vitamin and mineral supplements.
- **People taking medications**—Medications may interfere with the body's use of certain nutrients.
- **Cigarette smokers and alcohol users**—Heavy cigarette smokers require more vitamin C and possibly vitamin E than nonsmokers.[3,4] Alcohol consumption inhibits the absorption of B vitamins and may interfere with their metabolism.

Despite the benefits of supplements to some individuals, they can also carry risks. Concentrated doses of vitamins and minerals can result in toxicity, and supplements of other substances, such as herbs, may have side effects that outweigh any benefits they may provide. If you choose to take a dietary supplement, whether to ensure an adequate nutrient intake, prevent disease, or optimize health, use some common sense along with the information on the supplement label to assure that the supplement provides all the nutrients and other substances you need to satisfy your individual concerns, but does not contain ingredients or amounts that could cause adverse effects.

The information included on supplement labels is standardized (see figure and Chapter 2) and can be used to determine if a supplement includes the nutrients you want in appropriate amounts. For example, if you are looking for a vitamin/mineral supplement the Nutrition Facts panel will indicate if it provides minerals as well as vitamins. If you want to increase your calcium intake, check to see if it provides the amount of calcium that you want. If you have low iron stores, check to see if it provides iron. If you are over 50 or eat a vegan diet, check to see if it provides enough vitamin B$_{12}$ to meet your needs. Special supplement formulas for men, seniors, and women are available, but may not necessarily provide what you need even if you fit into the group they target. These formulations are not defined or regulated so it is up to the company to decide what they contain.

The amounts of nutrients contained in a dose vary depending on the supplement. Some contain less than or equal to 100% of the Daily Value while others supply two, three, or ten times the Daily Value. High doses of individual nutrients or combinations of several different nutrients or other substances can lead to nutrient imbalances or toxicities. To assess the safety of the amounts of nutrients in a supplement dose compare it to the Tolerable Upper Intake Levels (ULs) (see inside cover). If the supplement contains amounts of nutri-

Supplement Facts

Serving Size 1 Tablet

Each Tablet Contains	% DV	Each Tablet Contains	% DV
Vitamin A 5000 IU	100%	Chromium 120 mcg	100%
(20% as Beta Carotene)		Molybdenum 75 mcg	100%
Vitamin C 60 mg	100%	Chloride 72 mg	2%
Vitamin D 400 IU	100%	Potassium 80 mg	2%
Vitamin E 30 IU	100%		
Vitamin K 25 mcg	31%	Boron 150 mcg	*
Thiamin 1.5 mg	100%	Nickel 5 mcg	*
Riboflavin 1.7 mg	100%	Silicon 2 mg	*
Niacin 20 mg	100%	Tin 10 mcg	*
Vitamin B6 2 mg	100%	Vanadium 10 mcg	*
Folic Acid 400 mcg	100%	Lutein 250 mcg	*
Vitamin B12 6 mcg	100%	*Daily Value (%DV) not established.	
Biotin 30 mcg	10%		
Pantothenic Acid 10 mg	100%		
Calcium 162 mg	16%		
Iron 18 mg	100%		
Phosphorus 109 mg	11%		
Iodine 150 mcg	100%		
Magnesium 100 mg	25%		
Zinc 15 mg	100%		
Selenium 20 mcg	29%		
Copper 2 mg	100%		
Manganese 2 mg	100%		

SUGGESTED USE:
Adults - One tablet daily

WARNING: Accidental overdose of iron-containing products is a leading cause of fatal poisoning in children under 6. Keep this product out of reach of children. In case of accidental overdose, call a doctor or poison control center immediately.

Keep bottle tightly closed. Store at room temperature.

(George Semple)

ents in excess of the UL, symptoms of toxicity are more likely to occur. One nutrient to be particularly careful of is vitamin A; too much increases the risk of bone fractures.[5] To minimize your risk do not take supplements of preformed vitamin A and if you take a multivitamin look for one that contains vitamin A as β-carotene. When checking how much is in your supplement be aware that the % Daily Value of vitamin A listed on food and supplement labels is based on a Daily Value of 1500 μg (5000 IU) per day for adults. For women the RDA is only 700 μg (2330 IU) per day, so a supplement containing 100% of the Daily Value provides over twice the RDA.

Although the ULs are a good guide, they are not always available and don't always tell the whole story. For example, there are no ULs or Daily Values for herbs, carotenoids, and other phytochemicals, so it is difficult to assess whether the amount in a supplement is too low to be of benefit or high enough to be harmful. Even when ULs are available they don't consider specific individual conditions or circumstances. For instance, β-carotene supplements may increase the risk of lung cancer among smokers. Iron can be a more serious toxicity concern in those with an abnormality that causes excess iron absorption. People who tend to develop kidney stones should avoid vitamin C supplements. Medications may also interact with supplements. Individuals taking anticoagulant medications should not take supplements containing vitamin E or vitamin K. Individuals who routinely take medications should discuss nutrient–drug interactions and the need for specific vitamin and mineral supplementation with their doctor or pharmacist.

Supplements can be part of an effective strategy to promote good health, but they should never be considered a substitute for other good health habits and they should never be used instead of medical therapy to treat a health problem. If you choose to use dietary supplements a safe choice is a multivitamin/mineral supplement that does not exceed 100% of the Daily Values. Although there is little evidence that the average person can benefit from such a supplement, there is also little evidence of harm. If you suffer a harmful effect or illness that you think is related to the use of a supplement, seek medical attention and go to the Dietary Supplements Adverse Events Reporting Web site at www.cfsan.fda.gov/~dms/ds-rept.html for information on how to proceed.

Considering Supplements

Before you choose to take a dietary supplement consider the following:

- **Why do you want a supplement?** If you are taking it for insurance, does it provide both vitamins and minerals? If you want to supplement specific nutrients, are they contained in the product?

- **Does it contain potentially toxic levels of any nutrient?** Check the % Daily Value. For any nutrients that exceed 100%, check to see if they exceed the UL (see inside cover).

- **Does it contain any nonvitamin/ nonmineral ingredients?** If so, have any been shown to be toxic to someone like you?

- **Do you have a medical condition that recommends against certain nutrients or other ingredients?** Are you a smoker? Smoking increases the need for vitamin C, but also increases the risks associated with taking β-carotene.

- **Are you taking prescription medication with which an ingredient in the supplement may interact?** Check with your physician, dietitian, or pharmacist to help identify these interactions.

- **How much does it cost?** Compare product costs and ingredients before you buy. Just as more isn't always better, more expensive is not always better either.

- **What is the expiration date?** Some nutrients degrade over time so expired products will have less than is on the label. Look for the Dietary Supplement Verification Program (DSVP) mark (see figure) that tells you the product has met industry quality, purity, and potency standards.

[1] Millen, A., Dodd, K., and Subar, A. Use of vitamin, mineral, nonvitamin and nonmineral supplements in the United States: The 1987, 1992, and 2000 National Healthy Interview Survey results. *J. Am. Diet. Assoc.* 104:942–951, 2004.

[2] American Dietetic Association. Position of the American Dietetic Association: Fortification and nutritional supplements. *J. Am. Diet. Assoc.* 105:1300–1311, 2005.

[3] Food and Nutrition Board, Institute of Medicine. *Dietary Reference Intakes for Vitamin C, Vitamin E, Selenium, and Carotenoids.* Washington, DC: National Academies Press, 2000.

[4] Bruno, R. S., and Traber, M. G. Cigarette smoke alters human vitamin E requirements. *J. Nutr.* 135:671–674, 2005.

[5] Michaelsson, K., Lithell, H., Vessby, B., and Melhus, H. Serum retinol levels and the risk of fracture. *N. Engl. J. Med.* 348:287–294, 2003.

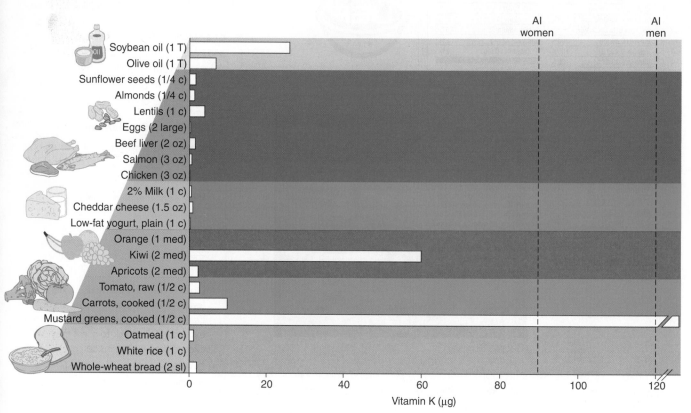

Figure 9.15 Vitamin K content of MyPyramid food groups
The best sources of vitamin K are leafy green vegetables and some plant oils; the dashed lines represent the AIs for adult men and women.

sources (**Figure 9.15**). Some of the vitamin K produced by bacteria in the human gastrointestinal tract is also absorbed. Vitamin K is destroyed by exposure to light and low- or high-acid conditions.

Vitamin K in the Body

prothrombin A blood protein required for blood clotting.

Vitamin K is a coenzyme needed for the production of the blood-clotting protein **prothrombin** and other specific blood-clotting factors. Blood-clotting factors are proteins that circulate in the blood in an inactive form. When activated they lead to the formation of fibrin, the protein that forms the structure of a blood clot (**Figure 9.16**). Injuries, as well as the normal wear and tear of daily living, produce small tears in blood vessels. To prevent blood loss, these tears must be repaired with blood clots.

There are other roles for vitamin K in the body but they are less well understood. For example, there are several vitamin K-dependent proteins in bone that may be involved in bone mineralization and demineralization. Several studies have demonstrated that low-dietary vitamin K intake is associated with low bone-mineral density or increased fractures.[36] Vitamin K dependent proteins in blood vessels may be involved in preventing calcification of blood vessels and loss of elasticity.[37]

Recommended Vitamin K Intake

Unlike other fat-soluble vitamins, the body uses vitamin K rapidly, so a constant supply is necessary. The vitamin K produced by bacteria in the gastrointestinal tract

Figure 9.16 Role of vitamin K in blood clotting
Several clotting factors, including prothrombin, require vitamin K for synthesis. These are needed for fibrinogen to be converted into its active form, fibrin, which is a structural component of blood clots. (Amethyst/Custom Medical Stock Photo, Inc.; Science Photo Library/Custom Medical Stock Photo, Inc.

contributes to needs, but this is not well absorbed and alone is not enough to meet needs. An AI for dietary vitamin K has been set at about 120 μg per day for men and 90 μg per day for women (see Table 9.1). The AI is not increased for pregnancy or lactation. An AI for infants was set based on the amount typically consumed in breast milk.

Vitamin K Deficiency

Abnormal blood coagulation is the major symptom of vitamin K deficiency. When vitamin K is deficient the blood does not clot to seal ruptured arteries or veins, and blood loss goes unchecked. If the deficiency is severe it can eventually cause death from blood loss. A deficiency is very rare in the healthy adult population, but it may result from fat malabsorption syndromes or the long-term use of antibiotics. The antibiotics kill the bacteria in the gastrointestinal tract that are a source of the vitamin. In combination with an illness that reduces the dietary intake of vitamin K, this may precipitate a deficiency. Injections of vitamin K are typically administered before surgery to aid in blood clotting. Since inappropriate blood clotting causes strokes and heart attacks, drugs that block vitamin K activity have been used to reduce blood clot formation in patients with cardiovascular disease (see Science Applied: Cows, Clover, and Coagulation).

Vitamin K deficiency is most common in newborns. There is little transfer of this vitamin from mother to fetus, and because the infant gut is free of bacteria, no vitamin K is made there. Further, breast milk is low in vitamin K. Therefore, to prevent uncontrolled bleeding, infants are typically given a vitamin K injection within 6 hours of birth.

Life Cycle

Vitamin K Toxicity and Supplements

A UL has not been established for vitamin K because there are no well-documented side effects, even with intakes up to 370 μg per day from food and supplements. Because vitamin K functions in blood clotting, high doses can interfere with anticoagulant drugs. Therefore, individuals prescribed these medications should consult with their physicians before taking supplements containing vitamin K.

SCIENCE

ScienceAppliedScienceApplied
ScienceAppliedScienceApplied
ScienceAppliedScienceApplied

APPLIED

(DAJ/Getty Images, Inc.)　　(www.victorianoizquierdo.com/Getty Images, Inc.)　　(Elena Schweitzer/Shutterstock)

Cows, Clover, and Coagulation

On a snowy night in 1933, a disgruntled farmer delivered a bale of moldy clover hay, a pail of unclotted blood, and a dead cow to the laboratory of Dr. Carl Link at the University of Wisconsin. Link, the University's first professor of biochemistry, was already making a name for himself in the scientific community when he was presented with the farmer's challenge to speed the typically deliberate pace of research. Why were his cows dying? What could he do to stop the bleeding disease that was killing them? Link had just begun to research hemorrhagic sweet clover disease, the condition that was killing the farmer's cows, but at the time the only advice he could offer was to find alternative feed and try blood transfusions to save the other animals. Link and his colleagues began a line of inquiry that ultimately led to the development of an anti-blood-clotting factor that today saves the lives of hundreds of thousands of people.

In the 1930s, hemorrhagic sweet clover disease was killing cows across the midwestern prairies of the United States and Canada. It occurred in cattle that were fed moldy, spoiled, sweet clover hay. These animals died because their blood did not clot. Even a minor scratch from a barbed wire fence could be fatal; once bleeding began, it did not stop. Six years after the farmer's challenge, Link and colleagues had isolated the anticoagulant *dicumarol* from moldy clover. Dicumarol is a derivative of coumarin, which gives clover its sweet scent; mold converts coumarin to dicumarol. Cows fed moldy clover consume dicumarol, which interferes with vitamin K activity and consequently prevents normal blood clotting.

The discovery of dicumarol enhanced our understanding of the blood-clotting mechanism and led to the development of anticoagulant drugs. These drugs help eliminate blood clots and prevent their formation. In carefully regulated doses, they are used to treat heart attacks, which occur when blood clots block one or more of the vessels supplying blood to the heart muscle. Dicumarol, first synthesized in 1940, was the first anticoagulant that could be administered orally to humans. Further work with dicumarol led Link to propose the use of a more potent derivative, called *warfarin*, as rat poison.

President Eisenhower suffered a heart attack in September, 1955. His recovery was aided by treatment with the anticoagulant sodium warfarin. A little over a year later, in November 1956, he was elected to his second term. (Ed Clark/Getty Images, Inc.)

When rats consume the odorless, colorless warfarin, their blood fails to clot, and they bleed to death. Warfarin was used as a rodenticide for nearly a decade before it was introduced into clinical medicine in 1954. Sodium warfarin, also known by the brand name Coumadin, soon became the most widely prescribed anticoagulant drug in the nation. It was used to treat President Dwight D. Eisenhower when he suffered a heart attack in 1955.

Sodium warfarin and dicumarol have been administered to millions of patients to prevent blood clots, which, can cause heart attacks and strokes. It is ironic that a substance that killed hundreds of cattle across the Great Plains and that efficiently kills rodents in our homes has saved so many human lives.

Outcome

Ana is now a happy, healthy 2-year-old. You would never know that a year ago she had been diagnosed with the vitamin D deficiency disease rickets. She developed rickets when she lived in an orphanage in China, where her diet was low in vitamin D and she was not exposed to enough sunlight to synthesize adequate amounts of the vitamin to meet her needs. Without adequate vitamin D, she was unable to absorb sufficient calcium to support bone growth and health. After diagnosing Ana with rickets, her pediatrician prescribed oral supplements of both vitamin D and calcium and recommended that Ana consume a calcium-rich diet. After only a week of treatment, Ana's laboratory values had improved, and X-rays showed that her bones were healing. After a few months, the bony protrusions on her ribs had disappeared, the slight bowing in her legs was corrected, and new teeth began to emerge. If Ana had not been treated when she was young and still growing, her skeletal deformities would have been permanent.

Ana now lives in Michigan, so she gets little sunshine during the winter months. She does not like to drink milk, an important dietary source of calcium and vitamin D, but she does drink soymilk that is fortified with both these nutrients. This, as part of an overall healthy diet, will help Ana continue to meet her vitamin D needs and avoid other vitamin deficiencies that could affect her health as she gets older.

APPLICATIONS

Personal Nutrition

1. Do you get enough vitamin A?

   a. Use iProfile and your food intake record from Chapter 2 to calculate your average daily intake of vitamin A.

   b. How does your vitamin A intake compare to the RDA for someone of your age and sex?

   c. What are three major food sources of vitamin A in your diet?

   d. Do the major food sources of vitamin A in your diet contain preformed vitamin A or carotenoids?

2. How much vitamin E is in your diet?

   a. Use iProfile and the food intake record you kept in Chapter 2 to calculate your average intake of vitamin E.

   b. How does your intake of vitamin E compare with the RDA?

   c. If your diet does not meet the RDA, suggest modifications that will add enough vitamin E to your diet to meet the RDA without increasing your energy intake.

General Nutrition Issues

1. Who is at risk of vitamin D deficiency in your town?

   a. Assume you have a friend or relative living in a nursing home. Find out about how much time nursing-home residents spend outdoors without sunscreen or clothing covering their skin. Do you think they are at risk for vitamin D deficiency? Why or why not?

   b. At higher northern and southern latitudes little vitamin D is synthesized in the winter months. Is your community located at a latitude greater than 40° north or south?

   c. How much time do the schoolchildren at your local elementary school spend outdoors during recess? Do you think they are at risk for vitamin D deficiency? Why or why not?

   d. Do a survey to determine the percentage of people who apply sunscreen daily. Why might sunscreen affect vitamin D status?

2. What supplements are your friends taking? Are they safe?

   a. Do a supplement survey of 10 people. Record all of the vitamin and mineral supplements they take including the dose and the number of doses taken per day as well as the reason they chose to take each supplement.

   b. Tabulate the total amount of each vitamin and mineral each person takes.

   c. Are any of the survey subjects consuming nutrients in excess of recommendations (RDA or AI)?

   d. Are any nutrients consumed in excess of the UL?

   e. Do you think these supplements will fulfill the expectations of the consumers? Why or why not?

Summary

9.1 Fat-Soluble Vitamins in the Modern Diet

- Vitamins A, D, E, and K are soluble in fat, which affects how they are absorbed, transported, stored, and excreted. Deficiencies of vitamins A and D are common in the developing world. In the United States, the risk of deficiencies of fat-soluble vitamins is increasing due to low intakes of fruits and vegetables and limited sun exposure.

9.2 Vitamin A

- Vitamin A is found both preformed as retinoids and in precursor forms called carotenoids. The major food sources of preformed vitamin A include liver, eggs, fish, and fortified dairy products. Carotenoids are found in plant foods such as yellow-, orange-, and red-colored fruits and vegetables and leafy green vegetables. Some carotenoids are precursors of vitamin A. The most potent is β-carotene.

- In the body the retinoids, which include retinol, retinal, and retinoic acid, are needed for vision and for the growth and differentiation of cells. Retinol is transported in the blood and can be converted into retinal or retinoic acid. Retinal binds to opsin in the eye to form rhodopsin. When light strikes rhodopsin to begin the visual cycle, it causes a nerve impulse to be sent to the brain so the light is perceived. Retinoic acid affects cell differentiation by altering gene expression. It is needed for healthy epithelial tissue and normal reproduction and immune function. Beta-carotene functions as an antioxidant, a role that is independent of its conversion to vitamin A.

- Vitamin A deficiency is a world health problem that increases the frequency of infectious disease and causes blindness and death in millions of children.

- Preformed vitamin A can be toxic at doses as low as ten times the RDA and can increase the risk of bone fractures and birth defects. Carotenoids are not toxic, but a high intake can give the skin an orange appearance.

9.3 Vitamin D

- Vitamin D can be made in the skin by exposure to sunlight, so dietary needs vary depending on the amount synthesized. Vitamin D is found in fish oils and fortified milk.

- Dietary vitamin D as well as vitamin D synthesized in the skin must be modified by the liver and then the kidney to form active vitamin D. Active vitamin D promotes calcium and phosphorus absorption from the intestines and acts with parathyroid hormone to cause the release of calcium from bone and calcium retention by the kidney. These roles are essential for maintaining proper levels of calcium and phosphorus in the body. Adequate vitamin D also protects against autoimmune diseases and cancer.
- Vitamin D deficiency in children results in a condition called rickets; in adults, vitamin D deficiency causes osteomalacia.
- Although it can be toxic in high doses, many experts now think that Americans do not get enough vitamin D.

9.4 Vitamin E

- Vitamin E is found in nuts, plant oils, green vegetables, and fortified cereals.

- Vitamin E functions primarily as a fat-soluble antioxidant. It is necessary for reproduction and protects cell membranes from oxidative damage.
- Vitamin E deficiency can cause hemolytic anemia and neurological problems.
- Many people take vitamin E supplements. There is little risk of toxicity, but there is also little documented evidence of any benefit from supplements.

9.5 Vitamin K

- Vitamin K is found in plants and is synthesized by bacteria in the gastrointestinal tract.
- Vitamin K is a coenzyme essential for the formation of blood clotting factors as well as proteins needed for normal bone mineralization.
- Deficiency causes bleeding and low-bone density. Since vitamin K deficiency is a problem in newborns, they are routinely given vitamin K injections at birth.

Review Questions

1. List two food sources of preformed vitamin A and two of provitamin A.

2. How is vitamin A involved in the perception of light?

3. How does vitamin A affect the proteins made by a cell?

4. Why does a deficiency of vitamin A cause night blindness? Dry eyes?

5. What is β-carotene?

6. Explain why β-carotene is not toxic, but preformed vitamin A is.

7. Why is vitamin D called the "sunshine vitamin?"

8. Name two sources of vitamin D in the diet.

9. What is the primary function of vitamin D?

10. Describe the symptoms of vitamin D deficiency in children.

11. Explain how vitamin D's affect on gene expression alters calcium absorption.

12. What is the function of vitamin E?

13. Name two sources of vitamin E in the diet.

14. What is the main function of vitamin K?

15. What are the symptoms of vitamin K deficiency?

References

1. Rajakumar, K., and Thomas, S. B. Reemerging nutritional rickets: A historical perspective. *Arch. Pediatr. Adolesc. Med.* 159:335–341, 2005.

2. Weisberg, P., Scanlon, K. S., Li, R., and Cogswell, M. E. Nutritional rickets among children in the United States: Review of cases reported between 1986 and 2003. *Am. J. Clin. Nutr.* 80(Suppl):1697S–1705S, 2004.

3. Holden, J. M., Eldridge, A. L., Beecher, G. R. et al. Carotenoid content of U.S. foods: An update of the database. *J. Food Composition and Analysis* 12:169–196, 1999.

4. Food and Nutrition Board, Institute of Medicine. *Dietary Reference Intakes: Vitamin A, Vitamin K, Arsenic, Boron, Chromium, Copper, Iodine, Iron, Manganese, Molybdenum,*

Nickel, Silicon, Vanadium, and Zinc. Washington, DC: National Academies Press, 2001.

5. Ross, A. C. Vitamin A and carotenoids. In *Modern Nutrition in Health and Disease*, 10th ed. M. E. Shils, M. Shike, A. C. Ross, et. al. eds. Philadelphia: Lippincott Williams & Wilkins, 2006, pp. 351–375.

6. Clagett-Dame, M., and DeLuca, H. F. The role of vitamin A in mammalian reproduction and embryonic development. *Annu. Rev. Nutr.* 22:347–381, 2002.

7. Wintergerst, E. S., Maggini, S., and Hornig, D. H. Contribution of selected vitamins and trace elements to immune function. *Ann. Nutr. Metab.* 51:301–323, 2007.

8. World Health Organization. *Micronutrient Deficiencies. Vitamin A Deficiency: The Challenge.* Available online at www.who.int/nutrition/topics/vad/en/index.html. Accessed April 23, 2009.

9. McCaffery, P. J., Adams, J., Maden, M., and Rosa-Molinar, E. Too much of a good thing: Retinoic acid as an endogenous regulator of neural differentiation and exogenous teratogen. *Eur. J. Neurosci.* 18:457–472, 2003.

10. Michaelsson, K., Lithell, H., Vessby, B., and Melhus, H. Serum retinol levels and the risk of fracture. *N. Engl. J. Med.* 348: 287–294, 2003.

11. Feskanich, D., Singh, V., Willett, W. C., and Colditz, G. A. Vitamin A intake and hip fractures among postmenopausal women. *JAMA.* 287: 47–54, 2002.

12. Cooper, D. A., Eldridge, A. L., and Peters, J. C. Dietary carotenoids and lung cancer: A review of recent research. *Nutr. Rev.* 57:133–145, 1999.

13. Pryor, W. A., Stahl, W., and Rock, C. L. Beta-carotene: From biochemistry to clinical trials. *Nutr. Rev.* 58:39–53, 2000.

14. Holick, M. F. Resurrection of vitamin D deficiency and rickets. *J. Clin. Invest.* 116:2062–2072, 2006.

15. DeLuca, H. F. Overview of the general physiologic features and functions of vitamin D. *Am. J. Clin. Nutr.* 80(Suppl):1689S–1696S, 2004.

16. Nagpal, S., Na, S., and Rathnachalam, R. Noncalcemic actions of vitamin D receptor ligands. *Endocr Rev* 26:62–68, 2005.

17. Garland, C. F., Garland, F. C., Gorham, E. D. et al. The role of vitamin D in cancer prevention. *Am. J. Public Health* 96:252–261, 2006.

18. Holick, M. F., and Chen, T. C. Vitamin D deficiency: A worldwide problem with health consequences. *Am. J. Clin. Nutr.* 87(Suppl.):1080S–1086S, 2008.

19. Food and Nutrition Board, Institute of Medicine. *Dietary Reference Intakes: Calcium, Phosphorus, Magnesium, Vitamin D, and Fluoride.* Washington, DC: National Academies Press, 1997.

20. Holick, M. F. Vitamin D deficiency: What a pain it is. *Mayo Clin. Proc.* 78(12):1457–1459, 2003.

21. Holick, M. F. Vitamin D: Importance in the prevention of cancers, type 1 diabetes, heart disease, and osteoporosis. *Am. J. Clin. Nutr.* 79:362–371, 2004.

22. Holick, M. F. Sunlight and vitamin D for bone health and prevention of autoimmune diseases, cancers, and cardiovascular disease. *Am. J. Clin. Nutr.* 80(Suppl):1678S–1688S, 2004.

23. Warner, C. L., and Greer, F. R. American Academy of Pediatrics, Section on Breastfeeding and Committee on Nutrition. Prevention of rickets and vitamin D deficiency in infants, children, and adolescents. *Pediatrics* 122:1142–1152, 2008.

24. Office of Dietary Supplements. Dietary Supplement Fact Sheet: Vitamin D. Available online at ods.od.nih.gov/factsheets/vitamind.asp/ Accessed September 25, 2009.

25. Blank, S., Scanlon, K. S., Sinks, T. H., and Falk, H. An outbreak of hypervitaminosis D associated with the overfortification of milk from a home-delivery dairy. *Am. J. Public Health* 85:656–659, 1995.

26. Vieth, R. Vitamin D toxicity, policy, and science. *J. Bone Miner. Res.* 22(Suppl. 2):V64–V68, 2007.

27. Traber, M. G., Burton, G. W., and Hamilton, R. L. Vitamin E trafficking. *Ann. N.Y. Acad. Sci.* 1031:1–12, 2004.

28. Sabat, R., Guthmann, F., and Rüstow, B. Formation of reactive oxygen species in lung alveolar cells: Effect of vitamin E deficiency. *Lung* 186(2):115–122, 2008.

29. Food and Nutrition Board, Institute of Medicine. *Dietary Reference Intakes for Vitamin C, Vitamin E, Selenium, and Carotenoids.* Washington, DC: National Academies Press, 2000.

30. Rimm, E. B., Stampfer, M. J., Ascherio, A. et al. Vitamin E consumption and the risk of heart disease in men. *N. Engl. J. Med.* 328:1450–1456, 1993.

31. Stampfer, M. J., Hennekens, C. H., Manson, J. E. et al. Vitamin E consumption and the risk of heart disease in women. *N. Engl. J. Med.* 328:1487–1489, 1993.

32. Harris, A., Devaraj, S., and Jailal, I. Oxidative stress, alpha-tocopherol therapy, and atherosclerosis. *Curr. Atheroscler. Rep.* 4:373–380, 2002.

33. Traber, M. G., Frei, B., and Beckman, J. S. Vitamin E revisited: Do new data validate benefits for chronic disease prevention? *Curr. Opin. Lipidol.* 19:30–38, 2008.

34. Bjelakovic, G., Nikolova, D., Gluud, L. L. et al. Mortality in randomized trials of antioxidant supplements for primary and secondary prevention: Systematic review and meta-analysis. *JAMA* 297:842–857, 2007.

34. Jialal, I., and Devaraj, S. Scientific evidence to support a vitamin E and heart disease health claim: Research needs. *J. Nutr.* 135:348–353, 2005.

35. Booth, S. L., Pennington, J. A. T., and Sadowski, J. A. Food sources and dietary intakes of vitamin K_1 (phylloquinone) in the American diet: Data from the FDA Total Diet Study. *J. Am. Diet. Assoc.* 96:149–154, 1996.

36. Bugel, S. Vitamin K and bone health. *Proc. Nutr. Soc.* 62:839–843, 2003.

37. Vermeer, C., Shearer, M. J., Zittermann, A. et al. Beyond deficiency: Potential benefits of increased intakes of vitamin K for bone and vascular health. *Eur. J. Nutr.* 43:325–335, 2004.

Focus On

Phytochemicals

Outline

functional foods Foods that provide a health benefit beyond that attributed to the nutrients they contain.

phytochemicals Substances found in plant foods (*phyto* means plant) that are not essential nutrients but may have health-promoting properties.

zoochemicals Substances found in animal foods (*zoo* means animal) that are not essential nutrients but may have health-promoting properties.

Food presents an unlimited array of tastes, textures, colors, and aromas. With this gastronomic variety and delight come a myriad of nutrient combinations. In addition, food contains substances that have not been identified as nutrients but may promote health and reduce disease risk. Foods have been used in folk medicine for centuries. Today, researchers continue to discover beneficial effects of various food components and explore the relationships among the consumption of specific foods, typical dietary patterns, and health. Foods that provide health benefits beyond basic nutrition are called **functional foods**.[1] **Table F3.1** provides examples of functional foods and their potential benefits. Health-promoting substances in plant foods are called **phytochemicals**, while those found in animal foods are called **zoochemicals**.

Table F3.1 Benefits of Functional Foods

Functional Food	Key Components	Potential Benefit
Whole-grain products	Fiber, lignans, phytoestrogens	Reduce the risk of cancer and heart disease.
Oatmeal	β-glucan, soluble fiber	Reduces blood cholesterol.
Grape juice	Phenols	Improves cardiovascular health.
Green or black tea	Tannins, catechins	Reduces the risk of certain types of cancer.
Fatty fish	Omega-3 fatty acids	Reduces the risk of heart disease.
Soy	Phytoestrogens, soy protein	Reduces the risk of cancer and heart disease, reduces symptoms of menopause.
Garlic	Organic sulfur compounds	Reduces the risk of cancer and heart disease.
Spinach, kale, collard greens	Lutein, zeaxanthin	Reduce the risk of age-related blindness (macular degeneration).
Nuts	Monounsaturated fatty acids	Reduce the risk of heart disease.

F3.1 Phytochemicals in the Modern Diet

Learning Objectives

- Distinguish phytochemicals from essential nutrients.
- Discuss how the color of fruits and vegetables is related to their phytochemical content.
- Give some examples of the health benefits of phytochemicals.

Phytochemicals include the hundreds, perhaps thousands, of biologically active non-nutritive chemicals found in plants. In the plants themselves, phytochemicals provide biological functions. For example, compounds in onions and garlic are natural pesticides that protect plants from insects. Gardeners often plant these near more vulnerable plant varieties to protect them from insect infestation. Most plant chemicals have no effect on human health, but many promote health, and a few can be toxic. For example, the phytochemicals in soy and tea have been shown to inhibit tumor growth.[2] On the other hand, chemicals in rhubarb leaves can cause symptoms ranging from burning in the mouth and throat, abdominal pain, nausea, vomiting, and diarrhea to convulsions, coma, and death from cardiovascular collapse (**Figure F3.1**). Despite the variety of effects these chemicals can have, the term "phytochemical" is generally used to refer to those substances found in plants that have health-promoting properties. Phytochemicals are responsible for the health-promoting properties afforded by a variety of natural functional foods.

The phytochemicals in our diet protect our health in a variety of ways. Some, such as carotenoids, are **antioxidants** (see Chapters 8 and 9). Others provide benefits because they mimic the structure or function of natural substances in the body. Phytoestrogens, such as those in soy for instance, have structures similar to the hormone estrogen and affect us by blocking or mimicking estrogen action. Phytosterols resemble cholesterol in structure and thus compete with cholesterol for absorption from the gastrointestinal tract. Their presence reduces cholesterol absorption and helps lower blood cholesterol—a major risk factor for cardiovascular disease. Some phytochemicals stimulate the body's natural defenses. For example, indoles and isothiocyanates found in broccoli stimulate the activity of enzymes that help deactivate **carcinogens**. Other phytochemicals are health-promoting due to their ability to alter the way in which cells communicate, to affect DNA repair mechanisms, or to influence other cell processes that may affect cancer development.[3] The phytochemicals described in this chapter are just a few of the ones that have been identified in our food. Many others have been studied and still more have yet to be isolated.

antioxidants Substances that are able to neutralize reactive oxygen molecules and thereby reduce oxidative damage.

carcinogen A substance that causes cancer.

Figure F3.1 Not all of the chemicals in plants benefit our health. The leaves of the rhubarb plant are poisonous. The stems have lower levels of the toxin and are safe to eat. (Image Source/Getty Images, Inc.)

Carotenoids

Carrots, sweet potatoes, acorn squash, apricots, and mangos get their yellow-orange color from the carotenoids they contain. These and other yellow-orange and red fruits and vegetables as well as leafy greens, in which the color of the carotenoids is masked by the green color of chlorophyl, are the major sources of dietary carotenoids. People who eat more of these have higher blood carotenoid levels. A high intake of carotenoid-containing fruits and vegetables has been associated with a reduced risk of certain cancers, cardiovascular disease, and age-related eye diseases.[4]

Carotenoids are phytochemicals that have antioxidant properties; some also have vitamin A activity[5] (see **Table F3.2**). The most prevalent carotenoids in the North American diet include β-carotene, α-carotene, β-cryptoxanthin, lycopene, lutein, and zeaxanthin. Beta-carotene is the best known and it provides the most vitamin A activity, but it may be a less effective antioxidant than others. Lycopene, the carotenoid that gives tomatoes their red color, does not provide vitamin A activity, but it is a more potent antioxidant than other dietary carotenoids[6] (**Figure F3.2**). The carotenoids lutein and zeaxanthin are antioxidants that accumulate in the macula, which is the central portion of the retina of the eye. High intakes of these are associated with reduced risk of **macular degeneration**, the leading cause of blindness in older adults.

macular degeneration
An incurable eye disorder that is caused by deterioration of the retina of the eye. It is the leading cause of blindness in adults over the age of 55 years.

Table F3.2 Phytochemicals in Foods

Phytochemical Name or Class	Food Sources	Biological Activities and Possible Effects
Carotenoids: α-carotene, β-carotene, β-cryptoxanthin, lutein, zeaxanthin, lycopene	Apricots, carrots, cantaloupe, tomatoes, peppers, sweet potatoes, squash, broccoli, spinach, and other leafy greens	Some are converted to vitamin A, provide antioxidant protection, some decrease the risk of macular degeneration.
Flavonoids: flavonols (quercetin, kaempferol, myricetin), flavones (apigenin), flavanols (catechins), anthrocyanidins (cyanidin, delphinidin)	Berries, citrus fruits, onions, margarine, purple grapes, green tea, red wine, and chocolate	Make capillary blood vessels stronger, block carcinogens and slow the growth of cancer cells.
Phytoestrogens including lignins and isoflavones such as genistein, biochanin A, and daidzein	Tofu, soy milk, soybeans, flax seed, and rye bread	Mimic effect of estrogen, induce cancer cell death, slow the growth of cancer cells, reduce blood cholesterol, may reduce risk of osteoporosis.
Phytosterols: β-sitosterol, stigmasterol, and campesterol	Nuts, seeds, and legumes	Decrease cholesterol absorption, reduce the risk of colon cancer by slowing growth of colon cells.
Capsaicin	Hot peppers	Modulates blood clotting.
Glucosinolates, isothiocyanates, indoles	Broccoli, brussels sprouts, and cabbage	Increase the activity of enzymes that deactivate carcinogens, alter estrogen metabolism, affect the regulation of gene expression.
Sulfides and allium compounds	Onions, garlic, leeks, and chives	Deactivate carcinogens, kill bacteria, protect against heart disease.
Inositol	Sesame seeds and soybeans	Protects against free radicals, protects against cancer.
Saponins	Beans and herbs	Decrease cholesterol absorption, decrease cancer risk, antioxidant.
Ellagic acid	Nuts, grapes, and strawberries	Anticancer properties, prevents the formation of carcinogens in the stomach.
Tannins, catechins	Tea and red wine	Antioxidants, cancer protection.
Curcumin	Turmeric and mustard	Reduces carcinogen formation, antioxidant, anti-inflammatory.
Sulforaphane	Broccoli and other cruciferous vegetables	Detoxifies carcinogens, shown to protect animals from breast cancer.
Limonene	Citrus fruit peels	Inhibits cancer cell growth.

Figure F3.2 The red color of tomatoes is due to the carotenoid lycopene, a potent antioxidant. Processing of tomatoes into tomato paste and sauce increases lycopene concentration and bioavailability. (© Datacraft/Age Fotostock America, Inc.)

Flavonoids

Like carotenoids, flavonoids are plant pigments that add color to your plate. They are found in fruits, vegetables, wine, grape juice, chocolate, and tea. One of the most abundant types of flavonoids is the anthocyanins, which give the blue and red colors to blueberries, raspberries, and red cabbage. Other types of flavonoids give the pale yellow color to potatoes, onions, and orange rinds. These compounds are strong antioxidants that protect against cancer and cardiovascular disease. Citrus fruits contain about 60 flavonoids that inhibit blood clotting and have antioxidant, anti-inflammatory, and anticancer properties[7] (see Off the Shelf: Chocolate: High-Fat Treat or Functional Food?).

Indoles, Isothiocyanates, and Alliums

Cruciferous vegetables such as broccoli, cauliflower, brussels sprouts, cabbage, and greens such as mustard and collards are particularly good sources of sulfur-containing phytochemicals (**Figure F3.3**). These stimulate the activity of enzymes that detoxify carcinogens. Sulforaphane, a phytochemical in broccoli, is particularly effective at boosting the activity of these enzyme systems and has been shown to protect animals from breast cancer.[8] Crucifers also contain phytochemicals called indoles. Indoles inactivate the hormone estrogen. Exposure to estrogen is believed to increase the risk of cancer; therefore, because indoles reduce estrogen exposure, they protect against cancer.

cruciferous A group of vegetables (also called crucifers) named for the cross shape of their four-petal flowers. They include broccoli, brussels sprouts, cabbage, cauliflower, kale, kohlrabi, mustard greens, rutabagas, and turnips. Their consumption is linked with lower rates of cancer.

Figure F3.3 Cruciferous vegetables are excellent sources of phytochemicals that may protect against cancer. (©iStockphoto)

(©iStockphoto)

Chocolate: High-Fat Treat or Functional Food?

Few foods provide as many mixed messages as chocolate. It is offered as a reward or treat and is consumed for comfort. It has been hailed as everything from an antidepressant to an aphrodisiac and been accused of causing acne, weight gain, and tooth decay. Yet we consume it with vigor. Is it simply the seductive flavor of chocolate that lures us into consuming this high-kcalorie, high-fat treat, or does it provide other benefits that contribute to our attraction to this confection?

One of the reasons we crave chocolate is because it makes us feel good. Chocolate contains several chemical compounds that may be responsible for the mood boost it induces. One study found that consuming chocolate causes the brain to produce natural opiates, which dull pain and increase feelings of well-being.[1] Other studies found that a compound in chocolate called anandamide can mimic the effects of tetrahydrocannabinol (THC)—the active chemical in marijuana—causing a chocolate "high." Chocolate also contains phenylethylamine, an amphetamine-like compound that raises blood pressure and blood sugar, increasing alertness and contentment. Chocolate also contains caffeine and related compounds that make us feel more alert.

In addition to making us feel good, chocolate provides small amounts of copper, magnesium, iron, and zinc. But what about all that fat and sugar? About 50% of the energy in chocolate is from fat and over half of this is from saturated fat, but in terms of heart health it may not be as bad as those numbers look. Much of the saturated fat is from stearic acid, which has been shown to have no effect on blood cholesterol levels (although it may increase cardiovascular disease risk in other ways). Some of the fat is from oleic acid, a monounsaturated fatty acid, which is beneficial to heart health. And, per gram, dark chocolate provides more antioxidants—which may protect against heart disease and other health problems—than red wine or blueberries.[2] Dark chocolate, which is rich in flavonoids, has been shown to improve arterial function, inhibit platelet activities that lead to heart disease, lower blood pressure, and improve insulin sensitivity.[3]

The sugar in chocolate can contribute to tooth decay, but the fat it contains may protect your teeth by coating them, preventing cavity-causing plaque. Chocolate provides about 150 kcalories per ounce, but it contributes only 2% of the energy in the American diet. It is therefore unlikely to be a significant reason for the increasing girth of American waistlines. Studies of chocolate's effect on acne have found no connection. Chocolate can cause headaches in individuals sensitive to tyrosine, but few people are affected.

So chocolate provides essential minerals and antioxidants, doesn't cause acne, and is no more likely to cause tooth decay than other carbohydrate-containing foods. Thus, although it cannot really be called a nutrient-dense food and should not be a mainstay of the diet, in moderation it has positive health effects and therefore can be considered a functional food.

(Mary Ellen Bartley/Foodpix/Jupiter Images Corp.)

[1]Kuwana, E. Discovering the sweet mysteries of chocolate. Available online at faculty.washington.edu/chudler/choco.html/. Accessed June 30, 2005.

[2]Halvorsen, B. L., Carlsen, M. H., Phillips, K. M. et al. Content of redox-active compounds (i.e., antioxidants) in foods consumed in the United States. Am. J. Clin. Nutr. 84(1):95–135, 2006.

[3]Corti, R., Flammer, A. J., Hollenberg, N. K., and Lüscher, T. F. Cocoa and cardiovascular health. Circulation 119:1433–41, 2009.

Figure F3.4 Garlic and onions provide sulfur-containing phytochemicals that may help protect against cancer and heart disease. (Ulrich Kerth/StockFood/Getty Images, Inc.)

Sulfur compounds called alliums are found in garlic, onions, leeks, chives, and shallots (**Figure F3.4**). These phytochemicals boost the activity of cancer-destroying enzyme systems, protect against oxidative damage, and defend against heart disease by lowering blood cholesterol, blood pressure, and platelet activity.[9] In addition, these compounds prevent bacteria in the gut from converting nitrates into nitrites, which can form carcinogens.

Phytoestrogens and Other Plant Hormones

Human hormones help regulate body processes and maintain homeostasis. Plants have hormones too. When ingested they can affect human health. Phytoestrogens are plant hormones that are believed to interrupt cancer development and affect health by interfering with the action of the human hormone estrogen. Phytoestrogens include isoflavones and lignins. These molecules are modified by the microflora in the intestines to form compounds that are structurally similar to estrogen. They are belived to block estrogen function by tying up estrogen receptors on cells. Isoflavones are found in soybeans, flaxseed, and barley; they may protect against some types of cancers as well as osteoporosis.[10,11] They are also thought to decrease hot flashes and other symptoms of menopause, although studies have shown this effect to be minimal[12] (see Chapter 6: Off the Shelf: Should You Increase Your Soy). Flaxseed is also rich in lignin. Lignin metabolites are structurally similar to estrogen and have been shown to inhibit the growth of estrogen-stimulated breast cancer cells.[13]

F3.2 Choosing a Phytochemical-Rich Diet

Learning Objectives

- List foods that are high in phytochemicals.
- Compare the health benefits of taking phytochemical supplements with those of a diet rich in unrefined plant foods.

It has not been possible to make quantitative recommendations for the intake of specific phytochemicals. Many of these substances have not been identified or classified. Many function differently depending on the form in which they are consumed. Their effects may vary if they are removed from the foods in which they are found. Therefore, to benefit the most from phytochemicals choose a diet based on plant foods. The impact of the total diet is more significant than that of any single phytochemical. For example, in some people a diet high in plant sterols, soy, almonds, and foods such as oats, barley, psyllium, okra, and eggplant that are high in soluble fibers has been shown to be as effective at lowering cholesterol as prescription medications.[14] Likewise, it has been hypothesized that a diet rich in flaxseed, cruciferous vegetables, and fruits and vegetables in general could significantly reduce the risk of breast, colon, prostate, lung, and other cancers.[15] Table F3.3 includes some suggestions for increasing the intake of foods that provide a variety of phytochemicals.

Table F3.3 Tips to Increase Phytochemicals

- Choose 5 different colors of fruits and vegetables each day.
- Try a new fruit or vegetable each week.
- Spice up your food—herbs and spices are a great source of phytochemicals.
- Add vegetables to your favorite entrees such as spaghetti sauces and casseroles.
- Try baked or dried fruit for dessert.
- Double your typical serving of vegetables.
- Add pesto, spinach, artichokes, or asparagus to pizza.
- Buy jars of chopped garlic, ginger, and basil to make it easy to add more of these to your cooking.
- Snack on whole-grain crackers.
- Add barley or bulgur to casseroles or stews.
- Switch to whole-wheat bread, brown rice, and whole-wheat pasta.
- Add fruit to your cereal or vegetables to your eggs.
- Dice up some tofu and add it to your stir fry.
- Include nuts in stir fries and baked goods.
- Sprinkle flaxseed in your oatmeal.

Eat More Fruits and Vegetables

The Dietary Guidelines and MyPyramid recommend a diet with plenty of fruits and vegetables; 2 cups of fruit and 2.5 cups of vegetables for a 2000-kcalorie diet. If these fruits and vegetables include a rainbow of colors—dark green-colored vegetables as well as yellow-orange, pale yellow, and deep red and purple fruits and vegetables—you are getting an abundance of carotenoids, flavonoids, and other phytochemicals (Figure F3.5).

Unfortunately most people do not follow these recommendations. Recent surveys of the typical American diet suggest that only 29% of those surveyed met their recommended intake for fruit and for vegetables.[16] In addition, white potatoes represented a disproportionately large share of the total vegetable intake (many of these consumed as french fries), while phytochemical- and nutrient-rich dark green and deep yellow vegetables accounted for a disproportionately small share.[17]

Figure F3.5 Choosing a rainbow of fruits and vegetables is a good way to include a variety of phytochemicals in your diet. (Top four photos: A. J. J. Estudi/Age Fotostock America, Inc.; bottom photo: Andy Washnik)

Make Half Your Grains Whole

Fruits and vegetables aren't the only source of dietary phytochemicals. In fact, whole grains deliver as many if not more phytochemicals and antioxidants than do fruits and vegetables.[18] Epidemiological studies have found that whole-grain intake is associated with a lower risk of cancer, cardiovascular disease, diabetes, and obesity. These health-promoting properties are believed to be due to the synergistic effects of the wide variety of nutrients and phytochemicals found in whole grains.[19] In addition to fiber, whole grains are rich in antioxidant phytochemicals called phenols as well as phytate, phytoestrogens such as lignan, and plant stanols and sterols. The bran and germ portions of whole-wheat flour contribute more than half of the total phenols, flavonoids, lutein, and zeaxanthin, as well as over 80% of the water-soluble and fat-soluble antioxidant activity.[20] These phytochemicals and vitamins are lost when the bran and germ are removed to make white flour. The Dietary Guidelines recommend Americans consume at least 3 servings, or half of their grain servings, as whole grains. The average intake in the United States today is less than 1 serving per day.[19]

Choose Plant Proteins

The amounts of health-promoting substances in the diet can further be enhanced by choosing plant sources of protein. Phytochemical-rich soybeans and flaxseed are good sources of protein and, other legumes, nuts, and seeds are high-protein foods that make important fiber and phytochemical contributions. The Dietary Guidelines and MyPyramid encourage the consumption of these high-phytochemical protein sources by recommending that Americans choose more beans, peas, nuts, and seeds.

What about Added Phytochemicals?

In addition to foods that are natural sources of phytochemicals, phytochemical supplements are available and many foods are fortified with phytochemicals. For example, special margarines such as Benecol® and Take Control® contain added plant sterols to help lower blood cholesterol, some brands of oatmeal are fortified with soy and flaxseed, and carrot juice is available with added lutein. These modified foods have also been called *nutraceuticals* because they blur the line between nutrients and pharmaceuticals, or *designer foods* because they are designed to provide specific health benefits (see Chapter 8: Off the Shelf: Are They Foods? Should You Choose Them?).

While phytochemical supplements and phytochemical-fortified foods may offer some specific advantages, they do not provide all the benefits obtained from a diet high in natural sources of these compounds. One reason is that most contain only a few of the many phytochemicals contained in foods. In addition, the benefits provided by many foods are believed to be due to the interactions among a variety of phytochemicals and nutrients and therefore cannot be replicated by a supplement that contains only one or a few of these substances. Finally, the amounts that can be added to supplements or foods may be too small to have an impact on overall health. For example, a multivitamin advertising that it provides lycopene may include about 0.3 mg per dose, whereas a half-cup serving of spaghetti sauce will give you about 20 mg.

References

1. American Dietetic Association. Position of the American Dietetic Association: Functional foods. *J. Am. Diet. Assoc.* 104:814–826, 2004.

2. Zhou, J. R., Yu, L., Mai, Z., and Blackburn, G. L. Combined inhibition of estrogen-dependent human breast carcinoma by soy and tea bioactive components in mice. *Intl. J. Cancer.* 108:8–14, 2004.

3. Zuzino, S. How Plants Protect Us. *Agriculture Research Magazine*, March 2008, pp 9–11. Available online at www.ars.usda.gov/News/docs.htm?docid=18510. Accessed August 29, 2009.

4. Krinsky N. I., Johnson E. J. Carotenoid actions and their relation to health and disease. *Mol. Aspects Med.* 6:459–516, 2005.

5. Rao, A. V., and Rao, L. G. Carotenoids and human health. *Pharmucol. Res.* 5:207–216, 2007.

6. Agarwal, S., Rao, A. V. Tomato lycopene and its role in human health and chronic diseases. *CMAJ.* 163:739–744, 2000.

7. Erdman, J. W., Balentine, D., and Arab, L. Flavonoids and heart health: Proceedings of the ILSI North America Flavonoids Workshop, May 31–June 1, 2005, Washington, DC. *J. Nutr.* 137:718S–737S, 2007.

8. Stan, S. D., Kar, S., Stoner, G. D., and Singh, S. V. Bioactive food components and cancer risk reduction. *J. Cell. Biochem.* 104:339–356, 2008.

9. Butt, M. S., Sultan, M. T., Butt, M. S., and Iqbal, J. Garlic: Nature's Protection against Physiological Threats. *Critical Reviews in Food Science and Nutrition.* 49:538–551, 2009.

10. Messina, M., Gardner, C., and Barnes, S. Gaining insight into the health effects of soy but a long way still to go: Commentary on the Fourth International Symposium on the Role of Soy in Preventing and Treating Chronic Disease. *J. Nutr.* 132:547S–551S, 2002.

11. Messina, M., and Messina, V. Soyfoods, soybean isoflavones, and bone health: A brief overview. *J. Ren. Nutr.* 1:63–68, 2000.

12. Vincent, A., and Fitzpatrick, L. A. Soy isoflavones: Are they useful in menopause? *Mayo Clin. Proc.* 75:1174–1184, 2000.

13. Rice, S., and Whitehead, S. A. Phytoestrogens oestrogen synthesis and breast cancer. *J. Steroid Biochem. Mol. Biol.* 108:186–195, 2008.

14. Jenkins, D. J., Kendall, C. W., Marchie, A. et al. Direct comparison of a dietary portfolio of cholesterol-lowering foods with a statin in hypercholesterolemic participants. *Am. J. Clin. Nutr.* 81:380–387, 2005.

15. Donaldson, M. S. Nutrition and cancer: A review of the evidence for an anti-cancer diet. *Nutr. J.* 3:19–30, 2004.

16. Casagrande, S. S., Wang, Y., Anderson, C., and Gary, T. L. Have Americans increased their fruit and vegetable intake? The trends between 1988 and 2002. *Am. J. Prev. Med.* 32: 1–7, 2007.

17. Krebs-Smith, A. M., and Kantor, L. S. Choose a variety of fruits and vegetables daily: Understanding the complexities. *J. Nutr.* 131:487S–501S, 2001.

18. Jones, J. M., Reicks, M., Adams, J. et al. Becoming proactive with the whole-grains message. *Nutr. Today* 39:10–17, 2004.

19. Slavin, J. Why whole grains are protective: Biological mechanisms. *Proc. Nutr. Soc.* 62:129–134, 2003.

20. Adom, K. K., Sorrells, M. E., and Liu, R. H. Phytochemicals and antioxidant activity of milled fractions of different wheat varieties. *J. Agric. Food Chem.* 53:2297–2306, 2005.

10

Water and the Electrolytes

Case Study

When Gabriele Andersen-Scheiss emerged from the tunnel into the Olympic stadium in 1984 for the final lap of the women's marathon, she didn't look much like a world-class athlete. The 37-year-old runner staggered around the track as if drunk, her left arm limp, her right leg stiff. She had completed about 26 of the 26.2 miles of the marathon, but it wasn't clear whether she now could negotiate a single lap around the track. What was wrong? Should someone stop her?

Medical officers rushed over to help, but she waved them off. After observing her as she proceeded around the track, doctors decided to allow her to continue unaided.

(David Tenenbaum/©AP/Wide World Photos)

Andersen-Scheiss was demonstrating the signs of serious dehydration. Because the medics could see that she was sweating profusely, though, they concluded that she was not yet suffering from heat stroke, the most severe and life-threatening form of heat-related illness. The gold medalist in this race, Joan Benoit, had crossed the finish line 20 minutes earlier, so Andersen-Scheiss was struggling simply to finish, not to win. One minute the crowd cheered her on, and the next they pleaded for the medics to stop her. Her final staggering lap around the track to the finish line lasted 5 minutes and 44 seconds. Medics immediately treated her for dehydration and heat exhaustion.

This case illustrates the importance of water in maintaining body systems. Water and the minerals dissolved in it make up the soup in which the reactions that maintain life occur. Water and mineral imbalances can come on rapidly and be devastating, but they can also be alleviated faster than other nutrient deficiencies.

(©iStockphoto)

Onodera/Dex Image/Getty Images, Inc.)

10.1 Water: The Internal Sea

Learning Objectives

- Discuss the forces that move water back and forth across cell membranes.
- Describe five functions of water in the body.
- List the sources of body water and describe the routes by which water is lost.
- Discuss the effects of dehydration.

The complex molecules necessary for the emergence of life were forged in the Earth's first seas. These primordial seas supported life because they were rich in inorganic minerals as well as organic substances. As organisms grew in complexity, the water and chemicals critical to their survival were incorporated into an internal sea. Just as the right amounts of water, organic molecules, and minerals were necessary for the beginning of life, the right combination is necessary in the body for the maintenance of life. This internal sea allows the reactions necessary for life to proceed.

Functions of Water in the Body

Water is an essential nutrient that we must consume in our diet to survive. Without water death occurs in only a few days. In the body, water serves as a medium in which chemical reactions take place; it also transports nutrients and wastes, provides protection, helps regulate temperature, participates in chemical reactions, and helps maintain acid-base balance (**Table 10.1**).

Table 10.1 A Summary of Water and the Electrolytes

Nutrient	Sources	Recommended Intake for for Adults[a]	Major Functions	Deficiency Diseases and Symptoms	Groups at Risk of Deficiency	Toxicity	UL[a]
Water	Drinking water, other beverages, and food	2.7–3.7 liters/d	Solvent, reactant, protector, transporter, regulator of temperature and pH	Thirst, weakness, poor endurance, confusion, disorientation	Infants, those with fever and diarrhea, elderly, athletes	Confusion, coma, convulsions	ND
Sodium	Table salt, processed foods	<2300 mg/d ideally 1500 mg/d	Major positive extracellular ion, nerve transmission, muscle contraction, fluid balance	Muscle cramps	Those consuming a severely sodium-restricted diet, excessive sweating	Contributes to high blood pressure	2300 mg/d
Potassium	Fresh fruits and vegetables, legumes, whole grains, milk, and meat	4700 mg/d or greater	Major positive intracellular ion, nerve transmission, muscle contraction, fluid balance	Irregular heartbeat, fatigue, muscle cramps	Those consuming poor diets high in processed foods, those taking thiazide diuretics	Abnormal heartbeat	ND
Chloride	Table salt, processed foods	<3600 mg/d, ideally 2300 mg/d	Major negative extracellular ion, fluid balance	Unlikely	None	None likely	3600 mg/d

[a]Recommended intakes for water, sodium, potassium, and chloride are Adequate Intakes (AIs); UL, Tolerable Upper Intake Level; ND, insufficient data to determine a UL.

Solvent One of the key functions of water in the body is as a **solvent**. A solvent is a fluid in which **solutes** can dissolve to form a solution. Water is an ideal solvent for some substances because it is **polar**; that is, the two sides or poles of the water molecule have opposite electrical charges. The polar nature of water comes from its structure, which consists of two hydrogen atoms and one oxygen atom. These atoms, like all atoms, are made up of a positively charged central core, or nucleus, with negatively charged **electrons** orbiting around it. To form a water molecule, the two hydrogen atoms move close enough to share their electrons with an atom of oxygen. But the sharing is not equal. The shared electrons spend more time around the oxygen atom than around the hydrogen atoms, giving the oxygen side of the molecule a slightly negative charge and the hydrogen side a slightly positive charge. This polar nature of water allows it to surround other charged molecules and disperse them. Table salt, which dissolves in water, consists of a positively charged sodium **ion** bound to a negatively charged chloride ion. When placed in water, the sodium and chloride ions move apart, or **dissociate**, because the positively charged sodium ion is attracted to the negative pole of the water molecule and the negatively charged chloride ion is attracted to the positive pole (**Figure 10.1**).

Transport Blood, which is 90% water, transports oxygen and nutrients to cells. It then carries carbon dioxide and other waste products away from the cells. Blood also distributes hormones and other regulatory molecules throughout the body so they can reach target cells. Water in urine helps to carry waste products, such as urea and ketones, out of the body.

Lubrication and Protection Water functions as a lubricant and cleanser. Watery tears lubricate the eyes and wash away dirt, synovial fluid lubricates the joints, and saliva lubricates the mouth, making it easier to chew, taste, and swallow food. Water inside the eyeballs and spinal cord acts as a cushion against shock. Similarly, during pregnancy, water in the amniotic fluid provides a protective cushion around the fetus.

Regulation of Body Temperature Body temperature is closely regulated to maintain a normal level of around 98.6°F (37°C). If the body temperature rises above 108°F or falls below 80°F, death is likely. The fact that water holds heat and changes temperature slowly helps keep body temperature constant when the outside temperature fluctuates, but water is also more actively involved in temperature regulation.

The water in blood helps regulate body temperature by increasing or decreasing the amount of heat lost from the surface of the body. When body temperature starts to rise, the blood vessels in the skin dilate, causing blood to flow close to the surface

solvent A fluid in which one or more substances dissolve.

solutes Dissolved substances.

polar Used to describe a molecule that has a positive charge at one end and a negative charge at the other.

electrons Negatively charged particles.

ion An atom or group of atoms that carries an electrical charge.

dissociate To separate two charged ions.

Figure 10.1 The polar nature of water
Electrons in a water molecule, shown as dots, spend more time around the oxygen atom, giving the oxygen side of the molecule a slightly negative charge, and the hydrogen side a slightly positive charge. When sodium chloride is added to water, the positive sodium ion is attracted to the negative pole of the water molecule, and the negative chloride ion is attracted to the positive pole.

Figure 10.2 Exercising in the heat can dramatically increase water losses from sweat. (Lori Adamski Peek/Getty Images, Inc.)

hydrolysis reaction Chemical reaction that breaks large molecules into smaller ones by adding water.

condensation reaction Chemical reaction that joins two molecules together. Hydrogen and oxygen are lost from the two molecules to form water.

pH A measure of the level of acidity or alkalinity of a solution.

Life Cycle

of the body where it can release some of the heat to the environment. This occurs with fevers as well as when environmental temperature rises. In a cold environment, blood vessels in the skin constrict, restricting the flow of blood near the surface and conserving body heat.

Water also helps regulate body temperature through the evaporation of sweat. When body temperature increases, the brain triggers the sweat glands in the skin to produce sweat, which is mostly water. As the sweat evaporates from the skin, heat is lost, cooling the body (**Figure 10.2**).

Chemical Reactions Water is involved in chemical reactions in the body. A **hydrolysis reaction** breaks large molecules into smaller ones by adding water. For example, water is added in the reaction that breaks a molecule of maltose into two glucose molecules (**Figure 10.3**). Water is also involved in reactions that join two molecules. This type of reaction is referred to as a **condensation reaction**. The formation of the disaccharide maltose from two glucose molecules is a condensation reaction and therefore requires the removal of a water molecule.

Acid-Base Balance The chemical reactions that occur in the body are very sensitive to acidity. Acidity is expressed in units of **pH**. The range of pH units is from 1 to 14, with 1 being very acidic, 14 being very basic or alkaline, and 7 being neutral (**Figure 10.4**). Most reactions in the body occur in slightly basic solutions, around pH 7.4. If body solutions become too acidic or too basic, chemical reactions cannot proceed efficiently. Water and the dissolved substances it contains are important for maintaining the proper level of acidity. Water serves as a medium for the chemical reactions that prevent changes in pH and it participates in some of these reactions. Water is also needed as a transport medium to allow the respiratory tract and kidneys to regulate acid-base balance.

Distribution of Body Water

Water is found in varying proportions in all the tissues of the body; blood is about 90% water, muscle about 75%, and bone about 25%. Adipocytes have a low water content—only about 10%. In adults, about 60% of total body weight is water but this varies with age and other factors that affect body composition. The percentage of

Hydrolysis reaction

Figure 10.3 Hydrolysis and condensation reactions The cleavage of the disaccharide maltose into two molecules of glucose is a hydrolysis reaction; disaccharide formation is a condensation reaction.

Condensation reaction

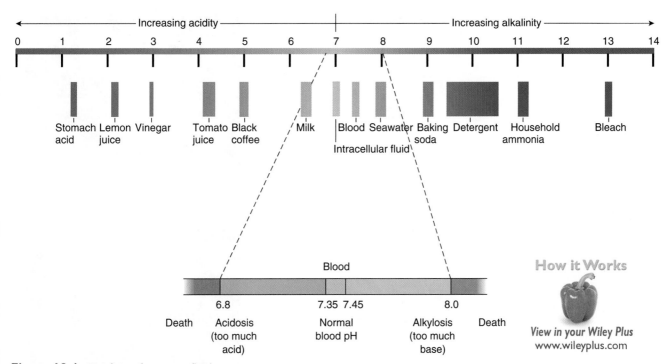

Figure 10.4 pH values of common fluids
Fluctuations from the normal blood pH range of 7.35 to 7.45 leads to acidosis (too much acid) or alkalosis (too much base) and, if severe, can be fatal.

water is higher in infants than in adults and decreases as adults age, primarily due to increases in body fat and a loss of muscle mass. Because women typically have a higher percentage of body fat than men, they have less body water. Obese individuals have a lower percentage of body weight as water and a higher percentage as fat than their lean counterparts.

About two-thirds of body water is found inside cells; this is known as **intracellular fluid**. The remaining one-third is outside cells, as **extracellular fluid** (**Figure 10.5a**). Extracellular fluid includes primarily blood plasma, lymph, and the fluid between cells, called **interstitial fluid**. Other extracellular fluids include fluid secreted by glands such as saliva and other digestive secretions, and fluid in the eyes, joints, and spinal cord. The concentration of substances dissolved in body water varies among these body compartments. The concentration of protein is highest in

intracellular fluid The fluid located inside cells.

extracellular fluid The fluid located outside cells. It includes fluid found in the blood, lymph, gastrointestinal tract, spinal column, eyes, joints, and that found between cells and tissues.

interstitial fluid The portion of the extracellular fluid located in the spaces between the cells of body tissues.

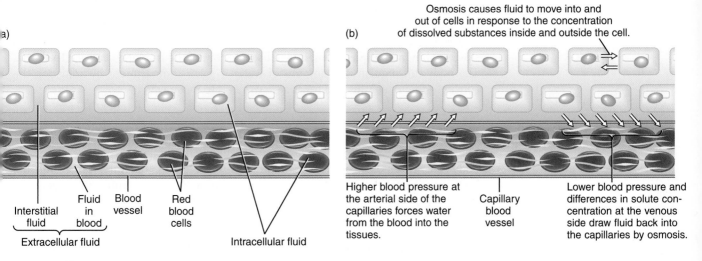

Figure 10.5 Forces that distribution body water
(a) Body water is distributed between intracellular and extracellular spaces.
(b) The amount of water in blood and tissues is determined by blood pressure and the force generated by osmosis.

Figure 10.6 Osmosis
When sugar is sprinkled on strawberries, osmosis draws water out of the strawberries to dilute the concentrated sugar solution on the surface. (Dennis Drenner)

intracellular fluid, lower in extracellular fluid, and even lower in interstitial fluid. Extracellular fluid has a higher concentration of sodium and chloride and a lower concentration of potassium, and intracellular fluid is higher in potassium and lower in sodium and chloride.

The movement of water from one compartment to another is affected by fluid pressure and osmosis, which depends on the concentration of solutes in each compartment (**Figure 10.5b**). The fluid pressure of blood against the blood vessel walls, or **blood pressure**, causes water to move from the blood into the interstitial space. The difference in the concentration of solutes between the blood in the capillaries and the fluid in the interstitial space causes much of this water to re-enter the capillaries by osmosis (see Chapter 3). Osmosis occurs when there is a selectively permeable membrane, such as a cell membrane, which allows water to pass freely but regulates the passage of other substances. Water moves across this membrane in a direction that will equalize the concentration of solutes on both sides. For example, when sugar is sprinkled on fresh strawberries, the water inside the strawberries moves across the skin of the fruit to try to equalize the sugar concentration on each side. As shown in **Figure 10.6**, this pulls water out of the fruit and causes it to shrink. The body can regulate the amount of water in each compartment by adjusting the concentration of solutes and relying on osmosis to move water.

blood pressure The amount of force exerted by the blood against the artery walls.

Water Balance

The amount of water in the body remains relatively constant over time. Since the body does not store water, to maintain this homeostasis the water taken into the body must equal the amount of water lost in urine, feces, and through evaporation (**Figure 10.7**). When water losses are increased, as they are in hot weather and with exercise, intake must increase to keep body water at a healthy level.

Water Intake Most of the water in the body comes from the diet—not only as water we drink but from the water in other liquids and in solid food (**Figure 10.8**). About 75% to 80% of total water intake comes from fluids, with food providing the remain-

Figure 10.7 Water balance
To maintain water balance, intake must equal output. This figure approximates the amounts of water from different sources that make up water intake and the amounts of lost water in an adult who is not sweating.

ing 20% to 25%.[1] Milk is 90% water, apples are about 85% water, and roast beef is about 50% water. A small amount of water is also generated inside the body by metabolism, but this is not significant in meeting body water needs (see Your Choice: Is Bottled Water Better?).

Water consumed in the diet is absorbed from the gastrointestinal tract by osmosis. This is possible because of the concentration gradient created by the absorption of nutrients from the lumen into the blood. As nutrients are absorbed, the solute concentration in the lumen decreases. Water therefore moves with the absorbed nutrients toward the area with the highest solute concentration. The rate of water absorption is affected by the volume of water and the concentration of nutrients consumed with it. Consuming a large volume of water increases the rate of water absorption; increasing the nutrients and other solutes it contains decreases the rate of absorption.

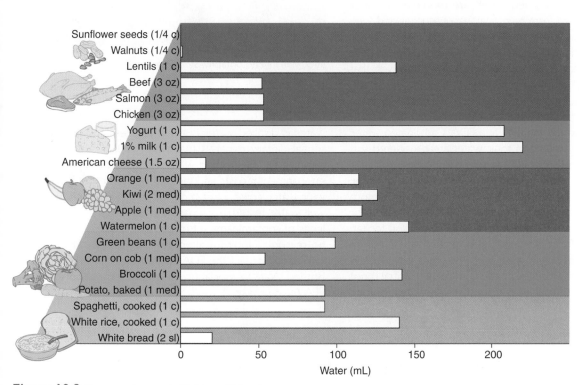

Figure 10.8 Sources of water in MyPyramid food groups
Fruits and vegetables, as well as many choices from other food groups, have a high water content.

Is Bottled Water Better?

Bottled water is an $8 billion industry in the United States.[1] Why are we paying for that glass of water? Is bottled really better?

Many Americans buy bottled water because they believe it is safer and purer than tap water. In reality, though, the standards for bottled water purity are comparable to the minimum standards for municipal water systems (tap water) set by the Environmental Protection Agency (EPA). Bottled water can be any water as long as it has no added ingredients except safe and suitable antimicrobial agents. Thus, it is not surprising that about 25% of the bottled water sold in the United States is tap water.[1]

The FDA has established standard definitions for bottled water products. Bottled water that comes from a tap must be clearly labeled as such. However, water that has been taken from a municipal water supply and then treated—for example, filtered and disinfected—need not indicate that it is tap water. "Distilled water" and "purified water" are examples of water that have been taken from municipal water supplies and then treated. If you want water that did not come from a tap, select artesian water, spring water, well water, or mineral water. These come from underground sources. Be aware, however, that words like "pure," "pristine," and "glacial" have no set definitions or meanings. No matter what it is called, bottled water, including flavored bottled water, must comply with the bottled water standards set by the EPA and FDA. Carbonated water, seltzer water, soda water, and tonic water are considered soft drinks and regulated under FDA food regulations.

So, Is bottled really better? When choosing your water, weigh the benefits against the risks. Bottled water is more expensive than tap water; as much as $10.00 per gallon for some bottled water versus less than $0.01 per gallon for tap water. The use of bottled water also generates 1.5 million tons of plastic waster per year, and consumes oil, which is used to produce the bottles. In addition, bottled water is not necessarily purer or safer than tap water.[2] The safest bottled

(Rick Mariani Photography/StockFood America)

water is distilled water, but it is tasteless and lacking in essential dietary minerals that water usually supplies. Before deciding to buy bottled water, consider the economic and environmental costs and look at the water-monitoring tests your water company is required to perform (or have your well water tested). Compare the test results with the legal limits of contaminants set by the EPA. You may find you have no reason to look for alternatives to the tap. For more information, contact the FDA (www.fda.gov), the International Bottled Water Association (www.bottledwater.org), or the EPA (www.epa.gov).

---

[1]Christiansen Bullers, A. Bottled Water: Better Than the Tap? *FDA Consumer* July–August 2002. Available online at www.fda.gov/FDAC/features/2002/402_h2o.html. Accessed August 24, 2008.

[2]National Resources Defense Council, Clean Water & Oceans: Drinking Water: In Depth: Report: Bottled Water—Pure Drink or Pure Hype? Executive Summary. Available online at www.nrdc.org/water/drinking/bw/exesum.asp/. Accessed May 25, 2009.

Water Losses Water is lost from the body in urine, in feces, through evaporation from the lungs and skin, and in sweat. A typical adult who is not sweating loses about 2.75 liters of water daily (see Figure 10.7).

Urinary Losses Typical urine output is 1 to 2 liters per day, but this varies depending on the amount of fluid consumed and the amount of waste to be excreted. The waste products that must be excreted in urine include urea and other nitrogen-containing products from protein breakdown, ketones from fat breakdown, phosphates, sulfates, and other minerals. The amount of urea that must be excreted is increased when dietary or body protein breakdown is increased. Ketone excretion is increased when body fat is broken down. In both cases, the need for water increases in order to produce more urine to excrete the extra wastes.

Fecal Losses The amount of water lost in the feces is usually small, only about 200 mL per day (less than a cup). This is remarkable because every day about 9 liters of fluid enter the gastrointestinal tract via food, water, and secretions. Under normal conditions, more than 95% is reabsorbed before the feces are eliminated. However, in cases of severe diarrhea, large amounts of water can be lost through the gastrointestinal tract.

Insensible Losses Water loss due to evaporation from the skin and lungs occurs without the individual being aware that it is occurring; such losses are therefore referred to as **insensible losses**. An inactive person at room temperature loses about 1 liter per day through insensible losses but the amount varies depending on body size, environmental temperature and humidity, and physical activity. For example, a very dry environment, such as in an airplane or in the desert, increases evaporative losses.

insensible losses Fluid losses that are not perceived by the senses, such as evaporation of water through the skin and lungs.

Sweat Losses Water lost in sweat is distinct from insensible losses because it is a detectable loss. The amount of water lost through sweat is extremely variable depending on the individual, his or her activity level, and the environmental conditions. An individual doing light work at a temperature of about 84°F will lose about 2 to 3 liters of sweat per day. Strenuous exercise in a hot environment can cause water losses in sweat to be as high as 2 to 4 liters in an hour.[2] Adequate water intake is essential to compensate for these losses. Athletes can estimate water loss by weighing themselves before and after exercise. Lost water can then be replaced by consuming at least the equivalent weight in fluids. For instance, an athlete who loses 2 lbs during a workout should consume an extra 2 to 4 pints or 1 to 2 liters of fluid (1 lb = 1 pint = 1/2 liter)(see Chapter 13).

Regulation of Water Intake The desire to drink, or thirst, is triggered by a decrease in the amount of water in the blood, which is sensed by the thirst center in the hypothalamus of the brain. A decrease in saliva secretion, which causes a dry mouth also stimulates thirst (**Figure 10.9**).

Over the course of days and weeks, fluid intake, driven by thirst and that typically consumed as beverages during meals, is adequate to maintain water homeostasis. However, this is not always the case in the short term. People don't or can't always drink when they are thirsty and thirst is quenched almost as soon as fluid is consumed and long before short-term water balance is restored. Also, the sensation of thirst often lags behind the need for water. For example, athletes exercising in hot weather lose water rapidly but do not experience intense thirst until they have lost so much body water that their physical performance is compromised.[3,4] A person with fever, vomiting, or diarrhea may also be losing water rapidly and thirst mechanisms may not be adequate to replace the fluid. Thirst is a powerful urge, but to maintain adequate levels of water in the body it is also necessary to regulate water excretion.

Regulation of Water Losses The amount of water lost by the body is regulated by increasing or decreasing the amount of water excreted in the urine. The kidneys serve as a filtering system that regulates the amount of water and dissolved substances

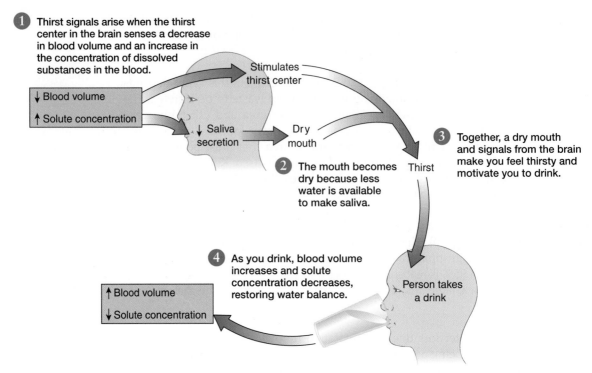

1. Thirst signals arise when the thirst center in the brain senses a decrease in blood volume and an increase in the concentration of dissolved substances in the blood.

↓ Blood volume

↑ Solute concentration

Stimulates thirst center

↓ Saliva secretion

Dry mouth

2. The mouth becomes dry because less water is available to make saliva.

Thirst

3. Together, a dry mouth and signals from the brain make you feel thirsty and motivate you to drink.

4. As you drink, blood volume increases and solute concentration decreases, restoring water balance.

↑ Blood volume

↓ Solute concentration

Person takes a drink

Figure 10.9 Regulation of water intake
The sensation of thirst helps motivate fluid intake in order to restore water balance.

antidiuretic hormone (ADH) A hormone secreted by the pituitary gland that increases the amount of water reabsorbed by the kidney and therefore retained in the body.

retained in the blood and excreted in urine. As blood flows through the kidneys, water and small molecules are filtered out of the blood vessels (see Chapter 3). Some of the water and molecules are reabsorbed into the blood and the rest are excreted in the urine. The amount of water that is reabsorbed depends on conditions in the body. When the concentration of solutes in the blood is high, **antidiuretic hormone (ADH)**, which is secreted from the pituitary gland, signals the kidneys to reabsorb water to reduce the amount lost in the urine. This reabsorbed water is returned to the blood, preventing the solute concentration in the blood from increasing further (**Figure 10.10**). When the solute concentration in the blood is low, ADH levels decrease so less water is reabsorbed and more is excreted in the urine, allowing blood solute concentration to increase to normal. The amount of sodium in the blood, blood volume, and blood pressure also play a role in regulating body water.

Recommended Water Intake

We need more water each day than any other nutrient. The DRIs recommend 3.7 liters (3700 grams) per day for men and 2.7 liters (2700 grams) per day for women.[1] The actual amount needed may vary depending on activity, heat and humidity, and diet. Activity increases water needs because it increases the amount of water lost in sweat; the amount is greater in hot and humid environments. The composition and adequacy of the diet also affect water needs. A low-kcalorie diet increases water needs because, as body fat and protein are broken down to fuel the body, ketones and urea are produced and extra water is needed for them to be excreted in the urine. A high-protein diet increases the amount of urea and other nitrogenous waste that must be excreted. A high-sodium diet increases water losses because the excess salt must be excreted in the urine. A high-fiber diet increases water needs because more water is held in the intestines and lost in the feces. Despite variations in our fluid needs, most people consume adequate fluids on a day-to-day basis to maintain body water at a normal level.[1]

Most beverages, whether water, milk, juice, or soda, help meet the overall need for water. Beverages containing caffeine, such as coffee, tea, and cola, increase water losses for a short period because caffeine is a diuretic. Over the course of a day, however, the increase in water loss is small, so the net amount of water that caffeinated beverages add

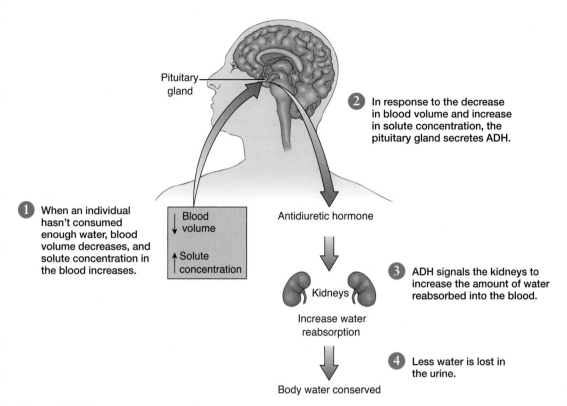

① When an individual hasn't consumed enough water, blood volume decreases, and solute concentration in the blood increases.

↓ Blood volume

↑ Solute concentration

② In response to the decrease in blood volume and increase in solute concentration, the pituitary gland secretes ADH.

Pituitary gland

Antidiuretic hormone

Kidneys

Increase water reabsorption

③ ADH signals the kidneys to increase the amount of water reabsorbed into the blood.

Body water conserved

④ Less water is lost in the urine.

Figure 10.10 Regulation of water loss
The kidneys help regulate water balance by adjusting the amount of water lost in the urine in response to the release of antidiuretic hormone (ADH).

to the body is similar to the amount contributed by noncaffeinated beverages. Alcohol is also a diuretic; the overall effect it has on water balance depends on the relative amounts of water and alcohol in the beverages being consumed.[1]

Water needs increase during pregnancy and lactation. During pregnancy, water is needed to increase blood volume, produce amniotic fluid, and nourish the fetus. The AI for pregnancy of 3 liters per day is based on the median total water intake during pregnancy. During lactation, the fluid secreted in milk, about 750 mL or 3 cups per day, must be replaced by the mother's fluid intake. Based on the median fluid intake during lactation, the AI is set at 3.8 liters per day.[1]

The fluid requirements per unit of body weight are higher for infants than for adults. One reason is that the infant's kidneys cannot concentrate urine as efficiently as adult kidneys, so water loss is greater. Moreover, insensible losses are proportionally greater in infants and children because body surface area relative to body weight is much greater than in adults. In addition to having greater water needs, infants are susceptible to **dehydration** because they cannot ask for a drink when they are thirsty. The AI for infants 0 to 6 months of age is 0.7 liters per day and is based on the amount of water consumed in human milk.[1]

Life Cycle

dehydration A condition that results when not enough water is present to meet the body's needs.

Water Deficiency: Dehydration

Even minor changes in the amount and distribution of body water can be life-threatening. Without food, an average individual can live for about 8 weeks, but a lack of water reduces survival to only a few days. A deficiency of water causes symptoms more rapidly than any other nutrient deficiency. Likewise, health can be restored in a matter of minutes or hours when fluid is replaced.

Dehydration occurs when the drop in body water is great enough for blood volume to decrease, thereby reducing the ability to deliver oxygen and nutrients to cells and remove waste products. Even mild dehydration—a body water loss of 1% to 2% of body weight—can impair physical and cognitive performance.[1] Early symptoms of dehydration include headache, fatigue, loss of appetite, dry eyes and mouth, and

Well hydrated

Mild dehydration

Severe dehydration

Figure 10.11 Urine color and hydration status
The darker an individual's urine color, the greater the level of dehydration. Pale yellow urine indicates good hydration.

water intoxication A condition that occurs when a person drinks enough water to significantly lower the concentration of sodium in the blood.

hyponatremia Low blood sodium concentration.

electrolytes Positively and negatively charged ions that conduct an electrical current in solution. Commonly refers to sodium, potassium, and chloride.

dark-colored urine (**Figure 10.11**). A loss of 5% body weight as water can cause nausea and difficulty concentrating. Confusion and disorientation can occur when water loss approaches 7% of body weight. A loss of about 10% to 20% can result in death.

Young athletes involved in sports with weight classes, such as wrestling and boxing, sometimes use dehydration to reduce their body weight so they can compete in a lower weight class. Being at the high end of the lower weight class is thought to provide an advantage over smaller opponents in that class.[5] However, when this is accomplished through even mild dehydration, exercise performance can be impaired (see Chapter 13).

Water Intoxication: Overhydration

An excess of water can affect the distribution of water among body compartments and can be just as dangerous as dehydration. However, it is difficult to consume too much water under normal circumstances; overhydration or **water intoxication**, may occur with illness or in certain situations during exercise. When there is too much water relative to the amount of sodium in the body, the concentration of sodium in the blood drops, a condition called **hyponatremia**. When this occurs, water moves out of the blood vessels into the tissues by osmosis, causing them to swell. Swelling in the brain can cause disorientation, convulsions, coma, and death.

The early symptoms of water intoxication may be similar to dehydration: nausea, muscle cramps, disorientation, slurred speech, and confusion. It is important to determine if the problem is dehydration or water intoxication because if you assume the symptoms are from dehydration and drink plain water the symptoms will worsen and can result in seizure, coma, or death. To help avoid water intoxication when exercising for more than an hour beverages, such as sports drinks, containing dilute solutions of sodium as well as sugar should be used to replace water losses (see Chapter 13).

10.2 Electrolytes: Salts of the Internal Sea

Learning Objectives

- Define the term "electrolyte" and explain the functions of electrolytes in the body.
- Contrast the dietary sources of sodium and potassium.
- Explain how blood pressure is regulated.

The water in the body—the internal sea—contains a variety of mineral salts. The right amounts and combinations of these are necessary for the maintenance of life. The distribution of these minerals affects the distribution of water in different body compartments. The properties of these minerals, including electrical charge, affect nerve and muscle functions in the body. Mineral salts dissociate in water to form ions. Positively and negatively charged ions are called **electrolytes**. Although there are many electrolytes in the body, in nutrition, the term is typically used to refer to the three principal electrolytes in body fluids: sodium, potassium, and chloride.

Sodium, Potassium, and Chloride in the Modern Diet

The modern diet is high in salt (sodium chloride) and low in potassium. The reason is that we eat a lot of processed foods, which are high in sodium and generally low in potassium, and too few fresh unprocessed foods such as fruits, vegetables, whole grains, and fresh meats, which are low in sodium and high in potassium (**Figure 10.12**).

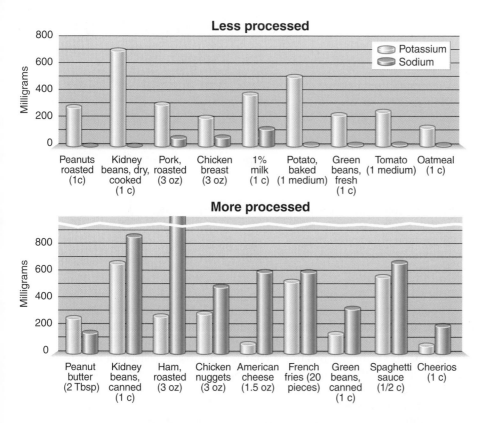

Figure 10.12 Effect of food processing on sodium and potassium

Less processed foods tend to be low in sodium and good sources of potassium, whereas more processed foods are generally higher in sodium and may also be lower in potassium.

About 77% of the salt Americans eat is from that added to food during processing and manufacturing. Only about 12% comes from salt found naturally in food, while 11% is from salt added in cooking and at the table.[6] Salt is 40% sodium and 60% chloride by weight, so 9 grams of salt contains 3.6 grams of sodium (9 g × 40% = 3.6 g) and 5.4 grams of chloride. Some of the sodium in processed foods is from salt added for flavoring; potato chips, lunchmeats, and canned soups are all high in sodium chloride. Some of the sodium is added as a preservative because it inhibits bacterial growth. In addition to sodium chloride other sodium salts, such as sodium bicarbonate, sodium citrate, and sodium glutamate are also used as preservatives. Less than 1% of the salt we consume is from tap water.[1] Softened water or mineral water is often higher in sodium than tap water and, if consumed in large quantities, can contribute significantly to daily sodium intake.

The human diet has not always been high in salt. Prehistoric diets consisted of plant foods such as nuts, berries, roots, and greens. These foods are high in potassium and low in salt. Fresh animal foods, such as meat and milk, are also low in sodium and high in potassium. Because of its value as a food preservative and flavor enhancer salt was highly prized by ancient cultures in Asia, Africa, and Europe, where it was used in rituals as well as in the preservation of food. Roman soldiers were paid in *sal*, the Latin word for salt from which we get our word salary. Today, rather than a prized commodity, salt is a substance we attempt to limit in the diet. The reason for restricting salt is that diets high in salt have been implicated as a risk factor for **hypertension**.

Sodium, Potassium, and Chloride in the Body

Almost all of the sodium, chloride, and potassium consumed in the diet is absorbed. Despite large variations in dietary intake, homeostatic mechanisms act to control the concentrations of these electrolytes in the body where they help regulate fluid balance and are important for nerve conduction and muscle contraction.

Regulation of Fluid Balance The distribution of fluid among body compartments depends on the concentration of electrolytes and other solutes. Water moves by osmosis in response to solute concentration. All body fluids are in osmotic balance. So,

hypertension Blood pressure that is consistently elevated to 140/90 mm Hg or greater.

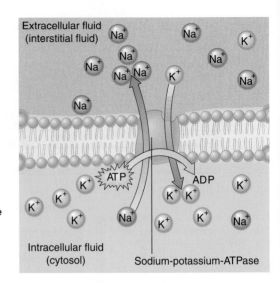

Figure 10.13 Sodium-potassium-ATPase
Each cycle of sodium-potassium-ATPase uses the energy in ATP to pump two potassium ions into the cell and expel three sodium ions.

for example, a change in the concentration of solutes in the blood causes a shift in water that affects blood volume as well as interstitial and intracellular fluid volumes. The concentration of specific electrolytes in body compartments differs dramatically. Potassium is the principal positively charged ion inside cells, where it is 30 times more concentrated than outside the cell. Sodium is the most abundant positively charged electrolyte in the extracellular fluid and chloride is the principal negatively charged extracellular ion.

The different intracelluar and extracellular concentrations of these electrolytes is maintained by cell membranes and an active transport system called the *sodium-potassium-ATPase*. Cell membranes keep the majority of sodium outside the cell and potassium inside, but some does leak across the membrane. The sodium-potassium-ATPase maintains the concentration gradient by pumping sodium out of the cell and pumping potassium into the cell (**Figure 10.13**). Maintaining this concentration gradient of electrolytes is important for nerve conduction and muscle contraction, but requires a great deal of energy: It is estimated that the sodium-potassium-ATPase pump accounts for 20% to 40% of resting energy expenditure in an adult. The pumping of sodium ions across cell membranes is also linked to nutrient transport. For example, glucose and amino acids are transported by systems that depend on the movement of sodium ions across cell membranes.

Nerve Conduction and Muscle Contraction The concentration gradient of sodium and potassium across nerve cell membranes is important for the conduction of nerve impulses (see Table 10.1). An electrical charge, or membrane potential, exists across nerve cell membranes because the number of negative ions just inside the cell membrane is greater than the number outside. This occurs because the cell membrane allows more positively charged ions to leak out of the cell than to leak into the cell. Nerve impulses are created by a change in the electrical charge across cell membranes. Stimuli, such as touch or the presence of neurotransmitters, change the cell membrane's permeability to sodium, allowing it to rush into the cell (**Figure 10.14**). This reverses, or depolarizes, the charge of the cell membrane at that location, and an electrical current is generated. The nerve impulse travels along the nerve cell as an electrical current. Once the nerve impulse passes, the original membrane potential is rapidly restored by another change in cell membrane permeability; then the original distribution of sodium and potassium ions across the cell membrane is restored by the sodium-potassium-ATPase pump in the cell membrane. A similar mechanism causes the depolarization of the muscle cell membranes, leading to muscle contraction.

Regulation of Electrolyte Balance In northern China, typical sodium chloride intake is greater than 13.9 grams per day; in the Kalahari Desert, it is less than 1.7 grams per day; and among the Yanomani Indians of Brazil, consumption may be less than

Nerve cell membrane

Figure 10.14 The role of sodium and potassium in nerve conduction
You feel a pinprick because it stimulates nerves beneath the surface of the skin. This stimulation increases the permeability of the nerve cell membrane to sodium, which rushes into the cell (shown here), initiating a nerve impulse.

0.06 gram of salt per day.[1] Despite these variations in intake, homeostatic mechanisms ensure that blood levels of sodium are not significantly different among these groups.

Sodium and chloride homeostasis is regulated to some extent by the intake of both water and salt. When salt intake is high, thirst is stimulated to increase water intake. When salt intake is very low, a salt appetite causes the individual to seek out the mineral. These mechanisms help ensure that appropriate proportions of salt and water are taken in. The kidneys are the primary regulator of sodium, chloride, and potassium balance in the body. Excretion of these electrolytes in the urine is decreased when intake is low and increased when intake is high. Because water follows sodium by osmosis, the ability of the kidneys to conserve sodium provides a mechanism to conserve body water.

Sodium plays a pivotal role in regulating extracellular fluid volume. When the concentration of sodium in the blood increases, water follows, causing an increase in blood volume. Changes in blood volume can change blood pressure. Changes in blood pressure trigger the production and release of proteins and hormones that affect the amount of sodium, and hence water, retained by the kidneys. For example, when blood pressure decreases, the kidneys release the enzyme **renin**, beginning a series of events leading to the production of **angiotensin II** (**Figure 10.15**). Angiotensin II increases blood pressure both by causing the blood vessel walls to constrict and by stimulating the release of the hormone **aldosterone**, which acts on the kidneys to increase sodium (and chloride) reabsorption. Water follows the reabsorbed sodium, helping to maintain blood volume and, consequently, blood pressure. As blood pressure increases it inhibits the release of renin and aldosterone so that blood pressure does not continue to rise.

The amount of potassium in the body is also tightly regulated. If blood levels begin to rise, mechanisms are activated to stimulate the cellular uptake of potassium. This short-term regulation prevents the amount of potassium in the extracellular fluid from getting lethally high. The long-term regulation of potassium balance depends on aldosterone release, which causes the kidneys to excrete potassium and retain sodium. Aldosterone release is stimulated by high-blood potassium, low-blood sodium, or angiotensin II.

renin An enzyme produced by the kidneys that converts angiotensin to angiotensin I.

angiotensin II A compound that causes blood vessel walls to constrict and stimulates the release of the hormone aldosterone.

aldosterone A hormone that increases sodium reabsorption by the kidney and therefore enhances water retention.

Recommended Sodium, Chloride, and Potassium Intakes

The AI for sodium for adults ages 19 to 50 years is 1500 mg per day and for chloride is 2300 mg per day, which is equivalent to 3.8 grams of salt per day[1] (see Table 10.1). This amount ensures an adequate intake of other nutrients and accounts for sodium losses in sweat. The UL is set at 2300 mg per day of sodium and 3600 mg per day of chloride. This is equivalent to 5.8 grams of salt, or about 1 teaspoon per day. The UL is based on the adverse effects of higher levels of sodium on blood

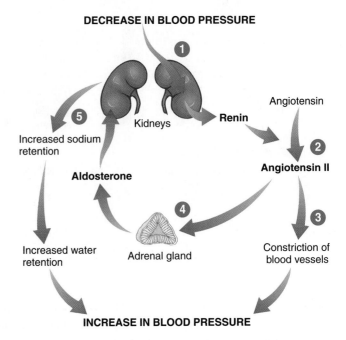

DECREASE IN BLOOD PRESSURE

Angiotensin

Renin

Kidneys

Increased sodium retention

Angiotensin II

Aldosterone

Increased water retention

Adrenal gland

Constriction of blood vessels

INCREASE IN BLOOD PRESSURE

1. A decrease in blood pressure triggers the kidneys to release the enzyme renin.

2. Renin converts angiotensin into angiotensin I, which is activated to angiotensin II.

3. Angiotensin II increases blood pressure by constricting the walls of blood vessels.

4. Angiotensin II stimulates release of aldosterone from the adrenal gland.

5. Aldosterone increases sodium reabsorption by the kidneys. Water follows the sodium, helping to maintain blood volume and blood pressure.

Figure 10.15 Regulation of blood pressure
A drop in blood pressure triggers events that cause blood vessels to constrict and the kidneys to retain water. An increase in blood pressure inhibits these events so that blood pressure does not continue to rise.

pressure. The Dietary Guidelines recommend that the general public consume a diet with less than 2300 mg of sodium per day and those with hypertension or at high risk of hypertension consume a diet with only 1500 mg of sodium per day.[6] The Daily Value for sodium of no more than 2400 mg of sodium per day (6 grams salt) is similar to the Dietary Guidelines recommendation for the general public.

The AI for potassium is set at 4700 mg per day; a level that will lower blood pressure and reduce the adverse effects of sodium on blood pressure. The Dietary Guidelines also recommend an intake of 4700 mg of potassium per day; the Daily Value is at least 3500 mg per day for adults. No UL has been set for potassium because potassium intake from foods is not a risk in healthy people with normal kidney function.

Life Cycle

There is no evidence that sodium and chloride requirements differ during pregnancy so pregnant women are advised to follow the recommendation for the general population for sodium intake[1] (see Chapter 14). At one time, a dietary salt restriction was common during pregnancy to prevent a spectrum of conditions involving high blood pressure known as hypertensive disorders of pregnancy. The cause of these disorders is not known, but salt restriction is no longer recommended. Potassium recommendations are not increased during pregnancy, but during lactation the AI is higher to account for the potassium lost in milk. In infants, sodium, chloride, and potassium needs are estimated from the amount consumed in human milk, which contains more chloride than sodium. This same chloride-to-sodium ratio has been recommended for infant formulas.

Electrolyte Deficiency

The electrolytes are found in plentiful amounts in the diet, and the kidneys of a healthy individual are efficient at regulating amounts in the body. However, illness and extreme conditions can increase electrolyte losses and affect overall health.

Sodium, chloride, and potassium depletion can occur when losses are increased due to heavy and persistent sweating, chronic diarrhea or vomiting, or kidney disorders that lead to excessive urinary losses. Medications can also interfere with electrolyte balance. For example, thiazide diuretics, which are used to treat hypertension, cause potassium loss. Generally, potassium supplements are prescribed along with or incorporated into medications that cause potassium loss. Deficiencies of any of the electrolytes can lead to electrolyte imbalance, which can cause disturbances in acid-base balance, poor appetite, muscle cramps, confusion, apathy, constipation, and, eventually, an irregular heartbeat. For example, the sudden death that can occur in fasting, anorexia nervosa, or starvation may be due to heart failure caused by potassium deficiency.

Electrolyte Toxicity

Electrolyte toxicity is rare when water needs are met and kidney function is normal. If, however, potassium supplements are consumed in excess or kidney function is compromised, blood levels of potassium can increase and potentially cause death due to an irregular heartbeat. A high oral dose of potassium generally causes vomiting which limits absorption, but if too much potassium enters the blood, it can cause the heart to stop.

It is difficult to consume more sodium than the body can handle because we usually drink more water when we consume more sodium. The primary concern with chronic high sodium intake is elevated blood pressure. Though rare, elevation of blood sodium can result from dehydration or from massive ingestion of salt, such as may occur from drinking seawater or consuming salt tablets. The symptoms of high blood sodium, or hypernatremia, are similar to those of dehydration. High sodium intake also increases calcium excretion and has been implicated as a risk factor for osteoporosis.[7]

10.3 Hypertension

Learning Objectives

- Define "hypertension" and list its symptoms and consequences.
- Discuss the effect of dietary salt intake on blood pressure.
- Describe the DASH diet and how it affects blood pressure.

A certain level of blood pressure is necessary to ensure that blood is delivered to all the body tissues. An optimal blood pressure is less than 120/80 millimeters of mercury (mm Hg). The higher number is systolic pressure, the maximum pressure in the artery. The lower number is diastolic pressure, the minimum pressure in the artery. Blood pressure from 120/80 to 139/89 is referred to as prehypertension. Prehypertension affects about 59 million Americans and indicates an increased risk for developing hypertension.[8] Blood pressure that is consistently 140/90 mm of mercury or greater indicates hypertension (see Appendix C).[9] High blood pressure damages artery walls, increases the workload of the heart, and can cause blood vessel walls to weaken or rupture. Hypertension is associated with increased risk of cardiovascular diseases such as atherosclerosis, heart attack, and stroke.[9] It also increases the risks for kidney disease and early death. Hypertension is a serious public health concern in the United States; about 33% of adult Americans and more than half of those over age 60 years have hypertension;[10] of these, 30% don't know they have it (**Figure 10.16**).

Figure 10.16 Everyone should have regular blood pressure monitoring, because hypertension has no outward symptoms. (Andersen Ross/Getty Images, Inc.)

What Causes Hypertension?

Most people with high blood pressure have *essential hypertension*—hypertension with no obvious external cause. It is a complex disorder, most likely resulting from disturbances in one or more of the mechanisms that control body fluid and electrolyte balance. High blood pressure that occurs as a result of other disorders is referred to as *secondary hypertension*. For example, if atherosclerosis causes a reduction in blood flow to the kidneys, the kidneys respond by releasing renin. This triggers events that lead to an increase in blood volume and a constriction of blood vessels. This raises blood pressure to the kidneys, but also raises blood pressure throughout the body.

Factors that Affect the Risk of Hypertension

The risk of developing high blood pressure is affected by genetics, age, existing disease conditions, and lifestyle factors. A family history of high blood pressure increases your risk of developing this disorder. The genetic basis of hypertension is also illustrated by the fact that it is more common in people of certain ethnic and racial backgrounds. For example, African Americans, Puerto Ricans, and Cuban and Mexican Americans have a higher incidence of hypertension than non-Hispanic whites.[11] The increased incidence among African Americans is reflected in their 1.8 times greater rate of death from stroke, 1.5 times greater rate of death from heart disease, and 4.2 times greater rate of hypertension-related kidney failure compared to whites.[10] The risk of hypertension increases with age. One reason is that as people age the arteries lose their elasticity. Diabetes also increases the risk of high blood pressure. Kidney damage is generally the cause of high blood pressure in type 1 diabetes. In type 2 diabetes, the higher incidence of hypertension may also be due to the effect of high insulin levels on sodium retention in the kidneys as well as the presence of excess body fat. A lack of physical activity, heavy alcohol consumption, smoking, stress, and a number of dietary factors can also increase blood pressure.[12] Obesity, particularly abdominal obesity, increases the risk of hypertension. Excess adipose tissue adds miles of capillaries through which blood must be pumped. Weight loss can prevent or delay the onset of hypertension in obese individuals.

Diet and Blood Pressure

The connection between sodium and blood pressure is well known. On average, as sodium intake goes up, so does blood pressure, but sodium is not the only mineral that affects blood pressure. Diets high in potassium, calcium, and magnesium are associated with a lower incidence of hypertension.

Salt Intake and Blood Pressure The relationship between salt intake and blood pressure was first identified by examining the incidence of hypertension in populations with different average dietary salt intakes. It was found that in populations consuming less than 4.5 grams of salt per day, average blood pressure was low and hypertension was rare or absent. In populations consuming 5.8 grams of salt or more per day, blood pressure increased with sodium intake.[13] More recent intervention trials have examined the effect of different levels of sodium intake on blood pressure. It was found that the lower the amount of sodium in the diet the lower the blood pressure.[14] When compared to an intake of 3300 mg of sodium (the average level consumed by Americans) an intake of 2400 mg of sodium reduced blood pressure in those with and without hypertension, and even more significant reductions were seen when sodium intake was reduced to 1500 mg of sodium per day. These studies and others are the basis for the current DRIs and Dietary Guidelines recommendation for Americans to consume less than 2300 mg of sodium per day. Despite the general effect of sodium intake on blood pressure, not everyone who consumes more than the recommended amount of sodium a day will develop hypertension. Individuals with hypertension, diabetes, and chronic kidney disease, as well as older individuals and African Americans tend to be more sensitive to salt intake.[1]

Potassium, Calcium, and Magnesium Intake and Blood Pressure Dietary patterns with high intakes of fiber and the minerals potassium, magnesium, and calcium are associated with lower blood pressure.[15] For example, populations and individuals consuming vegetarian diets, which are high in these nutrients, generally have lower blood pressure than nonvegetarians.[16] Population surveys, like NHANES, have shown that a dietary pattern low in calcium, potassium, and magnesium is associated with hypertension in American adults.[17] Despite these data, studies that have explored the impact of individual nutrients on blood pressure are often inconclusive. This may be because the impact of each individual nutrient is small and that other dietary components are also important in blood pressure regulation.

The first intervention trial to look at the effect of a dietary pattern high in potassium, calcium, and magnesium on blood pressure was the DASH trial, which stands for Dietary Approaches to Stop Hypertension[18] (see Science Applied: A Total Dietary Approach to Reducing Blood Pressure). In this trial the amount of dietary sodium was kept constant and different dietary patterns were compared in terms of their effect on blood pressure. The greatest reduction in blood pressure was found with a dietary pattern that was high in fruits and vegetables and included low-fat dairy products, and lean meat, fish, and poultry. This diet was higher in potassium, magnesium, calcium, and fiber, and lower in fat, saturated fat, and cholesterol than the typical American diet. The results of the DASH trial demonstrate that changing the dietary pattern can lower blood pressure. In addition, the DASH dietary pattern may also reduce cancer risk, prevent osteoporosis, and protect against heart disease (see Critical Thinking: A Diet for Health). The DASH dietary pattern or DASH Eating Plan is included in the recommendations for the Dietary Guidelines for Americans.[6] The MyPyramid recommendation of 4.5 cups of fruits and vegetables per day for a 2000 kcal diet is similar to the recommendations of the DASH Eating Plan.

Choosing a Diet and Lifestyle to Prevent Hypertension

Diet and lifestyle are both involved in regulating blood pressure. Maintaining body weight in a healthy range, staying active, and limiting alcohol consumption will help keep blood pressure in the normal range (**Table 10.2**). Consuming a diet rich in fresh fruits, vegetables, legumes, nuts and seeds, whole grains, lean meats, and low-fat dairy products is also important in keeping blood pressure normal (**Table 10.3**).

Table 10.2 Lifestyle Choices to Keep Blood Pressure in the Normal Range

- Eat plenty of fruits and vegetables—they are naturally low in salt and kcalories and rich in potassium.

- Choose and prepare foods with less salt.

- Aim for a healthy weight—blood pressure increases with increases in body weight and decreases when excess weight is reduced.

- Increase physical activity—it helps lower blood pressure, reduce the risk of other chronic diseases, and manage weight.

- If you drink alcoholic beverages, do so in moderation. Excessive alcohol consumption has been associated with high blood pressure.

- Quit smoking.

Source: Dietary Guidelines for Americans, 2005.

SCIENCE
ScienceAppliedScienceApplied
Science**AppliedScience**Applied
ScienceAppliedScienceApplied
APPLIED

(DAJ/Getty Images, Inc.)   (www.victorianoizquierdo.com/Getty Images, Inc.)   (Elena Schweitzer/Shutterstock)

A Total Dietary Approach to Reducing Blood Pressure

For over 30 years, the National Heart, Lung, and Blood Institute (NHLBI) of the National Institutes of Health (NIH) has been making recommendations for the treatment of high blood pressure through modifications of individual dietary components such as sodium and other minerals as well as fat, cholesterol, fiber, and protein. A review of these studies revealed enticing but conflicting and equivocal results. This led the NHLBI to pursue a study that would evaluate the effects of dietary patterns rather than individual dietary components on blood pressure.[1] As a result, the DASH (Dietary Approaches to Stop Hypertension) trial was conducted, finally providing conclusive evidence that diet does affect blood pressure.[2]

Designing the DASH trial presented several challenges. The study required large numbers of subjects to consume a specific diet for a fairly long period. To accrue enough subjects, the study needed to be run simultaneously from several different study centers. Subjects' diets had to be standardized across these centers.[1] Controlling dietary intake also presented challenges because the subjects lived at home but had to consume one meal a day, five days a week at the research study centers; the remaining meals were prepared by the research centers and sent home with the subjects to be consumed at home. To control for extra intake, subjects were also required to keep a daily diary of any nonstudy items consumed.

The DASH study population included 459 adults with slightly elevated blood pressure who were not taking blood pressure medications. Study subjects consumed a control diet for the first 3 weeks of the study, and their blood pressure was monitored. After 3 weeks, they were randomly assigned to one of three dietary groups for 8 weeks. During this intervention period, blood pressure was measured by individuals who did not know to which dietary groups the participants had been assigned.

The study diets included a "control" diet, a "fruits and vegetables" diet, and a "combination" diet. Each diet provided about 3000 mg of sodium—slightly lower than the typical U.S. intake—and enough kcalories to maintain body weight. The "control" diet was a typical American dietary pattern—low in fiber and high in fat and saturated fat. It matched the average U.S. nutrient intake except for potassium, magnesium, and calcium, which were set below average. The "fruits and vegetables" diet increased servings of fruits and vegetables and decreased sweets but was otherwise similar to the control diet. This diet was higher in fiber than the control, and the potassium and magnesium were above the typical American intake. The "combination" diet increased fruits, vegetables, and low-fat dairy products and reduced red meat, sweets, and sugar sweetened drinks; it was higher in potassium, calcium, magnesium, and fiber than the control diet and was lower in total fat, saturated fat, and cholesterol.

After 2 weeks, participants consuming the "fruits and vegetables" diet had a blood pressure reduction of 2.8 mm Hg systolic and 1.1 mm Hg diastolic. Those consuming the "combination" diet had a reduction in blood pressure of 5.5 mm Hg systolic and 3 mm Hg diastolic compared with the control group.[2] Estimates state that if the U.S. population adopted the DASH combination diet, the incidence of coronary heart disease would be reduced by 15% and stroke by 27%.

A second trial, DASH-Sodium, compared the effect of the DASH Eating Plan with a control diet (typical American diet) at three different levels of sodium intake.[3] The study included 412 participants with mild hypertension or prehypertension. In

A decrease in sodium intake lowered blood pressure more in the "control" diet than in the DASH diet. This is likely because blood pressures were already lower in the DASH diet group. The lowest blood pressure resulted from a combination of DASH and low sodium.

both the DASH diet and the control diet, lowering the sodium lowered blood pressure (see graphs). The combination of the DASH diet and the lowest sodium intake reduced blood pressure more than either the DASH diet alone or low sodium alone. Compared with the control diet with high sodium, the DASH diet with the lowest sodium lowered systolic blood pressure by 7.1 mm Hg in subjects without hypertension and by 11.5 mm Hg in those with hypertension—an effect equal to or greater than what would be expected from treatment with a single hypertension medication.

When many dietary factors are modified simultaneously, as in the DASH trial, it is impossible to determine which ones cause the effects seen. Therefore, the DASH trial taught scientists less about the physiology of hypertension than do studies that look at individual factors, but it provided more information about a daily dietary pattern that can prevent or reduce hypertension. The Dietary Guidelines for Americans now recommends the DASH Eating Plan as a healthy meal-planning tool for the general public.[4]

[1]Vogt, T. M., Appel, L. J., Obarzanek, E. et al. Dietary Approaches to Stop Hypertension: Rationale, design and methods. *J. Am. Diet. Assoc.* 99:12s–18s, 1999.

[2]Appel, L. J., Moore, T. J., Obarzanek, E. et al. A clinical trial of the effects of dietary patterns on blood pressure. DASH Collaborative Research Group. *N. Engl. J. Med.* 336:1117–1124, 1997.

[3]Sacks, F. M., Svetkey, L. P., Vollmer, W. M. et al. Effects on blood pressure of reduced dietary sodium and the Dietary Approaches to Stop Hypertension (DASH) diet. DASH-Sodium Collaborative Research Group. *N. Engl. J. Med.* 344:3–10, 2001.

[4]U.S. Department of Health and Human Services; U.S. Department of Agriculture. Dietary Guidelines for Americans, 2005. Available online at www.healthierus.gov/dietaryguidelines/. Accessed December 26, 2005.

Table 10.3 The DASH Eating Plan

Food Group	Serving Sizes	Daily Servings per Kcalorie Level			
		1600	2000	2600	3100
Grains[a]	1 slice bread, 1 oz dry cereal, 1/2 cup cooked rice, pasta, or cereal	6	7–8	10–11	12–13
Vegetables	1 cup raw leafy vegetables, 1/2 cup cooked vegetables, 6 oz vegetable juice	3–4	4–5	5–6	6
Fruits	6 oz fruit juice, 1 medium fruit, 1/4 cup dried fruit, 1/2 cup fresh, frozen, or canned fruit	4	4–5	5–6	6
Low-fat dairy	8 oz milk, 1 cup yogurt, 1½ oz cheese	2–3	2–3	3	3–4
Meats, fish, poultry	3 oz cooked meat, poultry, or fish	1–2	2 or less	2	2–3
Beans, nuts, and seeds	1/3 cup or 1½ oz nuts, 2 Tbsp or 1/2 oz seeds, 1/2 cup cooked dry beans or peas	3 per week	4–5 per week	1	1
Fat and oils[b]	1 tsp soft margarine, 1 Tbsp low-fat mayonnaise, 2 Tbsp light salad dressing, 1 tsp vegetable oil	2	2–3	3	4
Sweets	1 Tbsp sugar, 1 Tbsp jelly or jam, 1/2 oz jelly beans, 8 oz lemonade	0	5 per week	2	2

[a]Whole grains are recommended for most servings to meet fiber recommendations.

[b]Fat content changes the number of servings for fats and oils. One Tbsp regular salad dressing equals one serving, 1 Tbsp low-fat dressing equals 1/2 serving, and 1 Tbsp of fat-free dressing equals 0 servings.

Source: Dietary Guidelines for Americans, 2005.

Critical Thinking

A Diet for Health

Background

Rashamel's father died of a stroke at the age of 54 as a result of undiagnosed and untreated high blood pressure. Because he wants to live to see his grandchildren, Rashamel exercises for about 30 minutes on most days of the week, doesn't smoke, and watches his weight and salt intake. Despite these efforts, at his recent physical his blood pressure was 138/87, in the prehypertension category. Rashamel's doctor suggests he see a dietitian to help him manage his blood pressure with diet.

Data:

Rashamel is 43 years old and weighs 175 lbs. The dietitian recommends he follow the DASH Eating Plan to reduce his blood pressure. Rashamel's current diet is shown here.

(©iStockphoto)

CURRENT DIET

Breakfast	
Orange juice	3/4 cup
1% low-fat milk	I cup
Wheaties w/I tsp sugar	I cup
Whole-wheat bread w/ jelly	I slice
Margarine	I tsp
Lunch	
Tuna salad	3/4 cup
Wheat bread	2 slices
Chips	I oz
Cola	I can
Dinner	
Baked chicken	3 oz
White rice	I cup
Salad	I cup
Light salad dressing	I Tbsp
Dinner roll	I
Margarine	2 tsp
Cantaloupe	1/2 cup
Iced tea (sweetened)	12 oz
Snacks	
Cookies	2 large
Dried apricots	5
Milky Way candy bar	I
Cola	I can

Critical Thinking Questions

How healthy is Rashamel's current diet? Does it meet the recommendations of MyPyramid for grains, fruits, and vegetables for someone who eats 2600 kcalories per day? (see MyPyramid.gov)

▼

Now compare his diet to the recommendations of the DASH Eating Plan (see Table 10.3). Does he meet these recommendations? How many additional servings from grains, fruits, and vegetables would he need to add?

▼

Rashamel's wife is concerned about her risk for osteoporosis. Use Table 10.3 and iProfile to plan a day's meals that follow a 1600-kcalorie DASH Eating Plan and meet her calcium needs.

 iProfile Use iProfile to find out how much sodium is provided by your favorite snack foods.

Limiting sodium intake is also important for preventing hypertension. The amount of sodium recommended by the Dietary Guidelines and DRIs is significantly lower than the typical American intake of about 3300 mg per day. To reduce sodium intake Americans need to limit processed foods and added salt and increase their intake of fresh foods. **Table 10.4** provides some tips for reducing sodium intake. Food labels can be helpful in selecting lower-sodium foods (see Off the Label: Pass on the Salt). Foods with less salt may taste bland at first, but this preference for salt is learned. After consuming lower-salt foods for a period of time, the desire for salt decreases. Adding other flavorings such as onions, garlic, lemon juice, vinegar, black pepper, parsley, and other herbs to food may also help satisfy your taste for flavorful food without adding sodium.

Table 10.4 Tips for Reducing Sodium Intake

- **When shopping:**

  - Use food labels to select foods low in sodium.

  - Choose unprocessed foods—they have less sodium than processed foods.

  - Choose fresh or frozen vegetables rather than canned.

  - Choose fresh or frozen fish, shellfish, poultry, and meat more often than canned or processed forms.

- **When cooking:**

  - Prepare meals from scratch so you control the amount of salt added.

  - Do not add salt to the water when cooking rice, pasta, and cereals.

  - Flavor foods with ingredients such as lemon juice, onion or garlic powder (not salt), pepper, curry, dill, basil, oregano, or thyme rather than salt.

- **When eating:**

  - Limit salt use at the table.

  - Limit salted snack foods like potato chips, salted popcorn, and crackers, and replace them with fresh fruits and vegetables.

  - Limit cured, salted, or smoked meats such as bologna, corned beef, hot dogs, and smoked turkey to a few servings a week or less. Substitute sliced roasted turkey, chicken, or beef.

  - Limit salty or smoked fish such as sardines, anchovies, or smoked salmon (lox).

  - Limit foods prepared in salt brine such as pickles, olives, and sauerkraut.

  - Cut down on cheeses, especially processed cheeses.

  - Limit the amounts of soy sauce, Worcestershire sauce, barbecue sauce, ketchup, and mustard you add to food.

- **When eating out:**

  - Choose foods without sauces, or ask for them to be served on the side.

  - Ask that food be prepared without added salt.

  - Limit your fast food intake—it is usually very high in salt.

- **Reduce the salt in your diet gradually so that you learn to enjoy the unsalted flavors in foods.**

Off the Label
Pass on the Salt

Most of the sodium in the American diet comes from processed foods. Sodium chloride is the most common form in which sodium is added to foods; other sodium-containing ingredients include sodium hydroxide, sodium salts such as baking soda and baking powder, and monosodium glutamate (MSG).

Food labels list the sodium-containing ingredients in the ingredient list, and the Nutrition Facts panel gives the total amount of sodium in milligrams. To help you assess how the amount of sodium fits into the recommendations for a healthy diet, the sodium content of a serving is given as a percentage of the Daily Value. For example, the Nutrition Facts label here indicates that a serving of this spaghetti sauce contains 250 mg of sodium, or 10% of the Daily Value. In general, a food with 5% or less of the Daily Value is low in sodium, and one with 20% or more is high in sodium.

Food labels also include descriptors relating to salt or sodium content (see table). The spaghetti sauce shown here, labeled "Light in Sodium," contains 50% less sodium than regular spaghetti sauce. Additionally, a health claim that diets low in sodium may reduce the risk of high blood pressure can appear on foods that meet the definition of a low-sodium food and provide less than 20% of the Daily Value for fat, saturated fat, and cholesterol per serving. Medications such as pain relievers, antacids, and cough medications can also be a source of sodium in the diet. Drug facts labels on over-the-counter medications can help identify those that contain significant amounts of sodium.

Salt and Sodium on Food Labels

Sodium-free	Contains less than 5 mg of sodium per serving.
Salt-free	Must meet criterion for "sodium-free."
Very low sodium	Contains 35 mg or less of sodium per serving.
Low sodium	Contains 140 mg or less of sodium per serving.
Reduced or less sodium	Contains at least 25% less sodium per serving than a reference food.
Light in sodium	Contains at least 50% less sodium per serving than the average reference amount for the same food with no sodium reduction.
No salt added, without added salt, and unsalted	No salt added during processing, and the food it resembles and for which it substitutes is normally processed with salt. (If the food is not "sodium-free," the statement "not a sodium-free food" or "not for control of sodium in the diet" must appear on the same panel as the Nutrition Facts panel.)
Lightly salted	Contains at least 50% less sodium per serving than a reference amount. (If the food is not "low in sodium," the statement "not a low-sodium food" must appear on the same panel as the "Nutrition Facts" panel.)
Low-sodium meal	Contains 140 milligrams or less sodium per 100 grams.

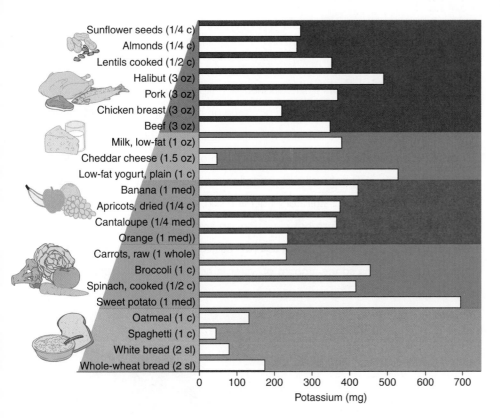

Figure 10.17 **Sources of potassium in MyPyramid food groups** Foods from all MyPyramid food groups are good sources of potassium, but whole unprocessed foods are the best.

The typical American diet contains only about 2000 to 3000 mg of potassium per day—well below the recommendation of 4700 mg per day. This is because most Americans do not consume the recommended amounts of fruits and vegetables—the best sources of potassium per kcalorie (**Figure 10.17**). Meat, milk, and cereal products also provide potassium.[6] Those who consume a diet that follows the MyPyramid and DASH Diet Plan recommendations for fruit and vegetable intake will easily meet the potassium recommendation (**Figure 10.18**). When diets are high in fruits and vegetables, intakes of 8000 to 11,000 mg per day are not uncommon.[1]

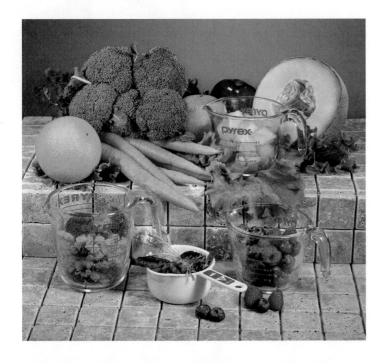

Figure 10.18 The amounts in the measuring cups shown here (about 2 cups of fruit and 2.5 cups of cooked vegetables) represent the amounts recommended by MyPyramid and the DASH Eating Plan for a 2000-kcalorie diet. (Andy Washnik)

Outcome

Despite her ailing appearance, Gabriele Andersen-Scheiss recovered rapidly. Once she finished her lap, she was given intravenous fluids, sprayed with a hose, and cold towels were placed on her body. After 2 hours she returned to the Olympic Village where she ate while doctors observed her for another few hours. Her dehydration had been caused by a combination of large fluid losses, a low fluid intake, and the fact that she was not well acclimatized to the southern California heat. As she ran, water evaporated from her respiratory tract and skin, and she produced large amounts of sweat to cool her body. In such hot conditions an athlete can lose several liters of water every hour. Andersen-Scheiss was not able to replace her fluid losses even with frequent drinks at water stations, so the amount of water in her body began to decline. Her blood volume decreased, and sufficient oxygen and nutrients could not be delivered to her exercising muscles. By the time she entered the stadium for her final lap, the lack of blood to her limbs had caused them to become numb. She observed, "I knew what I wanted to do, but my muscles wouldn't respond anymore." Andersen-Scheiss never ran another Olympic marathon but did go on to become a top elite Masters runner, setting many distance records. Her wobbly struggle to finish the women's Olympic marathon in 1984 is a vivid example of what happens when dehydration disrupts the balance of body fluids and electrolytes.

APPLICATIONS

Personal Nutrition

1. Do you drink enough fluid?
   a. Keep a log of all the fluids you consume in one day. Calculate your intake by totaling the volume of water, beverages, as well as foods that are liquid at room temperature.
   b. How does your intake on this day compare with the AI?
   c. How should your intake change if you added an hour of jogging or basketball to your day?

2. How does your diet compare to the DASH Eating Plan?
   a. Use one day of the food record you kept in Chapter 2 to compare the number of servings you ate from each of the food groups to the number of servings recommended by the DASH Eating Plan for your energy intake as shown in Table 10.3.
   b. Suggest modifications to your diet that would allow it to meet the DASH guidelines.
   c. What difficulties or inconveniences do you see with following this dietary pattern?
   d. What other dietary or lifestyle changes might you make if you are at high risk of hypertension?

3. How much sodium do processed foods add to your diet?
   a. Use iProfile or food labels to estimate the amount of sodium you consume from processed foods each day.
   b. Make a list of processed foods you commonly eat that contain more than 10% of the Daily Value for sodium (2400 mg) per serving.
   c. What less processed choices might you substitute for these?

 iProfile

General Nutrition Issues

1. Virginia's mother has high blood pressure and has had several strokes. A recent physical exam indicates that Virginia also has high blood pressure. Her physician prescribes medication to lower her blood pressure, but he believes that with some changes in diet and lifestyle Virginia's blood pressure can be brought into the normal range without drugs. Virginia works at a desk job. The only exercise she gets is when she takes care of her nieces and nephews one weekend a month. Her typical diet includes a breakfast of cereal, tomato juice, and coffee. She has a snack of doughnuts and coffee at work, and for lunch she joins coworkers for a fast-food cheeseburger, fries, and milkshake. When she gets home she has a soda and snacks on peanuts or chips. Dinner is usually a frozen dinner with milk.
   a. What dietary changes would you recommend for Virginia?
   b. What lifestyle changes would you recommend?

2. The recommendations of MyPyramid and the DASH Eating Plan are similar.
   a. Find the MyPyramid recommendations for a 2000-kcalorie diet by looking up the MyPyramid plan for a 40-year old woman who exercises for 30 to 60 minutes per day.
   b. Review the recommendations for the DASH Eating Plan for 2000 kcalories (Table 10.3).
   c. Make a chart that compares the amounts of food from each food group recommended by MyPyramid and the DASH Eating Plan.
   d. Which diet do you think would be easier to consume? Why?

Summary

10.1 Water: The Internal Sea

- Water is an essential nutrient that provides many functions in the body. The polar structure of water allows it to act as a solvent for the molecules and chemical reactions involved in metabolism. Water helps to transport other nutrients and waste products within the body and to excrete wastes from the body. It also helps to protect the body, regulate body temperature, and lubricate areas such as the eyes and the joints.

- The adult human body is about 60% water by weight. Body water is distributed between intracellular and extracellular compartments. The amount in each compartment depends largely on the concentration of solutes. Since water will diffuse by osmosis from a compartment with a lower concentration of solutes to one with a higher concentration, the body regulates the distribution of water by adjusting the concentration of electrolytes and other solutes in each compartment.

- Water cannot be stored, so intake must balance losses to maintain homeostasis. Water is lost from the body in urine and feces, through evaporation from the skin and lungs, and in sweat. The kidney is the primary regulator of water output. If water intake is low, antidiuretic hormone will cause the kidney to conserve water. If water intake is high, more water will be excreted in the urine.

- The recommended intake of water is 2.7 liters per day for women and 3.7 liters per day for men; needs vary depending on environmental conditions and activity level. Fluid intake is stimulated by the sensation of thirst, which occurs in response to a decrease in blood volume and an increase in the concentration of solutes.

- Dehydration can occur if water intake is too low or output is excessive. Mild dehydration can cause headache, fatigue, loss of appetite, dry eyes and mouth, and dark-colored urine. Water intoxication causes hyponatremia, which can result in abnormal fluid accumulation in body tissues.

10.2 Electrolytes: Salts of the Internal Sea

- The U.S. diet is abundant in sodium and chloride from processed foods and table salt but generally low in potassium, which is high in unprocessed foods such as fresh fruits and vegetables. Recommendations for health suggest that we increase our intake of potassium and consume less sodium.

- The minerals sodium, chloride, and potassium are electrolytes that are important in the maintenance of fluid balance and the formation of membrane potentials essential for nerve transmission and muscle contraction.

- The recommended salt intake is 3.8 grams per day for adults ages 19 to 50. Because salt is 40% sodium and 60% chloride by weight, this represents 1500 milligrams of sodium and 2300 milligrams of chloride. The Daily Value for sodium is somewhat higher—no more than 2400 milligrams of sodium per day. The UL for sodium, which is based on the increase in blood pressure seen with higher sodium intakes, is only 2300 milligrams per day. The DRIs recommend a potassium intake of 4700 milligrams per day; the Daily Value is at least 3500 milligrams per day for adults. This amount is significantly higher than the typical 2000 to 3000 milligrams consumed by most Americans. No UL has been set for potassium.

- Electrolyte and fluid homeostasis is regulated primarily by the kidneys. A decrease in blood pressure or blood volume signals the release of the enzyme renin, which helps form angiotensin II. Angiotensin II causes blood vessels to constrict and the hormone aldosterone to be released. Aldosterone causes the kidneys to reabsorb sodium and hence water, thereby preventing any further loss in blood volume. Failure of these regulatory mechanisms may be a cause of hypertension.

10.3 Hypertension

- A healthy blood pressure is less than 120/80 mm of mercury. Blood pressure from 120/80 to 139/89 is referred to as prehypertension, and blood pressure that is consistently 140/90 mm of mercury or greater indicates hypertension.

- Hypertension is common in the United States. A diet high in sodium increases blood pressure in most individuals. High intakes of the minerals potassium, magnesium, and calcium help lower blood pressure. Maintaining a healthy weight and exercise program helps prevent hypertension.

- Diets high in sodium and low in potassium are associated with an increased risk of hypertension. The DASH diet—a dietary pattern moderate in sodium; high in potassium, magnesium, calcium, and fiber; and low in fat, saturated fat, and cholesterol—lowers blood pressure.

- To reduce the risk of hypertension, public health recommendations suggest that Americans consume a dietary pattern that is high in fruits, vegetables, whole grains, legumes, nuts and seeds, and provides low-fat dairy products and lean meat, fish, and poultry. This dietary pattern contains less sodium and more potassium than the typical American diet. Blood pressure management also requires maintenance of a healthy weight, an active lifestyle, and a limit on alcohol consumption.

Review Questions

1. Describe the functions of water in the body.

2. How is the total amount of water in the body regulated?

3. How is the amount of water in each body compartment regulated?

4. What is the recommended water intake for adults?

5. List three factors that increase water needs.

6. Define electrolyte.

7. How do sodium, potassium, and chloride function in the body?

8. Explain how a drop in blood pressure is returned to normal.

9. What are the consequences of untreated hypertension?

10. What types of foods contribute the most sodium to the North American diet?

11. What types of foods are good sources of potassium?

12. What is the relationship between dietary sodium and blood pressure?

13. What is the DASH diet, and how does it affect blood pressure?

References

1. Institute of Medicine, Food and Nutrition Board. *Dietary Reference Intakes for Water. Salt and Potassium.* Washington, DC: National Academies Press, 2004.

2. Shen, H-P. Body fluids and water balance. In *Biochemical and Physiological Aspects of Human Nutrition.* 2nd ed. M. Stipanuk, ed. St. Louis: Saunders Elsevier, 2006, pp. 973–1000.

3. Murray, B. Hydrationand physical performance. *J. Am. Coll. Nutr.* 26: 542S–548S, 2007.

4. Coyle, E. F. Fluid and fuel intake during exercise. *J. Sports Sci.* 22:39–55, 2004.

5. Oppliger, R. A., Case, H. S., Horswill, C. A. et al. American College of Sports Medicine position statement: Weight loss in wrestlers. *Med. Sci. Sports Exerc.* 28:ix–xii, 1996.

6. U.S. Department of Health and Human Services; U.S. Department of Agriculture. Dietary Guidelines for Americans, 2005. Available online at www.healthierus.gov/dietaryguidelines/. Accessed May 19, 2009.

7. Teucher, B., Fairweather-Tait, S. Dietary sodium as a risk factor for osteoporosis: Where is the evidence? *Proc. Nutr. Soc.* 62:859–866, 2003.

8. U.S. Department of Health and Human Services. The Seventh Report of the Joint National Committee on Prevention, Detection, Evaluation, and Treatment of Blood Pressure. NIH Publication No. 04–5230, 2004.

9. Chobanian, A. V., Bakris, G. L., Black, H. R. et al. Seventh report of the Joint National Committee on Prevention, Detection, Evaluation, and Treatment of High Blood Pressure. Joint National Committee on Prevention, Detection, Evaluation, and Treatment of High Blood Pressure. National Heart, Lung, and Blood Institute. *Hypertension* 42:1206–1252, 2003.

10. American Heart Association. *Heart Disease and Stroke Statistics—2009 Update* (At-a-Glance Version). Available online at www.americanheart.org/presenter.jhtml?identifier=3037327. Accessed October 8, 2009.

11. Ostchega, Y., Yoon, S. S., Hughes, J., and Louis, *T. Hypertension Awareness, Treatment, and Control—Continued Disparities in Adults: United States, 2005–2006.* Available online at www.cdc.gov/nchs/data/databriefs/db03.pdf. Accessed August 25, 2008.

12. American Heart Association. Am I at Risk? Factors That Contribute to High Blood Pressure. Available online at www.americanheart.org/presenter.jhtml?identifier=2142. Accessed August 25, 2008.

13. Carvalho, J. J., Baruzzi, R. G., Howard, P. F. et al. Blood pressure in four remote populations in the Intersalt study. *Hypertension* 14:238–246, 1989.

14. Sacks, F. M., Svetkey, L. P., Vollmer, W. M. et al. Effects on blood pressure of reduced dietary sodium and the Dietary Approaches to Stop Hypertension (DASH) diet. DASH–Sodium Collaborative Research Group. *N. Engl. J. Med.* 344:3–10, 2001.

15. Houston, M. C., and Harper, K. J. Potassium, magnesium, and calcium: Their role in both the cause and treatment of hypertension. *J. Clin. Hypertens. (Greenwich)* 10(7 Suppl. 2): 3–11, 2008.

16. Craig, W. J., Mangels, A. R.; American Dietetic Association. Position of the American Dietetic Association: Vegetarian diets. *J. Am. Diet. Assoc.* 109:1266–1282, 2009.

17. Townsend M. S., Fulgoni, V. L. 3rd, Stern, J. S. et al. Low mineral intake is associated with high systolic blood pressure in the Third and Fourth National Health and Nutrition Examination Surveys: Could we all be right? *Am. J. Hypertens.* 18:261–269, 2005.

18. Appel, L. J., Moore, T. J., Obarzanek, E. et al. A clinical trial of the effects of dietary patterns on blood pressure. *N. Engl. J. Med.* 336:1117–1124, 1997.

11 Major Minerals and Bone Health

Case Study

Margie felt a searing pain in her hip when her foot struck the pavement, and the next thing she knew she was lying in the street. Her daughter and son-in-law would be arriving soon with her new grandson, and she had been rushing back from the corner store with some last-minute groceries. Stepping off the curb to cross the street had fractured her hip. The visit with her grandson would take place in the hospital rather than her home.

Margie is 75 years old, is 5' 2" tall, and weighs 115 pounds. She just retired from her engineering job and lives alone in her apartment. She is always busy taking care of her home and doing volunteer work at the library. Although she is generally healthy and has never felt the need for regular checkups, she does have a history of broken bones. Six months ago she broke her wrist after slipping and falling on an icy patch on the sidewalk. Five years ago she suffered a stress fracture in her foot while sightseeing in Washington, D.C. How could stepping off a curb cause her hip to break? How would it affect her future?

A health history reveals that Margie has never gotten much exercise, and her dietary calcium intake is about a quarter of the recommended 1200 mg per day. Her hip broke because the bone had been weakened by osteoporosis, a disease characterized by low bone density. Bone density is higher in people who exercise and consume adequate calcium. Margie's lifelong low-calcium intake and limited exercise increased her risk of developing this disease. Her hip fracture will require hospitalization, surgery, and a long period of rehabilitation. It may impair her ability to walk unassisted and cause prolonged or permanent disability. On a positive note, Margie is still in good health, so rehabilitation, diet, and medications can help her recover from the injury. Many older adults who experience a hip fracture due to osteoporosis require long-term nursing-home care and never regain their independence.

(Barbara Penoyar/Photodisc/Getty Images, Inc.)

(©iStockphoto)

(Disc. Inc./Getty Images)

Chapter Outline

11.1 What Are Minerals?

Learning Objectives

- Define *mineral* in terms of nutrition.
- Describe how interactions among minerals and other dietary components affect mineral bioavailability.

minerals In nutrition, elements needed by the body in small amounts for structure and to regulate chemical reactions and body processes.

major minerals Minerals needed in the diet in amounts greater than 100 mg per day or present in the body in amounts greater than 0.01% of body weight.

trace elements or trace minerals Minerals required in the diet in amounts of 100 mg or less per day or present in the body in amounts of 0.01% of body weight or less.

Minerals are inorganic elements needed by the body as structural components and regulators of body processes. Minerals may combine with other elements in the body, but they retain their chemical identity. Unlike vitamins, they are not destroyed by heat, oxygen, or acid. The ash that remains after a food is combusted in a bomb calorimeter contains the minerals that were present in that food.

Minerals have traditionally been categorized based on the amounts needed in the diet or present in the body. The **major minerals** include those needed in the diet in amounts greater than 100 mg per day or present in the body in amounts greater than 0.01% of body weight. The **trace elements** or **trace minerals** are minerals required by the body in an amount of 100 mg or less per day or present in the body in an amount of 0.01% or less of body weight (**Figure 11.1**). The major minerals include the electrolytes sodium, chloride, and potassium, which were discussed in Chapter 10. Calcium, phosphorus, and magnesium, discussed in this chapter, are major minerals that play a role in bone health, and sulfur is a major mineral that functions in association with other molecules, such as vitamins and amino acids. The trace elements are discussed in Chapter 12.

Minerals in the Modern Diet

Minerals are found in foods from all groups of MyPyramid (**Figure 11.2**). Most foods naturally contain minerals and some foods provide minerals that are added intentionally by fortification or accidentally through contamination. The mineral content of the diet can be maximized by eating a variety of foods, including many unprocessed foods such as fresh fruits, vegetables, whole grains, lean meats, and low-fat dairy products, as well as fortified foods (**Figure 11.3**). Dietary supplements are also a source of minerals.

Figure 11.1 Major and trace minerals in the periodic table The major minerals are shown in purple, and the trace elements are shown in blue.

GRAINS	VEGETABLES	FRUITS	MILK	MEAT & BEANS
Iron, Zinc, Selenium, Copper, Magnesium, Chromium, Sulfur, Manganese, Sodium, Potassium, Phosphorus	Iron, Calcium, Potassium, Magnesium, Molybdenum	Iron, Potassium	Calcium, Zinc, Phosphorus, Potassium, Iodine, Molybdenum	Iron, Zinc, Magnesium, Potassium, Chromium, Sulfur, Iodine, Selenium, Phosphorus, Copper, Manganese, Fluoride

Figure 11.2 Minerals in MyPyramid food groups Minerals are found in all food groups, but some groups are particularly good sources of specific ones.

Natural Sources In some foods, the amounts of minerals naturally present are predictable because the minerals are regulated components of the plant or animal. For instance, calcium is a component of milk; therefore, drinking a glass of milk reliably provides a known amount. Magnesium is a component of chlorophyll, so it is found in consistent amounts in leafy greens. For some minerals the amounts in food vary depending on the mineral concentration in the soil and water at the food's source. For example, the soil content of iodine is high near the ocean but usually quite low in inland areas. Therefore, foods grown near the ocean are better sources of iodine than those grown inland. In developed countries, modern transportation systems make foods produced in many locations available, so the diet is unlikely to be deficient in minerals that vary in concentration depending on where the food is produced. In countries where the diet consists predominantly of locally grown foods, individual trace element deficiencies and excesses are more likely to occur.

Processed Foods Food processing and refining can affect the mineral content of foods. Processing does not destroy minerals, but it can still cause losses. For example, as the structure of a food is broken down potassium is lost, and when the skins of fruits and vegetables and the bran and germ of grains are detached minerals such as magnesium, iron, selenium, zinc, and copper are removed. Processing also adds minerals to foods. Sodium is frequently added for flavor or as a preservative. The enrichment of grains has been adding iron to our breads, baked goods, and rice since the 1940s and today many breakfast cereals, breads, and juices are fortified with calcium. Some minerals enter the food supply inadvertently through contamination. For example, the iodine content of dairy products is increased by contamination from the cleaning solutions used on milking machines.

Dietary Supplements Supplements are also a source of minerals in the modern diet. Some, such as iron and calcium, are recommended for certain groups to meet their needs. Others, like chromium, zinc, and selenium are taken in the hopes that they will enhance athletic performance, stimulate immune function, or reduce cancer risk. High doses of minerals from supplements can be toxic. Because of the complex interactions among minerals, taking high doses of one can compromise the bioavailability of others, creating a mineral imbalance that can interfere with functions essential to human health. The body's regulatory mechanisms control the absorption and

Figure 11.3 The mineral content of the diet can be maximized by eating a variety of nutrient-dense foods. (Photo Disc)

excretion of minerals but have evolved to deal with the amounts of these elements that occur naturally in the diet. Large doses of mineral supplements may override this regulation, causing toxicity.

Understanding Mineral Needs

To maintain health, enough of each mineral must be consumed and the overall diet must contain all the minerals in the correct proportions. The wrong amounts or combinations can cause a deficiency or a toxic reaction. For some minerals, too much or too little causes obvious symptoms that impact short-term health. For example, an inadequate iron intake can cause a decrease in the number and size of red blood cells, reducing the blood's capacity to deliver oxygen and causing fatigue. These symptoms develop over a period of several months. Deficiencies of other minerals cause symptoms only in the long term. For example, a low calcium intake has no short-term consequences, but over the long term reduces bone density, increasing the risk of fractures later in life. Deficiencies of iron, iodine, and calcium are world health problems. Deficiencies of other minerals are rare, occurring only when the food supply is particularly limited or other factors affect mineral absorption or utilization.

Mineral toxicities occur most often as a result of environmental pollution or excessive use of supplements. For example, lead is toxic. Chronic exposure to lead from old lead paint, lead pipes, and soil and air contamination can cause growth retardation and learning disabilities in children (see Chapter 15). Even minerals such as iron that are essential in small doses can be toxic when consumed in excess.

Bioavailability of Minerals The body's ability to absorb specific minerals as well as the composition of the diet and the nutritional status and life stage of the consumer all affect bioavailability. Almost 100% of the sodium consumed in the diet is absorbed, whereas iron absorption may be as low as 5%. Calcium absorption is typically about 25% but during times of life when calcium needs are high, such as pregnancy and infancy, the proportion of dietary calcium absorbed is higher. For some minerals the amount absorbed depends primarily on the amount that is consumed. For others, the consumption of other minerals carrying the same charge affects absorption. Calcium, magnesium, zinc, copper, and iron all carry a 2^+ charge, and a high intake of one may reduce the absorption of others. For example, a high intake of calcium in a meal containing iron may reduce the absorption of the iron.

Other substances that are in the gastrointestinal tract at the same time as the mineral also affect bioavailability. Some substances enhance absorption. For example, when iron is consumed with acidic foods, the low pH helps to keep it in its more absorbable chemical form. Substances that bind minerals in the gastrointestinal tract can reduce absorption. **Phytic acid,** or **phytate**—an organic compound containing phosphorus that is found in whole grains, bran, and soy products—binds calcium, zinc, iron, and magnesium, limiting their absorption. Phytic acid can be broken down by yeast, so the bioavailability of minerals is increased in yeast-leavened foods such as breads. **Tannins,** found in tea and some grains, can interfere with iron absorption, and **oxalates**, which are organic acids found in spinach, rhubarb, beet greens, and chocolate, have been found to interfere with calcium and iron absorption (**Figure 11.4**). Dietary fiber also interferes with mineral absorption. Although North Americans generally do not consume enough of any of these components to cause mineral deficiencies, problems may occur in developing countries when the diet is high in cereal grains and marginal in certain minerals.

The ability to transport minerals from intestinal mucosal cells to the rest of the body also affects bioavailability. Some minerals must bind to plasma proteins or specific transport proteins to be transported in the blood. This binding helps regulate their absorption and prevents reactive minerals from forming free radicals that could cause oxidative damage. Nutritional status and nutrient intake can affect mineral transport in the body. For instance, when protein intake is deficient,

phytic acid or **phytate**
A phosphorus-containing storage compound found in seeds and grains that can bind minerals and decrease their absorption.

Life Cycle

tannins Substances found in tea and some grains that can bind minerals and decrease their absorption.

oxalates Organic acids found in spinach and other leafy green vegetables that can bind minerals and decrease their absorption.

Figure 11.4 Compounds such as phytate, oxalates, and tannins found in these foods decrease mineral absorption. (Charles D. Winters)

transport proteins (and proteins in general) cannot be synthesized. Therefore, even if a mineral is adequate in the diet, it cannot be transported to the cells where it is needed. Sometimes the intake of a specific mineral can affect how much of another is able to leave the mucosal cell and bind to a transport protein in the plasma.

Mineral Functions Minerals serve a wide range of vital structural and regulatory roles in the body. For example, calcium, phosphorus, magnesium, and fluoride affect the structure and strength of bones. Iodine is a component of the thyroid hormones, which regulate metabolic rate; chromium plays a role in regulating blood glucose levels; and zinc plays an important role in gene expression. Many of the minerals serve as **cofactors** necessary for enzyme activity (**Figure 11.5**). For instance, selenium is a cofactor for an antioxidant enzyme system.

Recommended Mineral Intakes As with other nutrients, the DRI recommendations for mineral intakes provide either an RDA value, when sufficient information is available to establish an EAR, or an AI, when population data is used to estimate needs. To help avoid toxic amounts of minerals, ULs have been established when adequate data are available. Recommendations are based on evidence from many types of research studies, ranging from laboratory studies done with animals and clinical trials using human subjects to epidemiological observations. In addition to planned experiments, information about trace element needs has come from the study of inherited diseases affecting trace element utilization and from the study of deficiency symptoms in individuals fed for long periods of time solely by total parenteral nutrition (TPN) solutions that were inadvertently deficient in specific essential minerals. As with other nutrients, when no other data are available, mineral needs can be estimated by evaluating the intake in a healthy population. It is assumed that if there are no deficiency symptoms, the diet must meet the requirement for that nutrient. One problem with this approach, however, is that deficiency symptoms may become apparent only when the deficiency is severe. Subtle signs of a mineral deficiency in a population may be difficult to detect, and deficiencies that have no symptoms for many years may be hard to identify.

cofactor An inorganic ion or coenzyme required for enzyme activity.

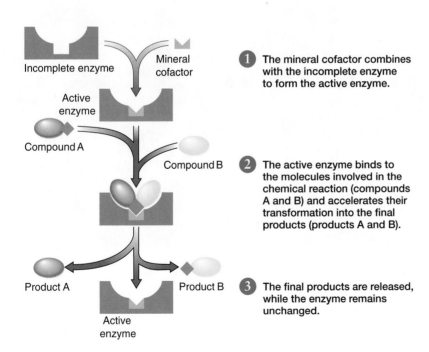

Figure 11.5 Minerals as cofactors
The binding of a cofactor to an enzyme activates the enzyme.

11.2 Calcium

Learning Objectives

- Explain the functions of calcium in the body.
- Compare the roles of parathyroid hormone, calcitonin, and vitamin D in the regulation of blood calcium levels.
- List foods that are good sources of calcium.

Calcium is the most abundant mineral in the body.[1] It provides structure to bones and teeth and has essential regulatory roles. Because of the importance of calcium in regulation, blood levels of this mineral are strictly controlled. However, this occurs at the expense of bone calcium; calcium is released from bone when blood levels drop. As a result, if the diet is not sufficient in calcium, over the long term, bone calcium is decreased and the risk of bone fractures due to **osteoporosis** is increased.

osteoporosis A bone disorder characterized by a reduction in bone mass, increased bone fragility, and an increased risk of fractures.

Calcium in the Diet

The main source of calcium in the U.S. diet is dairy products such as milk, cheese, and yogurt. Fish, such as sardines, that are consumed in their entirety, including the bones, are also a good source, as are legumes and some green vegetables such as broccoli, Chinese cabbage, and kale (**Figure 11.6**). Grains provide smaller amounts of calcium, but because they are consumed in such large quantities they make a significant contribution to dietary calcium intake (see Your Choice: Choose Your Beverage Wisely).

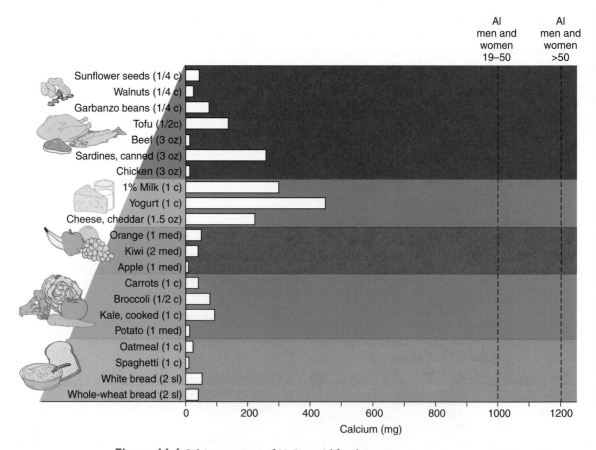

Figure 11.6 Calcium content of MyPyramid food groups
Calcium is provided by many different foods, but dairy products and fish consumed with bones are the best sources; the dashed lines represent the AI for adults ages 19 to 50 and for adults over age 50.

Choose Your Beverage Wisely

(©iStockphoto)

We think of sodas as thirst quenchers, snacks, or beverages to gulp with our meals. We consume them daily. The average woman in her twenties drinks two 12-oz sodas a day; teenage boys drink about two and a half a day.[1] There is no doubt that carbonated beverages have become part of American culture, but what do they offer nutritionally?

A 12-oz can of soda contains about 10 teaspoons of sugar and few other nutrients. Thus, soda adds 25 teaspoons of sugar to the average teenage boy's diet and 20 teaspoons to a young woman's diet.[1] This might not be too bad if the soda were replacing other low-nutrient-density foods like cookies or cakes, but for many people soda is replacing milk. Twenty years ago teenagers drank more milk than soda; today it is the opposite; they consume more soda than milk.

Replacing an 8-ounce glass of milk with a 12-ounce soda increases the amount of added sugar in the diet by about 40 grams and reduces protein, calcium, vitamin A, vitamin D, and riboflavin intake (see figure). Because milk is the major source of calcium in the American diet, calcium is the nutrient of greatest concern for soda drinkers. Teenage girls consume only 60% of the recommended amount of calcium, with soda drinkers consuming almost one-fifth less calcium than those who don't drink soda.[1]

A low-calcium intake early in life increases the risk of osteoporosis. Osteoporosis is a major problem among older adults today, and when these adults were children they drank twice as much milk as kids do today. By substituting soda for milk, children and teens are putting their bones at risk. In fact, the number of bone fractures among children and young adults has increased; this is hypothesized to be due to low-calcium intakes.[2]

	Low–fat milk	Cola soft drink
Serving size (oz)	8	12
Energy (kcal)	102	150
Protein (g)	8	0
Calcium (mg)	300	0
Phosphorus (mg)	235	45
Riboflavin (mg)	0.4	0
Vitamin A (μg)	144	0
Vitamin D (μg)	2.5	0
Caffeine (mg)	0	40

[1]Jacobson, M. F., Center for Science in the Public Interest. Liquid candy. How soft drinks are harming Americans' health. Available online at www.cspinet.org/sodapop/liquid_candy.htm/ Accessed March 19, 2009.

[2]NIH; NICHD. Calcium Crisis Affects American Youth, December 10, 2001. Available online at www.nichd.nih.gov/new/releases_bak_20040224/calcium_crisis.cfm. Accessed September 4, 2004.

Some of the calcium in the diet is added to foods during food processing. Baked goods such as breads, rolls, and crackers, to which nonfat dry milk powder has been added, provide calcium. Tortillas that are treated with lime water (calcium hydroxide) provide calcium. Tofu is a good source when calcium is used in its processing. In addition, there are numerous products on the market, such as orange juice and breakfast cereals, that are fortified with calcium.

Calcium in the Digestive Tract

Calcium is absorbed by both active transport and passive diffusion (**Figure 11.7**). Active transport depends on the availability of the active form of vitamin D, which induces the synthesis of calcium transport proteins in the intestine. Active transport accounts for most calcium absorption when intakes are low to moderate. Calcium absorption is higher at times when the body's need for calcium is greater. In young adults, about 25% of dietary calcium is absorbed. When vitamin D is deficent absorption drops to about 10%.[1] At high calcium intakes, passive transport becomes more important. As calcium intake increases, the percentage that is absorbed declines.

The bioavailability of calcium is decreased by the presence of tannins, fiber, phytates, and oxalates. For example, spinach is a high-calcium vegetable but only about 5% of its calcium is absorbed; the rest is bound by oxalates and excreted in the feces.[2] Vegetables such as kale, collard greens, turnip greens, mustard greens, and Chinese cabbage are low in oxalates so their calcium is well absorbed. Chocolate also contains oxalates, but chocolate milk is still a good source of calcium because the amount of oxalates from the chocolate added to a glass of milk is small. Fiber can also reduce calcium absorption but, with few exceptions, the effect is small. Phytates, however, can have a significant effect on the absorption of calcium from foods such as wheat bran and pinto, red, and white beans. It would take almost 10 servings of red beans to provide the same amount of absorbable calcium as 1 serving of milk. When calcium intake is low, dietary components that alter absorption have a greater effect on calcium status than when calcium intake is adequate.[3]

Life Cycle

The efficiency of calcium absorption varies with life stage. During infancy, about 60% of calcium consumed is absorbed. In young adults absorption is about 25%. In older adults absorption declines due to a decrease in blood levels of the active form of vitamin D or a decrease in responsiveness to vitamin D.[4] An additional decrease in calcium absorption occurs in women after menopause due to the decrease in estrogen.

During pregnancy, when calcium is needed for formation of the fetal skeleton, elevated estrogen helps increase calcium absorption. Calcium absorption increases to

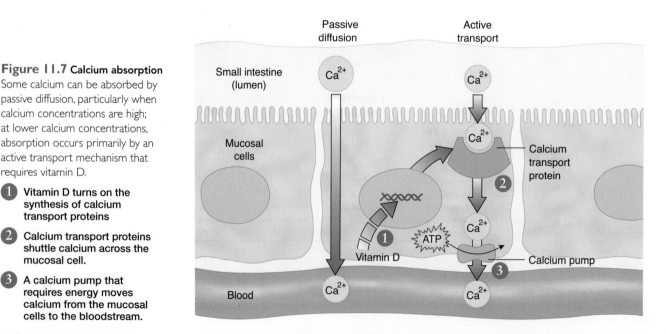

Figure 11.7 Calcium absorption Some calcium can be absorbed by passive diffusion, particularly when calcium concentrations are high; at lower calcium concentrations, absorption occurs primarily by an active transport mechanism that requires vitamin D.

1 Vitamin D turns on the synthesis of calcium transport proteins

2 Calcium transport proteins shuttle calcium across the mucosal cell.

3 A calcium pump that requires energy moves calcium from the mucosal cells to the bloodstream.

over 50% during pregnancy. Calcium need is also increased during lactation, but some of the calcium needed to make milk appears to come from the mother's bones. After lactation stops, an increase in calcium absorption and retention of calcium by the kidney help restore bone calcium.

Life Cycle

Calcium in the Body

Calcium accounts for 1% to 2% of adult body weight. Over 99% of the calcium in the body is found in the solid mineral deposit in bones and teeth.[1] The remaining 1% is present in intracellular fluid, blood, and other extracellular fluids, where it plays vital roles in nerve transmission, muscle contraction, blood pressure regulation, and the release of hormones (see **Table 11.1**).

Regulatory Roles of Calcium The calcium in body fluids plays critical roles in cell communication and the regulation of body processes. Calcium helps regulate enzyme activity and is necessary in blood clotting. It is involved in transmitting chemical and electrical signals in nerves and muscles. It is necessary for the release of neurotransmitters, which allow nerve impulses to pass from one nerve to another and from nerves to target tissues. Inside the muscle cells, calcium allows the two muscle proteins, actin and myosin, to interact to cause muscle contraction. The importance of calcium for proper nerve transmission and muscle contraction is illustrated by what happens when the concentration of calcium in the extracellular fluid drops too low. When this occurs the nervous system becomes increasingly excitable and nerves fire spontaneously, triggering contractions of the muscles, a condition known as *tetany*. Mild tetany can cause tingling of the lips, fingers, and toes, and more serious tetany results in severe muscle contractions, tremors, cramps, and even death. Tetany is typically caused by hormonal abnormalities, not a dietary calcium deficiency.

Calcium also plays a role in blood pressure regulation, possibly by controlling the contraction of muscles in the blood vessel walls and signaling the secretion of

Table 11.1 A Summary of Calcium, Phosphorus, Magnesium, and Sulfur

Mineral	Sources	Recommended Intake for for Adults	Major Functions	Deficiency Diseases and Symptoms	Groups at Risk of Deficiency	Toxicity	UL
Calcium	Dairy products, fish consumed with bones, leafy green vegetables, fortified foods	1000–1200 mg/d	Bone and tooth structure, nerve transmission, muscle contraction, blood clotting, blood pressure regulation, hormone secretion	Increased risk of osteoporosis	Postmenopausal women, elderly, those who consume a vegan diet, are lactose intolerant, or have kidney disease	Elevated blood calcium, calcification of the kidney, kidney stones, reduced absorption of other minerals	2500 mg/d from food and supplements
Phosphorus	Meat, dairy products, cereals, and baked goods	700 mg/d	Structure of bones and teeth, membranes, ATP, and DNA; acid-base balance	Bone loss, weakness, lack of appetite	Premature infants, alcoholics, elderly	Calcium resorption from bone	4000 mg/d
Magnesium	Greens, whole grains, nuts, seeds	310–420 mg/d	Bone structure, ATP stabilization, enzyme activity, nerve and muscle function	Nausea, vomiting, weakness, muscle pain, irregular heartbeat	Alcoholics, those with kidney and gastrointestinal disease	Nausea, vomiting, diarrhea, low blood pressure	350 mg/d from nonfood sources
Sulfur	High protein foods, preservatives	None specified	Part of amino acids, vitamins, acid-base balance	None when protein needs are met	None	None likely	ND

UL = Tolerable upper intake level, ND = not determined

substances that regulate blood pressure. The impact of adequate calcium on maintaining a healthy blood pressure was demonstrated by the DASH Trial (see Chapter 10, Science Applied: A Total Dietary Approach to Reducing Blood Pressure). In this trial a diet high in potassium, magnesium, and calcium was found to be more effective at lowering blood pressure than the control diet or an experimental diet lower in calcium.[5] Following the recommendations of the DASH Eating Plan can help keep both bones and blood pressure healthy.

Regulation of Blood Calcium The roles of calcium are so vital to survival that powerful regulatory mechanisms ensure that constant intracellular and extracellular concentrations are maintained. Slight changes in blood calcium levels trigger responses that quickly raise or lower them back to normal levels. This homeostasis is maintained by the hormones **parathyroid hormone (PTH)**, which raises blood calcium, and **calcitonin**, which lowers blood calcium (**Figure 11.8**). If the level of blood calcium falls too low, it triggers the secretion of more PTH from the parathyroid glands. PTH stimulates the release of calcium from bone, reduces calcium excretion by the kidney, and activates vitamin D. Activated vitamin D increases the amount of calcium absorbed from the gastrointestinal tract and, with PTH, stimulates calcium release from the bone and calcium retention by the kidney (see Chapter 9). The overall effect is to rapidly increase blood calcium levels. If blood calcium levels become too high, the secretion of PTH is reduced. This increases excretion of calcium by the kidney; decreases vitamin D activation, so less dietary calcium is absorbed; and reduces calcium release from bone. High blood calcium also stimulates the secretion of calcitonin from the thyroid gland. Calcitonin acts primarily on bone to inhibit the release of calcium. Together, low PTH levels and the presence of calcitonin cause a decrease in blood calcium levels.

parathyroid hormone (PTH) A hormone secreted by the parathyroid gland that increases blood calcium levels.

calcitonin A hormone secreted by the thyroid gland that reduces blood calcium levels.

Recommended Calcium Intake

The DRI values for calcium intake have been set at the amount that allows maximum calcium retention. Increasing dietary calcium above this level will not increase the amount of calcium retained in the body. Adults may continue to lose bone mass at this intake level due to other causes such as loss of estrogen, smoking, or a sedentary lifestyle, but this loss is not due to inadequate calcium intake.

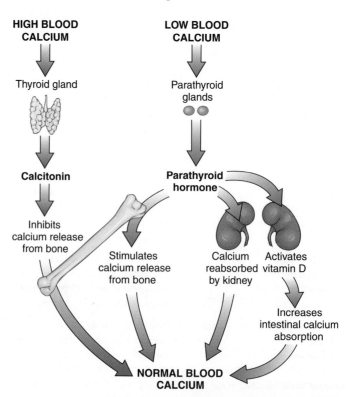

HIGH BLOOD CALCIUM
Thyroid gland
Calcitonin
Inhibits calcium release from bone

LOW BLOOD CALCIUM
Parathyroid glands
Parathyroid hormone
Stimulates calcium release from bone
Calcium reabsorbed by kidney
Activates vitamin D
Increases intestinal calcium absorption

NORMAL BLOOD CALCIUM

Figure 11.8 Regulation of blood calcium levels
Levels of calcium in the blood are very tightly regulated by parathyroid hormone and calcitonin.

Rather than an RDA, an AI has been determined for calcium because it was not possible to precisely estimate the dietary intake needed for maximum calcium retention. The AI for adults age 19 through 50 years is 1000 mg per day.[1] Since absorption decreases with age, the AI for men and women age 51 and older is increased to 1200 mg per day. In children and adolescents the AI is set at a level that will support bone growth. For adolescents the AI is higher than for adults—1300 mg per day for boys and girls age 9 through 18 years.

Infants thrive on the amount of calcium they obtain from human milk. For infants, an AI is set based on the mean intake of infants fed principally with human milk. Because calcium is not as well absorbed from infant formulas, formula-fed infants require more. There is no specific AI for formula-fed infants, but formulas are higher in calcium than breast milk to compensate for the reduced absorption.

Life Cycle

The AI for calcium during pregnancy is not increased above nonpregnant levels. This is because there is an increase in maternal calcium absorption during pregnancy that helps to supply the calcium needed for the fetal skeleton. In addition, since there is no correlation between the number of pregnancies and bone mineral density, the maternal skeleton does not appear to be used as a supply of calcium for the fetus.[1] However, during lactation, calcium is secreted in milk, and the source of this calcium does appear to be the maternal skeleton. This bone resorption occurs regardless of calcium intake and the calcium lost appears to be regained following weaning.[6] The AI is therefore not increased during lactation.

Calcium Deficiency and Toxicity

When calcium intake is not adequate, normal blood levels are maintained by resorbing calcium from bone. This provides a steady supply of calcium to maintain its roles in cell communication and regulation. Although there are no short-term symptoms of a calcium deficiency related to the removal of calcium from bone, a deficient diet affects bone mass. Low calcium intake during the years of bone formation results in lower bone density. Low intake during the adult years increases the rate of bone loss. As discussed later in this chapter both of these effects increase the risk of osteoporosis.

Too much calcium can also cause problems. Elevated blood calcium levels can cause symptoms such as loss of appetite, nausea, vomiting, constipation, abdominal pain, thirst, and frequent urination. Severe elevations may cause confusion, delirium, coma, and even death. Elevated blood calcium is rare and is most often caused by cancer or disorders that increase the secretion of PTH. But, it can also result from increases in calcium absorption due to excessive vitamin D intake or a high intake of calcium in combination with antacids. The consumption of large amounts of milk along with antacids used to be common in the treatment of peptic ulcers. This combination is associated with a condition called milk-alkali syndrome, which is characterized by high blood calcium along with calcification of the kidney that can lead to kidney failure. After the treatment of ulcers changed, the incidence of this condition declined, but it has risen again due to the increased use of calcium-containing antacids as calcium supplements and to treat heartburn.[7]

Too much calcium from supplements may also promote the formation of kidney stones. Kidney stones, which are usually composed of calcium oxalate or calcium phosphate, affect approximately 12% of the U.S. population. Although their cause is usually unknown, abnormally elevated urinary calcium, which can result from high doses of supplemental calcium, increases the risk of developing calcium stones.[1]

High calcium intake can also interfere with iron, zinc, magnesium, and phosphorus availability. Although calcium supplements inhibit iron absorption, there is no evidence that the long-term use of calcium supplements with meals affects iron status.[8] High intakes of calcium from supplements have also been found to reduce zinc absorption and thereby increase the amount of zinc needed in the diet.[9] There is no evidence of depletion of phosphorus or magnesium associated with calcium intake. Based on the occurrence of elevated blood calcium and kidney stones, as well as the potential for decreased absorption of other essential minerals, the UL for calcium in adults has been set at 2500 mg of calcium per day from food and supplements.[1]

11.3 Calcium and Bone Health

Learning Objectives

- Explain why bone remodeling is important.
- Discuss how the rates of bone formation and breakdown change throughout life.
- Describe dietary and lifestyle factors that affect the risk of osteoporosis.

hydroxyapatite A crystalline compound composed of calcium and phosphorus that is deposited in the protein matrix of bone to give it strength and rigidity.

cortical or **compact bone** Dense, compact bone that makes up the sturdy outer surface layer of bones.

trabecular or **spongy bone** The type of bone that forms the inner spongy lattice that lines the bone marrow cavity and supports the cortical shell.

bone remodeling The process whereby bone is continuously broken down and re-formed to allow for growth and maintenance.

osteoblasts Cells responsible for the deposition of bone.

osteoclasts Large cells responsible for bone breakdown.

Bone is composed of a protein framework, or matrix, that is hardened by deposits of minerals. The most abundant protein in this matrix is collagen. The mineral portion of bone is composed mainly of calcium associated with phosphorus as solid mineral crystals known as **hydroxyapatite**. In addition to calcium and phosphorus, bone contains magnesium, sodium, fluoride, and a number of other trace minerals. Healthy bone requires adequate dietary protein and vitamin C to maintain collagen, adequate vitamin D (discussed in Chapter 9) to promote calcium absorption, and a sufficient supply of minerals to ensure solidity. There is also growing evidence of the importance of vitamin K for bone health.[10]

There are two types of bone: **cortical** or **compact bone**, which makes up about 80% of the skeleton and forms the sturdy, dense outer surface layer, and **trabecular** or **spongy bone**, which forms an inner lattice that supports the cortical shell (**Figure 11.9**). Trabecular bone is found in the knobby ends of the long bones, the pelvis, wrists, vertebrae, scapulae, and the areas of the bone that surround the bone marrow.

Bone: A Living Tissue

Bone is a living, metabolically active tissue that is constantly being broken down and re-formed in a process called **bone remodeling**. Bone is formed by cells called **osteoblasts** and broken down or resorbed by cells called **osteoclasts**. During bone formation the activity of the bone-building osteoblasts exceeds that of the osteoclasts. When bone is being broken down, the osteoclasts resorb bone more rapidly than the osteoblasts can rebuild it (**Figure 11.10**).

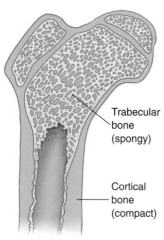

Figure 11.9 Types of bone
Cortical bone is compact bone that forms the dense outer layer; the spongy interior is referred to as trabecular bone.

Trabecular bone (spongy)

Cortical bone (compact)

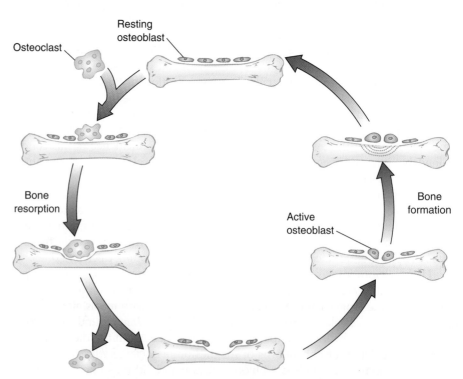

Resting osteoblast

Osteoclast

Bone resorption

Active osteoblast

Bone formation

Figure 11.10 Bone remodeling
During bone remodeling, osteoclasts (pink) breakdown bone, and osteoblasts (blue) build bone.

Most bone is formed early in life. In the growing bones of children, bone formation occurs more rapidly than breakdown. Even after growth stops, bone mass continues to increase into young adulthood when **peak bone mass** is achieved, somewhere between the ages of 16 and 30.[11] When bone breakdown and formation are in balance bone mass remains constant. After about age 35 to 45, the amount of bone broken down begins to exceed that which is formed. If enough bone is lost, the skeleton is weakened and fractures occur easily, a condition known as osteoporosis.

peak bone mass The maximum bone density attained at any time in life, usually occurring in young adulthood.

Osteoporosis

Osteoporosis is caused by a loss of both the protein matrix and the mineral deposits of bone, resulting in a decrease in the total amount of bone (**Figure 11.11**). Although both types of bone are lost with age, the greater surface area of the spongy trabecular bone gives it a higher turnover rate compared to cortical bone and it is therefore more vulnerable to bone loss. As a result, the regions in the skeleton that have higher amounts of trabecular bone, such as the spine and the upper part of the femur, are more susceptible to fracture later in life.

Health Impact of Osteoporosis Osteoporosis is a silent disease because it initially causes no symptoms. By the fifth or sixth decade of life the bones of individuals with this disorder have weakened enough to cause back pain and bone fractures of the spine, hip, and wrist. Spinal compression fractures may result in loss of height and a stooped posture (called a dowager's hump) (**Figure 11.12**). Osteoporosis is a major public health problem in the United States and around the world. In the United States, about 10 million people over age 50 have osteoporosis and another 34 million are at risk due to low bone mass, called *osteopenia*. Osteoporosis leads to 1.5 million fractures annually, which account for $12 to $18 billion per year in direct medical costs.[12]

Factors Affecting Osteoporosis Risk The causes of osteoporosis are not fully understood, but the risk depends on the level of peak bone mass and the rate at which bone is lost. These are affected by age, genetics, gender, hormone levels, and lifestyle (**Table 11.2**).

Figure 11.11 Healthy trabecular bone (right) is denser than trabecular bone weakened by osteoporosis (left). (Dr. Michael Klein/Peter Arnold, Inc.)

When weakened by osteoporosis, the front edge of the vertebrae collapses more than the back edge, so the spine bends forward.

Normal spine

Osteoporotic spine

Figure 11.12 Effects of osteoporosis
Osteoporosis of the spine leads to a stooped posture and decreased stature. (Larry Mulvehill/Photo Researchers)

Table 11.2 Factors Affecting the Risk of Osteoporosis

Risk Factor	How It Affects Risk
Gender	Fractures due to osteoporosis are about twice as common in women as in men. Men are larger and heavier than women and therefore have a greater peak bone mass. Women lose more bone than men due to postmenopausal bone loss.
Age	Bone loss is a normal part of aging, and risk increases with age.
Race	African Americans have denser bones than do Caucasians and Southeast Asians, so their risk of osteoporosis is lower.
Family history	Having a family member with osteoporosis increases risk.
Body size	Individuals who are thin and light have an increased risk because they have less bone mass.
Smoking	Tobacco use weakens bones.
Exercise	Weight-bearing exercise, such as walking and jogging, throughout life strengthens bone, and increasing weight-bearing exercise at any age can increase your bone density.
Alcohol abuse	Long-term alcohol abuse reduces bone formation and interferes with the body's ability to absorb calcium.
Diet	A diet that is lacking in calcium and vitamin D plays a major role in the development of osteoporosis. Low calcium intake during the years of bone formation results in a lower peak bone mass, and low calcium intake in adulthood can accelerate bone loss.

age-related bone loss
The bone loss that occurs in both cortical and trabecular bone of men and women as they advance in age.

Age The risk of osteoporosis increases with age. This is because bones become progressively less dense after about age 35 when bone breakdown begins to exceed bone formation. This **age-related bone loss** occurs in both men and women. Bone is lost at a rate of about 0.3% to 0.5% per year. Factors that increase bone loss in older adults include a decline in calcium and vitamin D intake, a decrease in physical activity, a decrease in the efficiency of vitamin D activation by the kidney, and a decrease in dietary calcium absorption.[4] In addition, older adults typically spend less time in the sun and wear more clothing to cover the skin when outdoors, which may reduce calcium absorption by decreasing the amount of vitamin D synthesized in the skin.

menopause The physiological changes that mark the end of a woman's capacity to bear children.

postmenopausal bone loss
The accelerated bone loss that occurs in women for about 5 years after estrogen production decreases.

Gender and Hormonal Factors About 80% of those affected by osteoporosis are women. Osteoporosis-related fractures occur in one out of every two women over age 50 compared to about one in every eight men over 50.[12] The risk of osteoporosis is greater in women than men because men have a higher peak bone mass to begin with and because bone loss is accelerated in women for about 5 years after **menopause** (**Figure 11.13**). This **postmenopausal bone loss** is related to the drop in estrogen levels that occurs around menopause. Declining estrogen affects bone cells, allowing an increase in bone breakdown. It also decreases intestinal calcium absorption.[13] During this 5- to 7-year period bone loss may be increased 10-fold to a rate of 3% to 5% per year. After the postmenopausal period, women continue to lose bone but at a slower rate.

Genetics Twin and family studies have shown that genetic factors are important determinants of bone density, bone size, bone turnover, and osteoporosis risk.[14] Hormonal and lifestyle factors such as nutrition, activity level, smoking, and alcohol consumption interact with genetic factors over time to determine actual bone density. Genetic differences among racial groups lead to differences in the risk of osteoporosis.[15] For example, the incidence of osteoporosis in African-American women is half that of white women despite similar environmental risk factors. The reason for this lower risk of fractures is that African-American women begin menopause with

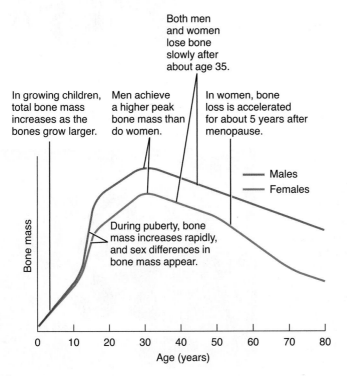

In growing children, total bone mass increases as the bones grow larger.

Men achieve a higher peak bone mass than do women.

Both men and women lose bone slowly after about age 35.

In women, bone loss is accelerated for about 5 years after menopause.

During puberty, bone mass increases rapidly, and sex differences in bone mass appear.

— Males
— Females

Bone mass

0   10   20   30   40   50   60   70   80
Age (years)

Figure 11.13 Bone mass by gender and age
Although both men and women lose bone after about age 35, women have a lower bone mineral density than men and experience accelerated bone loss after menopause.

higher bone density and have lower rates of postmenopausal bone loss. Bone density in Asians is generally lower than in non-Hispanic whites and that of Hispanics is similar to non-Hispanic whites, but bone density measures do not always explain racial differences in osteoporosis risk.[16,17]

Smoking and Alcohol Use Cigarette smoking and alcohol consumption both can decrease bone mass. Smoking affects ovarian function and calcium metabolism leading to an increase in bone loss and the risk of osteoporosis.[18] It is estimated that smoking increases the lifetime risk of developing a fracture of a vertebra by 13% in women and 32% in men and that it increases the risk of a hip fracture by 31% in women and 40% in men.[19] The effect of smoking may be partially reversed by smoking cessation. Although some evidence suggests that moderate drinking may decrease the risk of fracture in postmenopausal women, long-term heavy alcohol consumption can interfere with bone growth during adolescence and affect bone turnover in adults leading to bone loss.[20]

Exercise Weight-bearing exercise, such as walking and jogging, which puts direct weight over the skeleton, is good for bones. This mechanical stress stimulates the bones to become denser and stronger, increasing bone mass. In contrast, individuals who get no weight-bearing exercise, such as those with spinal cord injuries, those confined to bed, and astronauts in space, lose bone mass rapidly (see Science Applied: Bone: Lost in Space). Exercise during childhood and adolescence is thought to be particularly important for achieving a high peak bone mass. In adults who exercise regularly, there is a high correlation between muscle mass and bone mass, and both bone and muscle mass decrease with disuse.[21]

A greater body weight also increases bone mass.[22] Having greater body weight, whether that weight is due to an increase in muscle mass or to excess body fat, increases

(DAJ/Getty Images, Inc.)   (www.victorianoizquierdo.com/Getty Images, Inc.)   (Elena Schweitzer/Shutterstock)

Bone: Lost in Space

In 1962 when John Glenn became the first American to orbit the Earth, there was little concern about the effect that his 5-hour flight would have on his bones. By 1997, when Shannon Lucid spent 188 days aboard the Russian Mir space station, the effect of weightlessness on bone health had become a serious concern. Weight-bearing activities such as walking, jogging, and weight training are important for the maintenance of bone health. Under the force of Earth's gravity, these activities mechanically stress the bones, which stimulates the deposition of calcium into bone. When an astronaut goes into space, weightlessness eliminates this stimulus and calcium is lost from bone.[1] This elevates calcium levels in the rest of the body and may lead to kidney stones and calcification of the soft tissues.[2] Unless bone loss in space can be prevented, prolonged space flights may not be possible. Understanding and preventing bone loss in space will also benefit those on Earth who are at risk for osteoporosis.

Information on bone loss in space has been accumulating for 40 years. Studies done back in the 1960s and early 1970s during the Gemini and Apollo space missions showed that astronauts lost calcium from their bones during space travel. Skylab missions then offered an opportunity to study the effects of more extended periods in zero gravity. In one study, nine astronauts maintained a constant dietary intake and made continuous urine and fecal collections for 21 to 31 days before their flight, during their Skylab missions, and for 17 to 18 days after returning to Earth. The results showed that urinary calcium losses were increased during the flight. These losses occurred despite vigorous exercise regimens while in flight and were comparable to losses seen in normal adults subjected to prolonged bed rest.[3]

The study of bone metabolism in space continued with joint Russian-American studies, many conducted among astronauts who spent long periods on the Mir space station. Techniques used to study bones in space included measuring hormones and other indicators of bone metabolism in blood and urine samples before and after flights; measuring muscle strength and bone density before, during, and after return to Earth's gravity; and taking X-ray scans to determine bone mass. The most signif-

Shannon Lucid exercising on a treadmill aboard the Mir space station. (Courtesy NASA)

icant bone loss was found in weight-bearing parts of the skeleton; the lower vertebrae, hips, and upper femur—the same areas at risk for fracture in osteoporosis.[4] Once the astronauts returned to Earth, calcium loss slowed, but even after 6 months bone mass had not completely recovered in most subjects.[5] Biochemical measures indicate that the bone loss that occurs during space flight is due to an increase in bone resorption and decreased intestinal calcium absorption.[1] The decrease in calcium absorption is likely due to low levels of vitamin D from insufficient dietary intake and lack of ultraviolet light exposure during space flight.[1]

To try to counteract the effects of weightlessness, astronauts exercise in space on stationary bikes and treadmills and pull against bungee cords. Exercises that provide higher loads can counteract bone loss to some degree but do not prevent it.[1] In addition to weight-bearing exercise future studies may address nutritional factors such as vitamin D and calcium intakes as well as appropriate levels of other nutrients that affect bone metabolism such as vitamin K, sodium, and protein. Understanding how to optimize nutrient intake and exercise patterns for bone mineral retention in space will help astronauts remain healthy during long space flights and may do the same for elderly or bedridden persons on Earth who are at risk of bone loss due to inactivity.

[1] Smith, S. M., Wastney, M. E., O'Brien, K. O., et al. Bone markers, calcium metabolism, and calcium kinetics during extended-duration space flight on the Mir space station. *J. Bone Miner. Res.* 20:208–218, 2005.

[2] Whitson, P. A., Pietrzyk, R. A., Morukov, B. V., and Sams, C. F. The risk of renal stone formation during and after long duration space flight. *Nephron* 89:264–270, 2001.

[3] Whedon, G. D., Lutwak, L., Rambaut, P., et al. Mineral and nitrogen metabolic studies on Skylab flights and comparison with effects of earth long-term recumbency. *Life Sci. Space Res.* 14:119–127, 1976.

[4] Grigoriev, A. I., Oganov, V. S., Bakulin, A. V., et al. Clinical and physiological evaluation of bone changes among astronauts after long-term space flights. *Aviakosm. Ekolog. Med.* 32:21–25, 1998.

[5] Shackelford, L. C., Oganov, V., LeBlanc, A., et al. Bone mineral loss and recovery after shuttle-Mir flights. Available online at spaceflight.nasa.gov/history/shuttle-mir/science/hls/musc/sc-hls-bone.htm. Accessed June 17, 2005.

bone mass because it increases the amount of weight the bones must support in day-to-day activities. In postmenopausal women excess body fat may also reduce risk because adipose tissue produces estrogen, which helps maintain bone mass and enhances calcium absorption. Therefore, the risk and severity of osteoporosis is decreased in individuals with higher body weight and fat.

Diet Diet can have a significant effect on osteoporosis risk. A low calcium intake is the most significant dietary factor contributing to osteoporosis. Calcium is necessary for bone development. Adequate calcium intake during childhood and adolescence is an important factor in maximizing bone density; low calcium intakes during the years of bone formation result in a lower peak bone mass. If calcium intake is low after peak bone mass has been achieved, the rate of bone loss may be increased and, along with it, the risk of osteoporosis.

Despite its importance, calcium intake alone does not predict the risk of osteoporosis. Other dietary components affect bone mass and bone health by affecting calcium absorption, urinary calcium losses, and bone physiology. Low intakes of vitamin D reduce calcium absorption, thereby increasing the risk of osteoporosis. Diets high in phytate, oxalates, and tannins also reduce calcium absorption. High sodium has been implicated as a risk factor for osteoporosis because high dietary sodium intake increases calcium loss in the urine.[23] Adequate protein is necessary for bone health, but increasing protein intake increases urinary calcium losses. Despite this, high protein intakes are generally not associated with a higher risk of osteoporosis. This is because diets higher in protein are typically higher in calcium and may enhance calcium absorption. Bone mass depends more on the ratio of calcium to protein than the amount of protein alone. High levels of protein therefore do not have a negative effect on bone mass when calcium intake is adequate.[24] Higher intakes of zinc, magnesium, potassium, fiber, and vitamin C—nutrients that are plentiful in fruits and vegetables—are associated with greater bone mass[25] (see Critical Thinking: Osteoporosis Risk).

Preventing and Treating Osteoporosis

The best treatment for osteoporosis is to prevent it by achieving a high peak bone mass. Maximizing calcium deposition into bone is especially important during childhood and adolescence. Individuals with the highest peak bone mass after adolescence have a protective advantage over bone loss later in life.[12] A high peak bone mass can be achieved by maintaining an active lifestyle that includes weight-bearing exercise, limiting cigarette smoking and alcohol consumption, and consuming a diet that assures adequate calcium levels. Once osteoporosis has occurred, medications may help restore bone mass and prevent fractures.

Maximizing Dietary Calcium Americans typically do not consume enough calcium. The risk of osteoporosis can be minimized by consuming a diet that is adequate in calcium as well as vitamin D. Limiting intake of phosphorus, protein, and sodium may also be beneficial. Milk is the major source of calcium in the U.S. diet, but teenage boys and girls today drink more soda than milk. Since the 1970s, children and teens (ages 2 to 18 years) have more than doubled the number of kcalories they consume from soft drinks while cutting the kcalories they obtain from milk by 34%.[26] This has significantly reduced their calcium intake. Both the DASH Eating Plan and MyPyramid recommend 3 cups of milk or milk products plus 2 to 5 cups of vegetables daily to ensure adequate calcium intake. Ice cream, puddings, and soups made with milk are also good calcium sources but contribute discretionary kcalories from added sugar and fat.

Individuals who are lactose intolerant can meet their calcium needs by consuming high-calcium foods that contribute little or no lactose. For those who can tolerate some lactose, fermented dairy products such as yogurt and cheese may be tolerated. Lactose-free calcium sources include dark-green leafy vegetables such as

Critical Thinking
Osteoporosis Risk

(©iStockphoto)

Background:

Mika is nearly 50. Although she has no symptoms, she is worried about her risk for osteoporosis. Her mother is 75 and recently suffered a fractured hip due to reduced bone density caused by osteoporosis. Her previously independent mother is now living in a nursing home and struggling to return to her former life. Mika is frightened that she will face the same future. She finds the following osteoporosis risk factor questionnaire in a health magazine and fills it out. She also records her intake for one day.

FOOD	ENERGY (KCALS)	CALCIUM (MG)
Breakfast		
Eggs (2 large)	150	5
Toast with margarine (2 slices)	200	50
Orange juice (3/4 cup)	80	15
Coffee with cream (1 cup)	45	35
Lunch		
Bologna sandwich on white bread with mayonnaise	260	60
Lettuce and tomato (2 slices)	10	5
Milk (1 cup)	120	300
Apple (1 medium)	80	10
Snack		
Chips (1 oz)	150	10
Beer (12 fl oz)	140	20
Dinner		
Roast beef (3 oz)	225	5
Mashed potatoes and gravy (1 cup)	350	50
Green beans (1 cup)	35	60
Iced tea (12 oz)	4	0
Ice cream (1/2 cup)	140	70
Total	1989	695

Critical Thinking Questions

Evaluate Mika's risk for osteoporosis by looking at her answers on the questionnaire. Why would her milk intake and activity level as a child affect her risk now?

▼

How does Mika's calcium intake compare with the recommendations? Suggest changes she could make in her diet to increase her calcium without increasing her kcalorie intake.

▼

Do you think Mika should take a calcium supplement? Why or why not?

Data:

OSTEOPOROSIS QUESTIONNAIRE

Gender?	__ Male X Female
Age?	__ 12 to 18 years __ 19 to 30 years X 31 to 50 years __ 51 to 70 years __ > 70 years
Have you ever broken a bone?	__ Yes X No
What is your bone density?	X Never been measured __ Normal __ Low density
What is your Body Mass Index?	__ <18.5 kg/m² __ 18.5 to 24.9 X 25.0 to 29.9 __ 30.0 to 34.9 __ > 35
Do you smoke cigarettes?	X Yes __ No
How much alcohol do you drink?	__ > 2 drinks/day __ 1–2 drinks/day X Several drinks per week __ None
How much milk do you drink?	__ None X 2 or fewer glasses a day __ 3 or more glasses a day
How much milk did you drink as a child?	__ None X 2 or fewer glasses a day __ 3 or more glasses a day
How much milk did you drink as an adolescent?	X None __ 2 or fewer glasses a day __ 3 or more glasses a day
How often do you exercise?	X Less than 3 times a week __ 3 or more times a week
What types of activities do you participate in?	__ None X Walking, jogging, tennis __ Swimming, bicycling
What is your exercise history?	__ I have been active all my life. X I was active as a child but no longer exercise often. __ I recently started exercising.
If you are female, are you currently menstruating?	X Yes __ No
If you are postmenopausal, how long ago did menopause occur?	__ Less than 5 years ago __ More than 5 years ago
Do you have a family history of osteoporosis?	X Yes __ No

 iProfile Use iProfile to find out how much calcium is provided by the nondairy foods in your diet.

(a)

(b)

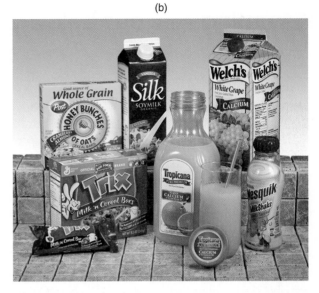

Figure 11.14 (a) Dairy products, fish consumed with bones, leafy greens, and legumes are good sources of calcium. (b) A variety of calcium-fortified foods are also available to help meet needs. (Felicia Martinez/PhotoEdit; Andy Washnik)

kale, broccoli, and mustard greens; soy products processed with calcium; and fish consumed with the bones (**Figure 11.14a**). Drinking milk treated with the lactose-digesting enzyme, lactase (Lactaid milk), or consuming lactase pills to help digest the lactose consumed with a meal can also help those with lactose intolerance to meet calcium needs (see Chapter 4). Calcium supplements and fortified foods such as break-fast cereals and juice products also provide calcium without lactose (**Figure 11.14b**) (see Off the Label: Counting All Your Calcium).

Calcium Supplements Individuals who do not meet their calcium needs with diet alone can benefit from calcium supplementation. In young individuals sup-plemental calcium can promote the development of a higher peak bone mass. In postmenopausal women, calcium supplements have a small but beneficial effect on bone mass.[27] Supplementation with 700 to 800 IU of vitamin D per day appears to reduce the risk of hip fractures in elderly persons.[28] Because calcium absorption decreases when large amounts are consumed at one time, calcium availability is better when a lower-dose calcium supplement (no more than 500 mg per dose) is taken twice a day than when a supplement that provides 100% of the RDA is taken once a day.

Osteoporosis Treatment Medications used to treat osteoporosis include hormones and drugs known as bisphosphonates. Replacing the hormones estrogen and prog-esterone, lost in menopause—known as *hormone replacement therapy*—has been shown to reduce bone loss and restore some lost bone, but this therapy carries risks and its use should be considered within the context of the individual's other health risks.[29] Administration of calcitonin, a hormone that acts by inhibiting bone resorp-tion, by injection or nasal spray can reduce bone loss, and its effects are enhanced by calcium supplementation.[30] Bisphosphonates are not hormones. They act by binding to the bone surface and inhibiting the activity of osteoclasts. They have been shown to prevent postmenopausal bone loss, increase bone mineral density, and reduce the risk of fractures in patients with osteoporosis.[30] Exercise can also be helpful in treat-ing osteoporosis. Minerals other than calcium that have been used to prevent and treat bone loss include magnesium, fluoride, and boron, but results from these have been equivocal.

Off the Label
Counting All Your Calcium

To find out if you get enough calcium, you'll need to count all your sources. You can obtain calcium from natural sources such as milk, yogurt, and leafy greens, from foods fortified with the mineral, and from calcium supplements.

You can see if a packaged food is a good source of calcium by looking at the label. The Nutrition Facts panel lists the % Daily Value for calcium. To calculate the milligrams of calcium in that food, multiply the % Daily Value by 1000 mg (the Daily Value for calcium). Descriptors such as "high in calcium" or "a good source of calcium" can help you identify foods that make a significant calcium contribution (see table). Foods high in calcium may include the health claim that a diet high in calcium helps reduce the risk of osteoporosis.

If you rely on supplements to increase your calcium count, be aware that a multivitamin and mineral supplement provides only a small amount of the calcium you need. To get a significant amount, use the Supplement Facts label to choose a supplement that contains a calcium compound alone or calcium with vitamin D (which aids calcium absorption).

The form of calcium in supplements is also important. Calcium carbonate is absorbed as well as the calcium from milk. Calcium citrate, calcium gluconate, calcium lactate, calcium citrate-malate, and calcium phosphate are absorbed as well as calcium from a mixed diet.[1] Avoid calcium preparations such as bone meal, coral calcium, powdered bone, dolomite, and oyster shell, which may contain contaminants that are dangerous if consumed routinely.[2]

Over-the-counter antacids can also be taken to supplement calcium intake. These have a Drug Facts, rather than a Supplement Facts, label. Many of these, such as Tums, which contains calcium carbonate, are safe, effective calcium supplements. However, antacids that contain aluminum and magnesium may actually increase calcium loss.

In short, to see if you are getting enough calcium, check the labels on your foods, supplements, and medications; consider the form of calcium in each; and watch for excesses of other nutrients and contaminants. Sound complicated? Maybe an extra glass of milk is easier.

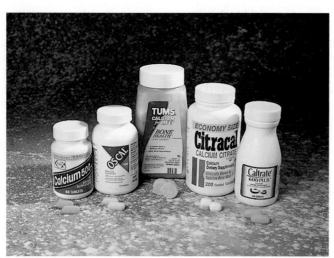

(George Semple)

Calcium on Food Labels

High-calcium, rich in calcium, excellent per source of calcium	Contains 200 mg of calcium or more per serving
Good source of calcium	Contains 100 mg to 190 mg of calcium per serving
More or added calcium	Contains at least 100 mg more per serving than reference food

[1]Mortensen, L., and Charles, P. Bioavailability of calcium supplements and the effect of vitamin D: Comparisons between milk, calcium carbonate, and calcium carbonate plus vitamin D. *Am. J. Clin. Nutr.* 63:354–357, 1996.

[2]Bourgoin, B. P., Evans, D. R., Cornett, J. R., et al. Lead content in 70 brands of dietary calcium supplements. *Am. J. Public Health* 83:1155–1160, 1993.

11.4 Phosphorus

Learning Objectives

- Describe the functions of phosphorus in the body.
- Plan a diet that meets the recommended intakes for calcium and phosphorus.

Phosphorus makes up about 1% of the adult body by weight, and 85% of this is found in bones and teeth.[1] The phosphorus in soft tissues has both structural and regulatory roles. In nature, phosphorus is most often found in combination with oxygen as phosphate (**Figure 11.15**).

Phosphorus in the Diet

Phosphorus is more widely distributed in the diet than calcium. Like calcium, it is found in dairy products such as milk, yogurt, and cheese, but meat, cereals, bran, eggs, nuts, and fish are also good sources (**Figure 11.16**). Food additives used in baked goods, cheese, processed meats, and soft drinks also contribute to dietary phosphorus.

Phosphorus in the Digestive Tract

Phosphorus is more readily absorbed than calcium. About 60% to 70% is absorbed from a typical diet. There is no evidence that the efficiency of absorption is affected by the amount in the diet. Vitamin D does aid phosphorus absorption via an active mechanism, but most absorption occurs by a mechanism that does not depend on vitamin D. Therefore, when vitamin D is deficient, phosphorus can still be absorbed, but its absorption is reduced.

Figure 11.15 Phosphate group
When inorganic phosphate (phosphorus combined with oxygen) joins with another molecule it is called a phosphate group.

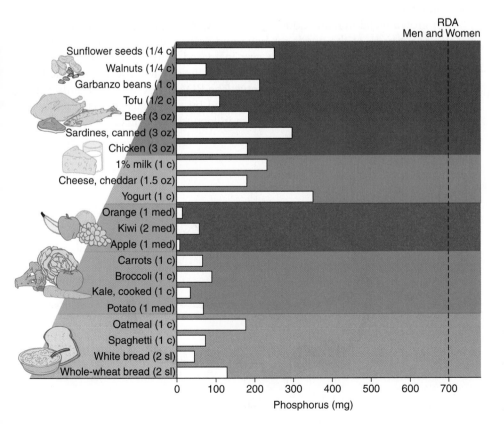

Figure 11.16 Phosphorus content of MyPyramid food groups
Adults can obtain their RDA of phosphorus (dashed line) by consuming foods in all the food groups.

Phosphorus in the Body

Phosphorus is an important component of a number of molecules with structural or regulatory roles (see Table 11.1). Phosphorus, along with calcium, forms hydroxyapatite crystals that provide rigidity to bones. Phosphorus is a component of the water-soluble head of phospholipid molecules, which form the structure of cell membranes. Phosphorus is a major constituent of the genetic material DNA and RNA and it is essential for energy metabolism because the high-energy bonds of ATP are formed between phosphate groups (**Figure 11.17**). Phosphorus is also a component of other high-energy compounds, including creatine phosphate, which provides energy to exercising muscles. Phosphorus-containing molecules are important in relaying signals to the interior of cells to mediate hormone action and perform other metabolic activities. Phosphorus is involved in regulating enzyme activity because the addition of a phosphate group can activate or deactivate certain enzymes. It is also part of the phosphate buffer system that helps regulate the pH in the cytosol of all cells so that chemical reactions can proceed normally.

Blood levels of phosphorus are not as strictly controlled as those of calcium, but levels are maintained in a ratio with calcium that allows bone mineralization. When blood levels of phosphorus are low, the active form of vitamin D is synthesized. This increases the absorption of both phosphorus and calcium from the intestine and increases their release from bone. When phosphorus intake is high, more is lost in the urine, so plasma levels rise only slightly. A rise in serum phosphorus indirectly stimulates PTH release, causing phosphorus excretion and calcium retention by the kidney as well as calcium release from bone. When PTH is not secreted (such as when calcium levels rise), phosphorus is retained by the kidney and calcium is excreted.

Recommended Phosphorus Intake

The RDA for phosphorus is set at 700 mg per day for men and women 19 to 50 years of age.[1] This is the amount needed to maintain normal blood phosphorus levels. Because neither absorption nor urinary losses change significantly with age, the RDA is the same for older adults.

Life Cycle

For growing children and adolescents, the RDA is based on the phosphorus intake necessary to meet the needs for bone and soft-tissue growth. There is no evidence that phosphorus requirements are increased during pregnancy; intestinal absorption increases by about 10%, which is sufficient to provide the additional phosphorus needed by the mother and fetus. The RDA is not increased during lactation because the phosphorus in milk is provided by an increase in bone resorption and a decrease in urinary excretion that are independent of dietary intake of either phosphorus or calcium.

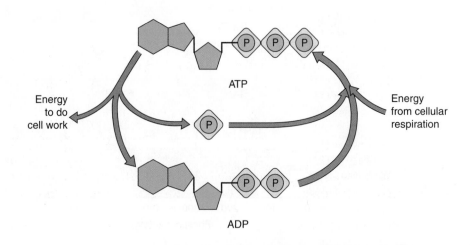

Figure 11.17 Phosphorus and ATP
Breaking the high-energy bond between the second and third phosphate groups of ATP releases energy for cellular work. The ADP (adenosine diphosphate) that is formed can be converted back to ATP by using the energy trapped by the electron transport chain of cellular respiration to add a phosphate group.

Phosphorus Deficiency

Phosphorus deficiency can lead to bone loss, weakness, and loss of appetite. Deficiency is rare in healthy people because phsophorus is so widely distributed in foods. Most people in the United States easily meet their needs; the average daily intake is about 1400 mg for adult men and 1000 mg for adult women.[1] Marginal phosphorus deficiencies are most common in premature infants, vegans, alcoholics, and the elderly. Marginal phosphorus status may also be caused by losses due to chronic diarrhea and overuse of aluminum-containing antacids, which prevent phosphorus absorption.

Phosphorus Toxicity

Toxicity from high phosphorus intake is rare in healthy adults, but excessive intakes can lead to bone resorption. Typical intake in the U.S. is above recommendations. One reason is the increased use of phosphorus-containing food additives. This has lead to concern about its impact on bone health.[12] High phosphorus intake has been found to increase bone resorption, but some of this can be prevented by adequate calcium intake.[31] Therefore levels of phosphorus intake typical in the United States are not believed to affect bone health as long as calcium intake is adequate. Based on the upper level of normal serum phosphate, a UL for phosphorus of 4 grams per day has been set for adults ages 19 to 70 years.[1]

11.5 Magnesium

Learning Objectives

- Describe the functions of magnesium in the body.
- Name three foods that are good sources of magnesium.

There are approximately 25 grams of magnesium in the adult human body. Magnesium is a mineral that affects the metabolism of calcium, sodium, and potassium.

Magnesium in the Diet

Magnesium is found in leafy greens such as spinach and kale because it is a component of chlorophyll. Nuts, seeds, bananas, and the germ and bran of whole grains are also good sources (**Figure 11.18**). Processed foods are generally poor sources. For example, removing the bran and germ of the wheat kernel reduces the magnesium content of a cup of white flour to only 28 mg, compared with the 166 mg in a cup of whole-wheat flour. In areas with hard water, the water supply may provide a significant amount of magnesium.

Magnesium in the Digestive Tract

About 50% of the magnesium in the diet is absorbed, and the percentage decreases as intake increases. The active form of vitamin D can enhance magnesium absorption to a small extent, and the presence of phytate decreases absorption. As calcium in the diet increases, the absorption of magnesium decreases, so the use of calcium supplements can reduce the absorption of magnesium.

Magnesium in the Body

About 50% to 60% of the magnesium in the body is in bone, where it is essential for the maintenance of structure. Most of the remaining body magnesium is present inside cells, where it is the second most abundant positively charged intracellular ion (after potassium). Magnesium is associated with the negative charge on

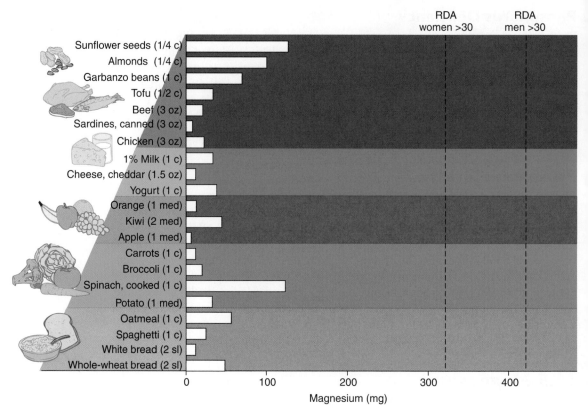

Figure 11.18 Magnesium content of MyPyramid food groups
Magnesium is found in nuts, seeds, legumes, and leafy greens; the dashed lines represent the RDA for adult men and women over age 30.

phosphate-containing molecules such as ATP (**Figure 11.19**). Magnesium is also involved in regulating calcium homeostasis and is needed for the action of vitamin D and many hormones including PTH.[32]

Magnesium is a cofactor for over 300 enzymes. It is necessary for the generation of ATP from carbohydrate, lipid, and protein (see Table 11.1). In some of these reactions it is involved indirectly as a stabilizer of ATP, and in others, directly as an enzyme activator. Magnesium is needed for the activity of the sodium-potassium ATPase pump, which is responsible for active transport of sodium and potassium across membranes. It is therefore essential for maintenance of electrical potentials across cell membranes and proper functioning of the nerves and muscles, including those in the heart. It is important for DNA and RNA synthesis and for almost every step in protein synthesis. Therefore, magnesium is particularly important for dividing growing cells.

The kidneys closely regulate blood levels of magnesium. When magnesium intake is low, excretion in the urine is decreased. As intake increases, urinary excretion increases to maintain normal blood levels. This efficient regulation permits homeostasis over a wide range of dietary intakes.

Figure 11.19 Magnesium and ATP

Magnesium stabilizes ATP structure by forming a magnesium-ATP complex. It is therefore important for all reactions that use or generate ATP.

Mg^{2+} ATP Complex

Recommended Magnesium Intake

The RDA for magnesium is 400 mg per day for young men and 310 mg per day for young women.[1] This is based on the maintenance of total body magnesium balance over time. The RDA is slightly higher for men and women over age 30; 420 and 320 mg/day, respectively. A serving of whole-grain breakfast cereal, spinach, or legumes contains about 100 mg of magnesium.

The requirement for pregnancy is increased by 35 mg per day to account for the addition of lean body mass. No increase is recommended for lactation because magnesium is released when bone is resorbed and urinary excretion is decreased. An AI is set for infants based on the magnesium content of human milk.

Life Cycle

Magnesium Deficiency

Magnesium deficiency is rare in the general population. It does occur in those with alcoholism, malnutrition, kidney disease, and gastrointestinal disease, as well as in those who use diuretics that increase magnesium loss in the urine. Deficiency symptoms include nausea, muscle weakness and cramping, irritability, mental derangement, and changes in blood pressure and heartbeat. Low blood magnesium levels affect levels of blood calcium and potassium; therefore some of these symptoms may be due to alterations in the levels of these other minerals.

Although overt deficiency is rare, the typical intake of magnesium in the United States is below the RDA. Low intakes of magnesium have been associated with a number of chronic diseases, including osteoporosis.[33] Low magnesium may also affect cardiovascular health. Dietary patterns higher in magnesium help reduce blood pressure and epidemiological evidence suggests that humans with good magnesium status are at a lower risk of atherosclerosis.[34] Areas with hard water, which is high in calcium and magnesium, tend to have lower rates of death from cardiovascular disease.

Magnesium Toxicity and Supplements

No adverse effects have been observed from ingestion of magnesium from food, but toxicity may occur from concentrated sources such as magnesium-containing drugs and supplements. Toxicity has been reported in elderly patients with impaired kidney function who frequently use magnesium-containing laxatives and antacids such as milk of magnesia. Magnesium toxicity is characterized by nausea, vomiting, low blood pressure, and cardiovascular changes. The UL for adults and adolescents over 9 years of age is 350 mg from nonfood sources of magnesium.

11.6 Sulfur

Learning Objective

• Discuss the role of sulfur in the body.

Dietary sulfur is found in organic molecules such as the sulfur-containing amino acids in proteins and the sulfur-containing vitamins. It is also found in some inorganic food preservatives such as sulfur dioxide, sodium sulfite, and sodium and potassium bisulfite, which are used as antioxidants.

In the body, the sulfur-containing amino acids methionine and cysteine are needed for protein synthesis. Cysteine is also part of the compound glutathione, which is important in detoxifying drugs and protecting cells from oxidative damage. The vitamins thiamin and biotin, essential for ATP production, contain sulfur. Sulfur-containing ions are important in regulating acid-base balance.

There is no recommended intake for sulfur, and no deficiencies are known when protein needs are met (see Table 11.1).

Outcome

Margie's hip fracture is not surprising, given her medical history. She is a small woman who never got much exercise or consumed much calcium—factors that contribute to a low peak bone mass. In addition, because she has been postmenopausal for a number of years, Margie has been losing bone faster than her body has replaced it. As a result, her bones are so brittle that the impact of stepping off a curb caused a bone in her hip to break. If Margie had had regular physical exams, her doctors would have noted her low bone density and begun treatment, which might have prevented the hip fracture.

After she broke her hip, Margie spent 4 months in a rehabilitation facility. She was lucky, however, and has been able to return to her old life. Now, a year later, she continues to treat her disease with bisphosphonate drugs, which inhibit bone resorption, as well as calcium and vitamin D supplements. As her mobility improves she is trying to increase the time she spends walking to 30 minutes on most days. She was thankful to be able to celebrate her grandson's first birthday in her own home.

APPLICATIONS

Personal Nutrition

1. **Do you get enough calcium?**
   a. Using iProfile and the food record you kept in Chapter 2, calculate your average calcium intake.
   b. How does your intake compare with the AI for calcium for someone of your age and gender?
   c. If your calcium intake is below the AI, suggest modifications to increase the amount of calcium in your diet without significantly increasing your energy intake.

2. **How much calcium do fortified foods contribute?**
   a. Choose three foods that are fortified with calcium and use their labels to determine how much calcium is in a serving of each.
   b. How many servings per day of each would you need to consume to meet your calcium needs?
   c. Are there other dietary components in any of these foods that would interfere with calcium absorption or utilization?

General Nutrition Issues

1. Many people in the United States must limit milk consumption due to lactose intolerance. How can they meet their calcium needs?

   a. Use iProfile to plan a day's diet that meets your calcium needs but does not include any dairy products or calcium-fortified foods.

   b. Is this a reasonable diet to follow every day? Would you recommend including fortified foods or calcium supplements? Why or why not?

2. Imagine you are a scientist with the U.S. Department of Agriculture and you have been assigned the task of deciding on a food or group of foods that will be fortified with calcium to assure that the population meets their calcium needs.

   a. What food or group of foods would you recommend? Why?

   b. Does the food or group of foods contain dietary components that interfere with calcium absorption?

   c. Is this a food or group of foods that is consumed by the population groups most at risk for calcium deficiency?

   d. How much calcium would you recommend adding? Would this amount meet recommendations but not put the population at risk of calcium toxicity?

Summary

11.1 What Are Minerals?

- Minerals are elements needed by the body to regulate chemical reactions and provide structure. They are found in both plant and animal foods.

- Minerals are added to some foods through fortification and get into others as a result of contamination. Dietary supplements are also a source of minerals.

- Mineral bioavailability is affected by body needs as well as interactions with other minerals, vitamins, and dietary components such as fiber, phytates, oxylates, and tannins.

11.2 Calcium

- Sources of calcium in the American diet include dairy products, fish consumed with bones, and leafy green vegetables. Fortified foods also contribute to calcium intake.

- Adequate calcium absorption depends on adequate levels of vitamin D. The absorption of calcium is reduced by the presence of tannins, fiber, phytates, and oxalates. Calcium absorption varies with life stage and is highest during infancy and pregnancy, when needs are greatest.

- Most of the calcium in the body is in bone. Calcium not found in bone is essential for cell communication, nerve transmission, muscle contraction, blood clotting, and blood pressure regulation. Blood levels of calcium are regulated by parathyroid hormone (PTH) and calcitonin. PTH stimulates the release of calcium from bone, decreases calcium excretion by the kidney, and activates vitamin D to increase the amount of calcium absorbed from the gastrointestinal tract and released from bone. Calcitonin blocks calcium release from bone.

- The AI for calcium ranges from 1000 to 1200 mg per day for adults and is 1300 mg per day in adolescents.

- Calcium deficiency can reduce bone mass and increase the risk of osteoporosis. Too much calcium can contribute to the formation of kidney stones, raise blood calcium levels, and interfere with the absorption of other minerals.

11.3 Calcium and Bone Health

- Bone is a living tissue that is constantly being broken down and reformed in a process known as bone remodeling. Early in life, bone formation occurs more rapidly than bone breakdown to allow bone growth and an increase in bone mass. Peak bone mass occurs in young adulthood. With age, bone breakdown begins to outpace formation, causing a decrease in bone mass; this is accelerated in women for about 5 years after menopause.

- Osteoporosis is a condition in which loss of bone mass increases the risk of bone fractures. The risk of osteoporosis is related to the level of peak bone mass and the rate of bone loss. These are affected by age, gender, hormone levels, genetics, smoking and alcohol use, exercise, and diet.

- Osteoporosis risk can be reduced by an active lifestyle and a diet adequate in calcium and vitamin D and not excessive in phosphorus, sodium, or protein. Osteoporosis is treated with supplements of calcium and vitamin D, medications that inhibit bone breakdown, and in some cases hormone replacement therapy.

11.4 Phosphorus

- Phosphorus is more widely distributed in the diet than calcium. It is found in dairy products such as milk, yogurt, and cheese, but meat, cereals, bran, eggs, nuts, and fish are also good sources. Food additives used in baked goods, cheese, processed meats, and soft drinks also contribute to dietary phosphorus.

- About 60% to 70% of the phosphorus in a typical diet is absorbed. Vitamin D aids phosphorus absorption via an active mechanism, but most absorption occurs by a mechanism that does not depend on vitamin D.

- Most of the phosphorus in the body is found in bones and teeth. In addition to its structural role in these tissues, phosphorus is an essential component of phospholipids,

ATP, and DNA. Phosphorus is also part of a buffer system that helps prevent changes in pH.

- The RDA for adults is 700 mg per day.
- Phosphorus deficiency is rare in healthy people because it is so widely distributed in foods. It can lead to bone loss, weakness, and loss of appetite.
- Toxicity from high phosphorus intake is rare in healthy adults, but excessive intakes can lead to bone resorption. The levels of phosphorus intake typical in the United States are not believed to affect bone health as long as calcium intake is adequate.

11.5 Magnesium

- Magnesium is found in leafy greens such as spinach and kale because it is a component of chlorophyll. Nuts, seeds, bananas, and the germ and bran of whole grains are also good sources.
- About half of the magnesium in the diet is absorbed, and the percentage decreases as intake increases. The active form of vitamin D can enhance magnesium absorption and the presence of phytates decreases absorption.
- Magnesium is important for bone health, and it is needed as a cofactor for numerous reactions throughout the body. In

reactions involved in energy metabolism it acts as an enzyme activator and stabilizer of ATP. It is also needed to maintain membrane potentials; thus it is essential for nerve and muscle conductivity. Homeostasis is regulated by the kidney.

- The RDA for magnesium is 400 mg per day for young men and 310 mg per day for young women.
- Magnesium deficiency is rare in the general population. It does occur in those with alcohoism, malnutrition, kidney disease, and gastrointestinal disease. Symptoms include nausea, muscle weakness and cramping, irritability, mental derangement, and changes in blood pressure and heartbeat.
- No adverse effects have been observed from ingestion of magnesium from food, but toxicity may occur from magnesium-containing drugs and supplements.

11.6 Sulfur

- Sulfur is in the diet as preformed organic molecules such as the amino acids methionine and cysteine, which are needed to synthesize proteins and glutathione; and the vitamins thiamin and biotin, needed for energy metabolism. Sulfur is also part of a buffer system that regulates acid-base balance. A dietary deficiency is unknown in the absence of protein malnutrition.

Review Questions

1. Explain the difference between major minerals and trace elements.

2. List four factors that can affect mineral bioavailability.

3. What is the major source of calcium in the North American diet?

4. What is the function of calcium in bones and teeth?

5. What are the roles of calcium in body fluids?

6. How are blood calcium levels restored when they drop too low? Rise too high?

7. What is bone remodeling?

8. How does the rate of bone formation and breakdown change throughout life?

9. How does the level of peak bone mass affect the risk of osteoporosis?

10. How is calcium intake related to the risk of osteoporosis?

11. What factors other than calcium intake are related to the risk of osteoporosis?

12. List sources of dietary calcium acceptable to those who are lactose intolerant.

13. Name some food sources of phosphorus.

14. What are the functions of phosphorus in the body?

15. Name some food sources of magnesium.

16. What is the function of magnesium in the body?

17. Where is sulfur found in the body?

References

1. Institute of Medicine, Food and Nutrition Board. *Dietary Reference Intakes for Calcium, Phosphorus, Magnesium, Vitamin D, and Fluoride*. Washington, DC: National Academies Press, 1997.

2. Heaney, R. P., Weaver, C. M., and Recker, R. R. Calcium absorption from spinach. *Am. J. Clin. Nutr.* 47:707–709, 1988.

3. Bronner, F., and Pansu, D. Nutritional aspects of calcium absorption. *J. Nutr.* 129:9–12, 1999.

4. Nordin, B. E. C., Need, A. G., Morris, H. A. et al. Effect of age on calcium absorption in postmenopausal women. *Am. J. Clin. Nutr.* 80:998–1002, 2004.

5. Conlin, P. R., Chow, D., Miller, E. R., III, et al. The effect of dietary patterns on blood pressure control in hypertensive patients: Results from the Dietary Approaches to Stop Hypertension (DASH) trial. *Am. J. Hypertens.* 13:949–955, 2000.

6. Prentice, A. Micronutrients and the bone mineral content of the mother, fetus and newborn. *J. Nutr.* 133(5 Suppl 2): 1693S–1699S, 2003.

7. Beall, D. P., and Scofield, R. H. Milk-alkali syndrome associated with calcium carbonate consumption. Report

of 7 patients with parathyroid hormone levels and an estimate of prevalence among patients hospitalized with hypercalcemia. *Medicine* (Baltimore). 74:89–96, 1995.

8. Minihane, A. M., and Fairweather-Tait, S. J. Effect of calcium supplementation on daily nonheme-iron absorption and long-term iron status. *Am. J. Clin. Nutr.* 68:96–102, 1998.

9. Wood, R. J., and Zheng, J. J. High dietary calcium intakes reduce zinc absorption and balance in humans. *Am. J. Clin. Nutr.* 65:1803–1809, 1997.

10. Shea, M. K., and Booth, S. L. Update on the role of vitamin K in skeletal health. *Nutr. Rev.* 66:549–557, 2008.

11. Wang, Q., and Seeman, E. Skeletal growth and peak bone strength. *Best Pract. Res. Clin. Endocrinol. Metab.* 22:687–700, 2008.

12. National Institutes of Health. Consensus Development Conference Statement. Osteoporosis Prevention, Diagnosis and Therapy, March 27–29, 2000. Available online at odp.od.nih.gov/consensus/cons/111/111_intro.htm/ Accessed October 8, 2009.

13. Van Cromphaut, S. J., Rummens, K., Stockmans, I. et al. Intestinal calcium transporter genes are upregulated by estrogens and the reproductive cycle through vitamin D receptor-independent mechanisms. *J. Bone Miner. Res.* 18:1725–1736, 2003.

14. Walker, M. D., Novotny, R., Bilezikian, J. P., and Weaver, C. M. Race and diet interactions in the acquisition, maintenance, and loss of bone. *J. Nutr.* 138:1256S–1260S, 2008.

15. National Institute of Arthritis and Musculoskeletal and Skin Diseases. *Osteoporosis Overview.* Available online at www.niams.nih.gov/Health_Info/Bone/Osteoporosis/ default.asp/. Accessed January 3, 2009.

16. Ferrari, S. Human genetics of osteoporosis. *Best Pract. Res. Clin. Endocrinol. Metab.* 22:723–735, 2009.

17. Looker, A. C. The skeleton, race, and ethnicity. *J. Clin. Endocrinol. Metab.* 87:3047–3050, 2002.

18. Kapoor, D., and Jones, T. H. Smoking and hormones in health and endocrine disorders. *Eur. J. Endocrinol.* 152:491–499, 2005.

19. Ward, K. D., and Klesges, R. C. A meta-analysis of the effects of cigarette smoking on bone mineral density. *Calcif. Tissue Int.* 68:259–270, 2001.

20. Sampson, H. W. Alcohol and other factors affecting osteoporosis risk in women. *Alcohol Res. Health* 26:292–298, 2002.

21. Anderson, J. J. The important role of physical activity in skeletal development: How exercise may counter low calcium intake. *Am. J. Clin. Nutr.* 6:1384–1386, 2000.

22. Reid, I. R. Relationships between fat and bone. *Osteoporos. Int.* 19:595–606, 2008.

23. Teucher, B., and Fairweather-Tait, S. Dietary sodium as a risk factor for osteoporosis: Where is the evidence? *Proc. Nutr. Soc.* 62:859–866, 2003.

24. Kerstetter, J. E., O'Brien, K. O., Caseria, D. M. et al. The impact of dietary protein on calcium absorption and kinetic measures of bone turnover in women. *Clin. Endocrinol. Metab.* 90:26–31, 2005.

25. New, S. A., Robins, S. P., Campbell, M. K. et al. Dietary influences on bone mass and bone metabolism: Further evidence of a positive link between fruit and vegetable consumption and bone health. *Am. J. Clin. Nutr.* 71:142–151, 2000.

26. Nielsen, S. J., and Popkin, B. M. Changes in beverage intake between 1977 and 2000. *Am. J. Prev. Med.* 27:205–210, 2004.

27. Shea, B., Wells, G., Cranney, A. et al. Meta-analysis of calcium supplementation for the prevention of postmenopausal osteoporosis. *Endocrine Reviews* 23:552–559, 2002.

28. Heike A., Bischoff-Ferrari, H. A., Willett, W. A. et al. Fracture prevention with vitamin D supplementation: A meta-analysis of randomized controlled trials. *JAMA.* 293:2257–2264, 2005.

29. U.S. Preventive Services Task Force. Hormone therapy for the prevention of chronic conditions in postmenopausal women: Recommendations from the U.S. Preventive Services Task Force. *Ann. Intern. Med.* 142:855–860, 2005.

30. South-Paul, J. E. Osteoporosis: Part II. Nonpharmacologic and pharmacologic treatment. *Am. Fam. Physician* 63:1121–1128, 2001.

31. Kerni, V. E., Kärkkäinen, M. U., Karp, H. J. et al. Increased calcium intake does not completely counteract the effects of increased phosphorus intake on bone: An acute dose-response study in healthy females. *Br. J. Nutr.* 99:832–839, 2008.

32. Konrad, M., and Schlingmann, K-P. Magnesium. In *Biochemical, Physiological, and Molecular Aspects of Human Nutrition,* 2nd ed. M. H. Stipanuk, ed. St. Louis: Saunders Elsevier, 2006, pp. 921–941.

33. Rude, R. K., and Gruber, H. E. Magnesium deficiency and osteoporosis: Animal and human observations. *J. Nutr. Biochem.* 12:710–716, 2004.

34. Al-Delaimy, W. K., Rimm, E. B., Willett, W. C. et al. Magnesium intake and risk of coronary heart disease among men. *J. Am. Coll. Nutr.* 23:63–70, 2004.

12 The Trace Elements

Case Study

Nissi has been feeling tired all the time and has noticed a lump in her neck that seems to be getting bigger. She lives in a small village in India. For generations her family has farmed the flood plains of the Ganges River valley as subsistence farmers—that is, they use their crops primarily to feed their family. Nissi's diet consists almost entirely of these nutritious homegrown grains, pulses (seeds, beans, and lentils), and vegetables. A typical meal might be flat fried bread, called chapattis; a porridge made with lentils, called dahl; vegetables such as potatoes and cauliflower; and yogurt. Nissi's mother takes her to the clinic, where the doctor determines that her malaise and swollen neck are caused by an iodine deficiency. He gives Nissi an injection of iodine. Soon she has more energy, and the bulge at the front of her neck begins to disappear.

How could an apparently healthy, well-nourished young girl have a nutritional deficiency? Despite the small amounts of iodine needed in the diet—only about 150 µg per day—iodine deficiency is a problem not only for Nissi but for others in her village and other villages and cities throughout India, because the repeated flooding of the Ganges River valley over the centuries has washed the iodine out of the soil. Food grown there is therefore low in iodine. A diet based solely on local foods, does not provide enough of this essential mineral to meet needs. Left untreated, Nissi's symptoms would have continued to worsen. If she had become pregnant, her baby would have been at risk for developmental abnormalities.

One way to prevent iodine deficiency is to include foods that are higher in iodine. However, this approach is not practical for Nissi, because all of the food grown in the region—and thus her entire diet—is deficient in iodine. The alternative for Nissi's family is to use iodized salt—salt to which iodine has been added.

Chapter Outline

12.1 Trace Elements in the Modern Diet

Learning Objective

- Discuss why bioavailability is so important in meeting trace element needs.

The trace elements, which include iron, zinc, copper, manganese, selenium, iodine, fluoride, chromium, and molybdenum, as well as several others, are required by the body in an amount of 100 mg or less per day or present in the body in an amount of 0.01% or less of body weight. Like the major minerals they provide a variety of essential structural and regulatory roles. Some of their functions are unique: Iodine is needed to make thyroid hormones, iron is needed to carry oxygen to body cells, and fluoride is needed for strong teeth. Other functions are similar and complementary; selenium, copper, zinc, iron, and manganese are each cofactors for antioxidant enzyme systems.

Although the trace elements are distinguished from the major minerals only by the amounts present in the diet and required in the body, the presence of such small amounts make them difficult to study. Usually mineral needs are evaluated by feeding a diet devoid of that nutrient. However, with some trace elements needs are so small that contamination from the environment and minerals already present in the body can obscure experimental results. Bioavailability is also more of a concern with trace elements because such small amounts are present in the diet. Phytates, tannins, oxalate, and fiber can bind minerals, reducing their absorption. For example, when the diet is based on unleavened grains, the phytate content may be high enough to decrease zinc absorption and cause a zinc deficiency. The interactions among the minerals that can affect their absorption and utilization also have a greater impact on trace element status. For example, a deficiency of copper can decrease available iron by reducing the amount of iron that can bind to iron transport proteins in the blood.

Determining the trace element content of foods is difficult and is compromised by the fact that the amounts of some are affected by the soil content where the food is grown or produced. For example, a loaf of bread made from wheat grown in one location may supply a different amount of selenium than a loaf made from wheat grown elsewhere. When modern transportation systems make foods produced in many locations available, this variation is unlikely to affect mineral status. But in countries where the diet consists predominantly of locally grown foods, individual trace element deficiencies and excesses are more likely.

12.2 Iron (Fe)

Learning Objectives

- List some dietary sources of heme and nonheme iron.
- Explain how the amount of iron in the body is regulated.
- Describe the primary function of iron and the physiological effects of iron deficiency and iron toxicity.

hemoglobin An iron-containing protein in red blood cells that binds oxygen and transports it through the bloodstream to cells.

Iron was identified as a major constituent of blood in the eighteenth century. By 1832, iron tablets were used to treat young women in whom "coloring matter" was lacking in the blood. Today we know that the red color in blood is due to the iron-containing protein **hemoglobin** and that a deficiency of iron decreases hemoglobin production. Despite the fact that iron is one of the best understood of the trace elements, iron deficiency remains the most common nutritional deficiency worldwide and is a problem among certain population groups in the United States.[1,2]

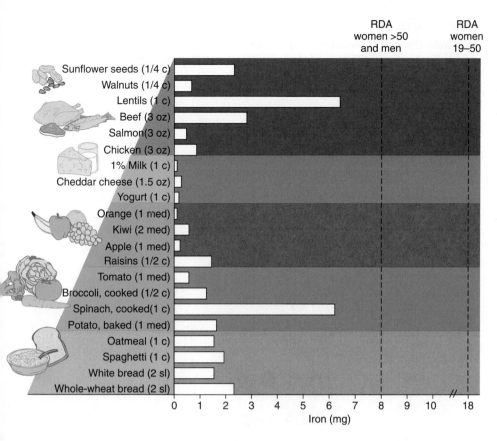

RDA
women >50
and men

RDA
women
19–50

Figure 12.1 Iron content of MyPyramid food groups
Both plant and animal foods are good sources of iron. The dashed lines represent the RDA for women of childbearing age and for men and postmenopausal women.

Iron in the Diet

Iron in the diet comes from both plant and animal sources (**Figure 12.1**). Much of the iron in animal products is **heme iron**—iron that is part of a chemical complex, called a heme group, found in proteins, such as hemoglobin in blood and **myoglobin** in muscle (**Figure 12.2**). Meat, poultry, and fish are good sources of heme iron. Heme iron accounts for about 5% to 10% of the dietary iron in western countries.[3]

Leafy green vegetables, legumes, and whole and enriched grains are good sources of **nonheme iron**. Another source of nonheme iron in the diet is iron cooking utensils, from which iron leaches into food. Leaching is enhanced by acidic foods. For example, 3 ounces of spaghetti sauce cooked in a glass pan contains about 0.6 mg of iron, but the same sauce cooked in an iron skillet contains about 5.7 mg, depending on how long it is cooked.

heme iron A readily absorbed form of iron found in animal products that is chemically associated with proteins such as hemoglobin and myoglobin.

myoglobin An iron-containing protein in muscle cells that binds oxygen.

nonheme iron A poorly absorbed form of iron found in both plant and animal foods that is not part of the iron complex found in hemoglobin and myoglobin.

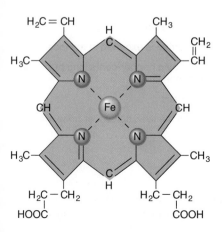

Figure 12.2 Heme group
A heme group contains four 5-membered nitrogen-containing rings that form a cage around a central iron ion. In hemoglobin and myoglobin the iron ion is in the Fe^{2+} state.

Iron in the Digestive Tract

Iron from the diet is absorbed into the intestinal mucosal cells. The amount absorbed depends on whether the iron is heme or nonheme iron as well as the presence of dietary components that enhance or inhibit iron absorption.

Heme iron is absorbed more efficiently than nonheme iron. When foods containing heme proteins are consumed, the iron-containing heme group is released from the proteins by protein-digesting enzymes. The heme binds to receptors on the surface of mucosal cells, allowing it to enter the cells, where the iron is released from the heme group (**Figure 12.3**). Heme iron absorption is not affected by the dietary factors that impact nonheme iron absorption.

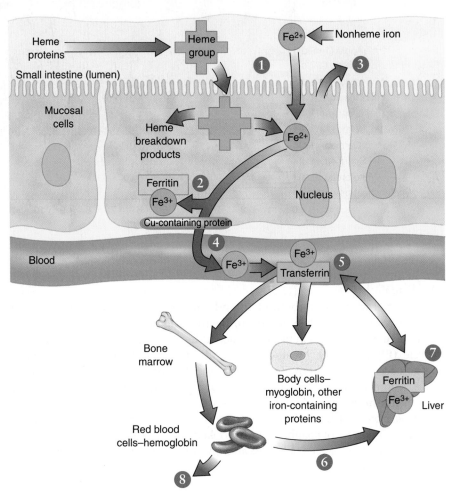

1. Heme iron is absorbed as part of the heme group. Nonheme iron is absorbed in the ferrous form (Fe^{2+}).

2. Once inside the mucosal cells, some iron may be bound to ferritin for storage.

3. When the mucosal cells die, iron that remains bound to ferritin is excreted in the feces.

4. Iron that enters the blood is converted to ferric iron (Fe^{3+}) by a copper-containing protein in the cell membrane. The Fe^{3+} binds to transferrin for transport.

5. Transferrin transports iron to liver, bone, and other body cells.

6. When red blood cells die they are broken down by cells in the liver, spleen, or bone marrow and the iron is released for reuse.

7. Excess iron is stored primarily in the liver, bound to ferritin.

8. Most iron loss is due to blood loss.

Figure 12.3 Iron absorption, transport, storage, and loss
The amount of iron that leaves the mucosal cells for transport to liver, bone, and other tissues is carefully regulated because little iron is lost from the body.

When foods containing nonheme iron are consumed, stomach acid helps convert the ferric form (Fe^{3+}) of iron to the ferrous form (Fe^{2+}). The ferrous form of iron remains more soluble when it enters the intestine and therefore is absorbed into the mucosal cells more readily. When foods containing nonheme iron are consumed with foods containing acids, such as ascorbic acid (vitamin C), citric acid, or lactic acid, iron absorption is enhanced because the acids help to keep iron in the ferrous (Fe^{2+}) form.[4] The best studied of these acids is vitamin C, which enhances nonheme iron absorption both by keeping the iron in its more absorbable form and by forming a complex with iron that remains soluble and more bioavailable.[3] Vitamin C can enhance nonheme iron absorption up to sixfold. Another dietary component that increases the absorption of nonheme iron is meat such as beef, fish, or poultry. For example, a small amount of ground beef in a pot of chili will enhance the body's absorption of nonheme iron from the beans.

Dietary factors that interfere with the absorption of nonheme iron include fiber, phytates found in cereals, tannins found in tea, and oxalates found in some leafy greens such as spinach. These prevent absorption by binding iron in the gastrointestinal tract. They are not consumed in large enough quantities in the diet of most developed countries to cause an iron deficiency. However, these components do contribute to iron deficiency in parts of the developing world where the diet is low in heme iron and factors that enhance nonheme iron absorption and high in foods that limit aborption.[5,6] The presence of other minerals may also interfere with iron absorption. For instance, calcium consumed in the same meal with iron decreases iron absorption. However, because numerous dietary factors affect iron absorption, the long-term effect of calcium as part of the diet as a whole is not as pronounced. For example, a study that examined the impact of the amount of calcium in a glass of milk consumed three times a day showed no decrease in nonheme-iron absorption over a 4-day period.[7]

Iron in the Body

Iron is essential for life but in excess it is toxic. To protect against the toxic effects of iron, the body regulates the amount that enters the blood from the mucosal cells of the gastrointestinal tract and has evolved ways to safely transport and store it.

Regulation of Iron Transport The amount of iron in the body is controlled primarily at the intestine. Iron that has entered the mucosal cells of the small intestine can be bound to the iron storage protein **ferritin** or picked up by the iron transport protein **transferrin**. Iron that remains bound to ferritin is excreted in the feces when mucosal cells die and are sloughed off into the intestinal lumen (see Figure 12.3). Iron that is picked up by transferrin is transported in the blood to the liver, bones, and other body tissues. The amount of iron transported from the mucosal cells to the rest of the body depends on need.

Several proteins regulate the transport and delivery of iron. Transferrin picks up iron from the intestinal mucosal cells in the small intestine as well as iron released from the breakdown of hemoglobin. Before iron can bind transferrin it must be converted to the ferric (Fe^{3+}) form. In the intestine this is accomplished by the action of a copper-containing protein located in the mucosal cell membrane (see Figure 12.3).[8] For the iron to be taken up by body cells the transferrin-iron complex must bind to cell membrane proteins called **transferrin receptors**. When iron stores are low expression of the gene for the transferrin receptor protein is increased, boosting the production of this protein and thereby allowing more iron to be transported into body cells. When iron is plentiful, less of the transferrin receptor protein is made and expression of the gene for ferritin is increased, enhancing ferritin production and the capacity to store iron. Therefore, when iron is plentiful more is stored in the mucosal cells and, thus, is lost when these cells die.

Iron Stores Iron that is transported out of the mucosal cell in excess of immediate needs can be stored in the protein ferritin, primarily in the liver, spleen, and bone marrow. Levels of ferritin in the blood can be used to estimate iron stores. When ferritin concentrations in the liver become high, some is converted to an insoluble storage protein called **hemosiderin**. Iron can be mobilized from body stores as needed, and deficiency signs appear only after stores are depleted.

ferritin The major iron storage protein.

transferrin An iron transport protein in the blood.

transferrin receptor Protein found in cell membranes that binds to the iron-transferrin complex and allows it to be taken up by cells.

hemosiderin An insoluble iron storage compound that stores iron when the amount of iron in the body exceeds the storage capacity of ferritin.

Iron Losses Iron is not readily excreted. Even when red blood cells die, the iron in their hemoglobin is not lost from the body. The red blood cells are removed from the blood by cells in the liver, spleen, and bone marrow and degraded; the iron is then attached to transferrin for transport back to body tissues including the bone, where it can be incorporated into new red blood cells (see Figure 12.3). Most iron loss even in

Table 12.1 A Summary of the Trace Elements

Mineral	Sources	Recommended Intake for Adults	Major Functions	Deficiency Diseases and Symptoms	Groups at Risk of Deficiency	Toxicity	UL
Iron	Red meats, leafy greens, dried fruit, whole and enriched grains	8–18 mg/d	Part of hemoglobin, which delivers oxygen to cells, myoglobin, which holds oxygen in muscle, and electron carriers in the electron transport chain; needed for immune function	Iron deficiency anemia: fatigue, weakness, small pale red blood cells, low hemoglobin	Infants and preschool children, adolescents, women of childbearing age, pregnant women, athletes	Gastrointestinal upset, liver damage	45 mg/d
Zinc	Meat, seafood, whole grains, eggs	8–11 mg/d	Regulates protein synthesis; functions in growth, development, wound healing, immunity, and antioxidant protection	Poor growth and development, skin rashes, decreased immune function	Vegetarians, low-income children, elderly	Decreased copper absorption, depressed immune function	40 mg/d
Copper	Organ meats, nuts, seeds, whole grains, seafood, cocoa	900 µg/d	A part of proteins needed for iron absorption, lipid metabolism, collagen synthesis, nerve and immune function, and antioxidant protection	Anemia, poor growth, bone abnormalities	Those who over-supplement zinc	Vomiting	10 mg/d
Manganese	Nuts, legumes, whole grains, tea	1.8–2.3 mg/d[a]	Functions in carbohydrate and lipid metabolism and antioxidant protection	Growth retardation	None	Nerve damage	11 mg/d
Selenium	Organ meats, seafood, eggs, whole grains	55 µg/d	Antioxidant protection as part of glutathione peroxidase, synthesis of thyroid hormones, spares vitamin E	Muscle pain, weakness, Keshan disease	Populations in areas with low selenium soil	Nausea, diarrhea, vomiting, fatigue, hair changes	400 µg/d
Iodine	Iodized salt, salt water fish, seafood, dairy products	150 µg/d	Needed for synthesis of thyroid hormones	Goiter, cretinism, mental retardation, growth and developmental abnormalities	Populations in areas with low-iodine soil and iodized salt is not used	Enlarged thyroid	1110 µg/d
Chromium	Brewers yeast, nuts, whole grains, mushrooms	25–35 µg/d[a]	Enhances insulin action	High blood glucose	Malnourished children	None reported	ND
Fluoride	Fluoridated water, tea, fish, toothpaste	3–4 mg/d[a]	Strengthens tooth enamel, enhances remineralization of tooth enamel, reduces acid production by bacteria in the mouth	Increased risk of dental caries	Populations in areas with unfluoridated water	Mottled teeth, kidney damage, bone abnormalities	10 mg/d
Molybdenum	Milk, organ meats, grains, legumes	45 µg/d	Cofactor for a number of enzymes	Unknown in humans	None	Arthritis and joint inflammation	2 mg/d

[a]Value is an Adequate Intake (AI).

UL = Tolerable Upper Intake Level; ND = insufficient data to determine a UL.

healthy individuals occurs through blood loss, including that lost during menstruation and the small amounts lost from the gastrointestinal tract. Some iron is also lost through the shedding of cells from the intestine, skin, and urinary tract.

Functions of Iron Iron in the body is essential for the delivery of oxygen to cells. It is a component of two oxygen-carrying proteins, hemoglobin and myoglobin. Most of the iron in the body is part of hemoglobin (**Table 12.1**). Hemoglobin in red blood cells transports oxygen to body cells and carries carbon dioxide away from cells for elimination by the lungs. Myoglobin is found in the muscle, where it enhances the amount of oxygen available for use in muscle contraction. Iron is also essential for ATP production as a part of several proteins involved in the citric acid cycle and the electron transport chain. Iron-containing proteins are involved in drug metabolism and immune function. Iron is also part of the enzyme catalase, which protects the cells from oxidative damage by destroying hydrogen peroxide before it can form free radicals.

Recommended Iron Intake

The RDA for iron is based on the amount needed to maintain normal function but only minimal iron stores. The RDA is set at 8 mg per day for adult men age 19 and older and for postmenopausal women (**Table 12.2**).[9] The RDA for menstruating

Table 12.2 **Dietary Reference Intake Values for Iron**

Gender/Life Stage	Recommended Intake
Infants	
0–6 months	0.27 mg/d[a]
7–12 months	11 mg/d
Children	
1–3 years	7 mg/d
4–8 years	10 mg/d
Males	
9–13 years	8 mg/d
14–18 years	11 mg/d
≥19 years	8 mg/d
Females	
9–13 years	8 mg/d
14–18 years	15 mg/d
19–50 years	18 mg/d
≥51 years	8 mg/d
Females taking oral contraceptives	
14–18 years	11.4 mg/d
19–50 years	10.9 mg/d
Pregnant women	27 mg/d
Lactating women	
≤18 years	10 mg/d
19–50 years	9 mg/d
Vegetarians[b]	
Men ≥19 years	14 mg/d
Women ≥51 years	14 mg/d
Menstruating women (19–50 years)	32 mg/d
Adolescent girls	27 mg/d

[a]This value is an AI; all other values are RDAs.
[b]Value is RDA × 1.8.

women is increased to 18 mg per day to compensate for the iron lost in menstruation. Other specific recommendations have been made for each gender and life-stage group by considering the percentage of dietary iron absorbed, iron losses from the body, and conditions that increase needs, such as growth and pregnancy. A separate RDA category has been created for vegetarians because iron is poorly absorbed from plant sources (see Table 12.2).

The recommended iron intake during pregnancy is increased to 27 mg per day to account for the iron deposited in the fetal and maternal tissues. The RDA during lactation is set lower than the RDA for menstruating women because little iron is lost in milk and menstruation is usually absent. The RDA for infants, children, and adolescents considers the additional iron needed for growth. An AI has been set for infants from newborn to 6 months based on the mean iron intake of infants principally fed human milk. Because the iron in human milk is more bioavailable than that in infant formula, it is recommended that infants who are not fed human milk or are only partially nourished with human milk be fed iron-fortified formula.[10]

Life Cycle

Iron Deficiency

When iron is deficient, hemoglobin cannot be produced. When not enough hemoglobin is available, the red blood cells that are formed are small (microcytic) and pale (hypochromic) and unable to deliver adequate oxygen to the tissues. This is known as **iron deficiency anemia** (**Figure 12.4**). Anemia is the last stage of iron deficiency. Earlier stages have no symptoms because they do not affect the amount of iron in red blood cells. Iron depletion can be detected by blood tests that measure indicators of iron levels in the plasma and in body stores (**Figure 12.5**).

iron deficiency anemia
An iron deficiency disease that occurs when the oxygen-carrying capacity of the blood is decreased because there is insufficient iron to make hemoglobin.

Symptoms The symptoms of iron deficiency anemia include fatigue, weakness, headache, decreased work capacity, an inability to maintain body temperature in a cold environment, changes in behavior, decreased resistance to infection, adverse

LABORATORY REPORT

Diagnosis: Iron Deficiency Anemia

Measurement	Value	Normal Range
Hematocrit	33ml/100ml	men 40–54 women 36–47
Hemoglobin	10.6g/100ml	men 14–18 women 12–16
Serum iron	55 μg/100ml	men 75–175 women 65–165
Ferritin	11 ng/ml	men 20–300 women 20–120

Figure 12.4 Iron deficiency anemia
Iron deficiency anemia is diagnosed when the volume of red blood cells (hematocrit), proteins containing iron (hemoglobin and ferritin), or serum iron levels are low. Under a microscope normal red blood cells (a) appear larger and darker in color than red blood cells from an individual with iron deficiency anemia (b). (B & B Photos/Custom Medical Stock Photo, Inc.; Custom Medical Stock Photo, Inc.)

(a)

(b)

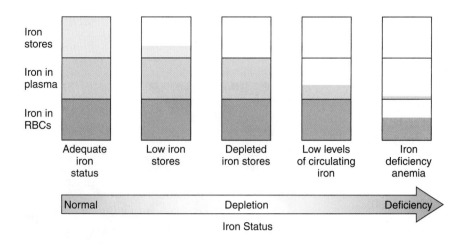

Figure 12.5 Stages of iron deficiency
Iron deficiency anemia is the final stage of iron deficiency. Inadequate iron first causes a decrease in the amount of stored iron, followed by low iron levels in the plasma. It is only after plasma levels drop that there is no longer enough iron available to maintain adequate hemoglobin in red blood cells.

pregnancy outcomes, impaired development in infants, and an increased risk of lead poisoning in young children. One strange symptom, thought to be related to iron deficiency, is **pica**. This is a compulsion to eat nonfood items such as clay, ice, paste, laundry starch, paint chips, and ashes. Pica can lead to the consumption of substances containing toxic minerals, such as lead-based paints, and it can introduce substances into the diet that inhibit mineral absorption (see Focus on Eating Disorders).

pica The compulsive ingestion of nonfood substances such as clay, laundry starch, and paint chips.

Groups at Risk for Iron Deficiency It is estimated that as much as 80% of the world's population may be iron deficient and 30% (2 billion people) suffer from iron deficiency anemia.[2] In the United States iron deficiency affects 2% of toddlers ages 1 to 2 years, and 3% of adolescent and adult women.[11] Among low-income and minority women and children, the incidence is even greater.

Women of reproductive age are at risk for iron deficiency anemia because of iron loss due to menstruation. Menstruation is absent during pregnancy but the need for iron is increased because of the expansion of maternal blood volume and the growth of other maternal tissues and the fetus. Iron deficiency is common among pregnant women even in industrialized countries and can lead to premature delivery and greater risk to the mother.

Iron deficiency is common in infants, children, and adolescents. In infants and children rapid growth increases iron needs. Toddlers may also be at risk because finicky eating habits often reduce intake (see Chapters 14 and 15). In adolescent boys, rapid growth and an increase in muscle mass and blood volume increase iron need. In adolescent girls, iron needs are increased because weight gain is almost as great as in boys and iron losses are increased by the onset of menstruation (see Chapter 15). Only about one-fourth of adolescent girls and women of childbearing age consume enough iron to meet the RDA.[12]

Athletes are another group at risk for iron deficiency. This may be due to a low iron intake, as well as increased losses due to prolonged training. Based on the amount lost, the EAR may be 30% to 70% higher for athletes than for the general population[9] (see Chapter 13 and Critical Thinking: Increasing Iron Intake and Uptake).

Life Cycle

Iron Toxicity

Iron is essential for cellular metabolism, but too much can be toxic. Iron promotes the formation of free radicals and causes cell death due to excess oxidation of cellular components. Iron toxicity can be acute, resulting from ingestion of a single large dose at one time, or chronic, due to the accumulation of iron in the body over time, referred to as *iron overload*. A UL has been set at 45 mg per day from all sources.

Critical Thinking
Increasing Iron Intake and Uptake

Background:

Hanna is a 23-year-old graduate student from South Carolina. She has been feeling tired and run down all semester. She recently read an article about iron deficiency in young women and became concerned about her iron status. She decided to go to the health center where she has blood drawn. The results of her tests indicate that she does not have iron deficiency anemia, but her iron stores are very low.

A review of her typical diet shows that Hanna's iron intake is less than the recommended amount. She decides to try to increase the amount of iron she gets from her diet before considering iron supplements.

(©iStockphoto)

Hanna consumes a vegetarian diet. At home her mother prepared meals using iron cookware, but the pans in Hanna's college apartment are stainless steel. Her typical diet is shown in the table.

Data:

TYPICAL DIET

FOOD	AMOUNT	IRON (MG)
Breakfast		
Grits with	I cup	0.5
butter	I tsp	0
Plantain	I	0.9
Whole wheat toast	I slice	1.2
Apple juice	3/4 cup	0.7
Tea with	I cup	0
sugar	I tsp	0
Lunch		
Apple	I medium	0.2
Cornbread with	I piece	1.5
butter	I tsp	0
Yogurt	I cup	0.2
Tomato	I medium	0.5
Tea with	I cup	0
sugar	I tsp	0
Dinner		
Rice	I cup	2.4
Peanuts	1/3 cup	0.9
Kale	I cup	1.2
Yams	I cup	1.1
Apple juice	3/4 cup	0.7
Tea with	I cup	0
sugar	I tsp	0
Total		12.0

Critical Thinking Questions

Does Hanna's iron intake meet the RDA for a young female vegetarian?

▼

How could Hanna increase her iron intake without adding iron to her diet?

▼

What could Hanna do to increase the absorption of the iron in her meals?

▼

Does Hanna's diet provide good vegetarian sources of calcium? Are there other nutrient deficiencies for which she may be at risk?

 iProfile Use iProfile to compare the amount of iron in the dark meat and white meat of poultry.

Acute Toxicity Even a single large dose of iron can be life-threatening. Iron poisoning can damage the intestinal lining and cause abnormalities in body pH, shock, and liver failure. Iron toxicity from supplements is one of the most common forms of poisoning among children under age 6 and is the leading cause of liver transplants in children. To protect children from accidental poisoning from iron-containing drugs and supplements, these products display a warning on the label (**Figure 12.6**).[13]

Iron Overload If too much iron enters the body, over time it accumulates in tissues such as the heart and liver. Iron overload can occur in people with conditions that cause abnormal red blood cell synthesis and in those with diseases requiring frequent blood transfusions, but the most common cause of chronic iron overload is **hemochromatosis**.[14] Hemochromatosis is an inherited condition that allows increased iron absorption. Hemochromatosis afflicts about 1 in 200 to 1 in 500 Americans, and is the most common genetic disorders in the caucasian population.[15]

Hemochromatosis has no symptoms early in life, but in middle age nonspecific symptoms such as weight loss, fatigue, weakness, and abdominal pain typically begin. If allowed to progress the accumulation of excess iron that occurs in hemochromatosis causes oxidative changes resulting in heart and liver damage, diabetes, certain types of cancer, and other chronic conditions. Iron deposits also darken the skin. To have these symptoms, an individual must inherit the hemochromatosis gene from both parents. The 1 in 10 people who inherit the gene from only a single parent don't have these serious symptoms but do absorb iron better than people who do not have the gene at all.

The rate at which iron accumulates and leads to serious symptoms in those with hemochromatosis depends on the amount of iron consumed and other dietary factors that affect iron absorption, as well as factors that cause iron loss such as menstruation and blood donations. The public health impact of hemochromatosis is potentially significant. The availability of red meat and the prevalence of iron-fortified foods in the American diet virtually assure that individuals with two genes for hemochromatosis will eventually accumulate damaging levels of iron. If individuals with hemochromatosis can be identified, treatment is simple: regular blood withdrawal. This will prevent the complications of iron overload, but to be effective it must be initiated before organs are damaged. Therefore, genetic screening to identify and treat young healthy individuals is essential in preventing complications.

Overconsumption of iron supplements or a diet high in absorbable iron can also increase iron stores. Although these iron stores are not high enough to cause the serious problems that occur with hemochromatosis, it has been hypothesized that people with high iron stores are at increased risk of the same diseases that occur in hemochromatosis—heart disease, diabetes, and cancer. Iron is hypothesized to promote heart disease by increasing the formation of oxidized LDL cholesterol, which

Life Cycle

hemochromatosis
An inherited condition that results in increased iron absorption.

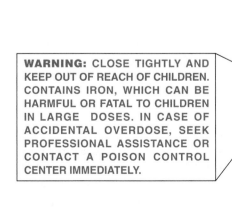

WARNING: CLOSE TIGHTLY AND KEEP OUT OF REACH OF CHILDREN. CONTAINS IRON, WHICH CAN BE HARMFUL OR FATAL TO CHILDREN IN LARGE DOSES. IN CASE OF ACCIDENTAL OVERDOSE, SEEK PROFESSIONAL ASSISTANCE OR CONTACT A POISON CONTROL CENTER IMMEDIATELY.

Figure 12.6 Why must labels on iron-containing supplements and medications carry a toxicity warning?

then leads to atherosclerosis. In some studies elevated levels of the iron-storage protein ferritin are associated with an increased risk of heart attacks, but the majority of studies do not support this association.[16] A relationship between higher iron stores and an increased risk of diabetes has been found in overweight and obese individuals with impaired glucose tolerance.[17] Iron is hypothesized to contribute to diabetes because it promotes the formation of free radicals, which contribute to insulin resistance and eventually decreased insulin secretion. The increase in free radical formation may also increase cancer risk.

Meeting Iron Needs: Consider the Total Diet

Both the amount and the bioavailability of iron from the diet need to be considered when meeting iron needs. The best sources of iron are red meats and organ meats such as liver and kidney. Good nonheme sources are legumes, dried fruit, leafy greens such as spinach and kale, and fortified grain products (**Figure 12.7**). Nonheme iron absorption can be enhanced by including meat, fish, poultry, and foods rich in vitamin C in meals containing iron, while decreasing the consumption of dairy products, which are high in calcium, at these meals.[3]

Because iron is a nutrient at risk for deficiency in the American diet, the iron content of packaged foods must be listed on food labels. It is given as a percent of the Daily Value for iron, which is 18 mg for adults. Therefore, if your breakfast cereal provides 10% of the Daily Value for iron, it contains about 1.8 mg of iron per serving.

Although diet is the ideal way to meet iron needs, supplements are often recommended for groups at risk for deficiency such as small children, women of childbearing age, and pregnant women. Iron is commonly available as an individual supplement or as part of multivitamin and mineral supplements. These contain nonheme iron. As with nonheme iron in the diet, to enhance the absorption of iron in a supplement, it should be consumed with foods containing vitamin C, such as orange juice; taken with a meal containing meat, fish, or poultry; and not taken with dairy products, calcium supplements, or substances that bind iron. Iron from supplements that contain the ferrous form (Fe^{2+}) of iron, such as ferrous sulfate, is more readily absorbed than iron from those with the ferric form (Fe^{3+}). Iron supplements can improve iron status, but large intakes of iron from supplements can interfere with the absorption of zinc and copper (**Table 12.3**). Iron-containing supplements should be taken only as suggested on the label and stored out of the reach of children or others who may consume them in excess.

Figure 12.7 The bioavailability of iron from plant sources and fortified foods such as flour is lower than that from ground beef and other animal sources. (Charles D. Winters)

Table 12.3 Benefits and Risks of Trace Element Supplements

Supplement	Claims	Actual Benefits or Risks
Iron	Increases energy	Needed to make hemoglobin to deliver oxygen to tissues. Supplements are beneficial if iron is deficient. High doses cause constipation, liver damage, and death.
Zinc	Treats colds, prevents aging, improves immune function, enhances fertility	Needed for enzyme function, protein synthesis, and vitamin and hormone function. Supplements do not enhance these effects and there is little evidence that they help prevent or treat colds. High doses cause copper deficiency, nausea, and vomiting.
Copper	Prevents heart disease and osteoporosis. Alleviates arthritis symptoms, maintains healthy skin and hair color, treats hypoglycemia	Supplements are useful for improving bone health and improving blood lipids in those with copper deficiency but there is no evidence that intakes above recommended levels prevent heart disease or are effective for the treatment of arthritis or skin conditions. High doses can cause vomiting.
Selenium	Protects against cancer. Promotes heart health, immune function	Antioxidant; evidence that it may protect against cancer in those with low levels. High doses cause loss of hair and nail changes.
Chromium	Controls diabetes, lowers cholesterol, reduces body fat, and increases lean tissue	Needed for insulin action. Supplements may improve blood sugar regulation but do not affect body composition. High doses may be related to headaches, sleep disturbances, and mood swings.
Vanadium	Aids insulin action; allows more rapid and intense muscle pumping for body builders	No evidence to support a benefit for body builders. Supplements can reduce insulin requirements but the dose required exceeds the UL.

12.3 Zinc (Zn)

Learning Objectives

- Describe how zinc absorption is regulated.
- Discuss the role of zinc in gene expression.

The essentiality of zinc in the human diet was first recognized about 30 years ago, when a syndrome of growth depression and delayed sexual development, seen in Iranian and Egyptian men consuming diets based on vegetable protein, was alleviated by supplemental zinc.[18] Although the diet was not low in zinc, it was high in grains containing phytates, which interfered with zinc absorption, causing a deficiency.

Zinc in the Diet

Zinc is found in foods from both plant and animal sources. Zinc from animal sources is better absorbed than that from plants because the zinc in plant foods is often bound by phytates. Zinc is abundant in red meat, liver, eggs, dairy products, vegetables, and some seafood (**Figure 12.8**). Whole grains are a good source, but refined grains are not because zinc is lost in milling and not added back in enrichment. Grain products leavened with yeast provide more zinc than unleavened products because the yeast leavening of breads reduces the phytate content.[9]

Zinc in the Digestive Tract

The gastrointestinal tract is the major site for regulation of zinc homeostasis. Both the amount of zinc in the mucosal cells and the amount that leaves these cells for distribution to the rest of the body are regulated.

Zinc transport proteins regulate the amount of zinc in the cytosol of the mucosal cells. Some of these proteins increase the amount of zinc absorbed into the mucosal cell by promoting the transport of zinc from the intestinal lumen into

Figure 12.8 Zinc content of MyPyramid food groups
Meat, seafood, dairy products, and fortified foods are good sources of zinc; the dashed lines represent the RDA for adult men and women.

the cell. Others reduce the amount of zinc in the cytosol of the mucosal cell by transporting zinc back into the lumen or into storage vesicles in the cell (**Figure 12.9**).[19] The amount of zinc that is in the cytosol can be regulated by increasing or decreasing the synthesis of proteins that transport zinc in versus those that transport it back out of the mucosal cells. For example, if zinc intake is low (see Figure 12.9a), expression of zinc transport proteins that move zinc from the lumen into the mucosal cells will increase relative to the expression of proteins that export zinc out of the mucosa. High zinc levels will have the opposite effect, increasing zinc export to the lumen relative to transport into the cell (see Figure 12.9b).

The amount of zinc that passes from the mucosal cell into the blood is regulated by a metal binding protein called **metallothionein**. When zinc intake is high, metallothionein is synthesized. Zinc in the mucosal cell binds to metallothionein, slowing its transfer into the blood; this provides more opportunity for export of zinc back into the lumen when zinc intakes are high or for it to be lost if the mucosal cell dies (see Figure 12.9b). Metallothionein also binds copper, and high levels can inhibit copper absorption.

Zinc in the Body

Once zinc has been absorbed, homeostasis can be maintained to some extent by regulating excretion. Zinc is secreted in pancreatic and intestinal juices, which enter the lumen of the intestine. When zinc levels in the body are low, the zinc that enters the gastrointestinal tract can be reabsorbed and recycled. When levels in the body are high, less is reabsorbed and more is therefore eliminated in the feces.

Zinc Functions Zinc is the most abundant intracellular trace element. It is found in the cytosol, in cellular organelles, and in the nucleus. Zinc is involved in the functioning of over 300 different enzymes, including a form of **superoxide dismutase (SOD)**, which is vital for protecting cells from free radical damage. It is needed to maintain adequate levels of metallothionein proteins, which also scavenge free radicals.[20] Zinc is also needed by enzymes that function in the synthesis of DNA and

metallothionein Refers to proteins that bind minerals. One such protein binds zinc and copper in intestinal cells limiting their absorption into the blood.

superoxide dismutase (SOD) An enzyme that protects the cell from oxidative damage by neutralizing superoxide free radicals. One form of the enzyme requires zinc and copper for activity, and another form requires manganese.

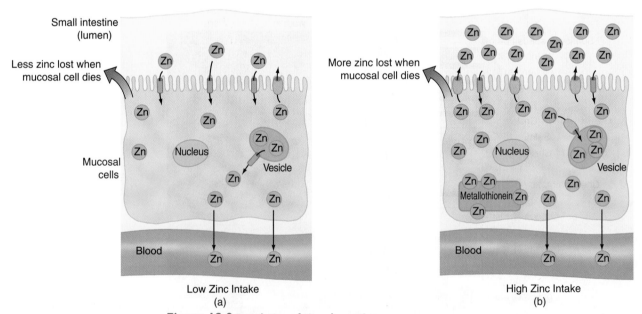

Figure 12.9 Regulation of zinc absorption

(a) When zinc intake is low, more zinc moves from the lumen into the mucosal cells and from vesicles into the cytosol, and little metallothionein is synthesized.

(b) When zinc intake is high, little zinc is transported from the lumen into the mucosal cells and more zinc moves out of the mucosal cells into the lumen and from the cytosol into vesicles. The synthesis of metallothionein, which binds zinc and limits its uptake into the blood, increases.

RNA, in carbohydrate metabolism, in acid-base balance, and in a reaction that is necessary for the absorption of folate from food. Zinc plays a role in the storage and release of insulin, the mobilization of vitamin A from the liver, and the stabilization of cell membranes. It influences hormonal regulation of cell division and is therefore needed for the growth and repair of tissues, the activity of the immune system, and the development of sex organs and bone.

Zinc and Gene Expression Some of the functions of zinc can be traced to its role in gene expression. For example, zinc stimulates the production of metallothionein by binding to a regulatory factor and activating the transcription of the gene for this protein. Zinc also plays a structural role in proteins essential for gene expression. Proteins containing zinc fold around the zinc atom to form a loop or "finger". These zinc fingers allow protein receptors to bind to regulatory regions on DNA, stimulating the transcription of specific genes and therefore the synthesis of the proteins for which they code (**Figure 12.10**). Protein receptors containing zinc fingers bind to vitamin A, vitamin D, and a number of hormones including thyroid hormones, estrogen, and testosterone, and are therefore essential for their activity. Without zinc, these nutrients and hormones could not interact with DNA to increase or decrease gene expression and, hence, the synthesis of certain proteins.

Recommended Zinc Intake

The RDA for zinc is 11 mg per day for adult men and 8 mg per day for adult women.[9] This is based on the amount of zinc needed to replace daily losses from the body.

During pregnancy, the recommendation for zinc intake is increased to account for the zinc that accumulates in maternal and fetal tissues. During lactation, the RDA is increased to compensate for zinc secreted in breast milk. For infants from newborn to 6 months, an AI has been established based on the zinc intake of breast-fed infants. RDAs have been established for older infants, children, and adolescents based on the amount of zinc lost from the body, the amount needed for growth, and the absorption of zinc from the diet.

Life Cycle

Zinc Deficiency

Zinc deficiency has been seen in individuals with a genetic defect in zinc absorption and metabolism called *acrodermatitis enteropathica*, in those fed total parenteral nutrition (TPN) solutions lacking zinc, and in those consuming diets low in protein and high in phytates. It may also occur in individuals with kidney disease, sickle cell anemia, alcoholism, cancer, and AIDS.

The symptoms of zinc deficiency include poor growth and development, skin rashes, hair loss, diarrhea, neurological changes, impaired reproduction, skeletal abnormalities, and reduced immune function.[20] Many of these symptoms reflect zinc's importance in protein synthesis and gene expression. Because it is needed for the proper functioning of vitamins A and D and the activity of numerous enzymes, some of the zinc deficiency symptoms resemble deficiencies of other essential nutrients. Decreased immune function is one of the main concerns with even moderate zinc

Figure 12.10 Zinc fingers and gene expression
Finger-like structures called zinc fingers allow nuclear protein receptors that bind to vitamin A, vitamin D, and hormones to interact with the regulatory region of a gene and thus affect gene expression.

deficiency. The impact of zinc deficiency on immune function is rapid and extensive, causing a decrease in the number and function of immune cells in the blood, which can lead to an increased incidence of infections.

Life Cycle

Symptomatic zinc deficiency is relatively uncommon in North America. However, a significant portion of the North American population does not consume adequate zinc; 10% of the U.S. population consumes less than half the recommended amount.[21] Groups likely to be at risk of deficiency in the United States include children from 1 to 3 years of age, adolescent females, and adults 71 years of age and older.[22] In developing countries zinc deficiency is more likely to have important health and developmental consequences. Through its relationship with immune function, it contributes to infection and overall mortality in children.[23] The risk of zinc deficiency is greater in areas of the world where the diet is high in phytate, fiber, tannins, and oxalates. Pregnant women, the elderly, low-income children, and vegans are at particular risk.

Zinc Toxicity

Zinc can be toxic when consumed in excess of recommendations. A single dose of 1 to 2 grams can cause gastrointestinal irritation, vomiting, loss of appetite, diarrhea, abdominal cramps, and headaches. This has occurred with consumption of foods and beverages contaminated with zinc that has leached from galvanized containers. Intakes in the range of 50 to 300 mg per day have been shown to decrease rather than enhance immune function and to reduce HDL cholesterol, the type of cholesterol that has a protective effect against heart disease.[9] Supplements providing 50 mg per day of zinc have been shown to interfere with the absorption of copper. When high zinc intake inhibits copper absorption, it leads to a reduction in the activity of the copper-dependent enzyme copper-zinc superoxide dismutase in red blood cells. A UL has been set at 40 mg per day from all sources based on the adverse effect of excess zinc on copper metabolism.

Zinc Supplements

Zinc is often marketed as a supplement to improve immune function and enhance fertility and sexual performance. For individuals consuming adequate zinc, there is no evidence that extra is beneficial. In individuals with a mild zinc deficiency, supplementation may result in improved wound healing, immunity, and appetite; in children it can result in improved growth and learning. In healthy older adults, supplements of zinc have been shown to improve the immune response[24] (see Chapter 16). Zinc supplements in lozenge form are currently popular for preventing and treating colds. Supplemental zinc is also used therapeutically to treat genetic diseases.

Figure 12.11 Zinc lozenges are marketed to reduce the prevalence and severity of the common cold. Do they really work? Do they pose a risk? (Andy Washnik)

Zinc and the Common Cold Americans suffer from about 1 billion colds a year and the common cold is a leading cause of doctor visits and missed days from school and work.[25] It has been suggested that zinc lozenges, containing either zinc gluconate or zinc acetate, reduce the duration and severity of the common cold by preventing the cold virus from binding to cells of the mucous membranes in the nose and throat.[26] The zinc swallowed in a mineral supplement will not have any effect because this zinc goes to your stomach and doesn't contact the mucosal surfaces affected by cold viruses. Although clinical trials to assess the efficacy of zinc lozenges have been inconsistent, many do support the value of zinc in reducing the duration and severity of symptoms when administered within 24 hours of the onset of common cold symptoms.[27,28] If zinc lozenges are used as a cold remedy, they should be used cautiously. Too much zinc can suppress the immune system, lower HDL cholesterol levels, and impair copper absorption. Zinc lozenges each contain about 11 to 14 mg of elemental zinc (**Figure 12.11**). Taking four of these in a day will exceed the UL of 40 mg per day.

Zinc and the Treatment of Genetic Abnormalities *Acrodermatitis enteropathica* is due to an inherited defect in zinc absorption, which results in zinc deficiency. This condition causes skin lesions, damages the eyes, and increases the risk of infection. If untreated, patients with acrodermatitis enteropathica usually die within the first few years of life. Symptoms can be reversed by providing supplemental zinc in amounts greater than 1 to 2 mg per kg per day for life. These large doses override the regulation of absorption, allowing enough zinc to get into the body. This therapy achieves a survival rate of 100%. Because treatment involves consumption of amounts well in excess of the UL, patients with this disorder must be monitored to ensure that the high zinc level does not cause copper deficiency.

Zinc supplements are also used to treat *Wilson's disease.* Wilson's disease is due to an inherited defect in the excretion of copper and causes copper to accumulate in the body leading to toxicity. A few drugs are available to remove copper from the body, but supplemental zinc acetate, which blocks the absorption of copper, increases copper excretion in the stool, and causes no serious side effects, is considered the best treatment.[29]

12.4 Copper (Cu)

Learning Objectives

- Explain why copper deficiency can lead to anemia.
- Describe how high intakes of zinc affect copper absorption.

The ability of copper to treat certain types of anemia helped establish the essentiality of this mineral in human nutrition.[30] Further understanding of the impact of copper deficiency in humans came from studying individuals who were inadvertently fed intravenous (TPN) solutions deficient in copper and those with a rare genetic disease called *Menkes disease* or *kinky hair disease*, in which there is a defect in intestinal copper absorption.

Copper in the Diet

The richest dietary sources of copper are organ meats such as liver and kidney. Seafood, nuts and seeds, whole-grain breads and cereals, and chocolate are also good sources (**Figure 12.12**). As with many other trace elements, soil content affects the amount of copper in plant foods.

Copper in the Digestive Tract

About 30% to 40% of the copper in a typical diet is absorbed.[9] The absorption of copper is affected by the presence of other minerals in the diet. As discussed, the zinc content of the diet can have a major impact on copper absorption. When zinc intake is high, it stimulates the synthesis of the protein metallothionein in the mucosal cells. Although metallothionein binds zinc, it binds to copper more tightly. Therefore, when metallothionein is synthesized, it binds copper, preventing it from being moved out of mucosal cells into the blood (**Figure 12.13**). The antagonism between copper and zinc is so great that phytates, which inhibit zinc absorption, actually increase the absorption and utilization of copper. Copper absorption is also reduced by high intakes of iron, manganese, and molybdenum. Other factors that affect copper absorption include vitamin C, which decreases copper absorption, and large doses of antacids, which also inhibit copper absorption and, over the long term, can cause copper deficiency.

Figure 12.12 Whole grain breads, nuts, and seeds are good sources of copper. (Food Collection/StockFood America)

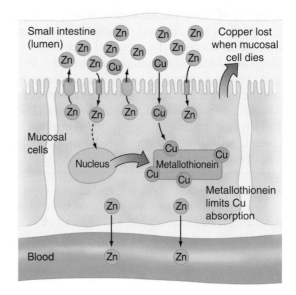

Small intestine (lumen)

Copper lost when mucosal cell dies

Mucosal cells

Nucleus

Metallothionein

Metallothionein limits Cu absorption

Blood

Figure 12.13 Inhibition of copper absorption by zinc
High levels of dietary zinc can inhibit copper absorption by stimulating the synthesis of metallothionein, which then preferentially binds copper and limits its absorption.

ceruloplasmin The major copper-carrying protein in the blood.

Copper in the Body

Once absorbed, copper binds to albumin, a protein in the blood, and travels to the liver, where it binds to the protein **ceruloplasmin** for delivery to other tissues. Copper must be transported bound to proteins such as albumin and ceruloplasmin because free copper ions can trigger oxidation leading to cellular damage. Copper can be removed from the body by secretion in the bile and subsequent elimination in the feces.

Copper functions in a number of important proteins and enzymes that are involved in iron and lipid metabolism, connective tissue synthesis, maintenance of heart muscle, and the functioning of the immune and central nervous systems.[9] The copper-containing plasma protein ceruloplasmin converts iron into a form that can bind to transferrin for transport from body cells and an analogous copper-containing protein found in intestinal cells is essential for the transport of absorbed iron from the intestine.[8] Copper is an essential component of a form of the antioxidant enzyme superoxide dismutase. Copper also plays a role in cholesterol and glucose metabolism; elevated blood cholesterol levels have been reported in copper deficiency. Copper is needed for the synthesis of the neurotransmitters norepinephrine and dopamine, and several blood-clotting factors. It may also be involved in the synthesis of myelin, which is necessary for transmission of nerve signals.

Recommended Copper Intake

The RDA for copper for adults is 900 μg per day. This recommendation is based on the amount of copper needed to maintain normal blood levels of copper and ceruloplasmin. During pregnancy, the RDA is increased to 1000 μg per day to account for the copper that accumulates in the fetus and maternal tissues. The RDA for lactation is 1300 μg per day to account for the copper secreted in human milk. The amount of copper in the North American diet is slightly above the RDA.

Copper Deficiency

Severe copper deficiency is relatively rare, occurring most often in preterm infants. Marginal copper deficiency may be more prevalent but has been difficult to diagnose. The most common manifestation of copper deficiency is anemia. This is due primarily to the importance of copper-containing proteins for iron transport. In copper deficiency, even if iron is sufficient in the diet, iron cannot be transported out of the intestinal mucosa. Copper deficiency causes skeletal abnormalities similar to those seen in vitamin C deficiency (scurvy). This is because the enzyme needed for the cross-linking of connective tissue requires copper. Copper deficiency has also been associated with impaired growth, degeneration of the heart muscle, degeneration of the nervous system, and changes in hair color and structure.[9] Because of copper's role in the development and maintenance of the immune system, a diet low in copper decreases the immune response and increases the incidence of infection.[31]

Copper Toxicity

Copper toxicity from dietary sources is extremely rare but has occurred as a result of drinking from contaminated water supplies or consuming acidic foods or beverages that have been stored in copper containers. Excessive copper intake causes abdominal pain, vomiting, and diarrhea. These symptoms may occur with copper intakes of 4.8 mg per day in some individuals, but there is evidence that people can adapt to higher exposures without experiencing any adverse effects. High doses of copper have also been shown to cause liver damage. The UL has been set at 10 mg of copper per day.[9]

12.5 Manganese (Mn)

Learning Objective

- Discuss the antioxidant function of manganese, copper, and zinc.

The best dietary sources of manganese are whole grains and nuts (**Figure 12.14**). Fruits and vegetables are fair sources; meat, dairy products, and refined grains are poor sources.

Manganese homeostasis is maintained by regulating both absorption and excretion. Manganese absorption increases when intake is low and decreases when intake is high. Manganese is eliminated by secretion into the intestinal tract in bile. It is a constituent of some enzymes and an activator of others. Manganese-requiring enzymes are involved in amino acid, carbohydrate, and cholesterol metabolism; cartilage formation; urea synthesis; and antioxidant protection. Like copper and zinc, manganese is needed for the activity of a form of superoxide dismutase. The form of the enzyme requiring manganese is located inside the mitochondria.

Recommended Manganese Intake

There is not sufficient evidence to set an RDA for manganese; the AI is 2.3 mg per day for men and 1.8 mg per day for women based on the amounts consumed in the healthy population. Recommended intakes are higher during pregnancy and lactation.[9]

Manganese Deficiency and Toxicity

Manganese deficiency in animals results in growth retardation, reproductive problems, congenital malformations in the offspring, and abnormalities in brain function, bone formation, glucose regulation, and lipid metabolism.

Although a naturally occurring manganese deficiency has never been reported in humans, a man participating in a study of vitamin K was inadvertently fed a diet deficient in manganese for 6 months. He lost weight, his black hair turned a red color, and he developed dermatitis and low blood cholesterol. Manganese deficiency was further studied in young male volunteers fed a manganese-deficient diet for 39 days. These men developed dermatitis and had altered blood levels of cholesterol, calcium, and phosphorus.[32]

Toxic levels of manganese result in damage to the nervous system. In humans, toxicity has been reported in mine workers exposed to high concentrations of inhaled manganese dust. The UL is 11 mg per day from all sources.[9]

Figure 12.14 Legumes, nuts, and whole grains are high in manganese. (Rita Maas/The Image Bank/Getty Images, Inc.)

12.6 Selenium (Se)

Learning Objectives

- Compare the antioxidant functions of selenium and vitamin E.
- Discuss the relationship between selenium and cancer.

Although selenium was discovered about 180 years ago, its essential role in human nutrition was not recognized until the 1970s when it was found to prevent a heart disorder in children living in regions of China with low soil selenium levels. Today selenium is known to be an important part of the body's antioxidant defenses.

Selenium in the Diet

Seafood, kidney, liver, and eggs are excellent sources of selenium (**Figure 12.15**). Fruits, vegetables, and drinking water are generally poor sources. Grains and seeds can be good sources depending on the selenium content of the soil where they were grown. For example, wheat grown in Kansas has a different selenium content from wheat grown in Michigan. Soil selenium can have a significant impact on the selenium intake of populations consuming primarily locally grown food. Selenium deficiency is not likely to be a problem when the diet includes foods produced in many different locations.

Selenium in the Body

Selenium absorption is efficient and does not appear to be regulated. Once absorbed, selenium homeostasis is maintained by regulating its excretion in the urine. Selenium is a mineral that functions mostly through association with proteins called **selenoproteins**. Several of these, including **glutathione peroxidase**, are enzymes

selenoproteins Proteins that contain selenium as a structural component of their amino acids. Selenium is most often found as selenocysteine, which contains an atom of selenium in place of the sulfur atom.

glutathione peroxidase A selenium-containing enzyme that protects cells from oxidative damage by neutralizing peroxides.

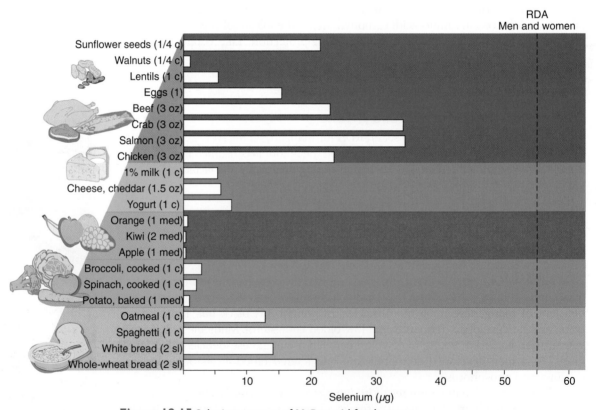

Figure 12.15 Selenium content of MyPyramid food groups
Both plant and animal foods are good sources of selenium. The dashed line represents the RDA for adult men and women.

that help protect cells from oxidative damage. Glutathione peroxidase neutralizes peroxides so they no longer form free radicals, which cause oxidative damage. By reducing free radical formation, selenium can reduce the need for vitamin E because this vitamin stops the action of free radicals once they are produced (**Figure 12.16**). Selenium is also needed for the synthesis of the thyroid hormones, which regulate basal metabolic rate.

Recommended Selenium Intake

The RDA for selenium for adults is 55 μg per day.[9] This is based on the amount needed to maximize the activity of the enzyme glutathione peroxidase in the blood. The estimated average intake of selenium in the United States meets or nearly meets this recommendation for all age groups.

An increase in selenium intake is recommended during pregnancy based on the amount transferred to the fetus and during lactation to account for the amount of selenium secreted in milk. The AI for infants is based on the amount contained in breast milk.

Selenium Deficiency

Symptoms of selenium deficiency include muscular discomfort and weakness. Deficiency was not identified in humans until the late 1970s, when it was observed in patients fed TPN solutions inadvertently deficient in selenium. At the same time scientists in China described a disease of the heart muscle called **Keshan disease**, which was linked to selenium deficiency.

Selenium and Keshan Disease Keshan disease causes an enlarged heart and poor heart function. It used to be endemic in regions of China where the diet was restricted to locally grown food and the soil was deficient in selenium (**Figure 12.17**).

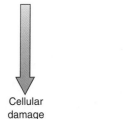

Cellular damage

Figure 12.16 Selenium spares vitamin E
Selenium is a part of the enzyme glutathione peroxidase, which neutralizes peroxides before they form free radicals. Fewer free radicals means less vitamin E is needed to eliminate them.

Keshan disease A type of heart disease that occurs in areas of China where the soil is very low in selenium. It is believed to be caused by a combination of viral infection and selenium deficiency.

r and nail brittleness and loss occur people living in regions of China with n selenium levels in the soil (intake of g/day).

Selenium deficiency causes muscular discomfort, weakness, and in some cases Keshan disease.

oil selenium

Deficient
Low
Normal
High
Very high
Not investigated

Figure 12.17 Levels of soil selenium in China
The soil content of selenium affects the selenium content of crops grown in the soil. Because the diet in rural China consists predominantly of locally grown foods, the incidence of Keshan disease corresponds to the belt of selenium deficient soil that crosses China from the northeast to the southwest.

Life Cycle

It affected primarily children and women of childbearing age. Selenium supplementation was found to dramatically reduce the incidence of Keshan disease, but it could not reverse heart damage once it had occurred. Although Keshan disease is now virtually eliminated by selenium supplementation, the disease itself is believed to be due to a combination of selenium deficiency and infection with a virus. When selenium is deficient the virus becomes more virulent, causing the symptoms of Keshan disease.[33]

Selenium and Cancer The role of selenium in cancer has been under investigation for three decades. An increased incidence of cancer has been observed in regions where selenium intake is low. In 1996 a study investigating the effect of selenium supplements on people with a history of skin cancer found that the supplement had no effect on the recurrence of skin cancer but the incidence of lung, prostate, and colon cancer all decreased in the selenium-supplemented group.[34] There was a great deal of excitement about this result and many believed selenium supplements could reduce cancer risk. Subsequent research, however, has not supported this result. Evidence now suggests that selenium supplements actually increase the incidence of certain types of skin cancer.[35] The reduction in the incidence of lung and prostate cancer seen in the 1996 study is now believed to have occured primarily in people who began the study with low levels of selenium. So, selenium deficiency can increase the risk of cancer, but supplements of selenium have not been shown to be of additional benefit in the general population (see Your Choice: Antioxidant Supplements: Are They Beneficial?).

Selenium Toxicity

In a region of China with very high selenium in the soil, an intake of 5 mg per day resulted in fingernail changes and hair loss (see Figure 12.17). Selenium toxicity has also been reported in the United States because of a manufacturing error that created mineral supplements containing a dose of 27 mg of selenium per day. The individuals who used these supplements had symptoms that included nausea, diarrhea, abdominal pain, fingernail and hair changes, nervous system abnormalities, fatigue, and irritability.[32] Hair and fingernail loss and gastrointestinal upset have been reported at much lower levels. The UL for adults is 400 μg per day from diet and supplements combined.[9]

Selenium Supplements

Selenium supplements are marketed with claims that they will protect against environmental pollutants, prevent cancer and heart disease, slow the aging process, and improve immune function. Although selenium does play a role in these processes, supplements that increase intake above the RDA will not provide additional benefits.

12.7 Iodine (I)

Learning Objectives

- Describe the function of iodine.
- Explain why iodine deficiency causes the thyroid gland to enlarge.
- Discuss factors that impact the iodine status of a population.

Iodine is needed for the synthesis of thyroid hormones. In the early 1900s, iodine deficiency was common in the central United States and Canada, but it has virtually disappeared due to the addition of iodine to table salt. Iodine deficiency, however, remains a world health problem.

(©iStockphoto)

Antioxidant Supplements: Are They Beneficial?

Many vitamins, minerals, and enzymes are marketed as supplements to boost our ability to defend against oxidative damage, keep us healthy by protecting us from heart disease and cancer, and even slow aging. The rationale for needing extra antioxidants is based on the fact that we are constantly bombarded with damaging reactive molecules, such as free radicals, that cause oxidative damage. Although nutrients are an important part of our antioxidant defense system, they are not the only source of antioxidant protection, and more is not always better.

Some free radicals in the body come from air pollution, radiation, and cigarette smoke. But, free radicals are also formed right in our bodies—some of the oxygen that our cells use in aerobic metabolism to produce ATP reacts with molecules in the body forming free radicals and other reactive molecules. If too many free radicals are generated the body's antioxidant defenses are overwhelmed. Sometimes cells are able to adapt by producing more antioxidant defenses. However, if the stress is too great or lasts too long, oxidative damage to DNA, proteins, carbohydrates, and lipids occurs, and cell death can result. The cumulative effect may play a role in aging and the development of a number of chronic diseases.

Our bodies are equipped with many types of antioxidant defenses. Some come from the diet, including vitamin C, vitamin E, and β-carotene and other carotenoids, as well as other phytochemicals (see Focus on Phytochemicals). Others are enzymes made in the body. Some rely on minerals, including zinc, copper, manganese, iron, and selenium for activity. Different antioxidants act in different locations under specific conditions to destroy particular types of reactive oxygen compounds (see figure). For example, vitamin C can inactivate reactive molecules in blood and other body fluids. Vitamin E and β-carotene can inactivate free radicals to protect lipids in cell membranes.

Do we get enough antioxidant nutrients and phytochemicals in our food? Can supplements boost our antioxidant defenses? Supplements containing antioxidant enzymes will not boost antioxidant defenses; because enzymes are proteins, when they are consumed they are broken down to amino acids and peptides in the gastrointestinal tract before they can be absorbed. Deciding whether antioxidant vitamins and minerals are beneficial is more difficult. If your diet is deficient in these nutrients, increasing your intake with a supplement will enhance antioxidant defenses. But whether consumption of these nutrients above the recommended intake will further improve the body's antioxidant defenses is still under investigation and we do not have sufficient information on optimum doses or the risk of toxicity. Also, because these nutrients interact, a deficiency of one could increase the need for another, and an excess of one may create a deficiency of another. For instance, vitamin C is necessary to regenerate the active form of vitamin E, selenium spares some of the need for vitamin E, and excesses of zinc can cause copper deficiency. Some antioxidants such as vitamin C can promote oxidative reactions under certain conditions. Therefore, it is possible for the wrong amounts to promote rather than prevent oxidative damage.

Antioxidant nutrients are important for good health, but based on our current understanding, it is best to boost antioxidant nutrients by eating more fruits, vegetables, and whole grains. They provide fiber and phytochemicals that you wouldn't get in a supplement, and these dietary components may be just as important in protecting you from chronic disease as are individual antioxidant nutrients.

Each of the antioxidant defenses functions in specific locations in the body and protects against specific types of damaging reactions.

Iodine in the Diet

The iodine content of foods varies depending on the soil where plants are grown or where animals graze. Iodine is found in seawater so seafood and plants grown near the sea are high in iodine. The soil in inland areas is generally low in iodine so plants grown inland have lesser amounts.

Most of the iodine in the North American diet comes from salt fortified with iodine, referred to as iodized salt. Iodized salt contains about 100 μg of iodine per gram. It is commonplace in the United States and only iodized salt is sold in Canada. Iodized salt should not be confused with sea salt, which is a poor source of iodine because the iodine is lost in the drying process.

Iodine in our diet also comes from contaminants and additives in foods. Dairy products may contain iodine because of the iodine-containing additives used in cattle feed and the use of iodine-containing disinfectants on cows, milking machines, and storage tanks. Iodine-containing sterilizing agents are also used in food service establishments, and iodine is used in dough conditioners and some food colorings.

Iodine in the Body

Iodine is absorbed completely and rapidly from the gastrointestinal tract in the form of iodide ions. Iodine can be eliminated from the body by excretion in the urine. More than half of the iodine in the body is located in the thyroid gland in the front of the neck. It is concentrated here because it is an essential component of the thyroid hormones, thyroxine (T_4) and triiodothyronine (T_3), which are made from the amino acid tyrosine (**Figure 12.18**). T_4 is the predominant thyroid hormone in the blood and is converted into the active T_3 form by a selenium-containing enzyme. The thyroid hormones act by affecting gene expression in target cells in a manner similar to vitamins A and D (**Figure 12.19**). Through gene expression, thyroid hormones promote protein synthesis and regulate basal metabolic rate, growth, and development.

Levels of the thyroid hormones are carefully controlled. If blood levels drop, **thyroid-stimulating hormone** is released from the anterior pituitary. This hormone signals the thyroid gland to take up iodine and synthesize thyroid hormones. When the supply of iodine is adequate, thyroid hormones can be made and their presence turns off the synthesis of thyroid-stimulating hormone (**Figure 12.20**).

thyroid-stimulating hormone A hormone that stimulates the synthesis and secretion of thyroid hormones from the thyroid gland.

Figure 12.18 Structure of the thyroid hormones
The thyroid hormones thyroxine (T_4) and triiodothyronine (T_3) are made from the amino acid tyrosine.

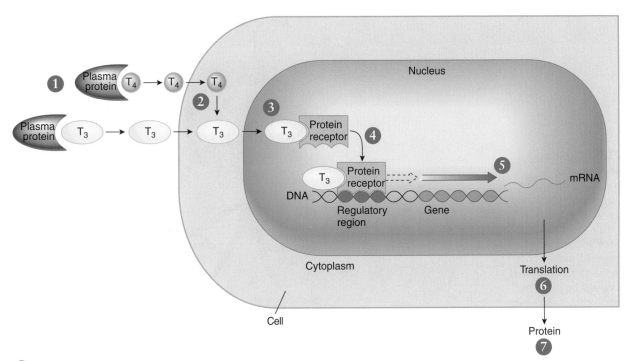

1. Thyroid hormones (T_4 and T_3) circulate in the blood bound to plasma proteins.

2. T_4 and T_3 enter the cell where a selenium-containing enzyme converts T_4 to T_3.

3. T_3 enters the nucleus and binds to a nuclear protein receptor.

4. The T_3-protein receptor complex then binds to a regulatory region of a target gene.

5. Transcription of the gene is turned on, increasing the amount of mRNA made.

6. mRNA directs translation, increasing the synthesis of the protein coded by this gene.

7. There is an increase in the amount of protein and hence the cellular functions and body processes affected by this protein.

Figure 12.19 Role of thyroid hormones in gene expression

Recommended Iodine Intake

The RDA for iodine in adult men and women is 150 μg per day. This is based on the amount needed to maintain normal iodine levels in the thyroid gland. Since the iodinization of salt, the intake of iodine in North America has met or exceeded the RDA.

The RDA is higher during pregnancy to account for the iodine that is taken up by the fetus and during lactation to account for the iodine secreted in milk. The recommended intake for infants is based on the amount obtained from breast milk.

Iodine Deficiency

Iodine deficiency reduces the production of thyroid hormones. Metabolic rate slows with insufficient thyroid hormones, causing fatigue and weight gain. The most obvious outward sign of deficiency is an enlarged thyroid gland called a **goiter (Figure 12.21)**. A goiter forms when reduced thyroid hormone levels cause thyroid-stimulating hormone to be released, stimulating the thyroid gland to make more thyroid hormones. Because iodine is unavailable, the hormones cannot be made and the stimulation continues, causing the thyroid gland to enlarge (see Figure 12.20). In milder cases of goiter, treatment with iodine causes the thyroid gland to return to normal size, but this result is not consistent in more severe cases.

A number of other iodine deficiency disorders occur because of the effect of iodine on growth and development. If iodine is deficient during pregnancy, it increases the risk of stillbirth and spontaneous abortion. Deficiency also can cause a condition

goiter An enlargement of the thyroid gland caused by a deficiency of iodine.

Life Cycle

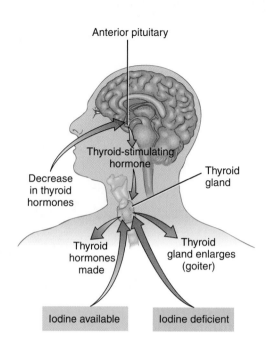

Figure 12.20 Regulating thyroid hormone levels
When thyroid hormone levels drop too low, thyroid-stimulating hormone is released and stimulates the thyroid gland to take up iodine and synthesize more hormones. If iodine is not available (brown arrows), thyroid hormones cannot be made and the stimulation continues, causing the thyroid gland to enlarge.

cretinism A condition resulting from poor maternal iodine intake during pregnancy that causes stunted growth and poor mental development in offspring.

goitrogens Substances that interfere with the utilization of iodine or the function of the thyroid gland.

called **cretinism** in the offspring. Cretinism is characterized by symptoms such as developmental disability, deaf mutism, and growth failure. Iodine deficiency during childhood and adolescence can also result in goiter and impaired mental function that lowers intellectual capacity.

Goitrogens The risk of iodine deficiency is increased by consuming **goitrogens**, substances in food that interfere with the utilization of iodine or with thyroid function. Goitrogens are found in turnips, rutabaga, cabbage, cassava, and millet. When these foods are boiled, the goitrogen content is reduced because some of these compounds leach into the cooking water. They are primarily a problem in African countries where cassava is a dietary staple. In the U.S. diet goitrogens are not a problem because they are present in foods that are not consumed in significant quantities in the typical diet.

Iodine Fortification Since it was first used in Switzerland in the 1920s, iodized salt has been the major means of combating iodine deficiency (see Off the Label: Should You Choose Salt Labeled "Iodized"?). Because of the fortification of table salt with iodine, cretinism and goiter are now rare in North America, but worldwide, 600 million people have goiter and 1.5 billion people are at risk for iodine deficiency.[36] Dramatic improvements in iodine status are seen in areas where iodization has been in place for over 5 years. For groups who do not have access to iodized salt or who will not use it, other forms of iodine supplementation, such as injections or oral doses of iodized oil, may be effective for control of iodine deficiency.[37]

Iodine Toxicity

Acute toxicity can occur with very large doses of iodine. Intakes between 200 and 500 μg per kilogram of body weight have caused death in laboratory animals.[32] Chronically high intakes of iodine can cause an enlargement of the thyroid gland that resembles goiter. The UL for adults is 1100 μg of iodine per day from all sources.[9] Goiter from excessive iodine can also occur if iodine intake changes drastically. For example, in a population with a marginal intake, a large increase in intake due to supplementation can cause thyroid enlargement even at levels that would not be toxic in a healthy population.

Figure 12.21 Iodine deficiency causes goiter, an enlargement of the thyroid gland seen as a swelling in the neck. (John Paul Kay/Peter Arnold, Inc.)

Off the Label
Should You Choose Salt Labeled "Iodized"?

(©iStockphoto)

When selecting a box of salt for the kitchen cupboard, you can choose one that just says "salt" or one that is labeled "iodized salt." Iodized salt is salt to which the trace element iodine has been added. Which should you choose?

The amount of iodine you consume in your diet depends as much on where the foods are grown as on which foods you choose. Foods from the ocean or produced near it, where the soil is rich in iodine are better sources of iodine than foods produced inland. This is because the iodine in inland areas has been washed into the oceans by glaciers, snow, rain, and flood waters. The iodine content of plants grown in iodine-deficient soil may be 100 times less than that of plants grown in iodine-rich soil.[1]

Iodine deficiency has been known for centuries in areas where the soil is depleted. In Europe the presence of iodine deficiency was recorded by classical art, which portrayed even the wealthy with goiter and cretinism. Leonardo da Vinci is said to have been more knowledgeable about goiter than medical professors of his time. A century ago, goiter was endemic in the central regions of North America. However, the iodinization of salt, which began in the early twentieth century, has virtually eliminated iodine deficiency in North America, Switzerland, and other European countries.

Why fortify salt? Salt was selected as the vehicle for added iodine because it is a food item consistently consumed by the majority of the population at risk. Also, iodine can be added to salt uniformly, inexpensively, and in a form that is well utilized by the body. It can be added in amounts that eliminate deficiency with typical consumption but not cause toxicity in people consuming larger amounts of iodized salt or individuals meeting iodine needs from other sources.

Since the introduction of iodized salt, iodine intake in the United States has been adequate, and iodine deficiency has been rare. However, recent U.S. surveys have shown a significant reduction in average iodine status.[2] Factors that may have contributed to this include increased consumption of processed foods, which contain non-iodized salt; reduced consumption of eggs, which are rich in iodine; and declining amounts of salt added in the home. Also, the iodine content of milk has decreased due to a reduction in the amount of iodine added to cattle feed, and the baking industry has eliminated some of the iodine-containing dough conditioners, thus reducing the iodine content of commercially manufactured breads.[2] If you live on the coast or buy food imported from many locations, you still probably get plenty of iodine. However, if you eat little seafood, live inland where the soil is deficient in iodine, and consume primarily foods grown locally, choose salt labeled "iodized" to ensure that your iodine needs are met.

(George Semple)

[1]Dunn, J. T. Iodine. In *Modern Nutrition in Health and Disease*, 10th ed. M. E. Shils, M. Shike, A. C. Ross, et al. eds. Philadelphia: Lippincott Williams & Wilkins, 2006, pp. 300–311.

[2]Pearce, E. N. National trends in iodine nutrition: Is everyone getting enough? *Thyroid* 17:823–827, 2007.

12.8 Chromium (Cr)

Learning Objective

- Explain the relationship between blood glucose levels and chromium.

It has been known since the 1950s that chromium is needed for normal glucose utilization, but only recently have scientists begun to understand the role of chromium in normal insulin function. The popular supplement chromium picolinate, is promoted to increase lean body mass.

Chromium in the Diet

Dietary sources of chromium include liver, brewer's yeast, nuts, and whole grains. Milk, vegetables, and fruit are poor sources. Refined carbohydrates such as white breads, pasta, and white rice are also poor sources because chromium is lost in milling and not added back in the enrichment process. Cooking in stainless steel cookware can increase chromium intake because chromium leaches from the steel into the food.

Chromium in the Body

After absorption, chromium is bound to the iron transport protein transferrin for transport in the blood. Chromium is involved in carbohydrate and lipid metabolism. When carbohydrate is consumed, insulin is released and binds to receptors in cell membranes. This binding triggers the uptake of glucose by cells, an increase in protein and lipid synthesis, and other effects. Chromium is believed to act as part of a small peptide that binds to the insulin receptor after insulin is bound, enhancing its effect[9] (**Figure 12.22**). When chromium is deficient, it takes more insulin to produce the same effect.

Recommended Chromium Intake

Based on the amount of chromium in a balanced diet, an AI has been set at 35 μg per day for men and 25 μg per day for women. The AI is increased during pregnancy and lactation. The AI for older adults is slightly lower because energy intake decreases with age.

Chromium Deficiency

Overt chromium deficiency is not a problem in the U.S. population. Deficiencies have been reported in patients receiving long-term TPN not containing chromium and in malnourished children. Deficiency symptoms include impaired glucose tolerance with

Figure 12.22 Chromium and insulin function

(a) When chromium is present, a small peptide inside cells becomes active and enhances the action of insulin by binding to the insulin receptor, which increases glucose uptake.

(b) When chromium is deficient, the active peptide is not formed and thus cannot bind the insulin receptor. The result is that insulin is less effective and less glucose can enter the cell.

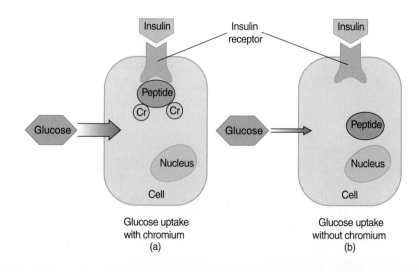

diabetes-like symptoms, such as elevated blood glucose levels and increased insulin levels.[38] Chromium deficiency may also cause elevated blood cholesterol and triglyceride levels, but the role of chromium in lipid metabolism is not fully understood.

Chromium Supplements and Toxicity

Chromium supplements, particularly as chromium picolinate, are marketed to reduce body fat and increase lean body tissue (**Figure 12.23**). This appeals to individuals wanting to lose weight as well as to athletes trying to build muscle. Because chromium is needed for insulin action and insulin promotes protein synthesis, it is likely that adequate chromium is necessary to increase lean body mass. However, most recent studies on the effects of chromium picolinate or other chromium supplements in healthy human subjects have found no beneficial effects on muscle strength, body composition, weight loss, or other aspects of health.[39] Chromium supplementation has been shown to have beneficial effects on blood glucose levels in individuals with type 2 diabetes.[40]

Controlled trials have reported no dietary chromium toxicity in humans.[9] Despite the apparent safety of chromium supplements, a few concerns have been raised. Two cases of renal failure have been associated with chromium picolinate supplements, but both of these individuals were taking other drugs known to cause renal toxicity, so it is unclear whether the effect was due to the chromium supplement.[41] The safety of chromium picolinate has also been questioned because of studies in cell culture that suggest it may cause DNA damage.[42] This effect is specific to the picolinate form of chromium and may be due to the ability of this form to generate DNA-damaging free radicals. Human studies using the standard supplemental doses of chromium picolinate have not detected an increase in DNA damage, but more work is needed to completely rule out any risk.[43] Despite these concerns, the DRI committee concluded that there was insufficient data to establish a UL for chromium.

Figure 12.23 Do chromium supplements help increase lean body mass and decrease body fat? (George Semple)

12.9 Fluoride (F)

Learning Objective

- Discuss the role of fluoride in maintaining dental health.

The importance of fluoride for dental health has been recognized since the 1930s, when an association between the fluoride content of drinking water and the prevalence of dental caries was noted (see Science Applied: From Colorado Brown Stain to Water Fluoridation).

Fluoride in the Diet

Fluoride is present in small amounts in almost all soil, water, plants, and animals. The richest dietary sources of fluoride are fluoridated water, tea, and marine fish consumed with their bones (**Figure 12.24**). Tea contributes significantly to total fluoride intake in countries that consume large amounts of the beverage. Brewed tea contains 1 to 6 mg of fluoride per liter depending on the amount of dry tea used, the brewing time, and the fluoride content of the water.[44] In the United States, most of the fluoride in the diet comes from toothpaste and from fluoride added to the water supply—usually 0.7 to 1.2 mg per liter. (Water companies often report fluoride levels in parts per million [ppm], 1 mg/liter = 1 ppm.) Because food readily absorbs the fluoride in cooking water, the fluoride content of food can be significantly increased when it is handled and prepared using fluoridated water. Cooking utensils also affect food fluoride content. Foods cooked with Teflon utensils can pick up fluoride from the Teflon, whereas aluminum cookware can decrease fluoride content. Fluoride is absorbed into the body in proportion to its content in the diet.

Figure 12.24 Dietary sources of fluoride include water, tea, fish eaten with bones, and toothpaste. (Charles D. Winters)

SCIENCE

ScienceAppliedScienceApplied
Science**AppliedScience**Applied
ScienceAppliedScienceApplied

APPLIED

(DAJ/Getty Images, Inc.)   (www.victorianoizquierdo.com/Getty Images, Inc.)   (Elena Schweitzer/Shutterstock)

From Colorado Brown Stain to Water Fluoridation

When Dr. Fredrick McKay set up his dental practice in Colorado Springs in 1901, he noticed that many of his patients had stained or mottled tooth enamel. McKay noted that those with stained teeth, a condition called "Colorado brown stain," seemed to be less susceptible to tooth decay.[1] At the time, dental caries were extremely prevalent, there was no known way to prevent the disease, and the most common way to treat it was to extract the affected teeth.

McKay believed that Colorado brown stain was due to something in the water supply. In 1930, he sent water samples to a chemist for analysis. Using a new methodology called spectrographic analysis, the chemist identified high levels of fluoride in McKay's samples. This finding led to the establishment of the Dental Hygiene Unit at the National Institutes of Health headed by Dr. H. Trendley Dean. His task was to investigate the association between fluoride intake and mottled enamel, which he termed "fluorosis."

Dean conducted epidemiological surveys to establish the prevalence of fluorosis across the country. He noted a strong inverse relationship between the prevalence of fluorosis and the prevalence of dental caries among children.[2] In other words, children with fluorosis had fewer dental caries. Further studies revealed that the protective effect of fluoride on dental caries was seen at water fluoride levels of 1 ppm, a level low enough to cause little fluorosis (see graph). Thus, work designed to identify the harm caused by too much fluoride had discovered the benefits of enough fluoride.

The first intervention trial to test the effectiveness of community water fluoridation began in 1945 and included four pairs of cities in Michigan, New York, Illinois, and Ontario. One city of each pair received the intervention—fluoridated water—and the second city served as a control. Surveys over a 13- to 15-year period found that the incidence of caries was reduced 50% to 70% among children in the communities with the fluoridated water.[3] In 1962, epidemiological studies of water consumption patterns and caries incidence in different climates and geographical locations across the country were used to make the first recommendation for an optimal range of fluoride concentration (0.7–1.2 ppm) in the water supply, with the lower range suggested for warmer climates, where more water is consumed, and the higher range for colder climates.[3]

Some people still believe that water fluoridation represents a public health hazard and increases the risk of cancer, but these beliefs are not supported by scientific fact. Based on epidemiological data and available evidence related to the adverse effects of fluoride, the small amounts consumed in drinking water do not pose a health risk.

Today, 69.2% of the U.S. population that is served by a public water system receives fluoridated water.[5] Fluoride intake has also increased due to the widespread use of fluoride toothpaste and fluoridated water in foods and beverages that are distributed in nonfluoridated areas. Although dental caries remains a public health problem, increased fluoride intake, combined with advances in dental care, have dramatically improved the dental health of the American public.

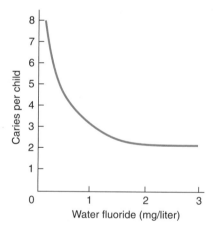

This graph illustrates the effect of water fluoridation level on dental caries in children 12 to 14 years of age.

---

[1]McKay, F. S. Relation of mottled enamel to caries. *J. Am. Dent. Assoc.* 15:1429–1437, 1928.

[2]Dean, H. T. Endemic fluorosis and its relation to dental caries. *Public Health Rep.* 53:1443–1452, 1938.

[3]Achievements in public health, 1900–1999: Fluoridation of drinking water to prevent dental caries. *Morb. Mortal. Wkly. Rep.* 48:933–940, 1999.

[4]National Research Council. The health effects of ingested fluoride: Report of the Subcommittee on the Health Effects of Ingested Fluoride, Committee on Toxicology, Board of Environmental Studies and Toxicology, Commission on Life Sciences. Washington, D.C.: National Academy Press, 1993.

[5]Centers for Disease Control and Prevention. Fact Sheet: Community Water Fluordination Statistics. Available online at www.cdc.gov/fluoridation/statistics.htm. Accessed September 9, 2009.

Fluoride in the Body

About 80% to 90% of ingested fluoride is absorbed. When taken with milk or other high-calcium foods, absorption is reduced. Fluoride has a high affinity for calcium and so is usually associated with calcified tissues such as bones and teeth. When fluoride is incorporated into the hydroxyapatite crystals of tooth enamel it makes the enamel more resistant to the acid that causes decay.

Recommended Fluoride Intake

Epidemiology has confirmed the effectiveness of fluoridated water in reducing dental cavities.[45] The criterion used to establish an AI for fluoride is the estimated intake shown to reduce the occurrence of dental caries maximally without causing unwanted side effects. The AI for fluoride from all sources is set at 0.05 mg per kg per day for everyone 6 months of age and older, because it protects against dental caries with no adverse effects.[44] Thus, for children age 4 through 8 years, the AI is set at 1.1 mg per day using a reference weight of 22 kg. For adult men age 19 and older, the AI is 3.8 mg per day based on a weight of 76 kg, for women, it is 3.1 mg per day based on a weight of 61 kg. The AI is not increased during pregnancy or lactation.

Life Cycle

Breast milk is low in fluoride, and ready-made infant formulas are prepared with unfluoridated water. Unless infant formula is prepared at home with fluoridated water, it contains little fluoride. The American Academy of Pediatrics suggests a supplement of 0.25 mg of fluoride per day for children 6 months to 3 years of age, 0.5 mg per day for ages 3 to 6 years, and 1.0 mg per day for ages 6 to 16 who are receiving less than 0.3 mg per liter of fluoride in the water supply.[46] These supplements are available by prescription for children living in areas with low water fluoride concentrations. Swallowed toothpaste is estimated to contribute about 0.6 mg per day of fluoride in young children.[44]

Fluoride Deficiency

Adequate dietary fluoride is important for bone and dental health. When fluoride is deficient tooth decay is more common. Because there are few food sources of fluoride and the fluoride content of water is variable, fluoride supplements or water fluoridation is often needed to minimize dental caries. Fluoride has its greatest effect on dental caries prevention early in life, during maximum tooth development up to the age of 13. During this time it can be incorporated into tooth enamel making the enamel more acid resistant. It has also been shown to protect teeth in other ways, making it beneficial for adults as well as children.[47] Fluoride in saliva reduces cavities by reducing acid produced by bacteria, inhibiting the dissolution of tooth enamel by acid, and increasing enamel remineralization after acid exposure.[44] Fluoride seems to stimulate new bone formation and has therefore been suggested to strengthen bones in adults with osteoporosis. Slow-release fluoride supplements have been shown to increase bone mass and prevent new fractures.[48]

Fluoride Toxicity

Fluoride can cause adverse effects in high doses. In children, fluoride intakes of 2 to 8 mg per day can cause stained, pitted teeth, a condition called **fluorosis (Figure 12.25)**. A recent increase in the prevalence of this condition in the United States has occurred due to the chronic ingestion of toothpaste containing fluoride.[49] In adults doses of 20 to 80 mg per day can result in changes in bone that can be crippling, as well as changes in kidney function and possibly nerve and muscle function. Death has been reported with an intake of 5 to 10 grams per day. Due to concern over excess fluoride intake, a warning is now required on fluoride-containing toothpastes.

fluorosis A condition caused by chronic overconsumption of fluoride, characterized by black and brown stains and cracking and pitting of the teeth.

Figure 12.25 Too much dietary fluoride causes staining and pitting of the teeth. These photos compare normal teeth (left) and teeth showing enamel fluorosis (right). [©E.H. Gill/Custom Medical Stock Photo, Inc. (right) ©NIH/Custom Medical Stock Photo, Inc.]

The label must state, "If you accidentally swallow more than used for brushing, seek professional help or contact a poison control center immediately."

The UL for fluoride is set at 0.1 mg per kg per day for infants and children less than 9 years of age and at 10 mg per day for people ages 9 through 70.[44]

12.10 Molybdenum (Mo)

Learning Objective

- Discuss how the molebdenum content of the soil affects the content of food.

Like many other trace elements, molybdenum is needed to activate enzymes. The molybdenum content of food varies with the molybdenum content of the soil where the food is produced. The most reliable sources include milk, milk products, organ meats, breads, cereals, and legumes.

Molybdenum is readily absorbed from foods. The amount in the body is regulated by excretion in the urine and bile. Molybdenum is a cofactor for enzymes necessary for the metabolism of sulfur-containing amino acids and nitrogen-containing compounds present in DNA and RNA, the production of uric acid (a nitrogen-containing waste product), and the oxidation and detoxification of various other compounds.

Although molybdenum deficiency in humans has been reported as a result of long-term TPN, a naturally occurring deficiency has never been reported. Deficiency has been induced in laboratory animals by feeding them high doses of the element tungsten, which inhibits molybdenum absorption. The resulting deficiency caused growth retardation, decreased food intake, impaired reproduction, and decreased life expectancy.

Based on the results of molybdenum balance studies, an RDA has been set at 45 μg per day for adults. The RDA is increased for pregnancy and lactation. An AI has been set for infants based on the amount of molybdenum in breast milk.

There are few data on adverse effects of high intakes of molybdenum in humans. A UL of 2000 μg per day was set based on impaired growth and reproduction in animals.[9]

12.11 Other Trace Elements

Learning Objective

- Name four essential trace elements for which no RDA or AI has been established.

Many other trace elements are found in minute amounts in the human body. Some of these may be essential for human health, and others, such as lead (see Chapter 15) may be present only as a result of environmental exposure. Arsenic, boron, nickel, silicon, and vanadium have been reviewed by the DRI committee and found to have a significant role in human health.[9] Arsenic is better known as a poison than an essential nutrient, but the organic forms of arsenic that occur in foods are nontoxic. It is hypothesized that arsenic is involved in the conversion of the amino acid methionine into compounds that affect heart function and cell growth. Arsenic deficiency has been correlated with nervous system disorders, blood vessel diseases, and cancer. Boron may be involved in vitamin D and estrogen metabolism. Nickel is thought to function in enzymes involved in the metabolism of certain fatty acids and amino acids, and it may play a role in folate metabolism. Silicon, the primary constituent of sand, is involved in the synthesis of collagen and the calcification of bone. Vanadium has been shown to have an insulin-like action and to stimulate cell proliferation and differentiation. There is not sufficient data to establish an AI or an RDA for any of these elements, but ULs have been set for boron, nickel, and vanadium. Other trace elements that play a physiological role include aluminum, bromine, cadmium, germanium, lead, lithium, rubidium, and tin. The specific functions of these have not been defined, and they have not been evaluated by the DRI committee. All the minerals, both those known to be essential and those that are still being assessed for their role in human health, can be obtained by choosing a variety of foods from each of the food groups of MyPyramid.

Outcome

Nissi's family and many others in the village are now using iodized salt. Nissi has grown to be an energetic teenager, with no trace of goiter. Iodine deficiency was common in Nissi's village, because the people grow the food they need and cannot afford expensive imports. The iodine content of food, like the content of many other trace elements, depends on where that food is grown or produced. The food grown near Nissi's village is low in iodine. A diet, such as that in the United States, made up of foods from many locations usually contains adequate amounts of all of the trace minerals.

About a year after Nissi was diagnosed with goiter, the Indian government began promoting the use of salt fortified with iodine and banned the production and sale of non-iodized salt. Some families in Nissi's village are still resistant to using the new salt, but information and education programs are spreading the message that iodized salt is safe and affordable. UNICEF also has established a program that allows children to bring samples of their salt to school to test its iodine content.

APPLICATIONS

Personal Nutrition

1. Are you at risk for iron deficiency?
   a. Use iProfile and the 3-day food intake record you kept in Chapter 2 to calculate your average daily intake of iron.
   b. How does your iron intake compare with the recommendation for someone of your age, gender, and life stage?
   c. If your intake is low, suggest modifications to your diet that would increase your iron intake enough to meet the RDA for someone your age and gender.
   d. If your diet already meets the recommendations for iron, make a list of foods you like that are good sources of iron.
   e. Identify the major food sources of iron in your diet and indicate whether they contribute heme iron.

2. Do you consume enough zinc?
   a. Use iProfile and your food record to calculate your zinc intake.
   b. If you eliminated meat from your diet, would you meet the RDA for zinc?
   c. What foods could you substitute for meats that are good sources of zinc?

General Nutrition Issues

1. What promises are made about trace element supplements?
   a. Using the Internet, search for information on a supplement discussed in this chapter—for instance, zinc lozenges or chromium picolinate.
   b. How does the information compare to the discussion in the text?
   c. Who provided the information? Does it promote the sale of a product?
   d. Is the information supported by scientific studies?

2. Imagine the diet in a developing country is deficient in iodine. Most of the food is grown and prepared locally. To solve the problem, the government imports iodized salt. When iodine deficiency continues to be a problem, a study

of the local diet finds it to be very low in added salt. Not enough of the imported iodized salt was used to have an effect on the iodine status of the population. Use the following information to suggest a way that iodine intake might be increased in this population:

> The following foods are typically consumed:
> Corn and corn tortillas
> Dried beans
> White rice
> Fresh tomatoes
> Fresh vegetables—greens and squash
> Pork
> Fresh fruits

A typical breakfast is cornmeal and fruit; lunch is a hot meal, usually with some kind of vegetable soup served with tortillas; and dinner is meat, beans, rice, tortillas, and fruit.

3. A researcher asked his new technician to prepare a diet for his laboratory animals. The technician is interrupted several times while mixing the diet and is unfamiliar with the scale he is using to weigh the diet ingredients. After the diet is fed to the animals for several months they begin to show signs of anemia. An error in diet preparation is suspected. The diet ingredients are:

Starch	Potassium
Sucrose	Magnesium
Casein (protein)	Chloride
Corn oil	Zinc
Mixed plant fibers	Iron
Vitamin A	Iodine
Vitamin D	Selenium
Vitamin E	Copper
Vitamin K	Manganese
B vitamin mix	Chromium
Calcium	Molybdenum
Sodium	

   a. What trace element deficiencies can cause anemia?
   b. What trace element excess can cause anemia?
   c. What vitamin deficiencies can cause anemia?
   d. What dietary components can contribute to anemia by interfering with the absorption of trace elements?

 iProfile

Summary

12.1 Trace Elements in the Modern Diet

- Trace elements are needed in minute amounts but deficiencies can be as devasting as deficiencies of nutrients required in larger amounts.

12.2 Iron (Fe)

- Iron is found in both plant and animal foods. Heme iron, the easily absorbable form, is found in animal products. Nonheme iron, which is not well absorbed, comes from both animal and plant sources.

- The amount of iron that is absorbed from the diet depends on the type of iron and the presence of other dietary components. The absorption of nonheme iron can be increased by consuming it with meat or acidic foods; its absorption is decreased by consuming it with foods containing phytates, oxalates, and tannins. If iron stores are low, more iron is bound to transferrin and transported from the intestinal mucosa to body cells. When body stores are adequate, less iron is transported from the mucosa and more is bound to ferritin and lost when mucosal cells die.

- Iron functions as part of hemoglobin, which transports oxygen in the blood, and myoglobin, which enhances the amount of oxygen available during muscle contraction. Iron is also a component of proteins involved in ATP production and is needed for activity of the antioxidant enzyme catalase.
- The RDA for iron for women age 19 to 50 is 18 mg per day, more than double the RDA of 8 mg per day for adult men and postmenopausal women.
- When iron is deficient, adequate hemoglobin cannot be made, resulting in iron deficiency anemia—the most common nutritional deficiency worldwide.
- Iron can be toxic. Ingestion of a single large dose can be fatal. The accumulation of iron in the body over time causes heart and liver damage and contributes to diabetes and cancer. The most common cause of chronic iron overload is hemochromatosis, a genetic disorder in which too much iron is absorbed.

12.3 Zinc (Zn)

- Good sources of zinc include red meats, eggs, dairy products, and whole grains.
- Zinc absorption is regulated by zinc transport proteins that determine how much zinc is in the mucosal cell and by metallothionein, a protein that binds zinc in the mucosal cell. When zinc intake is high more metallothionein is synthesized and zinc absorption is limited.
- Zinc is needed for the activity of many enzymes, including a form of the antioxidant enzyme superoxide dismutase. Many of the functions of zinc are related to its role in gene expression. Zinc is needed for tissue growth and repair, development of sex organs and bone, proper immune function, storage and release of insulin, mobilization of vitamin A from the liver, and stabilization of cell membranes.
- The RDA for zinc is 11 mg per day for adult men and 8 mg per day for adult women
- Zinc deficiency results in poor growth, delayed sexual maturation, skin changes, hair loss, skeletal abnormalities, and depressed immunity.
- Since copper also binds metallothionein, an excess of zinc can stimulate its synthesis and trap copper in the mucosal cells, causing a copper deficiency.

12.4 Copper (Cu)

- Good sources of copper in the diet include organ meats, seafood, nuts, and seeds.
- The absorption of copper is affected by the presence of other minerals in the diet. The zinc content of the diet can have a major impact on copper absorption.
- Copper functions in a number of important proteins that affect iron and lipid metabolism, synthesis of connective tissue, and antioxidant protection. Copper is transported in the blood bound to proteins such as ceruloplasmin.
- The RDA for copper for adults is 900 μg per day
- A copper deficiency can cause anemia and connective tissue abnormalities. Copper toxicity from dietary sources is extremely rare.

12.5 Manganese (Mn)

- Good dietary sources of manganese include whole grains and nuts. The AI is 2.3 mg per day for men and 1.8 mg per day for women.
- Manganese is necessary for the activity of some enzymes, including a form of the antioxidant enzyme superoxide dismutase. Manganese is involved in amino acid, carbohydrate, and lipid metabolism.

12.6 Selenium (Se)

- Dietary sources of selenium include seafood, eggs, organ meats, and plant foods grown in selenium-rich soils.
- Selenium protects against oxidative damage as an essential part of the enzyme glutathione peroxidase. Glutathione peroxidase destroys peroxides before they can form free radicals. Adequate dietary selenium reduces the need for vitamin E.
- The RDA for selenium for adults is 55 μg per day.
- Severe selenium deficiency is rare except in regions with very low soil selenium content and limited diets. In China, selenium deficiency contributes to the development of a heart condition known as Keshan disease. Low selenium intake has been linked to increased cancer risk.
- Very high selenium intake (5 mg per day) causes fingernail changes and hair loss.
- Selenium supplements are marketed with claims that they will protect against environmental pollutants, prevent cancer and heart disease, slow the aging process, and improve immune function. Supplements that increase intake above the RDA will not provide additional benefits.

12.7 Iodine (I)

- The best sources of iodine in the diet are seafood, foods grown near the sea, and iodized salt.
- Iodine is an essential component of thyroid hormones, which promote protein synthesis and regulate basal metabolic rate, growth, and development.
- The RDA for iodine in adult men and women is 150 μg per day
- When iodine is deficient, continued release of thyroid-stimulating hormone causes the thyroid gland to enlarge, forming a goiter. Iodine deficiency during pregnancy causes a condition in the offspring known as cretinism, which is characterized by growth failure and developmental disability. Iodine deficiency during childhood and adolescence can impair mental function. Although iodine deficiency is a world health problem, it has been virtually eliminated in North America through the use of iodized salt.
- Acute toxicity can occur with very large doses of iodine. Chronically high intakes of iodine can cause an enlargement of the thyroid gland that resembles goiter.

12.8 Chromium (Cr)

- Chromium is found in liver, brewer's yeast, nuts, and whole grains.
- Chromium is needed for normal insulin action and glucose utilization.

- Recommended chromium intake is 35 µg per day for men and 25 µg per day for women.
- Overt chromium deficiency is not a problem in the U.S. population.
- Chromium supplements are marketed to control blood sugar and increase lean body mass. Controlled trials have reported no dietary chromium toxicity in humans.

12.9 Fluoride (F)

- Most of the fluoride in the diet in the United States comes from fluoridated drinking water and toothpaste.
- Fluoride is necessary for the maintenance of bones and teeth. Adequate dietary fluoride helps prevent dental caries

- The recommended fluoride intake from all sources is set at 0.05 mg per kg per day for everyone 6 months of age and older, because it protects against dental caries with no adverse effects

12.10 Molybdenum (Mo)

- Molybdenum is a cofactor for enzymes involved in the metabolism of the amino acids methionine and cysteine and nitrogen-containing compounds such as DNA and RNA.

12.11 Other Trace Elements

- There is evidence that boron, arsenic, nickel, silicon, and vanadium may be essential in humans as well as animals. These elements may be necessary in small amounts but can be toxic if consumed in excess.

Review Questions

1. What are the functions of iron in the body?

2. Why does iron deficiency cause red blood cells to be small and pale?

3. List three life-stage groups at risk for iron deficiency anemia and explain why they are at risk.

4. List several good sources of iron in the diet and indicate if they contain heme or nonheme iron.

5. Discuss three factors that affect iron absorption.

6. Explain the roles of ferritin, transferrin, and transferrin receptors in regulating the amount of iron in the body.

7. What is hemochromatosis?

8. How does zinc affect the synthesis of proteins?

9. How does a high zinc intake reduce the amount of zinc that enters the blood?

10. Why does excess zinc cause a deficiency of copper?

11. Explain why a deficiency of copper can contribute to anemia.

12. What is the role of selenium in the body?

13. Why does selenium decrease the need for vitamin E?

14. What is a goiter and why does iodine deficiency cause it to form?

15. What is the role of chromium in the body?

16. What do zinc, copper, and manganese have in common?

17. How does fluoride function in dental health?

References

1. Centers for Disease Control and Prevention. Iron deficiency—United States. 1999–2000. *Morb. Mortal. Wkly. Rep.* 51:897–899, 2002. Available online at www.cdc.gov/mmwr/preview/mmwrhtml/mm5140a1.htm/ Accessed Jan 21, 2009.

2. World Health Organization. Micronutrient Deficiencies, Iron Deficiency Anemia: The Challenge. Available online at www.who.int/nutrition/topic/ida/en/ Accessed Jan 21, 2009.

3. Sharp, P., and Srai, S. K. Molecular mechanisms involved in intestinal iron absorption. *World J. Gastoenterol.* 13:4716–4724, 2007.

4. Teucher, B., Olivares, M., and Cori, H. Enhancers of iron absorption: Ascorbic acid and other organic acids. *Intl. J. Vit. Nutr. Res.* 74:403–419, 2004.

5. Zijp, I. M., Korver, O., and Tijburg, L. B. Effect of tea and other dietary factors on iron absorption. *Crit. Rev. Food Sci. Nutr.* 40:371–398, 2000.

6. Hurrell, R. F., Lynch, S., Bothwell, T. et al. SUSTAIN Task Force. Enhancing the absorption of fortification iron. A SUSTAIN Task Force report. *Intl. J. Vit. Nutr. Res.* 74:387–401, 2004.

7. Grinder-Pedersen, L., Bukhave, K., Jensen, M. et al. Calcium from milk or calcium-fortified foods does not inhibit nonheme-iron absorption from a whole diet consumed over a 4-d period. *Am. J. Clin. Nutr.* 80:404–409, 2004.

8. Anderson, G. J., Frazer, D. M., McKie, A. T., and Vulpe, C. D. The ceruloplasmin homolog hephaestin and the control of intestinal iron absorption. *Blood Cells Mol. Dis.* 29:367–375, 2002.

9. Food and Nutrition Board, Institute of Medicine. *Dietary Reference Intakes: Vitamin A, Vitamin K, Arsenic, Boron, Chromium, Copper, Iodine, Iron, Manganese, Molybdenum, Nickel, Silicon, Vanadium, and Zinc.* Washington, DC: National Academies Press, 2001.

10. O'Connor, N. R. Infant formula. *Am. Fam. Physician* 79:565–570, 2009.

11. Killip, S., Bennett, J. M., and Chambers, M. D. Iron deficiency anemia. *Am Fam Phys* 75:671–678, 2007.

12. Centers for Disease Control and Prevention. Recommendations to prevent and control iron deficiency in the United States. *Morb. Mortal. Wkly. Rep.* 47:1–29, 1998. Available online at www.cdc.gov/mmwr/preview/mmwrhtml/00051880.htm/ Accessed June 20, 2005.

13. Guidance for industry: Iron-containing supplements small entity compliance guide, October, 2003. Available online at www.fda.gov/Food/GuidanceCompliance RegulatoryInformation/GuidanceDocuments/Dietary Supplements/ucm073014.htm. Accessed September 8, 2009.

14. Siah, C. W., Trinder, D., and Olynyk, J. K. Iron overload. *Clin. Chem. Acta.* 358:24–36, 2005.

15. Rajpathak, S. N., Wylie-Rosett, J., Gunter, M. J. et al. Biomarkers of body iron stores and risk of developing type 2 diabetes. *Diabetes Obes. Metab.* 11:472–479, 2009.

16. Zegrean, M. Association of body iron stores with development of cardiovascular disease in the adult population: A systematic review of the literature. *Can. J. Cardiovasc. Nurs.* 19:26–32, 2009.

17. Fowler, C. F. Hereditary hemochromatosis: Pathophysiology, diagnosis, and management. *Crit. Care Nurs. Clin. N. Am.* 20:191–201, 2008.

18. Prasad, A. S. Discovery of human zinc deficiency and studies in an experimental human model. *Am. J. Clin. Nutr.* 53:403–412, 1991.

19. Liuzzi, J. P., and Cousins, R. J. Mammalian zinc transporters. *Annu. Rev. Nutr.* 24:151–172, 2004.

20. Tapiero, H., and Tew, K. D. Trace elements in human physiology and pathology: Zinc and metallothioneins. *Biomed. Pharmacother.* 57:399–411, 2003.

21. Wakimoto, P., and Block, G. Dietary intake, dietary patterns, and changes with age: An epidemiological perspective. *J. Gerontol. A. Biol. Sci. Med. Sci.* 56:65–80, 2001.

22. Briefel, R. R., Bialostosky, K., Kennedy-Stephenson, J. et al. Zinc intake of the U.S. population: Findings from the Third National Health and Nutrition Examination Survey, 1988–1994. *J. Nutr.* 130:1367S–1373S, 2000.

23. Black, R. E. Zinc deficiency, infectious disease, and mortality in the developing world. *J. Nutr.* 133:1485S–1489S, 2003.

24. Haase, H., Mocchegiani, E., and Rink, L. Correlation between zinc status and immune function in the elderly. *Biogerontology* 7:421–428, 2006.

25. National Institute of Allergy and Infectious Diseases. The common cold. NIAID fact sheet. National Institute of Allergy and Infectious Diseases, National Institutes of Health. Available online at: www.niaid.nih.gov/factsheets/cold.htm/ Accessed June 20, 2009.

26. Hulisz, D. Efficacy of zinc against common cold viruses: An overview. *J. Am. Pharm. Assoc.* 44:594–603, 2004.

27. Caruso, T. J., Prober, C. G., and Gwaltney, J. M., Jr. Treatment of naturally acquired common colds with zinc: a structured review. *Clin. Infect. Dis.* 45:569–574, 2007.

28. Prasad, A. S., Beck, F. W., Bao, B. et al. Duration and severity of symptoms and levels of plasma interleukin-1 receptor antagonist, soluble tumor necrosis factor receptor, and adhesion molecules in patients with common cold treated with zinc acetate. *J. Infect. Dis.* 197:795–802, 2008.

29. National Institute of Neurological Disorders and Stroke. NINDS Wilson's Disease Information Page. Available online at www.ninds.nih.gov/disorders/wilsons/wilsons. htm/ Accessed September 8, 2009.

30. Mills, E. S. The treatment of idiopathic (hypochromic) anemia with iron and copper. *Can. Med. Assoc. J.* 22:175–178, 1930.

31. Failla, M. L. Trace elements and host defense: Recent advances and continuing challenges. *J. Nutr.* 133 (5 suppl 1):1443S–1447S, 2003.

32. National Research Council, Food and Nutrition Board. *Recommended Dietary Allowances,* 10th ed. Washington, DC: National Academy Press, 1989.

33. Beck, M. A., Levander, O. A., and Handy, J. Selenium deficiency and viral infection. *J. Nutr.* 133(5 suppl 1): 1463S– 1467S, 2003.

34. Clark, L. C., Combs, G. F. Jr., Turnbull, B. W. et al. Effect of selenium supplementation for cancer prevention in patients with carcinoma of the skin. *JAMA* 276:1957–1968, 1996.

35. Duffield-Lillico, A. J., Slate, E. H., Reid, M. E. et. al. Selenium supplementation and secondary prevention of nonmelanoma skin cancer in a randomized trial. *J. Natl. Cancer Inst.* 95:1477–1481, 2003.

36. World Health Organization. Micronutrient Deficiencies: Iodine Deficiency Disorders. Available online at www.who.int/nutrition/topics/idd/en/ Accessed April 8, 2009.

37. World Health Organization. *Micronutrient Deficiencies: Iodine Deficiency Disorders.* Available online at www.who.int/nutrition/topics/idd/en/index.html. Accessed May 20, 2008.

38. Vincent, J. B. Recent advances in the nutritional biochemistry of trivalent chromium. *Proc. Nutr. Soc.* 63:41–47, 2004.

39. Di Luigi, L. Supplements and the endocrine system in athletes. *Clin. Sports Med.* 27:131–151, 2008.

40. Balk, E. M., Tatsioni, A., Lichtenstein, A. H. et al. Effect of chromium supplementation on glucose metabolism and lipids: A systematic review of randomized controlled trials. *Diabetes Care* 30:2154–2163, 2007.

41. Jeejeebhoy, K. N. The role of chromium in nutrition and therapeutics and as a potential toxin. *Nutr. Rev.* 57:329–335, 1999.

42. Stearns, D. M., Wise, J. P. Sr., Patierno, S. R., and Wetterhahn, K. E. Chromium (III) picolinate produces chromosome damage in Chinese hamster ovary cells. *FASEB J.* 9:1643–1648, 1995.

43. Vincent, J. B. The potential value and toxicity of chromium picolinate as a nutritional supplement, weight loss agent and muscle development agent. *Sports Med.* 33:213–230, 2003.

44. Institute of Medicine, Food and Nutrition Board. *Dietary Reference Intakes for Calcium, Phosphorus, Magnesium, Vitamin D, and Fluoride.* Washington, DC: National Academies Press, 1997.

45. Parnell, C., Whelton, H., and O'Mullane, D. Water fluoridation. *Eur. Arch. Paediatr. Dent.* 10:141–148, 2009.

46. American Academy of Pediatrics. Fluoride Supplementation Recommended Schedule. Available online at www.aap.org/oralhealth/cme/page44.htm. Accessed September 9, 2009.

47. American Dental Association. Fluoridation facts. Available online at: www.ada.org/public/topics/fluoride/facts/fluoridation_facts.pdf. Accessed October 11, 2009.

48. Rubin, C. D., Pak, C.Y., Adams-Huet, B. et al. Sustained-release sodium fluoride in the treatment of the elderly with established osteoporosis. *Arch. Intern. Med.* 161:2325–2333, 2001.

49. Beltrán-Aguilar E. D., Griffin S. O., and Lockwood S. A. Prevalence and trends in enamel fluorosis in the United States from the 1930s to the 1980s *J. Am. Dent. Assoc.* 133:157–165, 2002.

Focus On

Nonvitamin/Nonmineral Supplements

Outline

If you are looking for a dietary supplement, you won't have to look far. Currently, there are about 30,000 different products from which to choose.[1] They come as tablets, capsules, powders, softgels, gelcaps, and liquids. They are sold in health food stores, supermarkets, drug stores, and national discount chain stores, as well as through mail-order catalogs, television, the Internet, and direct sales. Most of these products contain vitamins and minerals, but a large number of the more popular dietary supplements contain nutrients other than vitamins or minerals and substances that are not classified as nutrients at all. Surveys have reported that over 50% of adult Americans use supplements and over 17% use nonvitamin/nonmineral supplements.[2,3] They are taken to improve athletic performance, promote weight loss, prevent and treat disease, slow aging, and for a variety of other reasons. Some of these contain protein, amino acids, or fatty acids. Others contain substances, such as hormones, enzymes, and coenzymes, which are made in the body but are not dietary essentials. Some contain plant-derived substances such as phytochemicals and herbs. For many there is scientific evidence of beneficial effects. For others the benefits are more questionable, and for a few, the risk of using them clearly outweighs any benefits they may provide.

F4.1 What Is a Dietary Supplement?

Learning Objectives

* List the types of substances that are included in dietary supplements.
* Explain the regulatory impact of classifying dietary supplements as foods, rather than drugs.

The term dietary supplement traditionally referred to products designed to add essential nutrients to the diet. But the 1994 Dietary Supplement Health and Education Act (DSHEA) broadened this definition to include any product intended for ingestion as a supplement to the diet. These products can include not only vitamins and minerals, but also herbs, botanicals, and other plant-derived substances as well as amino acids and concentrates, metabolites, constituents, and extracts of these substances. Products sold as dietary supplements must carry a standard label that meets the specifications of the DSHEA.[4] But just because a supplement is labeled, doesn't mean it is safe. Unlike most foods, dietary supplements may contain concentrations of nutrients and other substances that exceed levels normally found in the diet and may therefore present a risk, particularly for people taking medications or with certain medical conditions. Unlike drugs, dietary supplements are not strictly regulated in terms of dose or constituents.

Dietary Supplement Labels

According to FDA regulations, any product intended for ingestion as a supplement to the diet must include the words "dietary supplement" on the label and carry a "Supplement Facts" panel (**Figure F4.1** and Chapter 2). The Supplement Facts panel lists the recommended serving size and the name and quantity of each ingredient per serving. The nutrients for which Daily Values have been established are listed first, followed by other dietary ingredients for which Daily Values have not been established.[4]

Supplement Facts		
Serving Size: 2 Capsules		
Servings Per Container: 60		
	Amount Per Serving	**DV%**
Vitamin C (as ascorbic acid)	60mg	100%
Pantothenic Acid (as calcium, pantothenate)	20mg	200%
Vitamin B-6 (as pyridoxine hcl)	8mg	400%
Niacin	5mg	25%
Folate (as folic acid)	100mcg	25%
Zinc (as zinc gluconate)	5mg	33%
Copper (as copper gluconate)	500mcg	25%
NADH (Nicotinamide Adenine Dinucleotide)	1000mcg	*
Hoodia Gordonii Extract (20:1 Extract- Equal to 2000 mg of whole plant)	100mg	*
5-Hydroxytryptophan (Griffonia Simplicifolia)	25mg	*
N, N Dimethylglycine	50mg	*
Trimethylglycine	75mg	*
L-Phenylalanine	600mg	*
Decaffinated Green Tea Extract (Total Catechins 130mg, Epigaliocatechin Galiate (EGCG 70mg)	175mg	*
Salvia Scalarea Extract	50mg	*
Choline (as bitartrate)	75mg	*

*Daily Value (DV, not established)

Recommended Use: As a dietary supplement take two capsules before breakfast on a empty stomach (or before exercise) and two capsules at mid afternoon preferably with 8 oz of water.

Figure F4.1 Supplement facts This Supplement Facts panel from a supplement marketed to reduce appetite and aid in weight loss indicates that it contains vitamins, as well as certain amino acids, plant extracts, and some substances made in the body.

To ensure that dietary supplements do not contain contaminants and that the information listed on the supplement label is accurate, the FDA has established regulations regarding current Good Manufacturing Practices (cGMP) for dietary supplements.[5] These require manufacturers to evaluate their products for identity, purity, strength, and composition. The U.S. Pharmacopeia (USP) has also developed a voluntary dietary supplement verification program. Those manufacturers who participate in the program can include the USP-Verified mark on their product label (see Chapter 2, Figure 2.14).

Regulation of Dietary Supplements

Although dietary supplements are often taken as drugs to prevent or treat disease, their safety and marketing are not regulated as strictly as drugs. Drugs are required to undergo testing that must be reviewed by the FDA before they can be marketed to the public. Supplement manufacturers are responsible for ensuring product safety but these products do not require FDA review. If a problem arises with a specific product, the FDA must prove that the supplement represents a risk before it can be removed from the market. The exception to this rule is products that contain new ingredients. Any supplement containing an ingredient not sold in the United States before October 15, 1994, must provide the FDA with safety data prior to marketing the product. Ingredients sold prior to this date are presumed safe based on their history of use by humans.[4]

F4.2 Macronutrient Supplements

Learning Objective

- Explain why people might take supplements containing protein, amino acids, or fatty acids.

A varied balanced diet will meet nutrient needs for most healthy people (see Chapter 9: Off the Label: Think Before You Supplement). However, some people choose to supplement specific nutrients because they don't think they get enough in their diets or because they are looking for additional beneficial effects such as disease prevention or performance enhancement. For example, carbohydrate and protein supplements are frequently used by athletes. Carbohydrate pills wouldn't provide enough carbohydrate to have a significant effect so supplemental carbohydrate usually comes in the form of sports beverages, bars, or carbohydrate gels. These are packaged in convenient containers and are absorbed from the GI tract quickly to provide glucose to exercising muscles. Protein supplements are generally in the form of powders, drinks, and bars. They do not provide any benefits beyond that obtained from the protein in an adequate diet. Individual amino acids and fatty acids are also marketed for their effect on performance and body composition as well as disease prevention.

Amino Acids

Amino acids supplements are popular among athletes and dieters. The amino acids arginine, ornithine, and lysine are taken because they have been found to stimulate the release of growth hormone, which promotes muscle growth. Therefore, these are promoted to people who want to build muscle and lose fat. However, controlled studies have not found oral supplements of these amino acids taken before exercise to boost growth hormone release, or to increase muscle mass or strength above that obtained from training alone.[6] Branched-chain amino acids (leucine, isoleucine, and valine) are marketed to athletes because they are used as fuel during exercise. Despite this, supplements have not been demonstrated to enhance exercise performance.[7] Glutamine and glycine supplements are also marketed to athletes but neither has been found to enhance exercise performance. Because some amino acids share transport systems, supplementing one amino acid can cause a deficiency of others that use that same transport system (see Chapter 6).

Fatty Acids

Supplements of omega-3 fatty acids from fish oils and flaxseed are taken to reduce the risk of heart disease (**Figure F4.2**). Valid scientific evidence shows that omega-3 fatty acids protect against heart disease but supplements may not contain enough of these to have a beneficial effect.[8] Likewise supplemental flaxseed oil is unlikely to provide enough omega-3 fatty acids to have an effect on the total diet. Eating fish several times a week and sprinkling ground flaxseed on your cereal is a better option. If flaxseed is added to foods on a daily basis it will increase not only omega-3 fatty acid intake, but also the intake of fiber and phytochemicals. The risks of taking supplements containing omega-3 fatty acids are minimal for healthy people, but these products are not recommended for those taking blood-thinning medications because they inhibit blood clotting.

Figure F4.2 Fish oil and flaxseed oil supplements can increase your omega-3 fatty acid intake, but are not as beneficial to your health as eating fish and flaxseeds. (Andy Washnik)

F4.3 Substances Made in the Body

Learning Objectives

- Discuss why most enzyme supplements are ineffective.
- Describe the benefits of popular hormone supplements.

Many molecules essential to normal metabolic and physiological function are made in the body in amounts sufficient to meet needs and are therefore not essential in the diet. No deficiency symptoms occur when they are absent from the diet. Nonetheless supplements of many of these biological molecules are sold to enhance bodily functions. Most of these have little beneficial effect for healthy, well-nourished individuals.

Enzyme Supplements

Enzymes are proteins. Those needed for normal function are made in the body. When consumed in supplements, like other proteins, they are broken down into amino acids in the GI tract. The enzyme protein itself never reaches cells inside the body and therefore most enzyme supplements have little effect on body function (see Chapter 6). The exception to this is digestive enzymes that act in the gastrointestinal tract. When supplemented, these can perform their functions before they are broken down. For example, lactase, the enzyme that breaks down the milk sugar lactose, can benefit individuals with lactose intolerance when it is consumed along with foods containing lactose. The enzyme breaks down lactose that is in the GI tract. Eventually the lactase is also digested.

A number of other digestive enzymes including proteases, lipases, amylases, and plant enzymes, such as bromelain from pineapple and papain from papaya, are marketed to improve digestion in normal healthy people. Advertisements for these products claim that the digestive enzymes naturally present in food are destroyed by cooking, leaving partially digested substances in the GI tract and forcing the body to synthesize more of its own digestive enzymes. Despite the popularity of enzyme supplements there is no evidence that they are beneficial for healthy people.

Hormone Supplements

Hormones are another popular supplement ingredient. Protein or peptide hormones such as growth hormone have the same problem as enzymes—they are proteins so they are broken down in the gut before they can reach their target. Despite this, oral

Figure F4.3 Melatonin and DHEA are hormones that can be purchased in supplement form. DHEA use is banned by the International Olympic committee, the National College Athletic Association, and most major league sporting organizations. (Andy Washnik)

growth hormone supplements are sold. These supplements are claimed, by some, to increase muscle mass, to decrease body fat, and to boost stamina and sense of well-being. Even growth hormone injections, which are the only way to get the active hormone into the body, have not been shown to have a significant effect on muscle strength or the aging process.[9]

Hormones that are not proteins can be absorbed into the body intact and supplemental doses may affect body functions (**Figure F4.3**). Melatonin is a hormone made by the pineal gland in the brain. Although it is synthesized from the amino acid tryptophan, it is not a protein and supplemental doses can be absorbed intact from the GI tract. Supplements of melatonin are taken to delay aging, protect against free radical damage, and help with sleep disorders and jet lag. There is little evidence that it slows the aging process or that it reduces oxidative damage but there is significant evidence that links the hormone melatonin to sleep cycles in humans. It has been suggested that in situations where the body's production of melatonin is reduced (advancing age) or the normal sleep/wake cycle is disrupted, such as with jet lag, supplemental melatonin may improve both sleep duration and quality. Melatonin appears to decrease jet lag symptoms and hasten the return to normal energy levels. Melatonin may also improve sleep quality for people whose jobs require them to work on rotating shift schedules. However, adequate long-term studies examining the efficacy, toxicity, and optimal dosage and timing of melatonin administration are still lacking.[10]

Like melatonin, steroid hormones can be absorbed in the digestive tract and reach the bloodstream intact, thereby affecting function. DHEA (dehydroepiandrosterone), a steroid hormone made by the adrenal glands is a popular supplement. It is a precursor to the sex hormones, estrogen and testosterone. The production of DHEA in the body peaks in one's mid-twenties, and gradually declines with age in most people. Preventing this drop has been suggested to delay the aging process by maintaining levels of estrogen and testosterone. It has been claimed that DHEA improves energy level, strength, and immunity. Athletes use it as a substitute for anabolic steroids to increase muscle mass and decrease body fat. However, supplementation has not been found to be effective for increasing muscle size or strength or for treating advancing age, male sexual dysfunction, or menopausal symptoms.[11,12] The long-term effects of DHEA supplements have not been studied, but there is concern that they may interfere with normal levels of the sex hormones and have detrimental effects on the body, including liver damage.

Coenzyme Supplements

Many vitamins have coenzyme functions, but there are also coenzymes that are not dietary essentials. One of these is lipoic acid, which is a coenzyme needed for two reactions necessary for the production of ATP by aerobic metabolism. Although essential to energy metabolism, lipoic acid can be synthesized in adequate amounts by human cells so supplements do not accelerate the reactions catalyzed by this coenzyme.

Ubiquinone, also called coenzyme Q, is another coenzyme important for the production of ATP from carbohydrate, fat, and protein. It is needed in the electron transport chain; the final stage of aerobic metabolism where ATP is generated. Because, as its name implies, it is present ubiquitously, in animals, plants, and microorganisms, and it is synthesized in the human body, supplements are not necessary for most people. However, supplements may be beneficial in individuals with inherited defects in the function of their mitochondria.[13] Low levels of coenzyme Q are also a concern in those taking cholesterol-lowering statin drugs such as Crestor and Lipitor. Statins inhibit an enzyme needed for the synthesis of both cholesterol and ubiquinone, which can cause depletion of this coenzyme. Depletion of coenzyme Q in the mitochondria of muscle cells has been suggested as a cause of the muscle weakness that appears as a side effect in some individuals taking statins. Although coenzyme Q supplements increase blood levels of coenzyme Q, it is not clear whether levels increase in the muscle mitochondria where it is needed.[14]

Supplements Containing Structural and Regulatory Molecules

A number of structural and regulatory molecules are taken as supplements for a variety of different reasons. For instance, carnitine and creatine are both sold to enhance athletic performance (see Chapter 13). Carnitine is a molecule that is needed to transport fatty acids into the mitochondria where they are broken down by β-oxidation and aerobic metabolism to produce ATP. Supplements are marketed to increase endurance by improving the use of fat as an energy source during exercise. Supplements have not been shown to improve endurance but more recent studies focus on its potential to enhance recovery from exercise.[15] Creatine is a small molecule used to make a high-energy molecule, called creatine phosphate, which provides energy to the muscle for short bursts of activity. Creatine supplements have been shown to benefit some athletes by enhancing strength, performance, and recovery from high intensity exercise.[16] They do not improve endurance (see Chapter 13).

Glucosamine, chondroitin, and SAM-e are molecules needed for the maintenance of healthy joints and are sold to alleviate the pain and progression of arthritis. Glucosamine and chondroitin are molecules found in and around the cells of cartilage, the type of connective tissue that cushions joints. They are made in the body and consumed in the diet in meat. Supplements of both glucosamine and chondroitin are reported to reduce arthritis pain, stop cartilage degeneration, and possibly stimulate the repair of damaged joint cartilage (see Chapter 16: Your Choice: Do Glucosamine and Chondroitin Really Help Arthritis?). Supplements of these may be beneficial in relieving the symptoms of arthritis in some people[17] (**Figure F4.4**).

SAM-e, chemically known as S-adenosylmethionine, is present in the body normally as an intermediate in the metabolism of the amino acid methionine. SAM-e promotes the production of cartilage and is beneficial in the treatment of arthritis. It is also claimed to be effective for treating depression and liver disease. Although there is preliminary evidence that SAM-e may be beneficial in individuals with depression and arthritis, the results of large, well-controlled studies are not yet available and the risks of taking this supplement have not been adequately assessed.[18]

Supplements of inositol can also be found on the shelf. Inositol is a component of phospholipids in cell membranes where it plays a role in relaying messages to the inside of the cell. Inositol can be synthesized from glucose. There is no evidence that it is essential in the human diet, but it may have some clinical value in treating diseases such as diabetes and kidney failure.[19]

Figure F4.4 There is evidence that supplements containing glucosamine and chondroitin sulfate benefit people suffering from arthritis. The pills are large and about 3 a day is recommended to obtain these benefits. (Andy Washnik)

F4.4 Phytochemical Supplements

Learning Objective

- Explain why phytochemical supplements may not have the same benefits as foods containing these phytochemicals.

A diet rich in phytochemicals from fruits, vegetables, and whole grains has been shown to reduce the risk of heart disease and cancer (see Focus on Phytochemicals). Although we have not yet isolated and identified all of these health-promoting substances, some have been extracted, purified, and pressed into pills or capsules. These are advertised as having health-promoting properties but they do not appear to provide all the benefits obtained from whole foods that are rich sources of these as well as a host of other phytochemicals and nutrients.

Carotenoids

Carotenoids are a group of more than 600 yellow, orange, and red compounds found in living organisms. Carotenoids have antioxidant properties, and some also have vitamin A activity. The most prevalent carotenoids in the North American diet include β-carotene, α-carotene, β-cryptoxanthin, lycopene, lutein, and zeaxanthin. The major sources of carotenoids in the diet are fruits and vegetables (**Figure F4.5**).

Figure F4.5 Fruits and vegetables are the major source of dietary carotenoids. (Andy Washnik)

Lutein and zeaxanthin are carotenoids found in leafy green vegetables. They do not have vitamin A activity but are concentrated in the macula of the eye, where they protect against oxidative damage. Diets high in these carotenoids have been associated with a reduced incidence of age-related eye disorders (see Chapter 16), such as macular degeneration, and supplements of lutein have been shown to improve vision in individuals with macular degeneration.[20]

The most common carotenoid supplement is β-carotene. It is marketed for its antioxidant properties, but under some circumstances it may promote rather than prevent oxidative damage. For example, some studies show that when β-carotene is added to a vitamin E-deficient diet, it promotes oxidation.[21] But in the presence of vitamin E, β-carotene acts as an antioxidant. One explanation for the increase in the incidence of lung cancer among smokers supplemented with β-carotene is that pro-oxidant activity prevails over antioxidant activity. Because supplements don't provide the same balance of antioxidants and other substances found in foods their effect is sometimes unpredictable.

Flavonoids

Like carotenoids, flavonoids, which are often called bioflavonoids, are antioxidants. Supplements containing categories of flavonoids such as rutin and hesperidian and the flavonoid complex pycnogenol are advertised as cures for arthritis, heart disease, high blood pressure, and colds. Hesperidian is often called vitamin P but it does not meet the definition of a vitamin because it has not been shown to be essential in the diet. These are often included in supplements containing vitamin C because they are purported to promote the action of this vitamin. Although the foods containing these phytochemicals have been shown to have health-promoting properties, supplements have not been shown to have the same health effects.

F4.5 Herbal Supplements

Learning Objective

- Discuss the risks of herbal supplements.

Technically an herb is a nonwoody, seed-producing plant that dies at the end of the growing season. However, the term *herb* is generally used to refer to any botanical or plant-derived substance. Throughout history folk medicine has used herbs to prevent and treat disease. Today, herbs and herbal supplements are still popular in treating illness and promoting health. It is estimated that more than half of all patients diagnosed with cancer explore alternative medicine—mostly herbal medicine.[22] The seven most popular herbal medicinal products in the United States today are ginkgo biloba, St. John's wort, ginseng, garlic, echinacea, saw palmetto, and kava.[23]

Herbal supplements are readily available and relatively inexpensive. They can be purchased without a trip to the doctor or a prescription. Although consumers who want to manage their own health may view this as beneficial, it can also cause problems. When a drug is prescribed by a physician, it is assumed that it will have a beneficial effect, that each dose will contain the same amount of drug, that the physician or pharmacist has considered other medications and other medical conditions that may alter the effectiveness of the drug, and that the drug itself will not cause a severe side effect. These assumptions cannot be made with herbs. Some herbs may be toxic either alone or in combination with other drugs and herbs being consumed. Some may contain bacteria or other contaminants. And it is difficult to know what dose of an herb you are taking. Even those pressed and packaged into pills may not provide the same dose in each pill. Also, because consumers decide what to treat, herbal remedies can be used inappropriately or can be used instead of necessary medical intervention.

Some herbs may offer benefits, but serious side effects from excessive doses or unusual combinations of herbs and medications are not uncommon (**Table F4.1**). The use of herbal supplements also may be inappropriate at certain times. For example, St. John's wort can prolong and intensify the effects of narcotic drugs and anesthetic agents, so it should not be taken for 2 to 3 weeks prior to surgery. Herbal products should also be avoided during pregnancy. Blue cohosh (used to treat menstrual cramps), juniper (used for heartburn), pennyroyal or rosemary (used for digestive

Table F4.1 Potential Benefits and Side Effects of Common Herbal Ingredients

Product	Suggested Benefit	Side Effects
Astragalus (Huang ch')[a]	Immune stimulant	Interacts with immune suppressants
Cat's Claw (uña de gato)[a]	Relieves arthritis and indigestion, immune stimulant	Headache, dizziness, vomiting
Chamomile[a]	Aids indigestion, promotes relaxation	Allergy possible
Comfrey (borage, coltsfoot)[*,a]	As a poultice for wounds and sore joints, as a tea for digestive disorders	Do not take orally, even as a tea; obstruction of blood flow to liver resulting in liver failure and possibly death
Dong Quai[a,b]	Increases energy, reduces menopause symptoms	May cause birth defects
Echinacea (purple coneflower, snake root, Indian head)[a]	Topically for wound healing, internally as an immune stimulant, cold remedy	Allergy possible
Ephedra (Ma Huang, Chinese ephedra, epitonin)[*,a]	Relieves cold symptoms, weight loss	High blood pressure, irregular heartbeat, heart attack, stroke, death; large doses banned by the FDA
Ginger[a]	Relieves motion sickness and nausea	Gas, bloating
Ginkgo biloba[a] (maiden hair, kew tree, Pak ko)	Improves memory and mental function, improves circulation	GI distress, headache, allergic skin reactions
Ginseng[a]	Enhances immunity, improves sexual function	Diarrhea, headache, insomnia, low or high blood pressure
Kava[a]	Relieves anxiety and stress	Liver damage, visual disturbances, dizziness, GI discomfort
Lobelia[*,c] (Indian tobacco)	Relaxation, respiratory remedy, smoking cessation	Breathing problems, rapid heartbeat, low blood pressure, convulsions, coma, death
Milk thistle[a]	Protects against liver disease	Laxative effect, bloating, stomach upset
Saw palmetto[a]	Improves urinary flow with enlarged prostrate	Nausea, urine retention, decreased libido
St. John's wort[a] (hypericum)	Promotes mental well-being	Contains similar ingredients as the antidepressant drug fluoxetine (Prozac) and should not be used by people taking antidepressants, allergic reactions, nausea, anxiety
Valerian[a]	Mild sedative	GI upset, headache, restlessness, insomnia
Willow bark[d,*]	Pain and fever relief	Reye's syndrome, allergies
Yohimbe[b]	Aphrodisiac	Tremors, anxiety, high blood pressure, rapid heart beat, psychosis, paralysis

*Has been shown to have serious side effects and should be avoided.
[a]Office of Dietary Supplements, NIH. Dietary Supplement Fact Sheets available online at http://ods.od.nih.gov/Health_Information/Information_About_Individual_Dietary_Supplements.aspx. Accessed June 9, 2009.
[b]Liu J., Burdette J. E., Xu H. et al. Evaluation of estrogenic activity of plant extracts for the potential treatment of menopausal symptoms. *J. Agric. Food. Chem.* 49:2472–2479, 2001.
[c]Fetrow C. W. et al. Professional's Handbook of Complementary and Alternative Medicines. Philadelphia: Springhouse; 1999.
[d]Gagnier J.J., van Tulder M.W., Berman B. et al. Herbal medicine for low back pain. *Spine*; 32:82–92, 2007.

problems), sage (used for stomach upset), and thuja (used for respiratory infections), and even raspberry tea (used to treat morning sickness) may stimulate uterine contractions, which can increase the risk of miscarriage or premature labor.[24] Some guidelines to follow if you are considering taking herbs or herbal supplements are included in **Table F4.2**.

Table F4.2 Considerations When Choosing Herbal Supplements

- If you are ill or taking medications, consult your physician before taking herbs.
- Do not take herbs if you are pregnant.
- Do not give herbs to children.
- Do not assume herbal products are safe.
- Do not take herbs with known toxicities.
- Read label ingredients and the list of precautions.
- Start with low doses, and stop taking any product that causes side effects.
- Do not take combinations of herbs.
- Do not use herbs for long periods.
- Do not choose products that claim to be a secret cure and be wary of terms such as "breakthrough," "magical," "miracle cure," and "new discovery."

Ginkgo Biloba

Ginkgo biloba, also called "maiden hair," is the top-selling herbal medicinal product in the United States[21] (**Figure F4.6a**). It has been used for millennia in Chinese medicine to treat asthma and skin infections, but today it is marketed to enhance memory and to treat a variety of circulatory ailments.[25] Despite its popularity, a controlled clinical trial found ginkgo biloba supplements to have no measurable benefit on memory or other aspects of cognitive function in healthy adults.[26] Taking this product may cause side effects that include headaches and gastrointestinal symptoms[23] (see Table F4.1). Ginkgo biloba also interacts with a number of medications. It can cause bleeding when combined with warfarin or aspirin, elevated blood pressure when combined with a thiazide diuretic, and coma when combined with the antidepressant trazodone.[27]

St. John's Wort

St. John's wort is taken to promote mental well-being (**Figure F4.6b**). Analysis reveals that it contains low doses of the chemical found in the antidepressant drug fluoxetine (Prozac). Clinical trials on its effectiveness are inconsistent but a number do suggest that it is effective for the treatment of depression. Side effects include nausea and allergic reactions. St. John's wort should not be used in conjunction with prescription antidepressant drugs and it has been found to interact with anticoagulants, heart medications, birth control pills, and medications used to treat HIV infection.[25,28]

Ginseng

Ginseng has a long history in traditional medicine (**Figure F4.6c**). It has been used in Asia for centuries for its energizing, stress-reducing, and aphrodisiac properties. Today it is popular in the West for its effects on cardiovascular health, the central nervous system, endocrine function, and sexual function. Although there is animal and cell culture research that demonstrates potential benefits of ginseng on cardiovascular health and in the prevention of cancer, there are few clinical trials in humans

(a)

(Altrendo/Getty Images, Inc.)

(b)

(Michael Gadomski/Photo Researchers)

(c)

(Lynn Johnson/NG Image Collection)

(d)

(Mary Ellen Bartley/StockFood America)

(e)

(Linda Lewis/Botanica/Jupiter Images Corp)

Figure F4.6 Herbal supplements are derived from plants, many of which are common in fields, gardens, or kitchens. (a) The leaves of the ginkgo biloba plant are used to make the top-selling herbal supplement in the United States. (b) These yellow flowers of St. John's wort grow wild in fields and pastures and are considered a perennial weed. (c) Ginseng capsules, extracts, and powders are made from the dried root of the ginseng plant. (d) Garlic is used to spice food in the kitchen but extracts are also processed into pills or tablets and marketed as herbal supplements. (e) Flowers of the echinacea plant, like the ones shown here, can be seen growing along the roadside in the western United States.

to support these effects.[29,30] Despite these potential benefits and a history of use in Chinese medicine ginseng may not be safe for everyone. It can alter bleeding time and therefore should not be used by those taking warfarin, and it has been found to interact with other medications such as estrogens, corticosteroids, antidepressants, and morphine.[29,30] Even in those not taking other medications it may cause side effects such as diarrhea, headache, insomnia, and changes in blood pressure.[23]

Garlic

Throughout history garlic has been used for a lot more than to keep vampires away (**Figure F4.6d**). Hippocrates, who is considered the father of Western medicine, recommended garlic to treat pneumonia and other infections, as well as cancer and digestive disorders. Although it is no longer recommended for these purposes recent research has shown that it may lower blood cholesterol.[31] Eating enough garlic to lower cholesterol will probably keep your friends and family away as well as the vampires so supplement manufacturers have provided a way to increase intake without eating this odiferous food at every meal; some preparations contain a deodorized form. Even though we spice our food with it, garlic supplements are not safe for everyone. The National Institutes of Health has concluded that it could be harmful for people undergoing treatment for HIV infection.[28] Garlic may also interact with the anticoagulant drug warfarin, and could lead to bleeding.[27]

Echinacea

Petals of the echinacea plant were used by Native Americans as a treatment for colds, flu, and infections (**Figure F4.6e**). Today, the echinacea root is typically used as a cold remedy. Echinacea is hypothesized to act as an immune system stimulant, but there is little evidence that it is beneficial in either preventing or treating the common cold.[32] Although side effects have not been reported, allergies are possible.[23]

Saw Palmetto

Traditionally saw palmetto, which comes from the berries of the American dwarf palm, has been used to treat problems of the urinary and genital tract; enhance sperm production, breast size, or libido; and as a mild diuretic. Today it is marketed to treat prostate enlargement and therefore improve urinary flow. A review of the effectiveness of this supplement found that it provides mild to moderate improvement in urinary symptoms and flow measures but its long-term safety and effectiveness are unknown.[33] Possible side effects include constipation, decreased libido, headache, hypertension, nausea, and urinary retention.[23]

Kava

Kava is traditionally served as a special drink at ceremonies such as weddings and coming-out-of-mourning celebrations in the South Pacific. It is used today to relieve stress and anxiety. A meta-analysis of clinical trials concluded that short-term administration is effective in reducing anxiety.[34] However, kava may not be the safest way to relieve stress. In 2002 the FDA issued a warning about kava because it may cause liver damage, including hepatitis, cirrhosis, and liver failure. It has been taken off the market in many European countries, Canada, Australia, and Singapore because of this danger.

R e f e r e n c e s

1. Coates, P. Ongoing Research on Dietary Supplements at the National Institutes of Health Testimony Before the Subcommittee on Human Rights and Wellness Committee on Government Reform United States House of Representatives, September 22, 2004. Available online at http://dietary-supplements.info.nih.gov/News/Congressional_Testimony_Ongoing_Research_on_Dietary_Supplements_at_NIH.aspx Accessed September 8, 2009.

2. Radimer, K., Bindewald, B., Hughes, J. et al. Dietary supplement use by US adults: Data from the National Health and Nutrition Examination Survey, 1999–2000. *Amer. J. Epidemiol.* 160:339–349, 2004.

3. National Center for Complementary and Alternative Medicine. Using Dietary Supplements Wisely. Available online at http://nccam.nih.gov/health/supplements/wiseuse.htm. Accessed June 8, 2009.

4. FDA, U.S. Department of Health and Human Services. Dietary Supplement Labeling. Available online at http://www.fda.gov/Food/DietarySupplement/DietarySupplementLabeling/default.htm. Accessed June 8, 2009.

5. Food and Drug Administration. Current good manufacturing practice in manufacturing, packaging, labeling, or holding operations for dietary supplements; final rule. *Fed. Regist.* 72(121):34751–34958, June 25, 2007. Available online at http://edocket.access.gpo.gov/2007/07-3039.htm. Accessed October 10, 2009.

6. Chromiak, J. A., and Antonio, J. Use of amino acids as growth hormone-releasing agents by athletes. *Nutrition* 18:657–661, 2002.

7. Gleeson, M. Interrelationship between physical activity and branched-chain amino acids. *J. Nutr.* 135:1591S–1595S, 2005.

8. de Lorgeril, M., and Salen, P. Alpha-linolenic acid and coronary heart disease. *Nutr. Metab. Cardiovasc. Dis.* 14:162–169, 2004.

9. Jenkins, P. J. Growth hormone and exercise. *Clin. Endocrinol.* 50:683–689, 2000.

10. Caldwell, J. L. The use of melatonin: An information paper. *Aviat. Space Environ. Med.* 71:238–244, 2000.

11. Cameron, D. R., and Braunstein, G. D. The use of dehydroepiandrosterone therapy in clinical practice. *Treat. Endocrinol.* 4:95–114, 2005.

12. Dayal, M., Sammel, M. D., Zhao, J. et al. Supplementation with DHEA: Effect on muscle size, strength, quality of life, and lipids. *J. Womens Health* 14:391–400, 2005.

13. Marriage, B., Clandinin, M. T., and Glerum, D. M. Nutritional cofactor treatment in mitochondrial disorders. *J. Am. Diet. Assoc.* 103:1029–1038, 2003.

14. Keith, M., Mazer, C. D., Mikhail, P. et al. Coenzyme Q10 in patients undergoing CABG: Effect of statins and nutritional supplementation. *Nutr. Metab. Cardiovasc. Dis.* 18:105–11, 2008.

15. Kraemer, W. J., Volek, J. S., and Dunn-Lewis, C. L-carnitine supplementation: Influence upon physiological function. *Curr. Sports Med. Rep.* 7:218–223, 2008.

16. Paddon-Jones, D., Borsheim, E., and Wolfe, R. R. Potential ergogenic effects of arginine and creatine supplementation. *J. Nutr.* 134(10 Suppl):2888S–2894S, 2004.

17. Gregory, P. J., Sperry, M., and Wilson, A. F. Dietary supplements for osteoarthritis. *Am. Fam. Physician.* 15:177–184, 2008.

18. Ramos, L. Beyond the headlines: SAM-e as a supplement. *J. Am. Diet. Assoc.* 100: 414, 2000.

19. Ooms, L. M., Horan, K. A., Rahman, P. et al. The role of the inositol polyphosphate 5-phosphatases in cellular function and human disease. *Biochem. J.* 419:29–49, 2009.

20. Richer, S., Stiles, W., Statkute, L. et al. Double-masked, placebo-controlled, randomized trial of lutein and antioxidant supplementation in the intervention of atrophic age-related macular degeneration: The Veterans LAST study (Lutein Antioxidant Supplementation Trial). *Optometry* 75:216–230, 2004.

21. Palozza, P. Prooxidant actions of carotenoids in biologic systems. *Nutr. Rev.* 56:257–265, 1998.

22. Boon, H., and Wong, J. Botanical medicine and cancer: A review of the safety and efficacy. *Expert Opin. Pharmacother.* 5:2485–2501, 2004.

23. Ernst, E. The risk-benefit profile of commonly used herbal therapies: Ginkgo, St. Johns wort, ginseng, echinacea, saw palmetto, and kava. *Ann. Intern. Med.* 136:42–53, 2002.

24. Schweitzer, A. Dietary Supplements During Pregnancy. *J. Perinat. Educ.* 15(4): 44–45, 2006.

25. ODS, NIH Dietary Supplement Fact Sheets. Available online at http://ods.od.nih.gov/Health_Information/Information_About_Individual_Dietary_Supplements.aspx. Accessed June 9, 2009.

26. Solomon, P. R., Adams, F., Silver, A. et al. Ginkgo for memory enhancement: A randomized controlled trial. *JAMA* 288:835–840, 2002.

27. Hu, Z., Yang, X., Ho, P. C. et al. Herb-drug interactions: A literature review. *Drugs* 65:1239–1282, 2005.

28. Mills, E., Montori, V., Perri, D. et al. Natural health product-HIV drug interactions: A systematic review. *Intl. J. STD AIDS* 16:181–186, 2005.

29. Zhou, W., Chai, H., Lin, P. H. et al. Molecular mechanisms and clinical applications of ginseng root for cardiovascular disease. *Med. Sci. Monit.* 10:RA187–RA192, 2004.

30. Helms, S. Cancer prevention and therapeutics: Panax ginseng. *Altern. Med. Rev.* 9:259–274, 2004.

31. Hermansen, K., Dinesen, B., Hoie, L. H. et al. Effects of soy and other natural products on LDL: HDL ratio and other lipid parameters: A literature review. *Adv. Ther.* 20:50–78, 2003.

32. Caruso, T. J., and Gwaltney, J. M., Jr. Treatment of the common cold with echinacea: A structured review. *Clin. Infect. Dis.* 40:807–810, 2005.

33. Wilt, T., Ishani, A., and Mac Donald, R. Serenoa repens for benign prostatic hyperplasia. Cochrane Database Syst. Review (3):CD001423, 2002.

34. Pittler, M. H., and Ernst, E. Efficacy of kava extract for treating anxiety: Systematic review and meta-analysis. *J. Clin. Psychopharmacol.* 20:84–89, 2000.

13

Nutrition and Physical Activity

Case Study

As Tour de France champion Lance Armstrong pedaled his bicycle up the last 6 kilometers of a mountain in the French Alps, his normally smooth pedal stroke became choppy. He did not respond when other riders caught and passed him on what he later called "the hardest day of my life on the bike."

Just 7 days earlier, while climbing the last mountain of a ride that included four such climbs, Armstrong had taken the overall lead in the Tour de France. In the final 12 miles of that ascent, which rose up a 7.9% grade, he had amazed sports enthusiasts by accelerating past the best cyclists in the world as if they were standing still. Through the next 5 days in the mountains, he had continued to gain time over his closest rivals. But on this day and this climb, he was exhausted and falling farther behind as he pedaled along in low gear. What was wrong with the defending champion and leader of the Tour de France?

The key to understanding Armstrong's difficulty was revealed in an interview after the day's ride, when he said, "I didn't eat enough, and I had no energy." The Tour de France is arguably the most grueling sports event on the planet. What does an athlete need to eat and drink to fuel such intense, prolonged activity? The cook for the U.S. Postal Service team, with which Armstrong was riding, said the cyclists eat "pasta and more pasta." The cook had 88 lb of pasta with him and would need to buy more along the way. To meet the energy demands of the Tour, cyclists consume 6000 to 7000 kcalories per day. All that pasta may indeed be an important part of their success, but peak performance also depends on what else they eat and drink and when they consume it. What an athlete eats before, during, and after an event affects performance, particularly in a competition like the Tour de France, in which athletes need to perform strenuous endurance exercise day after day.

(Friedemann Vogel/Bongarts/Getty Images, Inc.)

(©iStockphoto)

(BRELOER/dpa/Landov)

Chapter Outline

13.1 Exercise, Fitness, and Health

Learning Objectives

- Describe the characteristics of a fit individual.
- Explain what is meant by the overload principle.
- Evaluate the impact of exercise on health.
- Discuss the role of exercise in weight management.

Exercise improves **fitness** and overall health. For some people, fitness means being able to easily walk around the block, mow the lawn, or play with their children. For more seasoned athletes, fitness means optimal performance of strenuous exercise. For everyone, fitness reduces the risk of chronic diseases such as cardiovascular disease, diabetes, and obesity. You don't need to run 10-kilometer races, ride the Tour de France, or compete in the Olympics to be physically fit. Even a small amount of exercise is better than none, and, within reason, more exercise is better than less. Whether you are 8 or 80, fitness through regular exercise can improve your overall health.

Exercise Improves Fitness

Fitness level is defined by endurance, strength, flexibility, and body composition. Engaging in regular exercise improves these parameters. When you exercise you breathe harder, your heart beats faster, and your muscles stretch and strain. Regular exercise causes adaptations that result in long-term physiological changes. This is known as the **overload principle**; the more you do, the more you are capable of doing. For example, if you run 3 times a week, in a few weeks you can run farther; if you lift weights a few days a week, in a few weeks you will have more muscle and will be able to lift more weight more easily; if you stretch to touch your toes every morning, in a few days it becomes less of a stretch. These adaptations improve overall fitness.

Cardiorespiratory Endurance Cardiorespiratory endurance determines how long you can continue a task, whether it is climbing stairs, raking leaves, or running a race. It requires muscle strength but also involves the cardiovascular and respiratory systems, referred to jointly as the **cardiorespiratory system**. Endurance is increased by **aerobic exercise**, the type of exercise that increases heart rate and uses oxygen. To be aerobic, an activity should be performed at an intensity low enough to allow you to carry on a conversation but high enough that you cannot sing while exercising. Aerobic activities include walking, dancing, jogging, cross-country skiing, cycling, and swimming.

Regular aerobic exercise strengthens the heart muscle and increases **stroke volume**, which is the amount of blood pumped with each beat of the heart. This in turn decreases **resting heart rate**, which is the rate at which the heart must beat to supply blood to the tissues at rest. Resting heart rate can be measured by counting the number of pulses, or heartbeats, per minute while at rest (**Figure 13.1**). The more fit a person is, the lower their resting heart rate and the more blood their heart can pump to muscles during exercise. In addition to increasing the amount of oxygen-rich blood that is pumped to muscles, regular aerobic exercise increases the muscle's ability to use oxygen to produce ATP. The body's maximum ability to generate ATP by aerobic metabolism during exercise is called **aerobic capacity**, or **VO₂ max**. Aerobic capacity is dependent on the ability of the cardiorespiratory system to deliver oxygen to the cells and the ability of the cells to use oxygen to produce ATP. The greater a person's aerobic capacity, the more intense activity he or she can perform before a lack of oxygen affects performance.

fitness The ability to perform routine physical activity without undue fatigue.

overload principle The concept that the body will adapt to the stresses placed on it.

cardiorespiratory system The circulatory and respiratory systems, which together deliver oxygen and nutrients to cells.

aerobic exercise Endurance exercise such as jogging, swimming, or cycling that increases heart rate and requires oxygen in metabolism.

stroke volume The volume of blood pumped by each beat of the heart.

resting heart rate The number of times that the heart beats per minute while a person is at rest.

aerobic capacity or **VO₂ max** The maximum amount of oxygen that can be consumed by the tissues during exercise. This is also called maximal oxygen consumption.

Figure 13.1 To estimate your heart rate, place your fingers over the carotid artery, which is at either side of your neck just below the jawbone, and count the number of pulses per minute. (Michael Newman/PhotoEdit)

Figure 13.2 Aerobic capacity can be estimated by measuring oxygen uptake while running to exhaustion on a treadmill. (Julian Calder/Getty Images, Inc.)

Aerobic capacity can be determined in an exercise laboratory by measuring oxygen uptake during exercise. To perform this measurement, an individual runs on a treadmill or rides a stationary bicycle while the gases he or she breathes are measured. Oxygen consumption or uptake is calculated by subtracting the amount of oxygen exhaled from the amount of oxygen inhaled. The workload is then increased by increasing the speed and/or grade of the treadmill or resistance on the bike until the individual can no longer continue (**Figure 13.2**). The amount of oxygen consumed at the highest workload achieved is the aerobic capacity. A trained athlete will have a greater aerobic capacity than an untrained individual.

Muscle Strength and Endurance Muscle strength and endurance enhance the ability to perform tasks such as pushing or lifting. In daily life, this could mean lifting heavy boxes, unscrewing the lid of a jar, or shoveling snow. Muscle strength and endurance are increased by repeatedly using muscles in activities that require moving against a resisting force. This type of exercise is called strength-training or resistance-training and includes activities such as weight lifting (**Figure 13.3**). Lifting a heavy weight stresses muscles. This stress or overload causes muscles to adapt by increasing in size and strength—a process called **hypertrophy**. The larger, stronger muscles can now easily lift the same weight that stressed them the first time. By progressively increasing the amount of weight at each exercise session, the muscle slowly hypertrophies.

When muscles are not used due to a lapse in training, an injury, or illness they become smaller and weaker. This process is called **atrophy**. For example, when an individual is bedridden and unable to move about, their muscles atrophy. Once they are up and active again, their muscles regain strength and size. There is truth behind the expression "use it or lose it."

Flexibility Fitness is not just about bulging muscles, it also involves flexibility. Flexibility determines range of motion—how far you can bend and stretch muscles and ligaments. If flexibility is poor, a person cannot easily bend to tie their shoes or stretch to remove packages from the car. Being flexible may reduce the risk of pulled muscles and tendons. In a competitive athlete, improving flexibility can increase speed. This is because too-tight muscles, tendons, and ligaments can restrict motion at a joint and thus decrease stride length and increase the energy needed to overcome this motion-resisting stiffness. Regularly moving the limbs, neck, and torso through their full ranges of motion helps increase and maintain flexibility (**Figure 13.4**).

Figure 13.3 Building muscle requires an increase in the amount of resistance exercise, not simply an increase in protein intake. (Wang Leng/Asia Images/Getty Images, Inc.)

hypertrophy An increase in the size of a muscle or organ.

atrophy Wasting or decrease in the size of a muscle or other tissue caused by lack of use.

Figure 13.4 Stretching muscles to increase and maintain flexibility is an important component of any exercise regimen. (RW Photographic/ Masterfile)

Figure 13.5 **Body composition**
Body composition, which refers to the percentage of fat versus non-fat or lean tissue (muscle, bones, cartilage, skin, nerves, and internal organs), is an indicator of health and finess.

Body Composition Exercise builds and maintains muscle. Individuals who are physically fit have a greater proportion of lean body tissue than unfit individuals of the same body weight (**Figure 13.5**). Not everyone who is fit is thin, but in a fit person who carries extra pounds, more of the weight is from muscle. How much body fat a person has is also affected by gender and age. In general, women have more stored body fat than men. For young adult women, the desirable percent of body fat is 21% to 32% of total weight; in adult men, the desirable percent is about 8% to 19%.[1] With aging, lean body mass decreases in both men and women, and there is an increase in the percentage of body fat even if body weight remains the same. Some of this change may be prevented by staying physically active (see Chapter 16).

Video

Health Benefits of Exercise

In addition to making the tasks of everyday life easier, maintaining fitness through regular activity offers many health benefits. A regular exercise program makes it easier to maintain a healthy body weight; helps maintain muscles, bones, and joints; and reduces the risk of osteoporosis.[2] It can help to prevent or delay the onset of cardiovascular disease, hypertension, diabetes, and colon cancer. It can also prevent depression and improve mood, sleep patterns, and overall outlook on life.

Weight Management People who exercise regularly are more likely to be at and maintain a healthy body weight. Exercise makes weight management easier because it increases energy needs so more kcalories can be consumed without weight gain. During exercise, energy expenditure can rise well above the resting rate and some of this increase persists for many hours after activity slows.[3] Exercise can also boost energy expenditure through its effect on body composition. Exercise increases lean tissue mass and because, even at rest, lean tissue uses more energy than fat tissue, this increases basal energy needs. The combination of increased energy output during exercise, the rise in expenditure that persists after exercise, and the increase in basal needs can have a major impact on total energy expenditure (**Figure 13.6**). Besides increasing energy needs, exercise also promotes the loss of body fat and slows the loss of lean tissue that occurs with energy restriction. This makes exercise an essential component of any weight-reduction program.

Cardiovascular Health Exercise reduces the risk of cardiovascular disease.[4] Because aerobic exercise strengthens the heart muscle, it reduces the number of times the heart must beat to deliver blood to the tissues at rest and during exercise. The changes that occur with exercise also help to lower blood pressure and increase HDL cholesterol levels in the blood. All of these effects help to reduce the risk of cardiovascular diseases such as heart attack and stroke.[5]

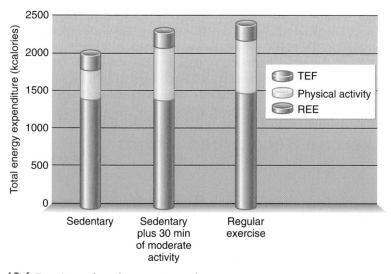

Figure 13.6 Exercise and total energy expenditure
Total energy expenditure is the sum of the energy used for resting energy expenditure (REE), physical activity, and the thermic effect of food (TEF). Exercise increases energy expenditure by increasing the amount of energy expended for physical activity, and if it is regular, it leads to an increase in muscle mass, which increases REE.

Diabetes Prevention and Management People with excess body fat are more likely to develop diabetes. By keeping body fat within the normal range, aerobic exercise can decrease the risk of developing type 2 diabetes. Physical activity that includes both aerobic exercise and strength training is also important in the treatment of diabetes because exercise increases the sensitivity of tissues to insulin.[6] Exercise can reduce or eliminate the need for medication to maintain normal blood glucose levels. Therefore, to prevent low blood glucose people with diabetes should develop exercise programs with the help of their physicians and dietitians.

Bone and Joint Health Just as lifting weights helps maintain muscle size and strength, weight-bearing exercise stimulates bones to become denser and stronger. One of the causes of bone loss, like muscle loss, is lack of use; therefore, weight-bearing exercise such as walking, running, and aerobic dance can increase peak bone mass and prevent bone loss, and therefore reduce the risk of osteoporosis (see Chapter 11). Exercise can also benefit individuals with arthritis because the strength and flexibility promoted by exercise helps manage pain and allow arthritic joints to move more easily.

Cancer Risk Individuals who exercise regularly may be reducing their cancer risk by as much as 40%.[7] There is evidence that exercise reduces breast cancer risk; the risk reduction is related to exercise intensity, duration, and the age at which the exercise is performed.[8] The evidence that exercise reduces colon cancer risk is also strong; active individuals are less likely to develop colon cancer than their sedentary counterparts.[7] When evaluating the impact of exercise on cancer risk, diet and other lifestyle factors also must be considered. It is possible that some of the effect is due to the fact that people who exercise regularly are more likely to have healthier overall diets and lifestyles.

Overall Well-Being Physical activity improves mood, boosts self-esteem, and increases overall well-being.[9] It has been shown to reduce depression and anxiety, and improve the quality of life.[10] The exact mechanisms involved are not clear but one hypothesis has to do with the production of **endorphins**. Exercise stimulates the release of these chemicals, which are thought to be natural mood enhancers that play a role in triggering what athletes describe as an "exercise high." In addition to causing this state of exercise euphoria,

endorphins Compounds that cause a natural euphoria and reduce the perception of pain under certain stressful conditions.

endorphins are thought to aid in relaxation, pain tolerance, and appetite control. Exercise may also benefit mental well-being by affecting the levels of certain mood-enhancing neurotransmitters in the brain, releasing muscle tension, improving sleep patterns, and reducing levels of the stress hormone cortisol. Exercise also raises body temperature, which is believed to have a calming effect. These changes in both the brain and the body can reduce anxiety, irritability, stress, fatigue, anger, self-doubt, and hopelessness.[10]

13.2 Exercise Recommendations

Learning Objectives

- Describe the amounts and types of exercise recommended to improve health.
- Classify activities as aerobic or anaerobic.
- Plan a fitness program that can be integrated into your daily routine.
- Explain overtraining syndrome.

Most Americans do not exercise regularly; 25% of adults get no physical activity at all during their leisure time.[5] Because of the health benefits of exercise, public health guidelines recommend an increase in activity level.[2,11,12] The most recent recommendations

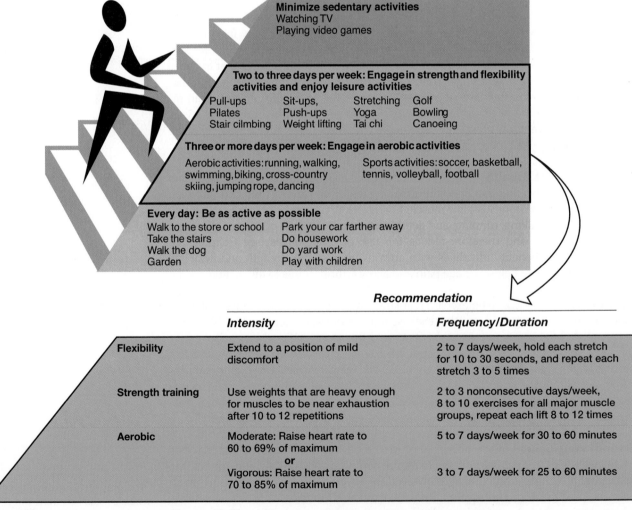

Minimize sedentary activities
Watching TV
Playing video games

Two to three days per week: Engage in strength and flexibility activities and enjoy leisure activities

Pull-ups	Sit-ups,	Stretching	Golf
Pilates	Push-ups	Yoga	Bowling
Stair cilmbing	Weight lifting	Tai chi	Canoeing

Three or more days per week: Engage in aerobic activities

Aerobic activities: running, walking, swimming, biking, cross-country skiing, jumping rope, dancing

Sports activities: soccer, basketball, tennis, volleyball, football

Every day: Be as active as possible

Walk to the store or school	Park your car farther away
Take the stairs	Do housework
Walk the dog	Do yard work
Garden	Play with children

Recommendation

	Intensity	Frequency/Duration
Flexibility	Extend to a position of mild discomfort	2 to 7 days/week, hold each stretch for 10 to 30 seconds, and repeat each stretch 3 to 5 times
Strength training	Use weights that are heavy enough for muscles to be near exhaustion after 10 to 12 repetitions	2 to 3 nonconsecutive days/week, 8 to 10 exercises for all major muscle groups, repeat each lift 8 to 12 times
Aerobic	Moderate: Raise heart rate to 60 to 69% of maximum **or**	5 to 7 days/week for 30 to 60 minutes
	Vigorous: Raise heart rate to 70 to 85% of maximum	3 to 7 days/week for 25 to 60 minutes

Figure 13.7 Exercise recommendations
Weekly activities should include areobic exercise, strength-training activities, and stretching. The recommended duration of aerobic exercise depends on the intensity.

advise at least 150 minutes of moderate physical activity per week.[2] This is similar to the Dietary Guidelines recommendation of 30 minutes of moderate exercise most days of the week to reduce chronic disease risk.[11] To be considered moderate, an activity must increase heart rate and breathing. As a rule of thumb an activity with an intensity rating of 5 to 6 on a scale of 1 to 10, with 1 being lying on the couch and 10 being maximal activity, is considered moderate. For most people, moderate activity is the equivalent of walking or jogging at a rate of 3 to 4 mph, cycling leisurely, or swimming slowly. Additional health benefits can be obtained by engaging in more vigorous activity or activity of longer duration.[2] Sixty minutes of moderate intensity activity on most days of the week is recommended to help manage body weight and prevent weight gain; for those who have lost weight and want to keep it off, 60 to 90 minutes of moderate intensity activity is recommended.[11]

Components of a Good Exercise Regimen

A well-planned exercise regimen includes aerobic exercise, which raises heart rate and therefore improves cardiorespiratory fitness; stretching, which promotes and maintains flexibility; and strength training, which increases the strength and endurance of specific muscles. Some aerobic and strength-training activities also help strengthen bone. Exercise should be integrated into an active lifestyle that includes a variety of everyday activities, enjoyable recreational activities, and a minimum amount of time spent in sedentary activities (**Figure 13.7**).

Aerobic Activity Aerobic exercise, such as walking, bicycling, skating, swimming, or jogging, should be performed for 30 to 60 minutes, depending on intensity, most days of the week. An activity is in the aerobic zone if it raises heart rate to 60% to 85% of its maximum (**Figure 13.8**). **Maximum heart rate** is the maximum number of beats per minute that the heart can attain. It is dependent on age and can be estimated by

maximum heart rate
The maximum number of beats per minute that the heart can attain. It declines with age and can be estimated by subtracting age in years from 220.

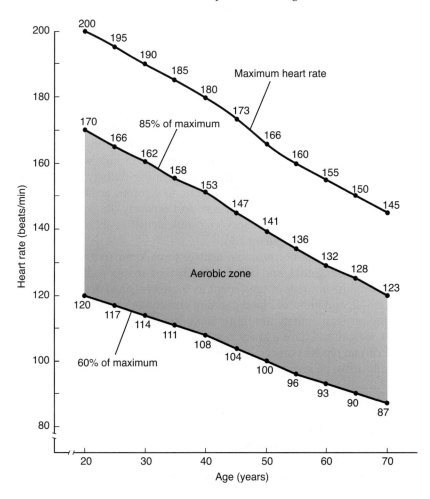

Figure 13.8 The aerobic zone
The aerobic zone (orange area) is between 60% and 85% of maximum heart rate.

subtracting your age from 220. For example, a 40-year-old individual would have a maximum heart rate of 180 beats per minute and should exercise at a pace that keeps his or her heart rate between 108 and 153 beats per minute (see Figure 13.8). Each exercise session should begin with a warm-up, such as mild stretching and easy jogging, to increase blood flow to the muscles, and end with a cool-down period, such as walking or stretching, to help prevent muscle cramps and slowly reduce heart rate. Aerobic activities of different intensities can be combined to meet recommendations and achieve health benefits. The total amount of energy expended in physical activity depends on the intensity, duration, and frequency of the activity. Vigorous physical activity, such as jogging, that raises heart rate to the high end of the aerobic zone (70–85%) improves fitness more and burns more kcalories per unit of time than does moderate-intensity activity, such as walking, that raises heart rate only to the low end of the aerobic zone (60–69%). For a sedentary individual beginning an exercise program, mild exercise such as walking can raise the heart rate into this range. As fitness improves, exercisers must perform more intense activity to raise their heart rates to this level.

Stretching Stretching may improve performance in activities such as dancing and gymnastics that require flexibility.[2] To improve and maintain flexibility, stretching exercises should be done at least 3 days a week. Muscles should be stretched to a position of mild discomfort and held for 10 to 30 seconds. Each stretch should be repeated 3 to 5 times. Although flexibility is an important component of fitness, time spent stretching should not be counted towards the goal of 150 minutes of physical activity per week.[2]

Strength Training Developing and maintaining strong muscles requires work, but you don't need to lift weights every day. Strength training, such as weight lifting, should be done 2 to 3 days a week at the start of an exercise program, and 2 days a week after the desired strength has been achieved. Each session should include a minimum of 8 to 10 exercises that train the major muscle groups. Each exercise should be repeated 8 to 12 times. The weights should be heavy enough to cause the muscle to be near exhaustion after the 8 to 12 repetitions. Increasing the amount of weight lifted will increase muscle strength, whereas increasing the number of repetitions will improve endurance.

Exercise Recommendations for Children

Life Cycle

Children and adolescents should spend at least 60 minutes per day in developmentally appropriate exercise.[11] Aerobic, muscle-strengthening, and bone-strengthening activities should be included in this 60 minutes.[2] For children muscle-strengthening activities can be unstructured play activities such as climbing on playground equipment or playing tug of war. Bone-strengthening activities include weight-bearing play such as hopscotch, jumping rope, basketball, and running. Activity for young children should be intermittent, with periods of moderate to vigorous activity lasting 10 to 15 minutes or more along with periods of rest and recovery. To promote the recommended amount of exercise, a variety of enjoyable activities should be stressed and competition deemphasized (**Figure 13.9**).

Modern lifestyles, do not promote activity in children and adolescents; television, computers, video games, and cell phone activities are often chosen over physical activity. Reducing the amount of time spent in these sedentary activities can increase fitness, lower BMI, and improve blood pressure and cholesterol levels.[13] Children who learn to enjoy physical activity are more likely to be active adults who maintain a healthy body weight and have a lower risk of cardiovascular disease, diabetes, osteoporosis, and certain types of cancer. Learning by example is always best. Children who have physically active parents are the leanest and the fittest.

Planning an Active Lifestyle

Almost everyone can participate in some form of exercise, no matter where they live, how old they are, or what physical limitations they have. Exercise classes are taught in nursing homes. People with heart disease, visual impairments, and physical disabilities compete in athletic events. You are never too old to exercise, and it is never too late to start.

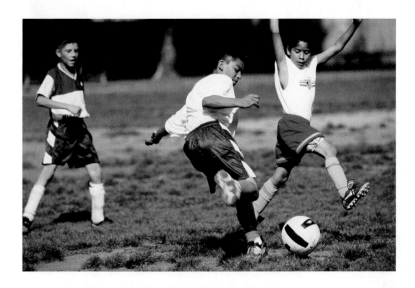

Figure 13.9 Children who participate in and enjoy exercise are more likely to have active lifestyles as adults. (Carl Schneider/Taxi/Getty Images, Inc.)

Find Convenient, Enjoyable Activities Incorporating exercise into day-to-day life may require a behavior change, and changing behavior is not easy. The first step in beginning an exercise program is to recognize the reasons for not exercising and identify ways to overcome them. Many people avoid exercise because they do not enjoy it, feel they have to join an expensive health club, have little motivation to do it alone, or find it inconvenient and uncomfortable. Finding a type of exercise that is enjoyable, a time that is realistic and convenient, and a place that is appropriate and safe are important first steps in adopting an exercise program. Riding your bike to class or work rather than driving or taking the bus, taking a walk on your lunch break, and enjoying a game of catch or tag with your children are all effective ways to increase your everyday activity level. The goal is to gradually make lifestyle changes that increase physical activity. Behavioral strategies such as those listed in **Table 13.1** may help promote regular exercise (see Critical Thinking: Incorporating Exercise Sensibly).

Table 13.1 **Suggestions for Starting and Maintaining an Exercise Program**

Start slowly. Set specific attainable goals. Once you have met them, add more.

- Walk around the block after dinner.
- Get off the bus or subway one stop early.
- Use half of your lunch break to exercise.
- Do a few biceps curls each time you take the milk out of the refrigerator.

Make your exercise fun and convenient.

- Opt for activities you enjoy—bowling and dancing are more fun than a treadmill in the basement.
- Find a partner to exercise with you.
- Choose times that fit your schedule.

Stay motivated.

- Vary your routine—swim one day and mountain bike the next.
- Challenge your strength or endurance once or twice a week and do moderate workouts on other days.
- Track your progress by recording your activity.
- Reward your success with a new book, movie, or some workout clothes.

Keep your exercise safe.

- Warm-up before you start and cool-down when you are done.
- Wear light-colored or reflective clothing that is appropriate for the environmental conditions.
- Don't overdo it—alternate hard days with easy days and take a day off when you need it.
- Listen to your body so you stop before an injury occurs.

Critical Thinking
Incorporating Exercise Sensibly

Background:

Nicole recently celebrated her forty-fifth birthday. Her promise to herself was to get back in shape. Nicole rarely gets any exercise and when she does she suffers for the next few days with sore muscles. When the family goes on outings, she finds that she tires long before her husband and children.

Before beginning her exercise program she checks with her physician, who recommends that she do stretching and strength-training exercises as well as aerobic activities that keep her heart rate between 60% and 85% of her maximum.

Data:

Nicole is 5' 7" tall and weighs 155 lbs. Although her body mass index is still within the healthy range, she is about 5 lbs above her usual weight. She would like to lose a few pounds, but more importantly she would like to increase her strength and endurance.

Nicole decides she will exercise for 90 minutes a day, 5 days a week. Her plan is to join a gym and stretch and lift weights for 30 minutes, followed by an

(Mike Kemp/Rubberball/Getty Images, Inc.)

hour of aerobic exercise outdoors, either jogging or riding a bicycle in the park.

After 3 days she realizes that her family is angry, she is tired, sore, and ready to give up.

Critical Thinking Questions

List 3 things that are wrong with Nicole's exercise program.
▼
What should her heart rate be to keep it in her aerobic zone?
▼
Calculate Nicole's EER before and after the addition of her exercise regimen. Do you think she will lose weight?
▼
Suggest some modifications to her exercise program that will keep her from getting sore and keep her family happy.

 iProfile Use iProfile to calculate your energy expenditure for one day.

Keep Exercise Safe Safety should be a consideration in planning any exercise regimen. Before beginning, everyone should check with their physician to be sure that their plans are safe considering their medical history. Then the location and environment for exercise can be considered. Busy work schedules often force people to exercise in the dark, early morning or evening hours. Exercisers who use the street for walking or jogging should wear light-colored, reflective clothing so they can be seen by motorists. Exercising with a partner is safer and more enjoyable.

Weather conditions can also be a safety concern. Physical activity produces heat, which normally is dissipated to the environment, partly by the evaporation of sweat. When the environmental temperature is high, heat is not efficiently transferred to the environment, and when humidity is high, sweat evaporates slowly, making it difficult to cool the body. Thus, exercise should be reduced or curtailed in hot and humid conditions. Cold environments can also pose problems for the outdoor exerciser. In general, cold does not impair exercise capacity, but the numbing of exposed flesh and the bulk of extra clothing can cause problems for joggers and bicyclists. Clothing must allow the body to dissipate heat while providing protection from the cold. For swimmers, cold water can cause performance to deteriorate.

Tailor Exercise Frequency, Intensity, and Duration Individuals should structure their fitness program based on their needs, goals, and abilities. For example, some people might prefer a short, intense workout such as 30 minutes of running, while others would rather work out for a longer time, at a lower intensity, such as a 1-hour walk. Some may choose to complete all their exercise during the same session, while others may spread their exercise throughout the day, in shorter bouts. Three short bouts of 10-minute duration can be as effective as a continuous bout of 30 minutes for reducing the risk of chronic disease.[2,14] A combination of intensities, such as a brisk 30-minute walk twice during the week in addition to a 20-minute jog on two other days, can meet recommendations. Also, what is best for a middle-aged man trying to reduce his risk of chronic disease is different from what is best for a 19-year-old college basketball player, and different still from what is best for an octogenarian trying to continue living independently. Young healthy athletes may require very intense activity to obtain a training effect. Older adults and those who have not previously been active can increase their fitness by exercising at a lower intensity if the duration and frequency of exercise are increased.

Don't Overdo It To improve cardiorespiratory fitness and muscle strength, the body must be stressed and respond to the stress by increasing aerobic capacity and muscle size and strength. Initially, training can cause fatigue and weakness, but during rest the body rebuilds to become stronger. If not enough rest occurs between exercise sessions, there is no time to regenerate so fitness and performance do not improve. In athletes, excessive training can lead to **overtraining syndrome**, which involves emotional, behavioral, and physical symptoms that persist for weeks to months. It is caused by repeatedly training without sufficient rest to allow for recovery. The most common symptom of overtraining syndrome is fatigue that limits workouts and is felt even at rest. Some athletes experience a decrease in appetite and weight loss as well as muscle soreness, increased frequency of viral illnesses, and increased incidence of injuries. They may become moody, easily irritated, depressed, have altered sleep patterns, or lose their competitive desire and enthusiasm. Overtraining syndrome occurs only in serious athletes who are training extensively, but rest is essential for anyone working to increase fitness (see Science Applied: Training: Sometimes Less Is Better).

overtraining syndrome
A collection of emotional, behavioral, and physical symptoms that occurs when training without sufficient rest persists for weeks to months.

13.3 Fueling Exercise

Learning Objectives

- Compare the fuels used to generate ATP by anaerobic and aerobic metabolism.
- Discuss the effect of exercise duration and intensity on the type of fuel used.
- Describe the physiological changes that occur in response to exercise.

Whether your goal is maintaining health or competing in athletic events, nutrition provides a launching pad from which physical fitness can be improved. Just as an automobile engine runs on energy from gasoline, the body machine runs on energy from the carbohydrate, fat, and protein in food and body stores. These fuels are needed whether you are writing a letter, walking around the block, or running a marathon. But before nutrients can be used to fuel activity, their energy must be converted into the high-energy compound ATP. ATP provides an immediate source of energy for all body functions, including muscle contraction. ATP can be generated both in the presence of oxygen by **aerobic metabolism** and in the absence of oxygen by **anaerobic metabolism** or **anaerobic glycolysis**. The way ATP is produced during activity depends on how long an activity is performed, the intensity of the activity, and the physical conditioning of the exerciser. This in turn affects how much carbohydrate, fat, and protein are used to produce this ATP.

aerobic metabolism
Metabolism in the presence of oxygen. In aerobic metabolism glucose, fatty acids, and amino acids are completely broken down to form carbon dioxide and water and produce ATP.

anaerobic metabolism
or **anaerobic glycolysis**
Metabolism in the absence of oxygen. Each molecule of glucose generates two molecules of ATP. Glucose is metabolized in this way when the blood cannot deliver oxygen to the tissues quickly enough to support aerobic metabolism.

SCIENCE

ScienceAppliedScienceApplied
Science**AppliedScience**Applied
ScienceAppliedScienceApplied

APPLIED

(DAJ/Getty Images, Inc.) (www.victorianoizquierdo.com/Getty Images, Inc.) (Elena Schweitzer/Shutterstock)

Training:
Sometimes Less is Better

The Ball State University swim team was talented. They trained long and hard. Why then couldn't they perform consistently well? In search of an answer, the coach enlisted the help of Dr. David Costill, director of the school's Human Performance Laboratory. Costill began by assessing the condition of the swimmers. He attached monitors to measure heart rates and took blood samples to measure lactic acid levels. These measurements would help assess how well the athletes' bodies were responding to their training schedule. With continued training, heart rates and lactic acid accumulation were expected to decrease. However, Costill found that many of the swimmers had high lactic acid levels after practice despite the fact that they were well-trained athletes.[1] Perhaps they were training too long and too hard.

Further studies helped to clarify the problems and suggest some solutions. Costill studied the swimmers on an increased training schedule; they swam at their normal pace but doubled the distance.[2] Some of the swimmers were unable to tolerate the heavier training schedule. Costill took muscle biopsies and found that muscle glycogen was depleted in these swimmers, indicating that they were running out of fuel. Their carbohydrate intake was not sufficient to meet the needs of the increased training, and their performance was suffering.[2] Other swimmers were able to tolerate the heavier training but it was not enhancing their performance. In addition, the extra training had other negative consequences. The swimmers' ratings of their muscle soreness, depression, anger, fatigue, and overall mood disturbances became more negative and they reported a reduction in their general sense of well-being.[3] Could cutting down on training actually improve performance?

Traditionally, it was believed that more training meant better strength and endurance. However, Costill believed that the swimmers were overtrained. To test his hypothesis, he divided the team into two groups. One group of swimmers trained for 1.5 hours in the morning and 1.5 hours in the afternoon. A second group participated only in the afternoon session. Costill found that the group that trained the most experienced a decline in speed, whereas the second group showed an improvement.

(Tim Davis/Photo Researchers)

So, doubling the training time did not enhance performance.[4] Costill suggested that the Ball State swimming coach cut training time in half: Instead of working out twice a day, the coach cut out the morning workout. The team now consisted of more rested swimmers who swam faster than before; they ended with their best season in 10 years.

Costill's work suggests that when athletes train too much they are not able to maintain muscle glycogen, and increases in the amount of energy and carbohydrate in the diet may not be able to keep up. Performance can be optimized by a combination of proper diet and the right amount of exercise. Just as dietary excesses and deficiencies can hurt performance, too little or too much training can result in less-than-peak performance. When excessive training continues, athletes are at risk for overtraining syndrome, characterized by underperformance, persistent fatigue, altered mood, and increased rates of infection.[5] Athletes can help prevent overtraining, by resting one day each week, alternating hard and easy training days, and optimizing their nutrition, especially carbohydrate and energy intake.

---

[1]*The Champion Within.* Infinite Voyage Video Series, Intellimation, Inc. Santa Barbara, CA: QED Communications, Inc., and Washington, D.C.: National Academy of Sciences, 1991.

[2]Costill, D. L., Flynn, M. G., and Kirwan, J. P. Effects of repeated days of intensified training on muscle glycogen and swimming performance. *Med. Sci. Sports Exerc.* 20:249–254, 1988.

[3]Morgan, W. P., Costill, D. L., Flynn, M. G. et al. Mood disturbances following increased training in swimmers. *Med. Sci. Sports Exerc.* 20:408–414, 1988.

[4]Costill, D. L., Thomas, R., Robergs, R. A. et al. Adaptations to swimming training: Influence of training volume. *Med. Sci. Sports Exerc.* 23:371–377, 1991.

[5]Pearce, P. Z. A practical approach to the overtraining syndrome. *Curr. Sports Med. Rep.* 1:179–183, 2002.

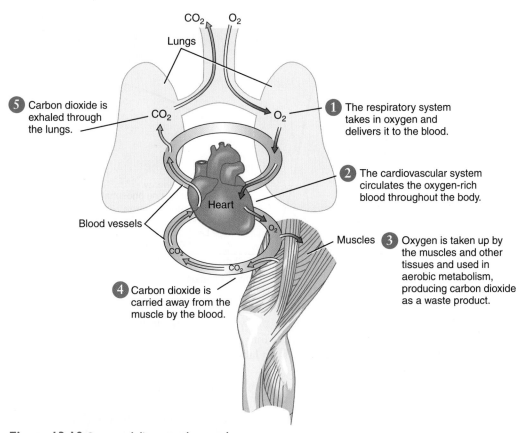

Figure 13.10 Oxygen delivery to the muscles
When you exercise, your muscles demand more energy, which requires oxygen. Your body responds by breathing faster and deeper in order to take in more oxygen and by increasing heart rate in order to deliver more oxygen to your muscles.

The Effect of Exercise Duration

Resting muscles do not need much energy. At rest the heart and lungs are able to deliver enough oxygen to meet energy demands using aerobic metabolism. During exercise, to increase the amount of energy provided by aerobic metabolism, the amount of oxygen available at the muscle must be increased (**Figure 13.10**). To do this breathing and heart rate are increased, but this takes time. When exercise first begins breathing and heart rate have not yet had enough time to increase the amount of oxygen available at the muscle.

Instant Energy: Stored ATP and Creatine Phosphate When you jump up to answer the phone or take the first steps of your morning jog your muscles increase their activity but your heart and lungs have not had time to step up oxygen delivery to them. To get the needed energy the muscles rely on small amounts of ATP that are stored in resting muscle. It is enough to sustain activity for a few seconds. As the ATP in muscle is used, enzymes break down another high-energy compound, called **creatine phosphate**, to replenish the ATP supply and allow activity to continue. But, like ATP, the amount of creatine phosphate stored in the muscle at any time is small. It will fuel muscle activity for about an additional 8 to 10 seconds before it, too, is used up. So, during the first 10 to 15 seconds of exercise, the muscles rely on energy from the ATP and creatine phosphate that is stored in them (**Figure 13.11**).

creatine phosphate
A compound found in muscle that can be broken down quickly to make ATP.

Short-Term Energy: Anaerobic Metabolism As exercise continues beyond 10 to 15 seconds the ATP and creatine phosphate in the muscles are used up but the heart and lungs have still not had time to increase oxygen delivery to the muscles. Therefore, the additional ATP needed to fuel muscle contraction must be produced without oxygen. By 30 seconds into activity, anaerobic pathways are operating at full capacity. This

Figure 13.11 Change in energy sources over time
The ATP for muscle contraction is first derived from ATP and creatine phosphate stored in the muscle, after which anaerobic glycolysis, which breaks down glucose, becomes the predominant source of ATP. After about 2 to 3 minutes oxygen delivery to the muscles has increased enough for aerobic metabolism, which uses fatty acids and glucose to produce ATP, to make a significant contribution to ATP production.

lactic acid A compound produced from the breakdown of glucose in the absence of oxygen.

anaerobic metabolism takes place in the cytosol. It includes glycolysis, which breaks glucose into the 3-carbon molecule pyruvate, releases electrons, and produces two molecules of ATP (**Figure 13.12**). At this point if oxygen is unavailable, the pyruvate and released electrons combine to form **lactic acid**. The lactic acid is transported out of the muscle for use in other tissues.

Anaerobic metabolism can produce ATP very rapidly, but can only use glucose as a fuel. This glucose may come from the breakdown of glycogen inside the muscle or from glucose delivered via the bloodstream. The glucose delivered in the blood comes from the breakdown of liver glycogen, the synthesis of glucose by the liver, or the ingestion of carbohydrate during exercise. Anaerobic metabolism predominates during the first few minutes of exercise (see Figure 13.11) and is also important during periods of intense exercise because oxygen cannot be delivered to the cells quickly enough to meet energy demands. Anaerobic metabolism uses glucose rapidly. Because the amount of glucose available is limited, if activity is to continue the body must use its glucose more efficiently and find a more plentiful fuel source.

Long-Term Energy: Aerobic Metabolism After 2 to 3 minutes of exercise, breathing and heart rate have increased to supply more oxygen to the muscles. When oxygen is available, ATP can be produced by aerobic metabolism. The reactions of aerobic metabolism take place in the mitochondria (see Figure 13.12). When glucose is broken down by aerobic metabolism, the pyruvate produced by glycolysis is converted to acetyl-CoA, so lactic acid is not formed. Acetyl-CoA is broken down by the citric acid cycle producing carbon dioxide and some ATP and releasing high-energy electrons. The electrons are shuttled to the electron transport chain, where their energy is harnessed to produce ATP and water is formed.

Aerobic metabolism produces ATP at a slower rate than anaerobic metabolism but is much more efficient, producing about 18 times more ATP for each molecule of glucose. In addition, aerobic metabolism can use fatty acids, and sometimes amino acids from protein, to generate ATP (see Figure 13.12). Fatty acids to fuel muscle contraction come from triglycerides stored in adipose tissue as well as small amounts stored in the muscle itself. During exercise, triglycerides are broken down into fatty acids and glycerol. Fatty acids from adipose tissue are released into the blood and are then taken up by the muscle cells. Inside the muscle cell, fatty acids from triglycerides within the muscle and those delivered by the blood must be transported into the mitochondria to produce ATP. To enter the mitochondria, fatty acids must be activated with the help of **carnitine**. Inside the mitochondria, fatty acids are broken into 2-carbon units by beta-oxidation to form acetyl-CoA (see Figure 13.12). Acetyl-CoA is metabolized via the citric acid cycle and electron transport chain to produce ATP, carbon dioxide, and water.

carnitine A molecule synthesized in the body that is needed to transport fatty acids and some amino acids into the mitochondria for metabolism.

When exercise continues at a low to moderate intensity, aerobic metabolism predominates and fat becomes the principal fuel source for exercising muscles. If exer-

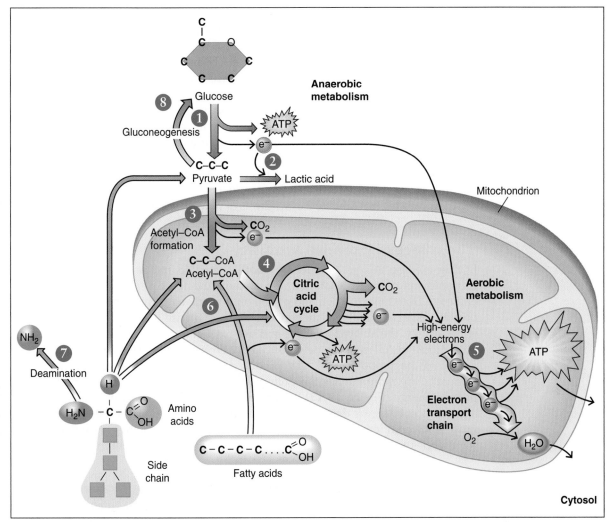

1. Glucose is split into 2 molecules of pyruvate, releasing electrons, and producing two molecules of ATP.

2. In the absence of oxygen the pyruvate and released electrons combine to form lactic acid.

3. When oxygen is available, the pyruvate is converted to acetyl-CoA.

4. Acetyl-CoA is broken down by the citric acid cycle.

5. The electrons released are shuttled to the electron transport chain, where their energy is harnessed to produce ATP.

6. Fatty acids are broken into 2-carbon units that form acetyl-CoA.

7. Amino acids are deaminated and then used as an energy source.

8. After deamination some amino acids can be used to synthesize glucose by gluconeogenesis.

Figure 13.12 Anaerobic versus aerobic metabolism
In the absence of oxygen, ATP is produced by the anaerobic glycolysis of glucose. When oxygen is present fatty acids and amino acids can also be used for energy.

cise intensity increases, the proportion of energy generated by anaerobic versus aerobic metabolism changes, as do the relative amounts of glucose and fatty acids used.

Protein Use During Exercise Although protein is not considered a major energy source, even at rest the body uses small amounts of amino acids to provide energy. The amount increases if the diet does not provide enough total energy to meet needs, if more protein is consumed than needed, if not enough carbohydrate is consumed, or if certain types of exercise are performed.

The amino acids available to the body come from the digestion of dietary proteins and from the breakdown of body proteins. When the nitrogen-containing amino group is removed from an amino acid (see Figure 13.12), the remaining carbon compound can be broken down to produce ATP by aerobic metabolism or in some cases used to make glucose via gluconeogenesis. Endurance exercise, which continues for many hours, increases the use of amino acids both as an energy source and as a raw material for glucose synthesis. When exercise stops, protein synthesis is accelerated so amino acids are needed to build and repair muscle. Repeated activity with a slight overload stimulates the muscle to adapt to the stress by breaking down existing muscle proteins and replacing them with greater amounts of new muscle proteins to meet the higher demand placed on the muscle. The need for amino acids for muscle building and repair is greater in strength athletes because they are actively overloading their muscles to stimulate the synthesis of new muscle tissue.

The Effect of Exercise Intensity

During exercise, ATP is produced by both anaerobic and aerobic metabolism. The contributions made by each of these systems overlap to ensure that muscles get enough ATP to meet the demand placed on them. The relative contribution of anaerobic versus aerobic metabolism depends on how intense the activity is. With very intense activity, the ability to deliver and use oxygen at the muscle becomes limiting. The amount of ATP that can be produced by aerobic metabolism cannot meet the demand, so the proportion of ATP produced anaerobically from glucose increases. Generally, the more intense the exercise, the more muscles must rely on glucose to provide energy (**Figure 13.13**). When intensity reaches the aerobic capacity of the athlete, most energy is derived from anaerobic metabolism of glucose. When the exercise is lower in intensity, the cardiorespiratory system can deliver enough oxygen to the muscles to allow aerobic metabolism to predominate, so fatty acids as well as

Figure 13.13 The effect of exercise intensity on fuel use

As exercise intensity increases, the proportion of energy supplied by carbohydrate increases. During exercise, the total amount of energy expended is greater than during rest. (Source: Adapted from Horton, E. S. Effects of low-energy diets on work performance. Am. J. Clin. Nutr. 35:1228–1233, 1982.) (Yva Momatiuk and John Eastcott/Minden Pictures/NG Image Collection; Alaska Stock Images/NG Image Collection; Rich Reid/NG Image Collection) some glucose are used as fuel. Thus, exercise intensity determines the contributions that carbohydrate and fat make as fuels for ATP production. In turn, which fuels are used affects how long exercise can continue before **fatigue** occurs.

High-Intensity Exercise Contributes to Fatigue If you run faster, you tire sooner. This is because more intense exercise relies more on anaerobic metabolism, which uses glucose more rapidly than aerobic metabolism and produces lactic acid. Until recently, it was assumed that lactic acid buildup was the cause of muscle fatigue, but we now know that although lactic acid buildup is associated with fatigue, it does not cause it.[15] Fatigue most likely has many causes, including glycogen depletion and changes in the muscle cells and the concentrations of molecules involved in muscle energy metabolism.

When athletes run out of glycogen, they experience a feeling of overwhelming fatigue that is sometimes referred to as "hitting the wall" or "bonking." Glycogen depletion is a concern for athletes because the amount of glycogen available to produce glucose during exercise is limited. There are between 60 and 120 grams of glycogen stored in the liver; stores are highest just after a meal. Liver glycogen is used to maintain blood glucose between meals and during the night. Eating breakfast replenishes the liver glycogen used overnight. There are about 200 to 500 grams of glycogen in the muscles of a 70-kg person. The glycogen in a muscle is used to fuel the activity of that muscle. Muscle glycogen levels can be increased by a combination of rest and a very high-carbohydrate diet.

Small amounts of lactic acid produced by anaerobic metabolism can be carried away from the muscle and used by other tissues as a fuel or by the liver to produce glucose. But, if the amount of lactic acid produced exceeds the amount that can be used by other tissues this by-product begins to build up in the muscles and subsequently the blood. **Anaerobic threshold** or **lactate threshold** refers to the exercise intensity at which lactic acid starts to accumulate in the blood faster than it can be metabolized. This is normally somewhere between 80% and 90% of maximum heart rate. Although the cause of muscle fatigue is not fully understood, it correlates with lactic acid buildup. When exercise stops and oxygen is available again, lactic acid can be either carried away by the blood to other tissues to be broken down or metabolized aerobically in the muscle.

Low-Intensity Exercise Can Continue Longer Lower-intensity exercise can be continued for longer periods because it relies on aerobic metabolism, which is more efficient than anaerobic metabolism and uses both glucose and fatty acids for energy. The body's fat reserves are almost unlimited so, if fat is the fuel, exercise can theoretically continue for a very long time. For example, it is estimated that a 130-lb woman has enough energy stored as body fat to run 1000 miles.[16] However, even aerobic activity uses some glucose, so if exercise continues long enough, glycogen stores will eventually be depleted and contribute to fatigue.

The Effect of Training

Training with repeated bouts of aerobic exercise causes physiological changes that increase aerobic capacity—the amount of oxygen that can be delivered to and used by the muscle cells. This in turn affects which fuels can be used by the exercising muscle cells.

Aerobic exercise causes adaptations in the cardiorespiratory system. The heart becomes larger and stronger so that the stroke volume is increased (**Figure 13.14**). The number of capillary blood vessels in the muscles increases so that blood is delivered to muscles more efficiently. And the total blood volume and number of red blood cells expands, increasing the amount of hemoglobin so more oxygen can be transported to the cells.

Training also causes changes at the cellular level that affect the ability of cells to use different types of fuel to produce ATP. There is an increase in the ability to store glycogen, and there is an increase in the number and size of muscle-cell mitochondria

fatigue The inability to continue an activity at an optimal level.

anaerobic threshold or **lactate threshold** The exercise intensity at which the reliance on anaerobic metabolism results in the accumulation of lactic acid.

Figure 13.14 Effect of exercise training on the heart Training increases the amount of blood pumped with each beat, so the heart of a trained athlete can pump more blood per minute than can the heart of an untrained individual.

Figure 13.15 Training increases the number of mitochondria in muscle cells, which increases aerobic capacity. (Don W. Fawcett/Visuals Unlimited)

(**Figure 13.15**). Because aerobic metabolism occurs in the mitochondria, this increases the cell's capacity to burn fatty acids to produce ATP. The use of fatty acids spares glycogen, which delays the onset of fatigue. Because trained athletes store more glycogen and use it more slowly, they can sustain aerobic exercise for longer periods at higher intensities than can untrained individuals. Conditioned athletes can also exercise at a higher percentage of their aerobic capacity before lactic acid begins to accumulate.

Living and working at high altitudes, where the atmosphere contains less oxygen, also causes adaptations that improve the ability of the cardiorespiratory system to deliver oxygen. Therefore, endurance athletes often train at high altitudes to enhance their aerobic capacity.

13.4 Energy and Nutrient Needs for Physical Activity

Learning Objectives

- Compare the energy and macronutrient needs of athletes and nonathletes.
- Explain why athletes are at risk for iron deficiency.
- Describe the female athlete triad.

Good nutrition is essential to performance whether you are a marathon runner or a mall walker. The diet must provide sufficient energy from the appropriate sources to fuel activity, protein to maintain muscle mass, micronutrients to allow utilization of the energy-yielding nutrients, and water to transport nutrients and cool the body. The major difference between the nutritional needs of a serious athlete and those of a casual exerciser is the amount of energy and fluid required.

Energy Needs

The amount of energy needed for activity depends on the intensity, duration, and frequency of the activity, as well as the characteristics of the exerciser, and even his or her location. For a casual exerciser, the energy needed for activity may increase energy expenditure by only a few hundred kcalories a day. For an endurance athlete, such as a marathon runner, the energy needed for training may increase expenditure by 2000 to 3000 kcalories per day. Some athletes require 6000 kcalories a day to maintain body weight. In general, the more intense the activity, the more energy it requires, and the more time spent exercising, the more energy it burns (**Table 13.2** and Appendix K). For example, walking for 30 minutes involves less work than running for the same amount of time and therefore requires less energy. Riding a bicycle for 60 minutes requires 6 times the energy needed to ride for 10 minutes. The body weight of the exerciser is another factor in determining energy needs. Moving a heavier body requires more energy than moving a lighter one. Therefore, it requires less energy for a 120-lb woman to walk for 30 minutes than it does for a 250-lb woman.

Table 13.2 Kcalorie Needs for Various Activities

Body Weight		100 lbs	125 lbs	140 lbs	155 lbs	170 lbs	185 lbs	200 lbs
Activity	Rate	Energy (kcal/hr)						
Bicycling	< 10 mph	137	171	191	212	233	252	273
	10–11.9 mph	228	285	318	353	388	420	455
	12–13.9 mph	319	399	445	494	543	588	637
	14–15.9 mph	410	513	572	635	698	756	819
	16–19 mph	501	627	699	776	853	924	1001
Running	12 min/mile	319	399	445	494	543	588	637
	10 min/mile	410	513	572	635	698	756	819
	8 min/mile	523	713	730	811	891	966	1047
	6 min/mile	683	855	953	1058	1163	1260	1365
Skiing, cross-country	2.5 mph	273	342	381	423	465	504	546
	4–4.9 mph	319	399	445	494	543	588	637
	5–7.9 mph	364	456	508	564	620	672	728
Swimming	leisurely	228	285	318	353	388	420	455
	50 yds/min	319	399	445	494	543	588	637
	75 yds/min	455	570	635	705	775	840	910
Walking	2 mph	68	86	95	106	116	126	137
	3 mph	105	131	146	162	178	193	209
	4 mph	182	228	254	282	310	336	364

The DRIs have developed equations to estimate energy requirements based on an individual's age, gender, size, and physical activity (PA) level (see Chapter 7 and inside cover). For the purposes of calculating estimated energy requirement (EER), an individual who performs no exercise other than the activities of daily living is in the "sedentary" PA category and one who performs less than an hour of moderate activity fits into the "low-active" PA category. Someone who engages in 60 minutes of moderate exercise each day is considered to be in the "active" PA category (see Chapter 7, Table 7.5). An "active" activity level can be achieved with less than 60 minutes of exercise if the exercise is more intense, for example, jogging at 5 mph or greater or swimming at a moderate to fast pace. Individuals who perform moderate exercise for more than 2.5 hours per day or more intense exercise for more than 1 hour per day are in the "very active" PA category. Calculating EER at different activity levels can demonstrate the dramatic impact activity can have on energy needs.[3] For example, the EER for a 25-year-old sedentary, 5'11"tall, 154-lb man is about 2500 kcalories. If this same person becomes a runner and trains several hours per day, his energy needs may increase to 3500 kcalories per day or more (**Figure 13.16**).

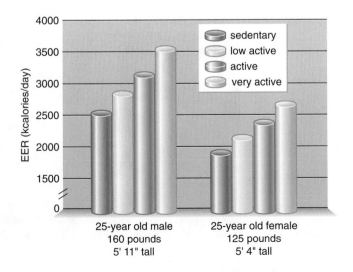

Figure 13.16 Effect of activity level on energy expenditure
Changing the amount of activity you routinely engage in can have a significant impact on your EER.

There are also some special considerations that affect the energy needed for activity. For example, because of the buoyancy of adipose tissue, the energy required for an individual with excess body fat to swim may be less than his lean counterpart. If a lean individual and an obese individual were in the weightlessness of space, it would require no more energy for one to leap across the room than for the other. There are also special circumstances that affect the amount of energy an individual needs for daily activity. A paraplegic in a wheelchair may have lower energy needs because many of the major muscles in the body are always inactive. At the other extreme, a person with the form of cerebral palsy that causes uncontrolled muscle movements may have higher energy needs because the muscles never stop moving.

Weight Loss Body weight and composition can affect exercise performance. Athletes involved in activities where small, light bodies offer an advantage—for instance, ballet, gymnastics, and certain running events—may restrict energy intake to maintain a low body weight. While a slightly leaner physique may be beneficial, dieting to maintain an unrealistically low weight may threaten health and performance. The general guidelines for healthy weight loss should be followed—reduce energy intake, increase activity, and change the behaviors that led to weight gain (see Chapter 7). To preserve lean body mass and enhance fat loss, weight should be lost at a rate of about 0.5 to 2 lbs per week. This can be accomplished by reducing total energy intake by 200 to 500 kcalories per day and increasing exercise. An athlete who needs to lose weight should do so in advance of the competitive season to prevent the restricted diet from affecting performance.[17]

Unhealthy Weight-Loss Practices Athletes are often under extreme pressure to achieve and maintain a body weight that optimizes their performance. Failure to meet weight-loss goals may have serious consequences such as being cut from the team or restricted from competition. This pressure may compel some athletes to use strict diets and maintain body weights that are not healthy. This, combined with the self-motivation and discipline that characterizes successful athletes, makes them vulnerable to eating disorders such as anorexia and bulimia.[18] In athletes with anorexia restricted food intake causes a deficiency of energy and nutrients, which can affect growth and maturation and impair exercise performance. In athletes with bulimia purging can cause dehydration and electrolyte imbalance, which affect performance and put overall health at risk. In addition to using restricted food intake or purging to keep body weight low, some athletes focus on the other side of the energy balance equation by exercising compulsively to burn kcalories (see Focus on Eating Disorders).

Athletes involved in sports with weight classes, such as wrestling and boxing, are at particular risk for unhealthy weight-loss practices because they are under pressure to lose weight before a competition so they can compete in lower weight classes (**Figure 13.17**). Competing at the high end of a weight class is thought to give one an advantage over smaller opponents. To lose weight rapidly these athletes may use

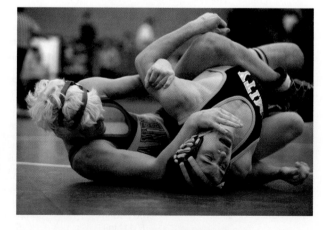

Figure 13.17 Energy restriction and dehydration used by wrestlers to keep weight down can harm health and impair exercise performance. (Enigma/Alamy)

sporadic diets that severely restrict energy intake or dehydrate themselves through such practices as vigorous exercise, fluid restriction, wearing plastic vapor-impermeable suits, and using hot environments such as saunas and steam rooms. They may also resort to even more extreme measures, such as self-induced vomiting and the use of diuretics and laxatives. These practices can be dangerous and even fatal. They may impair performance and can adversely affect heart and kidney function, temperature regulation, and electrolyte balance. In 1997 three young wrestlers died while trying to "make weight."[19] As a result of these deaths, wrestling weight classes were altered to eliminate the lightest weight class, plastic sweat suits were banned, a maximum wrestling room temperature of 75°F was established, weigh-ins were moved to 1 hour before competition, and mandatory weight-loss rules were put in place restricting the amount of weight that could be lost. There are minimum limits for percent body fat of 5% for college wrestlers and 7% for high school wrestlers.

Weight Gain In sports such as football and weight lifting in which being large is advantageous, an increase in body weight may be desirable. To gain weight, 500 to 1000 extra kcalories per day should be consumed. Strength training should accompany weight gain to promote an increase in lean tissue. To increase muscle mass many amateur and professional athletes have been drawn to the use of hormones called anabolic steroids. Although they do stimulate muscle growth, they are dangerous and illegal (see Your Choice: Ergogenic Hormones: Anything for an Edge).

Carbohydrate, Fat, and Protein Needs

The source of dietary energy can be as important as the amount of energy in an athlete's diet. In general, the diets of physically active individuals should contain the same proportion of carbohydrate, fat, and protein as is recommended to the general public—about 45% to 65% of total energy as carbohydrate, 20% to 35% of energy as fat, and 10% to 35% of energy as protein.

Carbohydrate Carbohydrate is needed to maintain blood glucose levels during exercise and to replace glycogen stores after exercise. The amount recommended for athletes depends on the total energy expenditure, type of sport, gender, and environmental conditions but ranges from 6 to 10 grams per kilogram of body weight per day.[17] For a 150-lb person burning 3000 kcalories per day, this would be about 60% of kcalories or about 450 grams of carbohydrate. Most of the carbohydrate in the diet should be complex carbohydrates from whole grains and starchy vegetables, with some naturally occurring simple sugars from fruit and milk. These foods provide vitamins, minerals, phytochemicals, and fiber as well as energy. Snacks and meals consumed before or during exercise should be lower in fiber to avoid cramping and gastrointestinal distress.

Fat Dietary fat supplies essential fatty acids, ensures the absorption of fat-soluble vitamins, and provides an important source of energy. Body stores of fat provide enough energy to support the needs of even the longest endurance events. For physically active individuals, diets providing 20% to 25% of energy as fat have been recommended to allow adequate carbohydrate intake.[17] Diets too high in fat do not contain enough carbohydrate to maximize glycogen stores and optimize performance. Excess dietary fat is unnecessary and excess energy consumed as fat, carbohydrate, or protein can cause an increase in body fat. Diets very low in fat (less than 20% of kcalories) have not been found to benefit performance.

Protein Protein is not a significant energy source, accounting for only about 5% to 10% of energy expended, but dietary protein is needed to maintain and repair lean tissues, including muscle. Enough protein is essential to maintain muscle mass and strength, but eating extra protein does not produce bigger muscles. Muscle growth is stimulated by exercise, not by increasing protein intake.

(©iStockphoto)

Ergogenic Hormones: Anything for an Edge

Athletes are always searching for things that will help them sprint faster, jump higher, or run farther. Some of the most effective substances used are hormones; however, they are also some of the most deadly. Because of the unfair advantage offered by these products, their use is banned in most athletic competitions and because of their risks, many are also illegal.

Anabolic Steroids have muscle-building effects. They attracted the attention of the athletic community when athletes from Eastern European nations began to dominate international strength events. These hormones accelerate protein synthesis and growth. The anabolic steroids used by athletes are synthetic versions of the human steroid hormone testosterone. Natural testosterone stimulates and maintains the male sexual organs and promotes the development of bones and muscles and the growth of skin and hair. The synthetic testosterone used by athletes has a greater effect on muscle development and bone, skin, and hair than it does on sexual organs. When synthetic testosterone is taken in conjunction with exercise and an adequate diet, muscle mass increases. However, these drugs also make the body think testosterone is being produced, and therefore the production of natural testosterone is reduced. Without natural testosterone, the sexual organs are not maintained; this leads to testicular shrinkage and a decrease in sperm production.[1] In adolescents, the use of synthetic testosterone causes bone growth to stop and height to be stunted. Use may also cause oily skin and acne, water retention, yellowing of eyes and skin, coronary artery disease, liver disease, and sometimes death. Psychological and behavioral side effects may lead to suicide. Because steroids are illegal and their manufacturing and distribution are not regulated, users can't be sure of their potency and purity.

Steroid Precursors are compounds that the body can convert into steroid hormones. The best known is androstenedione, or "andro," a precursor to testosterone marketed as an alternative to anabolic steroids to increase testosterone levels. The majority of studies have not supported that contention, but an increase in estrogen concentration has

been seen.[1] In addition, no studies have shown a significant ergogenic effect. Andro has been shown to lower HDL cholesterol, and therefore increase cardiovascular disease risk. Because andro is metabolized to estrogen and testosterone in the body, it may cause hormonal imbalances that could result in symptoms such as shrinkage of the testicles, impotence, and breast enlargement in men and male pattern baldness, deepening voice, increased facial hair, and abnormal menstrual cycles in women. In children it may cause earlier puberty and stunt bone growth. Steroid precursors, like anabolic steroids, are now classified as controlled substances and cannot be sold as dietary substances. They have been banned by all major national and international sports federations.

Human Growth Hormone is produced by the pituitary gland. In children it is important for tissue building during growth; in adults it maintains lean tissue, stimulates fat breakdown, increases the number of red blood cells, and boosts heart function. Genetically engineered growth hormone is used to treat children with growth failure. This hormone is appealing to athletes because it increases muscle protein synthesis, but ergogenic benefits among athletes remain unproven.[2] Prolonged use of growth hormone can cause heart dysfunction and high blood pressure, as well as excessive growth of the hands, feet, and facial features.

EPO, which is short for erythropoietin, is another popular hormone among endurance athletes. Natural erythropoietin is produced by the kidneys and stimulates cells in the bone marrow to differentiate into red blood cells. Genetically engineered EPO is used to treat anemia due to kidney disease, chemotherapy, HIV infection, and blood loss. It can enhance the performance of endurance athletes by increasing the ability to transport oxygen to the muscles.[3] It therefore increases aerobic capacity and spares glycogen. However, too much EPO can cause production of too many red blood cells and lead to excessive blood clotting, heart attacks, and strokes. The International Olympic Committee banned EPO in 1990 after it was linked to the death of more than a dozen cyclists.[4]

[1]Tokish, J. M., Kocher, M. S., and Hawkins, R. J. Ergogenic aids: A review of basic science, performance, side effects, and status in sports. *Am. J. Sports Med.* 32:1543–1553, 2004.

[2]Jenkins, P. J. Growth hormone and exercise. *Clin. Endocrinol.* 50:683–689, 2000.

[3]Ritter, S. K. Faster, higher, stronger. *Chemical Engineering News* 77:42–52, 1999.

[4]Birkeland, K. I., Stray-Gundersen, J., Hemmersbach, P. et al. Effect of rhEPO administration on serum levels of sTfR and cycling performance. *Med. Sci. Sports Exerc.* 32:1238–1243, 2000.

A diet that contains the RDA for protein (0.8 g/kg) provides adequate protein for most active individuals. Competitive athletes participating in endurance and strength sports may require more protein.[17] In endurance events such as marathons, protein is used for energy and to maintain blood glucose so these athletes may benefit from 1.2 to 1.4 grams of protein per kilogram per day. Strength athletes who require amino acids to synthesize new muscle proteins may benefit from 1.2 to 1.7 grams per kilogram per day. While this amount is greater than the RDA, it is not greater than the amount of protein habitually consumed by athletes.[20] For example, an 85-kg man consuming 3000 kcalories per day, 18% of which is from protein, would be consuming 135 grams, or 1.6 grams of protein per kilogram of body weight.

Vitamin and Mineral Needs

An adequate intake of vitamins and minerals is essential for optimal performance. These nutrients are needed for energy metabolism, oxygen delivery, antioxidant protection, and repair and maintenance of body structures. During exercise the amounts of many vitamins and minerals used in energy metabolism are increased and after exercise the amounts of those needed to repair tissue damage are increased. Exercise may also increase the losses of some nutrients. Nonetheless, most athletes can meet their needs by consuming the amounts of vitamins and minerals recommended for the general population. In addition, because athletes must eat more food to satisfy their higher energy needs, they consume extra vitamins and minerals in these foods, particularly if nutrient-dense choices are made. Athletes who restrict their intake to maintain a low body weight may be at risk for vitamin or mineral deficiencies.

B Vitamins B vitamins such as thiamin, riboflavin, and niacin are important for the production of ATP from carbohydrates and fat. Vitamin B_6, folate, and vitamin B_{12} are needed for proper synthesis of red blood cells, which deliver oxygen to body tissues. Vitamin B_6 is needed to break down glycogen to release glucose and to make the protein hemoglobin, which carries oxygen in red blood cells. Despite the importance of all of these roles during exercise the recommended intake of B vitamins is not any greater for athletes than for the rest of the population.

Antioxidant Nutrients Exercise increases the amount of oxygen at the muscle and the rate of metabolic reactions that produce ATP; oxygen utilization in active muscles can rise as much as 200-fold above resting levels.[21] This increased oxygen use increases the production of free radicals that can lead to oxidative damage and contribute to muscle fatigue.[22] Antioxidants, such as vitamins C and E, β-carotene, and selenium, help protect the body from oxidative damage. Despite the increase in free radical production that occurs during exercise there is no evidence that supplementation of antioxidants improves performance or that athletes require more of these nutrients than the general public.[23]

Iron and Anemia Iron is important for exercise because it is required for the formation of hemoglobin and myoglobin and a number of iron-containing proteins that are essential for the production of ATP by aerobic metabolism. Although a specific RDA has not been set for athletes the DRIs acknowledge that based on iron losses, the EAR may be 30% to 70% higher for athletes than for the general population.[24]

It is not uncommon for athletes, particularly female athletes, to have reduced iron stores.[25,26] If this deficiency progresses to anemia, it can impair exercise performance and reduce immune function. Low iron stores can be caused by inadequate iron intake, increased iron needs, increased iron losses, or a redistribution of iron due to exercise training. Iron intake can be a problem in athletes who are attempting to keep body weight low and in those who consume a vegetarian diet and therefore do not eat meat—an excellent source of readily absorbable heme iron. Iron needs may be increased in athletes because exercise stimulates the production of red blood cells, so more iron is needed for hemoglobin synthesis. An increase in iron losses with prolonged training, possibly because of increased fecal, urinary, and sweat losses, may

Normal   Sports anemia

Figure 13.18 Sports anemia
Training causes a decrease in the percentage of blood volume that is red blood cells. As training progresses, the number of red blood cells increases to catch up with the increase in total blood volume.

also occur.[17] Iron losses may also be increased by foot-strike hemolysis, the breaking of red blood cells from impact or the contraction of large muscles in events such as running. Although most of the iron from these cells is recycled, some is lost. Despite this, foot-strike hemolysis rarely causes anemia because the rupture of red blood cells stimulates the production of new ones.[25]

Some athletes experience a condition known as **sports anemia**, which is a temporary decrease in hemoglobin concentration that occurs during exercise training. This is an adaptation to training that does not seem to impair delivery of oxygen to tissues. It occurs when blood volume expands to increase oxygen delivery, but the synthesis of red blood cells lags behind the increase in plasma volume (**Figure 13.18**).

sports anemia Reduced hemoglobin levels that occur as part of a beneficial adaptation to aerobic exercise in which expanded plasma volume dilutes red blood cells.

Calcium and Bone Health Calcium is needed to maintain blood calcium levels and promote and maintain healthy bone density, which in turn reduces the risk of osteoporosis. In general, exercise—particularly weight-bearing exercise—increases bone density, thereby reducing the risk of osteoporosis. Although calcium needs are not different for athletes, in female athletes, too much exercise combined with restricted food intake can cause hormonal abnormalities that affect calcium metabolism and put bone health at risk. This **female athlete triad**, is a combination of restrictive eating patterns that can lead to eating disorders, abnormalities in hormone levels that cause **amenorrhea**, and disturbances in bone formation and breakdown that contribute to osteoporosis. Hormonal abnormalities occur when extreme energy restriction and exercise create a physiological condition similar to starvation. Estrogen levels drop, causing amenorrhea. Because estrogen is needed for calcium homeostasis in the bone and calcium absorption in the intestines, low levels lead to premature bone loss, low peak bone mass, and an increased risk of stress fractures. Neither adequate dietary calcium nor the increase in bone mass caused by weight-bearing exercise can compensate for bone loss due to low estrogen levels. Treatment for female athlete triad involves increasing energy intake and reducing activity so that menstrual cycles resume. This is essential for preserving long-term bone health.[27]

female athlete triad
The combination of disordered eating, amenorrhea, and osteoporosis that occurs in some female athletes, particularly those involved in sports in which low body weight and appearance are important.

amenorrhea Delayed onset of menstruation or the absence of three or more consecutive menstrual cycles.

13.5 Fluid Needs for Physical Activity

Learning Objectives

- Discuss dehydration in relation to performance and heat-related illness.
- Describe a scenario that might lead to hyponatremia.
- Explain why the types of fluid recommended for a 30 minute work-out and a 2-hour workout are different.

During exercise water is needed to eliminate heat and to transport both oxygen and nutrients to the muscles and waste products away from the muscles. The ability to dissipate the heat generated during exercise is affected by the hydration status of the exerciser as well as by environmental conditions. At rest in a temperate environment, an individual loses about 1.2 L (about 4.5 cups) of water per day, or 50 mL per hour, through evaporation from the skin and lungs. Exercise in a hot environment can increase losses more than 10-fold. Even when fluids are consumed at regular intervals during exercise it may not be possible to drink enough to compensate for losses from sweat and evaporation through the lungs. Failure to consume adequate fluids to replace water lost can be critical to even the most casual exerciser. If heat cannot be lost from the body, body temperature rises and exercise performance as well as health may be jeopardized.

Dehydration

Dehydration occurs when water loss is great enough for blood volume to decrease, thereby reducing the ability to deliver oxygen and nutrients to exercising muscles. Dehydration hastens the onset of fatigue and makes a given exercise intensity seem more difficult. Even mild dehydration—a body water loss of 2% to 3% of body weight—can impair exercise performance (**Figure 13.19**).[17] A 3% reduction in body weight can significantly reduce the amount of blood pumped with each heartbeat. This reduces the ability of the circulatory system to deliver oxygen and nutrients to cells and remove waste products. The decrease in blood volume that occurs with dehydration reduces blood flow to the skin and sweat production, which limits the body's ability to sweat and cool itself. Core body temperature can then increase and with it the risk of various **heat-related illnesses**.

The risk of dehydration is greater in hot environments, but it may also occur when exercising in the cold. Cold air tends to be dry air so evaporative losses from the lungs are greater. Insulated clothing may increase sweat losses and fluid intake may be reduced because a chilled athlete may be reluctant to drink a cold beverage. Female athletes tend to limit fluid intake to avoid the inconvenience of removing clothing to urinate.[17]

Children, older athletes, and obese individuals are at a greater risk for dehydration and heat-related illness. Children produce more heat, are less able to transfer heat from muscles to the skin, take longer to acclimatize to heat, and sweat less than adults. To reduce risks on hot days, children should rest periodically in the shade, consume fluids frequently, and limit the intensity and duration of activities. Also, children lose more heat in cold environments than adults because they have a greater surface area per unit of body weight. Therefore, they are more prone to **hypothermia**. Older athletes are at greater risk of dehydration because the thirst sensation decreases with age, and the kidneys may be less able to concentrate urine thus increasing the amount of fluid lost in urine. Excess weight increases the risk of heat-related illness because it increases the amount of work and therefore the amount of heat produced in a given activity. The fat also acts as an insulator, retarding the conduction of heat to the body surface. Obese individuals also have a smaller surface area-to-body mass ratio than lean people so they are less efficient at dissipating heat through blood flow to the surface and the evaporation of sweat.

heat-related illness
Conditions, including heat cramps, heat exhaustion, and heat stroke, that can occur due to an unfavorable combination of exercise, hydration status, and climatic conditions.

Life Cycle

hypothermia A condition in which body temperature drops below normal. Hypothermia depresses the central nervous system, resulting in the inability to shiver, sleepiness, and eventually coma.

Figure 13.19 Effect of dehydration on exercise performance
As the severity of dehydration increases, exercise performance declines. (Source: Adapted from Saltin, B., and Castill, D. I. Fluid and electrolyte balance during prolonged exercise. In Exercise, Nutrition, and Energy Metabolism. E. S. Horton, and R. I. Tergung, eds. New York: Macmillan, 1988.)

Heat-Related Illness

Exercising in hot weather can lead to heat-related illness. Both the temperature and humidity greatly affect the risk. As environmental temperature rises it becomes more difficult to dissipate heat and as humidity rises the ability to cool the body by evaporation declines.[28] When the humidity is high the same air temperature feels hotter than when the humidity is lower. For example, when the humidity is 100%, a temperature of 82°F feels the same as a temperature of 90°F and a humidity of only 50%. The risks associated with exercising in these conditions are similar (**Figure 13.20**). Conditioning with repeated bouts of exercise can reduce the risk of heat-related illness but cannot compensate for a lack of water. Dehydration reduces the ability to cool the body and increases the risk of these disorders even when it is not extremely hot or humid.

Heat-related illnesses include heat cramps, heat exhaustion, and heat stroke. Heat cramps are involuntary muscle spasms that occur during or after intense exercise, usually in the muscles involved in exercise. They are caused by an imbalance of the electrolytes sodium and potassium at the muscle cell membranes and can occur when water and salt are lost during extended exercise. Heat exhaustion occurs when fluid loss causes blood volume to decrease so much that it is not possible to both cool the body and deliver oxygen to active muscles. It is characterized by a rapid weak pulse, low blood pressure, fainting, profuse sweating, and disorientation. Someone experiencing the symptoms of heat exhaustion should stop exercising and move to a cooler environment. If exercise continues heat exhaustion may progress to heat stroke. Heat stroke, the most serious form of heat-related illness, occurs when the temperature regulatory center of the brain fails due to a very high core body temperature (greater than 105°F). Heat stroke is characterized by elevated body temperature, hot dry skin, extreme confusion, and unconsciousness. It requires immediate medical attention.

Hyponatremia

The evaporation of sweat helps cool the body during exercise. Sweat is a blood filtrate produced by sweat glands in the skin. It is made up of 99% water along with small amounts of minerals, primarily sodium and chloride, acids, and trace amounts of other substances. Because sweat is mostly water, for most activities sweat losses can be replaced with plain water. However, when sweating continues for more than 4 hours, as it may during endurance events such as marathons, enough sodium may be lost to affect electrolyte balance. A reduction in the concentration of sodium in the blood is referred to as **hyponatremia**. Hyponatremia can occur if an athlete loses large amounts of water and salt in sweat, and replaces the loss with water alone. This

hyponatremia Abnormally low concentration of sodium in the blood.

Figure 13.20 Heat index and the risk of heat-related illness The "heat index" or "apparent temperature" is a measure of how hot it feels when the relative humidity is added to the actual air temperature. To find the heat index find the intersection of the temperature on the left side of the table and the relative humidity across the top of the table. The shaded zones indicate the relative risk of heat-related illness with continued exposure and/or physical activity. (Source: National Weather Service. Available online at www.nws.noaa.gov/os/heat/index.shtml).

Relative humidity (%)

°F	40	45	50	55	60	65	70	75	80	85	90	95	100
110	136												
108	130	137											
106	124	130	137										
104	119	124	131	137									
102	114	119	124	130	137								
100	109	114	118	124	129	136							
98	105	109	113	117	123	128	134						
96	101	104	108	112	116	121	126	132					
94	97	100	102	106	110	114	119	124	129	135			
92	94	96	99	101	105	108	112	116	121	126	131		
90	91	93	95	97	100	103	106	109	113	117	122	127	132
88	88	89	91	93	95	98	100	103	106	110	113	117	121
86	85	87	88	89	91	93	95	97	100	102	105	108	112
84	83	84	85	86	88	89	90	92	94	96	98	100	103
82	81	82	83	84	84	85	86	88	89	90	91	93	95
80	80	80	81	81	82	82	83	84	84	85	86	86	87

Air temperature (left axis)

Heat index (apparent temperature)

With prolonged exposure and/or physical activity

| Extreme danger |
| Heat stroke highly likely |

| Danger |
| Heat stroke, heat cramps, and/or heat exhaustion likely |

| Extreme caution |
| Heat stroke, heat cramps, and/or heat exhaustion possible |

| Caution |
| Fatigue possible |

causes the sodium that remains in blood to be diluted so the amount of water is too great for the amount of sodium. This is analogous to taking a full glass of salt water, dumping out half, and replacing what was poured out with plain water. The sodium in the glass is now more dilute (**Figure 13.21**). It is also possible to develop hyponatremia when salt losses from sweating are not excessive. This can occur if an athlete drinks more water than is lost in sweat, diluting the sodium in their system. A study of runners in the Boston Marathon found that 13% of those tested had hyponatremia and 0.6% had serum sodium concentrations low enough for this condition to be considered critical.[29] It is the concentration of sodium that is important, not the absolute amount.

Hyponatremia causes a number of problems. Solutes in the blood help hold fluid in the blood vessels. As sodium concentration drops, water will leave the bloodstream by osmosis and accumulate in the tissues, causing swelling. Fluid accumulation in the lungs interferes with gas exchange, and fluid accumulation in the brain causes disorientation, seizure, coma, and death. The early symptoms of hyponatremia may be similar to dehydration: nausea, muscle cramps, disorientation, slurred speech, and confusion. Drinking water alone will make the problem worse and can result in seizure, coma, or death.

For most types of exercise hyponatremia is not a concern and lost electrolytes can be replaced during the meals following exercise. During long-distance events when hyponatremia is more likely, risk can be reduced by increasing sodium intake several days prior to competition, consuming sodium-containing sports drinks during the event, and avoiding Tylenol, aspirin, ibuprofen, and other nonsteroidal anti-inflammatory agents. These medications interfere with kidney function and may contribute to the development of hyponatremia. Mild symptoms of hyponatremia can be treated by eating salty foods or drinking sodium-containing beverages such as sports drinks. More severe symptoms require medical attention.

Recommended Fluid Intake for Exercise

Anyone exercising should consume extra fluids. Good hydration is important before exercise and since thirst is not a reliable indicator of immediate fluid needs, it is important to schedule regular fluid breaks during exercise. The amount and type of fluid that is best depends on how much water you lose and how long you exercise. Because many people do not consume enough during exercise, beverages consumed after exercise must restore hydration.

Normal blood
sodium concentration

Water and sodium
lost in sweat

Replacing just water
dilutes sodium
(hyponatremia)

Figure 13.21 Hyponatremia
Hyponatremia can occur when an athlete loses water and sodium in sweat but replaces these losses with plain water, diluting the remaining sodium in the blood.

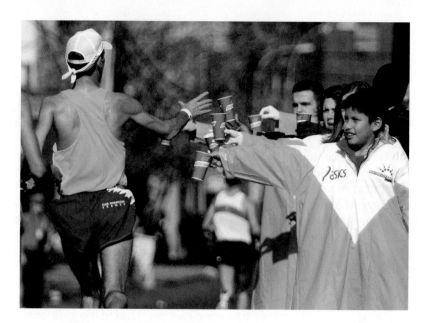

Figure 13.22 Consume fluids before, during, and after exercise to maintain adequate hydration. (Mario Tama/Getty Images, Inc.)

How Much Should You Drink? To ensure hydration adequate fluids should be consumed before, during, and after exercise. Exercisers should drink generous amounts of fluid in the 24 hours before the exercise session and about 2 cups of fluid at least 4 hours before exercise. During exercise, whether casual or competitive, exercisers should try and drink enough water to prevent weight loss in excess of 2% of body weight (**Figure 13.22**).[17] Drinking 6 to 12 oz of fluid every 15 to 20 minutes beginning at the start of exercise should maintain adequate hydration. To restore lost water after exercise, each pound of weight lost should be replaced with 16 to 24 oz (1 to 1.5 lbs) of fluid (**Table 13.3**).

Table 13.3 Recommended Fluid Intake

Before Exercise
- Begin exercise well hydrated by consuming generous amounts of fluid in the 24 hours before exercise.
- Consume about 2 cups of fluid at least 4 hours before exercise.

During Exercise
- Consume at least 6 to 12 ounces of fluid every 15 to 20 minutes.
- For exercise lasting 60 minutes or less, plain water is the only fluid needed but beverages containing carbohydrate and electrolytes will not hurt performance.
- For exercise lasting longer than 60 minutes, consuming a fluid containing about 6% to 8% carbohydrate may improve endurance.
- For exercise lasting longer than 60 minutes, a fluid containing electrolytes can increase fluid intake by stimulating thirst and increasing absorption.

After Exercise
- Begin fluid replacement immediately after exercise.
- Consume 16 to 24 ounces of fluid for each pound of weight lost.

What Should You Drink During Short Workouts? For exercise lasting an hour or less, water is the only fluid needed. For a 20-minute jog, 40 minutes at the gym, or a brisk walk through the park, sports drinks offer no advantage over a water bottle filled at the drinking fountain. Sports drinks will not hurt your performance in a short workout, but they may be counterproductive if the goal of exercise is weight loss. A typical sports drink contains about 50 kcalories per cup, so drinking a 16-oz bottle at the gym will replace about half of the 200 kcalories expended during your 40-minute ride on the stationary bicycle.

What Should You Drink During Long Workouts? For exercise lasting more than 60 minutes, beverages containing a small amount of carbohydrate and electrolytes are recommended. Exercise depletes body carbohydrate stores. Consuming carbohydrate in a beverage helps to maintain blood glucose levels, therefore providing a source of glucose for the muscle and delaying fatigue. A good sports drink should empty rapidly from the stomach, enhance intestinal absorption, and promote fluid retention. As the amount of carbohydrate in the beverage increases, the rate at which the solution leaves the stomach decreases. Beverages containing 15 to 20 grams of carbohydrate per cup (6% to 8%) are best. This is the amount of carbohydrate found in popular sports beverages such as Gatorade and PowerAde. Beverages containing larger amounts of carbohydrate, such as fruit juices and soft drinks, are not recommended unless they are diluted with an equal volume of water. Water and carbohydrate trapped in the stomach do not benefit the athlete.

Small amounts of minerals, including sodium and chloride, are lost in sweat, but sweat consists mostly of water, so the amounts lost during exercise lasting less than 3 to 4 hours are usually not enough to affect health or performance, particularly if sodium was present in the previous meal. Even though there may not be a physiological need to replace sodium, a beverage containing 500 to 700 mg of sodium per liter (around 150 mg in a cup) is recommended for exercise lasting more than an hour.[17] This is because the sodium enhances palatability and the drive to drink so it may cause an increase in fluid intake. The presence of small amounts of sodium and glucose also tend to slightly increase the rate of water absorption. A sodium-containing beverage will also help prevent hyponatremia in athletes who overhydrate and in those participating in endurance events, such as ultramarathons or iron man triathlons, in which significant amounts of sodium may be lost in sweat.

13.6 Food and Drink to Maximize Performance

Learning Objectives

- Discuss the advantages and disadvantages of carbohydrate loading.
- Explain the recommendations for food and drink during extended exercise.
- Plan pre- and post-competition meals for a marathon runner.

For most of us a trip to the gym requires no special nutritional planning but for competitive athletes when they eat and what they eat before, during, and after competition is as important as a balanced overall diet. Food eaten at these times may give or take away the extra seconds that can mean victory or defeat.

Maximizing Glycogen Stores

Glycogen provides a source of stored glucose. Larger glycogen stores allow exercise to continue for longer periods. Glycogen stores and, hence, endurance are increased by increasing carbohydrate intake (**Figure 13.23**). Serious endurance athletes who want to substantially increase their glycogen stores before a competition may choose to follow a dietary regimen referred to as **glycogen supercompensation** or **carbohydrate loading**. This involves resting for one to three days before competition while consuming a very high-carbohydrate diet.[30,31] The diet should provide 10 to 12 g of carbohydrate per kilogram of body weight per day. For a 150-pound person, this is equivalent to about 700 g of carbohydrate per day. Having a stack of pancakes with

glycogen supercompensation or **carbohydrate loading** A regimen designed to maximize muscle glycogen stores before an athletic event.

Figure 13.23 Effect of carbohydrate consumption on endurance
Endurance capacity is shown during cycling exercise after 3 days of a very-low-carbohydrate diet (less than 5% of energy from carbohydrate), a normal diet (about 55% carbohydrate), and a high-carbohydrate diet (82% carbohydrate). (Source: From Bergstrom, J., Hermansen, L., Hultman, E., and Saltin, B. Diet, muscle glycogen and physical performance. Acta. Physiol. Scand. 71:140–150, 1967.) (Jignesh Jhaveri/StockFood/Getty Images, Inc.)

syrup and a large glass of juice for breakfast will provide about a third of the carbohydrate recommended for a day. A number of commercial high-carbohydrate beverages, containing 50 to 60 g of carbohydrate in 8 fluid ounces, are available to help athletes consume the amount of carbohydrate recommended to maximize glycogen stores. These should not be confused with sports drinks designed to be consumed during competition, which contain only about 15 to 20 g of carbohydrate in 8 fluid ounces. Trained athletes who follow a carbohydrate-loading regimen can double their muscle glycogen content.[30]

Although glycogen supercompensation is beneficial to endurance athletes, it will provide no benefit and even has some disadvantages for people exercising for periods less than 90 minutes. For every gram of glycogen in the muscle, 3 grams of water are also deposited. This water can cause a 2- to 7-lb weight gain and may cause some muscle stiffness. The extra weight is a disadvantage for those competing in events of short duration. As glycogen is used, the water is released; this can be an advantage when exercising in hot weather.

What to Eat Before Exercise

An athlete who is hungry will not perform at his or her best, but the wrong meal can hinder performance more than the right one can enhance it. The size, composition, and timing of the preexercise meal are all important. The goal of meals eaten before exercise is to maximize glycogen stores and provide adequate hydration while minimizing hunger and any undigested food in the stomach that can lead to gastric distress.

Ideally, a preexercise meal should provide enough fluid to maintain hydration and be high in carbohydrate (60% to 70% of kcalories). This will help to maintain blood glucose and maximize glycogen stores. Muscle glycogen is depleted by exercise, but liver glycogen is used to supply blood glucose and is depleted even during rest if no food is ingested. So, first thing in the morning liver glycogen stores have been reduced by the overnight fast. A high-carbohydrate meal eaten 2 to 4 hours before the event will fill liver glycogen stores. In addition to being high in carbohydrate the preexercise meal should be moderate in protein (10% to 20%) and low in fat (10% to 25%) and fiber to minimize gastrointestinal distress and bloating during competition. A cup of pasta with tomato sauce and a slice of bread, or a turkey sandwich and a cup of juice are good choices. Spicy foods that could cause heartburn, and large amounts of simple sugars that could cause diarrhea, should be avoided unless the athlete is accustomed to eating these foods.

In addition to providing nutritional clout, a meal that includes "lucky" foods may provide some athletes with an added psychological advantage. Some athletes find that in addition to a precompetition meal, a small high-carbohydrate snack or beverage consumed shortly before an event may enhance endurance. Because foods affect people differently, athletes should test the effect of these meals and snacks during training, not during competition.

What to Eat During Exercise

Regardless of the type or duration of exercise, maintaining adequate fluid intake is important while exercising (see Table 13.3). For exercise that lasts more than an hour, consuming about 30 to 60 grams of carbohydrate per hour (the amount in a banana or an energy bar) can enhance endurance.[17] Consuming carbohydrate during exercise is particularly important for athletes who exercise in the morning when liver glycogen levels are low.

Carbohydrate intake should begin shortly after exercise commences and regular amounts should be consumed every 15 to 20 minutes during exercise. The carbohydrate should provide glucose, glucose polymers (chains of glucose molecules), or a combination of glucose and fructose.[17] Fructose alone is not as effective and may cause diarrhea. Some athletes may prefer to obtain this carbohydrate from a sports drink, while others prefer a high carbohydrate snack or energy gel consumed with water. Energy gels consist of a thick carbohydrate syrup packaged in a palm-sized packet. The contents can be sucked out of the packet, providing about 20 grams of carbohydrate (see Off the Label: What Are You Getting from That Sports Bar?).

During exercise sodium and other minerals are lost in sweat. Although the amounts lost during exercise lasting less than 3 to 4 hours are usually not enough to affect health or performance, a snack or beverage containing sodium is recommended for exercise lasting 1 hour or more. The sodium enhances the palatability of beverages and increases the drive to drink so even if sodium losses are small, consuming it during exercise may cause an increase in fluid intake.

What to Eat After Exercise

When exercise ends, the body must shift from the catabolic state of breaking down glycogen, triglycerides, and muscle proteins for fuel to the anabolic state of restoring muscle and liver glycogen, depositing lipids, and synthesizing muscle proteins. The goal for meals after exercise is to replenish fluid, electrolyte, and glycogen losses and to provide amino acids for muscle protein synthesis and repair. For example, a mixed meal such as pancakes and a glass of milk consumed soon after a strenuous competition or training session will help the athlete prepare for the next exercise session.

The first priority for all exercisers is to replace fluid losses. For serious athletes it may also be important to rapidly replenish glycogen stores. Appropriate postexercise intake can replenish muscle and liver glycogen within 24 hours of the athletic event. To maximize glycogen replacement, a high-carbohydrate meal or drink should be consumed within 30 minutes after the competition and again every 2 hours for 6 hours after the event. Ideally the meals should provide about 1.0 to 1.5 grams of carbohydrate per kilogram of body weight, which is about 70 to 100 grams of carbohydrate for a 70-kg (150-lb) person—the equivalent of about 2 and a half cups of pasta.[17] This type of regimen to restore glycogen is critical for athletes who must perform again the following day, but is not necessary if the athlete has 1 or more days to replace glycogen stores before the next intense exercise. Those not competing again the next day can replace glycogen more slowly by consuming high-carbohydrate foods for the next day or so. Most people do not need a special glycogen replacement strategy to ensure glycogen stores are full by their next gym visit. Eating a typical diet that provides about 55% of kcalories as carbohydrate will quickly replace the glycogen used during a 30 to 60 minute workout at the gym.

Off the Label

What Are You Getting from That Sports Bar?

©iStockphoto

Looking for a convenient snack that can give you an energy boost during your bike ride or day of skiing? A sports bar may be the answer, but which should you choose? There are hundreds of varieties. Some are high in protein and low in carbohydrate; others are high in carbohydrate and low in fat; and some claim to have just the right balance of everything. They promise to optimize performance, build lean muscle, reduce body fat, increase strength, and speed recovery.

Carbohydrate is the fuel that becomes limiting during prolonged exercise, so if you want to have the energy to keep pedaling or skiing, choose high-carbohydrate bars, called energy or endurance bars. They have the carbohydrate needed to prevent hunger and maintain blood glucose during sports activities. Use the label to check out the amount of carbohydrate, fat, protein, and energy in different bars. A bar that provides about 45 grams of carbohydrate (70% of kcalories) will help maintain your blood glucose level during exercise. Watch the fat and protein; in 300 kcalories you want no more than about 8 grams of fat and 16 grams of protein. Bars higher in fat or protein or lower in carbohydrate will not give you the blood glucose boost that you need to continue exercising.

Is a sports bars any better for you than a candy bar? A look at the label shows that there is a difference. Typically, sports bars are lower in fat, higher in fiber, and contain more vitamins and minerals than candy bars. Many contain vitamin C, vitamin E, calcium, iron, magnesium, copper, zinc, and a host of B vitamins. They must list the percent Daily Value for calcium, iron, and vitamins A and C. The Daily Values of other vitamins and minerals do not need to be included in the Nutrition Facts portion of the label, but all the nutrients added will appear in the ingredient list.

So, should you be packing a sports bar on your next outing? It won't take the place of the whole grains, fresh vegetables and fruits, low-fat dairy products, and lean meats or meat substitutes that make up a healthy diet. But, if having a compact, individually wrapped bar that can travel with you means the difference between consuming this snack or no food at all, sports bars can be beneficial. They may also provide a psychological edge if you believe they will enhance your performance.

If you choose to use these bars, wash them down with plenty of water. They don't provide fluid—an essential during any activity. Also remember that one sports bar provides around 200 to 300 kcalories. Even though they are eaten to support activity they still add to your overall energy intake and can contribute to weight gain if consumed in excess.

Nutrition Facts	Amount/Serving	% DV*	Amount/Serving	% DV*
Serving Size 1 bar (65g)	Total Fat 2g	3%	Total Carb 45g	15%
Calories 230	Saturated Fat 0.5g	3%	Dietary Fiber 3g	12%
Calories from Fat 20	Trans Fat 0g		Sugars 14g	
Calories from Sat Fat 5	Cholesterol 0mg	0%	Other Carb 28g	
*Percent Daily Values (DV) are based on a 2,000 calorie diet.	Sodium 90mg	4%	Protein 10g	
	Potassium 145mg	4%		

Vitamin A 0% • Vitamin C 100% • Calcium 30% • Iron 35% • Vitamin E 100%
Thiamin 100% • Riboflavin 100% • Niacin 100% • Vitamin B$_6$ 100%
Folate 100% • Vitamin B$_{12}$ 100% • Biotin 100% • Pantothenic Acid 100%
Phosphorus 35% • Magnesium 35% • Zinc 35% • Copper 35% • Chromium 20%

(George Semple)

568

13.7 Ergogenic Aids: Do Supplements Enhance Athletic Performance?

Learning Objectives

- Assess the health risks associated with anabolic steroids.
- Explain why creatine supplements affect sprint performance.
- Describe one way in which a supplement might improve endurance.

"Citius, Altius, Fortius"—faster, higher, stronger—the Olympic motto. For as long as there have been competitions, athletes have yearned for something—anything—that would give them the competitive edge. Anything designed to enhance performance can be considered an **ergogenic aid**; running shoes are mechanical aids; psychotherapy is a psychological aid; drugs are pharmacological aids. Many dietary supplements are also used as ergogenic aids. Although these supplements are often expensive and most have not been shown to improve performance, athletes are vulnerable to their enticements. When considering the use of an ergogenic supplement, an athlete should first weigh the health risks against potential benefits; dietary supplements do not have to be proven safe or effective before they can be sold (see Chapter 2 and Focus on Nonvitamin Nonmineral Supplements as well as **Table 13.4**). The following sections discuss some of the more popular products. Others are reviewed in **Table 13.5**.

ergogenic aid Anything designed to increase work or improve performance.

Table 13.4 Evaluating the Benefits and Risks of Ergogenic Supplements

Does the supplement meet your needs?
- Does the product contain the nutrient or other ingredient you are looking for?
- Has it been shown to provide the benefits you want?

Are the ingredients safe for you?
- Does it contain any ingredients that have been shown to be toxic to someone like you?
- Do you have a medical condition that would make it dangerous to take this product?
- Are you taking prescription medication that might interact with the supplement?

Is the dose safe?
- Does it contain potentially toxic levels of any nutrient? Check the % Daily Value for any nutrients that exceed 100%. If they do, do they exceed the UL?
- Follow the recommended dose on the package. More isn't always better and may cause side effects.

How much does it cost?
- More expensive is not always better.
- Compare costs and ingredients before you buy.

Vitamin Supplements

Many of the promises made to athletes about the benefits of vitamin supplements are extrapolated from their biochemical functions. For example, B vitamin supplements are promoted to enhance ATP production because of their roles in muscle energy metabolism. Vitamins B_6, B_{12}, and folic acid are promoted for aerobic exercise because they are involved in the transport of oxygen to exercising muscles. These vitamins are indeed needed for energy metabolism, and a deficiency of one or more of these will interfere with ATP production and impair athletic performance; however, providing more than the recommended amount does not deliver more oxygen to the muscle, cause more ATP to be produced, or enhance athletic performance. Because athletes must consume more food to meet energy needs, they consume more vitamins as well. A reasonably well-planned diet that is based on whole grains, vegetables, and fruits and includes lean meats and low-fat dairy products will provide enough of all the B vitamins to meet an athlete's needs.

Table 13.5 Claims, Benefits, and Risks of Popular Ergogenic Aids

Ergogenic Aid	Promoter Claims	Proven Benefits	Potential Risks
Arginine, ornithine, and lysine	Causes the release of growth hormone, which stimulates muscle development and decreases body fat.	No increase in lean body mass observed with supplementation.	Reduced absorption of other amino acids. Diarrhea at high doses.
Bee pollen	Causes faster recovery from training workouts, which enables a higher level of training.	No evidence that it improves training level.	Allergic reactions.
Bicarbonate (sodium bicarbonate, baking soda)	Helps buffer lactic acid produced during exercise and delays fatigue.	Increases blood pH and may enhance performance and strength during intense anaerobic activities.	Causes bloating, diarrhea, and high blood pH.
Branched chain amino acids (leucine, isoleucine, and valine)	Improves endurance and prevents fatigue.	Evidence of an effect is inconsistent.	No toxicity reported.
Caffeine	Increases the release of fatty acids from adipose tissue, spares glycogen, and enhances endurance.	Increases endurance in some individuals.	Dehydration, nervousness, anxiety, insomnia, digestive discomfort, abnormal heartbeat.
Carnitine	Enhances the utilization of fatty acids and spares glycogen.	No increase in fatty acid utilization or improvement in exercise performance found.	D,L-carnitine and D-carnitine forms can be toxic.
Chromium (chromium picolinate)	Increases lean body mass, decreases body fat, delays fatigue.	No effect on protein or lipid metabolism unless a chromium deficiency exists.	No toxicity reported in humans.
Coenzyme Q10	Increases mitochondrial ATP production, acts as an antioxidant, and may combat fatigue	No effect on exercise performance observed.	No toxicity reported.
Creatine (creatine monohydrate)	Increases ATP production and speeds recovery after high-intensity exercise.	Increases muscle creatine and creatine phosphate synthesis after exercise. Enhances strength, performance, and recovery from high-intensity exercise.	Stomach pain.
DHEA (dehydroepiandro-sterone)	Builds muscles, burns fat, and delays chronic diseases associated with aging.	No proven benefits.	Acne, oily skin, facial hair, voice deepening, hair loss, mood changes, liver damage, and stimulation of existing cancers.
Ginseng (*Panax ginseng* or Chinese ginseng)	Enhances performance.	Little evidence of ergogenic effects.	May increase the effects and side effects of other stimulants such as caffeine.
Glutamine	Increases muscle glycogen deposition following intense exercise, enhances immune function, and prevents the adverse effects of overtraining.	Little evidence that glutamine increases immune function, prevents the symptoms of overtraining, or increases glycogen synthesis.	No evidence of toxicity.
Glycerol	Improves hydration and endurance.	Evidence of an effect is equivocal.	May cause cellular dehydration, nausea, vomiting, diarrhea.
HMB (β-hydroxy-β-methylbutyrate)	Increases ability to build muscle and burn fat in response to exercise.	Some evidence of an increase in lean body mass and strength.	No toxicity in animals, but little information in humans.
Medium-chain triglycerides (MCT)	Provides energy without promoting fat deposition; reduces muscle protein breakdown during prolonged exercise.	Provides energy and must be metabolized before they can be stored as body fat. They increase endurance and fatty acid oxidation in mice, but there is no evidence of a benefit in humans.	None known.
Ribose	Increases cellular ATP and muscular power.	No research.	None known.
Vanadium (vanadyl sulfate)	Aids insulin action; allows more rapid and intense muscle pumping for body builders.	No evidence to support a benefit for body builders.	Reduces insulin production.

Supplements of vitamin E, vitamin C, and β-carotene are promoted to athletes because of their antioxidant functions. Exercise increases oxidative processes, and therefore increases the production of free radicals, which cause cellular damage and have been associated with fatigue during exercise. It has been suggested that antioxidant supplements reduce the levels of free radicals and hence delay fatigue. Research, however, has not found that supplementation of antioxidant nutrients improves performance.[32] There is also no clear evidence that antioxidant supplements reduce oxidative stress. In fact, free radical production is believed to serve as a signal to the muscle to adapt to the stress by enhancing its natural antioxidant defenses. Exercise training has been shown to increase the activity of the enzyme superoxide dismutase in muscle and a variety of protective enzymes in the blood, thus reducing the risk of oxidative damage to tissues.[21] Although antioxidant supplements do not appear to be ergogenic, as long as athletes do not consume them in amounts that exceed the ULs, there is little risk associated with their use.[24] A better way to ensure adequate antioxidant protection is a diet that includes plenty of whole grains, fruits, and vegetables, which are rich in antioxidant nutrients as well as antioxidant phytochemicals.

Mineral Supplements

Supplements of chromium, vanadium, selenium, zinc, and iron are marketed to strengthen muscles or enhance endurance. As with vitamin supplements, many of the claims made about these minerals are based on their physiological functions. And as with vitamins, there is little evidence that consuming more than the recommended amount provides any benefits.

Chromium supplements, as chromium picolinate, claim to increase lean body mass and decrease body fat. Chromium is needed for insulin action and insulin promotes protein synthesis. Therefore, adequate chromium status is likely to be important for lean tissue synthesis. The picolinate form is typically used because it is believed to be absorbed better than other forms of chromium. Studies in humans have not consistently demonstrated an effect of supplemental chromium picolinate on muscle strength, body composition, body weight, or other aspects of health.[33] Because no adverse effects have been associated with chromium intake from food or supplements, no UL has been established.

Vanadium, usually as vanadyl sulfate, is another mineral marketed for its ability to promote the action of insulin. Vanadium supplements promise to increase lean body mass, but there is no evidence that they have an anabolic effect, and toxicity is a concern.[34] A UL of 1.8 mg per day of elemental vanadium has been set for adults age 19 and older.

Selenium is marketed for its antioxidant properties and zinc for its role in protein synthesis and tissue repair, but neither of these supplements has been found to improve athletic performance in individuals with adequate mineral status. Iron is also marketed as an ergogenic mineral because it is needed for hemoglobin synthesis. If an iron deficiency exists, as it frequently does in female athletes, supplements can be of benefit.

Protein Supplements

Hundreds of protein supplements are available—from powders you mix in your beverage to bars you put in your backpack. They are often marketed to athletes with the promise of enhancing muscle growth or improving performance. Muscles enlarge in response to exercise. Adequate protein is necessary for this to occur, but consuming extra protein either as food or supplements does not increase muscle growth or strength.[34] The protein provided by expensive supplements will not meet an athlete's needs any better than the protein found in a balanced diet. If an athlete's diet provides enough energy, it usually provides enough protein without adding a supplement.

Amino Acid Supplements

Supplements of individual amino acids are also promoted to athletes. Supplements of some single amino acids affect hormone levels and muscle physiology, but their effect on exercise performance is unclear. Glycine supplements are promoted because glycine is a precursor to creatine, but it does not provide the ergogenic effects that creatine supplements do (see the next section).

Supplements of the amino acids ornithine, arginine, and lysine are marketed with the promise that they will stimulate the release of growth hormone, which increases the growth of muscles. Large doses of these amino acids have been shown to stimulate the release of growth hormone. However, growth hormone levels in the blood of athletes taking these amino acids are no greater than levels typically resulting from exercise alone.[35,36] Supplementing growth hormone itself has not been shown to have ergogenic benefits.[37] In addition, growth hormone is on the World Anti-Doping Agency's list of banned substances.

Glutamine supplements promise to increase muscle glycogen deposition following intense exercise, to prevent acid accumulation during intense exercise, to enhance immune function, and to prevent the adverse effects of overtraining such as fatigue and increased incidence of infections. Glutamine supplementation has not been found to increase glycogen synthesis or to improve weight-lifting performance.[38,39]

The branched-chain amino acids (leucine, isoleucine, and valine) are the predominant amino acids used for fuel during exercise and have been suggested to be the third fuel for skeletal muscle after carbohydrate and fat. Supplements of these are promoted to improve performance in endurance athletes by preventing muscle breakdown during and after exercise and accelerating the repair of muscles after exercise. Studies examining branched-chain amino acid supplements have not found them to enhance performance.[40]

There is currently little evidence to support the use of amino acid supplements by athletes, and in general these supplements are not recommended. High doses of individual amino acids may interfere with the absorption of other amino acids from the diet (see Chapter 6). In addition, there have been several reports of illness caused by contaminants in the supplements. Like any dietary supplement, amino acid supplements should be taken with caution and the risks weighed against potential benefits.

Supplements to Enhance Short, Intense Performance

Although amino acid supplements are not ergogenic, creatine and β-hydroxy-β-methylbutyrate (HMB), which are made from amino acids, do provide some benefits for athletes who seek to increase muscle mass and strength and improve performance in activities that depend on quick bursts of intense exercise. Bicarbonate will not increase muscle mass or strength but it may provide some advantages for intense activities (see Critical Thinking: Does it Provide an Ergogenic Boost?).

Creatine Supplements Creatine is a nitrogen-containing compound found primarily in muscle, where it is used to make creatine phosphate, which is a source of energy for short-term exercise. It can be synthesized in the liver, kidneys, and pancreas from the amino acids arginine, glycine, and methionine. It is also consumed in the diet in meat and milk. The more creatine in the diet, the greater the muscle creatine stores. Creatine supplements increase levels of both creatine and creatine phosphate in muscle (**Figure 13.24**). Higher levels of these provide muscles with more quick energy for short-term maximal exercise. Creatine supplementation has been shown to improve performance in high-intensity exercise lasting 30 seconds or less.[41,42] It is therefore beneficial for exercise that requires explosive bursts of energy, such as sprinting and weight lifting, but not for long-term endurance activities such as marathons.

Critical Thinking
Does it Provide an Ergogenic Boost?

(iStockphoto)

Background

Paulo is on the college track team. To improve his performance, he decides to try some ergogenic supplements. Based on the articles and advertisements he's read in sports magazines, he chooses creatine to improve his sprint times and chromium to increase his lean body mass. But before he begins taking these, he wants to explore their risks and benefits.

Data

The ads and articles about these supplements make the following claims:
- Creatine will increase muscle creatine phosphate levels to provide quick energy and speed recovery after exercise.
- Chromium will increase lean body tissue and enhance fat loss.

Critical Thinking Questions

Use the questions in Table 13.4 to help Paulo evaluate these claims.

▼

Based on the information given in this chapter, explain the advantages and risks of these products.

▼

Suggest places Paulo could look to get additional information he can trust.

▼

Would you recommend Paulo take these supplements? Why or why not?

 iProfile Use iProfile to compare the amount of protein in a powdered supplement with the amount in a chicken breast.

Creatine supplements are also taken by athletes to increase muscle mass and strength. Some of the increase in lean body mass that occurs when supplements are taken is believed to be due to water retention related to creatine uptake in the muscle. In addition to this an increase in muscle mass and strength may occur in response to the greater amount and intensity of training that may be achieved when muscle creatine levels are higher.[42,43]

Long-term creatine supplementation appears to be safe at intakes of up to 5 g per day, but the safety of higher doses over the long term has not been established.[44] These supplements can be used legally by athletes wanting to increase muscles mass, but ingestion of creatine before or during exercise is not recommended and the FDA has advised consumers to consult a physician before using creatine.

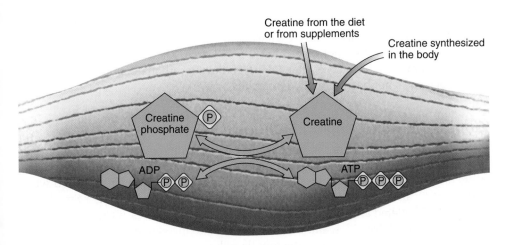

Figure 13.24 Creatine and creatine phosphate
The more creatine consumed, the greater the amount of creatine and creatine phosphate, which is made from it and stored in the muscles. During short bursts of intense activity, creatine phosphate can transfer a phosphate group to ADP, forming creatine and ATP that can be used for muscle contraction.

There are a number of substances used by athletes to enhance strength or endurance that have been banned by sporting organizations. Most have dangerous side effects and athletes who test positive for these drugs face sanctions (**Table 13.6**).

Table 13.6 Banned Ergogenic Aids

Ergoenic Aid	Claim/Effectiveness	Adverse Effects
Amphetamines (beans or greenies)	Decreases reaction time and increases endurance	Anxiety, irregular heartbeat, hallucinations, addiction, death
Anabolic steroids (testosterone or "T")	Increases muscle mass and strength, decreases body fat	Testicular atrophy, liver damage, heart disease, hypertension
Androstenedione (andro)	Increases testosterone production leading to increased muscle mass and strength	Unknown, may increase cardiovascular risk and cause side effects similar to anabolic steroids
Ephedra (ma huang, guarana)	Boosts metabolism, burns fat, increases alertness, increases endurance	Anxiety, irregular heartbeat, hallucinations, addiction
Erythropoietin (EPO)	Increases endurance, increases oxygen-carrying capacity of the blood	Increased blood viscosity, increased risk of heart attack, or pulmonary embolism
Human growth hormone (hGH)	Stimulates body growth to increase muscle mass	Muscle and cardiac abnormalities, carpal tunnel syndrome, abnormal growth

Source: Tokish, J. M., Kocher, M. S., and Hawkins, R. J. Ergogenic aids: A review of basic science, performance, side effects, and status in sports. *Am. J. Sports Med.* 32:1543–1553, 2004.

Beta-Hydroxy-Beta-Methylbutyrate β-hydroxy-β-methylbutyrate, known as HMB, is a metabolite of the branched chain amino acid leucine. Supplements of HMB are hypothesized to increase strength and lean body mass by decreasing muscle breakdown and speeding muscle repair. Early studies found that oral HMB supplements decreased muscle damage and increased muscle strength in response to resistance training.[45] However, more recent studies have not found these supplements to have an ergogenic effect on muscular strength, size, or endurance.[46]

Bicarbonate Bicarbonate may provide some advantage for intense activities. Because bicarbonate acts as a buffer in the body, supplementing it is thought to neutralize acid and thus delay fatigue and allow improved performance. Taking sodium bicarbonate, which is just baking soda from the kitchen cupboard, before exercise has been found to improve performance and delay exhaustion in sports, such as sprint cycling, that entail intense exercise lasting only one to seven minutes, but it is of no benefit for lower-intensity aerobic exercise.[47] Just because baking soda is an ingredient in your cookies does not mean that it is risk free. Many people experience abdominal cramps and diarrhea after taking sodium bicarbonate, and other possible side effects have not been carefully researched.

Supplements to Enhance Endurance

Sprinters and weight lifters can benefit from increases in creatine phosphate levels, but endurance athletes have different fuel concerns. Long-distance runners and cyclists are more concerned about running out of glycogen. Glycogen is spared when fat is used as an energy source, allowing exercise to continue for a longer time before glycogen is depleted and fatigue sets in. A number of substances, including carnitine, medium-chain triglycerides, and caffeine are taken to increase endurance by increasing the amount of fat available to the muscle cell.

Carnitine Carnitine supplements are marketed as fat burners—substances that increase the utilization of fat during exercise. Carnitine is an amino acid-like molecule produced in the body from the amino acids lysine and methionine. It is needed to transport fatty acids into the mitochondria where they are used to produce ATP by aerobic metabolism. Supplements promise to speed up the delivery of fatty acids to muscle mitochondria and therefore enhance the utilization of fat during exercise. Carnitine is made in the body, so it does not need to be supplied in the diet to ensure the efficient use of fatty acids. Studies that examined the effect of carnitine supplements found that they did not affect the utilization of fat as fuel during exercise or improve exercise endurance.[48]

Medium-Chain Triglycerides Most of the fatty acids used by the muscle to generate ATP are delivered in the blood, so theoretically, higher levels in the blood increase the availability of fatty acids as a fuel for exercise. Most of the fat consumed in the diet is absorbed in chylomicrons, which enter the lymphatic system before they appear in the blood. However, medium-chain triglycerides (MCT), those made up of fatty acids with medium-length carbon chains (8 to 10 carbons), do not need to be incorporated into chylomicrons. They are soluble in water so they can be absorbed directly into the blood. In addition to being absorbed much more quickly, the fatty acids cross cell membranes more easily and can enter the mitochondria for oxidation without the help of carnitine. When MCTs are ingested blood fatty acid levels increase. Despite this, research has not found that supplementation with MCT increases endurance, spares glycogen, or enhances performance.[49,50]

Caffeine Caffeine is a stimulant found in coffee, tea, and some soft drinks. It has been shown to enhance performance and endurance during prolonged exhaustive exercise and to a lesser degree it also enhances short-term high-intensity exercise.[51,52] Caffeine also improves concentration, enhances alertness, and reduces fatigue. How caffeine causes all these physiological effects is not completely understood, but it may enhance endurance by increasing the release of fatty acids. When fatty acids are used as a fuel source, glycogen is spared, delaying the onset of fatigue. Your morning coffee is probably not enough to have an effect but drinking 2.5 cups of percolated coffee up to an hour before exercising has been shown to improve endurance. The effectiveness of caffeine varies with each person. Athletes who are unaccustomed to caffeine respond better than those who routinely consume it. Caffeine is a diuretic but it does not cause significant dehydration during exercise. In some athletes caffeine may impair performance by causing gastrointestinal upset. Regardless of its effectiveness, athletes should know that consuming excess caffeine before a competition is illegal. The International Olympic Committee prohibits athletes from competing when urine caffeine levels are 12 μg per mL or greater. For urine caffeine to reach this level, an individual would need to drink 6 to 8 cups of coffee within about a 2-hour period. Caffeine is also found in pill form in products such as NoDoz, which contains about 100 mg of caffeine per tablet—about the same amount as that in a cup of coffee (**Table 13.7**).

Other Supplements

In addition to the nutrient and non-nutrient supplements discussed thus far there are hundreds of other products marketed to athletes. Most have no effect on performance. For example, bee pollen, which is a mixture of the pollen of flowering plants, plant nectar, and bee saliva has been promoted as an ergogenic aid even though it contains no extraordinary factors and has not been shown to have any performance-enhancing effects. In addition, ingesting or inhaling bee pollen can be hazardous to individuals allergic to various plant pollens.[53] Brewer's yeast is a source of B vitamins and some minerals but has not been demonstrated to have any ergogenic properties. Likewise, there is no evidence to support claims that wheat germ oil will aid endurance. As an oil, it is high in fat, but it is no better as an energy source than any other fat. Royal jelly is a substance produced by worker bees to feed to the queen bee. While it helps the queen bee grow to twice the size of worker bees

Table 13.7 The Caffeine Content of Foods and Medications

Food or Medication	Amount	Caffeine (mg)
Coffee, regular	1 cup (240 mL)	139
Coffee, decaffeinated	1 cup	3
Tea, brewed	1 cup	45
Pepsi	12 oz (1 can)	37
Diet Pepsi	12 oz (1 can)	50
Mountain Dew	12 oz (1 can)	54
Hot chocolate	1 cup	7
Brownie	1	14
Chocolate bar	1 oz	15
NoDoz	1 tablet	100
Excedrin	1 tablet	65
Empirin, Anacin	1 tablet	32

and to live 40 times longer, royal jelly does not appear to enhance athletic capacity in humans. Supplements of DNA and RNA are marketed to aid in tissue regeneration. In the body, they carry genetic information and are needed to synthesize proteins, but DNA and RNA are not required in the diet, and supplements do not help replace damaged cells. A variety of herbal products are also marketed to athletes. Most of these have not been studied extensively for their ergogenic effects so the evidence of their benefits is only anecdotal. Ginseng is promoted to increase endurance, but human clinical trials of Chinese ginseng (*Panax ginseng*) have not yet demonstrated conclusively that it enhances physical performance.[54] Ginseng supplements are generally considered safe based on over 2000 years of use with few reported side effects but the same is not true of all herbal products. Many can harm health as well as performance so athletes should consider the risks before using these products (see Focus on Nonvitamin/Nonmineral Supplements).

Figure 13.25 The impact of diet and supplements on exercise performance
Eating a healthy overall diet provides the foundation for optimization of performance. Foods and beverages used to supply energy and ensure hydration during an event can provide additional benefits but ergogenic aids provide little or no performance boost. (©iStockphoto)

A few specific supplements are beneficial in some cases

Sports foods and beverages used to refuel and rehydrate

An overall healthy diet

The Impact of Diet Versus Supplements

Supplements may garner most of the press when it comes to exercise performance, but they are only the very tip of the iceberg when it comes to the things athletes can do to enhance their performance. The foundation of good athletic performance is talent, hard work, and a healthy diet. A healthy diet is one that provides the right number of kcalories to keep weight in the desirable range; the proper balance of carbohydrate, protein, and fat to fuel activity and maintain tissues; plenty of water; and sufficient but not excessive amounts of essential vitamins and minerals. It is rich in whole grains, fruits and vegetables, high in fiber, moderate in fat and sodium, and low in saturated fat, cholesterol, *trans* fat, and added sugars. Whether you are a couch potato or an Olympic hopeful the recommendations of MyPyramid and the Dietary Guidelines can help you choose such a diet. This diet provides the foundation from which to optimize performance. Performance can be further improved by using appropriate foods and fluids to help refuel and rehydrate during workouts and events. Where do supplements fit in? Most of them don't, but a few specific types of athletes in specific events will receive an additional small benefit from a few select supplements (**Figure 13.25**).

Outcome

On that particular day in the Alps, Armstrong had passed up his last opportunity to pick up food and now was low on energy. Because it takes time for dietary carbohydrate to boost blood glucose levels, endurance athletes need to anticipate their needs by eating and drinking before they feel hungry or thirsty. By not eating, Armstrong had cut off the supply of glucose from his diet, so his body was forced to use his stored glycogen faster, depleting his muscle and liver stores. His liver could not supply blood glucose fast enough to meet his needs, so his blood sugar dropped. He developed the symptoms of hypoglycemia, including fatigue, mental confusion, dizziness, and hallucinations. The only way Armstrong was able to continue was to slow his pace.

Armstrong did finish the climb, and that evening he recovered by refueling and rehydrating. The next day he again looked like an elite athlete, and ultimately he rode victorious into Paris as the winner of his second consecutive Tour de France. The lesson he learned on that hard climb in the Alps helped him to win five more Tour de France races. You probably don't spend 6 hours a day exercising, but even your weekend run or ride can become much more difficult if your body can't provide the fuels your muscles and brain need.

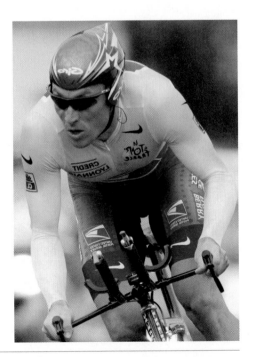

APPLICATIONS

1. How much exercise do you get?
   a. Keep a log of your activity for one day.
   b. Refer to Chapter 7, Table 7.4 to help you determine the number of hours you spend engaged in
      i. Activities of daily living
      ii. Moderate intensity activity
      iii. Vigorous activity
   c. Use Table 7.5 to determine your physical activity level and PA value.
   d. Use Table 7.6 to determine your estimated energy expenditure (EER).
   e. If you increased your exercise enough to move to the "active" physical activity level, what would your new EER be? (If you are already active, what would your EER be in the "very active" level?)
   f. Use iProfile to find foods that you could add to your diet to balance the added expenditure of this increase in activity.

2. What types and amounts of exercise work for you?
   a. Taking into consideration your typical weekly schedule of activities and events, design a reasonable exercise program for yourself. Include the types of activities, the times during the week you will be involved in each activity, and the length of time you will engage in each activity. Choose activities you enjoy and schedule them for practical lengths of time and at reasonable frequencies.
   b. What everyday changes have you made that will increase the energy expended in day-to-day activities?
   c. Which activities are aerobic, which are for strength training? Are any of your activities bone-strengthening?
   d. Can each of these activities be performed year-round? If not, suggest alternative activities and locations for inclement weather.

General Nutrition Issues

1. David is beginning an exercise program. He plans to run before lunch and then play racquetball every night after dinner. Once he begins his exercise program he finds that he feels lethargic and hungry before his late-morning run. After running, he doesn't have much of an appetite, so he saves his fast-food lunch until midafternoon. He is still hungry enough to eat dinner at home with his family, but finds that he is getting stomach cramps and is too full when he goes to play racquetball. His typical diet is listed below:

TYPICAL DIET		
BREAKFAST	LUNCH	DINNER
Orange juice	Big Mac	Steak
Coffee	French fries	Baked potato with sour cream and butter
	Milk shake	Green beans in butter sauce
		Salad with Italian dressing
		Whole milk

   a. How might David change his diet so it is better suited to his exercise program?
   b. Does his exercise program include both an aerobic and a strength-training component?
   c. Do you think David will be able to stick with this exercise program? Why or why not?
   d. Suggest some changes that would make David's exercise program more balanced.

2. Do a risk-benefit analysis of an ergogenic aid (a quick way to do this is to use the Internet to collect information). List the risks and benefits and then write a conclusion stating why you would or would not recommend this substance.

Summary

13.1 Exercise, Fitness, and Health

Video
- Regular exercise improves fitness. How fit an individual is depends on his or her cardiorespiratory endurance, muscle strength, muscle endurance, flexibility, and body composition.

- Regular exercise can reduce the risk of chronic diseases such as obesity, heart disease, diabetes, and osteoporosis. It can reduce overall mortality even in obese individuals.

- Exercise helps manage body weight by increasing energy expenditure and by increasing the proportion of body weight that is lean tissue.

13.2 Exercise Recommendations

- The current recommendation suggest a minimum 150 minutes per week of moderate activity, which includes cardiorespiratory and muscle-strengthening exercise.

- An activity is moderate if it increases heart rate and breathing and requires moderate exertion. Sixty minutes of moderate activity is recommended to prevent weight gain and 60 to 90 minutes is recommended for those working to maintain a weight loss.

- Exercise recommendations for children suggest a minimum of 60 minutes of activity per day, some of which is muscle-strengthening and bone-strengthening. Activities should be age appropriate.

- An exercise program should include activities that are enjoyable, convenient, and safe. Rest is important to allow the body to recover and rebuild. In serious athletes, inadequate rest can lead to overtraining syndrome.

13.3 Fueling Exercise

- During the first 10 to 15 seconds of exercise, ATP and creatine phosphate stored in the muscle provide energy to fuel activity. During the next 2 to 3 minutes, the amount of oxygen at the muscle remains limited, so ATP is generated by the anaerobic metabolism of glucose. After a few minutes, the delivery of oxygen at the muscle increases, and ATP can be generated by aerobic metabolism. Aerobic metabolism is more efficient than anaerobic metabolism and can utilize glucose, fatty acids, and amino acids as energy sources. The use of protein as an energy source increases when exercise continues for many hours.

- For short-term, high-intensity activity, ATP is generated primarily from the anaerobic metabolism of glucose from muscle glycogen stores. Anaerobic metabolism uses glucose rapidly. For lower-intensity exercise of longer duration, aerobic metabolism predominates, and both glucose and fatty acids are important fuel sources.

- Fitness training causes changes in the cardiovascular system and muscles that improve oxygen delivery and utilization and increase glycogen stores, allowing aerobic exercise to be sustained for longer periods at higher intensity.

13.4 Energy and Nutrient Needs for Physical Activity

- The diet of an active individual should provide sufficient energy to fuel activity. The EERs base energy needs on activity level as well as age, gender, and body size.

- To maximize glycogen stores, optimize performance, and maintain and repair lean tissue, a diet providing about 60% of energy from carbohydrate, 20 to 25% of energy from fat, and about 15 to 20% of energy from protein is recommended.

- Sufficient vitamins and minerals are needed to generate ATP from macronutrients, to maintain and repair tissues, and to transport oxygen and wastes to and from the cells. Most athletes who consume a varied diet that meets their energy needs also meet their vitamin and mineral needs. Those who restrict their food intake may be at risk for deficiencies. The pressure to compete and maintain a body weight that is optimal for their sport puts some athletes at risk for eating disorders. A combination of excessive exercise and energy restriction puts female athletes at risk for the female athlete triad. Increased iron needs and greater iron losses due to fitness training put athletes, particularly female athletes, at risk of iron deficiency.

13.5 Fluid Needs for Physical Activity

- Water is needed to ensure that the body can be cooled and that nutrients and oxygen can be delivered to body tissues. Adequate fluid intake before exercise ensures that athletes begin exercise well hydrated. Fluid intake during and after exercise must replace water lost in sweat and from evaporation through the lungs.

- If water intake is inadequate, dehydration can lead to a decline in exercise performance and increase the risk of heat-related illness. This can be life-threatening in severe cases.

- Drinking plain water during extended exercise increases the risk of hyponatremia, a relative deficiency of sodium in the blood.

- Plain water is an appropriate fluid to consume for most exercise. Beverages containing carbohydrate and sodium are recommended for exercise lasting more than an hour.

13.6 Food and Drink to Maximize Performance

- Competitive endurance athletes may benefit from glycogen supercompensation (carbohydrate loading), which maximizes glycogen stores before an event.

- Meals eaten before competition should help ensure adequate hydration, provide moderate amounts of protein, be high enough in carbohydrate to maximize glycogen stores, be low in fat and fiber to speed gastric emptying, and satisfy the psychological needs of the athlete.

- During exercise, athletes need beverages and food to replace lost fluid and provide carbohydrate and sodium.

- Postcompetition meals should replace lost fluids and electrolytes, provide carbohydrate to restore muscle and liver glycogen, and provide protein for muscle protein synthesis and repair.

13.7 Ergogenic Aids: Do Supplements Enhance Athletic Performance?

- Many types of ergogenic aids are marketed to improve athletic performance. An individual risk–benefit analysis should be used to determine whether a supplement is appropriate for you.

- Vitamin and mineral supplements are usually not necessary for athletes who meet their kcalorie needs.

- Protein needs can be met by diet; amino acid supplements are not recommended.

- Creatine supplementation has been shown to improve performance in short-duration high-intensity exercise.

- Caffeine use can improve performance in endurance activities, but high doses are illegal during athletic competitions.

- Anabolic steroids combined with resistance-training exercise increase muscle size and strength, but these supplements are illegal and have dangerous side effects.

- A healthy diet is the base for successful athletic performance. Beverages and foods that supply fluids and energy can enhance performance, and there are a few supplements that benefit specific activities.

Review Questions

1. What characterizes a fit individual?

2. What is aerobic exercise?

3. How does aerobic exercise affect resting heart rate?

4. What is strength training?

5. What causes muscle hypertrophy? Muscle atrophy?

6. List five of the health benefits of exercise.

7. How much of what types of exercise is recommended?

8. What is aerobic capacity? How is it affected by training?

9. From where does the ATP to fuel the first few minutes of exercise come?

10. What fuels are used to produce ATP in anaerobic metabolism?

11. Which is more efficient, aerobic or anaerobic metabolism?

12. What factors affect the availability of oxygen and the type of fuel used during exercise?

13. What fuels are used in exercise of long duration such as marathon running?

14. What are the recommendations for fluid intake before, during, and after exercise?

15. How does exercise affect protein needs?

16. What is glycogen supercompensation or carbohydrate loading?

17. Explain why creatine supplements are ergogenic. Are they safe?

References

1. Gallagher, D., Heymsfield, S., Heo, M. et al. Healthy percentage body fat ranges: An approach for developing guidelines based on body mass index. *Am. J. Clin. Nutr.* 72:694–701, 2000.

2. United States Department of Health and human Services. 2008 Physical Activity Guidelines for Americans. Available online at www.health.gov/paguidelines/. Accessed June 16, 2009.

3. Institute of Medicine, Food and Nutrition Board. *Dietary Reference Intakes for Energy, Carbohydrates, Fiber, Fat, Protein and Amino Acids.* Washington, DC: National Academies Press, 2002.

4. The President's Council on Physical Fitness and Sports. *Physical Activity Protects against the Health Risks of Obesity.* Available online at www.fitness.gov/digest_dec2000.htm. Accessed June 12, 2009.

5. Centers for Disease Control and Prevention. *Physical Activity and Health: A Report of the Surgeon General.* Available online at www.cdc.gov/nccdphp/sgr/adults.htm/. Accessed February 3, 2009.

6. Zanuso, S., Jimenez, A., Pugliese, G. et al. Exercise for the management of type 2 diabetes: A review of the evidence. *Acta. Diabetol.* June 3, 2009 [Epub].

7. Newton, R. U., and Galvão, D. A. Exercise in prevention and management of cancer. *Curr. Treat. Options Oncol.* 9:135–146, 2008.

8. Reigle, B. S., and Wonders, K. Breast cancer and the role of exercise in women. *Methods Mol. Biol.* 472:169–189, 2009.

9. Fontaine, K. R. *Physical Activity Improves Mental Health.* Available online at www.physsportsmed.com/index.php?art=psm_10_2000?article=1256. Accessed April 7, 2009.

10. Antunes, H. K., Stella, S. G., Santos, R. F. et al. Depression, anxiety and quality of life scores in seniors after an endurance exercise program. *Rev. Bras. Psiquiatr.* 27:266–271, 2005.

11. U.S. Department of Health and Human Services, U.S. Department of Agriculture. Dietary Guidelines for Americans, 6th edition, Washington, DC, 2005.

12. Healthy People 2010. Available online at www.healthypeople.gov/ Accessed September 17, 2009.

13. Swinburn, B., and Shelly, A. Effect of TV time and other sedentary pursuits. *Int. J. Obes. (Lond)* 32:S5132–S5136, 2008.

14. Haskell, W. L., Lee, I-M, Pate, R. R. et al. Physical Activity and Public Health Updated Recommendation for Adults: Updated Recommendation from the American College of Sports Medicine and the American Heart Association. *Circulation* 116:1081–1093, 2007.

15. Cairns, S. P. Lactic acid and exercise performance: Culprit or friend? *Sports Med.* 36:279–291, 2006.

16. Manore, M., and Thompson, J. *Sport Nutrition for Health and Performance.* Champaign, IL: Human Kinetics, 2000.

17. Rodriguez, N. R., DiMarco, N. M., and Langley, S. Position of the American Dietetic Association, Dietitians of Canada, and the American College of Sports Medicine: Nutrition and athletic performance. *J. Am. Diet Assoc.* 109:509–527, 2009.

18. Sundgot-Borgen, J., and Torstveit, M. K. Prevalence of eating disorders in elite athletes is higher than in the general population. *Clin. J. Sport Med.* 14: 25–32, 2004.

19. Remick, D., Chancellor, K., Pederson, J. et al. Hyperthermia and dehydration-related deaths associated with intentional rapid weight loss in three collegiate wrestlers—North Carolina, Wisconsin, and Michigan, November–December, 1997. *MMWR Morb Mortal Wkly Rep* 47:105–108, 1998. Available online at www.cdc.gov/mmwr/preview/mmwrhtml/00051388.htm. Accessed March 25, 2009.

20. Tipton, K. D., and Wolfe, R. R. Protein and amino acids for athletes. *J. Sports. Sci.* 22:65–79, 2004.

21. Jackson, M. J., Khassaf, M., Vasilaki, F. et al. Vitamin E and the oxidative stress of exercise. *Ann. N.Y. Acad. Sci.* 1031:158–168, 2004.

22. Finaud, J., Lac, G., and Filaire, E. Oxidative stress: Relationship with exercise and training. *Sports Med.* 36(4):327–358, 2006.

23. Margaritis, I., and Rousseau, A.S. Does physical exercise modify antioxidant requirements? *Nutrition Research Reviews* 21:3–12, 2008.

24. Food and Nutrition Board, Institute of Medicine. *Dietary Reference Intakes: Vitamin A, Vitamin K, Arsenic, Boron, Chromium, Copper, Iodine, Iron, Manganese, Molybdenum, Nickel, Silicon, Vanadium, and Zinc.* Washington, DC: National Academies Press, 2001.

25. Suedekum, N. A., and Dimeff, R. J. Iron and the athlete. *Curr. Sports Med. Rep.* 4:199–202, 2005.

26. Di Santolo, M., Stel, G., Banfi, G. et al. Anemia and iron status in young fertile non-professional female athletes. *Eur. J. Appl. Physiol.* 102(6):703–709, 2008.

27. Kazis, K., Iglesias, E. The female athlete triad. *Adolescent Medicine* 14:87–95, 2003.

28. NOAA's National Weather Service: *Heat Index.* Available online at www.weather.gov/os/heat/index.shtml. Accessed March 10, 2009.

29. Almond, C. S. D., Shin, A.Y., Fortescue, E. B. et al. Hyponatremia among runners in the Boston marathon. *N. Engl. J. Med.* 352:1550–1556, 2005.

30. Bussar, V. A., Fairchild, T. J., Rao, A. et al. Carbohydrate loading in human muscle: An improved 1 day protocol. *Eur. J. Appl. Physiol.* 87:290–295, 2002.

31. Burke, L.M. Nutrition strategies for the marathon. Fuel for training and racing. *Sports Med.* 37:344–347, 2007.

32. Urso, M. L. and Clarkson, P. M. Oxidative stress, exercise, and antioxidant supplementation. *Toxicology* 189:41–54, 2003.

33. Di Luigi, L. Supplements and the endocrine system in athletes. *Clin. Sports Med.* 27:131–151, 2008.

34. Nissen S. L., and Sharp R. L. Effect of dietary supplements on lean mass and strength gains with resistance exercise: A meta-analysis. *J. Appl. Physiol.* 94:651–659, 2003.

35. Kanaley, J. A., Growth hormone, arginine and exercise. *Curr. Opin. Clin. Nutr. Metab. Care* 11:50–54, 2008.

36. Chromiak, J. A., and Antonio, J. Use of amino acids as growth hormone-releasing agents by athletes. *Nutrition* 18(7–8):657–661, 2002.

37. Liu, H., Bravata, D. M., Olkin, I. et al. Systematic review: the effects of growth hormone on athletic performance. *Ann. Intern. Med.* 148:747–758, 2008.

38. van Hall, G., Saris, W. H., van de Schoor, P. A., and Wagenmakers, A. J. The effect of free glutamine and peptide ingestion on the rate of muscle glycogen resynthesis in man. *Int. J. Sports Med.* 21:25–30, 2000.

39. Antonio, J., Sanders, M. S., Kalman, D. et al. The effects of high-dose glutamine ingestion on weightlifting performance. *J. Strength Cond. Res.* 16:157–160, 2002.

40. Gleeson M. Interrelationship between physical activity and branched-chain amino acids. *J. Nutr.* 135:1591S–1595S, 2005.

41. Bemben, M. G., and Lamont, H.S. Creatine supplementation and exercise performance: Recent findings. *Sports Med.* 35:107–125, 2005.

42. Paddon-Jones, D., Borsheim, E., and Wolfe, R. R. Potential ergogenic effects of arginine and creatine supplementation. *J. Nutr.* 134(10 Suppl):2888S–2894S, 2004.

43. Volek, J. S., and Rawson, E. S. Scientific basis and practical aspects of creatine supplementation for athletes. *Nutrition* 20:609–614, 2004.

44. Shao, A., and Hathcock, J. N. Risk assessment for creatine monohydrate. *Regul. Toxicol. Pharmacol.* 45:242–251, 2006.

45. Nissen, S., Sharp, R., Ray, M. et al. Effect of leucine metabolite beta-hydroxy-beta-methylbutyrate on muscle metabolism during resistance-exercise training. *J. Appl. Physiol.* 81:2095–2104, 1996.

46. O'Connor, D. M., and Crowe, M. J. Effects of six weeks of beta-hydroxy-beta-methylbutyrate (HMB) and HMB/creatine supplementation on strength, power, and anthropometry of highly trained athletes. *J. Strength Cond. Res.* 21:419–423, 2007.

47. Raymer, G. H., Marsh, G. D., Kowalchuk, J. M., and Thompson, R. T. Metabolic effects of induced alkalosis during progressive forearm exercise to fatigue. *J. Appl. Physiol.* 96:2050–2056, 2004.

48. Brass, E. P. Carnitine and sports medicine: Use or abuse? *Ann. NY Acad. Sci.* 1033:67–78, 2004.

49. Jeukendrup, A. E., and Aldred, S. Fat supplementation, health, and endurance performance. *Nutrition* 20:678–688, 2004.

50. Horowitz, J. F., Mora-Rodriguez, R., Byerley, L. O., and Coyle, E. F. Preexercise medium-chain triglyceride ingestion does not alter muscle glycogen use during exercise. *J. Appl. Physiol.* 88:219–225, 2000.

51. Paluska, S. A. Caffeine and exercise. *Curr. Sports Med. Rep.* 2:213–219, 2003.

52. Sökmen, B., Armstrong, L. E., Kraemer, W. J. et al. Caffeine use in sports: Considerations for the athlete. *J. Strength Cond. Res.* 22:978–986, 2008.

53. Bauer, L., Kohlich, A., Hirschwehr, R. et al. Food allergy: Pollen or bee products? *J. Allergy Clin. Immunol.* 97:65–73, 1996.

54. Bahrke, M. S., Morgan, W. P., and Stenger, A. Is ginseng an ergogenic aid? *Int. J. Sport Nutr. Exerc. Metab.* 19:298–322, 2009.

14

Nutrition During Pregnancy and Lactation

Case Study

Jasmine is 26 years old and expecting her first baby. At her initial prenatal visit the obstetrician tells her that she and the baby seem healthy except that her iron stores are low. The doctor prescribes a prenatal supplement and gives her a pamphlet on nutrition during pregnancy. Jasmine is concerned because the pamphlet recommends that she gain 25 to 35 lb over the course of her pregnancy and suggests a dietary intake that includes much more than she usually eats. Jasmine has always worried about her weight. She typically skips breakfast, has only yogurt and a diet soda for lunch, and then eats a big dinner with her husband in the evening. Jasmine's sister, who has three young children, is now 25 lb heavier than she was before the birth of her first child 8 years ago, and Jasmine doesn't want to end up like that. She also remembers her grandmother telling her that gaining too much weight during pregnancy makes the delivery more difficult. So Jasmine decides to continue to follow her usual eating pattern. After all, she reasons, the prenatal supplement will give her all the nutrients her baby needs.

By the fourth month of her pregnancy, Jasmine has gained only 1 lb and is feeling tired and run down. She tells the doctor that she stopped taking the supplement because it was making her nauseous and constipated, and that she has been limiting what she eats because she is afraid of gaining too much weight. The doctor explains to Jasmine that during pregnancy, her body undergoes physiological changes that support the baby's growth. New tissues in her body plus the growth of the baby cause weight gain, and she will lose the weight after the baby is born. The obstetrician warns Jasmine that her diet must supply all of the nutrients necessary for the changes in her physiology, as well as for the growth and development of the infant. A deficiency of nutrients or energy may cause birth defects or increase the risk of having a baby that is born too soon or too small.

(Art Vandalay/Getty Images, Inc.)

(©iStockphoto)

(Bride/Getty Images, Inc.)

Chapter Outline

14.1 The Physiology of Pregnancy

Learning Objectives

- Explain why the mother's nutrient intake during pregnancy is so important.
- Discuss the risks associated with gaining too little or too much weight during pregnancy.
- List some types of exercise that are appropriate for pregnant women.
- Describe some of the nutrition-related discomforts and complications of pregnancy.

conception The union of sperm and egg (ovum) that results in pregnancy.

lactation Milk production and secretion.

fertilization The union of sperm and egg (ovum).

oviducts or **fallopian tubes** Narrow ducts leading from the ovaries to the uterus.

zygote The cell produced by the union of sperm and ovum during fertilization.

implantation The process by which the developing embryo embeds in the uterine lining.

Pregnancy, from **conception** to birth, usually lasts 40 weeks in humans. During pregnancy, a single cell grows and develops into an infant that is ready for life outside the womb. This development requires a safe environment to which oxygen and nutrients are provided in the right amounts and from which waste products are removed. Many physiological changes take place in the mother to support prenatal development and prepare her for **lactation**.

Prenatal Growth and Development

Reproduction requires the **fertilization** of an egg, or ovum, from the mother by a sperm from the father. Fertilization, which occurs in the **oviduct** or **fallopian tube**, produces a single-celled **zygote**. The zygote travels down the mother's fallopian tube into the uterus. Along the way it divides many times to form a ball of smaller cells. In the uterus the developing embryo imbeds in the uterine lining in a process known as **implantation (Figure 14.1)**.

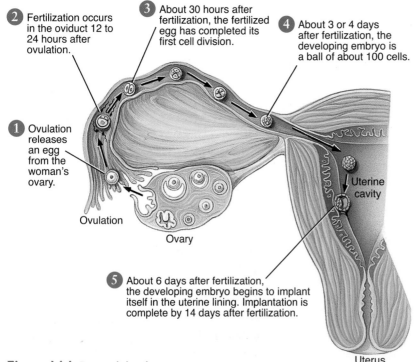

2 Fertilization occurs in the oviduct 12 to 24 hours after ovulation.

3 About 30 hours after fertilization, the fertilized egg has completed its first cell division.

4 About 3 or 4 days after fertilization, the developing embryo is a ball of about 100 cells.

1 Ovulation releases an egg from the woman's ovary.

Ovulation

Ovary

Uterine cavity

5 About 6 days after fertilization, the developing embryo begins to implant itself in the uterine lining. Implantation is complete by 14 days after fertilization.

Uterus

6 During the embryonic stage of development (2 to 8 weeks), cells differentiate and arrange themselves in the proper locations to form the major organ systems. The embryo shown here is about 5 to 6 weeks old and less than 3 cm long.

7 During the fetal stage of development (9 weeks until birth), the fetus grows, and internal and external body structures continue to develop. This fetus is about 16 weeks old and about 16 cm long.

Figure 14.1 Prenatal development
This cross section shows the path of the egg and developing embryo from the ovary, where the egg is produced, through the oviduct to the uterus, where most prenatal development occurs. (center/right photo: Biphoto Associates/Photo Researchers, Inc.; bottom right photo: Meitchik/Custom Medical Stock Photo, Inc.)

Prenatal growth and development continue after implantation. The cells differentiate into the multitude of specialized cell types that make up the human body, and arrange themselves in the proper shapes and locations to form organs and other structures. About 2 weeks after fertilization, implantation is complete and the developing offspring is known as an **embryo** (Figure 14.1). The embryonic stage of development lasts until the eighth week after fertilization, when rudimentary organ systems have been formed. The embryo at this point is approximately 3 cm long (a little more than an inch) and has a beating heart. All major external and internal structures have been formed. Beginning at the ninth week of development and continuing until birth, the developing offspring is known as a **fetus** (Figure 14.1). During the fetal period of development, structures that appeared during the embryonic period continue to grow and mature. Anything that interferes with development can cause birth defects. If the birth defects are severe, they may result in a **spontaneous abortion** or **miscarriage**.

The early embryo gets its nourishment by breaking down the lining of the uterus, but soon this source is inadequate to meet its growing needs. After about 5 weeks, the **placenta** takes over the role of nourishing the embryo (**Figure 14.2**). The placenta is a network of blood vessels and tissues that allows nutrients and oxygen to be transferred from mother to fetus and waste products to be transferred from the fetus to the mother's blood for elimination. The placenta is made up of tissue from both the mother and the fetus. The maternal portion of the placenta develops from the uterine lining. The fetal portion of the placenta develops from the outer layer of pre-embryonic cells. These cells divide to form branch-like projections that grow into the lining of the uterus where they are surrounded by pools of maternal blood. The projections contain blood vessels that supply the developing fetus. Although maternal and fetal blood do not mix, the close proximity of fetal blood vessels to maternal blood allows nutrients and oxygen to easily pass from mother to baby, and allows carbon dioxide and other wastes to pass from baby to mother for elimination (Figure 14.2). The placenta also secretes hormones that are necessary to maintain pregnancy.

embryo The developing human from 2 to 8 weeks after fertilization. All organ systems are formed during this time.

fetus The developing human from the ninth week to birth. Growth and refinement of structures occur during this time.

spontaneous abortion or **miscarriage** Interruption of pregnancy prior to the seventh month.

placenta An organ produced from both maternal and embryonic tissues. It secretes hormones, transfers nutrients and oxygen from the mother's blood to the fetus, and removes wastes.

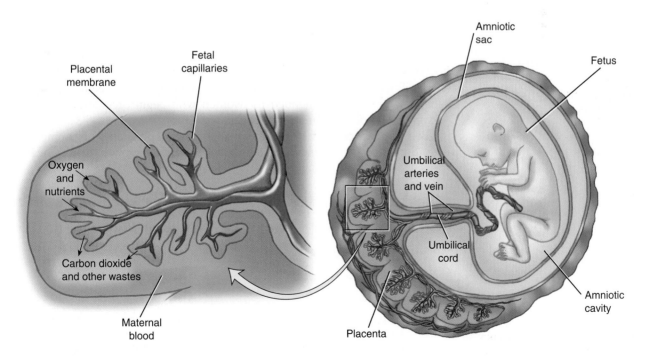

Figure 14.2 Placenta and amniotic sac
The placenta allows the transfer of nutrients and wastes between mother and baby. The amniotic sac and the fluid it contains protect the fetus.

gestation The time between conception and birth, which lasts about 9 months (or about 40 weeks) in humans.

small-for-gestational-age An infant born at term weighing less than 2.5 kg (5.5 lbs).

preterm or **premature** An infant born before 37 weeks of gestation.

low birth weight A birth weight less than 2.5 kg (5.5 lbs).

very low birth weight A birth weight less than 1.5 kg (3.3 lbs).

Figure 14.3 Even though incubators and other technological aids can help premature babies survive, they face greater risk for illness and death than full-term babies. (Brad Nelson/Phototake)

trimester A term used to describe each third, or 3-month period, of a pregnancy.

The pregnancy usually ends after 40 weeks of **gestation** with the birth of an infant weighing about 3 to 4 kg (6.6 to 8.8 lbs).[1] Infants who are born on time but have failed to grow normally in the uterus are said to be **small-for-gestational-age**. Those born before 37 weeks of gestation are said to be **preterm** or **premature**. Whether born too soon or just too small, **low birth weight** infants (those weighing less than 2.5 kg [5.5 lbs] at birth) and **very low birth weight** infants (those weighing less than 1.5 kg [3.3 lbs]), are at increased risk for illness and early death.[2] They often require special care and a special diet in order to successfully continue to grow and develop. Survival improves with increasing gestational age and birth weight. Today, with advances in medical and nutritional care, infants born as early as 25 weeks of gestation and those weighing as little as 1 kg (2.2 lbs) can survive (**Figure 14.3**).

Changes in the Mother

A woman's body undergoes many changes during pregnancy to support the growth and development of the embryo and fetus. These continuous physiological adjustments affect the metabolism and distribution of nutrients in her body. Maternal blood volume increases by 50%, and the heart, lungs, and kidneys work harder to deliver nutrients and oxygen and remove wastes. The placenta develops and the hormones produced by it orchestrate other changes: They promote uterine growth; they relax muscles and ligaments to accommodate the growing fetus and allow for childbirth; they promote breast development; and they increase fat deposition to provide the energy stores that will be needed during late pregnancy and lactation. These changes result in weight gain and can affect the type and level of physical activity that is safe for the pregnant woman.

Weight Gain During Pregnancy Gaining the right amount of weight during pregnancy is essential to the health of both mother and fetus. The recommended weight gain for healthy, normal-weight women is 25 to 35 lbs (11.4 to 15.9 kg). Typically the weight of the infant at birth is about 25% of the total pregnancy weight gain. The placenta, amniotic fluid, and changes in maternal tissues account for the rest. This includes increases in the size of the uterus and breasts, expansion of blood and extracellular fluid volume, and deposition of fat stores (**Figure 14.4**). The rate of weight gain is as important as the total weight gain. Little gain is expected in the first 3 months, or **trimester**, of pregnancy—usually about 2 to 4 lbs (0.9 to 1.8 kg). In the second and third trimesters, when the fetus grows from less than 1 lb to 6 to 8 lbs, the recommended maternal weight gain is about 1 lb (0.45 kg) per week. Women who are underweight, and women who are overweight or obese at conception should still gain weight at a slow, steady rate (**Figure 14.5**). Weight gains of up to 40 lbs (18 kg) are recommended for women who begin pregnancy underweight. Overweight and obese women should gain less (**Table 14.1**).[1]

Being underweight by 10% or more at the onset of pregnancy or gaining too little weight during pregnancy increases the risk of producing a low-birth-weight baby or

Table 14.1 Recommendations for Weight Gain During Pregnancy

Prepregnancy Weight Status[a]	Recommended Total Gain
Underweight (BMI <18.5 kg/m^2)	28–40 lbs (12.7–18.2 kg)
Normal weight (BMI 18.5–24.9 kg/m^2)	25–35 lbs (11.4–15.9 kg)
Overweight (BMI 25.0–29.9 kg/m^2)	15–25 lbs (6.8–11.4 kg)
Obese (BMI ≥ 30.0 kg/m^2)	11–20 lbs (5.0–9.1 kg)

Source: From Committee to Reexamine IOM Pregnancy Weight Guidelines, Institute of Medicine, National Research Council. *Weight Gain During Pregnancy: Reexamining the Guidelines.* Washington, DC: National Academies Press, 2009.

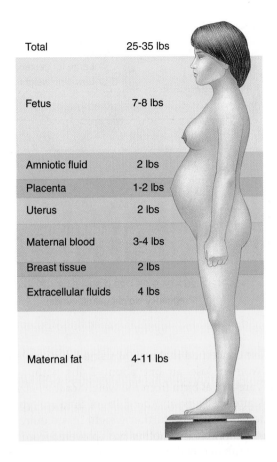

Total	25-35 lbs
Fetus	7-8 lbs
Amniotic fluid	2 lbs
Placenta	1-2 lbs
Uterus	2 lbs
Maternal blood	3-4 lbs
Breast tissue	2 lbs
Extracellular fluids	4 lbs
Maternal fat	4-11 lbs

Figure 14.4 Sources of weight gain in pregnancy
Weight gained during pregnancy is due to increases in the weight of the mother's tissues, as well as the weight of the fetus, placenta, and amniotic fluid.

preterm baby (**Figure 14.6**). It can also increase the child's risk of developing heart disease or diabetes later in life.[2] Excess weight, whether present before conception or gained during pregnancy, can also compromise the outcome of the pregnancy. The mother's risks for high blood pressure, diabetes, difficult delivery, and **cesarean section** are increased by excess weight, as is the risk of having a **large-for-gestational-age** baby (Figure 14.6). Maternal obesity may also increase the risk of neural tube defects and fetal death.[3] Despite this, dieting during pregnancy is not advised even for obese women. If possible, excess weight should be lost before the pregnancy begins or, alternatively, after the child is born and weaned.

cesarean section The surgical removal of the fetus from the uterus.

large-for-gestational-age An infant weighing more than 4 kg (8.8 lbs) at birth.

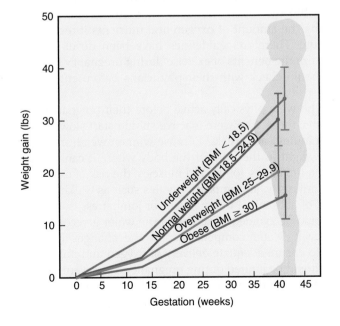

Figure 14.5 Recommended weight gain during pregnancy
The same pattern of weight gain is recommended for women who are normal weight, underweight, overweight, or obese at the start of pregnancy, but total weight gain recommendations differ. (Source: Adapted from Committee to Reexamine IOM Pregnancy Weight Guidelines, Institute of Medicine, National Research Council. *Weight Gain During Pregnancy: Reexamining the Guidelines.* Washington, DC: National Academies Press, 2009.)

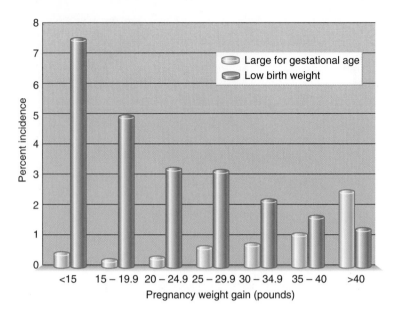

Figure 14.6 Relationship between maternal weight gain and birth weight Gaining more or less than the recommended amount of weight during pregnancy increases the incidence of large-for-gestational-age and low-birth-weight babies, respectively.

Figure 14.7 During pregnancy, exercising in the water can reduce stress on joints and help keep the body cool. (Tracy Frankel/The Image Bank/Getty Images, Inc.)

Some women are concerned that weight gained during pregnancy will be permanent, but most women lose all but about 2 lbs within a year of delivery. Approximately 10 lbs are lost at birth from the weight of the baby, amniotic fluid, and placenta. In the week after delivery, another 5 lbs of fluid are typically lost. Once this initial fluid and tissue weight is lost, further weight loss requires that energy intake be less than energy output. After the mother has recovered from delivery, a balanced, reduced-kcalorie diet combined with moderate exercise will promote weight loss and the return of muscle tone.

Physical Activity During Pregnancy For healthy, well-nourished women, carefully chosen moderate exercise is recommended during and after pregnancy.[4] Physical activity during pregnancy improves overall fitness, reduces stress, prevents excess weight gain, prevents low back pain, improves digestion, reduces constipation, improves mood and body image, and speeds recovery from childbirth. Some evidence suggests that physical activity may reduce the risk of pregnancy complications and the length of labor.[4] In healthy women moderate-intensity activity during pregnancy does not increase risk of low birth weight, preterm delivery, or early pregnancy loss, but too much strenuous exercise has the potential to harm the fetus by reducing the amount of oxygen and nutrients it receives or by increasing body temperature. Therefore, guidelines have been developed to minimize the risks and maximize the benefits of exercise during pregnancy (**Table 14.2**). All pregnant women should check with their physicians before engaging in any exercise program.

Women who were physically active before their pregnancy can continue their exercise programs; those who were inactive should start slowly with a goal of exercising for 150 minutes each week.[4] Because women weigh more during pregnancy and carry that weight in the front of the body where it can interfere with balance and put stress on the bones, joints, and muscles, the risk of exercise-related injury is increased. Low-intensity, low-impact activities such as walking are ideal.[4] Activities that have a risk of abdominal trauma, falls, or joint stress, such as contact and racquet sports, should be avoided.[5] Exercise in the water is recommended because the body's buoyancy in water compensates for the changes in weight distribution (**Figure 14.7**). To ensure adequate delivery of oxygen and nutrients to the fetus, intense exercise should be limited during pregnancy. To prevent overheating, plenty of fluids should be consumed, and exercise should be carried out in a well-ventilated environment.

Table 14.2 Guidelines for Physical Activity during Pregnancy

- Obtain medical permission before beginning an exercise program.
- Healthy woman should get 150 minutes of exercise each week
- Activity should be spread throughout the week
- Women who are inactive before pregnancy should increase activity very gradually.
- Regular exercise is preferable to intermittent activity.
- Stop exercising when fatigued and do not exercise to exhaustion.
- Choose activities that have minimal risk of falls or abdominal injury. Avoid scuba diving.
- Avoid strenuous exertion during the first trimester.
- After the first trimester avoid exercise that is performed lying on one's back.
- Avoid exercising in hot or humid environments.
- Drink plenty of liquids before, during, and after exercise.

Source: Modified from DHHS Physical Activity Guidelines for Americans, 2008 available online at http://www.health.gov/paguidelines/pdf/paguide.pdf Accessed May 13, 2009; and Position of the American Dietetic Association: Nutrition and lifestyle for a healthy pregnancy outcome. *J. Am. Diet. Assoc.* 108:553–561, 2008.

Discomforts of Pregnancy

The physiological changes that occur during pregnancy can cause uncomfortable side effects for the mother. Some are caused by changes in fluid distribution, others by hormonal changes that affect the digestive tract. Most of these problems are minor, but in some cases they may endanger the mother and the fetus.

Edema During pregnancy, blood volume expands to nourish the fetus, but this expansion may also cause the accumulation of extracellular fluid in the tissues, known as **edema**. Edema is common in the feet and ankles during pregnancy because the growing uterus puts pressure on the veins that return blood from the legs to the heart. This causes blood to pool in the legs, forcing fluid from the veins into the tissues of the feet and ankles (**Figure 14.8**). Edema can be uncomfortable but does not increase medical risks unless it is accompanied by a rise in blood pressure. Reducing fluid and sodium intake below the amount recommended for the general population is not recommended.

Morning Sickness Morning sickness is a syndrome of nausea and vomiting that occurs in about 80% of women during pregnancy.[6] The incidence peaks at about 8 to 12 weeks of pregnancy and symptoms usually resolve by week 20. The term "morning sickness" is somewhat of a misnomer because symptoms can occur anytime during the day or night. Although the cause is unknown this nausea and vomiting is hypothesized to be related to the hormonal changes of pregnancy. The symptoms may be alleviated to some extent by eating small frequent snacks of dry starchy foods, such as plain crackers or bread. In most women symptoms are mild and do not affect maternal or fetal health. Fewer than 1% of pregnant women have a severe and intractable form of nausea and vomiting called *hyperemesis gravidarum* that may result in weight loss; nutritional deficiencies; and abnormalities in fluids, electrolyte levels, and acid-base balance. Treatment may require intravenous nutrition to assure that needs are met and medications to reduce nausea.

edema Swelling due to the buildup of extracellular fluid in the tissues.

morning sickness Nausea and vomiting that affects many women during the first few months of pregnancy and in some women can continue throughout the pregnancy.

Figure 14.8 Edema in the feet and ankles is common during pregnancy. The swelling may be reduced by elevating the feet. (P. Marazzi/Science Photo Library/Photo Researchers)

Heartburn Heartburn, a burning sensation caused by stomach acid leaking up into the esophagus, is another common digestive complaint during pregnancy because the hormones produced to relax the muscles of the uterus also relax the muscles of the gastrointestinal tract. This involuntary relaxation of the gastroesophageal sphincter allows the acidic stomach contents to back up into the esophagus, causing irritation. The problem gets more severe as pregnancy progresses because the growing baby crowds the stomach (**Figure 14.9**). The fuller the stomach, the more likely that its contents will back up into the esophagus. Heartburn can be reduced by avoiding substances that are known to cause heartburn, such as caffeine and chocolate, and by consuming many small meals throughout the day rather than a few large meals. Limiting intake of high-fat foods that leave the stomach slowly, such as fried foods, rich sauces, and desserts, can also help reduce heartburn. Because a reclining position makes it easier for acidic juices to flow into the esophagus, remaining upright after eating, limiting eating in the hours before bedtime, and sleeping with extra pillows to produce a semi-reclining sleep position can also reduce heartburn.

Constipation and Hemorrhoids Constipation is a frequent complaint during pregnancy. The pregnancy-related hormones that cause muscles to relax also decrease intestinal motility and slow transit time. Constipation becomes more of a problem late in pregnancy when the enlarging uterus puts pressure on the gastrointestinal tract (see Figure 14.9). Iron supplements prescribed during pregnancy also contribute to constipation. Maintaining a moderate level of physical activity and consuming plenty of water and other fluids along with high-fiber foods such

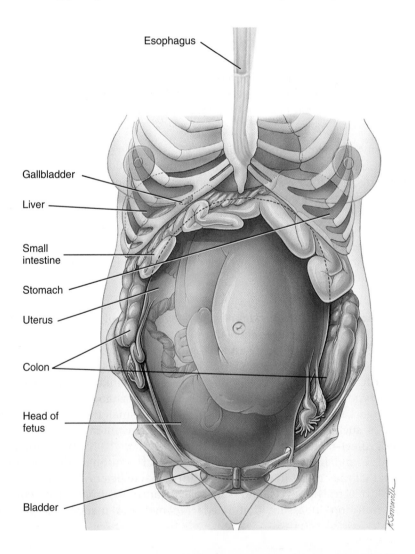

Figure 14.9 Crowding of the gastrointestinal tract
During pregnancy the uterus enlarges and pushes higher into the abdominal cavity, exerting pressure on the stomach and intestines.

as whole grains, vegetables, and fruits, are recommended to prevent constipation. Hemorrhoids are also more common during pregnancy, as a result of both constipation and physiological changes in blood flow.

Complications of Pregnancy

While most pregnancies are problem-free some women do experience complications that increase risks to both mother and baby.[7,8] Some, such as anemia, can be prevented by proper nutrition and good prenatal care. For others, such as hypertension and diabetes, the cause is not as well understood, making prevention difficult. However, if caught early, these complications can usually be managed, allowing for a healthy delivery (**Figure 14.10**).

High Blood Pressure About 5 to 10% of pregnant women experience high blood pressure during pregnancy. **Hypertensive disorders of pregnancy**, previously known as pregnancy-induced hypertension, refers to a spectrum of conditions involving elevated blood pressure during pregnancy. It accounts for nearly 16% of pregnancy-related maternal deaths in the United States.[9] It is especially common in mothers under 20 and over 35 years of age, low-income mothers, and mothers with chronic hypertension or kidney disease.

About one-third of the hypertensive disorders of pregnancy are due to chronic hypertension that was present before the pregnancy, but the remainder are related to the pregnancy. The least problematic of these is **gestational hypertension**, an abnormal rise in blood pressure that occurs after the 20th week of pregnancy. Gestational hypertension may signal the potential for a more serious condition called **preeclampsia**. Preeclampsia is characterized by high blood pressure along with fluid retention and excretion of protein in the urine; it can result in weight gain of several pounds within a few days. It is dangerous to the baby because it reduces blood flow to the placenta, and it is dangerous to the mother because it can progress to a condition called **eclampsia**, in which life-threatening seizures occur. Women with preeclampsia require bed rest and careful medical monitoring. The condition usually resolves after delivery.

The causes of preeclampsia are not fully understood. At one time, low-sodium diets were prescribed to prevent it, but studies have not found them to be effective.[10] Calcium may play a role in preventing the hypertensive disorders of pregnancy; calcium supplements have been found to reduce the risk of high blood pressure and preeclampsia.[11] Although calcium supplements are not routinely recommended for healthy pregnant women, pregnant teens, individuals with inadequate calcium intake, and women who are known to be at risk of developing hypertension during pregnancy may benefit from additional dietary calcium.

Gestational Diabetes Mellitus Consistently elevated blood glucose level during pregnancy in a woman without previously diagnosed diabetes is known as **gestational diabetes mellitus**. It occurs in about 7% of all pregnancies and is most common in obese women and those with a family history of type 2 diabetes.[2,12] It occurs more frequently among African American, Hispanic/Latino American, and Native American women than among Caucasian women.[13] In addition to its impact on the mother's health, gestational diabetes increases risks for the baby. Because glucose in the mother's blood passes freely across the placenta, when the mother's blood levels are high, the growing fetus receives extra glucose kcalories. This extra energy promotes rapid growth, resulting in babies who are large for gestational age and consequently at increased risk of complications during delivery. As with other types of diabetes, the treatment of gestational diabetes involves consuming a carefully planned diet, maintaining moderate daily exercise, and in some cases using medications to control blood glucose. This form of diabetes usually disappears when the pregnancy is completed, although the mother remains at higher risk for developing type 2 diabetes (see Chapter 4). Babies born to mothers with gestational diabetes are at risk of developing diabetes as adults.[14]

Figure 14.10 Prenatal care, which monitors the mother's blood pressure, weight, and blood sugar and the baby's size and heartbeat, can allow early identification and treatment of pregnancy complications. (Faye Norman/ Science Photo Library/Photo Researchers)

hypertensive disorders of pregnancy High blood pressure during pregnancy that is due to chronic hypertension, gestational hypertension, preeclampsia-eclampsia, or preeclampsia superimposed on chronic hypertension.

gestational hypertension The development of hypertension after the twentieth week of pregnancy.

preeclampsia A condition characterized by an increase in body weight, elevated blood pressure, protein in the urine, and edema. It can progress to **eclampsia**, which can be life-threatening to mother and fetus.

gestational diabetes mellitus A consistently elevated blood glucose level that develops during pregnancy and returns to normal after delivery.

14.2 The Nutritional Needs of Pregnancy

Learning Objectives

- Compare the nutrient needs of pregnant women with those of nonpregnant women.
- Discuss the possible effects of too little folic acid during pregnancy.

In order to produce a healthy baby, maternal intake must supply all the nutrients needed to provide for the growth and development of the fetus while continuing to meet the mother's needs. Because the increased need for energy is proportionately smaller than the increased need for protein, vitamins, and minerals, a well-balanced, nutrient-dense diet is required.

Energy Needs During Pregnancy

Energy needs increase during pregnancy to deposit and maintain the new fetal and maternal tissues. The estimated energy requirement (EER) for pregnancy is calculated by totaling the energy needs of nonpregnant women, the increase in energy needs due to pregnancy, and the energy deposited in tissues.[5] During the first trimester, total energy expenditure changes little, so the EER is not increased above nonpregnant levels. During the second and third trimesters, an additional 340 and 452 kcalories per day, respectively, is recommended (**Figure 14.11**). This is the amount of energy contained in a snack such as a sandwich, an apple, and a glass of milk.

Protein, Carbohydrate, and Fat Recommendations

The RDA for protein is increased during pregnancy. The additional protein is needed because protein is essential for the formation and growth of new cells. During pregnancy the placenta develops and grows, the uterus and breasts enlarge, and a single cell devel-

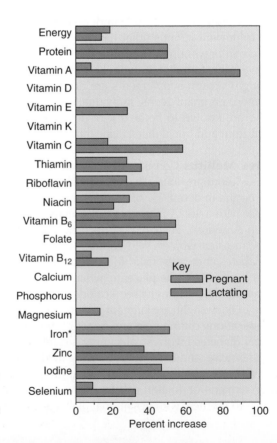

Figure 14.11 Energy and nutrient needs during pregnancy and lactation
This graph illustrates the percentage increase in recommended nutrient intakes for a 25-year-old woman during the third trimester of pregnancy and during lactation.
*The RDA for iron during lactation is equal to half the RDA for nonpregnant, nonlactating women.

ops into a fully formed infant. An additional 25 grams of protein per day above the RDA for nonpregnant women or 1.1 grams per kilogram per day is recommended for the second and third trimesters of pregnancy. For a woman weighing 136 lbs (62 kg), this increases protein needs to about 75 grams per day. This is the amount of protein in 3 cups of milk or yogurt plus 7 ounces of meat.

The RDA for carbohydrate is increased by 45 grams during pregnancy to provide sufficient glucose to fuel the fetal and maternal brains. Therefore the RDA for carbohydrate during pregnancy is 175 grams per day. This is well below the typical intake of about 300 grams per day, and therefore most women do not need to consciously increase carbohydrate intake.

Although total fat intake does not need to increase during pregnancy more of the essential fatty acids linoleic and alpha-linolenic acid are recommended because these are incorporated into the placenta and the fetal tissues. Since there is insufficient data to determine how much is required to meet these needs, AIs for these fatty acids have been established based on the median intake in the United States.

Despite increases in the recommended intakes of protein, carbohydrate, and specific fatty acids during pregnancy, the macronutrient distribution of the diet should be about the same as that recommended for the general population. If the additional energy needed during pregnancy comes from nutrient-dense choices the diet will provide the additional protein, carbohydrate, and fatty acids needed for a healthy pregnancy.

Water and Electrolyte Needs

The need for water is increased during pregnancy because of the increase in blood volume, the production of amniotic fluid, and the needs of the fetus. Throughout pregnancy a woman will accumulate about 6 to 9 liters of water. Some is intracellular, but most is due to increases in the volume of blood and interstitial fluid. The need for water from food and beverages is therefore increased from 2.7 liters per day in nonpregnant women to 3 liters per day.[5] This is equivalent to drinking a little more than an extra cup a day. Despite changes in the amount and distribution of body water during pregnancy there is no evidence that the requirements for potassium, sodium, or chloride are different from that of nonpregnant women.

Micronutrient Needs During Pregnancy

The need for many vitamins and minerals is increased during pregnancy. Due to growth in maternal and fetal tissues as well as increased energy utilization, the requirements for the B vitamins, such as thiamin, niacin, and riboflavin, increase. To form new maternal and fetal cells and to meet the needs for protein synthesis in fetal and maternal tissues, the requirements for folate, vitamin B_{12}, vitamin B_6, zinc, and iron increase. The needs for calcium, vitamin D, and vitamin C increase to provide for the growth and development of bone and connective tissue. For many of these nutrients, intake is easily increased when energy intake rises to meet needs, but for others there is a risk that inadequate amounts will be consumed.

Video

Calcium The fetus retains about 30 grams of calcium over the course of gestation. Most of the calcium is deposited in the last trimester when the fetal skeleton is growing most rapidly and the teeth are forming. Many women have trouble getting enough calcium to meet their own needs, let alone enough to provide this amount for the fetus. Fortunately they don't need to consume any more than is recommended for nonpregnant women because calcium absorption increases during pregnancy.[15] This increase is believed to be due in part to the rise in estrogen that occurs during pregnancy as well as an increase in the concentration of active vitamin D in the blood.[16] At one time there was concern that the calcium needed by the fetus would come from maternal bones if intake was not increased. It is now known that the increased need for calcium does not increase maternal bone resorption, and studies have found no correlation between the number of pregnancies a woman has had and the density of her bones.[17] Therefore, the AI for calcium for pregnant women age 19 and older—1000 mg per day—is not increased above nonpregnant needs. This AI can be met by consuming 3 to 4 servings of milk or other dairy products daily. Women who are lactose intolerant can meet their calcium needs with yogurt, cheese, reduced-lactose milk, calcium-rich vegetables, fish consumed with bones, calcium-fortified foods, or calcium supplements.

Vitamin D Adequate vitamin D is essential to ensure efficient calcium absorption, but the recommended intake for vitamin D during pregnancy is not increased above non-pregnant levels. Pregnant women who receive regular exposure to sunlight can synthesize sufficient vitamin D. If exposure to sunlight is limited, dietary sources such as milk must supply the needed amounts. The incidence of vitamin D deficiency has been increasing in all segments of the U.S. population but may be of particular concern among African-American women. One study found that over 40% of African-American women of childbearing age were vitamin D deficient.[18] Inadequate vitamin D may be a problem in African-American women because their milk intake is often low due to lactose intolerance and their darker pigmentation reduces the synthesis of vitamin D in the skin. If sufficient vitamin D is not consumed in the diet, careful supplementation should be considered. Most prenatal supplements provide 10 µg of vitamin D, which is twice the AI but well below the UL for pregnancy of 50 µg.[15]

Evidence is accumulating that the AI for vitamin D during pregnancy should be increased above current levels and that the amount typically contained in most prenatal supplements (10 µg/day) is insufficient.[19]

Vitamin C Vitamin C is important for bone and connective tissue formation because it is needed for the synthesis of collagen, which gives structure to skin, tendons, and the protein matrix of bones. Vitamin C deficiency during pregnancy increases the risk for premature birth and preeclampsia. The RDA is increased by 10 mg per day during pregnancy.[20] The requirement for vitamin C can easily be met by including citrus fruits and juices in the diet, and supplements are generally not necessary.

Folate Folate is needed for the synthesis of DNA and thus for cell division. During pregnancy, cells multiply to form the placenta, expand maternal blood, and allow for fetal growth. Adequate folate intake is crucial even before conception because rapid cell division occurs in the first days and weeks of pregnancy.

If maternal folate intake is low there is an increased risk of fetal abnormalities that involve the formation of the **neural tube**. During development, neural tissue forms a groove; the groove closes when the sides rise and fold together to form the neural tube (**Figure 14.12**). This neural tube closure occurs between 21 and 28 days of development. If it does not occur normally, the infant will be born with a neural tube defect. These defects include anencephaly, in which the brain and skull do not develop normally, and spina bifida, a condition in which the vertebrae do not close completely, causing part of the spinal cord to be exposed (see Chapter 8). Although the mechanism underlying the protective effect of folate is unknown it is likely to involve genes that regulate folic acid transport and metabolism.[21]

Because the neural tube closes so early in development, often before a woman even knows she is pregnant, the DRIs recommend that women capable of becoming pregnant consume 400 µg per day of synthetic folic acid from fortified foods, supplements, or a combination of the two, in addition to consuming a varied diet rich in natural sources of folate (see Chapter 8, Critical Thinking: Meeting Folate Recommendations). Since the initiation of folic acid fortification, the incidence of neural tube defects has been reduced by 25% in the U.S. and 50% in Canada[22,23] (see Science Applied: Folate: From Epidemiology to Health Policy).

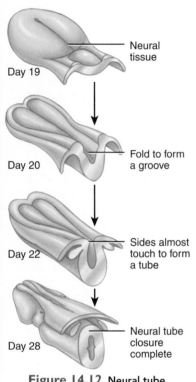

Day 19 — Neural tissue

Day 20 — Fold to form a groove

Day 22 — Sides almost touch to form a tube

Day 28 — Neural tube closure complete

Figure 14.12 Neural tube formation

The neural tube develops from a flat plate of neural tissue.

neural tube The portion of the embryo that develops into the brain and spinal cord.

SCIENCE

ScienceAppliedScienceApplied
Science**AppliedScience**Applied
ScienceAppliedScienceApplied

APPLIED

Folate: From Epidemiology to Health Policy

Until the late 1990s, neural tube defects (NTDs), such as spina bifida and anencephaly, affected approximately 3900 pregnancies in the United States each year. For decades researchers had suspected that NTDs might be related to the mother's dietary intake. Today, public health policies mandate the fortification of certain foods with folic acid, the synthetic form of folate.

The link between maternal folate status and NTDs was identified in the 1970s when lower first trimester red blood cell folate concentrations were found in women who later gave birth to NTD-affected babies.[1] An intervention study completed in 1980 demonstrated that folic acid supplementation in early pregnancy reduced the incidence of NTDs in women who had previously given birth to a baby with an NTD.[2] These findings were supported by a second, large-scale study, which randomly assigned nonpregnant women to receive either folic acid, other supplemental vitamins, or a placebo.[3] This trial, was stopped early when researchers concluded that folic acid supplementation alone reduced NTD recurrence by 71%.

A link between NTDs and folic acid was now clear, but early trials used 800 μg of folic acid. Could a smaller amount be as effective? Also, would folic acid supplementation prevent the first occurrence of NTDs? To answer these questions, women who had no previous NTD–affected pregnancies and were planning a pregnancy were randomly assigned to receive folic acid or a placebo for at least 1 month before conception and until at least the date of the second missed menstrual cycle.[4] The study evaluated 5453 pregnancies. In the 2391 women receiving the placebo, 6 babies were born with NTDs; in the 2471 women in the supplement group, there were no NTDs.[5] This and other studies helped determine that 400 μg of supplemental folic acid dramatically reduced the incidence of NTDs.[6,7]

These results led the Centers for Disease Control and Prevention and the U.S. Public Health Service to recommend that all women of childbearing age who are capable of becoming pregnant consume 400 μg per day of folic acid. But how could the population's folate intake be increased? Educating women to consume foods high in folate would be costly and ineffective. Folic acid supplements were recommended, but after 5 years only one-third of women of childbearing age were consuming a supplement containing the recommended amount.[8] Therefore, it was concluded that the most reliable way to increase folate consumption was through food fortification.

Fortification of the food supply requires a careful analysis to determine how much of the nutrient to add so it will provide the needed benefit without undue risk. The right amount of supplemental folic acid could reduce the incidence of NTD-affected pregnancies and the risk of heart disease in the general population. But, because a high folic acid intake can mask the symptoms of vitamin B_{12} deficiency, a level of fortification needed to be chosen that would reduce NTDs without compromising the elderly population at risk for B_{12} deficiency.

The foods chosen for fortification were enriched grain products such as bread, flour, cornmeal, pasta, grits, and rice. These products are regularly consumed by the target population— women of childbearing age of all races and cultures. The folic acid could be added to these grains while they were being enriched with other nutrients. The amount added, 140 mg per 100 g of grain product, was chosen because it balanced the need to provide enough folic acid to reduce the risk of NTDs with the possibility of masking vitamin B_{12} deficiency. The success of the folic acid fortification program can be seen in the decline in the estimated number of NTD-affected pregnancies as well as in the reduction in heart attacks in the United States that has occurred since the fortification of grains with folic acid.[9]

[1] Smithells, R. W., Sheppard, S., and Schorah, C. J. Vitamin deficiencies and neural tube defects. *Arch. Dis. Child.* 51:944–949, 1976.

[2] Smithells, R. W., Sheppard, S., Schorah, C. J. et al. Possible prevention of neural tube defects by periconceptional vitamin supplementation. *Lancet* 1:339–340, 1980.

[3] MRC Vitamin Study Research Group. Prevention of neural tube defects: Results of the MRC vitamin study. *Lancet* 338:131–137, 1991.

[4] Czeizel, A. E., and Dudás, I. Prevention of the first occurrence of neural-tube defects by periconceptional vitamin supplementation. *N. Engl. J. Med.* 327:1832–1835, 1992.

[5] Czeizel, A. E. Folic acid and the prevention of neural tube defects. *J. Pediatr. Gastroenterol. Nutr.* 20:4–16, 1995.

[6] Werler, M. M., Shapiro, S., and Mitchell, A. A. Periconceptional folic acid exposure and the risk of occurrent neural tube defects. *JAMA* 269:1257–1261, 1993.

[7] Daly, S., Mills, J. L., Molloy, A. M., et al. Minimum effective dose of folic acid for food fortification to prevent neural-tube defects. *Lancet* 350:1666–1669, 1997.

[8] Use of folic acid-containing supplements among women of childbearing age—United States, 1997. *MMWR* 47:131–134, 1998. Available online at cdc.gov/mmwr/preview/mmwrhtml/00051435.htm/ Accessed February 10, 2001.

[9] Bentley, T. G., Weinstein, M. C., Willett, W. C., and Kuntz, K. M. A cost-effective analysis of folic acid fortification policy in the United States. *Public Health Nutr.* 12:455–467, 2009.

Adequate folate continues to be important even after the neural tube closes. Cell division continues in both embryonic and fetal development and folate is central because of its role in DNA synthesis. Marginal folate status can impair growth in both the fetus and the placenta. If folate is inadequate during pregnancy, megaloblastic anemia—the type of anemia in which blood cells do not mature properly—may result (see Chapter 8). Low dietary folate intakes and low circulating folate levels are associated with increased risk of preterm delivery, low birth weight, and fetal growth retardation.[24] Thus, to maintain red blood cell folate levels in pregnant women, the RDA for folate is set at 600 μg dietary folate equivalents per day.[25] Natural sources of folate include orange juice, legumes, leafy green vegetables, and organ meats. A half cup of legumes plus a cup of raw spinach provide about a third of the RDA. Fortified sources include enriched breads, cereals, and other grain products; a serving of fortified cereal provides about 25% of the RDA. Folic acid supplements can also be used to meet this goal. Most prenatal supplements contain 400 μg of folic acid.

Vitamin B$_{12}$ Vitamin B$_{12}$ is essential for the regeneration of active forms of folate, so a deficiency of vitamin B$_{12}$ can also result in megaloblastic anemia. Vitamin B$_{12}$ is transferred from the mother to the fetus during pregnancy. Based on the amount transferred and the increased efficiency of vitamin B$_{12}$ absorption that occurs during pregnancy, the RDA for pregnancy is set at 2.6 μg per day.[25] This recommendation is easily met by a diet containing even small amounts of animal products. Vegetarian diets are generally safe for pregnant women but vegans must consume foods fortified with vitamin B$_{12}$ or take vitamin B$_{12}$ supplements daily to meet the needs of mother and fetus.

Zinc Zinc is involved in the synthesis of DNA, RNA, and proteins. It is therefore extremely important for growth and development. Zinc deficiency during pregnancy is associated with an increased risk of fetal malformations, prematurity, and low birth weight.[26] Because zinc absorption is inhibited by high iron intakes, iron supplements may compromise zinc status if the diet is low in zinc. The RDA is 11 mg per day for pregnant women 19 years of age and older.[27] A 3-oz serving of lean ground beef provides about 2 mg of zinc.

Iron Iron needs are high during pregnancy to allow for the synthesis of hemoglobin and other iron-containing proteins in both maternal and fetal tissues. The physiological changes of pregnancy allow for increased iron absorption and iron losses are decreased due to the cessation of menstruation. Nonetheless, iron-deficiency anemia is common during pregnancy. Part of the reason for this is that low iron stores are common among women of childbearing age so many women start pregnancy with diminished iron stores and quickly become deficient.

The RDA for iron during pregnancy is 27 mg per day compared with 18 mg for nonpregnant women.[27] It takes an exceptionally well-planned diet to meet iron needs during pregnancy. Red meats, leafy green vegetables, and fortified cereals are good sources of iron. Foods that enhance iron absorption, such as citrus fruit and meat, should also be included in the diet. Iron supplements are typically recommended during the second and third trimesters of pregnancy (see Critical Thinking: Nutrient Needs for a Successful Pregnancy).

When iron needs are not met, iron-deficiency anemia may occur. Iron-deficiency anemia during pregnancy has been associated with an increased risk of low birth weight and preterm delivery.[28] The fetus draws iron from the mother to ensure adequate fetal hemoglobin production, mostly during the last trimester. Babies born prematurely may not have had time to accumulate sufficient iron, but babies born at term usually have adequate iron stores even if the mother is deficient.

Critical Thinking

Nutrient Needs for a Successful Pregnancy

Background

Tina is 3 months pregnant. From the start—before she tried to conceive—she has been careful about her nutritional health. She even took a prenatal vitamin supplement before she knew she was pregnant to be sure she got enough folic acid. Now that she is approaching her second trimester, her doctor is concerned about her intake of iron. Even though there is iron in her supplement, she needs to increase the iron in her diet.

Data

Tina is 26 years old, 5′4″ tall, and weighed 126 pounds before she became pregnant. She typically exercises for about 40 minutes per day.

FOOD	IRON (mg)	PROTEIN (g)	ENERGY (kcal)
Breakfast			
I cup corn flakes	0.4	2	130
with I cup reduced-fat milk	0.1	8	121
3/4 cup orange juice	1.1	1.3	105
I cup decaffeinated coffee			
with sugar and cream	0.1	0	51
Lunch			
Tuna sandwich			
3 oz tuna	1.2	21.7	170
2 tsp mayonnaise	0.5	0.1	66
2 slices white bread	2.5	6.6	240
20 french fries	1.3	3.2	203
I can orange soda	0.2	0	180
3 chocolate chip cookies	0.8	1.7	144
I apple	0.4	0	80
Dinner			
3 oz chicken leg	1.5	29.6	250
1/2 cup peas	1.2	7.9	67
I piece corn bread	0.8	4	152
I tsp margarine	0	0	33
I cup lettuce and tomato salad	1.3	5	25
I Tbsp Italian dressing	0	0	69
I cup reduced-fat milk	0.1	8	121
Total	**13.5**	**99.1**	**2207**

(©Mark Burstyn/Masterfile)

According to this table, Tina's diet meets her current energy needs. But, after her first trimester she will need additional kcalories, protein, and other nutrients.

Critical Thinking Questions

Once Tina is in her second trimester, how many extra kcalories will she need? What about protein and iron?

▼

Compare Tina's intake to the recommendations of MyPyramid for Moms shown in Table 14.2. Does she meet the food group recommendations for her first trimester? What should she add during her second trimester?

▼

Suggest a snack that will meet these food group recommendations and provide the additional kcalories she needs.

▼

What about iron? Does her current diet meet her needs without the supplement? How much iron does the snack you suggested provide?

iProfile   Use iProfile to find good food sources of iron.

Based on the information you provided, these are your recommended a from each food group. For more information, go to MyPyramid.gov.

	GRAINS Make half your grains whole	VEGETABLES Vary your veggies	FRUITS Focus on fruits	MILK Get your calcium-rich foods	MEAT & B Choose lean wit
1st Trimester	7 ounces	3 cups	2 cups	3 cups	6 ounces
2nd Trimester	8 ounces	3 cups	2 cups	3 cups	6^1/$_2$ ounces
3rd Trimester	9 ounces	3^1/$_2$ cups	2 cups	3 cups	6^1/$_2$ ounces

*These are only estimates of your needs. Check with your health care provider to make sure you are gaining weight appropriately.

*The calories and amounts of food you need change with each trimester of pregnancy. Your plan may show different amounts of food for different months, to meet your changing nutritional needs. Changing the amount of calories you eat each trimester also helps you gain weight at the correct rate.

Know your limits on fats, sugars, and sodium

	OILS Aim for this much	EXTRAS Limit excess solid fats and sug to this much
1st Trimester	6 teaspoons	290 Calories
2nd Trimester	7 teaspoons	360 Calories
3rd Trimester	8 teaspoons	410 Calories

Figure 14.13 MyPyramid for pregnancy
This MyPyramid plan for Moms (www.MyPyramid.gov) is for a 26-year-old woman who is 5 feet 4 inches tall, gets 30 to 60 minutes of exercise a day, and weighed 125 pounds before she became pregnant. Energy needs are not increased during the first trimester, so the recommended amounts from each group for the first trimester are the same as for a nonpregnant woman.

Meeting Nutrient Needs with Food and Supplements

The energy and nutrient needs of pregnancy can be met by following the recommendations of the Dietary Guidelines and MyPyramid for Pregnancy (**Figure 14.13**). Additional grains, vegetables, and fruits provides energy, protein, folate, vitamin C, and fiber, particularly if whole grains are chosen. An extra serving of milk provides energy, protein, calcium, vitamin D, and riboflavin. Additional lean meat provides energy, protein, vitamin B_6, vitamin B_{12}, iron, and zinc. For example, adding a snack such as a turkey sandwich on whole-grain bread, an apple, and a glass of low-fat milk will provide all the extra energy and nutrients needed daily for a healthy pregnancy.

Supplements Even when a healthy diet based on MyPyramid for Pregnancy is consumed it is difficult to meet all vitamin and mineral needs. Generally, supplements of folic acid are recommended before and during pregnancy, and iron supplements are recommended during the second and third trimesters.[2] A multivitamin and mineral supplement may also be necessary in those whose food choices are limited, such as vegetarians, or in those whose needs are very high, such as pregnant teenagers. A prenatal supplement, however, must be taken in conjunction with, not in place of, a carefully planned diet (see Off the Label: What's in a Prenatal Supplement?).

Off the Label
What's in a Prenatal Supplement?

(©)iStockphoto)

Most pregnant women leave their first prenatal doctor's visit with a prescription for a prenatal vitamin and mineral supplement. What's in these supplements? Do they meet all the needs of pregnancy?

A look at a label shows that a typical prenatal supplement contains more than 15 vitamins and minerals. It supplies enough folate, iron, and many other micronutrients to meet recommendations, but taking the supplement does not mean that pregnant women can ignore their diet. Some nutrients in these supplements are present in amounts that do not meet the needs of pregnancy, and others are missing altogether. For example, the tablet whose ingredients are shown in the Supplements Facts panel below does not provide any magnesium and contains only 200 mg of calcium, which is only 20% of the recommended intake for a pregnant woman aged 19 or older. To meet her magnesium and calcium needs, a pregnant woman taking this tablet would still need to consume plenty of whole grains, nuts, seeds, and leafy greens to provide magnesium and enough milk or other high calcium foods to provide about 1000 mg of calcium.

Even if all the calcium and magnesium needed for pregnancy could be packed into a little pill, it still would not provide everything needed in an adequate diet. Prenatal supplements do not contain the protein needed for tissue synthesis or the complex carbohydrates required for energy. They lack fiber, which helps prevent constipation, and they do not contain fluid needed for expanding blood volume and maintaining normal bowel function. They also don't contain other food components such as the phytochemicals supplied by a diet rich in whole grains, fruits, and vegetables. Thus, taking a multivitamin and mineral supplement during pregnancy can be beneficial, but remember not to exceed the recommended dosage or allow the supplement to take the place of a carefully planned diet.

(Andy Washnik)

Supplement Facts

Serving Size 1 Tablet
Servings Per Container 60

Amount Per 1 Tablet	% Daily Value
Vitamin A (as beta carotene) 5000 IU	63%
Vitamin C (as ascorbic acid) 85 mg	100%
Vitamin D (as cholecalciferol) 400 IU	200%
Vitamin E (as d-alpha tocopheryl) acetate (Covitol™) 22 IU	67%
Vitamin K 90 mcg	100%
Thiamin 1.4 mg	100%
Riboflavin 1.6 mg	100%
Niacin (as niacinamide) 17 mg	100%
Vitamin B6 (as pyridoxine HCl) 2.6 mg	137%
Folic acid 1000 mcg	167%
Vitamin B12 (as cyanocobalamin) 2.6 mg	100%
Pantothenic Acid (as as d-calcium pantothenate) 6 mg	100%
Iron (as iron fumarate) 27 mg	100%
Iodine (kelp) 220 mcg	100%
Zinc (as monomethionine & gluconate) 11mg	100%
Selenium (as sodium selenate) 60 mcg	100%
Copper (as copper sulfate) 1000 mcg	100%
Calcium (as calcium carbonate) 200 mg	20%

* Daily Values based on RDAs for pregnant women ages 19-50
Other ingredients: stearic acid, vegetable stearate, silicon dioxide, croscarmellose sodium, microcrystalline cellulose, natural coating (contains hydroxypropyl methylcellulose, titanium dioxide, riboflavin, polyethylene glycol and polysorbate)

Figure 14.14 This African American woman in Georgia is eating a white clay called kaolin, which some women crave during pregnancy. Eating kaolin is also a traditional remedy for morning sickness. This example of pica may be related to cultural beliefs and traditions. (© Michael DiBari, Jr./ AP/wide world photos)

pica An abnormal craving for and ingestion of unusual food and nonfood substances.

Food Cravings and Aversions Most women change their diets during pregnancy. Some changes are made in an effort to improve nutrition to ensure a healthy infant, but other changes are based on cravings, aversions, or cultural or family traditions. Foods that are commonly craved include fruit and fruit juices, sweets, candy (particularly chocolate), and dairy products. Common aversions include coffee and other caffeinated drinks, alcohol, meat, fish, poultry, eggs, highly seasoned foods, or fried foods. It has been suggested that hormonal or physiological changes during pregnancy—in particular, changes in taste and smell—may be the cause of such cravings and aversions.

Usually the food cravings of pregnant women can be indulged within reason with no harmful effects. But abnormal cravings leading to consumption of nonfood substances can have serious consequences. **Pica** is an abnormal craving for and ingestion of nonfood substances having little or no nutritional value (see Focus on Eating Disorders). Pica has been described since antiquity but its cause is still a mystery. It was once thought that pica was an attempt to meet micronutrient needs. It is now believed that pica may be more related to cultural factors than the need for micronutrients. It is more common in African-American women and in those with a family or personal history of the practice (**Figure 14.14**).[29] Women with pica commonly consume clay, laundry starch, ice and freezer frost, baking soda, cornstarch, and ashes. Consuming large amounts of these can reduce the intake of nutrient-dense foods, reduce nutrient absorption from food, increase the risk of consuming toxins and harmful microorganisms, and even cause intestinal obstructions. Complications of pica include iron-deficiency anemia, lead poisoning, and parasitic infections.[29] Anemia and hypertensive disorders of pregnancy are more common in mothers who practice pica, but it is not clear if pica is a result of these conditions or a cause. In newborns, anemia and low birth weight are often related to pica in the mother.

14.3 Factors that Increase the Risks of Pregnancy

Learning Objectives

- Explain how maternal nutritional status, health status, age, and income level affect the risks of pregnancy.
- Explain the purpose of the Special Supplemental Nutrition Program for Women, Infants, and Children.
- Describe the effects of maternal drug and alcohol use on pregnancy outcome.

Most of the 4 million women who give birth every year in the United States are healthy during pregnancy and produce healthy babies. However, childbearing is not without risks. In the United States, 13 out of every 100,000 women die as a result of childbirth. Thirteen percent of babies are born too soon, 9.7% are of low or very low birth weight, and 6.8 out of each 1000 born alive die within the first year of life.[7,8] The reasons for poor pregnancy outcome vary. Malnutrition is a factor in some women. Others are at increased risk because of their age and preexisting health problems or socioeconomic factors such as limited access to health care, lack of a supportive home environment, or insufficient resources to acquire nutritious foods (**Table 14.3**). Some women and babies are at risk because they are exposed to harmful substances from the diet or environment.

Maternal Nutritional Status

Proper nutrition is important before pregnancy to support conception and maximize the likelihood of a healthy pregnancy. At any time during pregnancy, maternal malnutrition due to a deficiency or excess of energy or individual nutrients can affect pregnancy outcome.

Table 14.3 **Factors that Increase Pregnancy Risks**

Maternal Factor	Maternal Risk	Infant/Fetal Risk
Prepregnant BMI < 19.8 or gaining too little weight during pregnancy	Anemia, premature rupture of the membranes, hemorrhage after delivery	Low birth weight, preterm birth
Prepregnancy BMI > 26 or gaining too much weight during pregnancy	Hypertensive disorders of pregnancy, gestational diabetes, difficult delivery, cesarean section	Large-for-gestational-age, low Apgar scores (a score used to assess the health of a baby in the first minutes after birth), and neural tube defects
Malnutrition	Decreased ability to conceive, anemia	Fetal growth retardation, low birth weight, birth defects, preterm birth, spontaneous abortion, stillbirth, increased risk of chronic disease later in life
Phenylketonuria	High blood levels of phenylketones	Mental retardation if low phenylalanine diet is not carefully followed by mother
Hypertension	Stroke, heart attack, premature separation of the placenta from the uterine wall	Low birth weight, fetal death
Diabetes	Difficulty adjusting insulin dose, preeclampsia, cesarean section	Large-for-gestational-age, congenital abnormalities, fetal death
Frequent pregnancies: 3 or more during a 2-year period	Malnutrition	Low birth weight, preterm birth
Poor obstetric history or history of poor fetal outcome	Recurrence of problem in subsequent pregnancy	Birth defects, death
Age:		
Teenage	Malnutrition, hypertensive disorders of pregnancy	Low birth weight
Older than 35	Hypertensive disorders of pregnancy, gestational diabetes	Down syndrome and other chromosomal abnormalities
Alcohol consumption	Poor nutritional status	Alcohol-related birth defects, alcohol-related neurodevelopmental disorders, fetal alcohol syndrome
Cigarette smoking	Lung cancer and other lung diseases, miscarriage	Low birth weight, miscarriage, stillbirth, preterm birth, sudden infant death syndrome, respiratory problems
Cocaine use	Hypertension, miscarriage, premature labor and delivery	Intrauterine growth retardation, low birth weight, preterm birth, birth defects, sudden infant death syndrome

Nutritional Status Before Pregnancy A woman's nutritional status before she becomes pregnant may affect her ability to conceive and successfully complete a pregnancy. Starvation diets, anorexia nervosa, and excessive exercise, such as marathon running, can reduce body fat and affect hormone levels. If hormone levels are too low, ovulation does not occur and conception is not possible. Too much body fat can also reduce fertility by altering hormone levels. Deficiencies or excesses of nutrients can also affect pregnancy outcome. For instance, a deficiency of folate or an excess of vitamin A early in pregnancy can cause birth defects.

Nutritional status can also be affected by some birth control methods and these can therefore have an impact on a subsequent pregnancy. For example, oral contraceptives are associated with reduced blood levels of vitamins B_6 and B_{12}.[25] If conception occurs soon after oral contraceptive use stops, these levels will not have had time to return to normal before pregnancy begins.

Malnutrition During Pregnancy Maternal malnutrition can cause fetal growth retardation, low infant birth weight, birth defects, premature birth, spontaneous abortion, and stillbirth. The effect of malnutrition depends on how severe the nutrient deficiency or excess is and when during the pregnancy it occurs. In general, poor nutrition early in pregnancy affects embryonic development and the potential of the embryo to survive, and poor nutrition in the latter part of pregnancy affects fetal growth.

Immediate Effects of Maternal Malnutrition A low energy intake during early pregnancy is not likely to interfere with fetal growth because the energy demands of the embryo are small. However, if the embryo does not receive adequate amounts of the nutrients needed for cell division and differentiation, such as folate and vitamin A, malformations or death can result. Inadequate folate intake in the first few weeks of pregnancy may affect neural tube development.[25] Too much vitamin A is of particular concern because the risk of kidney problems and central nervous system abnormalities in the offspring increases even when maternal intake is not extremely high. High intakes early in pregnancy are the most damaging. A UL of 3000 μg per day has been established for pregnant women ages 19 to 50 years.[27] Supplements consumed during pregnancy should therefore contain β-carotene, which is not damaging to the fetus.

Malnutrition is most devastating during the first trimester. After the first trimester, nutrient deficiencies or excesses are less likely to cause developmental defects (malformations) because most organs and structures have already formed. However, undernutrition in the mother after the first trimester can interfere with fetal growth. Even a mild energy restriction during the last trimester, when the fetus is growing rapidly, can affect birth weight. Malnutrition also interferes with the growth and function of the placenta. Then in turn, a poorly developed placenta cannot deliver sufficient nutrients to the fetus and the result is a small infant who may also have other developmental abnormalities.

Long-Term Effects of Maternal Malnutrition It has been proposed that problems in maternal nutrition can cause adaptations that change fetal structure, physiology, and metabolism and can affect the child's risk of developing chronic diseases later in life. Evidence for this comes from epidemiological studies that suggest that individuals who were small at birth or disproportionately thin or short have higher rates of heart disease, high blood pressure, high blood cholesterol, and diabetes in middle age.[30]

Maternal Health Status

The general health as well as nutritional status of the mother affects the outcome of pregnancy. Women who begin pregnancy with chronic diseases such as hypertension, diabetes, and phenylketonuria (PKU) must manage their health carefully to assure a healthy pregnancy. The effect of hypertension depends on when it develops and how severe it is. As in nonpregnant individuals, high blood pressure in pregnant women increases the risk of stroke and heart attack, but in pregnancy it also increases the risk of low birth weight and premature separation of the placenta from the wall of the uterus, resulting in fetal death.

Women with diabetes must carefully manage diet and medication to ensure that glucose levels stay in the normal range throughout pregnancy. Uncontrolled diabetes early in pregnancy increases the risk of birth defects. When normal blood glucose is maintained throughout pregnancy, the risk of complications is greatly reduced. The need for insulin increases during the second and third trimesters, so women with preexisting diabetes may need to adjust their medication dosage. When maternal blood glucose is elevated, it provides extra nutrients to the growing fetus, resulting in large-for-gestational-age newborns who are at increased risk.

Reproductive History Frequent pregnancies, with little time between, increase the risk of poor pregnancy outcomes. One reason is that the mother may not have replenished nutrient stores depleted in the first pregnancy when she becomes pregnant again. An interval of less than 18 months increases the risk of delivering a full-term but small-for-gestational-age infant. An interval of only 3 months has been shown to increase the risk of a preterm or small-for-gestational-age infant as well as neonatal death.[31] Women with a history of poor pregnancy outcome are also at increased risk. For example, a woman who has had a number of miscarriages is more likely to have another, and a woman who has had one child with a birth defect has an increased risk for defects in subsequent children.

The Pregnant Teenager Pregnancy places a stress on the body at any age, but this is compounded when the mother herself is still growing. Although the rate of teen pregnancy has been decreasing, from 62 babies per 1000 teens in 1991, to 42 per thousand in 2006, it remains a major public health problem.[32] Pregnant teens are at greater risk of developing hypertensive disorders of pregnancy and are more likely to deliver preterm and low-birth-weight babies. To produce a healthy baby, a pregnant teenager needs early medical intervention and nutritional counseling.

Adolescent girls continue to grow and mature physically for about 4 to 7 years after menstruation begins. Therefore the diet of a pregnant teen must provide both for her growth and that of her baby. Even teenagers who deliver normal-birth-weight infants may stop growing themselves.[33] Because the nutrient needs of a pregnant teen may be higher than those of a pregnant adult, the DRIs include a special set of nutrient recommendations for pregnant teens (**Figure 14.15**). Consuming a diet that

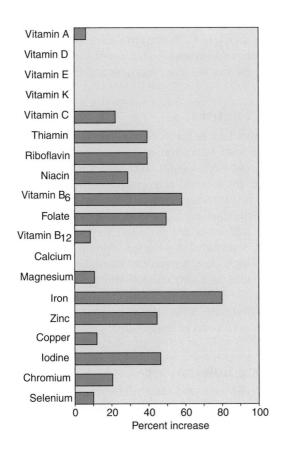

Figure 14.15 Nutrient needs of pregnant teens The percentage increase in micronutrient needs above nonpregnant levels is shown here for a 14- to 18-year-old teen during pregnancy.

Figure 14.16 Prenatal care with careful medical monitoring can help older women have uncomplicated pregnancies and healthy babies. (Stewart Cohen/Stone/Getty Images)

meets these needs can be challenging. Even nonpregnant teens often fall short of meeting their nutrient needs. Nutrients that are commonly low in the diets of pregnant teens are calcium, iron, zinc, magnesium, vitamin D, folate, and vitamin B_6.[20,25]

The Older Mother The nutritional requirements for older women during pregnancy are no different than for women in their twenties, but pregnancy after the age of 35 does carry additional risks because older women are more likely to start pregnancy with medical conditions such as cardiovascular disease, kidney disease, obesity, and diabetes. During pregnancy, they also are more likely to develop gestational diabetes, hypertensive disorders of pregnancy, and other complications. They also have a higher incidence of low-birth-weight deliveries and of chromosomal abnormalities, especially **Down syndrome**. Today, careful medical monitoring throughout pregnancy is reducing the risks to older mothers and their babies (**Figure 14.16**).

Down syndrome A disorder caused by extra genetic material that results in distinctive facial characteristics, mental retardation, and other abnormalities.

Socioeconomic Factors

One of the greatest risk factors for poor pregnancy outcome is low-income level. Poverty limits access to food, education, and health care. Low-income women have a higher incidence of low-birth-weight and preterm infants.[34] Many low-income women do not receive any medical care until late in pregnancy. Women who begin prenatal care after the first trimester are at a higher risk for poor pregnancy outcomes such as premature birth, low birth weight, or growth retardation. One federally funded program that addresses the nutritional needs of pregnant women is the Special Supplemental Nutrition Program for Women, Infants, and Children (WIC). WIC participation has been shown to reduce health-care costs by providing preventative care to low-income pregnant women through nutrition education and food vouchers.[35] This program provides services to pregnant women, to nonlactating women for 6 months after birth, to lactating women for 12 months after birth, and to infants and children up to 5 years of age.

Exposure to Toxic Substances

During development, cells are particularly vulnerable to damage because they are dividing rapidly, differentiating, and moving to form organs and other structures. Anything that interferes with this development can cause a baby to be born too soon or too small or can result in birth defects. A **teratogen** is any chemical, biological, or

teratogen A substance that can cause birth defects.

physical agent that causes birth defects. Even some vitamins have been found to be teratogens. The placenta prevents some teratogens from passing from the mother's blood to the embryonic or fetal blood, but it cannot prevent the passage of all hazardous substances.

Each organ system develops at a different rate and time, so each has a critical period when exposure to a teratogen or other insult can disrupt development and cause irreversible damage (**Figure 14.17**). If the damage is severe, it may result in a miscarriage. Because the majority of cell differentiation occurs during the embryonic period, this is the time when exposure to teratogens can do the most damage, but vital body organs can still be affected during the fetal period. As discussed previously, deficiencies or excesses of energy or nutrients during pregnancy can affect the health of the embryo and fetus and cause developmental errors. Other substances present in the environment, consumed in the diet, or taken as medications or recreational drugs can also act as teratogens.

Environmental Toxins In a pregnant woman, exposure to environmental toxins—such as cleaning solvents, lead and mercury, some insecticides, or paint—can affect her developing child. Therefore, pregnant women need to be aware of the potential toxins in their food, water, and environment. Fish has both benefits and risks for pregnant women. It is a source of lean protein for tissue growth and of omega-3 fatty acids and iodine needed for brain development, but if it is contaminated with mercury, consumption during pregnancy can cause developmental delays and brain damage. Rather than avoid fish, pregnant women should be informed consumers. Exposure to mercury can be controlled by avoiding fish such as shark, swordfish, king mackerel, or tilefish, which can be high in mercury, and by limiting tuna intake to no more than 6 oz of albacore per week. Up to 12 oz per week of varieties of fish and shellfish that are lower in mercury, such as shrimp, canned light tuna, salmon, pollock, and catfish, can be safely consumed.[36]

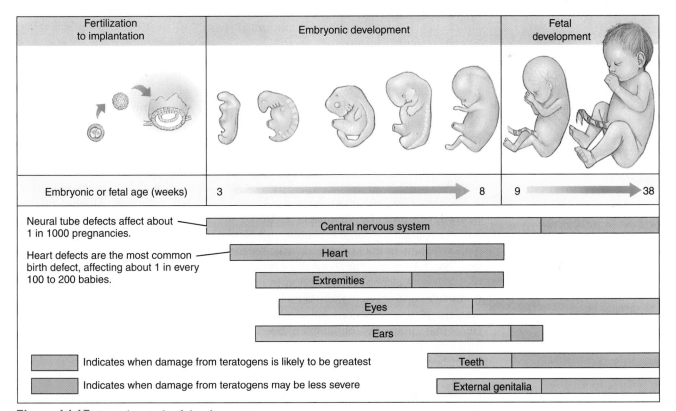

Figure 14.17 Critical periods of development
The critical periods of development are different for various body systems. Heart defects are the most common birth defect. (Source: Adapted from Moore, K., and Persaud, T. The Developing Human, 5th ed. Philadelphia: W. B. Saunders Company, 1993.)

Caffeine and Herbs Caffeine-containing beverages like coffee are a part of our typical diet, but consuming too much caffeine during pregnancy has been associated with reductions in birth weight and an increased risk of miscarriage.[37] It is recommended that pregnant women avoid consuming more than 200 mg of caffeine per day. This is the amount in about 2 cups of regular coffee or 5 cups of tea or cola beverages (see Table 13.8). Herbal teas are also popular beverages. Some are consumed to treat the discomforts of pregnancy. For example, ginger and raspberry leaves are often used to treat morning sickness. Because there is not a great deal of research on herbal teas and other herbal products, pregnant women should avoid them until they are shown to be safe during pregnancy.[2]

Food-Borne Illness The immune system is weakened during pregnancy, increasing susceptibility to and the severity of certain food-borne illnesses. *Listeria* infections are about 20 times more likely during pregnancy and are especially dangerous for pregnant women, often resulting in miscarriage, premature delivery, stillbirth, or infection of the fetus.[38] About one-quarter of babies born with *Listeria* infections do not survive. The bacteria are commonly found in unpasteurized milk, soft cheeses, and uncooked hot dogs and lunch meats.

Toxoplasmosis is an infection caused by a parasite. If a pregnant woman becomes infected, there is about a 40% chance that she will pass the infection to her unborn baby.[39] Some infected babies develop vision and hearing loss, intellectual disability, and/or seizures. The toxoplasmosis parasite is found in cat feces, soil, and undercooked infected meat. Pregnant women should follow the safe food-handling recommendations discussed in Chapter 17.

Alcohol Alcohol consumption during pregnancy is one of the leading causes of preventable birth defects (see Focus on Alcohol). Alcohol is a teratogen that is particularly damaging to the developing central nervous system.[40] It also indirectly affects fetal growth and development because it is a toxin that reduces blood flow to the placenta, thereby decreasing the delivery of oxygen and nutrients to the fetus. The use of alcohol can also impair maternal nutritional status, further increasing the risk to the embryo or fetus. Despite this, about 12% of women report drinking alcohol during pregnancy.[2]

Prenatal exposure to alcohol can cause a spectrum of disorders depending on the dose, timing, and duration of the exposure. One of the most severe outcomes of drinking alcohol during pregnancy is **fetal alcohol syndrome (FAS)**, which causes facial deformities, growth retardation, and permanent brain damage (**Figure 14.18**). Newborns with the syndrome may be shaky and irritable, with poor muscle tone and alcohol withdrawal symptoms. Other problems include heart and urinary tract defects, impaired vision and hearing, and delayed language development. Intellectual disability is the most common and most serious effect. Not all babies exposed to alcohol have FAS, but many have some alcohol-related problems. **Alcohol-related neurodevelopmental disorders (ARND)** are functional or mental impairments linked to prenatal alcohol exposure, and **alcohol-related birth defects (ARBD)** are malformations in the skeleton or major organ systems. These conditions are less severe than FAS, but occur about three times more often.

Because alcohol consumption in each trimester has been associated with abnormalities and because there is no level of alcohol consumption that is known to be safe, complete abstinence from alcohol is recommended during pregnancy. Warning labels that appear on containers of beer, wine, and hard liquor state that "According to the Surgeon General, women should not drink alcoholic beverages during pregnancy because of the risk of birth defects."

Cigarette Smoke If a woman smokes cigarettes during pregnancy, her baby will be affected before birth and throughout life. The carbon monoxide in tobacco smoke binds to hemoglobin, reducing oxygen delivery to fetal tissues. The nicotine absorbed from cigarette smoke is a teratogen that can affect brain development.[41] It also constricts arteries and limits blood flow, reducing both oxygen and nutrient delivery to

Figure 14.18 Facial characteristics shared by children with fetal alcohol syndrome include a low nasal bridge, a short nose, distinct eyelids, and a thin upper lip. (David Young-Wolff/PhotoEdit)

fetal alcohol syndrome A characteristic group of physical and mental abnormalities in an infant resulting from maternal alcohol consumption during pregnancy.

alcohol-related neurodevelopmental disorders A spectrum of learning and developmental disabilities and behavioral abnormalities in a child due to maternal alcohol consumption during pregnancy.

alcohol-related birth defects Malformations in the skeleton or major organ systems in a child due to maternal alcohol consumption during pregnancy.

the fetus.[42] Cigarette smoking during pregnancy reduces birth weight and increases the risk of preterm delivery, stillbirth, neurobehavioral problems, and early death.[2,41] Even exposure to cigarette smoke from the environment has been found to increase the risk of low birth weight. The risk of **sudden infant death syndrome (SIDS, or crib death)** and respiratory problems are also increased in children exposed to cigarette smoke both in the uterus and after birth. The effects of maternal smoking follow children throughout life; they are more likely to have frequent colds and develop lung problems later in life.[43]

sudden infant death syndromes (SIDS), or **crib death** The unexplained death of an infant, usually during sleep.

Legal and Illicit Drug Use The use of drugs—whether over-the-counter, prescribed, or illicit—can also affect both fertility and pregnancy outcome. For example, the acne medications Accutane and Retin-A, which are derivatives of vitamin A, can cause birth defects if taken during pregnancy. A woman who is considering pregnancy should discuss her plans with her physician in order to determine the risks associated with any medication she is taking.

Substance abuse during pregnancy is a national health issue. It is estimated that from 1% to 11% of babies born each year have been exposed to drugs during the prenatal period. These numbers include only the use of illicit drugs and would be much larger if alcohol and nicotine were included.[44]

Marijuana and cocaine are drugs that are commonly used during pregnancy. Both cross the placenta and enter the fetal blood. There is little evidence that marijuana affects fetal outcome, but cocaine use increases the risk of complications to the mother and creates problems for the infant before, during, and after delivery. Cocaine is a central nervous system stimulant, but many of its effects during pregnancy occur because it constricts blood vessels, thereby reducing the flow of oxygen and nutrients to the rapidly dividing fetal cells. Cocaine use during pregnancy is associated with a high rate of miscarriage, intrauterine growth retardation, spontaneous abortion, premature labor and delivery, low-birth-weight, and birth defects.[45] Exposure to cocaine, opiates, or amphetamines has been shown to affect infant behavior and impact learning and attention span during childhood.[46]

14.4 Lactation

Learning Objectives

- Compare the nutritional needs of lactating women with those of nonpregnant nonlactating women of childbearing age.
- Explain the relationship between suckling and milk production and let down.

The nutrient requirements of pregnancy include those needed to prepare for lactation. After childbirth, the breast-feeding mother's nutrient intake must support milk production and can influence the nutrient composition of her milk.

The Physiology of Lactation

Lactation involves both the synthesis of the milk components, such as milk proteins, lactose, and milk lipids, and the movement of these milk components through the milk ducts to the nipple. Throughout pregnancy, hormones prepare the breasts for lactation by stimulating the enlargement and development of the milk ducts and the milk-producing glands, called *alveoli* (**Figure 14.19**). During the first few days after childbirth, the breasts produce and secrete a small amount of a clear yellow fluid called **colostrum**. Colostrum is immature milk. It is rich in protein, including immune factors that help protect the newborn from disease. Within about a week of childbirth, there is a rapid increase in milk secretion, and its composition changes from colostrum to that of mature milk.

colostrum The first milk, which is secreted in late pregnancy and up to a week after birth. It is rich in protein and immune factors.

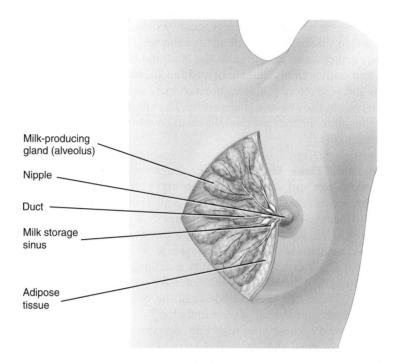

Figure 14.19 **Anatomy of lactation**
During lactation, milk travels from the milk-producing glands through the ducts to milk storage sinuses and then to the nipple.

prolactin A hormone released by the anterior pituitary that acts on the milk-producing glands in the breast to stimulate and sustain milk production.

let-down A hormonal reflex triggered by the infant's suckling that causes milk to be released from the milk glands and flow through the duct system to the nipple.

oxytocin A hormone produced by the posterior pituitary gland that acts on the uterus to cause uterine contractions and on the breast to cause the movement of milk into the secretory ducts that lead to the nipple.

Milk production and release is triggered by hormones that are released in response to the suckling of the infant. The pituitary hormone **prolactin** stimulates milk production; the more the infant suckles, the more milk is produced. The release of milk from the milk-producing glands and its movement through the ducts and storage sinuses is referred to as **let-down** (**Figure 14.20**). The let-down of milk is caused by **oxytocin**, another hormone produced by the pituitary gland that is released in response to the suckling of the infant. As nursing becomes more automatic, oxytocin release and the let-down of milk may occur in response to the sight or sound of an

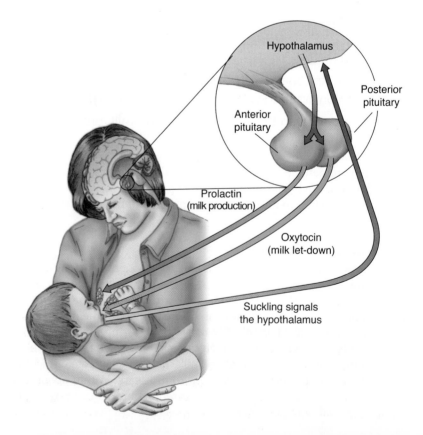

Figure 14.20 **Hormones of lactation**
When the infant suckles, nerve receptors in the nipple send signals to the hypothalamus, which signals the release of prolactin and oxytocin.

infant. It can be inhibited by nervous tension, fatigue, or embarrassment. The let-down response is essential for successful breast-feeding and makes suckling easier for the child. If let-down is slow, the child can become frustrated and difficult to feed.

Maternal Nutrient Needs During Lactation

The need for many nutrients is even greater during lactation than during pregnancy. This is because the mother is still providing for all of the energy and nutrient needs of the infant, who is growing faster and is more active than the fetus. Meeting the needs of lactation requires a varied nutrient-dense diet. Most lactating women can meet all their needs without supplements.

Energy and Macronutrient Needs During the first 6 months of lactation, approx-imately 600 to 900 mL (2.5 to 3.75 cups) of milk is produced daily, depending on how much the infant consumes. Human milk contains about 160 kcalories per cup (240 mL) so providing an infant with 3 cups of milk would require the mother to expend approximately 500 kcalories. Much of this must come from the diet, but some can come from mobilization of maternal fat stores, which increase during pregnancy. The EER for lactation is estimated by adding the total energy expenditure of nonlac-tating women and the energy in milk and then subtracting the energy supplied by maternal fat stores.[5] This is equal to an additional 330 kcalories per day during the first 6 months of lactation, and 400 kcalories per day during the second 6 months (see Figure 14.11). To ensure adequate protein for milk production, the RDA for lactation is increased by 25 grams per day. The RDA for carbohydrate and the AIs for linoleic and alpha-linolenic acids are also higher during lactation.[5]

Even though some of the energy for lactation comes from maternal fat stores, the impact of lactation on maternal weight loss is variable. Some studies report that breast-feeding does not affect the amount of weight lost, whereas others suggest it does so initially or if breast-feeding continues for at least 6 months.[47] Beginning 1 month after birth, most lactating women lose 1 to 2 lbs (0.5 to 1 kg) per month for 6 months. Some women will lose more, and others may maintain or even gain weight regardless of whether or not they breast-feed. Rapid weight loss is not recommended during lactation because it can decrease milk production. However, regular exercise can make weight loss easier and does not impair milk production.

Water Needs During Lactation The amount of milk a woman produces depends on how much her baby demands. The more the infant suckles, the more milk is pro-duced. To avoid dehydration and ensure adequate milk production, lactating women need to consume about 1 liter of additional water per day. The AI of 3.8 liters per day, of which about 3.1 liters is from drinking water and other beverages, is based on typ-ical intake during lactation.[10] Consuming an extra glass of milk, juice, or water at every meal and whenever the infant nurses can help ensure adequate fluid intake.

Micronutrient Needs During Lactation The recommended intakes for several vitamins and minerals are increased during lactation to meet the metabolic needs of synthesizing milk and to replace the nutrients secreted in the milk itself (see Figure 14.11). Maternal intake of some vitamins including C, B_6, B_{12}, A, and D can affect milk composition. When maternal intake is low, the amounts in milk are decreased. The recommended intakes of vitamin B_6, vitamin B_{12}, other B vitamins, and vitamins A, C, and E are increased above nonlactating levels. Because vitamin B_{12} may be de-ficient in the breast milk of vegan mothers, their infants should be supplemented with vitamin B_{12}.

For other nutrients, levels in the milk are maintained at the expense of maternal stores. For example, much of the calcium secreted in human milk comes from an in-crease in maternal bone resorption. However, the AI for calcium is not increased above nonlactating levels because the loss of calcium from maternal bones is not pre-vented by increases in dietary calcium. In addition, the lost bone calcium is fully re-stored within a few months of weaning, and therefore women who breast-feed have not been found to have a long-term deficit in bone mineral density.[48] Folate needs are increased above nonpregnant levels to account for the amount needed to replace folate secreted in milk.[25]

Iron needs are not increased during lactation because little iron is lost in milk, and, in most women, losses are decreased because menstruation is absent. The RDA for lactation is 9 mg per day, half that of nonlactating women.

14.5 The Nutritional Needs of Infancy

Learning Objectives

- Compare the energy and macronutrient needs of newborns with those of adults.
- List micronutrients that are likely to be deficient in infants.
- Explain the best way to monitor the adequacy of an infant's dietary intake.

When a child is born and the umbilical cord is cut, he or she suddenly becomes actively involved in obtaining nutrients rather than being passively fed through the placenta. The energy and nutrients the infant consumes must support his or her continuing growth and development and increasing level of activity (**Table 14.4**).

Table 14.4 Energy and Nutrient Needs of Infants Compared to Adults

Nutrient/Energy	Newborn Recommendation (0–6 mo)	Adult Recommendation
Energy[a]	493–606 kcal/day (~100 kcal/kg/day)	2403–3067 kcal/day (~30 kcal/kg/day)
Protein	9.1 g/day 1.52 g/kg/d	46–56 g/day 0.8 g/kg/day
Carbohydrate	at least 60 g/day 40% of energy intake[b]	at least 130 g/day 45%–65% of energy intake
Fat Linoleic acid α-linolenic acid	50% of energy[b] 4.4 g/day[c] 0.5 g/day[d]	20%–35% of energy 12–17 g/day 1.1–1.6 g/day
Fluid	0.7 liters	2.7–3.7 liters

[a]The energy values are based on EER prediction equations for infants 0–6 months of age and for adults ≥19 years of age.
[b]Based on the composition of human milk.
[c]Refers to all omega-6 polyunsaturated fatty acids.
[d]Refers to all omega-3 polyunsaturated fatty acids.

Energy Needs During Infancy

During the first few months after birth, growth is more rapid than at any other time of life. As a result, newborn infants need more kcalories per pound of body weight than at any other time. EERs for infants are calculated from total energy expenditure plus the energy deposited in tissues due to growth[5] (see inside cover). After the first few months growth slows some and activity increases. Differences in growth rates and activity levels are reflected in the separate EER prediction equations for infants 0 to 3 months, 4 to 6 months, and 7 to 12 months.

Fat Recommendations

Healthy infants consume about 55% of their energy as fat during the first 6 months of life, and 40% during the second 6 months. This is far greater than the 20% to 35% of energy from fat recommended in the adult diet (**Figure 14.21**). The high propor-

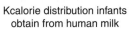

Kcalorie distribution infants
obtain from human milk

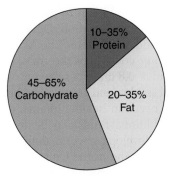

Recommended kcalorie distribution
for adults

Figure 14.21 Kcalorie distribution in infant versus adult diets
A comparison of the proportions of kcalories from carbohydrate, fat, and protein in human milk with the proportions recommended for an adult illustrates how much more fat infants need.

tion of fat increases the energy-density of the diet, allowing the infant's small stomach to hold enough to meet energy needs. An AI for total fat has been set at 31 grams per day for infants from birth to 6 months of age and at 30 grams per day for infants 7 to 12 months of age.

In addition to getting enough fat infants need the right kinds of fat. A sufficient supply of the long-chain polyunsaturated fatty acids docosahexaenoic acid (DHA, an omega-3 fatty acid) and arachidonic acid (an omega-6 fatty acid) are important for nervous system development. These fatty acids are constituents of cell membranes and are incorporated into brain tissue and the retina of the eye. Breast milk contains both of these fatty acids. Infant formulas supplemented with DHA and arachidonic acid are available but the addition of these fatty acids to infant formulas is not required in the United States.[49] Infants can synthesize these fatty acids from linoleic and α-linolenic acid, but since breast-fed infants have higher plasma concentrations of these long-chain polyunsaturated fatty acids than infants fed non-fortified formula, it is hypothesized that the rate of conversion may not be optimal. Evidence that inclusion of these fatty acids in infant formulas benefits growth, visual function, and cognitive development is equivocal.[50] AIs for infants have been set for total omega-3 and total omega-6 fatty acids based on the amounts of these types of fatty acids in human milk.[5]

Carbohydrate Intake

Carbohydrate, like fat, is a major contributor to energy intake in the infant. The source of carbohydrate for breast-fed infants and most bottle-fed infants is lactose. About 39% of the energy in breast milk is from lactose. As the infant grows and solid foods are introduced into the diet, the percentage of kcalories from carbohydrate in the diet increases and the percent from fat decreases.

Protein Requirements

The infant's protein requirement per unit of body weight is very high compared with the adult requirement: The AI is 1.52 grams per kilogram per day from birth to 6 months of age, compared with 0.8 grams per kilogram per day for an adult. The ideal protein source for newborns is human milk. Infant formulas are designed to mimic its amino acid pattern. A diet too high in protein may lead to dehydration because the excretion of metabolic wastes produced when excess protein is consumed increases water loss.

Water Needs

Infants have a higher proportion of body water than adults and they lose proportionately more body water in urine and through evaporation. Urine losses are high because the infant kidneys are poorly developed and unable to reabsorb much of the water that passes through them. Infants lose proportionately more water through evaporation because they have a larger surface area relative to their total body volume.

These factors, in addition to the fact that infants cannot tell us they are thirsty, put them at risk for dehydration. Despite this infants who are exclusively breast-fed do not require additional water. The AI is based on the volume of human milk consumed and the water content of the milk. It is set at 0.7 liters per day for infants 0 to 6 months and at 0.8 liters per day for older infants (7 to 12 months).[10] In older infants some fluid is obtained from other beverages and foods. Although breast milk can meet fluid needs in healthy infants, when water losses are increased by diarrhea or vomiting additional fluids may be needed.

In the developing world, dehydration from diarrhea is the most common cause of infant death, and in the United States it kills one child each day. The cause of the diarrhea is usually a bacterial or viral infection. The fluid intake of infants with diarrhea should be monitored carefully, and a pediatrician should be contacted. Mixtures of sugar, water, and electrolytes are available to replace lost fluids.

Micronutrient Needs of Infants

Human milk and formula are designed to meet the nutrient needs of young infants. Nonetheless, infants may still be at risk for deficiencies of iron, vitamin D, and vitamin K, and suboptimal levels of fluoride. The breast-fed infants of vegan mothers may also be at risk of vitamin B_{12} deficiency.

Iron Iron is the nutrient most commonly deficient in infants who are consuming adequate energy and protein. Iron deficiency is usually not a problem during the first 4 to 6 months of life because infants have iron stores at birth and the iron in human milk, though not particularly abundant, is very well absorbed. The AI for iron from birth to 6 months is only 0.27 mg per day.[27] After 4 to 6 months, iron stores are depleted but iron needs remain high to provide for hemoglobin synthesis, tissue growth, and iron storage. The RDA for infants 7 to 12 months jumps to 11 mg per day.[27] To meet needs after 4 to 6 months the diets of breast-fed infants should contain other sources of iron, such as iron-fortified rice cereal. Formula-fed infants can obtain iron from fortified formula.

Vitamin D Newborns are also potentially at risk for vitamin D deficiency. Breast milk is relatively low in vitamin D, so breast-fed infants who do not receive adequate exposure to sunlight, such as those living in cold climates, may not obtain adequate vitamin D. To synthesize adequate vitamin D, about 15 minutes per day of sun exposure, with only the face uncovered, is needed for light-skinned babies; a longer time is required for darker-skinned babies (**Figure 14.22**). An AI of 5 μg per day of vitamin D has been set for infants 0 to 12 months of age. Infant formulas contain 10 μg of vitamin D per liter of formula. It is recommended that all breast-fed infants receive 10 μg of oral vitamin D daily beginning during the first 2 months of life and continuing until they are obtaining this amount of dietary vitamin D from other sources.[51]

Vitamin K Vitamin K, which is essential for normal blood clotting, is another nutrient for which newborns are at risk of deficiency. Little of this vitamin crosses the placenta from mother to fetus, and because the gut is sterile at birth, no microbial vitamin K synthesis occurs. Breast milk is also low in vitamin K, so breast-fed infants are at risk of hemorrhage due to vitamin K deficiency. To prevent this it is recommended that all breast-fed infants receive a single intramuscular injection containing 0.5 to 1.0 mg of vitamin K after the first feeding is completed and within the first 6 hours of life.[52] This provides them with enough vitamin K to last until their intestines are colonized with the bacteria that synthesize it.

Figure 14.22 Dark skin pigmentation reduces the amount of vitamin D that can be synthesized in the skin, putting darker-skinned babies at greater risk for deficiency. (Photodisc/Getty Images, Inc.),

Fluoride Fluoride is important in the development of teeth, even before they erupt. Breast milk is low in fluoride, and formula manufacturers use unfluoridated water in preparing liquid formula. Therefore, breast-fed infants, infants fed premixed formula, and those fed formula mixed with low-fluoride water are often supplemented beginning at 6 months of age. In areas where the drinking water is fluoridated, infants fed formula reconstituted with tap water should not be given fluoride supplements.

Vitamin B$_{12}$ Breast milk and infant formula typically contain enough vitamin B$_{12}$ to meet the infant's needs. An exception is the breast milk of a vegan mother, which may be deficient in vitamin B$_{12}$. Therefore, breast fed-infants of vegan mothers should be supplemented with vitamin B$_{12}$.

Assessing Infant Growth

Although nutrient needs for infants are fairly well defined, it is difficult to calculate an infant's actual nutrient intake—particularly if they are breast-feeding. The best indicator of adequate nourishment is normal growth. Most healthy infants follow standard patterns of growth, so their growth can be monitored using growth charts[53] (see Appendix B).

Growth Charts Growth charts plot typical growth patterns of infants, children, and adolescents in the United States (**Figure 14.23**). They can be used to monitor an infant's pattern of growth and to compare length, weight, and head circumference to

CDC Growth Charts: United States

Weight-for-age percentiles: Boys, birth to 36 months

This infant's birth weight was at the 40th percentile, and he remained at this percentile into childhood.

SOURCE: Developed by the National Center for Health Statistics in collaboration with the Nation Center for Chronic Disease Prevention and Health Promotion (2000).

Figure 14.23 Monitoring infant growth
The black line on this weight-for-age growth chart for boys from birth to 36 months shows the pattern of growth for an infant whose birth weight was at the 40th percentile.

standards for infants of the same age. The resulting ranking, or percentile, indicates where the infant's growth falls in relation to population standards. For example, if a newborn boy is at the 20th percentile for weight, it means that 19% of newborn boys weigh less and 80% weigh more. Children usually continue at the same percentiles as they grow.

Whether an infant is 6 lbs or 8 lbs at birth, the pattern of growth should be approximately the same—rapid initially and slowing slightly as the infant approaches 1 year of age. A rule of thumb is that an infant's birth weight should double by 4 months and triple by 1 year of age. In the first year of life, most infants increase their length by 50% (**Figure 14.24**). Small infants and premature infants often follow a pattern parallel to but below the growth curve for a period of time and then experience catch-up growth that brings them onto the growth curve in a place compatible with their genetic growth potential.

Abnormal Growth Slight fluctuations in growth rate are normal, but a consistent pattern of not following the growth curve or a sudden change in growth pattern is cause for concern and could indicate overnutrition or undernutrition. A rapid increase in weight without an increase in height may be an indicator that the infant is being overfed. Because overweight children grow into overweight adults, this pattern of weight increase should be addressed early in life.

Growth that is slower than the predicted pattern indicates **failure to thrive**. This is a catch-all term for any type of growth failure in a young child. The cause may be a congenital condition, the presence of disease, poor nutrition, neglect, abuse, or psychosocial problems. The treatment is usually an individualized plan that includes adequate nutrition and careful monitoring by physicians, dietitians, and other health-care professionals. Just as there are critical periods in fetal life, there are critical periods for growth and development during infancy when undernutrition can permanently affect development.

Figure 14.24 An infant's length is measured in the recumbent position using a lengthboard with a fixed headpiece and a movable footpiece. (Paul Conklin/PhotoEdit, Inc.)

failure to thrive The inability of a child's growth to keep up with normal growth curves.

14.6 Feeding the Newborn

Learning Objective

- List the advantages and disadvantages of breast-feeding and bottle-feeding.

Newborns have small stomachs, can consume only liquids, and have high nutrient requirements. The ideal food for the newborn is breast milk, but infant formula can also meet a newborn's needs. From birth until 4 to 6 months of age infants don't need anything other than breast milk or formula. Solid food should not be introduced into the diet until the child is at least 4 to 6 months of age because the infant's feeding abilities and gastrointestinal tract are not mature enough to handle solid foods.

A relatively common problem in infants is **colic**. Colic involves daily periods of inconsolable crying that cannot be stopped by holding, feeding, or changing the infant. Colic usually begins at a few weeks of age and continues through the first 2 to 3 months. It occurs in both breast- and bottle-fed infants. Although its cause is unknown, it is hypothesized that colic is related to intestinal gas caused by milk intolerance, improper feeding practices, or immaturity of the central nervous system.

colic Inconsolable crying that is believed to be due to pain from gas buildup in the gastrointestinal tract or immaturity of the central nervous system.

Meeting Nutrient Needs with Breast-Feeding

It is estimated that if all women in the United States breast-fed their babies it could decrease annual health-care costs by $3.6 billion.[54] Breast milk meets the nutrient needs of the human newborn, requires no special preparation, and the amount available varies with demand. Thus, breast-feeding is the preferred form of infant nutrition and is usually the recommended choice for feeding the newborn of a healthy, well-nourished mother.[55,56]

Nutritional Advantages of Breast Milk The nutrient composition of breast milk is specifically designed for the human infant and changes over time as the infant develops, meeting the nutrient needs of the child for up to the first year of life. The first fluid that is produced by the breast after delivery is colostrum. This yellowish fluid is higher in water, protein, immune factors, minerals, and some vitamins than mature breast milk. It is produced for up to a week after delivery. While colostrum is produced, it may seem that the newborn is not receiving enough to eat; however, supplemental bottle feedings are not necessary. The nutrients in colostrum meet infant needs until mature milk production begins. Colostrum also has beneficial effects on the gastrointestinal tract, acting as a laxative that helps the baby excrete the thick, mucusy stool produced during life in the womb.

Lactalbumin is the predominant protein in human milk. In the infant's stomach it forms a soft, easily digested curd. The amino acids methionine and phenylalanine, which are difficult for the infant to metabolize, are present in lower amounts in human milk proteins than in cow's milk proteins. Human milk is also a good source of taurine, an amino acid needed for bile salt formation and eye and brain function.

The lipids in human milk are easily digested. They are high in cholesterol and the fatty acids linoleic acid, arachidonic acid, and DHA, which are essential for normal brain development, eyesight, and growth. The fat content of breast milk changes throughout a feeding, gradually increasing during the nursing session. Thus, for the baby to attain satiety and obtain adequate energy, it is important for nursing to continue long enough for the infant to obtain the higher-fat milk.

Lactose is the primary carbohydrate in human milk. It is digested slowly so it stimulates the growth of acid-producing bacteria. It also promotes the absorption of calcium and other minerals and provides a source of the sugar galactose for nervous system development.

Breast milk is low in sodium and the zinc, iron, and calcium present are in forms that are easily absorbed.[56] About 50% of the iron in human milk is absorbed, compared with only 2% to 30% from many other foods.

Other Advantages of Breast-Feeding Breast-feeding can be a relaxing, emotionally enjoyable interaction for both mother and infant. In addition to its nutritional advantages breast-feeding is convenient, inexpensive, and has immunological and physiological benefits for both mother and child (**Table 14.5**).

During the first few months of life, the immune factors provided first by colostrum, and later by mature milk, compensate for the infant's immature immune system. These include antibody proteins and immune system cells that pass from the mother into her milk. Breast milk also contains a number of enzymes and other proteins that prevent the growth of harmful microorganisms. Several carbohydrates have been identified that protect against disease-causing microorganisms, including viruses that cause diarrhea. One substance favors the growth of the beneficial bacterium *Lactobacillus bifidus* in the infant's colon, which inhibits the growth of harmful bacteria. Breast-fed babies have fewer allergies, ear infections, respiratory illnesses, and urinary tract infections than formula-fed babies, and have fewer problems with constipation and diarrhea. There is also evidence that breast-feeding protects against sudden infant death syndrome, diabetes, and chronic digestive diseases.[56]

In addition to providing disease protection the strong suckling required by breast-feeding aids in the development of facial muscles, which help in speech development and the correct formation of teeth. Breast-fed babies are also less likely to be overfed, because the amount of milk consumed cannot be monitored visually. In bottle-feeding, it is often tempting to encourage the baby to finish the entire bottle whether or not he or she is hungry.

Table 14.5 Advantages and Disadvantages of Breast- and Formula-Feeding

Advantage/Disadvantage	Breast-Feeding	Formula-Feeding
Nutrients	Ideal food for human babies. Composition changes as they eat and grow.	Modeled after human milk, but certain components cannot be duplicated. Composition does not change with time. Must be prepared carefully to supply the correct nutrient mix and ratio of nutrients to fluid.
Amount	Underfeeding can be a problem in newborns if the mother is not well versed in breast-feeding and the signs of dehydration in the infant.	Overfeeding is a risk because of the desire of caregivers to have the baby empty the bottle.
Immunity	Immune factors are transferred from mother to infant.	There are no immune factors in formula.
Allergies	Allergies to breast milk are very rare and the risk of food allergies is reduced.	There are a variety of choices if the infant is allergic to one type of formula.
Risk from mother	Certain contaminants such as environmental pollutants, medications, illicit drugs, and disease-causing organisms such as HIV can pass from mother to baby.	None.
Environmental contamination	Breast milk is sterile, but pumped milk can become contaminated if stored improperly.	Bacterial contamination is a risk if formula is prepared under unsanitary conditions or stored improperly.
Ease for caregivers	No equipment to wash, always available, but may require more time from the mother.	Requires more preparation and washing, but other family members can share responsibility for feeding.
Ease for baby	Suckling is harder for the baby but aids in development of teeth and facial muscles needed for speech. Weak or sick infants can easily consume pumped breast milk.	Easier for baby, which is especially important for weak or sick infants.*
Benefit to mother	Promotes uterine contractions, which help the uterus return to prepregnancy size. May promote loss of weight and body fat. May reduce risk of breast cancer.	May allow more sleep.*
Cost	Cheaper, but the mother must be well nourished.	More expensive than nursing and cost includes formula as well as equipment and energy used in preparation.

*Breast milk fed from a bottle can be used to nourish weak or sick infants and can give the mother a break from breast-feeding.

For the mother, breast-feeding has the advantage of providing a readily available and inexpensive source of nourishment for her infant. It requires no preparation or bottles and nipples that must be washed. It is more ecological because it doesn't require energy for manufacture or generate waste from discarded packaging. Physiologically, breast-feeding causes contractions that help the mother's uterus return to normal size more quickly and may promote weight loss in some women. Women who breast-feed may have a lower risk of developing osteoporosis and breast and ovarian cancer. Lactation also inhibits ovulation, lengthening the time between pregnancies; however, it does not reliably prevent ovulation and so cannot be effectively used for birth control. Oral contraceptives can be used immediately postpartum, but those containing only progestin are preferable because they do not affect milk volume or composition. Oral contraceptives containing estrogen may decrease milk volume.

How Much Is Enough? A strong, healthy baby will be able to suckle shortly after birth. Within a week, milk production and breast-feeding are usually fully established (**Figure 14.25**). During the early weeks of breast-feeding the infant should be fed about 8 to 12 times every 24 hours (every 2 to 3 hours) or whenever the infant shows early signs of hunger. A feeding should last approximately 8 to 12 minutes at each breast. A well-fed newborn should urinate enough to soak six to eight diapers a day and gain about one-third to one-half pound per week.

How Long Should Breast-Feeding Continue? Physiologically, lactation can continue as long as suckling is maintained. Breast-feeding alone is sufficient to support optimal growth for about 6 months and the American Academy of Pediatrics and many other health organizations recommend exclusive breast-feeding for the first 6 months of life.[55,56] However, currently only about 17% of infants are exclusively breast-fed for 6 months. Breast-feeding along with supplemental feeding of solids is recommended for at least the first year of life and beyond for as long as mutually desired by mother and child. After 12 months, the baby no longer needs breast milk to meet nutrient needs. As the infant obtains more and more of its energy from solid foods, milk production decreases due to reduced demand by the infant. However, breast-feeding beyond 12 months continues to provide nutrition, comfort, and an emotional bond between mother and child. In developing nations it may continue to give children the nutritional advantage needed to fight infection and stay healthy. The World Health Organization recommends that infants in developing nations be breast-fed for 2 years or more.[57]

Practical Aspects of Breast-Feeding Breast-feeding does not always come naturally to mother or infant and can require practice and patience. Effective suckling by the infant and relaxation of the mother are essential to successful breast-feeding. Some foods and other substances in the mother's diet, such as garlic or spicy foods, contain chemicals or flavors that pass into breast milk and cause adverse reactions in some babies. These reactions seem to be individual to the mother and child. As long as a food does not affect the infant's response to feeding, it can be included in the mother's diet. Caffeine in the mother's diet can make the infant jittery and excitable, so large amounts should be avoided while breast-feeding. Alcohol, which is harmful for infants, passes into breast milk. It is most concentrated an hour to an hour and a half after consumption and is cleared from the milk at about the same rate it disappears from the bloodstream. Therefore, occasional limited alcohol consumption while breast-feeding is probably not harmful if intake is timed to minimize the amount present in milk when the infant is fed.

Breast-feeding does not mean that a mother must be available for every feeding. Milk may be pumped from the breast and stored for later feedings (**Figure 14.26**). Since pumped milk is exposed to pumps and bottles, care must be taken to avoid contamination. If pumped milk is not immediately fed to the baby, it should be refrigerated. It can be kept refrigerated for 24 to 48 hours, but if it will not be used

Figure 14.25 By the time an infant is a week old, mother and child have usually adjusted to breast-feeding. (Richard Lord/The Image Works)

Figure 14.26 Breast pumps can be used to pump milk for bottle-feedings, relieving a mother of responsibility for all feedings. (Myrleen Ferguson Cate/PhotoEdit)

within that period, it should be frozen in clean containers. Warming breast milk in a microwave is not recommended because this destroys some of its immune properties and it may result in dangerously hot portions of the milk. The best way to warm milk is by running warm water over the bottle.

Meeting Nutrient Needs with Bottle-Feeding

A hundred years ago a baby who could not be breast-fed had little chance of survival. Today, infants who cannot breast-feed can still thrive. There are many commercially available infant formulas modeled after the nutrient content of breast milk.

When Is Bottle-Feeding Best? There are some situations when breast-feeding is not the best choice. An infant who is small or weak may not have the strength to receive adequate nutrition from breast-feeding. In this case, formula, which provides almost the same nutrients as breast milk, can be used, or pumped breast milk can be offered to the infant in a bottle.

Bottle-feeding prevents the transmission of drugs and disease via breast milk. Women who are taking medications should check with their physician as to whether it is safe to breast-feed. If prescription drugs are taken by the mother for only a short time, a breast pump may be used to maintain milk production and the milk discarded, until the medication is no longer needed. Because alcohol and drugs such as cocaine and marijuana can be passed to the baby in breast milk, alcoholic and drug-addicted mothers are counseled not to breast-feed. Nicotine from cigarette smoke is also rapidly transferred from maternal blood to milk, and heavy smoking may decrease the supply of milk. Tuberculosis and certain viral infections can be transmitted to the infant in breast milk, but common illnesses such as colds, flu, and skin infections should not interfere with breast-feeding. Human immunodeficiency virus (HIV), the virus that causes AIDS, can be transmitted to the infant in breast milk. In the United States, women who are infected with HIV are advised not to breast-feed, but in developing nations, the risk of malnutrition associated with not breast-feeding often outweighs the risk of passing this infection on to the infant.

How Much Is Enough? As with breast-fed infants, formula-fed infants should be fed on demand every few hours. Newborns have small stomachs, so at each feeding they may consume only a few ounces of formula. As the infant grows, the amount consumed at each feeding will increase to 4 to 8 oz. Caregivers should respond to cues from the infant that hunger is satisfied, even if a bottle of formula is not finished. Encouraging infants to finish every bottle can result in overfeeding and excess weight gain. As with breast-fed infants, adequate intake can be judged from the amount of urine produced and the amount of weight gained.

Practical Aspects of Bottle-Feeding Infant formula must be prepared carefully in order to avoid mixing errors and contamination. If the proper measurements are not used in preparing formula, the child can receive an excess or deficiency of nutrients and an improper ratio of nutrients to fluids. If the water and all the equipment used in preparing formula are not clean or if the prepared formula is left unrefrigerated, food-borne illness may result. Because sanitation is often a problem in developing nations, infections that lead to diarrhea and dehydration occur more commonly in formula-fed than in breast-fed infants. Commercially prepared formulas are sterile and powdered formulas contain no harmful microorganisms. To avoid introducing harmful microorganisms, the water used to mix powdered formula should be boiled for 1 to 2 minutes and allowed to cool before mixing. Hands should be washed before preparing formula, and bottles and nipples should be washed in a dishwasher or placed in a pan of boiling water for 5 minutes. Formula should be prepared immediately before a feeding, and any excess should be discarded. Opened cans of ready-to-feed and liquid concentrate formula should be covered and refrigerated and used within the time indicated on the can. Formula may be fed either warm or cold, but the temperature should be consistent.

Figure 14.27 Proper feeding position during bottle-feeding allows the formula to be swallowed easily and prevents air from being swallowed. (Zephyr Picture/Photolibrary)

The position of the child is important during feeding. The infant's head should be higher than his or her stomach, and the bottle should be tilted so that there is no air in the nipple (**Figure 14.27**). If the hole in the nipple is too large, the infant may feel full before receiving adequate nutrition. If the hole is too small, the infant may tire before nutrient needs are met. Just as breast-fed infants alternate breasts, bottle-fed infants should be held alternately between the left and right arms to promote equal development of the head and neck muscles.

Infants should never be put to bed with a bottle of formula. At night, while the child sleeps, the flow of saliva is decreased and the sugary formula is allowed to remain in contact with the teeth for many hours. This causes the rapid and serious decay of the upper teeth referred to as **nursing bottle syndrome**. Usually, the lower teeth are protected by the tongue and are unaffected (**Figure 14.28**).

Formula Choices Infant formulas can never duplicate the living cells, active hormones, enzymes, and immune system molecules in human milk, but formulas today try to replicate human milk as closely as possible in order to match the growth, nutrient absorption, and other parameters obtained with breast-feeding. Formula is available in ready-to-feed, liquid concentrate, or powdered forms (see Your Choice: Which Infant Formula Is Best?). Although most formulas are based on cow's milk, unmodified cows' milk should never be fed to infants. It is difficult for an infant to digest and its higher protein and mineral content taxes the kidneys and predisposes the infant to dehydration. Young infants may also become anemic if fed cow's milk because it contains little absorbable iron and can lead to iron loss by causing small amounts of gastrointestinal bleeding. Unmodified goat's milk is also not recommended for infants. Although it is less allergenic and more easily digested than cow's milk, it is low in vitamin D as well as iron, vitamin B_{12}, and folate, which can lead to an iron deficiency or megaloblastic anemia. Cow's milk and goat's milk can be introduced at about 12 months of age when organ systems are more mature and missing nutrients can be provided by other foods.

In addition to formulas for healthy infants, there are special formulas available for infants with allergies, premature infants, and those with genetic abnormalities that alter dietary needs. For infants who cannot tolerate human milk or cow's milk-based formula, soy protein formulas are available. And for those who are allergic to soy protein, formulas made from predigested proteins (elemental formulas), called protein hydrolysates, are an option.

Premature infants have special needs because they do not have fully developed organ systems or metabolic pathways. If they are too small or weak to nurse or take a bottle, pumped breast milk or formula can be fed through a tube. Some nutrients that are produced in the bodies of full-term infants are essential in the diets of premature infants. For example, preterm infants are less able to synthesize

nursing bottle syndrome Extreme tooth decay in the upper teeth resulting from putting a child to bed with a bottle containing milk or other sweet liquids.

Figure 14.28 Nursing bottle syndrome causes rapid decay of the child's upper front teeth. (K. L. Boyd/Custom Medical Stock Photo, Inc.)

(©iStockphoto)

Which Infant Formula Is Best?

Selecting an infant formula can be confusing. Is one safer or more nutritious? Is cow's milk formula better than soy-based? Should you choose a formula supplemented with iron or fatty acids? Is premixed better than powdered?

The safety and nutrient content of commercially prepared infant formulas are equivalent because they are regulated by the FDA. The FDA specifies minimum amounts of 29 nutrients based on levels in breast milk and requires formula labels to include use-by dates. If used before this date the formula will contain at least the levels of nutrients listed on the label.

The biggest difference between formulas is in the type of protein and sugar they contain. Most are based on cow's milk. The standard cow's milk-based formulas contain heat-treated cow's milk protein (at reduced concentrations) and the sugar lactose. Infants who cannot tolerate cow's milk formulas can consume soy-based formulas or hydrolyzed cow's milk formulas, referred to as elemental formulas. Soy formulas are made with soy protein and contain sucrose or corn syrup instead of lactose. In elemental formulas, the proteins have been broken down to amino acids. They are more expensive than soy-based formulas but may be necessary for infants who are allergic to both milk and soy proteins.

Another difference between formulas is the amounts of iron and long chain fatty acids. Most infant formulas are fortified with iron. The American Academy of Pediatrics recommends iron-fortified formulas for all infants. The fats in formula come from vegetable oils and provide little of the long-chain polyunsaturated fatty acids DHA (docosahexanoic acid) and arachidonic acid. Arachidonic acid and DHA are found in breast milk and are thought to help infant development. Formulas supplemented with these fatty acids are available, but they are more expensive and it is still not clear whether they improve growth or visual or neurological development.

Formulas are marketed in three basic forms: ready-to-feed, liquid concentrates, and powdered. Ready-to-feed formulas require no preparation and are packaged in many sizes.

Liquid concentrates and powdered formulas are prepared for use by mixing them with specific amounts of water. When properly prepared, all provide the needed nutrients in appropriate concentrations. Problems arise when formulas are mixed incorrectly or when the water used to prepare them is contaminated. Water for formula should come from a safe source and be boiled before use.

In short, ready-to-feed formulas are easiest to use but may cost more and are heavier and bulkier to carry home from the store. Liquid concentrates are a good compromise because they provide more formula for less weight and are easy to mix. Powders are the least expensive and the easiest to transport home, but they require more measuring and mixing. Since all of these products are nutritionally comparable, this choice depends on the needs of the caregivers.

(Charles D. Winters)

the amino acids tyrosine and cysteine and the fatty acid DHA. These and other substances, such as taurine and carnitine, are needed in greater amounts in the diets of premature babies. The energy, protein, and micronutrient requirements of preterm infants are also higher due to their rapid growth and development. Preterm infant formulas are available to meet the needs of premature babies.

Genetic abnormalities that prevent the normal metabolism of specific nutrients may alter dietary needs. For instance, infants with the genetic disease PKU lack an enzyme needed to metabolize the amino acid phenylalanine (see Chapter 6). If a child with PKU is fed breast milk or a formula that contains too much phenylalanine, the by-products of phenylalanine metabolism accumulate and cause brain damage. This can be prevented by feeding infants with PKU a special formula that provides only enough phenylalanine to meet the need for protein synthesis. Because this special diet must be started as soon as possible, infants born in the United States and Canada are tested for PKU at birth.

Outcome

After her doctor's visit, Jasmine realized that the health of her baby was more important to her than whether or not she was a few pounds overweight after the delivery. Her doctor helped her understand that she needed to eat a diet higher in energy, protein, and many micronutrients than the one she consumed before she became pregnant. Jasmine took a prenatal supplement to help meet her micronutrient needs, but a pill can't provide the kcalories and protein she needs to build new tissues or fiber to prevent constipation. To construct her diet, Jasmine looked up her MyPyramid Plan for Moms. It called for an increase in her intake of grains and vegetables, which added energy, fiber, protein, folate, and vitamin C to her diet, and extra-lean meat, which provided iron, protein, zinc, and B vitamins. After 9 months Jasmine had gained 32 pounds and gave birth to a healthy 7 lb 8 oz baby boy. She breast-fed him for a year. While she was lactating, her need for energy, fluid, and certain micronutrients were even higher than they were during pregnancy. Although she felt like she was eating all the time, after 6 months she was back to her prepregnancy weight.

APPLICATIONS

Personal Nutrition

1. **If you were a 25-year-old pregnant woman, would your diet meet your needs?**

   a. Pick one day of the food record you kept in Chapter 2. Use iProfile to determine whether this diet meets the third trimester energy and protein recommendations of a 5'5" tall, 25-year-old sedentary pregnant woman who weighed 130 lbs at the beginning of her pregnancy? If it doesn't, what foods would you add to the diet to meet the needs of pregnancy?

   b. Does this diet meet the iron and calcium needs of a 25-year-old pregnant woman? List three foods that are good sources of each.

   c. Does this diet meet the folate needs of a 25-year-old pregnant woman? What foods could you add to a diet that is low in folate to meet needs without supplements? What foods in this diet are fortified with folic acid?

2. **How do the energy and nutrient needs of nonpregnant, pregnant, and lactating women differ?**

   a. For each of the following, describe any differences between the needs of nonpregnant, pregnant, and lactating women of similar age and size.
   - Energy
   - Protein
   - Calcium
   - Iron
   - Folate

   b. For each of the above, explain why the requirements for pregnancy and lactation do or do not differ from those for the nonpregnant state.

 iProfile

General Nutrition

1. **Use the Internet to find out about the WIC program in your area.**

   a. Would it be easy for you to use this program if you were a pregnant or lactating woman or had a young child?

   b. What income levels does it serve?

2. **Marina is 16 years old and is pregnant with her first child. She is 5'4" and weighs 110 lbs. She eats breakfast at home with her mother and two brothers and has lunch in the school cafeteria. After school she often has a snack with friends and then has dinner at home. A day's sample diet is listed here:**

SAMPLE DIET

FOOD	SERVING SIZE	FOOD	SERVING SIZE
Breakfast		*Snack*	
Pastry	1	Ice cream cone	1
Fruit punch	6 oz	*Dinner*	
Lunch		Chicken	1 drumstick
Hamburger	1	Rice	1 cup
on bun	1	Refried beans	1/2 cup
Canned peaches	1/2 cup	Tortillas	3
Diet cola	12 oz	Fruit punch	12 oz

   a. What is the RDA or AI for folate, vitamin D, calcium, iron, and zinc for a 16-year-old pregnant woman?

   b. Does Marina's diet meet the recommendations for these nutrients?

   c. Use iProfile to determine how many kcalories her diet provides?

   d. Will Marina gain the recommended amount of weight if she consumes this diet throughout her pregnancy?

   e. What dietary changes would you suggest to meet the needs of the second trimester of pregnancy and to ensure a healthy pregnancy for both Marina and her baby?

Summary

14.1 The Physiology of Pregnancy

- Pregnancy begins with the fertilization of an egg by a sperm. About two weeks after fertilization implantation is complete. The embryo grows, and the cells differentiate to form the organs and structures of the body. Growth and maturation continue in the fetal period, which begins at

9 weeks, and continues until birth, about 38 weeks after fertilization.

- During pregnancy, the placenta develops; maternal blood volume increases; the uterus and supporting muscles expand; body fat is deposited; the heart, lungs, and kidneys work harder; the breasts enlarge; and total body weight increases. Changes in the mother and growth of the fetus result in weight gain. Recommended weight gain during pregnancy is 25–35 lbs for normal-weight women. Normal-weight, underweight, overweight, and obese mothers should all gain weight at a steady rate during pregnancy.

- During healthy pregnancies, a carefully planned program of moderate-intensity exercise can be beneficial and safe.
- Changes in blood volume and hormone levels and the enlargement of the uterus can result in edema, morning sickness, heartburn, constipation, and hemorrhoids during pregnancy.
- The hypertensive disorders of pregnancy include chronic hypertension, gestational hypertension, and preeclampsia, which can lead to life-threatening eclampsia. Gestational diabetes can result in a large-for-gestational-age baby.

14.2 The Nutritional Needs of Pregnancy

- During pregnancy, the requirements for energy, protein, water, vitamins, and minerals increase. The B vitamins are needed to support increased energy and protein metabolism; calcium, vitamin D, and vitamin C are needed for bone and connective tissue growth; protein, folate, vitamin B_{12}, and zinc are needed for cell replication; and iron is needed for red blood cell synthesis.
- Even with a nutrient dense diet, which follows a MyPyramid Plan for Moms, supplements of folic acid and iron are recommended during pregnancy.

14.3 Factors that Increase the Risks of Pregnancy

- Nutritional status is important before, during, and after pregnancy. Poor nutrition before pregnancy can decrease fertility or lead to a poor pregnancy outcome. Malnutrition during pregnancy can affect fetal growth and development and the risk that the child will develop chronic disease later in life.
- Poor maternal health status, age that is under 20 or over 35 years, a short interval between pregnancies, a history of poor reproductive outcomes, and poverty all increase the risks of complications for the mother and baby.

- Because the embryo and fetus are developing and growing rapidly, they are susceptible to damage from physical, chemical, or other environmental teratogens. Mercury in food, food-borne pathogens, cigarette smoking, alcohol use, and certain prescription and illegal drugs can interfere with growth and development of the embryo and fetus.

14.4 Lactation

- Milk production and let-down are triggered by the hormones prolactin and oxytocin, respectively. They are released in response to the suckling of the infant.
- During lactation the need for protein, water, and many vitamins and minerals is even greater than during pregnancy.

14.5 The Nutritional Needs of Infancy

- Newborns grow more rapidly and require more energy and protein per kilogram of body weight than at any other time in life. Fat and water needs are also proportionately higher than in adults.
- A diet that meets energy, protein, and fat needs may not necessarily meet the needs for iron, fluoride, and vitamins D and K.
- Growth, which is assessed using growth charts, is the best indicator of adequate nutrition in an infant.

14.6 Feeding the Newborn

- Breast milk is the ideal food for new babies. It is designed specifically for the human newborn; is always available; requires no special equipment, mixing, or sterilization; and provides immune protection.
- There are many infant formulas on the market that are patterned after human milk and provide adequate nutrition to the baby. Infant formulas are the best option when the mother is ill or is taking prescription or illicit drugs, or when the infant has special nutritional needs. The major disadvantages of formula-feeding are the potential for bacterial contamination, overfeeding, and the possibility of errors in mixing formula.

Review Questions

1. List three physiological changes that occur in the mother's body during pregnancy.

2. List three common digestive system discomforts that afflict pregnant women and explain why they occur.

3. Explain why the hypertensive disorders of pregnancy can be a risk to the mother and baby.

4. Why does gestational diabetes increase the risk of having a large-for-gestational-age baby?

5. How do energy and protein requirements change during pregnancy?

6. Why does the recommendation for iron intake increase during pregnancy?

7. How much weight should a woman gain during pregnancy?

8. How do the recommendations for weight gain differ for underweight, overweight, and obese women?

9. What kind of exercise is safe during pregnancy?

10. Why are folic acid supplements recommended even before pregnancy for women of childbearing age?

11. Are vegetarian diets safe for pregnant women? Why or why not?

12. Why does malnutrition early in pregnancy have different effects than malnutrition during the last trimester?

13. How does maternal age affect nutrient requirements during pregnancy?

14. How does alcohol consumed by a woman during pregnancy affect the child?

15. Why is the need for energy and some nutrients greater during lactation than pregnancy?

16. What is the best indicator of adequate nutrition in an infant?

17. What are the advantages of breast-feeding?

18. When is bottle-feeding a better choice?

References

1. Committee to Reexamine IOM Pregnancy Weight Guidelines, Institute of Medicine, National Research Council. *Weight Gain During Pregnancy: Reexamining the Guidelines*. Washington, DC: National Academies Press, 2009.

2. Kaiser, L., and Allen, L. A. Position of the American Dietetic Association: Nutrition and lifestyle for a healthy pregnancy outcome. *J. Am. Diet. Assoc.* 108: 553–561, 2008.

3. American College of Obstetricians and Gynecologists. ACOG Committee Opinion number 315, September 2005. Obesity in pregnancy. *Obstet. Gynecol.* 106(3): 671–675, 2005.

4. United States Department of Health and Services. 2008 Physical Activity Guidelines for Americans. Available online at http://www.health.gov/paguidelines/. Accessed May 13, 2009.

5. Institute of Medicine, Food and Nutrition Board. *Dietary Reference Intakes for Energy, Carbohydrates, Fiber, Fat, Protein and Amino Acids*. Washington, DC: National Academies Press, 2002.

6. Quinlan, J. D., and Hill, D. A. Nausea and vomiting of pregnancy. *Am. Fam. Physician* 68:121–128, 2003.

7. National Center for Health Statistics, Centers for Disease Control and Prevention. *FastStats: Infant Health*. Available online at www.cdc.gov/nchs/fastats/infant_health.htm. Accessed July 3, 2008.

8. National Center for Health Statistics, Centers for Disease Control and Prevention. *Deaths: Final Data for 2004*. Available online at www.cdc.gov/nchs/products/pubs/pubd/hestats/finaldeaths04/finaldeaths04.htm. Accessed July 30, 2008.

9. Chang, J., Elam-Evans, L. D., Berg, C. J. et al. Pregnancy-related mortality surveillance—United States, 1991–1999. *MMWR Morb. Mortal. Wkly. Rep.* 52:1–8, 2003.

10. Food and Nutrition Board, Institute of Medicine. *Dietary Reference Intakes Water, Potassium, Sodium, Chloride, and Sulfate*. Washington, DC: National Academies Press, 2004.

11. Kumar, A., Devi, S. G., Batra, S. et al. Calcium supplementation for the prevention of pre-eclampsia. *Int. J. Gynaecol. Obstet.* 104: 32–36, 2009.

12. Centers for Disease Control and Prevention. National Agenda for Public Health Action: A National Public Health Initiative on Diabetes and Women's Health. Available online at www.cdc.gov/diabetes/pubs/action/facts.htm/ Accessed April 11, 2009.

13. Office of Minority Health and Health Disparities, Centers for Disease Control and Prevention. *Eliminate Disparities in Diabetes*. Available online at www.cdc.gov/omhd/AMH/factsheets/diabetes.htm. Accessed February 23, 2009.

14. Damm, P. Future risk of diabetes in mother and child after gestational diabetes mellitus. *Int. J. Gynaecol. Obstet.* 104(Suppl. 1):S25–S26, 2009.

15. Food and Nutrition Board, Institute of Medicine. *Dietary Reference Intakes for Calcium, Phosphorus, Magnesium, Vitamin D, and Fluoride*. Washington, DC: National Academies Press, 1997.

16. Prentice, A. Micronutrients and the bone mineral content of the mother, fetus and newborn. *J. Nutr.* 133(5 Suppl 2): 1693S–1699S, 2003.

17. Kalkwarf, H. J., and Specker, B. L. Bone mineral changes during pregnancy and lactation. *Endocrine* 17:49–53, 2002.

18. Nesby-O'Dell, S., Scanlon, K. S., Cogswell, M. E. et. al. Hypovitaminosis D prevalence and determinants among African American and white women of reproductive age: Third National Health and Nutrition Examination Survey, 1988–1994. *Am. J. Clin. Nutr.* 76:187–192, 2002.

19. Hollis, B. W., and Wagner, C. L. Assessment of dietary vitamin D requirements during pregnancy and lactation. *Am. J. Clin. Nutr.* 79: 717–726, 2004.

20. Food and Nutrition Board, Institute of Medicine. *Dietary Reference Intakes for Vitamin C, Vitamin E, Selenium, and Carotenoids*. Washington, DC: National Academies Press, 2000.

21. Mitchell, L. E., Adzick, N. S., Melchionne, J. et al. Spina bifida. *Lancet* 364:1885–1895, 2004.

22. Centers for Disease Control and Prevention. Spina Bifida and Anencephaly Before and After Folic Acid Mandate—United States, 1995–1996 and 1999–2000, *MMWR Morb. Mortal. Wkly. Rep.* 17: 362–365, 2004. Available online at www.cdc.gov/MMWR/preview/mmwrhtml/mm5317a3.htm. Accessed April 17, 2008.

23. De Wals, P., Tairou, F., Van Allen, M. I. et al. Reduction in neural-tube defects after folic acid fortification in Canada. *N. Engl. J. Med.* 357: 135–142, 2007.

24. Scholl, T. O., and Johnson, W. G. Folic acid: Influence on the outcome of pregnancy. *Am. J. Clin. Nutr.* 71(Suppl.):1295S–1303S, 2000.

25. Food and Nutrition Board, Institute of Medicine. *Dietary Reference Intakes for Thiamin, Riboflavin, Niacin, Vitamin B-6, Folate, Vitamin B-12, Pantothenic Acid, Biotin, and Choline*. Washington, DC: National Academies Press, 1998.

26. King, J. C. Determinants of maternal zinc status during pregnancy. *Am. J. Clin. Nutr.* 71(Suppl.):1334S–1343S, 2000.

27. Food and Nutrition Board, Institute of Medicine. *Dietary Reference Intakes for Vitamin A, Vitamin K, Arsenic, Boron, Chromium, Copper, Iodine, Iron, Manganese, Molybdenum, Nickel, Silicon, Vanadium, and Zinc*. Washington, DC: National Academies Press, 2001.

28. Scholl, T.O. Iron status during pregnancy: Setting the stage for mother and infant. *Am J Clin Nutr* 81:1218S–1222S, 2005.

29. Mills, M.E. Craving more than food: The implications of pica in pregnancy. *Nurs Womens Health* 11:266–273, 2007.

30. Gluckman, P.D., Hanson, M.A., Cooper, C., and Thornburg, K.L. Effect of in utero and early-life conditions on adult health and disease. *N Engl J Med* 359:61–73, 2008.

31. Centers for Disease Control and Prevention. Pediatric and Pregnancy Nutrition Surveillance System, Health Indicators. Available online at www.cdc.gov/pednss/what_is/pnss_health_indicators.htm#Maternal%20Health%20Indicators/ Accessed January 12, 2006.

32. National Center for Health Statistics, Centers for Disease Control and Prevention. *FastStats: Teen Births.* Available online at www.cdc.gov/nchs/fastats/teenbrth.htm Accessed July 12, 2009.

33. Casanueva, E., Roselló-Soberón, M. E., and De-Regil, L. M. Adolescents with adequate birth weight newborns diminish energy expenditure and cease growth. *J Nutr* 136:2498–2501, 2006.

34. Kramer, M. S., Seguin, L., Lydon, J., and Goulet, L. Socio-economic disparities in pregnancy outcome: Why do the poor fare so poorly? *Paediatr. Perinat. Epidemiol.* 14:194–210, 2000.

35. Nason, C. S., Alexander, G. R., Pass, M. A., and Ballard, J. M. An evaluation of a Medicaid managed maternity program: The impact of comprehensive care coordination on utilization and pregnancy outcomes. *J. Health Hum. Serv. Admin.* 26:239–227, 2003.

36. U.S. Food and Drug Administration, Center for Food Safety and Applied Nutrition. Food Safety for Moms-to-Be. Available online at www.cfsan.fda.gov/~pregnant/safeats.html. Accessed April 19, 2009.

37. Weng, X., Odouli, R., and Li, D. K. Maternal caffeine consumption during pregnancy and the risk of miscarriage: A prospective cohort study. *Am. J. Ostet. Gynecol.* 198:279e1–279e8. Epub 2008.

38. Delgado, A.R. Listeriosis in pregnancy. *J Midwifery Womens Health* 53(3):255–259, 2008.

39. Center for the Evaluation of Risks to Human Reproduction (CERHR). *Toxoplasmosis.* Available online at http://cerhr.niehs.nih.gov/common/toxoplasmosis.html. Accessed July 16, 2008.

40. Goodlett, C. R., and Horn, K. H., Mechanisms of alcohol-induced damage to the developing nervous system. *Alcohol Res Health* 25:175–184, 2001. Available online at http://pubs.niaaa.nih.gov/publications/arh25–3/175–184.pdf/ Accessed April 20, 2009.

41. Rogers, J.M. Tobacco and pregnancy: Overview of exposures and effects. *Birth Defects Res. C. Embryo Today* 84:1–15, 2008.

42. Xiao, D., Huang, X., Yang, S., and Zhang, L. Direct effects of nicotine on contractility of the uterine artery in pregnancy. *J. Pharmacol. Exp. Ther.* 322(1): 180–185, 2007.

43. National Center for Chronic Disease Prevention and Health Promotion. *Women and Smoking: A Report of the Surgeon General*, March 2001. Available online at www.surgeongeneral.gov/library/womenandtobacco/. Accessed April 20, 2009.

44. The National Council on Alcoholism and Drug Dependence. Alcohol- and Other Drug-Related Birth Defects, Facts and Information. Available online at www.ncadd.org/facts/defects.html/ Accessed July 14, 2008.

45. Fajemirokun-Odudeyi, O., and Lindow, S. W. Obstetric implications of cocaine use in pregnancy: A literature review. *Eur. J. Obstet. Gyncol. Reprod. Biol.* 112:2–8, 2004.

46. Schiller, C., and Allen, P. J. Follow-up of infants prenatally exposed to cocaine. *Pediatr. Nurs.* 31:427–436, 2005.

47. Haiek, L. N., Kramer, M. S., Ciampi, A., and Tirado, R. Postpartum weight loss and infant feeding. *J. Am. Board Fam. Pract.* 14:85–94, 2001.

48. Kovacs, C.S. Calcium and bone metabolism during pregnancy and lactation. *J. Mammary Gland Biol. Neoplasia* 10:105–118, 2005.

49. American Academy of Pediatric Committee on Nutrition. New infant formula additives approved by FDA. *AAP News* 20:209, 2002.

50. Wright, K., Coverston, C., Tiedeman, M., and Abegglen, J. A. Formula supplemented with docosahexaenoic acid (DHA) and arachidonic acid (ARA): A critical review of the research. *J. Spec. Pediatr. Nurs.* 11:100–112, 2006.

51. Warner, C. L., Greer, F. R.; American Academy of Pediatrics, Section on Breastfeeding and Committee on Nutrition. Prevention of rickets and vitamin D deficiency in infants, children, and adolescents. *Pediatrics* 112:1142–1152, 2008.

52. American Academy of Pediatrics, Committee on Fetus and Newborn. Controversies concerning vitamin K and the newborn. *Pediatrics* 112:191–192, 2003.

53. U.S. Department of Health and Human Services, Centers for Disease Control and Prevention, National Center for Health Statistics. CDC Growth Charts: United States, Advance Data, No. 314, June 8, 2000 (revised). Available online at www.cdc.gov/growthcharts/ Accessed February 8, 2009.

54. Weimer, J. The Economic Benefits of Breast Feeding: A Review and Analysis. Food Assistance and Nutrition Research Report No. 13. Washington, DC: Food and Rural Economics Division, Economic Research Service, US Department of Agriculture; 2001.

55. American Academy of Pediatrics, Section on Breast-Feeding. Breast-feeding and the use of human milk. *Pediatrics* 115:496–506, 2005.

56. American Dietetic Association. Position of the American Dietetic Association: Promoting and supporting breastfeeding. *J. Am. Diet. Assoc.* 105:810–818, 2005.

57. WHO Fact Sheet No. 178: Reducing mortality from major childhood killer diseases. September 1997. Available online at www.who.int/inf-fs/en/fact178.html/ Accessed March 15, 2009.

15 Nutrition from Infancy to Adolescence

Case Study

Thirteen-year-old Felicia has been overweight since she was 3. When she entered the eighth grade, she was 5 feet tall and weighed 140 lb. At a recent checkup, her physician noted that her blood pressure was elevated and her cholesterol levels were at the high end of normal. The physician recommended that Felicia and her mother meet with a dietitian to discuss ways to manage Felicia's weight and improve her diet.

At that meeting, Felicia explained that she knows she should eat less and exercise more but can't find a way to make those changes. She spends most of her school day sitting at a desk. Physical education class meets only twice a week. She has to eat what is on the school menu because she gets a reduced-cost lunch as part of the National School Lunch Program. It is difficult for her to exercise after school because she goes to the library study program until her mother gets out of work at 5 P.M. Felicia gets a little more exercise on weekends by going out with friends, but they often go out for ice cream or fast food and Felicia feels left out if she doesn't join them.

The dietitian helps Felicia figure out some changes that will help reduce her kcalorie intake. She also works with Felicia's mother to plan low-kcalorie, nutritious dinners that the entire family will enjoy. Finally, Felicia and her mother decide to get some regular exercise by walking after dinner. These evening walks soon progress to activities that include the whole family, such as skating and bike riding. Felicia is on the right track, as good nutrition and exercise patterns learned early in life are key to maintaining long-term health later on.

(Blend Images/SUPERSTOCK)

(©iStockphoto)

(Darell/Stone/Getty Images)

Chapter Outline

15.1 Starting Right for a Healthy Life

Learning Objectives

- Discuss the healthfulness of children's diets in the U.S.
- Describe the impact of a child's nutrient intake on his or her long-term health.

Nutrient intake during childhood helps shape the adult that a child will become. A nutritious well-balanced eating pattern and active lifestyle allow children to grow to their potential and can prevent or delay the onset of the chronic diseases that plague American adults. Therefore, teaching healthy eating and exercise habits will benefit not only today's children, but tomorrow's adults (**Figure 15.1**).

What Are American Children Eating?

The diets of children today are not as healthy as they could be. Most children and adolescents in the United States consume more saturated fat and sodium and less calcium and fiber than is recommended. The typical diet contains too few fruits and vegetables and whole grains and too many processed foods that are high in fat, salt, or sugar.[1] When analyzed using the Healthy Eating Index, 60% to 80% of children between 2 and 9 years of age consumed diets that "need improvement." As children get older, the quality of their diet gets worse; they drink less milk and eat less fruit (**Figure 15.2**).[2]

Comparing the diets of children today with those of 25 years ago shows that intake of milk, vegetables, eggs, and grains has decreased while intake of cheese, fruits, juices, and sweetened beverages has increased. Children today eat more meals away from home and consume larger portion sizes.[1] Studies in adults as well as children suggest that the larger the portion served, the more the individual will eat. For example, when given lunch portions double the age-appropriate standard, children ages 3 to 5 consumed 15% more kcalories than when served the standard portion.[3] The amount of energy children consume from snacks has also increased and eating more kcalories from snacks is associated with being overweight.[4]

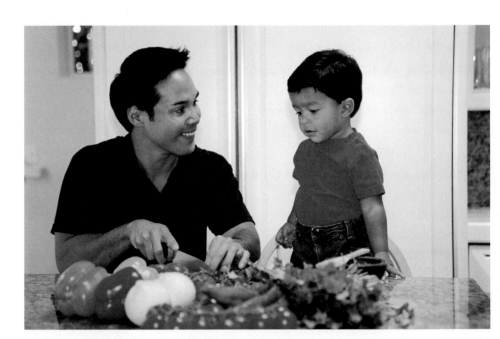

Figure 15.1 The foods and nutrients this child eats influence the eating habits and health of the adult he will become. (Banana Stock/Age Fotostock America, Inc.)

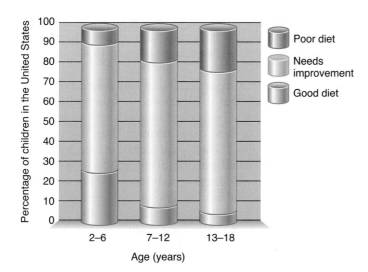

Figure 15.2 Diet quality of U.S. children.
The classification of children's diets as "poor", "needs improvement" or "good," is based on the Healthy Eating Index, which is a measure of diet quality based on how well the diet conforms to government dietary guidance. (Source: Centers for Disease Control and Prevention, 2001–2002 *National Health and Nutrition Examination Survey.*)

The Health of American Children

The high-kcalorie, high-saturated fat diet and low-activity lifestyle that contributes to obesity and chronic disease in adults is having the same effect in kids. As with adult obesity, childhood obesity increases the risks of chronic disease. Inactive, overweight children may have high blood cholesterol and glucose levels and elevated blood pressure. These factors increase the risk of developing heart disease, diabetes, and hypertension.[5,6]

Obesity Overweight and obesity are major problems in children in the United States. Over the last 25 years the total amount of energy consumed by American children has increased, and along with it the prevalence of obesity.[7] More than twice as many children and almost three times as many teens are overweight today as in 1980. About 16% of children and teens ages 2 to 19 are now overweight (**Figure 15.3**).[6]

In addition to the health issues, obese children and adolescents in the United States face social and psychological challenges. They are less well accepted by their peers than normal-weight children and are frequently ridiculed and teased. They often have a poor self-image and low self-esteem, particularly during the teenage years. Obese adolescents may be discriminated against by adults as well as by their peers. This contributes to feelings of rejection, social isolation, and low self-esteem.

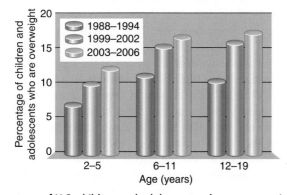

Figure 15.3 Percentage of U.S. children and adolescents who are overweight.
Results from the National Health and Nutrition Examination Surveys illustrate that the percentage of children and adolescents who are overweight is continuing to increase, even among very young children. (Source: Ogden, C. L., Flegal, K. M., Carroll, M. D., and Johnson, C. L. Prevalence and trends in overweight among U.S. children and adolescents, 1999–2000. JAMA 288:1728–1732, 2002; and Ogden, C. L., Carroll, M. D., and Flegal, K. M. High body mass index for age among U.S. children and adolescents, 2003–2006. JAMA 299:2401–2405, 2008.)

Figure 15.4 The social isolation experienced by many overweight teens contributes to inactivity and overeating, further exacerbating their weight problems. (Robert E. Daemmrich/Stone/Getty Images)

The isolation of obese adolescents from teen society results in boredom, depression, inactivity, and withdrawal—all of which can cause an increase in eating and a decrease in energy output, worsening the problem (**Figure 15.4**).

Type 2 Diabetes Until recently, type 2 diabetes was considered a disease that affected primarily adults over 40, but it is now on the rise among America's youth. About 3700 children and adolescents are diagnosed with type 2 diabetes in the United States each year. Most of these cases are in children 10–19 years and the incidence is higher among minorities.[8,9] The typical picture of type 2 diabetes in this population is a child from age 10 to mid-puberty, overweight, with a family history of the disease. Little is known about this disease in children, but it is a progressive disease that increases in severity with time from diagnosis. The longer an individual has diabetes, the greater the risk of complications that involve the circulatory system or nervous system and that can lead to blindness, kidney failure, heart disease, or amputations (see Chapter 4). Keeping children's weight in the healthy range and maintaining an active lifestyle can prevent diabetes.

Elevated Blood Cholesterol and Heart Disease Children in the United States currently consume more than the recommended maximum of 10% of their energy from saturated fat.[10] This can lead to elevated blood cholesterol levels. Children's diets are also lower in fiber than recommended.[1] Fiber has a role in decreasing the risk of heart disease, and diets high in fiber tend to be lower in fat, cholesterol, and energy. The recommended level for blood cholesterol in children ages 2 to 18 is less than 170 mg per 100 mL. In the United States, many children have blood cholesterol levels higher than this. Elevated blood cholesterol levels during childhood and adolescence are associated with higher blood cholesterol and higher mortality rates from cardiovascular disease in adulthood.[11]

The American Academy of Pediatrics recommends blood cholesterol screening for high-risk children and teenagers. This includes those with parents or grandparents who have a history of abnormal blood cholesterol levels or who developed heart disease prematurely (≤55 years of age for men or ≤65 years for women). Screening is also recommended for children whose family history is unknown and children who have other risk factors, including obesity, diabetes, or high blood pressure.[12] To reduce the risk of developing high blood cholesterol levels and, subsequently, heart disease, the Dietary Guidelines recommend that the diets of children 2 to 3 years of age contain between 30% and 35% of kcalories from fat and the diets of children and adolescents 4 to 18 years of age provide between 25% and 35% of energy from fat. To keep the diet low in cholesterol, saturated fat, and *trans* fat, most fats should come from foods rich in polyunsaturated and monounsaturated fatty acids, such as fish, nuts, and vegetable oils.[13] Low-fat diets have been found to promote healthy blood lipid levels in children without interfering with their growth.[14]

Hypertension People who have blood pressure at the high end of normal as youngsters are more likely to develop high blood pressure as adults.[15] Blood pressure can be affected by the amount of body fat, activity level, and sodium intake, as well as by the total pattern of dietary intake, so attention should be paid to these nutritional and lifestyle factors in children. This is particularly important if there is a family history of hypertension. As in adults, an active lifestyle, maintenance of a healthy body weight, and a diet moderate in sodium and high in whole grains fruits, vegetables, low-fat dairy products, and lean meats is recommended to maintain normal blood pressure.

Healthy Eating Is Learned for Life

Much of what we choose to eat as adults depends on what we learned to eat as children. Children learn by example, therefore the eating patterns, attitudes, and feeding styles of their caregivers influence what they learn to eat. When caregivers drink milk, choose whole grains, and eat plenty of fruits and vegetables, children follow their example. Likewise, if a child's role models eat a diet high in fat and low in fruits and vegetables, the child will follow suit. The eating and exercise habits developed during childhood and adolescence are important because they establish a pattern that may last a lifetime and affect how healthy people will be as they get older.

15.2 Nourishing Infants, Toddlers, and Young Children

Learning Objectives

- Explain why growth is the best indicator of nutrient intake.
- Compare the energy and protein requirements of infants and children with those of adults.
- Give examples of how environment influences children's nutrient intake.
- Summarize the recommendations for preventing and managing food allergies.

Nourishing a growing child is not always an easy task. The foods offered must supply enough energy and nutrients to meet the needs of maintenance, activity, and growth, as well as suit children's tastes. This can be a challenge to caregivers whether they are feeding infants (ages 4 months to 1 year) sampling solid foods for the first time, toddlers (ages 1 to 3 years) experimenting with new foods, or young children (ages 4 to 8 years) eating meals at school or with friends.

Monitoring Growth

The best indicator that a child is receiving adequate nourishment, neither too little nor too much, is a normal growth pattern. If a child does not get enough to eat, growth may be slowed. If intake is excessive, that child is at risk for becoming obese and developing the chronic diseases that are increasingly common in American adults.

The ultimate size (height and weight) that a child will attain is affected by genetic, environmental, and lifestyle factors. A child whose parents are 5 feet tall may not have the genetic potential to grow to 6 feet, but when adequately nourished, most children follow standard patterns of growth. Growth is most rapid in the first year of life, when an infant's length increases by 50%, or about 10 inches. In the second year of life, children generally grow about 5 inches; in the third year, 4 inches; and thereafter, about 2 to 3 inches per year. During adolescence, there is a period of growth that is almost as rapid as that of infancy. Growth can be monitored by comparing a child's growth pattern to standard patterns using growth charts (see Appendix B).[16] For infants, charts are available to monitor weight-for-age, length-for-age, and head circumference-for-age. For children and adolescents ages 2 to 20 years, weight-for-age, length-for-age, and body mass index (BMI)-for-age charts are available. The BMI-for-age growth chart is recommended for identifying children who are underweight, overweight, or obese (**Figure 15.5**).

Although growth often occurs in spurts and plateaus, overall growth patterns are predictable. If a child's overall pattern of growth changes, his or her dietary intake should be evaluated to determine the reason for the sudden change. Children who fall below the fifth percentile of the BMI-for-age distribution are considered underweight and their intake should be evaluated to be sure they are meeting their needs. Malnutrition during childhood can cause lasting damage for which adequate nutrition later on may not be able to compensate. Children are considered overweight when their BMI is greater than or equal to the 85th percentile and less than the 95th percentile and are considered obese when their BMI is greater than or equal to the

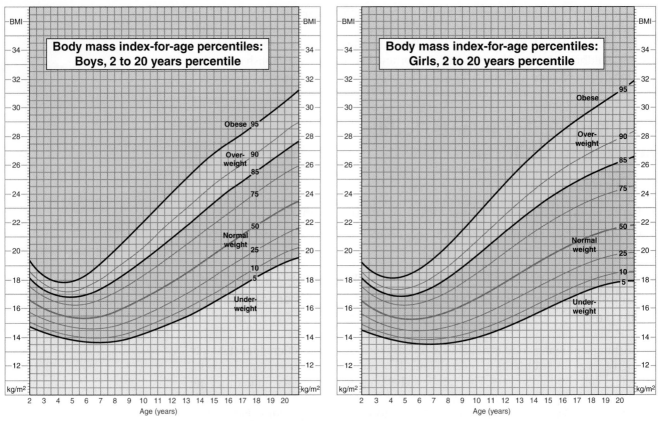

Figure 15.5 Body mass index-for-age percentiles for boys and girls ages 2 to 20 years.
The colored areas represent BMI values associated with underweight, normal weight, overweight, and obese in boys (left) and girls (right).

95th percentile (see Figure 15.5). An increase in activity and/or decrease in energy intake may be needed to keep a child's weight in the healthy range.

Nutrient Needs of Infants and Children

As children grow, their nutrient requirements per unit of body weight decrease, but total needs increase because they gain weight and become more active. Recommended intakes are not different for boys and girls until about 9 years of age, at which time sexual maturation causes differences in nutrient requirements between the sexes.

Energy and Energy-Yielding Nutrients The amount of energy and protein needed per kilogram of body weight decreases with age, but the total amount of each increases as body size increases. The average 2-year-old needs about 1000 kcalories and 13 grams of protein per day. By age 6, that child will need about 1600 kcalories and 19 grams of protein per day (**Figure 15.6**).[17]

Infants need a high-fat diet (40% to 55% of energy intake) to support their rapid growth and development, but by age 4, the recommended proportion of kcalories from fat is reduced to provide adequate energy without increasing the risk of developing chronic disease (see Off the Label: Reading Labels on Food for Young Children). The acceptable range for fat intake is 30% to 40% of energy for children ages 1 to 3 years and 25% to 35% of energy for those 4 through 18 years of age compared to 20% to 35% for adults.[17] To reduce the risk of developing high blood cholesterol levels and, subsequently, heart disease, the diets of children over the age of 3 should also be low in cholesterol, saturated fat, and *trans* fat.[17] Children's diets must provide adequate amounts of essential fatty acids; specific AIs have been set for linoleic and alpha-linolenic acid.[17]

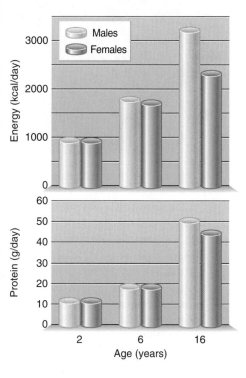

Figure 15.6 Total energy and protein needs by age and gender.
The total need for both energy and protein increases with age.

Carbohydrate recommendations for children are the same as those for adults: 45% to 65% of energy. Specific fiber recommendations have not been made for infants, but for children an AI has been established based on data that show an intake of 14 grams of fiber per 1000 kcalories reduces the risk of heart disease. As in the adult diet, most of the carbohydrate in a child's diet should be from whole grains, fruits, and vegetables. These will provide the recommended amount of fiber. Fiber supplements are not recommended for children since high intakes can limit the amount of food and, consequently, the nutrients that a small child can consume. Foods high in added sugars, such as cookies, candy, and soda, should be limited.[1]

Water and Electrolytes By 1 year of age, a child's kidneys have matured and the amount of fluid lost through evaporation has decreased, so total fluid losses decline. As with adults, under most situations drinking enough to satisfy thirst will provide sufficient water. In children 1 to 3 years of age about 1.3 liters (5½ cups) of water daily will meet needs; about 4 cups of this should be from water and other fluids. Older children, ages 4 to 8, need about 1.7 liters (7 cups) per day.[18] Water needs increase with illness, when the environmental temperature is high, and when activity increases sweat losses.

A UL of 2.3 grams of sodium per day has been set for adults and teens 14 to 18 years of age because a high sodium intake is associated with elevated blood pressure. The UL is somewhat lower in children and younger teens (see inside cover). The typical sodium intake in children and teens currently exceeds the UL.[18]

Micronutrients Children are smaller than adolescents and adults, and for the most part the recommended amounts of micronutrients are also smaller (see inside cover). Generally, a nutrient-dense diet that follows the MyPyramid recommendations for children will meet needs. Consuming the recommended amounts of meats and whole and enriched grains helps ensure enough B vitamins. Adequate fruits and vegetables provide vitamin C and vitamin A. Milk provides calcium and vitamins A and D. Fortified breakfast cereals help compensate for poorer diets by providing the recommended amounts of a variety of vitamins and minerals in a single serving. However, despite the relative abundance of vitamins and minerals in the modern diet, poor food choices put many children in the United States today at risk for deficiencies of calcium, vitamin D, and iron.

Off the Label
Reading Labels on Food for Young Children

Children have different nutrient needs than adults. Therefore, the labels on foods designed for young children must follow different rules. The most obvious difference is how fat is listed in the Nutrition Facts. Labels for foods intended for children younger than 2 years list total fat but may not list the amount of saturated fat, polyunsaturated fat, monounsaturated fat, cholesterol, kcalories from fat, or kcalories from saturated fat.[1] These labels also may not carry most claims about a food's nutrient content or health effects. The reason is that dietary fat is needed for brain development and meeting energy needs during the rapid growth and development of infancy and early childhood. It is hoped that excluding information about fat content on the label will prevent caregivers from restricting fats in the diets of young children.

As children develop, the amount of fat in their diet can safely be reduced. Therefore, labels on foods designed for 2- to 4-year-olds must include information on cholesterol and saturated fat per serving and may provide kcalories from fat and saturated fat, as well as polyunsaturated and monounsaturated fat per serving. The serving sizes listed must be based on servings appropriate for small children.

Another difference between standard food labels and those for foods designed for children under age 4 is the absence of percent Daily Values for total fat, saturated fat, cholesterol, total carbohydrate, fiber, and sodium.[1] For children under 4 years, the FDA has set Daily Values only for vitamins, minerals, and protein. Labels include the percent Daily Values for these nutrients when they are present in significant amounts.

Nutrient and health claims allowed on young children's foods include claims that describe the percentage of vitamins or minerals as they apply to the Daily Values for children under age 2, such as "provides 50% of the Daily Value for vitamin C." Also for children under 2, the descriptors "unsweetened" and "unsalted" are allowed. "No sugar added" and "sugar free" are approved only for use on dietary supplements for children.

Many of the foods consumed by young children do not have special labels because they are also adult foods. When selecting these foods, keep in mind that the needs of young children, especially for fat, are different than the needs of adults.

Nutrition Facts
Serving Size 1/4 cup (15g)
Servings Per Container About 30

Amount Per Serving		
Calories 60		
Total Fat		1g
Sodium		0mg
Potassium		50mg
Total Carbohydrate		10g
Fiber		1g
Sugars		0g
Protein		2g

Daily Value	Infants 0-1	Children 1-4
Protein	7%	6%
Vitamin A	0%	0%
Vitamin C	0%	0%
Calcium	15%	10%
Iron	45%	60%
Vitamin E	15%	8%
Thiamin	45%	30%
Riboflavin	45%	30%
Niacin	25%	20%
Phosphorus	15%	10%

Nutrition facts label for foods for children under age 2.

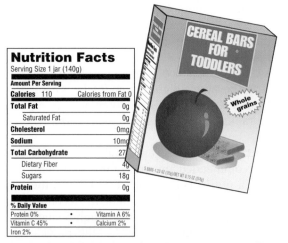

Nutrition Facts
Serving Size 1 jar (140g)

Amount Per Serving	
Calories 110	Calories from Fat 0
Total Fat	0g
Saturated Fat	0g
Cholesterol	0mg
Sodium	10mg
Total Carbohydrate	27g
Dietary Fiber	4g
Sugars	18g
Protein	0g

% Daily Value			
Protein 0%	•	Vitamin A 6%	
Vitamin C 45%	•	Calcium 2%	
Iron 2%			

Nutrition facts label for foods for children 2 to 4 years of age.

[1]Kurtzweil, P. Labeling rules for young children's foods. *FDA Consumer* 29:14–18, March 1995.

Calcium, Vitamin D, and Bone Health The AI for calcium for toddlers is 500 mg per day and for young children it is 800 mg per day. Adequate calcium intake during childhood is essential for achieving maximum peak bone mass, which is important in preventing osteoporosis later in life (see Chapter 11). Calcium intake in school-age American children has been declining, primarily due to a decrease in the consumption of milk (**Figure 15.7**).[1] Low intakes of milk, combined with limited sun exposure, may also put many children at risk of vitamin D deficiency.[19] Vitamin D is needed for calcium absorption, so is also essential for bone health. The AI is 5 μg per day; however, our expanding understanding of the role of vitamin D in health and disease prevention has led many experts to recommend 20 to 25 μg of vitamin D per day for children and adults when exposure to sunlight is not adequate (see Chapter 9).

Iron and Anemia The RDA for iron for infants 7 to 12 months of age is 11 mg per day. This drops to 7 mg per day for toddlers, but for young children ages 4 to 8 it is 10 mg per day, which is higher than the RDA for adult men. Good sources of iron that are acceptable to small children include fortified grains and breakfast cereals, raisins, eggs, and lean meats, but many children may still not get enough. Although the iron intake of American children has increased over the last 20 years, the incidence of iron deficiency remains above the levels targeted by Healthy People 2010 for toddlers, preschool children, and adolescent girls.[20] Iron deficiency can lower a child's resistance to illness and slow recovery time. It can affect learning ability, intellectual performance, stamina, and mood.[21,22] If anemia is diagnosed, iron supplements are usually prescribed until iron stores are repleted. These supplements should be kept out of the reach of children. Overdoses of iron-containing supplements are the leading cause of poisoning deaths among children under 6 years of age.[23] To help protect children, products containing iron include a warning about the hazards to children of ingesting large amounts of iron.

Feeding Infants

Although breast milk or infant formula meets most nutritional needs until 1 year of age semisolid and solid foods can be gradually introduced into the infant's diet starting between 4 and 6 months of age. Introducing solid foods earlier provides no nutritional or developmental advantages. Despite this, some parents offer semisolid foods

Figure 15.7 Three cups of milk supplies about 900 mg of calcium—enough to meet the AI for children up to age 8. (Jamie Grill/Age Fotostock America, Inc.)

Age	Birth to 4 months	4 to 6 months	6 to 9 months	9 to 12 months
Developmental milestone	The infant takes milk by *suckling*. Solid food placed in the mouth is usually pushed out as the tongue thrusts forward.	Solid food is accepted without being expelled by the tongue. The infant can hold his or her head up and sit, with or without support.	The infant can sit without support, chew, hold food, and easily move hand to mouth.	The infant can drink from a cup and feed him/herself.
Foods	Breast milk or iron-fortified infant formula	Breast milk or formula, iron-fortified infant cereal. After cereals, puréed vegetables and fruits can be introduced.	Breast milk or formula, iron-fortified infant cereal, puréed or strained vegetables, fruits, meats and beans, limited finger foods.	Breast milk or formula, iron-fortified infant cereal, chopped vegetables, soft fruits, meats and beans, fruit juice, nonchoking finger foods such as dry cereal, cooked pasta, and cut well-cooked vegetables.

Figure 15.8 Nourishing a developing infant
(Raul Touzon/NG Image Collection; Laura Dwight/PhotoEdit; Alamy; iStockphoto)

before this age often by adding infant cereal to the baby's bottle because they think the infant is hungry or the added food will help the child sleep through the night. Studies have shown that there is no difference in sleeping patterns based on such feeding practices and it may cause choking and increase the risk of food allergies.[24]

Before 4 to 6 months of age the infant's feeding abilities and gastrointestinal tract are not mature enough to handle foods other than breast milk or formula. The young infant takes milk by a licking motion of the tongue called suckling, which strokes or milks the liquid from the nipple. Solid food placed in the mouth at an early age is usually pushed out as the tongue thrusts forward. By 4 to 6 months of age the early reflex to bring the tongue to the front of the mouth to suckle has diminished, and the tongue is held farther back in the mouth, allowing solid food to be accepted without being expelled. By this age, the infant also can hold his or her head up steadily and is able to sit, either with or without support (**Figure 15.8**). Internally, the digestive tract has developed, and enzymes are present for starch digestion. The kidneys are more mature and better able to concentrate urine. With all of these changes, the child is ready to begin a new approach to eating.

What Foods to Introduce First? The most commonly recommended food to be fed first to a child is iron-fortified infant rice cereal mixed with formula or breast milk. Rice cereal is the recommended first food because it is easily digested and rarely causes allergic reactions. After rice has been successfully included in the diet, other grains can be introduced, with wheat cereal offered last because it is most likely to cause an allergic reaction. After cereals are introduced, pureed vegetables or fruits can be tried; some suggest that vegetables be offered before fruits so that the child will learn to enjoy food that is not sweet before being introduced to sweet foods. Once teeth have erupted, foods with more texture can be added (Figure 15.8). For the 6- to 12-month-old child, small pieces of soft or ground fruits, vegetables, and meats are appropriate (**Table 15.1**).

Table 15.1 Typical Meal Patterns for Infants

Food	Serving Size	Servings per Day		
		4–6 Months	6–9 Months	9–12 Months
Formula or breast milk[a]	8 oz	4	4	4
Dry infant cereal	2 Tbsp	2	4	4
Vegetables	2–3 Tbsp	—	2	3
Fruits	2 Tbsp	—	2	4
Fruit juice	4 oz	—	—	1 (in a cup)
Meats (or egg yolks)	1 Tbsp	—	2–4 (strained)	4–6 (chopped)
Finger foods		—	1[b]	4[c]

[a]Includes formula or breast milk added to cereal.
[b]Dry toast, teething biscuits.
[c]Table foods except "choking" foods (e.g., foods in shapes and sizes that are likely to cause choking, such as large pieces of meat, whole grapes, or hot dogs or carrots cut in circular slices).

Honey should not be fed to children less than a year old because it may contain spores of *Clostridium botulinum*, the bacterium that causes botulism poisoning (see Chapter 17). Older children and adults are not at risk from botulism spores because the environment in a mature gastrointestinal tract prevents the bacterium from growing.

Increasing Variety with Developmentally Appropriate Choices As the child becomes familiar with more variety, food choices should be made from each of the food groups in MyPyramid. At 1 year of age, whole cow's milk should be offered and continued until 2 years of age, after which reduced fat milks can be used. Cow's milk should not be used before 1 year of age because it is difficult to digest and the infant's kidneys are too immature to handle its higher protein and mineral content. To avoid choking, foods that can easily lodge in the throat, such as carrots, grapes, and hot dogs, should not be offered to infants or toddlers.

As children become more independent, they will want to feed themselves. Although this is not always a neat and clean process, it is important for development. By the age of 8 or 9 months, infants can hold a bottle and self-feed finger foods such as crackers. By 10 months, most infants can drink from a cup, so water and fruit juices can be offered (Figure 15.8). The amount of juice offered to children should be limited. The American Academy of Pediatrics recommends 4 to 6 ounces per day of 100% juice for children ages 1 to 6 and 8 to 12 oz for children age 7 and older.[25] Drinking too much juice can cause diarrhea, over- or undernutrition, and dental caries. It is recommended that juice not be offered to children in containers that can be carried around, encouraging continuous sipping.

A Caution about Food Allergies Although true food allergies are relatively rare, they are more common in infants.[26] Their immature digestive tracts allow incompletely digested proteins to be absorbed causing a reaction involving the immune system. Exposure to an **allergen** for the first time causes the immune system to produce anti-bodies to that allergen (see Chapters 3 and 6). When the allergen is encountered again by eating the same food, allergy symptoms such as vomiting, diarrhea, asthma, hives, eczema, runny nose and swelling of tissues, hay fever, and general cramps and aches may result as the immune system battles the allergen. The symptoms may occur almost immediately or take up to 24 hours to appear, and can vary from mild to severe and life-threatening. Foods that commonly cause allergies include wheat, peanuts, eggs, milk, nuts, fish, shellfish, and soy (see Your Choice: How can You Find Peanut-Free Foods?).

allergen A substance, usually a protein, that stimulates an immune response.

(©iStockphoto)

How Can You Find Peanut-Free Foods?

An allergy to peanuts is one of the most common food allergies. It is rarely outgrown, and life-threatening reactions occur from exposure to minuscule amounts. Because reactions result from such low levels of peanut exposure, individuals with this allergy must avoid consuming any peanut protein and some people are so sensitive that they must avoid all contact with peanuts.

Shopping for safe foods for someone with peanut allergy is challenging. Individuals with peanut allergy or their caregivers need to rely on food labels to identify safe and unsafe choices. Peanuts, peanut butter, and peanut butter candy are obvious foods to avoid. Others are not so obvious; some foods, such as cookies and crackers, contain peanut flour and peanut oil. Crude peanut oil (less refined), which still contains some peanut protein was found to cause an allergic reaction in many allergic subjects, whereas refined peanut oil did not cause a reaction in the majority of peanut-allergic individuals.[1] The ingredient list may not indicate if the oil is crude or refined, and other peanut-derived ingredients may be hidden in the list, but allergen labeling makes it easier to identify products containing peanuts and other allergens. Labels are required to indicate whether the product contains any of the top eight food allergens; milk, eggs, fish, shellfish, peanuts, tree nuts, wheat, and soy.[2] This is most often done by listing them at the end of the ingredient list after the word "Contains," for example, "Contains milk, peanuts."

In the case of peanut allergy, even foods that do not contain peanuts or peanut products can pose a risk if they are manufactured in the same location as peanut-containing foods. For instance, the cheese "sandwich" crackers, M&Ms, and granola bars shown in the photo seem like safe foods, but a thorough reading of the label reveals that this is not the case. Because all of these products were manufactured in facilities that process peanuts for products such as peanut butter sandwich crackers, peanut M&Ms, and granola bars with peanuts, cross contamination with small amounts of peanuts is possible. To warn consumers of this the label includes a statement such as "May contain peanuts," "Manufactured on equipment that processes peanuts," or "Manufactured in a facility that processes peanuts." This information protects both the company from legal action and the allergic individual from inadvertently consuming peanut-containing products.

Parents of children with allergies must read labels carefully. These products do not look like they contain peanuts, but the labels indicate that they may have inadvertently become contaminated with peanuts during manufacturing. (George Semple)

[1]Crevel, R. W., Kerkhoff, M. A., and Koning, M. M. Allergenicity of refined vegetable oils. *Food Chem. Toxicol.* 38:385–393, 2000.
[2]FDA, CFSAN. Food Allergen and Consumer Protection Act of 2004. Available online at www.cfsan.fda.gov/~dms/alrgact.html/. Accessed June 8, 2009.

To monitor for food allergies when solid foods are introduced to infants, it is important to introduce new foods one at a time. Each new food should be offered for a few days without the addition of any other new foods. If an allergic reaction occurs, it is most likely due to the newly introduced food. Foods that cause allergy symptoms such as rashes, digestive upsets, or respiratory problems should be discontinued before any other new foods are added. After an infant is about 3 months of age, the risk of developing food allergies is reduced because incompletely digested proteins are less likely to be absorbed. Many children who develop food allergies before the age of 3 years will outgrow them. For example, most children allergic to eggs at 1 year of age will no longer be allergic by age 5. Allergies that appear after 3 years of age are more likely to be a problem for life.

Adverse reactions to foods are also caused by **food intolerances**. In contrast to food allergies, food intolerances do not involve antibody production by the immune system. Rather, they are caused by foods that create problems during digestion. Food intolerances can be caused by chemical components in foods, by toxins that occur naturally in foods, by substances added to foods during processing or preparation, or simply by large amounts of foods, such as onions or prunes, that cause local gastrointestinal irritation. Lactose intolerance is an example of a food intolerance caused by a reduced ability to digest milk sugar. It is not an allergy to milk proteins.

food intolerance An adverse reaction to a food that does not involve antibody production by the immune system.

Diagnosing Food Allergies Several laboratory methods are available to identify foods that are likely to cause an individual's allergic reaction, but they cannot determine the source of the problem with 100% reliability. The cause of a food allergy can be confirmed by using an **elimination diet** and **food challenge**. This involves eliminating all foods suspected of causing an allergic reaction from the diet. Once a diet that causes no symptoms has been established, it should be consumed for 2 to 4 weeks. Then in the food challenge, small amounts of a food suspected of causing a reaction are reintroduced under a doctor's supervision. If no reaction to the food occurs, then increasing amounts are introduced until a normal portion is offered. If there is still no reaction, then the food can be ruled out as an allergen.

elimination diet and **food challenge** A regimen that eliminates potential allergy-causing foods from an individual's diet and then systematically adds them back to identify any foods that cause an allergic reaction.

Preventing and Managing Food Allergies Preventing the development of food allergies is not always possible. Breast-feeding can reduce the risk of food allergies and is recommended for infants from families with a history of allergies.[27] Infants who are breast-fed are less likely to be exposed to foreign proteins that cause food allergies. In addition, their gut matures earlier and they are protected by antibodies and other components of human milk. There is no evidence that delaying the introduction of solid food, including foods thought to be highly allergenic, past 6 months protects against the development of food allergies.[27]

Once a food allergy has developed, the best way to manage it is to avoid consuming the offending food. The information on food labels can be helpful in identifying foods that contain allergy-causing ingredients (see Chapter 6, Off the Label: Is It Safe for You?).

Feeding Children

The development of nutritious eating habits begins in infancy and childhood. Parents and caregivers influence which foods children learn to eat through the examples they set and the amounts and types of foods offered. Children are more likely to eat foods that are available and easily accessible, and they tend to eat greater quantities when larger portions are provided.[28] Caregivers are responsible for deciding what foods should be offered to a child, when they should be offered, and where they should be eaten. The child must then decide whether to eat, what foods to eat, and how much to consume.[29] As children get older their choices are affected more by social activities, what they see at school, and what their friends are eating.

What to Offer? Children should be offered a balanced and varied diet adequate in energy and essential nutrients and appropriate to the child's developmental needs. A healthy meal plan is based on whole grains, vegetables, and fruits; is adequate in milk and other high-protein foods; and is moderate in fat and sodium. Food choices to meet these goals can be determined by following the MyPyramid recommendations and spreading these amounts throughout the meals and snacks served each day (**Figure 15.9**). For example, a 6-year-old, moderately active boy would only need 5 ounces of grains. These could include a half cup of cereal at breakfast, some crackers for a snack, half a sandwich at lunch, and a half cup of rice at dinner. This child would need 3 cups of milk a day but these may be consumed in smaller portions throughout the day (**Table 15.2**). The need for nutrient-dense choices from all food groups is just as important for children as it is for adults.

Getting a child to eat all the foods recommended by MyPyramid may not always be easy. To increase variety new foods should regularly be introduced into a child's diet. Children's food preferences are learned through repeated exposure to foods; children develop an increased preference for a food if it is offered a minimum of 8 to 10 times.[1] Children are also more likely to try a new food if it is introduced at the beginning of a meal, when the child is hungry, and if the child sees his or her parents or peers eating it. If a new food becomes associated with a bad experience, such as burning the mouth, the child will be unlikely to try it again. Incorporating refused foods into familiar dishes can also increase the variety of the diet. If vegetables are refused, they can be added to soups and casseroles. Fruit can be served on cereal or in milkshakes. Cheese can be included in recipes such as macaroni and cheese, cheese sauce, and pizza. Milk can be added to hot cereal, cream soups, puddings, and custards, and powdered milk can be used in baking. Meats can be added to spaghetti sauce, stews, casseroles, burritos, or pizza.

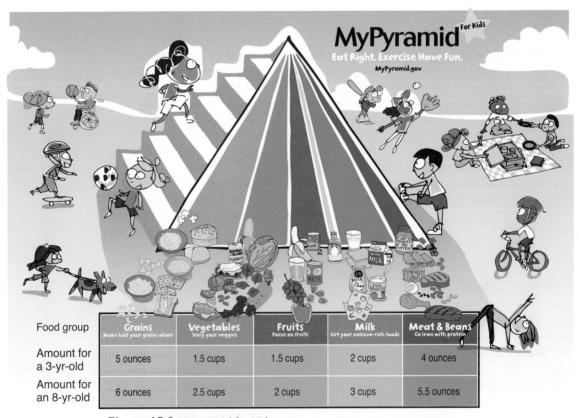

Food group	Grains Make half your grains whole	Vegetables Vary your veggies	Fruits Focus on fruits	Milk Get your calcium-rich foods	Meat & Beans Go lean with protein
Amount for a 3-yr-old	5 ounces	1.5 cups	1.5 cups	2 cups	4 ounces
Amount for an 8-yr-old	6 ounces	2.5 cups	2 cups	3 cups	5.5 ounces

Figure 15.9 MyPyramid for Kids
MyPyramid for kids recommends amounts from each food group based on age, gender, and physical activity; the recommendations shown here are for 3- and 8-year-old children who are active (get over 60 minutes of activity a day).

Table 15.2 A Typical Meal & Snack Pattern for Three- and Eight-Year-Old Children

Food	Amount	
	3-Year-Old	**8-Year-Old**
Breakfast		
Cheerios	1/2 cup	1 cup
Milk, 2%	1/2 cup	1 cup
Banana	1/2 medium	1
Snack		
Peanut butter	2 Tbsp	2 Tbsp
Wheat crackers	5	5
Water		
Lunch		
Vegetable soup	1/2 cup	1 cup
Grilled tuna sandwich	1/2	1
Tomato	1/4	1/2
Milk, 2%	1/2 cup	1 cup
Snack		
Pretzels	2	4
Orange sections	1/2 cup	1/2 cup
Dinner		
Rice	1/2 cup	1 cup
Chicken	1 drumstick	2 drumsticks
Broccoli	4 florets	4 florets
Milk, 2%	1/2 cup	1 cup
Ice cream	1/2 cup	1/2 cup
Yogurt	1/2 cup	3/4 cup
Berries	3/8 cup	3/4 cup

Children often have periods known as **food jags**, when they will eat only certain foods and nothing else. For example, a child may refuse to eat anything other than peanut butter and jelly sandwiches for breakfast, lunch, and dinner. The general guideline is to continue to offer other foods along with those the child is focused on. What a child will not touch at one meal, he or she may eat the next day or the next week. No matter how erratic children's food intake may be, caregivers should offer a variety of appropriate healthy food choices at each meal and let their children select what and how much they will eat (**Figure 15.10**).

food jag When a child will only eat one food item meal after meal.

Figure 15.10 Children should be allowed to select what and how much they will eat from a variety of healthy choices. (Courtesy Mary Grosvenor)

SCIENCE

ScienceAppliedScienceApplied
Science**AppliedScience**Applied
ScienceAppliedScienceApplied

APPLIED

(DAJ/Getty Images, Inc.)   (www.victorianoizquierdo.com/Getty Images, Inc.)   (Elena Schweitzer/Shutterstock)

Is Breakfast Food Really Brain Food?

Did your mother tell you that breakfast is the most important meal of the day? Research tells us that she was probably right. Breakfast provides the first dietary energy source of the day, fueling your body and your brain. A study that evaluated the contribution of breakfast to daily nutrient intake found that children who eat breakfast have healthier diets than those who skip breakfast.[1] Breakfast eaters are more likely to meet nutrient intake recommendations, and compared with breakfast skippers, they have higher daily intakes of vitamins A and C, riboflavin, folic acid, calcium, zinc, iron, and fiber and lower intakes of fat and cholesterol.[2–4] Children and adolescents who skip breakfast do not, on average, make up the nutrient deficits later in the day.

Breakfast may also help maintain a healthy weight. Compared with breakfast eaters, breakfast skippers tend to have a lower total daily energy intake, and studies have shown that children and teens who eat breakfast are less likely to be overweight.[2,4]

The impact of eating breakfast on cognitive and academic performance, psychosocial function, and school attendance has been studied widely.[2] Children who are hungry are more likely to have academic, emotional, and behavioral problems.[5] Eating breakfast could therefore improve cognitive performance simply by alleviating hunger. This is particularly important in children whose diets barely meet nutrient requirements, but even well-nourished children benefit from the short-term effects of eating breakfast. Breakfast provides energy and nutrients to the brain. Glucose is the primary energy source for the brain, and blood glucose levels affect the performance of tasks involving recall and memory.[6] Without breakfast, the brain must rely on energy from body stores for morning activities.

Studies have found that compared with nonbreakfast eaters, children in school breakfast programs have higher nutrient intakes, and the improvements in intakes are associated with improvements in academic performance, reductions in hyperactivity, better psychosocial behaviors, and less absence and tardiness.[7,8] One study compared children in grades 3 through 6 who participated in the National School Breakfast Program with those who were eligible but did not participate. Over the school year, students who participated in the School Breakfast Program showed improved cognitive performance and reduced tardiness and absenteeism.[9] Breakfast consumption may therefore enhance learning not only by fueling the brain, but also by improving school attendance, which provides children greater learning opportunities.[10]

Any breakfast is probably better than none, but a healthy breakfast can maximize the potential benefits. Ideally, breakfast should provide a quarter to a third of the day's nutrients without excessive kcalories. For example, a breakfast of orange juice, toast with jelly, and oatmeal with milk and raisins provides about 450 kcalories as well as protein; B vitamins; vitamins C, A, and D; and the minerals calcium and iron. But if the only food a child will eat in the morning is a bowl of sweetened cereal, that is better than nothing. Despite the high-sugar, low-fiber content of many breakfast cereals marketed to children, these cereals have few other nutritional strikes against them. For example, although 40% of the energy in Cap'n Crunch comes from simple sugars, this food is still low in fat and provides 20% or more of the Daily Value for thiamin, riboflavin, niacin, vitamin B_6, folate, vitamin B_{12}, pantothenic acid, and iron. When a half cup of reduced-fat milk is added to the cereal, it also provides 15% of the Daily Value for calcium. Even children who cannot or will not eat breakfast before they leave the house can snack on fruit, yogurt, a bag of dry cereal, or half a sandwich on the way to school or during recess. Having breakfast at school is also an option. The National School Breakfast program provides meals free or at a reduced cost for families who meet income guidelines.

[1]Basiotis, P., Lino, M., and Anand, R. Eating breakfast greatly improves schoolchildren's diet quality. *Fam. Econ. Nutr. Rev.* 12:81–83, 1999.

[2]Rampersaud, G. C., Pereira, M.A., Girard, B. L., et al. Breakfast habits, nutritional status, body weight, and academic performance in children and adolescents. *J. Am. Diet. Assoc.* 105:743–760, 2005.

[3]Nicklas, T.A., O'Neil, C. E., and Berenson, G. S. Nutrient contribution of breakfast, secular trends, and the role of ready-to-eat cereals: A review of the data from the Bogalusa Heart Study. *Am. J. Clin. Nutr.* 67:757S–763S, 1998.

[4]Barton, B.A., Eldridge, A. L., Thompson, D., et al. The relationship of breakfast and cereal consumption to nutrient intake and body mass index: The national heart, lung, and blood institute growth and health study. *J. Am. Diet. Assoc.* 105:1383–1389, 2005.

[5]Alaimo, K. Olson, C., and Frongillo, E. Food insufficiency and American school-aged children's cognitive, academic, and psychosocial development. *Pediatrics* 108:44–53, 2001.

[6]Benton, D., and Parker, P.Y. Breakfast, blood glucose, and cognition. *Am. J. Clin. Nutr.* 67(Suppl.)772S–778S, 1998.

[7]Kennedy, E., and Davis, C. USDA School Breakfast Program. *Am. J. Clin. Nutr.* 67: 798S–803S, 1998.

[8]Kleinman, R. E., Hall, S., Green, H., et al. Diet, breakfast, and academic performance in children. *Ann. Nutr. Metab.* 46 (Suppl. 1): 24–30, 2002.

[9]Meyers, A. F., Sampson, A. E., Weitzman, M., et al. School breakfast program and school performance. *Am. J. Dis. Child.* 143: 1234–1239, 1989.

[10]Pollitt, E., and Mathews, R. Breakfast and cognition: An integrative summary. *Am. J. Clin. Nutr.* 67(Suppl.): 804S–813S, 1998.

How Often to Offer Meals and Snacks? Children have small stomachs and high nutrient needs; therefore they should consume nutritious meals and snacks throughout the day. For young children a meal or snack should be offered every 2 to 3 hours and, because children thrive on routines and feel secure in knowing what to expect, a consistent pattern should be maintained from day to day. A missed meal or snack can leave a child without sufficient energy to perform optimally at school or play. A good breakfast is particularly important for ensuring optimal performance at school (see Science Applied: Is Breakfast Food Really Brain Food?). Snacks should be as nutritious as meals and should focus on fruits, vegetables, low-fat dairy products, lean meats, and whole-grain products, not soda and chips (**Table 15.3**).

Table 15.3 Healthy Snacks for Young Children

Focus on Fruit—make popsicles from fruit juice, cut fruit into interesting shapes, try frozen grapes, make trail mix with raisins, dried cranberries, and other dried fruit.

Vary Your Veggies—dip baby carrots in ranch dressing, add peanut butter to celery, serve salsa with baked tortilla chips.

Get Your Calcium-Rich Foods—include milk with after-school cookies, try melted cheese on a tortilla, top some fruit with yogurt, snack on string cheese, make a yogurt and fruit shake.

Make Half Your Grains Whole—try whole-grain breadsticks or pretzels, have graham crackers instead of cookies, pop some corn.

Go Lean with Protein—put peanut butter on apple slices or crackers, snack on some turkey slices, roll some black beans into a tortilla, spread hummus on crackers.

Meals at Day Care or School All meals need to contribute to a child's nutrient intake, but parents may have little input into what children eat while at day care or school. Ensuring that meals eaten away from home are nutritious is not easy because there is no guarantee that what is served or brought from home will be eaten. A packed lunch should contain foods the child likes and that do not require refrigeration (even if a refrigerator is available, the child is likely to forget to put the lunch in it). Even the most carefully planned lunch is not nutritious if it is not eaten.

For children who buy their lunch at school, the National School Lunch Program provides low-cost meals designed to meet nutrient needs and promote healthy diets. The goals of this program are to improve the dietary intake and nutritional health of America's children, and to promote nutrition education by teaching children to make appropriate food choices.[30] Each lunch meal must provide one-third of the RDA for protein, vitamin A, vitamin C, iron, calcium, and energy and provide no more than 30% of energy from fat and 10% from saturated fat. Within these guidelines, each school or school district can decide which foods to serve and how they are prepared. An analysis of the foods students chose to eat from the meal offered found that students who participated in the school lunch program consumed more vegetables, dairy products, and meat and meat substitutes, and fewer soft drinks and/or fruit drinks, than nonparticipants (**Figure 15.11**).[31]

In addition to lunches, federal guidelines regulate foods sold in snack bars and vending machines that compete with school lunch programs. These must provide at least 5% of the RDA for one or more of the following: protein, vitamin A, vitamin C, niacin, riboflavin, calcium, and iron.

Vitamin and Mineral Supplements As with adults, children who consume a well-selected, varied diet can meet all their vitamin and mineral requirements with food. In fact, average intakes of most vitamins and minerals for children 2 to 11 years of age exceed 100% of the recommended amounts.[1] Occasional skipped meals and unfinished dinners are a normal part of most children's eating behavior. However, children with particularly erratic eating habits, those on regimens to manage obesity,

Figure 15.11 Participation in the National School Lunch Program increases intake of calcium, riboflavin, phosphorus, magnesium, zinc, and vitamins B₆ and B₁₂. (Baerbel Schmidt/Stone/Getty Images, Inc.)

Figure 15.12 Companionship and conversation at meals help create a positive eating environment and foster good eating patterns. (©Masterfile)

those with limited food availability, and those who consume a vegan diet may benefit from supplements that provide no more than 100% of the Daily Values. If a children's supplement is offered, it should be monitored by caregivers and stored safely.

Eating Environment Factors such as whether families eat together, watch TV during meals, and choose food prepared at home or at a restaurant influence children's eating patterns.[28] To develop sound eating habits children need companionship, conversation, and a pleasant location at mealtimes. Caregivers should sit with children and eat what they eat (**Figure 15.12**). Children should be given plenty of time to finish eating. Slow eaters are unlikely to finish eating if they are abandoned by siblings who run off to play and adults who leave to wash dishes.

To make mealtime a nutritious, educational, and enjoyable experience, it should not be a battle zone. Threats and bribes are counterproductive and can create a problem where none had previously existed. Food is not a reward or a punishment: It is simply nutrition.

15.3 Nutrition and Health Concerns in Children

Learning Objectives

- Discuss the relationship between food intake patterns and dental caries.
- Explain why children should have their blood lead levels tested.
- Describe the impact of the modern U.S. lifestyle on childhood obesity.

A number of diet and lifestyle factors put children at risk for illness and malnutrition. Some are a greater risk in young children because of their size and stage of development and others are problems that may continue into adolescence.

Dental Caries

Children and teens typically eat more sugar than is recommended. Added sugars reduce the nutrient density of foods, so excessive consumption of foods high in added sugars make it difficult to meet nutrient needs. In addition, a diet high in sugary foods promotes tooth decay, causing dental caries, commonly known as cavities. Decay occurs when there is prolonged contact between sugar and bacteria on the surface of the teeth. Because the primary teeth guide the growth of the permanent teeth, maintaining healthy primary teeth is just as important as preserving permanent ones.

Much of the added sugar in children's diets come from soft drinks and other sweetened beverages; when these are sipped slowly between meals the contact time between sugar and teeth is prolonged, hence increasing the risk of tooth decay (**Figure 15.13**). Changing the types of beverages consumed by children may impact the incidence of dental caries. A study found fewer caries in children who drank more milk and more in those who consumed soda and juice.[32] Although sugary foods are the most cavity-promoting, any carbohydrate-containing food can cause tooth decay, especially if the food sticks to the teeth (see Chapter 4).

Both diet and dental hygiene can affect the risk of dental caries. Preventing tooth decay involves limiting high carbohydrate snacks, especially those that stick to teeth; brushing teeth frequently to remove sticky sweets; and consuming adequate fluoride. It is recommended that children consume 3 servings of dairy foods daily, limit intake of juices to 4 to 6 oz of 100% juice per day for children 1 to 6 years and 8

Figure 15.13 When juice is sipped slowly over a long period, it provides a continuous supply of sugar to feed cavity-causing bacteria. (Tom Merton/Age Fotostock America, Inc.)

to 12 oz for children 7 years and older, and restrict other sugared beverages to occasional use.[25,32] Children's teeth should be brushed as soon as they erupt and children 3 years of age and older should be examined by a dentist regularly.

Diet and Hyperactivity

Hyperactivity is a problem in 5% to 10% of school-age children, occurring more frequently in boys than in girls. This syndrome involves extreme physical activity, excitability, impulsiveness, distractibility, short attention span, and a low tolerance for frustration. Hyperactive children have more difficulty learning but usually are of normal or above-average intelligence. Hyperactivity is now considered part of a larger syndrome known as **attention deficit hyperactivity disorder (ADHD)**.

One popular misconception is that hyperactivity is caused by a high sugar intake, but research on sugar intake and behavior has failed to support this hypothesis.[33,34] Hyperactive behavior that is observed after sugar consumption is likely the result of other circumstances in that child's life. For example, the excitement of a birthday party rather than the cake is most likely the cause of hyperactive behavior. Other situations that might cause hyperactivity include lack of sleep, overstimulation, the desire for more attention, or lack of physical activity.

Specific foods and food additives have also been implicated as a cause of hyperactivity. In 1975, an allergist named Dr. Benjamin Feingold published a book suggesting that hyperactive behavior and learning disabilities were caused by high intakes of artificial colors and flavors. Despite the appeal of this type of dietary management, numerous studies done over the years have failed to provide sufficient scientific evidence for the efficacy of this diet to treat children with hyperactivity. There are, however, some children with behavioral problems who are sensitive to specific additives and who may benefit from a diet that eliminates these.[34]

Another possible cause of hyperactive behavior in children is caffeine. Caffeine is a stimulant that can cause sleeplessness, restlessness, and irregular heartbeats. Beverages, foods, and medicines containing caffeine are often a part of children's diets. For example, caffeinated beverages such as Coke and Mountain Dew are commonly included in children's fast-food meals.

attention deficit hyperactivity disorder (ADHD) A condition that is characterized by a short attention span, acting without thinking, and a high level of activity, excitability, and distractibility.

Lead Toxicity

Lead is an environmental contaminant that can be toxic, especially in children under 6 years of age. Children are particularly susceptible because they absorb lead much more efficiently than do adults. It is estimated that infants and young children may absorb as much as 50% of ingested lead, whereas adults absorb only about 10–15%.[35] Malnourished children are at particular risk because malnutrition increases lead absorption due to the fact that lead is better absorbed from an empty stomach and when other minerals such as calcium, zinc, and iron are deficient. Once absorbed from the gastrointestinal tract, lead circulates in the bloodstream and then accumulates in the bones and, to a lesser extent, the brain, teeth, and kidneys. Lead disrupts the activity of neurotransmitters and thus interferes with the functioning of the nervous system. Higher levels of lead can contribute to iron-deficiency anemia, altered kidney function, nervous system changes, and even seizures, coma, and death. In young children, lead poisoning can cause learning disabilities and behavior problems.[35–37]

Lead is found naturally in the earth's crust, but over the years industrial activities have redistributed it in the environment. Lead is now found in soil contaminated with lead paint dust; it enters drinking water from old corroded lead plumbing, lead solder on copper pipes, or brass faucets. It is found in polluted air, in leaded glass, and in glazes used on imported and antique pottery. Lead from these can contaminate food and beverages.

Because of the risks of lead toxicity from environmental contamination, lead is no longer used in house paint, gasoline, or solder. As a result, the number of children ages 1 to 5 years with elevated blood lead levels ($\geq$10 μg/100 mL) has decreased from about 78% in 1976–1980 to less than 2% in 1999–2002.[36] Despite these gains, certain groups remain at higher risk of elevated blood lead levels (**Figure 15.14**). Low-income children are at particular risk. Low-income families are more likely to live in older buildings that still have lead paint and lead plumbing. Even when other variables, such as race, are controlled for, low-income children are more likely to have elevated blood lead levels than middle- or high-income children. Typical blood lead levels for non-Hispanic black children remain higher than those for Mexican-American and non-Hispanic white children, in part reflecting differences in socioeconomic status. In addition, there is evidence that even blood lead levels below 10 μg/100 mL, which were once thought to be safe, may impair IQ in young children.[35,37]

Reducing the prevalence of lead toxicity in children is one of the national health objectives for Healthy People 2010 (**Table 15.4**). The effects of lead poisoning are permanent, but if high levels are detected early, the lead can be removed with medical treatment. Most children in the United States are at sufficient risk of lead exposure that they should have their blood lead concentration measured at least once.[38]

Figure 15.14 Percentage of children aged 1 to 5 years with elevated blood lead levels. Although blood lead levels have declined, they remain higher in non-Hispanic black and Mexican-American children than among white children. (Source: CDC, Blood lead levels-United States, 1999–2002, MMWR 54: 513–516, 2005.)

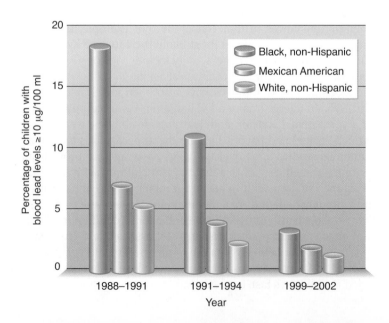

Table 15.4 What Can Be Done to Reduce Lead Exposure

Reducing exposure from lead paint: If you live in a house built before 1978, it may contain lead paint or lead paint may have been sanded or scrapped off at some time.

- Wash floors and other surfaces weekly with warm water and detergent.
- Wipe soil off shoes before entering the house.
- Cover exposed soil in the yard with grass or mulch.

Reducing exposure from tap water: If your home has old plumbing, lead may be leaching into your tap water. More lead leaches into hot water than cold, and water that has been standing in the pipes has more lead.

- Use cold water for drinking and cooking.
- Allow water to run for 30 seconds before use.

Reducing exposure from food containers: Pottery glazes and lead crystal contain lead. The FDA limits the amount of lead allowed in ceramic foodware, but the lead content of pottery designed for ornamental use is not regulated.

- Look for engraved warnings such as "Not for Food Use—May Poison Food" and "For Decorative Purposes Only" to identify pottery that should not be used to serve food.
- Do not store acidic foods such as fruit juices or tomato juice in ceramic containers.
- Limit the use of antique or collectible housewares for food or beverages to special occasions.
- Use your lead crystal stemware to drink from, but do not store anything in lead crystal.
- Pregnant women should not routinely use lead crystal glasses.
- Infants should not be fed from crystal baby bottles.

For additional information: Contact the Centers for Disease Control and Prevention at www.cdc.gov/health/lead or the Environmental Protection Agency's National Lead Information Center at www.epa.gov/lead/pubs/nlic.htm

Childhood Obesity

Although genes are important determinants of body size and weight, changes in lifestyle that have led to decreases in activity and increases in energy intake are the major reasons for the increase in obesity that has occurred among American children.[1,4] Reversing this trend requires changes in the way children play and eat (see Critical Thinking: At Risk for Malnutrition).

The Impact of Television Many children today spend more time watching television than they do in any activity other than sleep. Television affects nutritional status in a number of ways: it introduces children to foods they might otherwise not be exposed to, it promotes snacking, and it reduces physical activity (**Figure 15.15**).

Figure 15.15 Television watching influences activity level, snacking behavior, and the kinds of foods children choose. (Donna Day/Stone/Getty Images)

Critical Thinking
At Risk for Malnutrition

Background

Jamar is 8 years old and has been gaining weight. All he wants to do is lie around and watch TV. Previously he enjoyed playing basketball with his friends and was eager to go on hikes with the family. Jamar's parents are both overweight. They are concerned that Jamar will also have a weight problem, so they take him to see their pediatrician. The nurse weighs and measures Jamar and draws a blood sample for routine analysis.

Data

Last year Jamar's BMI was at the 50th percentile, but it is now almost at the 75th. The blood sample reveals that Jamar has iron deficiency anemia. The pediatrician prescribes an iron supplement and refers Jamar and his parents to a dietitian. By reviewing Jamar's diet and exercise patterns the dietitian learns that he gets 25 minutes of exercise during recess at school and that he has been watching TV or playing video games for about 6 hours a day. Below are the results of a food frequency questionnaire that she recorded:

(©iStockphoto)

FOOD	FREQUENCY	
	SERVINGS/DAY	SERVINGS/WEEK
Milk and dairy products		
Regular fat	6	
Reduced fat		
Fat-free		
Meat and eggs		
Red meat		1
Chicken		2
Fish		1
Eggs		
Grains and cereals		
Whole grains	2	
Refined grains	4	
Fruit and juices		
Citrus	1	
Other	2	
Vegetables		
Dark green leafy		
Other	1	
Added fats	3	
Snack foods		
Chips, etc.	2	
Candy	1	

Critical Thinking Questions

Why is Jamar's energy balance out of balance? Does he get the amount of daily activity recommended for a child his age? Evaluate his diet by comparing the number of servings per day he consumes from the various food groups to the MyPyramid recommendations for an 8-year-old boy.

▼

Why is he anemic? What foods groups does he consume that are good sources of iron? How would his intake of dairy products affect his iron status?

▼

How might Jamar's iron deficiency anemia have contributed to his weight gain?

▼

Suggest some dietary changes that could increase his iron intake and decrease his energy intake.

 iProfile   Use iProfile to find the iron content of several fast food meals.

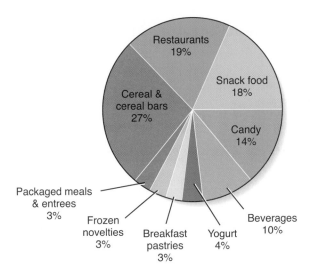

Figure 15.16 Types of foods advertised on children's Saturday morning television.
A high percentage of foods advertised on children's television are high in fat, sugar, or salt and low in nutrient density. (Source: Batada, A, Seitz, M, Wotan, M, et al. Nine out of ten Food Advertisements Shown During Saturday Morning Children's Television Programming are for Food High in Fat. Sodium or Added Sugars, or Low in Nutrients J. Am. Diet. Assoc. 108: 673–678, 2008.)

Through advertising, television has a strong influence on the foods selected by young children; children exposed to advertising choose advertised food products more often than children who are not exposed.[39] Food is the most frequently advertised product category on children's TV. The majority of these ads target highly sweetened products such as sweetened breakfast cereals; sweets such as candy, cookies, doughnuts, and other desserts; snacks; and beverages; and more recently, the proportion from fast-food meal promotions has been growing (**Figure 15.16**).[40] The more hours of TV a child watches, the more he or she asks for advertised food items, and the more likely these items are to be in the home. Television also promotes snacking behavior. Although snacks are an important part of a growing child's diet, while watching TV many children snack on sweet and salty foods that are low in nutrient density. In terms of overall diet, more hours of TV watching have been associated with higher intakes of energy, fat, sweet and salty snacks, and carbonated beverages and lower intakes of fruits and vegetables.[39]

Perhaps the most important nutritional impact of television is that it reduces activity. Hours spent watching television are hours when physical activity is at a minimum. One study showed that children who watch 4 or more hours of TV per day are 40% more likely to be overweight than those who watch an hour or less a day.[41] Generally the more physically active a child is the less TV he or she watches. In addition to television, children and adolescents today replace time spent at more physically demanding activities with time spent playing computer and video games.

The Impact of Fast Food Children and teens generally love fast food, and there is nothing wrong with an occasional fast-food meal. But a steady diet of burgers, fries, and soda will likely contribute to an overall diet that is high in energy, fat, sugar, and salt and low in calcium, fiber, and vitamins A and C (**Figure 15.17**).

The portions served at fast-food restaurants are a major contributor to children's increased energy intake. A meal that includes a hamburger, small fries, and a small drink will provide about 600 kcalories, 12 grams of saturated fat, and 36 grams of sugar. But a meal with a Big Mac, a large order of fries, and a large drink will increase the numbers to 1390 kcalories, 15 grams of saturated fat, and 94 grams of sugar. A steady diet of such meals can significantly increase kcalorie intake and consequently body weight. Choosing carefully from the old fast-food standbys such as plain, single-patty hamburgers or newer low-fat options such as grilled chicken sandwiches can keep fat and energy intake reasonable (see **Table 15.5**).

Figure 15.17 Consuming too much fast food and making poor fast-food choices can result in a diet high in fat and low in fruits and vegetables. (Arthur R. Hill/Visuals Unlimited)

Table 15.5 Make Healthier Fast-Food Choices

Instead of ...	Choose ...
Double-patty hamburger with cheese, mayonnaise, special sauce, and bacon	Regular single-patty hamburger without mayonnaise, special sauce, and bacon
Breaded and fried chicken sandwich	Grilled chicken sandwich
Chicken nuggets or tenders	Grilled chicken strips
Large French fries	Baked potato, side salad, or small order of fries
Fried chicken wings	Broiled skinless wings
Crispy-shell chicken taco with extra cheese and sour cream	Grilled-chicken soft taco without sour cream
Nachos with cheese sauce	Tortilla chips with bean dip
12-in. meatball sub	6-in. turkey breast sub with lots of vegetables
Thick-crust pizza with extra cheese and meat toppings	Thin-crust pizza with extra veggies
Doughnut	Cinnamon and raisin bagel with low-fat cream cheese

Some food groups are limited in typical fast-food meals. For example, the few pieces of shredded lettuce and the slice of tomato that garnish a burger or taco make only a small contribution to the 2 cups of vegetables that should be included in the diet of an average 8-year-old boy. Typically fast-food meals are also lacking in milk and fruits. Many fast-food franchises now offer vegetables, salads, yogurt, fruit, and milk, which can increase calcium and vitamin intake if selected. Even if they are not, keep in mind that a fast-food meal is only one part of the total diet. If the missing milk, fruits, and vegetables are consumed at other times during the day and overall energy intake balances output, the total diet can still be a healthy one.

Preventing and Treating Obesity The Institute of Medicine Committee on Prevention of Obesity in Children and Youth has developed a prevention-focused plan to decrease the prevalence of childhood obesity in the United States.[42] The committee recommends action by federal, state, and local governments; industry and the media; health-care professionals; community and nonprofit organizations; schools; and parents and families. One recommendation is that the food, beverage, restaurant, entertainment, leisure, and recreation industries help encourage healthy, appropriately portioned foods and develop products and opportunities that stimulate physical activity. The report also recommends changes in the food label and the development of advertising and marketing guidelines that help minimize the risk of obesity. At the community level recommendations focus on programs that encourage healthy eating behaviors and regular exercise by providing children with safe places to walk, bike, play games, and engage in other physical activities. The report targets schools because they are a place where children can be reached with information about energy balance, good nutrition, and physical activity. Schools can offer foods and beverages that meet acceptable nutritional standards. In addition, children should achieve at least 60 minutes of physical activity daily.[5] These recommendations apply at school and home because parents make daily decisions regarding food choices and opportunities for recreation, they determine the setting for foods eaten in the home, and they are responsible for other rules and policies that influence the extent to which various members of the family engage in healthful eating and physical activity.

These strategies will help reduce the prevalence of obesity in the population, but weight problems must also be addressed in individuals. Because children are still growing, weight loss is rarely recommended. Rather, overweight children should be encouraged to slow their weight gain while they continue to grow taller. This allows them to "grow into" their weight. A child who is at the 85th percentile for BMI at age 7 and gains only a few pounds a year can be at the 75th percentile by age 9. This requires that the child's behavior be modified to reduce energy intake to a moderate level and to increase activity.

Changing Behavior As with adults, weight gain in children is related to patterns of eating and exercise. Any permanent change in weight requires a permanent change in lifestyle. Changing eating patterns and activity is key to developing and maintaining a healthy weight. Because children, like adults, may overeat for comfort, self-reward, or out of boredom, parent involvement in helping the child find other sources of gratification can be vital.

Reducing Intake Modifying a child's food consumption patterns can be difficult. Denying food may promote further overeating by making the child feel that there will not be enough to satisfy hunger. The child may then overeat whenever there is a chance. Thus, energy intake restrictions should be relatively mild and the focus instead should be on offering nutrient-dense foods such as whole grains, fruits and vegetables, lean meats, and reduced-fat dairy products. Planning ahead can help manage eating at social events. For example, a teenage girl with a weight problem could plan how much she will eat at a pizza party and then increase her exercise to burn off the excess kcalories.

Increasing Activity One of the major contributors to the increase in body weight among children is lack of physical activity. Watching television, playing video games, and surfing the Web have replaced neighborhood games of tag and soccer for many children. Whether or not a child is overweight, he or she should be physically active. Guidelines recommend that children be physically active for at least an hour per day (**Table 15.6**).[5,13] Children have short attention spans, so their activities should be intermittent. Periods of moderate to vigorous activity lasting 10 to 15 minutes or more each day should be interspersed with periods of rest and recovery. Children and adolescents should be exposed to a variety of different types of activities that are of various levels of intensity and that include both muscle-strengthening and bone-strengthening activities.[5] Learning to enjoy sports and exercise in childhood will set the stage for an active lifestyle in adulthood (**Figure 15.18**). For inactive children, physical activity should be increased gradually in order to make exercise a positive experience. A good way to start is to encourage activities such as games, walks after dinner, bike rides, hikes, swimming, and volleyball that can be enjoyed by the whole family. This sends a positive message to "be more active." Again, involvement of the whole family is key to increasing activity.[43]

Figure 15.18 To help children balance food intake and physical activity, exercise should be fun. Riding bikes, using rollerblades, and skateboards, and playing basketball and frizbee all count toward this goal. (Masterfile)

Table 15.6 Exercise Guidelines for Children and Adolescents

- **Children and adolescents should do 60 minutes or more of physical activity daily.**

  - **Aerobic:** Most of the 60 or more minutes a day should be either moderate- or vigorous-intensity aerobic physical activity, and should include vigorous-intensity physical activity at least 3 days a week.

  - **Muscle-strengthening:** As part of their 60 or more minutes of daily physical activity, children and adolescents should include muscle-strengthening physical activity on at least 3 days of the week.

  - **Bone-strengthening:** As part of their 60 or more minutes of daily physical activity, children and adolescents should include bone-strengthening physical activity on at least 3 days of the week.

- **It is important to encourage young people to participate in physical activities that are appropriate for their age, that are enjoyable, and that offer variety.**

Source: DHHS, 2008 Physical Activity Guidelines for Americans. Available online at http://www.health.gov/paguidelines/pdf/paguide.pdf. Accessed May 13, 2009.

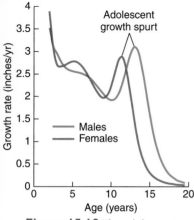

Figure 15.19 The adolescent growth spurt.
During a 1-year growth spurt, boys can gain 4 inches in height and girls 3.5 inches.

puberty A period of rapid growth and physical changes that ends in the attainment of sexual maturity.

adolescent growth spurt An 18- to 24-month period of peak growth velocity that begins at about ages 10 to 13 in girls and 12 to 15 in boys.

menarche The onset of menstruation, which occurs normally between the ages of 10 and 15 years.

15.4 Adolescents

Learning Objectives

- Describe how growth and body composition are affected by puberty.
- Compare the energy needs of adolescents with those of children and adults.
- Explain why iron and calcium are of particular concern during the teen years.
- Use MyPyramid to plan a day's diet that would appeal to a teenager.

Once a child has reached about 9 to 12 years of age, the physical changes associated with sexual maturation begin to occur. These physical changes, along with the social and psychological changes that accompany them, have a significant impact on the nutritional needs and nutrient intakes of adolescents. The DRIs divide recommended intakes for adolescence into ages 9 through 13 and ages 14 through 18.

The Changing Body: Sexual Maturation

During adolescence, organ systems develop and grow, **puberty** occurs, body composition changes, and the growth rates and nutritional requirements of boys and girls diverge. During the teenage years, boys and girls grow about 11 inches and gain about 40% of their eventual skeletal mass.[45] From ages 10 to 17, girls gain about 53 lbs and boys about 70 lbs. During adolescence, there is an 18- to 24-month period of peak growth velocity, called the **adolescent growth spurt**. In girls, the growth spurt occurs between the ages of 10 and 13. In boys, it occurs between ages 12 and 15 (**Figure 15.19**).

The hormonal changes that occur with sexual development orchestrate growth and affect body composition. During the growth spurt, boys tend to grow taller and heavier than girls and do so at a faster rate. Boys gain fat but also add so much lean mass as muscle and bone that their percentage of body fat actually decreases. In girls, **menarche**, the onset of menstruation, is typically followed by a deceleration in growth rate and an increase in fat deposition. By age 20, females have about twice as much adipose tissue as males and only about two-thirds as much lean tissue (**Figure 15.20**).

Nutrient intake during childhood and adolescence can affect sexual development. Nutritional deficiencies can cause poor growth and delayed sexual maturation. Taller, heavier children usually enter puberty sooner than shorter, lighter ones.[44]

Figure 15.20 Body composition of males and females.
After puberty, males have a higher percentage of lean body mass and less body fat than females. (Source: Adapted from Forbes, G. B. Body composition. In Present Knowledge in Nutrition, 6th ed. M. L. Brown, ed. Washington, DC: International Life Sciences Institute-Nutrition Foundation, 1990.)

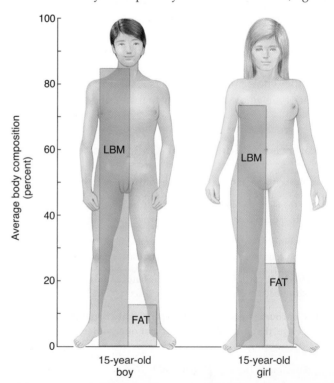

Adolescent Nutrient Needs

The physiological changes that occur during adolescence affect nutrient needs. Total nutrient needs are greater during adolescence than at any other time of life. Because there is a large individual variation in the age at which these growth and developmental changes occur, the stage of maturation is often a better indicator of nutritional requirements than actual chronological age. The best indicators of adequate intake are satiety and growth that follows the curve of the growth charts.

Energy and Energy-Yielding Nutrients The proportion of energy from carbohydrate, fat, and protein recommended for adolescents is similar to that of adults, but the total amount of energy needed by teenagers exceeds adult needs. Energy requirements for boys are greater than those for girls because boys have more muscle and a greater body size. Adolescent girls need 2100 to 2400 kcalories per day, whereas boys require about 2200 to 3150 kcalories per day (see Figure 15.6). Protein requirements for both groups reach the adult recommendation of 0.8 grams per kilogram by about age 19, but since boys are generally heavier, they require more total protein than girls. These higher requirements for males continue throughout life.

Micronutrients The requirements for many vitamins and minerals are greater during adolescence than childhood. Some of these are increased because of increased energy needs and others are increased because of their roles in growth and maturation.

Vitamins The need for most of the vitamins rises to adult levels during adolescence. The requirement for B vitamins, which are involved in energy metabolism, is much higher in adolescence than in childhood because of higher energy needs. The rapid growth of adolescence further increases the need for vitamin B_6, which is important for protein synthesis, and for folate and vitamin B_{12}, which are essential for cell division. The high kcalorie intakes of teens help them meet most of their vitamin needs, but inadequate intakes of riboflavin and vitamin D put some teens at risk for deficiency. Riboflavin is frequently low in teens' diets, especially in those of girls, possibly due to low milk intake. Vitamin D is important to support the rapid skeletal growth that occurs during adolescence. Low blood levels of vitamin D are a problem due to low intakes as well as limited synthesis from sunlight in those with dark skin pigmentation or inadequate exposure to sunlight during the winter months (see Chapter 7).[45]

Iron Iron-deficiency anemia is common in adolescence. Iron is needed to synthesize hemoglobin for the expansion of blood volume and myoglobin for the increase in muscle mass. Because blood volume expands at a faster rate in boys than in girls, boys require more iron for tissue synthesis than girls. However, the iron loss due to menstruation makes total needs greater in young women. The RDA is set at 11 mg per day for boys (this is greater than the 8 mg RDA for adult men) and 15 mg per day for girls ages 14 to 18.[46] Girls are more likely than boys to consume less than the recommended amount because they require more iron, tend to eat fewer iron-rich foods, and consume fewer overall kcalories. As a result, iron deficiency is common in adolescent females, affecting about 9% of girls ages 12 to 15 and 16% of young women ages 16 to 19.[47]

Calcium The adolescent growth spurt increases both the length and the mass of bones, and adequate calcium is essential to form healthy bone. Calcium retention varies with growth rate, with the fastest-growing adolescents retaining the most calcium. The AI for calcium during adolescence is 1300 mg per day for both sexes (300 mg greater than the RDA for adults ages 19 to 50), but intake is typically below this in both adolescent boys and girls.[48] Fewer than 10% of girls and only 25% of boys ages 9 to 13 consume the recommended amount of calcium.[49] This low intake in combination with a sedentary lifestyle in childhood and adolescence can impede skeletal growth and bone mineralization and increase the risk of developing osteoporosis later in life.

Foods common in the teen diet that are good sources of calcium include milk, yogurt and frozen yogurt, ice cream, and cheese added to hamburgers, nachos, and pizza. Although milk and cheese are the biggest source of calcium in teen diets, they

Figure 15.21 Percentage of energy from milk and soft drinks. Since the 1970s, children and teens (ages 2–18) have more than doubled the number of kcalories they consume from soft drinks while cutting the kcalories they obtain from milk by 34%. (Source: Nielsen, S. J., and Popkin, B. M. Changes in beverage intake between 1977 and 2001. Am. J. Prev. Med. 27: 205–210, 2004.)

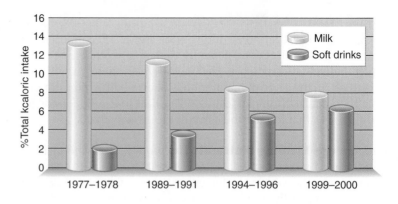

can be high in saturated fat, so adolescents should be encouraged to consume reduced-fat dairy products and vegetable sources of calcium. One factor that has contributed to low calcium intake among teens is the use of soda as a beverage, rather than milk (**Figure 15.21**). In addition to calcium, milk is an important source of vitamin D, phosphorus, magnesium, potassium, protein, riboflavin, vitamin A, and zinc. Adolescent girls are likely to drink less milk in order to cut kcalories, favoring low-kcalorie soft drinks (see Chapter 11: Your Choice: Choose Your Beverage Wisely.).

Zinc During adolescence, the increase in protein synthesis required for the growth of skeletal muscle and the development of organs increases the need for zinc. The RDA is 11 mg per day for boys and 9 mg per day for girls ages 14 to 18. A long-term deficiency results in growth retardation and altered sexual development. Although severe zinc deficiency is rare in developed countries, even mild deficiency can cause poor growth, affect appetite and taste, impair immune response, and interfere with vitamin A metabolism. Since adolescents are growing rapidly and maturing sexually, adequate zinc is essential for this age group.[46] Good sources of zinc include meats and whole grains. The fortification of many breakfast cereals with zinc has increased the average zinc intake in the United States.[50]

Meeting Adolescent Nutrient Needs

During adolescence, physiological changes dictate nutritional needs but peer pressure may dictate food choices. Parents often have little control over what adolescents eat and skipped meals and meals away from home are common. A food is more likely to be selected because it tastes good, it is easy to grab on the go, or friends are eating it than because it is healthy. No matter when foods are consumed throughout the day, an adolescent's diet should follow the recommendations of MyPyramid for the appropriate age, gender, and activity level (**Figure 15.22**). For example, an 18-year-old boy who exercises more than an hour a day would need a diet containing about 3200 kcalories a day. This diet should include 10 ounces of grains. This may seem like a huge amount, but it is not when spread over the course of a day. A large bowl of cereal and a slice of toast for breakfast is 3 ounces; two tacos for lunch and crackers after school provide 4 more; and a dinner of spaghetti and garlic bread can add another 3 or 4. As shown in Figure 15.22, the diet should also provide 4 cups of vegetables and 2.5 cups of fruit.

Fruits and vegetables are the food groups most likely to be lacking in the teen diet: French fries, which are high in fat and salt, are the most frequently consumed vegetable. Less than 16% of children or teens eat green beans, corn, green peas, or lima beans on a given day and the percentage consuming dark green and deep yellow vegetables is even lower despite recommendations to consume more of these vegetables. Fruit consumption declines in the teenage years. Seventy percent of children under 5 years of age consume some fruit or fruit juice on any one day, but that number drops to less than half among teens.[51] Sources of fruits and vegetables acceptable to teens include fruit juice, salads, and tomato sauce and vegetables on pizza and spaghetti.

Snacks are an important part of the adolescent diet; they provide about a quarter of the kcalories for a typical teen. Unfortunately many of these snacks are burgers, fries,

Food group	GRAINS	VEGETABLES	FRUITS	MILK	MEAT & BEANS
Amount for an 11-yr-old male	7 ounces	3 cups	2 cups	3 cups	6 ounces
Amount for an 11-yr-old female	6 ounces	2.5 cups	2 cups	3 cups	5.5 ounces
Amount for an 18-yr-old male	10 ounces	4 cups	2.5 cups	3 cups	7 ounces
Amount for an 18-yr-old female	8 ounces	3 cups	2 cups	3 cups	6.5 ounces

Figure 15.22 MyPyramid recommendations for teens.
The recommendations shown here are for 11- and 18-year-old boys and girls who engage in more than 60 minutes of activity daily.

potato chips, candy, cookies, and other high-fat, high-sodium, high-sugar foods. Most of these choices are low in calcium, fiber, folate, vitamins A and C, and iron and make the typical teen diet, especially that of teenage boys, high in fat, saturated fat, cholesterol, and sodium. To improve the teen diet, meals and snacks offered at home should be low in saturated fat and sodium and high in dairy products, vegetables, and fruits.

15.5 Special Concerns of Teenagers

Learning Objectives

- Explain how a vegetarian diet could be high in saturated fat.
- Discuss how teens' concerns for appearance and performance can affect their nutritional status.
- Describe why peer pressure affects nutrition in teenagers.

As teens grow and become more independent they are responsible for decisions about their diet and lifestyle. Choices they make regarding the foods they eat, their appearance, and their physical activities as well as the use of tobacco, alcohol, and illegal drugs can affect their nutrition as well as their overall health.

Vegetarian Diets

Some children and adolescents consume vegetarian diets because their families are vegetarians, but teens may also decide to consume a vegetarian diet even if the rest of the family does not. Some do it for health reasons or to lose weight, but most give up meat because they are concerned about animals and the environment. About 2% of children and teens ages 6 to 17 or about one million school-aged youth are vegetarian.[52]

We typically think of vegetarian diets as healthful alternatives and for many teens, they are. One study found that teenage vegetarians were much more likely than their meat-eating counterparts to meet the Healthy People 2010 objectives of less than 30% of kcalories from fat and less than 10% from saturated fat, 2 servings of fruit, and more than 3 servings of vegetables daily.[53] However, as with any diet, vegetarian foods must be carefully chosen to meet needs and avoid excesses. Meatless diets can be low in iron and zinc, and vegan diets, which contain no animal products, may put teens at risk of vitamin B_{12} deficiency and inadequate calcium and vitamin D intake. If the diet includes high-fat dairy products it can be high in saturated fat and cholesterol. If only refined grains are chosen and fruit and vegetable intake goals are not met the diet can be low in fiber. For example, a slice of cheese pizza and a can of cola provide calcium but are low in iron and fiber and high in fat and sugar. In contrast, a vegetarian lunch of whole grain pita bread stuffed with hummus (chickpeas), tomatoes, and spinach, along with some dried fruit and a glass of reduced-fat milk, is low in saturated fat and cholesterol, high in complex carbohydrate and fiber, and contains good sources of calcium and plant sources of iron. The key to a healthy vegetarian diet, like all healthy diets, is to choose a variety of nutrient-dense vegetables, fruits, grains, legumes, and dairy products (or other calcium sources).

Eating for Appearance and Performance

Appearance is probably of more concern during adolescence than at any other time of life. Many girls want to lose weight even if they are not overweight. Some boys also want to reduce their weight, but more want to gain weight to achieve a muscular, strong appearance and enhance their athletic abilities (see Critical Thinking: Less Food May Not Mean Fewer Kcalories).

Eating Disorders Although eating disorders are usually not diagnosed until adolescence, the excessive concern about weight and body image that characterizes these conditions may begin as early as the preschool years. As children grow, the pressure of taking on the responsibilities of adulthood, combined with pressure from peers and society to be thin, may contribute to the development of eating disorders. It is estimated that 0.5% of adolescent females have anorexia and 1 to 5% have bulimia.[54] Disordered eating is often hidden by other eating patterns. For example, many women choose vegetarian diets for weight control and vegetarian college women have been found to be at greater risk of disordered eating than nonvegetarians.[55] The nutritional consequences of an eating disorder can affect growth and development and have a lifelong impact on health (see Focus on Eating Disorders).

The Impact of Athletics Despite all the benefits of exercise, nutrition misinformation and the desire to excel in a sport can cause adolescent athletes to take dietary supplements, use anabolic steroids, or consume inappropriate training diets and experiment with fad diets, all of which can impact health (see Chapter 13).

Teen athletes may require more water, energy, protein, carbohydrate, and micronutrients than their less active peers, but supplements are rarely needed to meet these needs. If the extra energy needs of teen athletes are met with whole grains, fresh fruits and vegetables, and dairy products, their protein, carbohydrate, and micronutrient needs will easily be met. An exception is iron, which may need to be supplemented, particularly in female athletes. The combination of poor iron intake, iron losses from menstruation and sweat, and increased needs for building new lean tissue puts many female athletes at risk for iron-deficiency anemia.[56]

Critical Thinking
Less Food May Not Mean Fewer Kcalories

(Image Source/Getty Images, Inc.)

Background

Jenny is a busy 16-year-old high school junior. Until recently she hadn't paid much attention to her diet because she ate all her meals at home or at school. Now she has a part-time job and frequently eats dinner and snacks on her own. She notices that she has gained a few pounds and decides that she should change her diet. Despite eating less food with her new diet she continues to gain weight.

Data

JENNY'S DIET		JENNY'S NEW DIET	
FOOD	ENERGY (KCAL)	FOOD	ENERGY (KCAL)
Breakfast			
Corn flakes	97	Bagel	187
Low-fat milk	120		
Orange juice	112		
Toast	140		
Margarine	68		
Lunch			
Hamburger	260		
Apple	81		
Low-fat milk	120		
Corn chips	153		
Snack			
Slice of pizza	200	Frozen yogurt	288
Cola	185	Candy bar	300
		Potato chips	230
Dinner			
Ham and cheese sandwich	350	Double burger	576
Potato chips	150	French fries	315
Cola	185	Vanilla shake	503
Total	**2221**		**2319**

Critical Thinking Questions

Why is Jenny continuing to gain weight on her new diet despite eating a smaller breakfast and skipping lunch?

▼

How could Jenny modify her new diet to reduce her kcalorie intake and still fit her busy schedule?

 iProfile Use iProfile to find foods that are nutrient-dense and filling, but still low in kcalories.

Many of the most dangerous practices associated with adolescent sports are those that attempt to control body weight. Some sports such as football demand that the athlete be large and heavy (**Figure 15.23**). In order to "bulk up," high school athletes may experiment with anabolic steroids, androstenedione, and creatine. Anabolic steroids are illegal, and although they do increase muscle mass, the risks far outweigh the benefits (see Chapter 13: Your Choice: Ergogenic Hormones: Anything for an Edge). Androstenedione is a testosterone precursor that has been sold as a dietary supplement. The FDA has asked manufacturers to stop distributing dietary supplements containing androstenedione. The benefits of this supplement have not been substantiated and the long-term health effects have not yet been determined. Creatine improves exercise performance in sports requiring short bursts of activity and has not been associated with serious side effects.[57] Nonetheless, the best and safest way for young athletes to increase muscle mass is the hard way: lift weights and eat more. Lifting weights three times a week will stimulate the muscles to enlarge and adding snacks such as milkshakes and peanut butter sandwiches will provide the energy and protein needed to support muscle growth (see Chapter 13).

Female athletes involved in sports that require lean, light bodies, such as gymnastics and ballet, are likely to abuse weight-loss diets. Sexual maturation, which causes an increase in body fat and changes in weight distribution, can be disturbing to young women involved in such sports. The combination of hard training and weight restriction can lead to a syndrome known as the female athlete triad that includes disordered eating, amenorrhea, and osteoporosis[58] (see Focus on Eating Disorders and Chapter 13).

Weight loss is also a concern for adolescents participating in sports such as wrestling that require athletes to fit into a specific weight class on the day of the event. In these athletes, dangerous methods of quick weight loss—such as severe energy intake restriction, water deprivation, self-induced vomiting, and diuretic and laxative abuse—are common practice. Low-energy diets can interfere with normal growth and may be too limited in variety to meet these athletes' needs for vitamins and minerals. Even more of a danger is the practice of restricting water intake and encouraging sweat loss to decrease body weight. This may achieve the temporary weight loss necessary to put the athlete in a lower weight class, but dehydration is dangerous and can impair athletic performance (see Chapters 10 and 13).

Figure 15.23 High school football players often use dietary supplements and illegal ergogenic aids to gain muscle mass and strength. (Dennis MacDonald/ Age Fotostock America, Inc.)

Oral Contraceptive Use

Oral contraceptive hormones may be prescribed to adolescent girls for a number of reasons and can change nutritional status because they affect nutrient metabolism. Oral contraceptives may cause a rise in fasting blood sugar and a tendency toward abnormal glucose tolerance in those with a family history of diabetes. They may also cause changes in body composition, including weight gain due to water retention and an increase in lean body mass. Oral contraceptives may reduce the need for iron by reducing menstrual flow and increasing iron absorption. Therefore, a special RDA for iron of 11.4 mg per day has been established for those taking oral contraceptives.[46]

Teenage Pregnancy

Because adolescent girls continue to grow and mature for several years after menstruation starts, the diet of a pregnant teenager must meet her own nutrient needs for growth and development as well as the needs of pregnancy. These elevated needs put the pregnant adolescent at nutritional risk. In order for the mother and fetus to remain healthy, special attention must be paid to all aspects of prenatal care, including nutrient intake (see Chapter 14). Due to the special nutrient needs of this group, the DRIs have included a life-stage group for pregnant girls age 18 or younger.

Life Cycle

Tobacco Use

Approximately 20% of high school students in the United States smoke cigarettes.[59] Smoking affects hunger, body weight, and nutritional status, and increases the risk of cardiovascular disease and lung cancer. Many teens start smoking in order to promote weight loss or maintenance. Because smoking is associated with lower body weights in adult women, some teens believe smoking will curb their appetite and help them stay thin or lose weight.[60] Smokers often do not want to quit because they fear that they will gain weight. Smoking impacts nutrient intake. A comparison of the diets of smokers and nonsmokers found that smokers had higher intakes of total and saturated fat and consumed fewer fruits and vegetables leading to lower intakes of folate, vitamin C, and fiber.[61] This dietary pattern can affect nutritional status and further increase the risk of developing heart disease and cancer. In addition to being associated with lower intakes of vitamin C, the increase in oxidative stress caused by smoking increases the requirement for vitamin C so the DRIs recommend that smokers consume an extra 35 mg per day.[62]

Alcohol Use

Although it is illegal to sell alcohol to adolescents, alcoholic beverages are commonly available at teen social gatherings, and the peer pressure to consume them is strong. Surveys of American youth suggest that almost 45% of students in 9th through 12th grades have had at least one drink during the previous month; of these, 26% have engaged in **binge drinking**.[63] Alcohol is a drug that has short-term effects that occur soon after ingestion and long-term health consequences that are associated with overuse. It provides 7 kcalories per gram but no nutrients. Alcohol consumption displaces foods that are nutritious. Once ingested, alcohol alters nutrient absorption and metabolism. The metabolism of alcohol as well as its impact on nutritional and overall health are discussed in Focus on Alcohol.

binge drinking The consumption of five or more drinks in a row for males or four or more for females.

Outcome

After a few months of consuming healthy, low-kcalorie meals and exercising regularly, Felicia has lost a few pounds. More important, she has begun to feel better about herself and is even more motivated to change her old habits to improve her health and appearance. Her fitness has improved enough for her to ride her bike to school. She has begun helping her mother find healthy recipes and has learned to make lower-kcalorie choices when she eats out or snacks with friends. For example, instead of ice cream she has sorbet or low-fat frozen yogurt, and she passes on burgers and fries in favor of a grilled chicken sandwich and a salad. When she is hungry she reaches for fruit or raw vegetables. Felicia now takes a multivitamin and mineral supplement to make sure she gets enough iron and drinks fat-free milk with her meals for a low-kcalorie source of calcium. She still eats lunch in the school cafeteria, but now she makes better choices from the foods offered.

Felicia, now 15 years old, has grown 3 inches and gained only 5 pounds over the last 2 years. Her BMI is at about the 90th percentile. Her self-confidence has increased so much that she is considering trying out for the field hockey team next year. If she grows another 2 inches and gains weight slowly, by the time she is 17 she will have a BMI in the healthy range.

APPLICATIONS

Personal Nutrition

1. **What food groups are included in a fast-food lunch?**
   a. How much food from each food group of MyPyramid is provided by a Big Mac, a small order of fries, and a 16-oz cola?
   b. Estimate how many discretionary kcalories this meal provides.
   c. Go to www.MyPyramid.gov to see how much food from each food group is recommended for you and how many discretionary kcalories you can allow each day.
   d. If you consumed this fast-food lunch how much more food from each group would you need to consume to satisfy the daily recommendations of MyPyramid?
   e. Select foods from each group to complete your intake for the day without exceeding your discretionary kcalorie allowance.

2. **What's in your favorite fast-food meal?**
   a. Use iProfile to look up the nutrient composition of your favorite fast-food meal.
   b. What is the percent of kcalories from carbohydrate and fat in the meal?
   c. Compare the amount of energy, fat, protein, iron, calcium, vitamin C, and vitamin A in this meal to the recommended amounts of each for a person of your age and gender.

General Nutrition Issues

1. **Is this girl growing normally?**

Age	Height (Inches)	Weight (lbs)
6	45	44
7	48	53
8	50	77
9	52	97

   a. Use the height and weight measurements recorded in the table above for a girl from age 6 to age 9 to calculate her BMI at each age and plot these values on the appropriate BMI-for-age growth chart in Figure 15.5.
   b. What recommendations do you have about this girl's weight?

2. **What recommendations would you make for each of the following young athletes?**
   a. Frank is a wrestler. His usual weight is just at the low end of a weight class and he wants to lose enough weight to be in the next lower class.
   b. Sam is a football player. He has been getting hit hard in the last few games and wants to bulk up. He is looking into taking supplements to speed up the process.
   c. Talia is a dancer who has recently gained a few pounds. Her coach notices that she no longer drinks or snacks during practice.

Summary

15.1 Starting Right for a Healthy Life

- The current diet of American children is low in fruits and vegetables and whole grains and high in processed foods that are excessive in fat, salt, or sugar.
- Good nutrition during childhood sets the stage for nutrition and health in the adult years.
- Healthy eating habits learned in childhood will extend into the adult years

15.2 Nourishing Infants, Toddlers, and Young Children

- Growth that follows standard patterns is the best indicator of adequate nutrition. BMI-for-age growth charts can be used to evaluate whether a child is normal weight, underweight, overweight, or obese.
- Energy and protein needs per kilogram of body weight decrease as children grow, but total needs increase because of the increase in total body weight and activity level.

Children need a greater percentage of fat and the same percentage of carbohydrates as adults. Dietary carbohydrates should come primarily from whole grains, vegetables, fruits, and milk. Baked goods, candy, and soda should be limited.

- Under most situations water needs in children can be met by consuming enough fluid to alleviate thirst. Activity and a hot environment increase water needs. As with adults, the typical sodium intake in children and teens currently exceeds the recommended amounts.

- Calcium and iron intakes are often low in children's diets. Adequate calcium is important for preventing osteoporosis later in life but calcium intake is declining due to reductions in the consumption of dairy products. Iron intake has increased over the last 20 years but the incidence of iron deficiency in toddlers, preschool children, and adolescent girls remains above the levels targeted by Healthy People 2010.

- Introducing solid foods between 4 and 6 months of age adds iron and other nutrients to the diet and aids in muscle development. Newly introduced foods should be appropriate to the child's stage of development and offered one at a time to monitor for food allergies.

- Food allergies are caused by the absorption of allergens, most of which are proteins. Food allergies involve antibody production by the immune system and are more common in infancy because the infant's immature gastrointestinal tract is more likely to absorb whole proteins. Specific foods that cause allergies can be identified by an elimination diet and food challenge. Unlike food allergies, food intolerances do not involve the immune system.

- In order to meet nutrient needs and develop nutritious habits, a variety of healthy foods should be offered at meals and snacks throughout the day. The National School Lunch Program provides low-cost school lunches designed to meet nutrient needs and promote healthy diets. Some children can benefit from vitamin/mineral supplements, but children who consume a well-selected, varied diet can meet all their vitamin and mineral requirements with food.

15.3 Nutrition and Health Concerns in Children

- Dietary patterns high in sugars combined with poor dental hygiene put children at risk of dental caries. Sugar intake as well as food additives have been blamed for hyperactive behavior, but there is little evidence that these are the cause of hyperactivity.

- Children's health is harmed by lead. Lead disrupts the activity of neurotransmitters and thus interferes with the functioning of the nervous system. Due to reductions in the use of lead the number of children with high blood lead levels has been declining, but the incidence remains higher in certain minorities.

- Obesity is a growing problem among children. Watching television contributes to childhood obesity by promoting high-fat, high-sugar, and high-salt foods and by reducing the amount of exercise children get. Fast food can also add excess kcalories to a child's diet unless nutrient-dense choices are made throughout the rest of the day. Solutions to the problem of childhood obesity involve action from government, industry, health-care providers, communities, schools, and parents and families. Individuals who are overweight need to change behaviors to decrease food intake and increase activity.

15.4 Adolescents

- During adolescence body composition changes and the nutritional requirements of boys and girls diverge. Males gain more lean body tissue, while females have a greater increase in body fat.

- During adolescence, accelerated growth and sexual maturation have an impact on nutrient requirements. Total energy and protein requirements are higher than at any other time of life. Vitamin requirements increase to meet the needs of rapid growth. The minerals calcium, iron, and zinc are likely to be low in the adolescent diet. Calcium intake is often low because teens are drinking soda instead of milk. Iron-deficiency anemia is common, especially in girls as they begin losing iron through menstruation.

- Adolescent nutrient needs can be met by following the recommendations of MyPyramid. Since meals are frequently missed, healthy snacks should be included in the diet.

15.5 Special Concerns of Teenagers

- Teens often turn to vegetarian diets, sometimes for environmental reasons and sometimes for weight control. Poorly planned vegetarian diets can put teens at risk of iron, zinc, calcium, vitamin D, or vitamin B_{12} deficiency. Poor food choices can result in vegetarian diets that are high in saturated fat and cholesterol and low in fiber.

- Psychosocial changes occurring during the adolescent years make physical appearance of great concern. Eating disorders are more common in adolescence than at any other time. Adolescent athletes are susceptible to nutrition misinformation, and they may experiment with dangerous practices such as using anabolic steroids to increase muscle mass or fad diets and fluid restriction to lose weight.

- During the teen years, pregnancy, the use of oral contraceptives, and tobacco may affect nutritional status. Alcohol consumption and over-consumption often start in the teen years and can have negative nutritional and social consequences.

Review Questions

1. How does nutrient intake during childhood affect health later in life?

2. What improvements should be made in the diets of American children?

3. How can parents and caregivers influence children's food choices?

4. What is the best way to determine if a child is eating enough?

5. What factors influence the maximum height a child will reach?

6. What nutritional problems can be signaled by sudden changes in weight patterns?

7. How do the recommendations for fat intake change as a child gets older?

8. When should solid and semisolid foods be introduced into an infant's diet?

9. How should new foods be introduced to monitor for the development of food allergies?

10. Why is anemia a problem in young children? in teenage girls?

11. Why are snacks an important part of children's diets?

12. Why is breakfast important?

13. Why are malnourished children at greater risk of lead toxicity than adults or well-nourished children?

14. How does watching TV impact the nutritional status of children?

15. How can fast foods be incorporated into a healthy diet?

16. How does the treatment of obesity in children differ from treatment in adults?

17. What is the adolescent growth spurt? How does it affect nutrient requirements?

18. Describe two physiological differences between males and females after puberty that affect their nutrient needs.

19. Explain why soda intake among teens may be contributing to osteoporosis.

20. Why are vegetarian diets not always healthier than diets that include meat?

21. Why might participation in athletics contribute to the development of eating disorders in adolescents?

References

1. Nicklas, T. A., and Hayes, D. Position of the American Dietetic Association: Nutrition guidance for healthy children ages 2 to 11 years. *J. Am. Diet. Assoc.* 108:1038–1047, 2008.

2. U.S. Department of Agriculture, Center for Nutrition Policy and Promotion. The quality of children's diets in 2003–04 as measured by the Healthy Eating Index—2005. Nutrition Insight 43, April 2009. Available online at www.cnpp.usda.gov/Publications/Nutritioninsights/insight43.pdf. Accessed September 29, 2009.

3. Orlet Fisher, J., Rolls, B. J., and Birch, L. L. Children's bite size and intake of an entree are greater with large portions than with age-appropriate or self-selected portions. *Am. J. Clin. Nutr.* 77:1164–1170, 2003.

4. Nicklas, T. A., Yang, S. J., Baranowski, T., et al. Eating patterns and obesity in children. The Bogalusa Heart Study. *Am. J. Prev. Med.* 25:9–16, 2003.

5. DHHS, 2008 Physical Activity Guidelines for Americans available online at http://www.health.gov/paguidelines/pdf/paguide.pdf Accessed May 13, 2009.

6. Ogden, C. L., Carroll, M. D., and Flegal, K. M. High body mass index for age among U.S. children and adolescents, 2003–2006. *JAMA* 299:2401–2405, 2008.

7. Nielsen, S. J., Siega-Riz, A. M., and Popkin, B. M. Trends in energy intake in U.S. between 1977 and 1996: Similar shifts seen across age groups. *Obes. Res.* 10:370–378, 2002.

8. National Diabetes Information Clearinghouse. *National Diabetes Statistics, 2007.* Available online at http://diabetes.niddk.nih.gov/dm/pubs/statistics/index.htm#13. Accessed April 30, 2009.

9. Mayer-Davis, E. J. Type 2 diabetes in youth: Epidemiology and current research toward prevention and treatment. *J. Am. Diet. Assoc.* 108:S45–S51, 2008.

10. Center for Disease Control, National Health and Nutrition Examination Survey. Intake of Calories and Selected Nutrients for the United States Population, 1999–2000. Available online at www.cdc.gov/nchs/data/nhanes/databriefs/calories.pdf/ Accessed April 30, 2009.

11. Academy of Pediatrics, Committee on Nutrition. *Cholesterol in Childhood.* Available online at http://aappolicy.aappublications.org/cgi/reprint/pediatrics;101/1/141.pdf. Accessed September 4, 2008.

12. Daniels, S. R., Greer, F. R., and the Committee on Nutrition. Lipid screening for cardiovascular health in childhood. *Pediatr.* 122:198–208, 2008.

13. U.S. Department of Health and Human Services, U.S. Department of Agriculture. *Dietary Guidelines for Americans 2005,* 6th ed. Washington, DC, 2005.

14. Obarzanek E., Kimm, S.Y., Barton, B. A., et al. Long-term safety and efficacy of a cholesterol-lowering diet in children with elevated low-density lipoprotein cholesterol: Seven-year results of the Dietary Intervention Study in Children (DISC). *Pediatrics* 107:256–264, 2001.

15. Luma, G. B. and Spiotta, R. T. Hypertension in children and adolescents. Am Fam Physician. 73(9):1558–1568, 2006.

16. U.S. Department of Health and Human Services, Centers for Disease Control and Prevention, National Center for Health Statistics. CDC Growth Charts: United States. Advance Data, No. 314, June 8, 2000 (revised). Available online at www.cdc.gov/growthcharts/ Accessed April 30, 2009.

17. Institute of Medicine, Food and Nutrition Board. *Dietary Reference Intakes for Energy, Carbohydrate, Fiber, Fat, Protein and Amino Acids.* Washington, DC: National Academies Press, 2002.

18. Institute of Medicine, Food and Nutrition Board. *Dietary Reference Intakes for Water, Potassium, Sodium, Chloride, and Sulfate.* Washington, DC: National Academies Press, 2004.

19. Rovner, A. J., and O'Brien, K. O. Hypovitaminosis D among healthy children in the United States: A review of the current evidence. *Arch. Pediatr. Adolesc. Med.* 162:513–519, 2008.

20. Centers for Disease Control and Prevention (CDC). Iron deficiency—United States, 1999–2000. *MMWR* 51:897–899, 2002.

21. Haas, J. D., and Brownlie, T. IV. Iron deficiency and reduced work capacity: A critical review of the research to determine a causal relationship. *J. Nutr.* 131:676S–690S, 2001.

22. Grantham-McGregor, S., and Ani, C. A review of studies on the effect of iron deficiency on cognitive development in children. *J. Nutr.* 131:649S–668S, 2001.

23. U.S. Food and Drug Administration. Preventing iron poisoning in children. FDA Backgrounder. January 15,

1997. Available online at vm.cfsan.fda.gov/~dms/bgiron.html. Accessed September 29, 2009.

24. Macknin, M. L., Medendorp, S.V., and Maier, M. C. Infant sleep and bedtime cereal. *Am. J. Dis. Child*. 143:1066–1068, 1989.

25. American Academy of Pediatrics. The use and misuse of fruit juice in pediatrics. *Pediatrics* 107: 1210–1213, 2001.

26. Formanek, R., Food allergies: When food becomes the enemy. *FDA Consumer*, July/Aug, 2001. Available online at www.fda.gov/fdac/features/2001/401_food.html/ Accessed November 17, 2003.

27. Greer, F. R., Sicherer, S. H., and Burks, A. W. Effects of early nutritional interventions on the development of atopic disease in infants and children: the role of maternal dietary restriction, breastfeeding, timing of introduction of complementary foods, and hydrolyzed formulas. *Pediatrics* 121:183–191, 2008.

28. Patrick, H., and Nicklas, T. A. A review of family and social determinants of children's eating patterns and diet quality. *J. Am. Coll. Nutr.* 24:83–92, 2005.

29. Slatter, E. *Child of Mine*. Palo Alto, CA: Bull Publishing, 1986.

30. U.S. Department of Agriculture, Food and Nutrition Service. *National School Lunch Program*. Available online at www.fns.usda.gov/cnd/Lunch/AboutLunch/NSLPFactSheet.pdf. Accessed February 20, 2009.

31. U.S. Department of Agriculture, Food and Nutrition Service. *Children's Diets in the Mid-1990s: Dietary Intake and Its Relationship with School Meal Participation*. Special Nutrition Programs Report No. CN-01-CD1, January 2001. Available online at www.fns.usda.gov/OANE/menu/Published/CNP/FILES/ChilDiet.pdf. Accessed April 20, 2009.

32. Marshall, T. A., Levy, S. M., Broffitt, B., et al. Dental caries and beverage consumption in young children. *Pediatrics*. 112:e184–191, 2003.

33. Cormier, E., and Elder, J. H. Diet and child behavior problems: Fact or fiction? *Pediatr. Nurs.* 33:138–143, 2007.

34. Rojas, N. L., and Chan, E. Old and new controversies in the alternative treatment of attention-deficit hyperactivity disorder. *Ment. Retard. Dev. Disabil. Res. Rev.* 11:116–130, 2005.

35. Chandramouli, K., Steer, C. D., Ellis, M., and Emond, A. M. Effects of early childhood lead exposure on academic performance and behavior of school age children. *Arch. Dis. Child.* September 21, 2009 [Epub].

36. Centers for Disease Control and Prevention. Blood lead levels—United States, 1999–2002. *MMWR Morb. Mortal. Wkly. Rep.* 54:513–516, 2005. Available online at www.cdc.gov/mmwr/preview/mmwrhtml/mm5420a5.htm. Accessed April 20, 2009.

37. Jusko, T. A., Henderson, C. R. Jr, Lanphear, B. P., et al. Blood lead concentrations below 10 microg/dL and child intelligence at 6 years of age. *Environ. Health. Perspect.* 116: 243–248, 2008.

38. American Academy of Pediatrics Policy Statement. Lead Exposure in Children: Prevention, Detection, and Management. *Pediatrics* 116: 1036–1046, 2005.

39. Coon, K. A., and Tucker, K. L. Television and children's consumption patterns. A review of the literature. *Minerva Pediatr.* 54:423–436, 2002.

40. Batada, A., Seitz, M., Woxan, M. et. al. Nine out of ten food advertisements shown during Saturday morning children's television programming are for food high in fat, sodium, or added sugars, or low in nutrients. *J. Am. Diet. Assoc.* 108:673–678, 2008.

41. Eisenmann, J. C., Bartee, R. T., and Wang, M. Q. Physical activity, TV viewing, and weight in U.S. youth: 1999 Youth Risk Behavior Survey. *Obes. Res.* 10:379–385, 2002.

42. Institute of Medicine, Food and Nutrition Board. *Preventing Childhood Obesity: Health in the Balance*. Washington, DC: National Academies Press, 2005.

43. Centers for Disease Control Making Physical Activity a Part of a Child's Life. Available online at http://www.cdc.gov/physicalactivity/everyone/getactive/children.html. Accessed May 4, 2009.

44. Mandel, D., Zimlichman, E., Mimouni, F. B., et al. Age at menarche and body mass index: A population study. *J. Pediatr. Endocrinol. Metab.* 17:1507–1510, 2004.

45. Weng, F. L., Shults, J., Leonard, M. B. et al. Risk factors for low serum 25-hydroxyvitamin D concentrations in otherwise healthy children and adolescents. *Am. J. Clin. Nutr.* 86:150–158, 2007.

46. Institute of Medicine, Food and Nutrition Board. *Dietary Reference Intakes for Vitamin A, Vitamin K, Arsenic, Boron, Chromium, Copper, Iodine, Iron, Manganese, Molybdenum, Nickel, Silicon, Vanadium, and Zinc*. Washington, DC: National Academies Press, 2001.

47. Centers for Disease Control and Prevention. Iron Deficiency—United States, 1999–2000. *MMWR Morb. Mortal. Wkly. Rep.* 51:897–899, 2002. Available online at www.cdc.gov/MMWR/preview/mmwrhtml/mm5140a1.htm. Accessed September 11, 2008.

48. Institute of Medicine, Food and Nutrition Board. *Dietary Reference Intakes for Calcium, Phosphorus, Magnesium, Vitamin D, and Fluoride*. Washington, DC: National Academies Press, 1997.

49. National Institute of Child Health and Human Development. *Milk Matters, About milk matters* Available online at www.nichd.nih.gov/milk/about/index.cfm. Accessed April 27, 2009.

50. Arsenault, J. E., and Brown, K. H. Zinc intake of US preschool children exceeds new dietary reference intakes. *Am. J. Clin. Nutr.* 78: 1011–1017, 2003.

51. USDA/ARC Children's Nutrition Research Center at Baylor College of Medicine. Survey Tracks Trends in Children's Dietary Habits. Available online at www.kidsnutrition.org/consumer/archives/mealtime.htm/ Accessed September 11, 2005.

52. The Vegetarian Resource Group. How Many Teens are Vegetarian? How Many Kids Don't Eat Meat. Available online at www.vrg.org/press/2000novteen.htm/ Accessed September 29, 2009.

53. Zlotkin, S. Adolescent vegetarians: How well do their dietary patterns meet the healthy people 2010 objectives? *Arch. Pediatr. Adolesc. Med.* 156:426–427, 2002.

54. American Academy of Pediatrics. Policy Statement. Identifying and Treating Eating Disorders. *Peds* 111:204–211, 2003.

55. Klopp, S. A., Heiss, C. J., and Smith, H. S. Self-reported vegetarianism may be a marker for college women at risk for disordered eating. *J. Am. Diet. Assoc.* 103:745–747, 2003.

56. Rodriguiez, N. R., Dimarco, N. M., and Langley, S. Position of the American Dietetic Association, Dietitians of Canada, and the American College of Sports Medicine: Nutrition and athletic performance. *J. Am. Diet. Assoc.* 109:509–527, 2009.

57. Bemben, M. G., and Lamont, H. S. Creatine supplementation and exercise performance: Recent findings. *Sports Med.* 35:107–125, 2005.

58. Kazis, K., and Iglesias, E. The female athlete triad. *Adolesc. Med.* 14:87–95, 2003.

59. Palmersheim, K. A. Trends in cigarette smoking among high school youth in Wisconsin and the United States, 1993–2004. *WMJ* May;104(4):23–27, 2005.

60. Facchini, M., Rozensztejn, R., and Gonzalez, C. Smoking and weight control behaviors. *Eat. Weight Disord.*. 10:1–7, 2005.

61. Palaniappan, U., Jacobs Starkey, L., O'Loughlin, J., and Gray-Donald, K. Fruit and vegetable consumption is lower and saturated fat intake is higher among Canadians reporting smoking. *J. Nutr.* 131:1952–1958, 2001.

62. Food and Nutrition Board, Institute of Medicine. *Dietary Reference Intakes for Vitamin C, Vitamin E, Selenium and Carotenoids*. Washington, DC: National Academies Press, 2000.

63. YRBSS, 2007 National Youth Risk Behavior Survey Overview. Available online at www.cdc.gov/HealthyYouth/yrbs/pdf/yrbs07_us_overview.pdf. Accessed April 26, 2009.

16 Nutrition and Aging: The Adult Years

Case Study

(Amana Images, Inc/Alamy)

Min is 70 years old and has always eaten well and gotten plenty of exercise. When her husband died last year, though, her life changed. Right after his death, her family spent a lot of time with her, bringing groceries, helping with the cooking, or sharing a meal or snack. Now they don't visit as often, and Min usually eats alone. She used to walk every morning with her friends, but during the year and a half that her husband was ill she stopped because she wasn't comfortable leaving him alone. She has gained a few pounds and is tired all the time. At her last doctor's visit she learned that both her blood pressure and her blood sugar are slightly elevated. She tried walking with her friends a few weeks ago but found she could no longer keep up with them. She was so embarrassed that she doesn't plan to walk with them again.

Although we tend to focus on the physical changes that occur with aging, Min's case demonstrates that the psychological and social changes that are common in the elderly can also have a significant effect on lifestyle and nutritional status. Older adults and those of us who care for them need to consider all these factors when managing nutritional health.

(©iStockphoto)

na Stock/Age Fotostock America, Inc.)

Chapter Outline

Figure 16.1 Aging is a process that occurs continuously in individuals of all ages. (©Tony Freeman/PhotoEdit)

life span The maximum age to which members of a species can live.

life expectancy The average length of life for a population of individuals.

16.1 What Is Aging?

Learning Objectives

• Define aging.

• Explain what is meant by compression of morbidity.

Biologically, aging is not something that begins at age 55, 65, or 75; it is a process that begins with conception and continues throughout life (**Figure 16.1**). It can be defined as the inevitable accumulation of changes with time that are associated with and responsible for an ever-increasing susceptibility to disease and death. The maximum age to which any human can live—the **life span**—is about 100 to 120 years. Life span is a characteristic of a species; dogs can live about 20 years, gorillas 39 years, and mice only about 3 years. Life span is believed to be genetically determined. The only experimental treatment that has been found to extend the life span of a variety of mammalian species is a nutritional manipulation called *kcaloric restriction*.[1] Restricting the energy intake of animals to about 70% of typical intake slows and/or delays the aging processes. Although the underlying biological mechanism responsible for its life span extending effects are still not known, kcaloric restriction is believed to act by affecting the organism's genes.[2] Despite promising data from animal studies, kcaloric retriction is not currently considered a viable option for extending life in humans (see Science Applied: Eat Less—Live Longer?).

How Long Can Americans Expect to Live?

Although humans can live to be 120 years, most do not live that long. **Life expectancy**, the average length of time that a person can be expected to live, varies between and within populations. It is affected by genetics, lifestyle, and environmental factors. In the United States in 1900, life expectancy was 50 years, but today, with advances in technology and improved nutrition and health care, the average is about 77.8 years.[3] With this increase in life expectancy, the number of older adults is increasing. During the twentieth century, the population of older adults, those 65 years of age and older, grew from 3 million in 1900 to 35 million in 2000, or about 12.4% of the population (**Figure 16.2**). Over the same time period the oldest-old population, those over the age of 85 years, grew from just over 100,000 to 4.2 million. This increase in the number of older adults is expected to continue. By 2030, it is projected that nearly 20% of the total U.S. population, or 71.5 million Americans, will be older than 65 years of age.[4]

As the older population grows larger it will also grow more ethnically diverse, reflecting demographic changes in the U.S. population as a whole over the last several decades. In 2003 most older adults were whites, who accounted for nearly 83% of the U.S. older population. African Americans made up just over 8% of the older population, Asians about 3%, and Hispanics accounted for almost 6%. By 2050 it is projected that the older population will be only 61% white, with 18% Hispanic, 12% African American, and 8% Asian.[4]

Figure 16.2 Number of persons age 65 and older and 85 and older, 1900–2050 Projections indicate that in the next few decades there will be almost 80 million people in the United States who are 65 or older. (Source: U.S. Census Bureau, Decennial Census Data and Population Projections.)

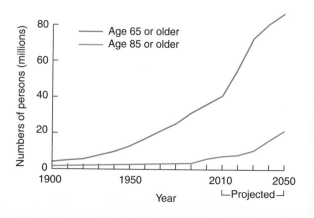

SCIENCE

ScienceAppliedScienceApplied
ScienceAppliedScienceApplied
ScienceAppliedScienceApplied

APPLIED

(DAJ/Getty Images, Inc.)   (www.victorianoizquierdo.com/Getty Images, Inc.)   (Elena Schweitzer/Shutterstock)

Eat Less—Live Longer?

Throughout history humans have searched for ways to stay young, avoid the ravages of old age, and extend life. Researchers have found that limiting kcaloric intake extends life and maintains health and vitality—at least in animals. Is this true in humans as well?

Kcaloric restriction, which refers to undernutrition without malnutrition, involves a diet providing 30% to 40% fewer kcalories than would typically be consumed, but containing all the necessary nutrients to support life. Since the 1930s, studies have described the life-extending effect of kcalorie restriction in rats and other organisms.[1,2] A kcalorie-restricted diet has been shown to extend the maximal life span of organisms as diverse as worms, insects, and rodents by as much as 50%. It also reduces age-related chronic disease, improves immune function, increases resistance to numerous stressors and toxins, and maintains function later into life.

To explore the possibility that kcaloric restriction would lengthen life and reduce chronic disease in animals more closely related to humans, in the late 1980s researchers began to study the effect of this diet in rhesus monkeys. Adult monkeys were fed nutritionally adequate diets containing 30% fewer kcalories than a control group. After 20 years, 80% of the kcalorie-restricted animals were still alive, compared to only 50% of the control animals.[3] The kcalorie-restricted group had a lower incidence of diabetes, cancer, cardiovascular disease, and brain atrophy. This study confirms that kcalorie restriction can slow aging in a primate species.

The fact that kcaloric restriction has extended the life of every species tested suggests that it would do the same in humans. Human studies are the only way to know for sure how effective this diet would be. However, a study of kcaloric restriction in humans is fraught with problems, including the fact that it would take decades to produce results. Instead, scientists have looked at the people of Okinawa. They provide one of the best examples of how kcaloric restriction might affect health and longevity in humans.[4] Okinawans have active lives and consume a nutrient-dense diet of vegetables and fish and typically eat only until they are 80% full. Okinawans enjoy the longest life expectancy in the world (81.2 years). They maintain

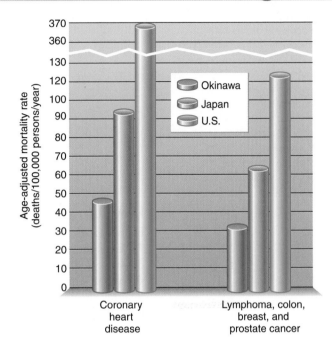

a low BMI and the incidence of the chronic diseases of aging, such as heart disease and cancer, is much lower among Okinawans than among people living in the United States or on mainland Japan (see graph).

Despite the health and longevity enjoyed by the Okinawan people, some scientists doubt that kcaloric restriction will actually extend the human life span. They point out that throughout history, groups of humans, for economic reasons, have in effect been on lifelong kcaloric restriction without a corresponding extension of life span past 120 years. Also, humans are not caged animals living under controlled conditions, so their longevity is affected by many factors. A mathematical model that factored in information related to the kcaloric intake and longevity of typical Japanese citizens, Japanese sumo wrestlers who must eat large amounts of food, and Okinawan men who eat less than is typical predicted that humans following this restrictive regimen would increase their life span by only 3% to 7%—far less than the almost 50% extension in rodent species.[5] Would the extra few years be worth decades of deprivation?

[1]McCay, C. M., Crowell, M. F., and Maynard, L. A. The effect of retarded growth upon the length of life and upon ultimate size. *J. Nutr.* 10, 63–79, 1935.

[2]Masoro, E. J. Subfield history: Caloric restriction, slowing aging, and extending life. *Sci. Aging Knowl. Environ.* 2003: RE2, 2003.

[3]Colman, R. J., Anderson, R. M., Johnson, E. K. et al. Caloric restriction delays disease onset and mortality in rhesus monkeys. *Science* 325:201–204, 2009.

[4]Willcox, B. J., Willcox, D. C., Todoriki, H. et al. Caloric restriction, the traditional Okinawan diet, and healthy aging: The diet of the world's longest-lived people and its potential impact on morbidity and life span. *Ann. N.Y. Acad. Sci.* 1114:434–455, 2007.

[5]Phelan, J. P., and Rose, M. R. Why dietary restriction substantially increases longevity in animal models but won't in humans. *Aging Res. Rev.* 4: 339–350, 2005.

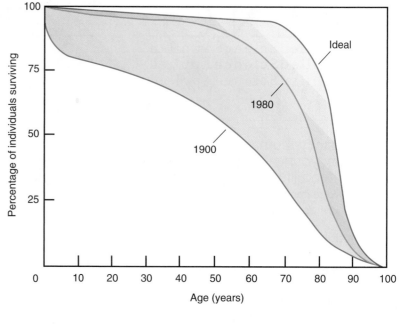

Figure 16.3 Effect of compression of morbidity on survival
The decline in deaths from infectious diseases between 1900 and 1980 allowed more people to survive into adulthood. Delaying the onset of chronic diseases will allow more people to remain healthy and survive into their seventies and eighties. (Source: Adapted from Fries, J. F. Aging, natural death, and the compression of morbidity. N. Engl. J. Med. 303:130–135, 1980.)

compression of morbidity
The postponement of the onset of chronic disease such that disability occupies a smaller and smaller proportion of the life span.

How Long Can Americans Expect To Be Healthy?

Even though average life expectancy in the United States has increased to almost 78 years, the average healthy life expectancy is only about 69 years.[5] This means that, on average, the last 9 years of life are restricted by disease and disability. The goal of successful aging is to increase not only life expectancy but the number of years of healthy life that an individual can expect. This is achieved by slowing the changes that accumulate over time and postponing the diseases of aging long enough to approach or reach the limits of life span before any adverse symptoms appear. This is referred to as **compression of morbidity**. When applied to the population as a whole, this term means that people are healthier and living longer (**Figure 16.3**); applied to the individual, it means staying healthy through the later years of life.

Because the incidence of disease and disability increases with increasing age, the older population accounts for a large part of the public health budget.[6] Thus, keeping older adults healthy is beneficial not only for the aging individuals themselves, but for the health-care system as well. Postponing the changes that occur with age is an important public health goal.

16.2 What Causes Aging?

Learning Objectives

- Describe the biological causes of aging.
- Discuss genetic, environmental, and lifestyle factors that affect the aging process.

reserve capacity The amount of functional capacity that an organ has above and beyond what is needed to sustain life.

Although universal to all living things, aging is a process we don't fully understand. We do know that as organisms become older, the number of cells they contain decreases and the function of the remaining cells declines. As tissues and organs lose cells, the ability of the organism to perform the physiological functions necessary to maintain homeostasis decreases; disease becomes increasingly common and the risk of malnutrition increases. This loss of cells and cell function occurs throughout life, but the effects are not felt for many years because organisms begin life with extra functional capacity, or **reserve capacity**. Reserve capacity allows an organism to continue functioning normally despite a decrease in the number and function of cells. In young adults, the reserve capacity of organs is four to ten times that required to sustain life. As a person ages and reserve capacity decreases, the effects of aging become evident in all body systems.

There are two major hypotheses to explain why aging occurs. One favors the idea of a genetic clock and argues that the cell death associated with aging is a genetically programmed event. The other views the events of aging as the result of cellular wear and tear. The actual cause of the cell death associated with aging is probably some combination of both of these, and the rate at which cell death occurs and at which aging proceeds is determined by the interplay among our genetic makeup, our lifestyle, and the environment in which we spend our years.

Programmed Cell Death

One hypothesis about aging proposes that cell death is triggered when genes that disrupt cell function are activated.[8] This causes the selective, orderly death of individual cells or groups of cells and is referred to as **programmed cell death**. This hypothesis is supported by the fact that cells grown in the laboratory divide only a certain number of times before they die. Cells from older individuals will divide fewer times than those from younger individuals, and cells from longer-lived species will divide more times than those from shorter-lived species. If cells in an organism stop reproducing and continue to die, the total number of cells will decline, resulting in a loss of organ function.

programmed cell death
The death of cells at specific predictable times.

Wear and Tear

A second hypothesis suggests that aging is the result of an accumulation of cellular damage. This wear and tear may result from errors in DNA synthesis, increases in glucose levels, or damage caused by free radicals. Free radicals are reactive chemical substances that are generated from both normal metabolic processes and exposure to environmental factors (see Chapter 8). They cause oxidative damage to proteins, lipids, carbohydrates, and DNA, and may also indirectly harm cells by producing toxic products. For example, age spots—brown spots that appear on the skin with age—are caused by the oxidation of lipids, which produces a pigment called lipofuscin, or age pigment. The damage done to cells by free radicals is associated with aging and has been implicated in the development of a number of chronic diseases common among older adults, including cardiovascular disease and cancer.

Genetics, Environment, and Lifestyle

The rate at which the changes associated with aging accumulate depends on the genes people inherit, the environment they live in, and their lifestyle (**Figure 16.4**). Genes determine the efficiency with which cells are maintained and repaired. Individuals with less cellular repair capacity will lose cells more readily and consequently age more quickly. Likewise, genes determine susceptibility to age-related diseases

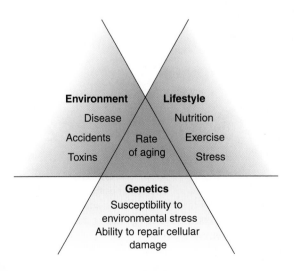

Figure 16.4 Factors that affect the rate of aging
The rate at which individuals age is affected by their genetic makeup, the environment in which they live, and the lifestyle choices they make.

such as cardiovascular disease and cancer. However, individuals who inherit a low capacity to repair cellular damage may still live long lives if they reside in an environment with few factors that damage cells and if they eat well and exercise regularly. In contrast, individuals with exceptional cellular repair ability may accumulate cellular damage rapidly and die young if they smoke cigarettes, consume a diet high in saturated fat and low in antioxidant nutrients, and live sedentary lives. No matter what individuals' genes predict about how long they will live, their actual **longevity** is also affected by lifestyle factors and the extent to which they are able to avoid accidents and disease.

longevity The duration of an individual's life.

16.3 Nutritional Needs and Concerns of Older Adults

Learning Objectives

- Compare the nutrient recommendations for older adults to those for young adults.
- List nutrients that may need to be supplemented in the diets of adults over the age of 50 years.

Older adults are a diverse population. There are 70-year-olds running marathons while others are confined to wheelchairs (**Figure 16.5**). The physiological and health changes that accompany aging affect the requirements for some nutrients, how nutrient needs must be met, and the risk of malnutrition. In order to best address the nutrient needs of adults, the DRIs divide adulthood into four age categories: young adulthood, ages 19 through 30; middle age, 31 through 50 years; adulthood, ages 51 through 70; and older adults, those over 70 years of age. Recommendations have been developed to meet the needs of the majority of healthy individuals in each age group. Although the incidence of chronic diseases and disabilities increases with advancing age, these conditions are not considered when making general nutrient intake recommendations.

Energy and Macronutrient Needs

Adult energy needs typically decline with age. This is due to a decrease in all components of total energy expenditure. Basal metabolic rate (BMR) decreases as adults get older, in part due to a decrease in lean body mass. There is a 2 to 3% drop in BMR

Figure 16.5 Chronological age is not always the best indicator of a person's health. A person who is 75 may have the vigor and health of someone who is 55, or vice versa. Some older adults are healthy, independent, and active, while others are chronically ill, dependent, and at high risk for malnutrition. (Alaska Stock Images/NG Image Collection; Thinkstock/Getty Images, Inc.)

every decade after about age 20. The thermic effect of food also declines with age and is about 20% lower in older than in younger adults. These decreases are reflected in the energy needs of older adults. For example, the estimated energy requirement (EER) for an 80-year-old man is almost 600 kcalories per day less than that for a 20-year-old man of the same height, weight, and physical activity level. For women, the difference in EER between an 80- and a 20-year-old of the same height, weight, and physical activity level is about 400 kcalories per day.[10] The decrease in EER that occurs with age is even greater if activity level declines, which it typically does. Decreased physical activity is estimated to account for about one-half of the decrease in total energy expenditure that occurs with aging.[11] The decrease in activity also contributes to the reduction in lean body mass and BMR.

Protein Protein is needed at all ages to repair and maintain tissues. Therefore, unlike energy requirements, the requirement for protein does not decline with age. The RDA for older as well as younger adults is 0.8 grams per kilogram of body weight per day. As a result, an adequate diet for older adults must be somewhat higher in protein relative to energy intake. Due to the diversity of older adults, actual need depends on the individual. In some, the protein requirement may be less than the RDA because there is less lean body mass to maintain, whereas in others it may be greater than the RDA because protein absorption or utilization is reduced.

Fat The digestion and absorption of fat does not change in older adults. Therefore, although total fat intake may be lower due to lower energy needs, the recommendations regarding the proportion and types of dietary fat apply to older as well as younger adults. A diet with 20% to 35% of energy from fat that contains adequate amounts of the essential fatty acids and limits saturated fat, *trans* fat, and cholesterol is recommended. Following these recommendations will allow older adults to meet their nutrient needs without exceeding their energy requirements and may delay the onset of chronic disease. However, there are certain situations, such as being underweight, where greater fat intake may be warranted.

Carbohydrates and Fiber As with fat, the recommended proportion of energy from carbohydrate (45% to 65% of energy) does not change with age, but the total amount needed may be lower in older adults due to lower energy needs. Dietary carbohydrate should come from whole grains, fruits, vegetables, and dairy products, and foods high in added sugars should be limited. This pattern will help assure adequate nutrients without excess energy.

The recommendations for fiber intake for older adults are slightly lower than for younger adults because the AIs for fiber are based on total energy needs.[10] Fiber, from whole grains, fruits, vegetables, and legumes, when consumed with adequate fluid, helps prevent constipation, hemorrhoids, and diverticulosis—conditions that are common in older adults. High-fiber diets may also be beneficial in the prevention and management of diabetes, cardiovascular disease, and obesity.

Water The recommended water intake for older adults is the same as that for younger adults; however, changes in the homeostatic mechanisms that regulate water balance may make meeting these needs more challenging. With age there is a reduction in the sense of thirst, which can decrease fluid intake.[9] In addition, the kidneys are no longer as efficient at conserving water, so water loss increases. Other physical and psychological changes also increase the risk of dehydration. For instance, difficulty in swallowing and restricted mobility may limit access to water even in the presence of thirst. Depression, which decreases water intake, and medications such as laxatives and diuretics, which increase water loss, also contribute to dehydration in the elderly. The elderly may also voluntarily restrict fluid intake to avoid accidents due to incontinence or because numerous trips to the bathroom increase pain from arthritis. In addition to impairing organ function, inadequate fluid intake contributes to the development of constipation.

Micronutrient Needs

Although the recommended intake for many of the micronutrients is no different for older adults than for younger adults the decrease in energy intake that occurs with age causes a decline in the intakes of micronutrients, especially the B vitamins, calcium, iron, and zinc (**Figure 16.6**).[9] Changes in digestion, absorption, and metabolism also affect micronutrient status. In turn, inadequate levels of certain micronutrients contribute to the development of some of the disorders that are common in older adults.

B Vitamins The only B vitamins for which recommendations differ between older and younger adults are vitamins B_6 and B_{12}. The RDA for vitamin B_6 is greater in people ages 51 and older than for younger adults because higher dietary intakes are needed to maintain the same functional levels in the body. Vitamin B_{12} is a nutrient of concern for older adults because of both reduced absorption and low dietary intakes, especially among the poor. Absorption of vitamin B_{12} naturally present in food is reduced in many older adults due to an inflammation of the stomach that reduces stomach acid so food-bound vitamin B_{12} cannot be released. The RDA for vitamin B_{12} is not increased (Figure 16.6), but it is recommended that individuals over the age of 50 meet their RDA for vitamin B_{12} by consuming foods fortified with vitamin B_{12}, such as breakfast cereals or soy-based products, or by taking a supplement containing vitamin B_{12}.[12] This recommendation is made because the vitamin B_{12} in fortified foods and supplements is not bound to proteins, so it is absorbed even when stomach acid is low.

The RDA for folate is the same for adults of all ages but folate intake is a concern in older adults for several reasons. Deficiencies of folate and vitamin B_{12} contribute to anemia, which is common in older adults. In addition, low folate, along with inadequate levels of vitamin B_6 and B_{12}, may result in an elevated homocysteine level, which increases the risk of cardiovascular disease. Due to the importance of folate in DNA synthesis, low folate intake has also been hypothesized to cause DNA

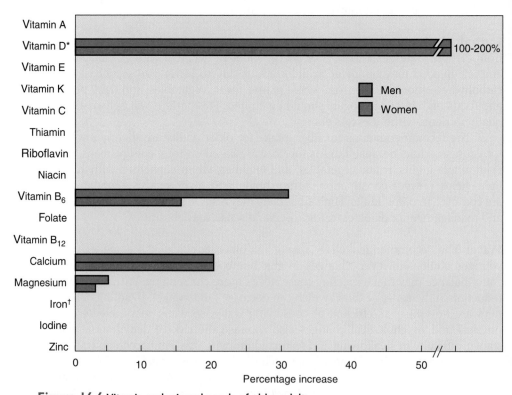

Figure 16.6 Vitamin and mineral needs of older adults
The percentage increase in micronutrient recommendations are shown here for adults age 51 and older compared to those of young adults ages 19 through 30.
*The AI for individuals 51 to 70 years is increased by 100%. For those over age 70 it is increased by 200%.
†The RDA for iron is decreased by over 50% in women over 50.

changes that contribute to cancer development.[13] The fortification of enriched grain products with folate, which began in 1998, has increased intake of this vitamin. However, when folate is consumed in excess it can mask the symptoms of vitamin B_{12} deficiency. Diets that include highly fortified products, such as breakfast cereals, and folate supplements, may exceed the UL for folate. Levels above the UL increase the risk that vitamin B_{12} deficiency will be masked and therefore go untreated (see Chapter 8).[13]

Antioxidant Vitamins The recommended intake of antioxidant vitamins is not increased in older adults, but low dietary intakes of vitamins C and E and carotenoids are a concern due to low fruit and vegetable consumption among the elderly. Only 32% of individuals 65 years of age and older consume 5 or more servings of fruits and vegetables daily.[14] As discussed below, eye disorders as well as mental impairment have been correlated with low levels of antioxidants in the elderly.

Calcium and Vitamin D Low intakes of both calcium and vitamin D contribute to osteoporosis in the elderly. Although calcium intake early in life prevents osteoporosis by ensuring a high bone density, low intakes in older adults can contribute to osteoporosis by accelerating bone loss. Calcium status is a problem in the elderly because intakes are low, primarily due to low intakes of dairy products, and because intestinal absorption typically decreases with age. The current AI for adults over age 50 is 1200 mg per day, which is 200 mg greater than the AI set for younger adults.[15] Although the decrease in estrogen that occurs at menopause causes bone loss, it cannot be prevented by increasing calcium intake, so the AIs for older men and women are not different.

Because vitamin D is necessary for calcium absorption, a deficiency may also contribute to osteoporosis. Vitamin D deficiency is a concern in the elderly for a number of reasons. Intakes of this vitamin are often low in the elderly population, usually due to limited consumption of milk, which is fortified with vitamin D. The amount of provitamin D formed in the skin is also reduced in the elderly. This occurs both because the capacity to synthesize provitamin D when the skin is exposed to sunlight is reduced and because the elderly spend less time outdoors and tend to wear clothing that covers or shades their skin when they go out. Even if adequate amounts of provitamin D are consumed or formed, the capacity to activate provitamin D in the kidney decreases with age. Using bone loss as an indicator of adequacy, the AI for vitamin D for men and women age 51 to 70 has been doubled from that of younger age groups to a value of 10 μg per day. For individuals over age 70, this is further increased to 15 μg per day. As discussed in Chapter 9, many experts now believe that in the absence of adequate exposure to sunlight, 20 to 20 μg of vitamin D is needed per day in all adults and children.[16]

Iron The iron needs of women decline sharply at menopause when blood loss through menstruation stops. The RDA for iron for women over 50 years of age is less than half of that of menstruating women. The iron needs of men do not change. Nonetheless, iron-deficiency anemia does occur, especially when energy intake is low. Common causes are chronic blood loss from disease and medications and poor iron absorption due to low stomach acid and antacid use. The problem is more common in people 85 years or older. In non-institutionalized adults 65 and older about 11% of men and 10.2% of women are anemic. In men and women 85 years or older this increases to 25% and 20%, respectively.[9]

Zinc The RDA for zinc is not changed in older adults, but lower energy intakes as well as malabsorption, physiological stress, trauma, muscle wasting, and prescription and over-the-counter medications can all contribute to poor zinc status.[17] The consequences of poor zinc status may include loss of taste acuity and impaired immune function and wound healing. Loss of taste acuity can contribute to malnutrition by reducing food intake. Reduction in immune function and wound healing increases the risk of infection, which can also impair nutritional status.

16.4 Factors that Increase the Risk of Malnutrition

Learning Objectives

- Describe how the normal physiological changes of aging can affect nutritional status.
- Explain how changes in body composition affect energy needs.
- Explain how the nutrient needs of older adults are affected by disease and medication use.
- Discuss social and economic factors that increase the risk of malnutrition.

Low energy intakes and poor food choices put many older adults at risk of malnutrition, but these are not the only reasons malnutrition is so prevalent among this group. Many of the physiological changes associated with aging can affect nutritional status. In addition, the elderly have a higher frequency of acute and chronic illnesses and are therefore more likely to be taking multiple medications. All of these factors can contribute to malnutrition (**Figure 16.7**). There are also social and economic changes that are common with aging that increase the risk of **food insecurity** and, consequently, malnutrition (**Table 16.1**).

food insecurity An inability to consistently acquire foods that are nutritionally adequate and individually, socially, and culturally acceptable.

Physiological Changes

It is difficult to determine which of the changes that occur with aging are inevitable consequences of the aging process and which are the result of disease states. But whether caused by disease or the inescapable loss of cells and cell function, the changes that occur in organs and organ systems can affect nutritional status by altering the appeal of food, nutrient digestion and absorption, nutritional requirements, and the ability to obtain food.

Sensory Decline Beginning around age 60, there is a progressive decline in the ability to taste and smell; this becomes more severe in persons over 70. The deterioration of these senses can contribute to impaired nutritional status by decreasing the appeal and enjoyment of food.[9] Some studies suggest that the drop in taste acuity is due to a reduction in the number of taste buds on the tongue; others suggest that it is the result of changes in sensitivity to specific flavors such as salty and sweet. The ap-

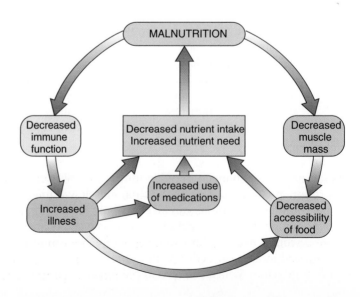

Figure 16.7 Causes and consequences of malnutrition
The decreases in muscle mass and immune function that occur with age contribute to malnutrition and, in turn, malnutrition makes these problems worse.

Table 16.1 Factors that Increase the Risk of Malnutrition Among the Elderly

- **Reduced food intake** due to:

  Decreased appetite due to lack of exercise, depression, or social isolation

  Changes in taste, smell, and vision

  Dental problems

  Limitations in mobility

  Medications that restrict meal times or affect appetite

  Lack of money to buy food

  Lack of nutrition knowledge

- **Reduced nutrient absorption and utilization** due to:

  Gastrointestinal changes

  Medications that affect absorption

  Diseases such as diabetes, kidney disease, alcoholism, and gastrointestinal disease

- **Increased nutrient requirements** due to:

  Illness with fever or infection

  Injury or surgery

- **Increased nutrient losses** due to:

  Medications that increase excretion of nutrients

  Diseases such as gastrointestinal and kidney disease

peal of food is also affected by the decline in the sense of smell. Odors provide important clues to food acceptability before food enters the mouth and once in the mouth some molecules reach the nasal cavity where their odor is detected. It is the blending of the odor message from the nasal cavity and the taste message from the tongue that provides the overall food flavor. When the sense of smell is diminished, food is not as flavorful.

Vision also typically declines with age, making shopping for and preparation of food difficult. **Macular degeneration** is the most common cause of blindness in older Americans. The macula is a small area of the retina of the eye that distinguishes fine detail. With age, oxidative damage reduces the number of viable cells in the macula. As the macula degenerates, visual acuity declines, ultimately resulting in blindness. **Cataracts** are another common reason for declining sight (**Figure 16.8**). Of people who live to age 85, half will have cataracts that impair vision. Oxidative damage is believed to cause both macular degeneration and cataracts. Therefore, a diet high in foods containing antioxidant nutrients might slow or prevent these eye disorders.[9]

Alterations in Gastrointestinal Function Aging causes changes in the gastrointestinal tract and its accessory organs that may alter the palatability as well as the digestion of food and the absorption of nutrients. One change is a decrease in the secretion of saliva into the mouth. Saliva provides lubrication for easy swallowing and mixes with food to allow it to be tasted. A reduction in saliva causes dryness which makes swallowing difficult and decreases the taste of food. Saliva is also an important defense against tooth decay because it helps wash material away from the teeth and it contains substances that kill bacteria. Thus, a dry mouth increases the likelihood of tooth decay and **periodontal disease**. Loss of teeth and improperly fitting dentures limit food choices and can contribute to poor nutrition in the elderly.

Changes in stomach emptying and stomach secretions can also affect nutritional status. In older adults the rate of stomach emptying may be slower, which can reduce hunger and, therefore, nutrient intake. Reductions in gastric secretions can

Figure 16.8 Cataracts cause the lens of the eye to become cloudy and impair vision. When cataracts obscure vision the affected lens can be removed and replaced with an artificial plastic lens. (©Science VU/Visuals Unlimited)

macular degeneration
Degeneration of a portion of the retina that results in a loss of visual detail and blindness.

cataracts A disease of the eye that results in cloudy spots on the lens (and sometimes the cornea), which obscure vision.

periodontal disease
A degeneration of the area surrounding the teeth, specifically the gum and supporting bone.

atrophic gastritis
An inflammation of the stomach lining that causes a reduction in stomach acid and allows bacterial overgrowth.

affect the absorption of some nutrients. It is estimated that 10% to 30% of American adults over age 50 and 40% of those in their 80s have **atrophic gastritis**. This inflammation of the stomach lining is accompanied by a decrease in the secretion of stomach acid and in severe cases a reduction in the production of intrinsic factor.[12] When stomach acid is reduced, the enzymes that release vitamin B_{12} from food do not function properly and the vitamin B_{12} naturally present in food cannot be absorbed. Absorption of iron, folate, calcium, and vitamin K may also be reduced. Reduced stomach acid secretion also allows microbial overgrowth in the stomach and small intestine.[12] The increase in the numbers of microbes in the gut further reduce B_{12} absorption by competing for available vitamin B_{12}.

With age there is a reduction in digestive enzymes from the pancreas and small intestine, but there is enough reserve capacity that digestion and absorption are rarely significantly impaired. In the colon there are functional changes, including decreased motility and elasticity, weakened abdominal and pelvic muscles, and decreased sensory perception, which can lead to constipation. Low fiber and fluid intakes and lack of activity also contribute to constipation. Constipation is a problem that occurs in fewer than 2% of persons in the nonelderly population but affects as many as 26% of men and 34% of women over 65 years of age.[18] It is estimated that more than 75% of elderly patients in hospitals and nursing homes use laxatives for bowel regulation. Maintaining regular exercise and consuming adequate fluid and fiber are safer ways to prevent constipation.

Changes in Other Organs Age-related changes in organs other than those of the gastrointestinal tract may also affect nutrient metabolism. Most absorbed nutrients travel from the intestine to the liver for metabolism or storage. The liver has a greater regenerative capacity than most organs, but with age, there is a decrease in liver size and blood flow and an increase in fat accumulation, which eventually decrease the liver's ability to metabolize nutrients and break down drugs and alcohol. With age, the pancreas may become less responsive to blood glucose levels, and the body cells may become more resistant to insulin, resulting in diabetes. Changes in the heart and blood vessels reduce blood flow to the kidneys, making waste removal less efficient. The kidneys themselves become smaller and their ability to filter blood and to excrete the products of protein breakdown declines.[19] In some individuals blood urea levels may increase if protein intake is too high. The ability of the kidneys to concentrate urine also decreases with age, as does the sensation of thirst, increasing the risk of dehydration.

Excess Body Fat The incidence of obesity in older age groups, as with younger adults, has increased over the past 25 years. In 2003–2004, 31% of individuals 60 years of age or older were obese.[20] Although the risk of death associated with obesity is lower in older than in younger adults, obesity still increases the risk of health complications that reduce the quality of life. It contributes to a higher risk of cardiovascular disease, certain cancers, hypertension, stroke, sleep apnea, type 2 diabetes, and arthritis. Obesity also contributes to suboptimal physical functioning.[11]

As with younger adults moderate weight loss can decrease obesity-related complications in older adults and, if combined with physical activity, improve physical function and quality of life. The approach to weight loss in the older population must place more emphasis on preventing the loss of muscle and bone mass that occurs with age because it can be further accelerated with weight loss.[11] Including exercise as part of a weight-loss regimen can improve strength, endurance, and overall well-being.

Weight Loss and Changes in Body Composition Although obesity is a problem among older adults, after the age of 60 the incidence of obesity decreases. In those over 80 years of age obesity is only half as common as in 50 to 59 year olds.[11] In these older adults, extreme thinness and unintentional weight loss are important health risks and increase the risk of malnutrition. Numerous studies have demonstrated that in older adults low BMI is associated with a higher risk of mortality.[21]

Even when body weight is in a healthy range the changes in body composition that occur with age can affect nutritional and overall health. With age, there is an increase in body fat, especially in the abdomen, and a decrease in lean tissue, including a loss of muscle mass and strength, referred to as **sarcopenia** (**Figure 16.9**).[22,23] In

sarcopenia Progressive decrease in skeletal muscle mass and strength that occurs with age.

Figure 16.9 Changes in the proportion of muscle and fat with age
(a) With age, the proportion of muscle mass decreases and that of body fat increases. (Source: Adapted from Cohen, S. H., et al. Compartmental body composition based on the body nitrogen, potassium, and calcium. Am. J. Physiol. 239:192–200, 1980.)
(b) Magnetic resonance image of a thigh cross-section from a 25-year-old man (left) and a 65-year-old man (right); note that although the thighs are of similar size, the thigh from the older man has more fat (shown in white) around and through the muscle, indicating significant muscle loss. (© Courtesy S. A. Jubias and K. E. Conley, University of Washington Medical Center)

older adults the wasting of lean tissue can result in a high percentage of body fat even when body weight is low or stable. The maximum amount of fat mass occurs at age 60 to 70, and after this both lean tissue and fat mass decrease.[11] The decline in muscle size and strength affects both the skeletal muscles needed to move the body and the heart and respiratory muscles needed to deliver oxygen to the tissues (see Figure 16.9). Therefore, both strength and endurance are decreased, making the tasks of day-to-day life more difficult. The changes in muscle strength contribute not only to **physical frailty**, which is characterized by general weakness, impaired mobility and balance, and poor endurance, but also to the risk of falls and fractures. In the oldest old (those 85 years of age and older), loss of muscle strength becomes the limiting factor determining whether they can continue to live independently. Some of the reduction in muscle strength and mass is due to changes in hormone levels and in muscle protein synthesis, but a lack of exercise is also an important contributor.[22]

Aging is also accompanied by a decrease in bone mass, often resulting in osteoporosis, which further increases the risk of fractures. Although obesity makes many chronic conditions worse, the loss of bone and the risk of osteoporosis is reduced in individuals who weigh more. This is partly due to the added mechanical stress on the bones caused by carrying excess body weight and partly due to the release of estrogen by body fat (see Chapter 11).

Reduced Hormone Levels Some of the hormonal changes that occur with age are considered part of the normal aging process. Others may be a symptom of a disease process. For example, about 4% to 8.5% of adults in the United States have thyroid levels that are below normal. Many of these individuals have no symptoms of this decline. It is not clear whether administering thyroid hormones to individuals with no symptoms offers any benefits.[24] If the decrease causes symptoms the patient is treated by administering hormones.[25]

physical frailty Impairment in function and reduction in physiological reserves severe enough to cause limitations in the basic activities of daily living.

menopause Physiological changes that mark the end of a woman's capacity to bear children.

Estrogen The most striking and rapidly occurring age-related hormonal change is **menopause**. Menopause normally occurs in women between the ages of 45 and 55. During menopause, the cyclical release of the female hormones estrogen and progesterone slows and eventually stops, causing ovulation and menstruation to cease. The period of decline in estrogen is accompanied by changes in mood, skin, and body composition (an increase in body fat and a decrease in lean tissue). The reduction in estrogen decreases the risk of breast cancer but increases the risk of heart disease to a level more similar to that in men. Reduced estrogen also increases the risk of osteoporosis by increasing the rate of bone breakdown and decreasing calcium absorption from the intestine. Estrogen used to be prescribed liberally to older women to alleviate the symptoms of menopause and reduce the risk of osteoporosis and heart disease. This "hormone replacement therapy" is no longer as common because studies have found that while it does reduce menopausal symptoms and the risk of bone fractures it increases the risks of heart disease, blood clots, stroke, breast cancer, and problems with memory and thinking.[26]

Menopause does not occur in men, but with age men do experience a gradual decrease in testosterone levels, which may contribute to a decrease in muscle mass and strength.

Growth Hormone Growth hormone stimulates growth and protein synthesis. Levels gradually decline with age in both men and women and may be responsible for some of the decrease in lean body mass, increase in fat mass, and bone loss that occurs with age. A few small, short-term studies have demonstrated improvements in body composition with growth hormone treatments, but there is little data on the benefits, safety, or cost effectiveness of long-term growth hormone administration.[27] When compared to a program of regular exercise, growth hormone injections did not produce any greater increases in muscle size or strength.[28] In addition, growth hormone administration has side effects including edema, carpal tunnel syndrome, and decreases in insulin sensitivity. Despite the widespread use of growth hormone and products that supposedly increase growth hormone release in the body, until more is known about the long-term effects of growth hormone administration, the use of these products for anti-aging purposes is not recommended.[28]

DHEA DHEA (dehydroepiandrosterone) is a precursor to the sex hormones, testosterone, estrogen, and progesterone. Even though low levels of this hormone are not known to be the cause of age-associated disorders, DHEA supplements are sold over-the-counter and claim to strengthen bones, muscles, and the immune system, and to prevent diabetes, obesity, heart disease, and cancer. Although some of these effects have been demonstrated when DHEA is administered to animals, beneficial effects of DHEA supplementation in humans have not been clearly established.[29]

Melatonin Melatonin is a hormone that is secreted by the pineal gland. It is involved in regulating the body's cycles of sleep and wakefulness. A decline in melatonin is hypothesized to influence aging by affecting body rhythms and triggering genetically programmed aging at a cellular level. Melatonin is also an antioxidant and may enhance immune function and reduce inflammation in the brain.[30] It is sold as a dietary supplement, but its ability to extend normal longevity in humans has not been determined.[31]

Insulin One of the most common hormone-related changes that occurs with aging is elevated blood glucose. This is due to both a decrease in the amount of insulin released by the pancreas and a decrease in insulin sensitivity of the tissues. This decreased insulin sensitivity is related to poor diet, inactivity, increased abdominal fat mass, and decreased lean mass. About 20% of individuals 60 years of age or older have diabetes, and many of these cases are undiagnosed.[32] Individuals with diabetes are treated with diet and lifestyle prescriptions, medications to reduce blood glucose, and, when necessary, administration of the hormone insulin.

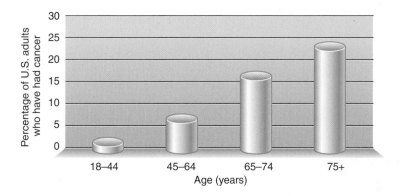

Figure 16.10 Effect of age on cancer incidence
The incidence of cancer increases with age. One reason for the higher incidence is that the immune system's ability to destroy cancer cells declines.

Changes in Immune Function The ability of the immune system to fight disease declines with age. As it does, the incidence of infections, cancers, and autoimmune diseases increases, and the effectiveness of immunizations declines (**Figure 16.10**). In turn, the increases in infections and chronic disease that occur can affect nutritional status. Some of the decrease in immune function may be due to nutritional deficiencies.[33] The immune response depends on the ability of cells to differentiate, divide rapidly, and secrete immune factors, so nutrients that are involved in cell differentiation, cell division, and protein synthesis can influence the immune response. Nutrient deficiencies are common in older adults, including deficiencies of zinc, iron, β-carotene, folic acid, and vitamins B_6, B_{12}, C, D, and E. Supplements of some of these individual nutrients have been shown to increase certain aspects of the immune response, but have not been shown to reduce mortality from infections. When a multivitamin/mineral supplement is used enhanced immune responses and a reduction in the occurrence of common infections are seen. These effects are greater among individuals showing evidence of nutrient deficiencies before supplementation.[33] High doses of some nutrients, including zinc, copper, and iron, depress immune function, so supplements should not contain more than 100% of the Daily Value.

Acute and Chronic Illness

With age there is an increase in the incidence of both acute and chronic illness. The reduction in reserve capacity and decline in immune function make infectious disease more frequent and more serious in the elderly. In addition, most older adults have at least one chronic medical condition.[9] The incidence of cardiovascular disease, diabetes, osteoporosis, hypertension, cancer, arthritis, and Alzheimer's disease all increase with age. Some of these diseases change nutrient requirements, some decrease the appeal of food, and some impair the ability to obtain and prepare an adequate diet by affecting mobility and mental status. All of these can increase the risk of food insecurity and malnutrition.

Conditions that Decrease Mobility More than half of the older population suffers from some form of physical disability, and the incidence increases with increasing age. Over 6.8 million older adults have disabilities that make it difficult to carry out the activities of daily life.[4] These limitations affect the ability to maintain good nutritional health by making it hard to shop, prepare food, get around the house, or go out to eat. Arthritis, a condition that causes pain upon movement, is the most common cause of disability in older individuals affecting approximately 59% of all older adults. Fifty percent of individuals 70 years of age and older with arthritis need help with the activities of daily living, including preparing and eating meals[9] (see Your Choice: Do Glucosamine and Chondroitin Really Help Arthritis?). Osteoporosis and its associated fractures can also affect mobility, which in turn affects the ability to acquire and consume a healthy diet.

(©iStockphoto)

Do Glucosamine and Chondroitin Really Help Arthritis?

Osteoarthritis is a type of arthritis that occurs when the connective tissue that cushions the joints degenerates, allowing the bones to rub together causing pain (see figure). The treatment goals are to control pain and slow or reverse disease progression. Traditionally, arthritis has been treated with drugs that reduce inflammation, such as aspirin and ibuprofen, and with pain relievers such as acetaminophen. These drugs can reduce pain and inflammation but do not repair the tissue. They also have side effects if taken over long periods of time. Supplements containing glucosamine and chondroitin sulfate offer an alternative.

Glucosamine and chondroitin sulfate are compounds found in and around the cells of cartilage, the connective tissue that cushions joints. These compounds are needed for the synthesis of large molecules that bind water to form a porous, gel-like material that allows cartilage to resist crushing forces and cushion the joints. Glucosamine may also inhibit inflammation and contribute to the lubricating and shock-absorbing properties of cartilage. Supplements of both glucosamine and chondroitin sulfate are said to reduce arthritis pain, stop cartilage degeneration, and possibly stimulate the repair of damaged cartilage.

Much of the research indicates that these supplements are safe and beneficial, but how beneficial? Some studies found large improvements, while others found only small effects. Furthermore, the relief provided varied by individual. A study that integrated results from many different trials concluded that these supplements had moderate to large effects on osteoarthritis symptoms.[1] The benefits occurred after the supplements had been taken for approximately 4 to 6 weeks, and the effects were sustained for 4 to 8 weeks after the supplements were discontinued.[2] A multicenter trial to evaluate the effects of glucosamine and chondroitin sulfate on osteoarthritis of the knee found that the combination of supplements did not reduce pain in all subjects but was effective in some patients with moderate to severe knee pain.[3]

Should you try these supplements? The risks are low, and the observed benefits make this treatment promising. However, until these compounds are fully tested, the Arthritis Foundation and the American College of Rheumatology urge patients with osteoarthritis to continue proven treatments and disease-management techniques and to inform their physicians if they are considering using these supplements.

In a normal joint (left), cartilage and fluid cushion the bones; in a joint with osteoarthritis (right), the cartilage has eroded away so there is nothing to prevent the bones from rubbing together.

Normal joint   Osteoarthritis

[1]McAlindon, T. E., LaValley, M. P., Gulin, J. P., and Felson, D. T. Glucosamine and chondroitin for treatment of osteoarthritis: A systematic quality assessment and meta-analysis. *JAMA* 283:1469–1475, 2000.

[2]Hochberg, M. C., and Dougados, M. Pharmacological therapy of osteoarthritis. *Best Pract. Res. Clin. Rheumatol.* 15:583–593, 2001.

[3]Clegg, D. O., Reda, D. I., Harris, C. L., et al. Glucosamine, chondroitin sulfate, and the two in combination for painful knee osteoarthritis. *N. Engl. J. Med.* 354:795–808, 2006.

Conditions that Impair Mental Status Altered mental status can affect nutrition by interfering with the response to hunger and the ability to eat and to obtain and prepare food. Although many individuals maintain adequate nervous system function into old age, the incidence of dementia increases with age. **Dementia** refers to an impairment in memory, thinking, and/or judgment that is severe enough to cause personality changes and affect daily activities and relationships with others. Causes of dementia include multiple strokes, alcoholism, dehydration, medication side effects and interactions, and **Alzheimer's disease**. Low levels of vitamin B_{12} and vitamin E have also been suggested to affect mental function in the elderly. With aging there is a decrease in blood vitamin B_{12} levels and a rise in metabolites indicative of poor vitamin B_{12} status. In most cases, vitamin B_{12} supplements do not improve neurological function; however, in some elderly patients with mild dementia and low blood levels of vitamin B_{12}, supplementation does improve mental function.[10] The relationship between vitamin E and cognitive impairment is also controversial. In the elderly, lower blood levels of vitamin E have been associated with poor memory and mental functioning and those who suffer from dementia have lower plasma levels of vitamin E.[34] The effect of vitamin E and vitamin C supplements on preventing dementia is inconsistent, but some evidence suggests that vitamin E supplements may slow the progression of the disease.[34]

Over half of the cases of dementia in the elderly are due to Alzheimer's disease, a progressive, incurable loss of mental function. The brains of patients with Alzheimer's disease are characterized by the accumulation of an abnormal protein and a loss of certain types of nerve cells. Its cause is unknown, but there does appear to be a genetic component in some cases. Many ineffective nutritional remedies have been marketed for Alzheimer's disease. Because the brains of patients with Alzheimer's contain high levels of aluminum, many people tried to reduce exposure by restricting the use of aluminum cookware and aluminum-containing deodorants. Aluminum restriction has not been shown to be helpful in treating or preventing Alzheimer's disease.[35] Supplements of choline and lecithin have been promoted to increase levels of the neurotransmitter acetylcholine, which is deficient in Alzheimer's patients. Antioxidant supplements have been suggested to prevent free radical damage, which contributes to the pathology of this disease. None of these are effective for preventing or treating Alzheimer's disease.

Prescription and Over-the-Counter Medications The use of prescription and over-the-counter medications can affect nutritional status in a number of ways. Because health problems increase with increasing age, older adults are more likely to take medications; almost half of older Americans take multiple medications daily (**Figure 16.11**).[36] The more medications taken, the greater the chance of side effects

dementia A deterioration of mental state resulting in impaired memory, thinking, and/or judgment.

Alzheimer's disease A disease that results in the relentless and irreversible loss of mental function.

Figure 16.11 It is not uncommon for older adults to take multiple medications daily. (Jose Luis Pelaez/Getty Images, Inc.)

such as increased or decreased appetite, changes in taste, constipation, weakness, drowsiness, diarrhea, and nausea. Illness related to incorrect doses or inappropriate combinations of medications is also a significant health problem in the elderly. Both the effects of drugs on nutritional status and the effects of nutritional status on the effectiveness of the medications must be considered.

Effect of Medications on Nutritional Status Medications can affect nutritional status by altering appetite, nutrient absorption, metabolism, or nutrient excretion (**Table 16.2**). The impact is greatest in individuals who must take medications for extended periods, those who take multiple medications, and those whose nutritional status is already marginal.

Table 16.2 Commonly Used Drugs that May Cause Nutritional Deficiencies

Drug Group	Drug	Potential Deficiency
Antacids	Sodium bicarbonate	Folate, phosphorus, calcium, copper
	Aluminum hydroxide	Phosphorus
Anticonvulsants	Phenytoin, phenobarbital, primidone	Vitamins D and K
	Valproic acid	Carnitine
Antibiotics	Tetracycline	Calcium
	Gentamicin	Potassium, magnesium
Antibacterial agents	Neomycin	Fat, nitrogen
	Boric acid	Riboflavin
	Trimethoprim	Folate
	Isoniazid	Vitamins B_6 and D, niacin
Anti-inflammatory agents	Sulfasalazine	Folate
	Prednisone	Calcium
	Aspirin	Vitamin C, folate, iron
Anticancer drugs	Colchine	Fat, vitamin B_{12}
	Methotrexate	Folate, calcium
Anticoagulant drugs	Warfarin	Vitamin K
Antihypertensive drugs	Hydralazine	Vitamin B_6
Diuretics	Thiazides	Potassium
	Furosemide	Potassium, calcium, magnesium
Hypocholesterolemic agents	Cholestyramine	Fat, fat-soluble vitamins, iron, folate, vitamin B_{12}
Laxatives	Mineral oil	Fat-soluble vitamins
	Phenolphthalein	Potassium, calcium
	Senna	Fat, calcium, vitamin B_6, folate, vitamin C
Tranquilizers	Chlorpromazine	Riboflavin

Source: Adapted from Roe, D. A. *Diet and Drug Interactions*. New York: Van Nostrand Reinhold, 1989.

Some medications directly affect the gastrointestinal tract. More than 250 drugs, including blood pressure medications, antidepressants, decongestants, and the pain reliever ibuprofen (found in Advil, Motrin, and Nuprin), can cause mouth dryness, which can decrease interest in eating by interfering with taste, chewing, and swallowing. Aspirin is a stomach irritant and can cause small amounts of painless bleeding in the gastrointestinal tract, resulting in iron loss. Digoxin, which is a heart stimulant, can cause gastrointestinal upset, loss of appetite, and nausea. Narcotic pain medications such as codeine can lead to constipation, nausea, and vomiting.

Other drugs can decrease nutrient absorption. Cholestyramine (Questran), which is used to reduce blood cholesterol, and Orlistat and Alli, used to promote weight loss, can decrease the absorption of fat-soluble vitamins, vitamin B_{12}, iron, and folate. Antacids that contain aluminum or magnesium hydroxide (Rolaids or Maalox) combine with phosphorus in the gut to form compounds that cannot be absorbed; chronic use can result in loss of phosphorus from bone and possibly accelerate osteoporosis. Repeated use of stimulant laxatives can deplete calcium and potassium. Mineral oil laxatives prevent the absorption of fat-soluble vitamins. If it is not possible to prevent constipation by consuming a diet high in fiber and fluid, bulk-forming laxatives such as Metamucil and Citrucel are a safer choice.

The metabolism of drugs can also affect nutritional status. For example, anticonvulsive drugs (used to prevent seizures) increase the liver's capacity to metabolize and eliminate vitamin D, therefore increasing the need for vitamin D.

Some drugs affect nutrient excretion. Diuretics, which are used to treat hypertension and edema, cause water loss, but some types (thiazides) also increase the excretion of potassium. People taking thiazide diuretics are advised to include several good sources of potassium in their diet each day or are prescribed supplements.

Effect of Food and Nutritional Status on the Effectiveness of Medications

Food components can either enhance or retard the absorption and metabolism of drugs. Some drugs, such as the pain medication Darvon, are absorbed better or faster if taken with food. Other drugs, such as aspirin and ibuprofen, should be taken with food because they are irritating to the gastrointestinal tract. Since food can delay how quickly drugs leave the stomach, some medications are best taken with just water. Other drugs interact with specific foods. For instance, the antibiotic tetracycline should not be taken with milk because it binds with calcium, making both unavailable. The metabolism of atorvastatin (Lipitor), taken to lower cholesterol, is blocked by a compound in grapefruit so eating grapefruit or drinking grapefruit juice can result in drug toxicity.[37]

Nutritional status can also affect drug metabolism. If nutritional status is poor, the body's ability to detoxify drugs may be altered. For example, in a malnourished individual, theophylline, used to treat asthma, is metabolized slowly, resulting in high blood levels of the drug, which can cause loss of appetite, nausea, and vomiting.

Specific nutrients can also affect the metabolism of drugs. High-protein diets enhance drug metabolism in general, and low-protein diets slow it. Vitamin K hinders the action of anticoagulants taken to reduce the risk of blood clots. On the other hand, omega-3 fatty acids, such as those in fish oils, inhibit blood clotting and may intensify the effect of an anticoagulant drug and cause bleeding. It is safe to eat fish while taking anticoagulant drugs; however, the use of fish oil supplements is not recommended. Drugs can also interact with each other. For example, alcohol affects the metabolism of over 100 medications. Drug interactions can exaggerate or, in some cases, diminish the effect of a medication. Individuals taking any medication should consult their doctor, pharmacist, or dietitian regarding how the drug could affect the action of other drugs they may be taking, how the drug could affect their nutrition, and how their nutrition could affect the action of the drug.

Economic, Social, and Psychological Factors

There are a variety of social and economic changes that often accompany aging. These factors are all interrelated and affect nutritional status by decreasing the motivation to eat and the ability to acquire and enjoy food.

Income Approximately 3.4 million older adults live below the poverty level.[38] Poverty is an even greater problem for African-American and Hispanic households. About 7.9% of elderly whites are poor compared to 21.9% of elderly African Americans and 22.7% of elderly Hispanics.[39] Many older adults must live on a fixed income when they retire from their jobs, making it difficult to afford health care, especially medications, and a healthy diet. Food is often the most flexible expense in one's budget, so limiting the types and amounts of foods consumed may be the only option available for older adults trying to meet expenses. Substandard housing and inadequate food preparation facilities can make the situation worse because food cannot easily be prepared and eaten at home. In 2007, 7.3 million elderly Americans experienced food insecurity.[40]

Dependent Living Although many older adults continue to live independently in their own homes, the physical decline and psychological issues associated with aging cause some to eventually require assistance in living (**Figure 16.12**). Poor eyesight and other physical restrictions can limit the ability to drive a car. Without help, many older adults may be unable to get to markets and food programs, restricting the types of food available to them. While a social support system consisting of family members, friends, and other caregivers can help many people stay at home, others may require assisted-living facilities, where they have their own apartments but can obtain assistance around the clock. For some, however, a nursing home is required to obtain the appropriate care.

Those in nursing homes are at increased risk for malnutrition because they are more likely to have medical conditions that increase nutrient needs or that interfere with food intake or nutrient absorption, and because they are dependent on others to provide for their care. In addition, 50% of institutionalized elderly suffer from some form of disorientation or confusion, which further increases the likelihood of decreased nutrient intake. Even when adequate meals are provided, many nursing home residents require assistance in eating and frequently do not consume all of the food served, increasing the likelihood of fluid and energy deficits.[41]

Depression Social, psychological, and physical factors all contribute to depression in the elderly.[41] Social factors such as retirement and the death or relocation of friends and family can cause social isolation and depression. Physical factors such as disability cause loss of independence. This reduces the ability to engage in normal daily activities, visit with friends and family easily, and provide for personal needs, further contributing to depression. Depression can make meals less appetizing and decrease the quantity and quality of foods consumed, thereby increasing the risk of malnutrition.

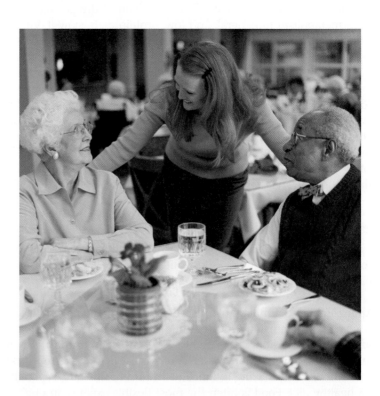

Figure 16.12 Many older people live in assisted living facilities and nursing homes, where nutritious meals are prepared for them. (©Ryan McVay/PhotoDisc/Getty Images, Inc.)

16.5 Keeping Older Adults Healthy

Learning Objectives

- Explain how exercise and a nutritious diet affect the degenerative changes of aging.
- Describe the purpose of the DETERMINE checklist.

There is no secret dietary factor that will bestow immortality, but good nutrition and an active lifestyle are major determinants of successful aging. A good diet can extend an individual's healthy life span by preventing malnutrition and delaying the onset of chronic diseases. The diseases that are the major causes of disability in older adults—cardiovascular disease, hypertension, diabetes, cancer, and osteoporosis—are all nutrition-related. Exercise and a lifetime of healthy eating will not necessarily prevent these diseases, but they may slow the changes that accumulate over time, postponing the onset of disease symptoms. For example, the risk of developing cardiovascular disease can be decreased by exercise and a diet low in saturated fat, *trans* fat, and cholesterol and high in whole grains, fruits, and vegetables. The risk of osteoporosis may be reduced by adequate calcium intake and exercise throughout life. And the likelihood of developing certain types of cancer can be reduced by consuming a diet low in saturated fat and high in whole grains, vegetables, and fruits. Regular exercise can slow the loss of lean body mass, maintain fitness and independence, and allow an increase in food intake without weight gain, so micronutrient needs are more easily met.

Despite the fact that the nutrient needs of older adults are not drastically different from those of young adults, it is more challenging to meet these needs. Some of this challenge is due to changes in health and social and economic conditions that are more common in this population. Meeting needs requires consideration of each person's medical, psychological, social, and economic circumstances. For some, government aid is needed to assure adequate nutrition.

A Healthy Diet Plan for Older Adults

The first step toward meeting the nutrient needs of the elderly is to plan a healthy diet. Because older adults need less energy but the same amounts of most micronutrients, their food choices must be nutrient dense. Meals and snacks should include plenty of liquids because dehydration is a common problem. In some cases, nutrient supplements may be necessary to meet needs.

MyPyramid To determine the recommended amounts from each group needed to meet, but not exceed, energy needs go to the MyPyramid Web site (www.MyPyramid.gov) and enter the individual's age, gender, and activity level. **Figure 16.13** shows the amounts of food from each group needed to meet the energy needs of 50- and 70-year-old sedentary men and women.

To meet micronutrient needs without exceeding kcalorie needs, nutrient-dense choices must be made from each food group. To ensure adequate fiber, whole grains should be chosen from the grains group. To maximize vitamin and phytochemical intake, a variety of fruits and orange, dark green, and starchy vegetables should be included. To maximize nutrient density, low-fat dairy products and lean meats should be chosen. To ensure foods are eaten, those offered should be easy to prepare and well seasoned to enhance appeal. In older adults, there is room for only a few discretionary kcalories. For example, a 70-year old woman who gets less than 30 minutes of exercise a day is only allotted 130 discretionary kcalories per day.

Dietary Supplements Many older adults may benefit from supplementing particular nutrients. Vitamin D supplements may be advantageous because production of this vitamin in the skin is decreased in the elderly and exposure to sunlight may be

Food group	GRAINS	VEGETABLES	FRUITS	MILK	MEAT & BEANS
Amount for a 50-yr-old male	7 ounces	3 cups	2 cups	3 cups	6 ounces
Amount for a 50-yr-old female	6 ounces	2.5 cups	1.5 cups	3 cups	5 ounces
Amount for a 70-yr-old male	6 ounces	2.5 cups	2 cups	3 cups	5.5 ounces
Amount for a 70-yr-old female	5 ounces	2 cups	1.5 cups	3 cups	5 ounces

Figure 16.13 MyPyramid recommendations for older adults The amounts of food from each food group shown here are the recommendations for sedentary (<30 minutes of activity/day) 50- and 70-year-old men and women.

limited. A calcium supplement may be necessary to meet needs, particularly in older women, because it can be difficult to consume 1200 mg of calcium from food without exceeding energy needs. Supplemental vitamin B_{12} from pills or fortified foods is recommended for older adults because the absorption of vitamin B_{12} often decreases with age. However, supplements should not take the place of a balanced, nutrient-dense diet high in whole grains, fruits, and vegetables. These foods also contain phytochemicals and other substances that may protect against disease. Older adults should be cautious to avoid overdoses, and the resulting toxicities, when selecting supplements.

A multivitamin and mineral supplement containing no more than 100% of the Daily Value for any nutrient is the safest way to supplement the diet. Supplements containing megadoses should be avoided. Supplements of nonnutrient substances should be taken with care. Most of these provide no proven benefit, many are costly, and others can be toxic. For example, lecithin is claimed to lower cholesterol and to treat Alzheimer's disease, but there is no proof that it does either. RNA is claimed to rejuvenate old cells, improve memory, and prevent wrinkling, but there are no controlled studies to support any of these claims. Superoxide dismutase (SOD), an enzyme that protects against oxidative damage, is said to slow aging and treat Alzheimer's disease. However, SOD is a protein that is broken down to amino acids in the gastrointestinal tract, so oral supplements will not increase blood or tissue levels of this enzyme. Coenzyme Q, a synthetic version of a compound in the electron transport chain, is marketed to older adults as a way to slow aging by enhancing the immune system. However, it does not boost immune function and may pose a risk to people with poor circulation.

The hypothesis that aging is caused by oxidative damage has contibuted to the popularity of antioxidant supplements. Although antioxidant supplements will not retard the aging process, there is evidence that adequate intakes may reduce the incidence of disease. Antioxidants, including vitamin E and vitamin C, have been found to preserve the function of immune system cells and may therefore help protect the body from infectious disease.[42] And, there is evidence that diets high in antioxidants from fruits and vegetables and other plant foods are associated with a reduced incidence of various chronic diseases, including cardiovascular disease and some types of cancer. Unfortunately, intervention trials have not consistently found that antioxidant supplements reduce the risk of cardiovascular disease or cancer.[43,44] So, rather than taking an antioxidant supplement older adults, like everyone else, should consume a diet plentiful in plant foods high in these nutrients. When antioxidant nutrients are obtained from foods, they bring with them phytochemicals, some of which offer additional antioxidant protection and some of which protect us from chronic disease in other ways (**Figure 16.14**).

As discussed earlier, supplements of hormones such as DHEA and melatonin are also marketed for their anti-aging properties. As with other supposed age-defying supplements, few benefits have been identified. Anyone considering taking dietary supplements should check with their physician first. This is particularly important for older adults who are taking medications that may interact with ingredients in supplements.

Physical Activity for Older Adults

Regular physical activity can extend the years of active independent life, reduce disability, and improve the quality of life for older adults. It helps to maintain muscle mass, bone strength, and cardiorespiratory function. Exercise also increases energy expenditure, so more food can be eaten, increasing the chances that adequate amounts of all essential nutrients will be consumed and reducing the risk of weight gain. To maximize the benefits of exercise, a physical activity program for older adults should include activities that improve endurance, strength, flexibility, and balance.[45,46] While there are some risks associated with participation in regular physical activity, the risks associated with a sedentary lifestyle far exceed them. **Table 16.3** lists the exercise recommendations for older adults.

Figure 16.14 Older adults can increase their antioxidant intake by consuming supplements (top) (©Charles D. Winters) or, better yet, foods that are good sources of antioxidants (bottom), which also provide fiber, energy, other micronutrients, and phytochemicals. (©Charles D. Winters)

Table 16.3 Exercise Guidelines for Older Adults

- All older adults should avoid inactivity. Some physical activity is better than none, and older adults who participate in any amount of physical activity gain some health benefits.

- For substantial health benefits, older adults should do at least 150 minutes a week of moderate-intensity, or 75 minutes a week of vigorous-intensity aerobic physical activity, or an equivalent combination.

- Aerobic activity should be performed in episodes of at least 10 minutes, and preferably, spread throughout the week.

- For additional health benefits, older adults should increase their aerobic physical activity to 300 minutes a week of moderate-intensity, or 150 minutes a week of vigorous-intensity aerobic physical activity, or an equivalent combination.

- Older adults should also do muscle-strengthening activities that are moderate or high intensity and involve all major muscle groups on 2 or more days a week.

- Older adults should do exercises that maintain or improve balance if they are at risk of falling.

- Older adults whose activity is limited by chronic conditions, should be as physically active as their abilities and conditions allow.

- Older adults with chronic conditions should discuss their limitations with their health care providers in order to understand whether and how their conditions affect their ability to do regular physical activity safely.

Adapted from DHHS, 2008 Physical Activity Guidelines for Americans. Available online at http://www.health.gov/paguidelines/pdf/paguide.pdf. Accessed May 13, 2009.

Figure 16.15 Water aerobics classes provide older adults with a low impact aerobic activity and social interaction. (Photo and Co/ Getty Images, Inc.)

Getting Started Before starting an exercise program or increasing the level of physical activity older adults should check with their physician. Those who have been inactive should begin with very low-intensity physical activities. To maximize enjoyment and optimize adherence, activities should be tailored to the individual's needs and interests. Exercise classes or other group-based activities can be a good way for older adults to start an exercise program. Classes enhance social interaction and improve compliance by fostering a mutual commitment to continuing the activity. Classes also provide instruction on proper technique, which can minimize injuries, and supervision in the event of an injury or other emergency.

Endurance Endurance activities appropriate for older adults include low-impact aerobic activities such as walking, biking, and swimming. These aerobic activities provide protection against chronic disease; the benefit increases if intensity increases from low to moderate. Water activities such as water aerobics and swimming do not stress the joints, so they can be used to improve endurance in those with arthritis or other bone and joint disorders (**Figure 16.15**). Some weight-bearing exercise, such as walking, is encouraged to promote bone health. Safe walking environments include shopping malls or lighted sidewalks. Lifestyle activities such as vacuuming, sweeping, mopping, and gardening can also enhance endurance. To provide benefits endurance activities need to be performed for at least 10 minutes without rest.[46]

Figure 16.16 Weight training at any age improves muscle strength and endurance. (©Ingram Publishing/ Alamy Images)

Strength Resistance-training has been shown to increase strength and lean body mass as well as to slow the decrease in bone density common in the elderly. Strength exercise should be performed 2 or more days per week.[46] Lifting small weights or stretching elastic bands at a level that requires some physical effort can provide resistance training (**Figure 16.16**). Weight machines and calisthenics can also be used to increase strength. Both upper- and lower-body muscles should be included in a strengthening regimen. Muscles of the lower body are particularly important for maintaining mobility and independence.

Flexibility Flexibility makes the tasks of everyday life easier and may reduce the risk of injuries.[45,46] Flexibility exercises can be done as part of a cool down after strength training. Flexibility exercises should include those that move the muscle through a full range of motion such as arm circles, as well as those that stretch a muscle its full length and hold it for 10 to 30 seconds. The movements should be smooth and stretches held steady without bouncing. Stretching can be incorporated into lifestyle activities such as putting away the dishes on high and low shelves and tying shoes.

Balance Improvements in strength and endurance also improve balance but specific balance activities provide additional benefits, including reducing the risk of falls in the elderly. Balance exercises should include those that improve balance while standing still, such as balancing on one leg or standing upright with the eyes closed, as well as those that improve balance while moving around, such as walking along a straight line or heel to toe walking. Tai chi is a low-impact activity that improves muscle tone and balance. Balance activities can also be incorporated into daily routines, for example, standing on one foot while waiting in line at the grocery store.

Figure 16.17 The social interaction provided by congregate meals is as beneficial to older adults as the meals provided. (Thinkstock/Getty Images, Inc.)

Preventing Food Insecurity

Once a diet that will meet needs has been developed, steps must be taken to assure that the elderly individual is capable of obtaining and consuming this diet. Preventing food insecurity and ensuring adequate nutrient intake may involve providing nutrient-dense meals or instruction regarding nutrient needs, economic food choices, and food preparation. It may also require assistance with shopping and food preparation.

Overcoming Economic Limitations Being able to afford a healthy diet is a problem for many older individuals. Reduced-cost food and meals at senior centers, food banks, and soup kitchens are available to people on limited incomes as are coupons and debit cards that can be used to purchase food. Programs that provide education about low-cost nutritious food choices can also help reduce food costs.

Overcoming Social Limitations Another problem that contributes to poor nutrient intake is loneliness (**Figure 16.17**). Living, cooking, and eating alone can decrease interest in food. This can be a problem not only for the elderly but for anyone who typically eats alone.

Buying single servings of food is an option, although it can be expensive. To avoid spoilage of perishable items, grocers can be asked to break up packages of meat, eggs, fruits, and vegetables so small amounts can be purchased. Alternatively, large packages can be purchased and shared among friends. Cooking larger portions and freezing foods in meal-size batches can be helpful not only with cost but also to relieve the boredom of eating the same leftovers several days in a row. Creativity and flexibility in what defines a meal can also help. An easy single meal can be prepared by topping a potato with cooked vegetables and cheese, or with leftover chili or spaghetti sauce (**Figure 16.18**). Yogurt or a bowl of cereal with fruit and milk is also a nutritious dinner option.

Overcoming Physical Limitations Difficulty in cooking due to limited mobility can also reduce food intake. Precooked foods, frozen dinners, canned foods, or salad bar items, as well as instant foods such as cereals, rice and noodle dishes, and soups that just require adding water, can provide a meal with almost no preparation. Medical nutritional products such as Ensure or Boost can also be used to supplement intake. These canned, fortified products have a long shelf life and can meet nutrient needs with a small volume. Food can also be ordered by phone if it is affordable. Eating out at senior centers or low-cost restaurants or sharing shopping and cooking chores with a friend can reduce cooking demand and increase social interaction. Home health services can help with cooking and feeding, and most senior centers, health departments, and social service agencies offer meals, rides, and in-home care.

Figure 16.18 Selecting acceptable foods that are nutritious and easy to prepare is important in meeting the needs of the elderly. (©Tony Freeman/PhotoEdit)

Overcoming Medical Limitations Medical conditions and the use of medications often affect food choices. Meals need to be appealing and easy to prepare and consume, as well as compatible with medical conditions. For instance, an individual with dental problems may not be able to chew fresh fruits and vegetables. Therefore, a texture modification is required. Fully cooked, canned, or soft fruit or fruit juices can be substituted for hard-to-chew fruits, and cooked vegetables can replace raw ones. Eggs and stewed meats can provide easy-to-chew protein sources. To overcome changes in the sense of taste and smell, spicy or acidic foods may be limited or emphasized, depending on individual tastes.

Special diets are typically prescribed for individuals with medical conditions such as hypertension, heart disease, diabetes, and kidney disease. These diets may contribute to malnutrition if they restrict favorite foods and if individuals prescribed the diet are not provided with enough information about how to substitute foods that will provide adequate energy, nutrients, and eating pleasure.[9] Education about what foods are appropriate and how to read food labels can help identify products that fit within dietary restrictions.

The use of prescription or over-the-counter medications to treat medical conditions can also affect eating habits. Physicians, pharmacists, and dietitians can provide information about possible effects on food intake. Purchasing all prescription medications from the same pharmacy will ensure that the pharmacist is aware of all medications taken and can advise of possible interactions. Health-care providers also need to be informed about all nonprescription medications and vitamin, mineral, or other dietary supplements used and whether or not medications are taken according to the prescription instructions.

Nutrition Programs for the Elderly

To address concerns over the nutritional health of the elderly, the federal Nutrition Screening Initiative was developed to promote screening for and intervention in nutrition-related problems in older adults.[47] This program is working to increase the awareness of nutritional problems in the elderly by involving practitioners and community organizations as well as relatives, friends, and others caring for the elderly in evaluating the nutritional status of the aging population. This program developed the DETERMINE checklist (**Table 16.4**) based on an acronym for the physiological, med-

Table 16.4 DETERMINE: A Checklist of the Warning Signs of Malnutrition

Disease	Any disease, illness, or condition that causes changes in eating can predispose a person to malnutrition. Memory loss and depression can also interfere with nutrition if they affect food intake.
Eating poorly	Eating either too little or too much can lead to poor health.
Tooth loss/mouth pain	An unhealthy mouth, teeth, or gums can make eating difficult.
Economic hardship	Having to or choosing to spend less than $25 to $30 per person per week on food interferes with nutrition.
Reduced social support	Being alone on a daily basis has a negative effect on morale, well-being, and eating.
Multiple medicines	The more medicines a person takes, the greater the chances of side effects such as weakness, drowsiness, diarrhea, changes in taste and appetite, nausea, and constipation.
Involuntary weight loss/gain	Unintentionally losing or gaining weight is a warning sign that should not be ignored. Being overweight or underweight also increases the risk of malnutrition.
Needs assistance in self-care	Difficulty walking, shopping, and cooking increase the risk of malnutrition.
Elder above age 80	The risks of frailty and health problems increase with increasing age.

ical, and socioeconomic situations that increase the risk of malnutrition among the elderly. The elderly themselves, family members, and caregivers can use this tool to identify when malnutrition is a potential problem (see Critical Thinking: Averting Malnutrition).

To help meet the nutrient needs of older adults, the federal Older Americans Act provides nutrition services to older individuals who are in economic need, particularly low-income minorities. Programs that provide nutritious meals in communal settings promote social interaction and can improve nutrient intake. The Congregate and Home-Delivered Nutrition Programs established by the Older Americans Act provide congregate meals at locations such as senior centers, community centers, schools, and churches. For those who are unable to attend congregate meals, home-delivered meals are available.

Although such programs are a first step in meeting nutritional needs, currently most provide only one meal a day for five days a week. Each meal served must provide at least a third of the RDA. In practice, participants in these elder nutrition programs are receiving 40% to 50% of their daily intake from this one meal.[48] These and other programs addressing the nutritional needs of older adults are described in **Table 16.5**.

Table 16.5 **National Programs Promoting Better Nutrition among Older Americans**

- **Older Americans Act—Title III Congregate and Home-Delivered Nutrition Programs**
  Serves at least one meal five days a week to persons 60 years and older. Meals are served at home or in churches, schools, senior centers, or other facilities.

- **Older Americans Act—Title VI Congregate and Home-Delivered Nutrition Programs**
  Provides home-delivered and congregate meals to Native-American organizations.

- **Older Americans Act—Title III Health Promotion and Disease Prevention Program**
  Provides health-promotion and disease-prevention services in areas where there are large numbers of economically needy older adults.

- **Nutrition Screening Initiative**
  Promotes nutritional screening and more attention to nutrition in all health-care and social-service settings that provide for older adults.

- **Supplemental Nutrition Assistance Program (SNAP)**
  Provides coupons or debit cards to low-income individuals including the elderly. These can be used instead of cash to purchase food.

- **Nutrition Program for the Elderly**
  Provides grants, cash, and commodity foods to states and tribes to supplement congregate and home-delivered meal programs.

- **Commodity Supplemental Food Program—Elderly**
  Provides food, nutrition education, and health-service referrals to individuals with low incomes, including the elderly.

- **Child and Adult Care Food Program (Adult Day Care)**
  Provides cash reimbursements and food commodities to community day-care centers that serve meals and snacks to children and elderly with special needs.

- **Food Distribution Program on Indian Reservations**
  Distributes commodity foods to low-income persons, including the elderly, living on or near Indian reservations.

Critical Thinking
Averting Malnutrition

(©iStockphoto)

Background

Shirley is an 82 year old woman who lives alone in the city. She recently had her teeth extracted because of periodontal disease. As a result of her dental problems, she has eaten only cottage cheese and milk for the past few weeks. Even though she is now feeling better, her granddaughter, Anna, begins to worry about Shirley's nutrition. Anna reviews the DETERMINE checklist and finds that eight of the items on the checklist apply to her grandmother. This confirms her concerns about the risk of malnutrition. Anna takes Shirley to a dietitian who asks her to recall the diet she ate before her teeth were extracted.

Data

Shirley needs a diet that includes foods that are not only easy to prepare and carry home on the bus but that are also easy to chew. To ensure she has the foods she needs to stay healthy Anna decides to take Shirley shopping once a month for the heavy, bulky items like paper goods, laundry soap, rice, cereal, and canned foods. Shirley can handle the smaller, more perishable items when she takes the bus to the store.

Shirley's Original Diet

FOOD	AMOUNT
Breakfast	
Bran flakes	I cup
Low-fat milk	I cup
Coffee	I cup
Low-fat milk	I Tbsp
Sugar	2 tsp
Lunch	
Chicken soup	I cup
Saltine crackers	6 crackers
Apple	I small
Dinner	
Low-fat milk	I cup
Instant white rice	I cup
Beef	3 oz
Peas	I cup

Critical Thinking Questions

How is Shirley doing? Does she meet the recommendations of MyPyramid for someone of her age who gets less than 30 minutes of activity per day?

▼

Suggest foods Shirley could add to improve her diet.

▼

What factors other than nutrient content need to be considered when recommending foods that will improve Shirley's diet?

▼

Would you recommend any dietary supplements for Shirley?

iProfile Use iProfile to find snacks that are nutrient dense and easy to chew.

Outcome

Min was lonely and became more and more depressed after her husband died. She didn't like to eat by herself, so she stopped cooking healthy meals. Instead, she ate easy-to-prepare convenience foods that were high in fat and included few vegetables or fruits. She became too depressed to seek out her old walking buddies, her fitness declined, and she rarely left the house. Her family became concerned and began visiting and phoning more often. After spending a weekend with her grandchildren, Min realized she was still loved and needed. She decided it was time to take care of herself. She began taking an exercise class, which helped her regain her fitness so she could walk with her friends. She realized that her diet of convenience foods had led to some weight gain. To improve her diet she pulled out some of the healthy recipes she used to cook when her husband was alive, cutting the amounts in half or freezing the extra portions for another day. On Wednesday nights she began attending church suppers. Eating there allowed her to meet people and helped her enjoy her meals again. Although Min still misses her husband, a year after his death she again has an active social life and is in good nutritional health.

APPLICATIONS

Personal Nutrition

1. **How does age affect energy needs?**
   a. How does your average energy intake from the food record you kept in Chapter 2 compare to the EER for a person who is your height, weight, and activity level but is 75 years old?
   b. Use iProfile to suggest modifications in your food choices that would allow you to meet the nutrient needs of a 75-year-old without exceeding the energy needs.
   c. Use the MyPyramid Website to determine the amounts of food you should consume from each food group if you were 75 years old, but at your current weight and height.

2. **How do medical conditions and dietary restrictions affect food choices?**
   a. How might you modify your food choices to accommodate a low-sodium diet?
   b. How might you modify your food choices to accommodate a restriction of protein to 0.6 gram per kilogram of body weight?
   c. How might you modify your food choices to accommodate a loss of smell and taste?
   d. How might you modify your food choices to accommodate a dry mouth and poorly fitting dentures?

General Nutrition Issues

1. **What information and resources are available for the elderly and their families?**
   a. Use the Internet to determine what kind of nutrition information is available to individuals planning for the care of their elderly parents or relatives. What are the costs?
   b. Assume that you have an elderly friend who lives and eats alone. Find resources in your area that would be able to provide meals and other services for your friend.

2. **What do seniors need to know about nutrition?**
   a. Prepare an outline for a 20-minute lecture on nutrition and aging that could be given at a senior center in your area.
   b. Define two goals for the lecture.
   c. What are five main points that you should discuss.

Summary

16.1 What Is Aging?

- Aging is the accumulation of changes over time that results in an ever-increasing susceptibility to disease and death. The longest an organism can live, or life span, is a characteristic of a species. The average age to which people in a population live, or life expectancy, is a characteristic of a population.

- As a population, we are living longer but not necessarily healthier lives. The elderly are the fastest-growing segment of the U.S. population. Compression of morbidity, that is, increasing the number of healthy years, is an important public health goal. A healthy diet and lifestyle cannot stop aging but can postpone the onset of many of the physiological changes and diseases that are common in older adults.

16.2 What Causes Aging?

- As organisms become older, the number of cells they contain decreases and the function of the remaining cells declines. This reduces reserve capacity lowering the organism's ability to maintain homeostasis and increasing the risk of disease.

- The loss of cells and cell function that causes aging is believed to be due to both genetic factors that limit cell life and the accumulation of cellular damage over time.

- How long we live and how long we remain healthy is determined by a combination of genetic, environmental, and lifestyle factors.

16.3 Nutritional Needs and Concerns of Older Adults

- Energy needs are lower in older adults due to a decrease in basal metabolic rate and the thermic effect of food and a reduction in physical activity, but the need for protein, water, fiber, and most micronutrients remains the same. Intakes of fiber and water are often less than recommended, increasing the risk of dehydration and constipation.

- Low intakes, reduced absorption, and changes in the metabolism of certain micronutrients including vitamin B_{12}, vitamin D, and calcium puts older adults at risk of deficiency. Iron requirements decrease in women after menopause but many older adults are at risk of iron deficiency due to blood loss from disease or medications.

16.4 Factors that Increase the Risk of Malnutrition

- The risk of malnutrition increases with age due to the physiological changes that accompany aging. There are changes in the sense of smell that affect the appeal of food, changes in vision that affect the ability to prepare food, changes in digestion and absorption that decrease the intake and absorption of nutrients, changes in metabolism that affect nutrient utilization, changes in weight and body composition that increase health risks and reduce independence, changes in hormonal patterns that affect body function, and changes in immune function that increase the risk of infectious and chronic disease.

- Both infectious and chronic diseases affect nutrient requirements and the ability to consume a nutritious diet. Aging increases the incidence of diseases that reduce mobility and mental capacity, limiting the ability to acquire, prepare, and consume food. The medications used to treat disease also affect nutrition, especially when the medications are taken over long periods of time and when multiple medications are taken simultaneously.

- Low-income levels increase the risk of malnutrition among the elderly by limiting the ability to purchase food. Loss of independence contributes to depression, which makes meals less appetizing and decreases the quantity and quality of foods consumed.

16.5 Keeping Older Adults Healthy

- A healthy diet and regular exercise can prevent malnutrition, delay the onset of chronic conditions, and increase independence in older adults. MyPyramid can be used to determine the amounts of food from each food group needed by older adults. Meals for the elderly must be

nutrient-dense, provide plenty of fluid and fiber, and consider individual medical, psychological, social, and economic circumstances. Supplements of calcium, vitamin D, and vitamin B_{12} may be beneficial. In some cases, assistance with shopping and meal preparation may be needed.

- A physical activity program for older adults should include activities that improve endurance, strength, flexibility, and balance. Activities should be tailored to the individual's needs and likes. Exercise classes are advantageous for older adults because they provide both social interaction and professional support and instruction. A well-planned exercise program can reduce the risk of chronic disease, improve mobility, increase independence, and reduce the risk of falls and injuries.

- The DETERMINE checklist helps identify older adults who are at risk for malnutrition.

- The federal Older Americans Act includes programs that provide older adults with low-cost or free meals in their homes or in a social setting. Although these programs are helpful, they do not ensure adequate nutrition for all elderly.

Review Questions

1. What is life expectancy? How does it differ from healthy life expectancy? How does it differ from life span?

2. What is meant by compression of morbidity?

3. What factors determine at what age the consequences of aging become apparent?

4. Why are older adults at risk for malnutrition?

5. List three physiological changes that occur with aging.

6. List three ways in which medication use and nutrition interact.

7. What social and economic factors increase nutritional risk among the elderly?

8. Why are the energy needs of older adults reduced?

9. Why are older adults at risk for vitamin B_{12} deficiency? Vitamin D deficiency?

10. How can nutrition affect the risk of developing macular degeneration?

11. Should obese adults over 70 years of age lose weight? Why or why not?

12. Explain how physical disabilities and mental illness affect nutritional status.

13. Why is it important that elderly individuals consume a nutrient-dense diet?

14. Compare the MyPyramid recommendations for a 65-year-old male and an 85-year-old male.

15. List some activities that are appropriate for older adults to improve endurance, strength, flexibility, and balance.

16. What is the purpose of the DETERMINE checklist?

References

1. Masoro, E. J. Overview of caloric restriction and ageing. *Mech. Aging Dev.* 126:913–922, 2005.

2. Lamming, D. W., Latorre-Esteves, M., Medvedik, O., et al. HST2 mediates SIR2-independent life-span extension by calorie restriction. *Science.* 309:1861–1864, 2005.

3. Centers for Disease Control and Prevention. Deaths: Final data for 2005. *Natl Vital Stat Rep* 56:1–124, 2008. Available online at www.cdc.gov/nchs/data/nvsr/nvsr56/nvsr56_10.pdf. Accessed April 1, 2009.

4. Federal Interagency Forum on Aging-Related Statistics. *Older Americans 2008: Key Indicators of Wellbeing, Population.* Available online at www.agingstats.gov/agingstatsdotnet/Main_Site/Data/Data_2008.aspx. Accessed September 30, 2009.

5. World Health Organization. *The World Health Report, 2003. Healthy Life Expectancy. Annex Table 4 Healthy Life Expectancy (HALE) in All Member States, Estimates for 2002.* Available online at www.who.int/whr/2003/en/Annex4-en.pdf. Accessed September 12, 2008.

6. DHHS, Administration on Aging A Profile of Older Americans: 2008 Health and Health Care Available online at http://www.aoa.gov/AoARoot/Aging_Statistics/ Profile/ 2008/14.aspx. Accessed May 11, 2009.

7. Schiller, J. S., and Bernadel, L. Summary health statistics for the U.S. population: National Health Interview, 2002. *Vital Health Stat.* 10:1–101, 2004.

8. Troen, B. R. The biology of aging. *Mt. Sinai J. Med.* 70:3–22, 2003.

9. American Dietetic Association. Position of the American Dietetic Association: Nutrition across the spectrum of aging. *J. Am. Diet. Assoc.* 105: 616–633, 2005.

10. Institute of Medicine, Food and Nutrition Board. *Dietary Reference Intakes for Energy, Carbohydrate, Fiber, Fat, Protein, and Amino Acids*. Washington, D.C.: National Academies Press, 2002.

11. Villareal, D. T., Apovian, C. M., Kushner, R. F., and Klein, S. American Society for Nutrition; NAASO, the Obesity Society. Obesity in older adults: Technical review and position statement of the American Society for Nutrition and NAASO, the Obesity Society. *Am. J. Clin. Nutr.* 82:923–934, 2005.

12. Institute of Medicine, Food and Nutrition Board. *Dietary Reference Intakes for Thiamin, Riboflavin, Niacin, Vitamin B6, Folate, Vitamin B12, Pantothenic Acid, Biotin, and Choline*. Washington, D.C.: National Academies Press, 1998.

13. Rampersaud, G. C., Kauwell, G. P., and Bailey, L. B. Folate: A key to optimizing health and reducing disease risk in the elderly. *J. Am. Coll. Nutr.* 22:1–8, 2003.

14. Centers for Disease Control and Prevention. 5 a Day. Available online at apps.nccd.cdc.gov/5ADaySurveillance/ displayV.asp/ Accessed December 17, 2004.

15. Institute of Medicine, Food and Nutrition Board. *Dietary Reference Intakes: Calcium, Phosphorus, Magnesium, Vitamin D, and Fluoride*. Washington, D.C.: National Academies Press, 1997.

16. Holick, M. F., and Chen, T. C. Vitamin D deficiency: A worldwide problem with health consequences. *Am. J. Clin. Nutr.* 87(Suppl.):1080S–1086S, 2008.

17. Chernoff, R. Micronutrient requirements in older women. *Am. J. Clin. Nutr.* 81:1240S–1245S, 2005.

18. Schaefer, D. C., and Cheskin, L. J. Constipation in the elderly. *Am. Family Physician* 58:907–914, 1998.

19. Esposito, C., Plati, A., Mazzullo, T. et al. Renal function and functional reserve in healthy elderly individuals. *J. Nephrol.* 20:617–625, 2007.

20. Ogden, C. L., Carroll, M. D., Curtin, L. R. et al. Prevalence of overweight and obesity in the United States 1999–2004, *JAMA* 295:1549–1555, 2006.

21. Thomas, D. R. Weight loss in older adults. *Rev. Endocr. Metab. Disord.* 6:129–136, 2005.

22. Nikolic, M., Bajek, S., Bobinac, D. et al. Aging of human skeletal muscles. *Coll. Anthropol.* 29:67–70, 2005.

23. St-Onge, M. P. Relationship between body composition changes and changes in physical function and metabolic risk factors in aging. *Curr. Opin. Clin. Nutr. Metab. Care* 8:523–528, 2005.

24. Col, N. F., Surks, M. I., and Daniels, G. H. Subclinical thyroid disease: Clinical applications. *JAMA* 291:239–243, 2004.

25. Surks, M. I., Ortiz, E., Daniels, G. H. et al. Subclinical thyroid disease: Scientific review and guidelines for diagnosis and management. *JAMA* 291:228–238, 2004.

26. U.S. Preventive Services Task Force. Hormone therapy for the prevention of chronic conditions in postmenopausal women: Recommendations from the U.S. Preventive Services Task Force. *Ann. Intern. Med.* 142:855–860, 2005.

27. Toogood, A. A. The somatopause: An indication for growth hormone therapy? *Treat. Endocrinol.* 3:201–209, 2004.

28. Thorner, M. O. Statement by the Growth Hormone Research Society on the GH/IGF-I axis in extending health span. *J. Gerontol. A Biol. Sci. Med. Sci.* 64:1039–44, 2009.

29. Cameron, D. R., and Braunstein, G. D. The use of dehydroepiandrosterone therapy in clinical practice. *Treat. Endocrinol.* 4:95–114, 2005.

30. Bondy, S. C., Lahiri, D. K., Perreau, V. M. et al. Retardation of brain aging by chronic treatment with melatonin. *Ann. N.Y. Acad. Sci.* 1035:197–215, 2004.

31. Karasek, M. Does melatonin play a role in the aging process. *J. Physiol. Pharmacol.* 58:105–113, 2007.

32. National Institute of Diabetes and Digestive and Kidney Diseases. National Diabetes Information Clearinghouse, National Diabetes Statistics, 2007. Available online at http://diabetes.niddk.nih.gov/DM/PUBS/statistics/#allages. Accessed October 1, 2009.

33. Chandra, R. K. Impact of nutritional status and nutrient supplements on immune responses and incidence of infection in older individuals. *Aging Res. Rev.* 3:91–104, 2004.

34. Cherubini, A., Martin, A., Andres-Lacueva, C. et al. Vitamin E levels, cognitive impairment and dementia in older persons: The InCHIANTI study. *Neurobiol. Aging* 26:987–994, 2005.

35. McDaniel, M. A., Maier, S. F., and Einstein, G. O. "Brain-specific" nutrients: A memory cure? *Nutrition* 19:957–975, 2003.

36. Hajjar, E. R., Cafiero, A. C., and Hanlon, J. T. Polypharmacy in elderly patients. *Am. J. Geriatr. Pharmacother.* 5:314–316, 2007.

37. Karch, A. M. The grapefruit challenge: The juice inhibits a crucial enzyme, with possibly fatal consequences. *Am. J. Nurs.* 104:33–35, 2004.

38. Administration on Aging. *A Profile of Older Americans: 2007*. Available online at www.agingcarefl.org/aging/ AOA-2007profile.pdf. Accessed September 14, 2008.

39. U.S. Census Bureau Poverty Status of People by Family Relationship, Race, and Hispanic: 1959 to 2006 available online at http://www.census.gov/hhes/www/poverty/ histpov/hstpov2.html. Accessed May 12, 2009.

40. Nord, M., Andrews, M., and Carlson, S. *Household Food Security in the United States, 2007*. November 2008. Available online at www.ers.usda.gov/Publications/ERR66/. Accessed April 20, 2009.

41. Dorner, B., Niedert, K. C., and Welch, P. K.; American Dietetic Association. Position of the American Dietetic Association: Liberalized diets for older adults in long-term care. *J. Am. Diet. Assoc.* 102:1316–1323, 2002.

42. De la Fuente, M. Effects of antioxidants on immune system aging. *Eur. J. Clin. Nutr.* 56(Suppl 3):S5–S8, 2002.

43. Stanner, S. A., Hughes, J., Kelly, C. N., and Buttriss, J. A. Review of the epidemiological evidence for the "antioxidant hypothesis." *Public Health Nutr.* 7:407–422, 2004.

44. Clarke, R., and Armitage, J. Antioxidant vitamins and risk of cardiovascular disease. Review of large-scale randomised trials. *Cardiovasc. Drugs Ther.* 16:411–415, 2002.

45. American College of Sports Medicine. Physical activity programs and behavior counseling in older adult populations. *Med. Sci. Sports Exerc.* 36:1997–2003, 2004.

46. DHHS, 2008 Physical Activity Guidelines for Americans. Available online at http://www.health.gov/paguidelines/ pdf/paguide.pdf. Accessed May 13, 2009.

47. American Academy of Family Physicians. Nutrition Screening Initiative. Available online at www.aafp.org/ nsi/index.html/ Accessed August 2, 2002.

48. U.S. Department of Health and Human Services, Administration on Aging. Elderly Nutrition Program. Available online at www.aoa.gov/nutrition/default.htm/ Accessed August 2, 2002.

17

Food Safety

Case Study

One hundred children at Loghill Elementary School were absent or went home sick on Friday. Forty of them vomited at school. It might have been the stomach flu, but only a few of the teachers and parents became ill, even though they were in contact with the children and presumably would have been just as likely as the children to catch the flu. When this many people in one place become ill at the same time, foodborne illness is always suspect.

Even though almost everyone had recovered by Monday, the local health department was notified. Inspectors came to the school to investigate the cause of the illnesses and were able to trace the source to the "Welcome Back, Spring" celebration held the day before everyone became ill. For this event, the first graders made cupcakes, the second graders made cookies, the third graders made popcorn balls, and the fourth graders made frozen custard. After interviewing the children and adults who were sick, the inspectors determined that only those who ate frozen custard became ill, and they all began having symptoms within 48 hours of consuming it. Symptoms included nausea and vomiting, diarrhea, abdominal pain, and fever. Many of the sick children were seen by physicians, and the organism *Salmonella enteritidis* was isolated from their stool samples. Further investigation revealed that the recipe the fourth graders used to make the frozen custard included six grade-A raw eggs. The students had cranked the custard by hand, and it had taken about 2 hours to harden.

(Masterfile)

(©iStockphoto)

attlberger/Getty Images, Inc.)

Chapter Outline

17.1 How Can Food Make Us Sick?

Learning Objectives

• Name the primary cause of foodborne illness in the United States.

• Explain why a contaminated food does not cause illness in everyone who eats it.

The American food supply is most likely the safest in the world, however, it is not risk-free. *Salmonella* bacteria contaminate chickens sold in the United States, industrial waste has polluted some of our waterways, pesticide residues are found on our fruit, and concerns about mad cow disease are rising. Headlines announce *Escherichia coli* (*E. coli*) in meat and apple juice; *Salmonella* in eggs, on vegetables, and in cereal; *Cyclospora* on fruit; *Cryptosporidium* in drinking water; and hepatitis A in frozen strawberries. It is estimated that 76 million people in the United States become ill, 325,000 are hospitalized, and 5000 die each year from food-related illness.[1]

If given a choice, most people would elect to consume food that contains no harmful substances. However, it is nearly impossible to choose a diet that is free of all potential hazards. Food has always carried the risks of bacterial contamination and naturally occurring toxins. Today, modern agricultural technology, trade patterns, food processing, and changes in dietary habits have increased the risks associated with bacterial contamination and introduced new risks. Regulatory agencies, food manufacturers and retailers, as well as consumers, must work together to maximize the safety of the food supply (**Figure 17.1**).

foodborne illness An illness caused by consumption of food containing a toxin or disease-causing microorganism.

pathogen A biological agent that causes disease.

toxins Substances that can cause harm at some level of exposure.

What Is Foodborne Illness?

Foodborne illness in the broadest sense is any illness that is related to the consumption of food or contaminants or toxins in food. However, most of the foodborne illness in the United States is caused by the contamination of food with **pathogens**, that is, microorganisms or microbes that can cause disease. **Toxins** produced by these microorganisms, as well as chemical and physical contaminants from the environment and those used in the processing and packaging of food, can also cause foodborne illness. Chemical contaminants include substances such as drugs used in raising cattle

Figure 17.1 Choosing safe, nutritious foods is one way that consumers help control the safety of the foods they eat. (Eric Glenn/DK Stock/Getty Images, Inc.)

and producing milk, pesticides and fertilizers used in growing crops, and wastes from industry that accumulate in the environment. Physical contaminants include substances as diverse as broken glass, packaging materials, and insect wings. Even substances we use to protect the food supply such as packaging and preservatives have the potential to cause harm if not properly used.

How Does Food Get Contaminated?

Often food is contaminated where it is grown or produced. *Salmonella enteritidis* may enter eggs directly from hens infected with the bacteria. Fish and seafood may be contaminated by agricultural runoff, sewage, and other toxins in the waters where they live. Molds may grow on grains during unusually wet or dry growing seasons. Food can also be contaminated during processing or storage, at retail facilities, and even at home. This often occurs by **cross-contamination** from a contaminated food or piece of equipment to an uninfected one. For example, *E. coli* from a single cow can contaminate processing equipment and be transferred to thousands of pounds of hamburger. Careful sanitation and handling can control most of these sources of foodborne illness.

cross-contamination
The transfer of contaminants from one food or object to another.

When Do Contaminants Make Us Sick?

Even when a food is contaminated, it does not cause every individual who consumes it to become ill. The potential of a substance to cause harm depends on how potent it is, the amount or dose that is consumed, how frequently it is consumed, and who consumes it. Some contaminants in food cause harm even when minute amounts are consumed, and almost any substance can be toxic if a large enough amount is consumed. Many substances have a **threshold effect**; that is, they are harmless up to a certain dose or threshold, after which negative effects increase with increasing intake. Body size, nutritional status, and how a substance is metabolized by the body can also affect toxicity. Small doses are more dangerous in children and small adults because the amount of toxin per unit of body weight is greater. Poor nutritional or health status may decrease the body's natural ability to detoxify harmful substances. Substances that are stored in the body are more likely to be toxic because they accumulate over time. They are deposited in bones, adipose tissue, liver, or other tissues until toxicity symptoms occur. Substances that are easily excreted when consumed in excess are less likely to cause toxicity. The interaction of toxins with one another and with other dietary factors also affects toxicity. For example, mercury, which is extremely toxic, is not absorbed well if the diet is high in selenium, and the absorption of lead is decreased by the presence of iron and calcium in the diet.

threshold effect A reaction that occurs at a certain level of ingestion and increases as the dose increases. Below that level there is no reaction.

17.2 Keeping Food Safe

Learning Objectives

- Explain how a HACCP system helps prevent food-borne illness.
- Discuss the roles of the federal agencies responsible for the safety of the U.S. food supply.
- Discuss the role of the consumer in keeping food safe.

Ensuring the safety of the food supply is a responsibility shared by the government, food manufacturers and retail establishments, and consumers. The steps taken to avoid foodborne illness require weighing the benefits a food provides against the potential risks it presents. This type of risk-benefit analysis is done by regulatory agencies when they evaluate the safety and sanitation of food-processing methods and food service establishments. Not every potential contaminant is harmful, nor can all be avoided, but those that have a great potential for harm need to be addressed. Consumers should also consider the risks and benefits when they choose which foods to buy, which to eat, and how to handle, store, and cook these foods.

The Government's Role

The safety of the food supply is monitored by agencies at the international, federal, state, and local levels (**Table 17.1**). Federal agencies set standards and establish regulations for the safe and sanitary handling of food and water and for the information on food labels. They regulate the use of agricultural chemicals, additives, and packaging materials; inspect food-processing and storage facilities; monitor both domestic and imported foods for contamination; and investigate outbreaks of foodborne illness. State agencies have the primary responsibility for milk safety and the inspection of restaurants, retail food stores, dairies, grain mills, and other food-related establishments within their borders (**Figure 17.2**). As a result, regulations vary from state to state. To provide guidance, the U.S. Food and Drug Administration (FDA) publishes the **food code** which offers recommendations for safeguarding public health when food is served to the consumer.[2]

food code A set of recommendations published by the FDA for the handling and service of food sold in restaurants and other establishments that serve food.

Figure 17.2 Both state and local governments regulate the safety of food sold at restaurants. (John Miller/ Getty Images, Inc.)

Table 17.1 Agencies That Monitor the Food Supply

International organizations

- **Food and Agriculture Organization of the United Nations (FAO):** Specializes in promoting and sharing knowledge in all aspects of food quality and safety and in all stages of food production: harvest, post-harvest handling, storage, transport, processing, and distribution.
- **World Health Organization (WHO):** Develops international food safety policies, food inspection programs, and standards for hygienic food preparation; promotes technologies that improve food safety and consumer education about safe food practices. Works closely with the FAO.

Federal organizations

- **U.S. Food and Drug Administration (FDA):** Ensures the safety and quality of all foods sold across state lines with the exception of red meat, poultry, and egg products; inspects food processing plants; inspects imported foods with the exception of red meat, poultry, and egg products; sets standards for food composition; oversees use of drugs and feed in food-producing animals; and enforces regulations for food labeling, food and color additives, and food sanitation.
- **U.S. Department of Agriculture (USDA) Food Safety and Inspection Service (FSIS):** Enforces standards for the wholesomeness and quality of red meat, poultry, and egg products produced in the United States or imported from other countries. If a food is suspect, it can be tested for contamination and denied entry into the country.
- **U.S. Environmental Protection Agency (EPA):** Regulates pesticide levels and must approve all pesticides before they can be sold in the United States; establishes water quality standards.
- **National Marine Fisheries Service:** Oversees the management of fisheries and fish harvesting. Operates a voluntary program of inspection and grading of fish products.
- **National Oceanic and Atmospheric Administration (NOAA):** Oversees fish and seafood products. Its Seafood Inspection Program inspects and certifies fishing vessels, seafood processing plants, and retail facilities for compliance with federal sanitation standards.
- **Centers for Disease Control and Prevention (CDC):** Monitors and investigates the incidence and causes of food-borne diseases.

State and local organizations

- Oversee all food within their jurisdiction. Inspect restaurants, grocery stores, and other retail food establishments, as well as dairy farms and milk processing plants, grain mills, and food manufacturing plants within local jurisdictions.

Concern about the prevalence of foodborne illness led to the establishment of the National Food Safety Initiative. The goal of this program is to reduce the incidence of foodborne illness by improving food safety practices and policies throughout the United States. The focus is on reducing the risk of microbial foodborne illness.[3] To accomplish this the program promotes the implementation of a science-based system to monitor the safety of the food supply and track foodborne illness once it has occurred.

Identifying Potential Problems Food safety used to be monitored by conducting spot-checks of manufacturing conditions and products. These checks often relied on visual inspection to detect contamination and typically did not find a problem until after it had already occurred. The current system for safeguarding the food supply, which is promoted by the National Food Safety Initiative, is called **Hazard Analysis Critical Control Point (HACCP)**. This is a science-based approach designed to prevent food contamination rather than catch it after it occurs (**Figure 17.3**).

The HACCP approach to food safety involves establishing standardized procedures to prevent, control, or eliminate contamination before food reaches consumers (**Table 17.2**). It focuses on identifying points in the handling of food, called **critical control points**, where chemical, physical, or microbial contamination can be prevented, controlled, or eliminated. The HACCP system requires the food manufacturing and food service industries to anticipate where contamination might occur. It also establishes record-keeping procedures to verify that the system is working consistently. The advantages of the HACCP system over standard inspections by the FDA are that it is preventative rather than punitive, it is easier to manage, and the responsibility for food safety is placed on the manufacturer, not the regulatory agencies.

Hazard Analysis Critical Control Point (HACCP)
A food safety system that focuses on identifying and preventing hazards that could cause foodborne illness.

critical control points
Possible points in food production, manufacturing, and transportation at which contamination could occur or be prevented.

Table 17.2 Seven Principles of HACCP

1. Conduct a hazard analysis.	Analyze the processes associated with the production of a food to identify the potential biological, chemical, and physical hazards and determine what type of preventive measures, such as changes in temperature, pH, or moisture level, could be used to control or avoid these hazards.
2. Identify critical control points.	Identify steps in a food's production called critical control points, at which the potential hazard can be prevented, controlled, or eliminated—for example, cooking, cooling, packaging, and metal detection.
3. Establish critical limits.	Establish preventive procedures with measurable limits for all critical control points. For example, for a cooked food this might be a minimum cooking time and temperature required to ensure elimination of harmful microbes. If these critical limits are not met, the food safety hazards are not being prevented, eliminated, or reduced to acceptable levels.
4. Establish monitoring procedures.	Establish procedures to monitor the critical limits. For example, how and by whom will the cooking temperature be monitored? Adjustments can be made while continuing the process.
5. Establish corrective actions.	Establish plans to discard the potentially hazardous product and to correct the out-of-control process when monitoring shows that a critical limit has not been met—for example, reprocessing or discarding food if the minimum cooking temperature is not met.
6. Establish verification procedures.	Establish procedures to verify the scientific or technical validity of the hazard analysis, the adequacy of the critical control points, and the effectiveness of the HACCP plan. An example of verification is the testing of time and temperature recording devices to verify that a cooking unit is working properly.
7. Establish record-keeping and documentation procedures.	Prepare and maintain a written HACCP plan. This would include records of hazards and their control methods, the monitoring of each critical control point, and notations of corrective actions taken. Each principle must be backed by sound scientific knowledge—for example, published studies on the time and temperatures needed to control specific foodborne pathogens.

Source: U.S. Food and Drug Administration. Available online at www.cfsan.fda.gov/~lrd/bghaccp.html/.

Figure 17.3 How does the current system for safeguarding the food supply differ from the traditional spot-checks by food safety inspectors? (Thinkstock Images/Getty Images, Inc.)

Tracking Foodborne Illness In addition to requiring the application of HACCP principles to identify and prevent potential and actual food hazards, the government has established a system for tracking foodborne illness once it has occurred. Rapid identification of the source of the contaminant that caused an outbreak of foodborne illness can help stop its spread. The National Food Safety Initiative established a national computer network linking public health laboratories. This enables epidemiologists to quickly respond to serious and widespread food contamination problems.[4] With this system, the distinctive DNA of a pathogenic strain of a microorganism can be tracked. For example, if outbreaks of foodborne illness in Ohio and Minnesota are both caused by the same strain of an organism, epidemiologists know that the outbreaks were caused by the same food source. They can focus their search for the source of contamination on foods distributed to both locations. To confirm the source, the DNA fingerprint isolated from the organisms found in people who became ill can be matched to the DNA fingerprint from a contaminated food source.

The Role of Food Manufacturers and Retailers

The responsibility of providing safe food to the marketplace falls on the shoulders of food manufacturers. It is their job to establish and implement a HAACP system for their particular business. Once in place it allows the company to anticipate where contamination might occur and to then prevent hazardous food from reaching the consumer. For example, contamination with *Salmonella* has been identified as a risk in the production of liquid egg products. To produce these products, eggs are removed from their shells; mixed together in large vats; heated, in a process called **pasteurization**, to kill *Salmonella* and other microbial contaminants; packaged; and then refrigerated or frozen. The critical control point for preventing contaminated eggs from reaching consumers is the pasteurization process. To monitor the effectiveness of pasteurization in the liquid egg industry, bacterial tests are performed on samples of eggs following pasteurization. All the eggs are held refrigerated or frozen until the results of the bacterial tests have been obtained. If the eggs are *Salmonella*-free, they are released to the market. If they contain *Salmonella*, the entire batch of eggs is discarded and pasteurization conditions are adjusted to ensure that *Salmonella* is killed in the next batch. Extensive record keeping enables the manufacturer to trace which eggs were pasteurized when, for how long, and at what temperature, and when and where they were shipped in the event of an outbreak of foodborne illness (**Figure 17.4**).

Food manufacturers are also responsible for proper labeling of their products. In addition to nutritional labeling some products also contain safe-handling labels as well as some type of product dating. A "use by" date also called a "best if used by," "freshness," or "quality assurance" date refers to the last date the product is likely to be at peak flavor, freshness, and texture. Beyond this date, the product's quality may diminish, but the food may still be safe if it has been handled and stored properly.

pasteurization The process of heating food products to kill disease-causing organisms.

Figure 17.4 Liquid egg products, which are used in institutions that must serve large numbers of people, are produced using HACCP guidelines to help ensure their safety. (Brian Leatart/Foodpix/Jupiter Images Corp)

A "sell by" or "pull by" date indicates when the grocery store should take the product off the shelf. You should buy the product before the date, but if the food has been handled and stored properly, it is usually still safe for consumption after it. For example, milk usually can be used for up to about 7 days after the sell-by date. Some foods also have an "expiration date." This is used to specify the last date that the food should be eaten or used.

Once food has left the manufacturer it goes to restaurants and other retail establishments. These businesses are responsible for preventing contaminated food from reaching the consumer. They must monitor the food that enters the establishment and prevent infected food, utensils, and employees from cross-contaminating food served to customers. In retail establishments food has many opportunities to be contaminated because of the large volume of food that is handled and the large number of people involved in food preparation. Although most of the foodborne illness in the United States is caused by food prepared in private homes, an outbreak in a commercial or institutional establishment usually involves more people at a time and is more likely to be reported.

Even when a restaurant uses extreme care in food preparation, customers can be a source of contamination. Because customers serve themselves at salad bars, cross-contamination from one customer to another is a risk. To limit this, salad and dessert bars in restaurants are usually equipped with "sneeze guards" (**Figure 17.5**).

Figure 17.5 Clear plastic shields placed above salad bars prevent customers from contaminating food with microorganisms transmitted by coughs and sneezes. (Catherine Karnow/© Corbis)

The Role of the Consumer

Consumers should be actively involved in preventing foodborne illness. Individuals must decide what foods they will consume and evaluate the risks involved. A food that has been manufactured, packaged, and transported with the greatest care can still cause foodborne illness if it is not carefully handled at home. For example, contaminated eggs, chicken, or hamburger can cause microbial foodborne illness if they are not thoroughly cooked. Just as manufacturers are asked to identify critical control points in food handling where contamination can be prevented and monitored, consumers can take a similar approach in selecting, storing, preparing, and serving food and leftovers (see Critical Thinking: Safe Picnic Choices). Consumers can also protect themselves and others by reporting incidents involving unsanitary, unsafe, deceptive, or mislabeled food to the appropriate agencies (**Table 17.3**).

Table 17.3 **How to Report Food-Related Issues**

Before reporting a suspected case of food contamination, get all the facts. Determine whether you have used the product as intended and according to the manufacturer's instruction. Check to see if the item is past its expiration date. After these steps have been taken, report the incident to the appropriate agency:

- **Problems related to any food except meat and poultry, including adverse reactions:** Report emergencies to the FDA's main emergency number, which is staffed 24 hours a day: 301–443–1240. Nonemergencies can be reported to the FDA consumer complaint coordinator in your area, which you can find at www.fda.gov/safety/reportaproblem.

- **Issues related to meat and poultry:** Report first to your state department of agriculture and then to the USDA Meat and Poultry Hotline (1–888-MPHotline or mphotline.fsis@usda.gov).

- **Restaurant food and sanitation problems:** Report directly to your local or state health department.

- **Issues related to alcoholic beverages:** Report to the U.S. Department of the Treasury's Bureau of Alcohol, Tobacco, Firearms, and Explosives.

- **Pesticide, air, and water pollution:** Report first to your state environmental protection department and then to the U.S. EPA.

- **Products purchased at the grocery store:** Return to the store. Grocery stores are concerned with the safety of the foods they sell, and they will take responsibility for tracking down and correcting the problem. They will either refund your money or replace the product.

Critical Thinking
Safe Picnic Choices

(J. Graham/Alamy)

Background

Tamika is organizing the annual class picnic. She decides to try to apply the HAACP food safety principles she learned in her food science class to keep the food safe. HAACP is designed to prevent or eliminate potential food hazards before they can make anyone sick. The first step in HAACP is to analyze the points in food preparation and storage where food contamination can occur.

Data

The picnic is a potluck so the food will be made in people's homes where most contamination occurs. Also, it is summertime so the food will sit in the temperature danger zone for several hours allowing pathogenic bacteria present in the food to multiply.

Tamika can analyze the potential for contamination in her own kitchen, but it is not possible to check every step in the preparation of each food that others are making for the picnic. She decides to find out what people are bringing and perhaps suggest some different choices if the foods seem to present a significant risk. She collects the following list of food items that her friends intend to bring:

PICNIC MENU

Chicken salad	Cheese and crackers
Tamales	Apple pie
Fruit salad	Cookies
Raw vegetables and onion dip	Mushrooms stuffed with crab meat
Chips and salsa	Fried chicken

Critical Thinking Questions

Is this picnic safe?

▼

Which foods are the least risky?

▼

Which foods carry the highest risks?

▼

What can Tamika do to reduce the risk of foodborne spoilage during the picnic?

▼

After the picnic is over, what foods would you consider safe to keep as leftovers and what would you throw out?

 iProfile Use iProfile to find the number of kcalories in your favorite picnic foods.

17.3 Pathogens in Food

Learning Objectives

- Distinguish food-borne infection from food-borne intoxication.
- Discuss three types of bacteria that commonly cause food-borne illness.
- Explain how viruses, molds, parasites, and prions can make us sick.
- Describe how careful food handling can prevent food-borne illness.

foodborne infection Illness produced by the ingestion of food containing microorganisms that can multiply inside the body and cause injurious effects.

foodborne intoxication Illness caused by consuming a food containing a toxin.

Most of the foodborne illness in the United States is caused by consuming food contaminated with pathogens (**Table 17.4**). The pathogens that most commonly affect the food supply include bacteria, viruses, molds, and parasites. An illness caused by consuming food contaminated with pathogens that multiply in the gastrointestinal tract or other parts of the body is called a **foodborne infection**. An illness caused by consuming food containing toxins produced by a pathogen is referred to as a **foodborne intoxication**. Unlike foodborne infections, which are usually caused by ingesting large numbers of pathogens, intoxication can be caused by only a few microorganisms that have produced a toxin. These food toxins may be difficult to destroy.

Table 17.4 Which Bug Has You Down?

Microbe	Sources	Symptoms	Onset	Duration
Bacteria				
Salmonella	Fecal contamination, raw or undercooked eggs and meat, especially poultry	Nausea, abdominal pain, diarrhea, headache, fever	6–48 hrs	1–2 days
Campylobacter jejuni	Unpasteurized milk, undercooked meat and poultry, untreated water	Fever, headache, diarrhea, abdominal pain	2–5 days	1–2 wks
Listeria monocytogenes	Raw milk products, soft ripened cheeses, deli meats and cold cuts, raw and undercooked poultry and meats, raw and smoked fish, raw produce	Fever, headache, stiff neck, chills, nausea, vomiting. May cause spontaneous abortion or stillbirth in pregnant women.	Days to weeks	Days to weeks
Vibrio vulnificus	Raw seafood from contaminated water	Cramps, abdominal pain, weakness, watery diarrhea, fever, chills	15–24 hrs	2–4 days
Staphylococcus aureus	Human contamination from coughs and sneezes, eggs, meat, potato and macaroni salads	Severe nausea, vomiting, diarrhea	2–8 hrs	24–48 hrs
Escherichia coli O157:H7	Fecal contamination, undercooked ground beef	Abdominal pain, bloody diarrhea, kidney failure	5–48 hrs	3 days to 2 wks or longer
Clostridium perfringens	Fecal contamination, deep-dish casseroles	Fever, nausea, diarrhea, abdominal pain	8–22 hrs	6–24 hrs
Clostridium botulinum	Canned foods, deep casseroles, honey	Lassitude, weakness, vertigo, respiratory failure, paralysis	18–36 hrs	10 days or longer (must administer antitoxin)
Bacillus cereus	Starchy foods and food mixtures such as soups and casseroles	Diarrhea, abdominal cramps, nausea, vomiting	30 min–15 hrs	24 hrs
Shigella	Fecal contamination of water or foods, especially salads such as chicken, tuna, shrimp, and potato salad	Diarrhea, abdominal pain, fever, vomiting	12–50 hrs	5–6 days
Yersinia enterocolitica	Pork, dairy products, and produce	Diarrhea, vomiting, fever, abdominal pain; often mistaken for appendicitis	24–48 hrs	Weeks
Viruses				
Noroviruses	Fecal contamination of water or foods, especially shellfish and salad ingredients	Diarrhea, nausea, vomiting	1–2 days	2–6 days
Hepatitis A virus	Human fecal contamination of food or water, raw shellfish	Jaundice, liver inflammation, fatigue, fever, nausea, anorexia, abdominal discomfort	10–50 days	1–2 wks to several months
Parasites				
Giardia lamblia	Fecal contamination of water and uncooked foods	Diarrhea, abdominal pain, gas, anorexia, nausea, vomiting	5–25 days	1–2 wks but may become chronic
Cryptosporidium parvum	Fecal contamination of food or water	Severe watery diarrhea	Hours	2–4 days but sometimes weeks
Trichinella spiralis	Undercooked pork, game meat	Muscle weakness, flu-like symptoms	Weeks	Months
Anisakis simplex	Raw fish	Severe abdominal pain	1 hr–2 wks	3 wks
Toxoplasma gondii	Meat, primarily pork	Toxoplasmosis (can cause central nervous system disorders, flu-like symptoms, and birth defects in women exposed during pregnancy)	10–23 days	May become chronic carrier

Source: U.S. Food and Drug Administration, Center for Food Safety and Nutrition. Foodborne Pathogenic Microorganisms and Natural Toxins Handbook: The "Bad Bug Book."

In most cases, the symptoms of a microbial foodborne illness include abdominal pain, nausea, diarrhea, and vomiting. These relatively mild symptoms are often mistaken for the flu. Foodborne illness can also cause more severe symptoms such as spontaneous abortion; hemolytic uremic syndrome, which can lead to kidney failure and death; and long-lasting conditions like arthritis and Guillain-Barré syndrome,

Figure 17.6 *Salmonella* can infect the ovaries of hens and contaminate the eggs before the shells are formed, so that the bacteria are present inside the shell when the eggs are laid. (B. Anthony Stewart/Getty Images, Inc.)

Life Cycle

which is the most common cause of acute paralysis. Young children, pregnant women, elderly persons, and individuals with compromised immune systems, such as patients with AIDS and cancer, are most susceptible to severe reactions. Avoiding microbial foodborne illness requires a knowledge of how contamination occurs and how to handle, store, and prepare food safely.

Bacteria

Bacteria are present in the soil, on our skin, on most surfaces in our homes, and in the food we eat. Most of the bacteria in our environment are harmless, some are beneficial, and some are pathogenic, causing disease either by growing in the body or by producing toxins in food. Pathogenic bacteria may also produce toxins within the body. Usually a large number of bacteria must be consumed to cause illness. Some common causes of bacterial infections include *Salmonella, E. coli, Campylobacter jejuni, Listeria monocytogenes,* and *Vibrio vulnificus. Staphylococcus aureus* and *Clostridium* are common causes of foodborne intoxication.

Salmonella It is estimated that 2 to 4 million people in the United States become infected with *Salmonella* each year. Most of these people just experience abdominal pain and diarrhea, but some infections are more serious.[6] *Salmonella* is found in animal and human feces and infects food through contaminated water or improper handling. *Salmonella* outbreaks have been caused by contaminated meat, meat products, dairy products, seafood, fresh vegetables, and cereal, but poultry and eggs are the most common food sources. Poultry products are often contaminated because poultry farms house large numbers of chickens in close proximity, allowing one infected chicken to infect thousands of others (**Figure 17.6**). One way to reduce infection is to spray chicks with beneficial bacteria. The chicks ingest the bacteria when they preen their feathers and the beneficial bacteria colonize the digestive tract leaving no room for pathogens.

Even if food contaminated with *Salmonella* is brought into the kitchen, careful handling and cooking of the food can prevent the organisms from causing illness. Washing hands, cutting boards, and utensils can prevent cross-contamination. If a contaminated food is stored in the refrigerator, the multiplication of the *Salmonella* will be slowed. In contrast, if a contaminated food is left at room temperature, the *Salmonella* will multiply rapidly, and when the food is eaten, large numbers of bacteria will be ingested with it (**Figure 17.7**). *Salmonella* is killed by heat—so foods likely to be contaminated, such as poultry and eggs, should be cooked thoroughly.

Figure 17.7 Exponential bacterial growth
The size of a population of bacterial cells doubles each time the cells divide; thus, if 10 bacterial cells contaminate an egg salad sandwich during preparation and it sits in your warm car for 4 hours, during which the cells divide every 20 minutes, there will be 40,960 bacterial cells in the sandwich by the time you eat it. (© Snowflake Studios/StockFood America)

Escherichia coli (E. coli) *Escherichia coli* (*E. coli*) is a bacterium that inhabits the gastrointestinal tracts of humans and other animals. It comes in contact with food through fecal contamination of water or unsanitary handling of food. Some strains of *E. coli* are harmless, but others can cause serious foodborne illness. One strain of *E. coli*, found in water contaminated by human or animal feces, is the cause of "travelers' diarrhea." Another strain, *E. coli* O157:H7, produces a toxin that causes abdominal pain, bloody diarrhea, and, in severe cases, hemolytic uremic syndrome, which can lead to kidney failure and even death. *E. coli* O157:H7 can live in the intestines of healthy cattle and contaminate the meat after slaughter. This strain was responsible for the deaths of several children who consumed undercooked, contaminated hamburgers from a fast-food chain in 1993. In 1996, lettuce contaminated with *E. coli* O157:H7 caused illness in 71 people.[7] Transmission of *E. coli* is also a risk at day-care centers from cross-contamination if caregivers do not carefully wash their hands after diaper changes.

Although *E. coli* on food can multiply slowly, even at refrigerator temperatures, if a contaminated food is thoroughly cooked to 160°F, both the bacteria and the toxin are destroyed. Ground beef contaminated with *E. coli* O157:H7 is a particular risk because, unlike other meats that are likely only to be contaminated on the surface, the grinding mixes the bacteria throughout the meat (**Figure 17.8**). The *E. coli* on the outside of the meat are quickly killed during cooking, but those in the interior survive if the meat is not cooked thoroughly.

Figure 17.8 Meat grinders and *E. coli* contamination
E. coli-contaminated meat that comes into contact with a grinder may contaminate hundreds of pounds of ground beef. During grinding the bacteria is mixed throughout the meat.

Campylobacter There are several species of *Campylobacter* that cause foodborne infections: *Campylobacter jejuni* causes most cases of the illness. *Campylobacter* infection is now the leading cause of bacterial diarrheal illness in the United States, affecting an estimated 2 million people each year.[8] Common sources are undercooked chicken, unpasteurized milk, and untreated water. This organism grows slowly in the cold and is killed by heat, so, as with *Salmonella*, thorough cooking and careful storage help prevent infection.

Life Cycle

Listeria Another cause of bacterial foodborne infection is *Listeria monocytogenes*. Although most cases of *Listeria* infection result in flu-like symptoms, in high-risk groups such as pregnant women, children, the elderly, and the immunocompromised, it can cause meningitis and serious blood infections and has one of the highest fatality rates of all foodborne illnesses. Each year in the United States, an estimated 2,500 persons become seriously ill due to infection with *Listeria monocytogenes*, and of these, 500 die.[9] *Listeria* is a very resistant organism that survives at higher and lower temperatures than most bacteria; it can survive and grow at refrigerator temperatures. *Listeria* frequently contaminates dairy products, but it is destroyed by pasteurization. It is found in processed ready-to-eat foods such as hot dogs and lunchmeats. Because consumers consider ready-to-eat foods safe, they often do not handle them as carefully as raw foods. To prevent infection, ready-to-eat meats should be heated to steaming and unpasteurized dairy products should be avoided.

Vibrio *Vibrio vulnificus* and *Vibrio parahaemolyticus* are two species of *Vibrio* bacteria that cause vomiting, diarrhea, and abdominal pain in healthy people and can be deadly if they infect people with compromised immune systems. The most common way people become infected is by eating raw or undercooked shellfish, particularly oysters. *Vibrio* bacteria grow in warm seawater, so the incidence of *Vibrio* infection is higher during the summer months, when warm water favors growth.

Staphylococcus aureus *Staphylococcus aureus* is a common cause of microbial foodborne intoxication. These bacteria live in human nasal passages and can be transferred through coughing or sneezing when handling food. The bacteria then produce toxins as they grow on the food. When ingested the toxin causes symptoms, which include nausea, vomiting, diarrhea, abdominal cramps, and headache. Foods that are common sources of *Staphylococcus aureus* include cooked ham, salads, bakery products, and dairy products.

Clostridium perfringens The bacterium *Clostridium perfringens* may cause illness by both infection and intoxication. It is found in soil and in the intestines of animals and humans. It thrives in conditions with little oxygen (anaerobic conditions) and is difficult to kill because it forms heat-resistant **spores**. Spores are a stage of bacterial life that remains dormant until environmental conditions favor growth. *Clostridium perfringens* is often called the "cafeteria germ" because foods stored in large containers, such as those used to serve food in cafeteria lines, have anaerobic centers that provide an excellent growth environment. Sources include improperly prepared roast beef, turkey, pork, chicken, and ground beef.

spore A dormant state of some bacteria that is resistant to heat but can germinate and produce a new organism when environmental conditions are favorable.

Clostridium botulinum Another strain of *Clostridium*, *Clostridium botulinum*, produces the deadliest bacterial foodborne toxin. Although the bacteria themselves are not harmful, the toxin, produced as the bacteria begin to grow and develop, blocks nerve function, resulting in vomiting, abdominal pain, double vision, dizziness, and paralysis causing respiratory failure. If untreated, botulism poisoning is often fatal, but today modern detection methods and rapid administration of antitoxin have reduced mortality. Low-acid foods, such as potatoes or stews, that are held in anaerobic conditions provide an optimal environment for botulism spores to germinate. Canned foods, particularly improperly home-canned foods, can also be a source of botulism. Canned foods should be discarded if the can is bulging because this indicates the presence of gas produced by bacteria as they grow. Once formed, botulism toxin can be destroyed by boiling, but if the safety of a food is in question, it should be discarded; even a taste of botulism toxin can be deadly.

Infant botulism is a type of botulism that is seen only in infants. Though rare, it occurs worldwide and is the most common form of botulism in the United States.[10] It occurs when ingested botulism spores germinate in the gastrointestinal tract, producing toxin, some of which is absorbed into the bloodstream causing weakness, paralysis, and respiratory problems. In the absence of complications, infants generally recover. Only infants get botulism from ingesting spores because in adults, competing intestinal microflora prevent spores from germinating. Because botulism spores can contaminate honey, it should never be fed to infants under 1 year of age (**Figure 17.9**).

Viruses

Viruses make us ill by entering our cells and converting them into virus-making factories (**Figure 17.10**). The viruses that cause human disease cannot grow and reproduce in foods, but the virus particle can contaminate food and then infect the consumer when the food is eaten.

Noroviruses Noroviruses are a group of viruses that cause gastroenteritis, or what we commonly think of as the "stomach flu." Symptoms usually involve more vomiting than diarrhea and resolve within 2 days. Noroviruses, which include caliciviruses and Norwalk-like viruses, are an extremely common cause of foodborne illness, but the technology to diagnose the infection was not available until the early 1990s. Noroviruses are now recognized as the most common cause of infectious gastroenteritis among persons of all ages and are believed to be responsible for about 50% of all foodborne gastroenteritis outbreaks in the United States.[11] Noroviruses spread primarily from one infected person to another, but they can also be spread by eating food that is contaminated with the virus or by touching a contaminated surface and

Life Cycle

Figure 17.9 Why are *Clostridium botulinum* spores in honey dangerous only to babies under 1 year old? (Caroline Kopp/Foodpix/Jupiter Images Corp)

viruses Minute particles not visible under an ordinary microscope that depend on cells for their metabolic and reproductive needs.

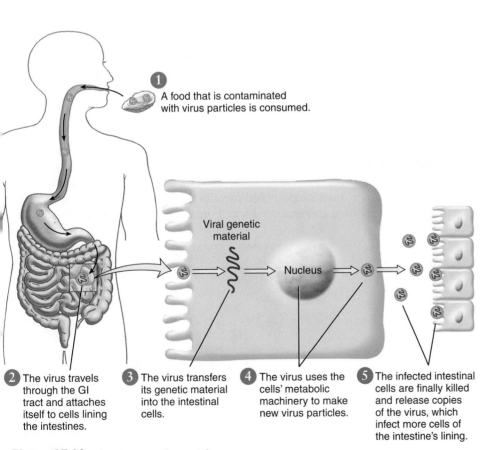

① A food that is contaminated with virus particles is consumed.

② The virus travels through the GI tract and attaches itself to cells lining the intestines.

③ The virus transfers its genetic material into the intestinal cells.

④ The virus uses the cells' metabolic machinery to make new virus particles.

⑤ The infected intestinal cells are finally killed and release copies of the virus, which infect more cells of the intestine's lining.

Viral genetic material

Nucleus

Figure 17.10 How viruses make us sick
Viruses make us sick by reproducing inside our cells. Viruses that cause food-borne illness enter the body through the gastrointestinal tract. Other types of viruses may enter the body through open cuts, the respiratory tract, or the genital tract.

Figure 17.11 Mold can grow at refrigerator temperatures and it will grow on almost anything if it remains in the refrigerator long enough. (Charles D. Winters)

then putting your fingers in your mouth. If kitchen workers have the virus on their hands they can contaminate a salad or sandwich as they prepare it. Infected fishermen can contaminate oysters as they harvest them. Shellfish can also become contaminated with norovirus if the water where they live is polluted with human or animal feces. Worldwide about one in ten oysters is believed to be contaminated.[12] Because noroviruses are destroyed by cooking, water and uncooked foods such as raw shellfish and salads are the most common cause of norovirus foodborne illness.

Hepatitis A Hepatitis A is a highly contagious viral disorder that causes inflammation of the liver, jaundice, fever, nausea, fatigue, and abdominal pain. It can be contracted from food contaminated by unsanitary handling or from eating raw or undercooked shellfish caught in sewage-contaminated waters. Hepatitis A can require a recovery period of several months, but it usually does not require treatment and does not cause permanent liver damage. Hepatitis in drinking water is destroyed by chlorination. Cooking destroys the virus in food, and good sanitation can prevent its spread. A vaccine that protects against hepatitis A infection is available.

Molds

mold Multicellular fungi that form a filamentous branching growth.

Many types of **mold** grow on foods such as bread, cheese, and fruit (**Figure 17.11**). Molds produce toxins that can lead to food intoxication. More than 250 different mold toxins have been identified. Aflatoxin is a mold toxin that is among the most potent mutagens and carcinogens known. It is produced by the mold *Aspergillus flavus*. This mold commonly grows on corn, rice, wheat, peanuts, almonds, walnuts, sunflower seeds, and spices such as black pepper and coriander. The level of aflatoxin that may be present in foods in the United States is regulated to prevent toxicity. Another mold that produces toxins and contaminates grain, particularly rye, is ergot. It causes hallucinations and is a natural source of the hallucinogenic drug LSD. Today, modern milling removes the part of the grain that harbors the mold, so the disease ergotism is rare. Cooking and freezing stops mold growth but does not destroy the mold toxins that have already been produced. If a food is moldy, it should be discarded, the area where it was stored should be cleaned, and neighboring foods should be checked to see if they have also become contaminated.

Parasites

parasites Organisms that live at the expense of others.

Some **parasites** are tiny single-celled animals, while others are worms that are easily seen with the naked eye. Parasites are killed by thorough cooking. They may be transmitted through consumption of contaminated food and water. *Giardia lamblia* (also called *Giardia duodenalis*) is a single-celled parasite that can infect the gastrointestinal tract through water or food contaminated with human or animal feces (**Figure 17.12**).

Figure 17.12 This electron micrograph shows *Giardia* (green) attached to the microvilli of the human small intestine. (CNRI/Science Photo Library/Photo Researchers)

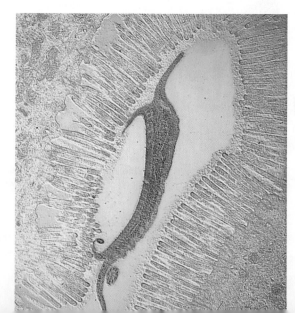

It is the most frequent cause of diarrhea not due to bacteria.[6] *Giardia* is sometimes contracted by hikers who drink untreated water from streams contaminated with animal feces, and it is becoming a problem from cross-contamination in day-care centers. *Cryptosporidium parvum* is another single-celled parasite that is commonly spread by contaminated water, but cases have also been reported from consuming unpasteurized apple cider and contaminated raw fruits and vegetables.[13,14]

Trichinella spiralis is a parasite found in raw and undercooked pork, pork products, and game meats, particularly bear. Once ingested, these small, worm-like organisms find their way to the muscles, where they grow, causing flu-like symptoms, muscle weakness, fever, and fluid retention. Trichinosis, the disease caused by *Trichinella* infection, can be prevented by thoroughly cooking meat to kill the parasite before it is ingested. The parasites are also destroyed by curing, smoking, canning, or freezing.

Fish are another common source of parasitic infections. Fish can carry the larvae (the worm-like stage of an organism's life cycle) of parasites such as roundworms, flatworms, flukes, and tapeworms. One such infection, Anisakis disease, is caused by the larval form of the small roundworm *Anisakis simplex*, or herring worm, found in raw fish.[6] Once consumed, these parasites invade the stomach and intestinal tract, causing severe abdominal pain. The fresher the fish is when it is eviscerated, the less likely it is to cause this disease because the larvae move from the fish's stomach to its flesh only after the fish dies. Parasitic infections from fish can be avoided by consuming cooked fish or freezing fish for 72 hours before consumption. If raw fish is consumed, it should be very fresh (**Figure 17.13**).

Figure 17.13 As the popularity of eating raw fish, such as this sushi, has increased so has the incidence of parasitic infections from fish. (Hoi Fung Tsoi/Getty Images, Inc.)

Prions

The strangest, scariest, yet rarest food-borne illness is caused not by a microbe but by a protein, called a **prion**, short for proteinaceous infectious particle. Abnormal prions are believed to be the cause of mad cow disease, or bovine spongiform encephalopathy (BSE), a deadly degenerative neurological disease that affects cattle. A human form of this disease, called variant Creutzfeldt-Jakob disease (vCJD), has been identified. People are believed to contract it by eating tissue from a cow infected with BSE (see Your Choice: Should You Bypass the Beef?).[15] Symptoms of vCJD begin as mood swings and numbness, and within about 14 months the nervous tissue damage progresses to dementia and death.

The abnormal prions that cause BSE and vCJD differ from normal proteins in the way they are folded—that is, in their three-dimensional structure. These rogue proteins reproduce by corrupting neighboring proteins, essentially changing their shape, so they too become abnormal prions (**Figure 17.14**). Because the abnormal prion proteins are not degraded normally, they accumulate and form clumps called plaques. These plaques cause the deadly nervous tissue damage.

prion A pathogenic protein that is the cause of degenerative brain diseases called spongiform encephalopathies.

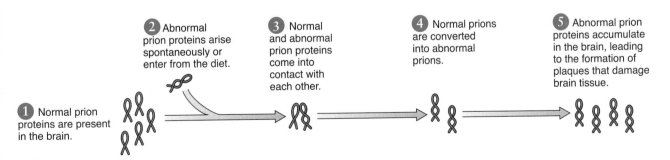

1 Normal prion proteins are present in the brain.

2 Abnormal prion proteins arise spontaneously or enter from the diet.

3 Normal and abnormal prion proteins come into contact with each other.

4 Normal prions are converted into abnormal prions.

5 Abnormal prion proteins accumulate in the brain, leading to the formation of plaques that damage brain tissue.

Figure 17.14 How prions multiply
Abnormal prions can reproduce by coming in contact with normal prion proteins and causing them to fold abnormally.

Figure 17.15 Fight Bac!
The Fight Bac! educational campaign recommends that consumers follow four steps—clean, separate, cook, and chill—to prevent foodborne illness.

Reducing the Risk of Microbial Foodborne Illness

Despite the variety of organisms that can cause foodborne illness, most cases can be avoided if food is handled properly (**Figure 17.15**; see **Table 17.5**). The first critical control point in preventing foodborne illness is making safe selections at the store to reduce the contaminants that are brought into the home. Food should come from reputable vendors and appear fresh. Foods that are discolored or smell contaminated and those in damaged packages should not be purchased or consumed.

Table 17.5 Tips for Handling Food Safely

Choose foods wisely

Voluntary freshness dates should be checked and foods with expired dates avoided. Jars should be closed and seals unbroken. Cans that are rusted, dented, or bulging should be rejected. Frozen foods should not contain frost or ice crystals, and food packaging should be secure. Frozen foods should be selected from below the frost line in the freezer. When shopping, cold foods should be purchased last.

Store foods properly

Fresh or frozen foods brought from the store should be refrigerated or frozen immediately at the proper temperature. Food that has been in your refrigerator for longer than is safe should be discarded.

Wash

Hands, cooking utensils, and surfaces should be washed with warm soapy water before each food preparation step. This will prevent cross-contamination.

Thaw

Foods should be thawed in the refrigerator or microwave.

Cook thoroughly

Cooking temperatures should be checked. Thorough cooking destroys most bacteria, toxins, viruses, and parasites.

Refrigerate promptly

Cooked food can be recontaminated, so it should be refrigerated as soon as possible after it is served.

Reheat thoroughly

Foods should be reheated to 165°F to destroy microorganisms that have recontaminated cooked foods and toxins that have been produced.

When in doubt, throw it out.

YOUR CHOICE

Should You Bypass the Beef?

In December 2003 it was announced that a case of mad cow disease, or bovine spongiform encephalopathy (BSE), had been identified in the United States. The agent that causes BSE and variant Creutzfeldt-Jakob disease (vCJD), the human form of the disease, is a protein called a prion. Prions in food cannot be killed, because they aren't alive. Prions can be passed from an infected animal to an uninfected host, most likely from consumption of a food contaminated with central nervous system tissue.[1] BSE is believed to have originated from sheep that carried a similar disease, called scrapie. It moved into cattle in Britain when they were fed protein supplements containing the remains of slaughtered, diseased sheep. The disease was then passed to people when they ate products from infected cows. The only way to determine if a cow is infected with BSE is to kill the animal and analyze its brain tissue, by which time its meat could be on the shelf. Should this cattle disease affect what you choose to eat?

To prevent people from getting vCJD, we need to prevent cows from getting BSE and prevent humans from eating products from infected cows. Safeguards that have been in place for some time have helped keep U.S. beef BSE-free. Since 1997 the USDA has restricted the import of ruminants and most ruminant products from Europe, where BSE was first identified.[2] The practice of including proteins from cows and other ruminants in protein supplements fed to cows also was banned. Other precautions that were put in place included increasing the number of cows tested at slaughter and holding products from cattle being tested until the results of tests are in. In addition, material from cows that can't walk (downer cows) is banned from the food supply; high-risk tissues such as brain, spinal cord, eyes, and intestines are kept out of the human food supply; and only slaughter methods that do not cause brain tissue to contaminate other parts of the cow are used.[2]

Even though cooking does not destroy prions, the risk of contracting vCJD is extremely small; meat (if free of central nervous system tissue) and milk have not been demonstrated to transmit BSE or vCJD. The meat from cows identified with BSE in the United States has not entered the food supply and thus far there has been no known instance of U.S. beef causing a case of vCJD. Even in Britain, where over 180,000 cows were infected, only about 167 definite or probable cases of vCJD have been identified.[4] If you love your burgers, be assured that precautions taken by U.S. agencies will continue to keep infected meat from reaching the shelves.

(Alan Carey/Photo Researchers)

---

[1]U.S. Food and Drug Administration, Center for Food Safety and Nutrition. *Foodborne Pathogenic Microorganisms and Natural Toxins Handbook: The "Bad Bug Book."* Available online at www.fda.gov/Food/FoodSafety/Foodborneillness/FoodborneillnessFoodbornePathogensNaturalToxins/BadBugBook/default.htm. Accessed October 5, 2009.

[2]Food and Drug Administration. Bovine Spongeform Encephalopathy (BSE). Available online at www.fda.gov/oc/opacom/hottopics/bse.html. Accessed August 8, 2009.

[3]The National Creutzfeldt-Jakob Disease Surveillance Unit. University of Edinburgh. Available online at www.cjd.ed.ac.uk/. Accessed October 5, 2009.

Canning temperature for low-acid foods in pressure cooker

Range of cooking temperatures to kill most bacteria. The amount of time needed decreases as the temperature increases.

Minimum temperature for reheating foods. Warming temperatures control growth but allow survival of some bacteria.

Some growth may occur: Many bacteria survive.

Danger Zone
Temperatures in this zone allow rapid bacterial growth and production of bacterial toxins. Foods should only be allowed to remain in this temperature range for minimal amounts of time.

Some bacterial growth may occur in this zone.

Cold temperatures allow slow growth for a few cold-tolerant organisms but stop the growth of most.

Freezing temperatures prevent bacterial growth but some bacteria are able to survive.

Figure 17.16 Effect of temperature on bacterial growth Bacterial growth is most rapid between 40° and 135°F.

Store Food Properly Once selected, foods need to be stored appropriately. The goal is to keep foods from remaining at temperatures that promote bacterial growth (**Figure 17.16**). Cold foods should be kept cold, at 40°F or less, and hot foods should be kept hot, at more than 135°F. Refrigerator temperature should be set between 38° and 40°F and freezers at 0°F. Produce should be stored in the refrigerator. Fresh meat, poultry, and fish should be frozen immediately if it will not be used within a day or two. Processed meats such as hot dogs and bologna must also be kept refrigerated but can be kept longer than fresh meat (**Table 17.6**).

Prevent Cross-Contamination The next critical control point for food in the home is preparation. A clean kitchen is essential for safe food preparation. Hands, countertops, cutting boards, and utensils should be washed with warm soapy water before each food preparation step. Food should be thawed in the refrigerator, in the microwave oven, or under running water—not at room temperature. Foods that are eaten raw should not be prepared on the same surfaces as foods that are going to be cooked. For example, if a chicken contaminated with *Salmonella* is cut up on a cutting board and the unwashed cutting board is then used to chop vegetables for a salad, the vegetables will become contaminated with *Salmonella*. When the chicken is cooked, the bacteria will be killed, but the contaminated vegetables are not cooked, so the bacteria can grow and cause foodborne illness. Cross-contamination can also occur when uncooked foods containing live microbes come in contact with foods that have already been cooked. Therefore, cooked meat should never be returned to the same dish that held the raw meat, and sauces used to marinate uncooked foods should never be used as a sauce on cooked food. To remind consumers how to handle meat, the packaging is labeled with safe handling guidelines (**Figure 17.17**).

Figure 17.17 Meat labels offer safe handling guidelines. (Dennis Drenner)

Cook Food Thoroughly Cooking is one of the most important critical control points in preventing foodborne illness. Heat will destroy most harmful microorganisms. A meat thermometer should be used when cooking meat because color

Table 17.6 How Long Can Food Be Safely Stored?

Product	Refrigerator (40°F)	Freezer (0°F)
Eggs		
Fresh, in shell	3 wks	Don't freeze
Raw yolks, white	2–4 days	1 yr
Hardcooked	1 week	Don't freeze
TV dinners, frozen casseroles	Keep frozen until ready to serve	3–4 mos
Soups & stews with vegetables or meat	3–4 days	2–3 mos
Hamburger, ground, & stew meats		
Hamburger & stew meats	1–2 days	3–4 mos
Ground turkey, veal, pork, lamb & mixtures of these	1–2 days	3–4 mos
Hotdogs		
Opened package	1 wk	In freezer wrap, 1–2 mos
Unopened package	2 wks	In freezer wrap, 1–2 mos
Lunch meats		
Opened	3–5 days	In freezer wrap, 1–2 mos
Unopened	2 wks	In freezer wrap, 1–2 mos
Bacon & sausage		
Bacon	7 days	1 mo
Sausage, raw from pork, beef, turkey	1–2 days	1–2 mos
Smoked breakfast links, patties	7 days	1–2 mos
Ham		
Ham, canned—label says keep refrigerated	6–9 mos	Don't freeze
Ham, fully cooked—whole	7 days	1–2 mos
Ham, fully cooked—slices	3–4 days	1–2 mos
Fresh Meat and Poultry		
Steaks, beef	3–5 days	6–12 mos
Chops, pork	3–5 days	4–6 mos
Chops, lamb	3–5 days	6–9 mos
Roasts, beef	3–5 days	6–12 mos
Roasts, pork & veal	3–5 days	4–6 mos
Chicken or turkey, whole	1–2 days	1 yr
Chicken or turkey pieces	1–2 days	9 mos
Meat and Poultry Leftovers		
Cooked meat & meat dishes	3–4 days	2–3 mos
Fried chicken	3–4 days	4 mos
Cooked poultry dishes	3–4 days	4–6 mos
Chicken nuggets, patties	1–2 days	1–3 mos

Source: Partnership for Food Safety Education. Available online at www.fightbac.org/doubt.cfm/.

is not always a good indicator of safety (**Table 17.7**). Fish should be cooked until the flesh is opaque and separates easily with a fork. Eggs should not be eaten raw, since *Salmonella* can contaminate the inside of the shell; they should be cooked until the yolk and white are firm.

Cooked food should be refrigerated as soon as possible after serving. The best temperatures for bacterial growth are the temperatures at which food is usually kept between service and storage. Large portions of food should be divided before

Table 17.7 What Cooking Temperatures Are Safe?

Food Item	Internal Temperature (°F) or Description
Beef, veal, lamb	
Ground products	160
Nonground products	
Medium-rare	145
Medium	160
Well done	170
Poultry	
Ground products	165
Whole bird and poultry parts	165
Stuffing (cooked alone or in a bird)	165
Pork	
Noncured products	
Medium	160
Well done	170
Ham	
Fresh (raw)	160
Pre-cooked (to reheat)	140
Eggs & egg dishes	
Eggs	Cook until yolk and white are firm
Egg dishes	160
Fish & shellfish	
Fish	145 or until flesh is opaque and flakes easily
Shrimp, lobster, crab	Cook until flesh is pearly and opaque
Scallops	Cook until milky white or opaque and firm
Clams, mussels, oysters	Cook until shells open
Leftovers & Casseroles	165

Source: Partnership for Food Safety Education. *Cook to Safe Temperature*. Available online at www.fightbac.org/images/pdfs/cook.pdf.

refrigeration so they will cool quickly. Most leftovers should only be kept for a few days. For example, cooked pasta can be kept refrigerated for 3 to 5 days; cooked beef, poultry, pork, vegetables, soup, and stews for 3 to 4 days; and stuffing and meat in gravy for 1 to 2 days. When leftovers are reheated, they should be heated to 165°F to destroy any bacteria that may have grown in them.

Food Safety Away from Home When you prepare your own food you can monitor the safety of the ingredients and food preparation steps, but at restaurants, picnics, and potlucks, you must rely on others to keep your food safe. Consumers should choose restaurants with safety in mind. Restaurants should be clean, and cooked foods should be served hot. Cafeteria steam tables should be kept hot enough that the water is steaming and food is kept above 135°F. Cold foods such as salad bar items should be kept refrigerated or on ice to keep food at 41°F or colder.

Picnics, potlucks, and other large events where food is served provide a prime opportunity for microbes to flourish because food is often left at room temperature or in the sun for hours before it is consumed. Foods that last well without refrigeration, such as fresh fruits and vegetables, breads, and crackers, should be selected for these occasions (see Critical Thinking: Safe Picnic Choices).

Food safety is also a concern when food must be carried out of the home. Any food that is transported should be kept cold. Lunches should be transported to and from work or school in a cooler or an insulated bag. They should be refrigerated upon arrival or kept cold with ice packs. Most foods that are brought home from work or school uneaten should be thrown out and not saved for another day.

17.4 Chemical Contaminants in Food

Learning Objectives

- Illustrate how contaminants move through the food chain and into our foods.
- Compare the risks and benefits of using pesticides with those of growing food organically.
- Describe how to minimize the risks of exposure to chemical contaminants.

Chemicals used in agricultural production and industrial wastes contaminate the environment and can find their way into the food supply. How harmful these chemicals are depends on how long they remain in the environment and whether they are stored in the organisms that consume them or can be broken down and excreted by these organisms. Some contaminants are eliminated from the environment quickly because they are broken down by microorganisms or chemical reactions. Others remain in the environment for very long periods, and when taken up by plants and small animals, they are not metabolized or excreted. For example, fat-soluble contaminants concentrate in body fat and cannot be excreted. When these plants or small animals are consumed by larger animals that are in turn eaten by still larger animals, the contaminants accumulate, reaching higher concentrations at each level of the food chain (**Figure 17.18**). This process is called **bioaccumulation**. Because the toxins are not eliminated from the body, the greater the amount consumed, the greater the amount present in the body.

bioaccumulation The process by which compounds accumulate or build up in an organism faster than they can be broken down or excreted.

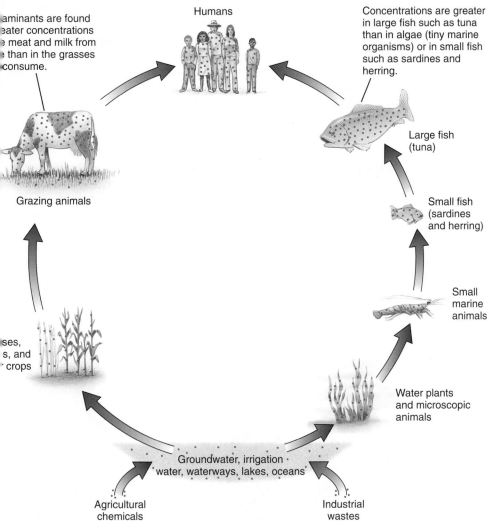

Humans

...aminants are found ...eater concentrations ...e meat and milk from ...e than in the grasses ...consume.

Grazing animals

...ses, ...s, and ...crops

Groundwater, irrigation water, waterways, lakes, oceans

Agricultural chemicals

Industrial wastes

Water plants and microscopic animals

Small marine animals

Small fish (sardines and herring)

Large fish (tuna)

Concentrations are greater in large fish such as tuna than in algae (tiny marine organisms) or in small fish such as sardines and herring.

Figure 17.18 Contaminants in the food chain
Industrial pollutants and agricultural chemicals that contaminate the water supply enter the food chain and accumulate as they are passed through the chain. An animal that occupies a higher level in the food chain has higher concentrations of these contaminants because it consumes all the contaminants that have been eaten by organisms at lower feeding levels.

Risks and Benefits of Pesticides

Pesticides are applied to crops growing in the field to prevent plant diseases and insect infestations and to produce after harvesting to prevent spoilage and extend shelf life. Crops grown using pesticides generally produce higher yields and look more appealing because insect damage is limited. Residues of these chemicals remain on the fruits and vegetables that reach consumers. Pesticides can also travel from the fields where they are applied into water supplies, soil, and other parts of the environment, so pesticide residues are found not only on treated produce but also in meat, poultry, fish, and dairy products.[16]

Regulating Pesticides In order to protect public health and the environment the types of pesticides that can be used on food crops, how often they may be used, and the amount of residue that can remain when foods reach consumers, are regulated. Before a pesticide can be used in food production it must be approved and registered by the Environmental Protection Agency (EPA). A major consideration in approving pesticides is whether they pose an unreasonable risk to humans. To determine this, the EPA assesses the risks associated with individual pesticides and with groups of pesticides that have a common toxic effect. The EPA also establishes maximum pesticide residue limits in food, or **tolerances**. In setting the tolerance the EPA must determine that the pesticide can be used with a "reasonable certainty of no harm." The EPA considers the known incidence of toxicity and the predicted exposure that consumers will have to the toxin. Tolerance levels are then set at the minimum amount of the pesticide needed to be effective; these levels are often several hundred times lower than the level found to cause harm in test animals.[16] To protect children, for whom the same amount of pesticide provides a larger dose per unit of body weight, the EPA is required to set tolerances that are safe for children as well as adults.[16] The FDA and U.S. Department of Agriculture (USDA) then monitor pesticide residues in foods.

In general, the amounts of pesticides to which people are exposed through foods are small. According to the FDA's pesticide residue monitoring program, pesticide residue levels in both domestic and imported foods are well below federally permitted limits (**Figure 17.19**).[17,18] Despite this, some individuals and special-interest groups are concerned that the pesticides remaining on foods do pose a risk to human health. Repeated consumption of large doses of any one pesticide could be harmful, but this is unlikely because most people consume a variety of foods produced using many different pesticides.

Reducing Pesticide Risks To reduce the risks posed by pesticides, new, more effective chemical pesticides are being developed, and the use of older, more toxic products is decreasing in the United States. One class of pesticide that is less likely to be harmful is biopesticides. These include naturally occurring substances that control pests, microorganisms that control pests, and pesticidal substances that are produced by plants through **genetic engineering**. In addition to developing safer pesticides, production methods are being implemented to make low-pesticide and pesticide-free produce available to the consumer.

tolerances The maximum amount of pesticide residues that may legally remain in food, set by the EPA.

Life Cycle

genetic engineering A set of techniques used to manipulate DNA for the purpose of changing the characteristics of an organism or creating a new product.

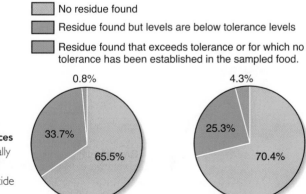

Figure 17.19 Pesticide tolerances An analysis of samples of domestically produced food and imported food from 100 countries found no pesticide residues in 65.5% of domestic and 70.4% of import samples.

Natural Toxins Many toxins that occur in plants function as natural pesticides that offer protection from bacteria, molds, and insect pests. These naturally pest-resistant crops are advantageous in developing countries because they thrive without the use of expensive added pesticides. Plants high in natural pesticides are being produced through special breeding programs as well as genetic engineering. The natural toxins in plants can also be isolated and applied to crops like synthetic pesticides.

As with all chemical toxins, natural toxins move through the food supply. For example, a cow that has foraged on toxic plants can pass the toxin into her milk and poison the consumer of the milk. Abraham Lincoln's mother died from drinking milk from a cow that had eaten poisonous snakeroot plants. The potential for toxicity, however, depends on the dose of toxin and the health of the consumer. Most natural toxins in the food supply are consumed in doses that pose little risk to the consumer.

Integrated Pest Management **Integrated pest management (IPM)** is a method of agricultural pest control that combines chemical and nonchemical methods and emphasizes the use of natural toxins and effective pesticide application. For example, increasing the use of naturally pest-resistant crop varieties that thrive without the use of added pesticides can reduce costs and do less environmental damage. Integrated pest management programs use information about the life cycles of pests and their interactions with the environment to manage pest damage economically, and with the least possible hazard to people, property, and the environment.

Organic Techniques **Organic food** production methods emphasize the recycling of resources and the conservation of soil and water to protect the environment. Organic food is produced without using most conventional pesticides, fertilizers made with synthetic ingredients, sewage sludge, genetically modified ingredients, irradiation, antibiotics, or growth hormones.

Organic farming techniques reduce the exposure of farm workers to pesticides and decrease the quantity of pesticides introduced into the food supply and the environment. However, organic foods are not risk-free. Manure is often used for fertilizer and runoff can pollute lakes and streams. If the manure is not treated properly, the food crop can be contaminated with bacteria that cause foodborne illness. Irrigation water, rain, and a variety of other sources can introduce traces of synthetic pesticides and other agricultural chemicals not approved for organic use into organically grown foods. The threshold for pesticide residues in organic foods is set at 5% of the EPA's pesticide-residue tolerance.[19] In addition, organic foods are usually more expensive and available in less variety than conventionally grown foods.

The USDA's National Organic Program has developed standards for organic foods. These national standards define both substances approved for and prohibited from use in organic food production. For example, an organic food may not include ingredients that are treated with irradiation, produced by genetic modification, or grown using sewage sludge or industrially synthesized fertilizers and pesticides. Certain natural pesticides and other manufactured agents are permitted. Farming and processing operations that produce and handle foods labeled as organic must be certified by the USDA. Products meeting the definition of "100% organic" or "organic" may display the USDA organic seal shown in **Figure 17.20** (see also **Table 17.8**).

integrated pest management (IPM) A method of agricultural pest control that integrates nonchemical and chemical techniques.

organic food Food that is produced, processed, and handled in accordance with the standards of the USDA National Organic Program.

Figure 17.20 The USDA organic seal can appear on the label of agricultural products that meet the definition of "100% organic" or "organic."

Table 17.8 Labeling of Organic Foods

Labeling Term	Meaning
100% organic	Contains (by weight or fluid volume, excluding water and salt) 100% organically produced raw or processed ingredients. May display USDA seal.
Organic	Contains (by weight or fluid volume, excluding water and salt) not less than 95% organically produced raw or processed agricultural products. May display USDA seal.
Made with organic ingredients	Contains (by weight or fluid volume, excluding water and salt) at least 70% organically produced ingredients. Cannot display USDA seal.

Figure 17.21 Milk from cows treated with genetically engineered bovine somatotropin is indistinguishable from other milk, but dairies that do not use bovine somatotropin may choose to indicate this on their labels. (Courtesy Lori Smolin)

polychlorinated biphenyls (PCBs) Carcinogenic industrial compounds that have found their way into the environment and, subsequently, the food supply. Repeated ingestion causes them to accumulate in biological tissues over time.

Life Cycle

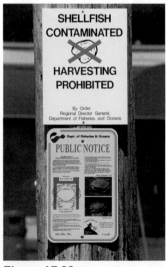

Figure 17.22 It is unsafe to consume shellfish from contaminated waters. (Paul A. Souders/© Corbis)

Antibiotics and Hormones in Food

Animals, like humans, are treated with antibiotics when they are sick. In addition, some animals are given antibiotics to prevent disease and to promote growth. This increases the amount of meat produced and reduces costs, but if used improperly, residues of these drugs can remain in the meat. To prevent passing these chemicals on to consumers, the FDA regulates which drugs can be used to treat animals used for food production and when they can be administered.[20] The USDA monitors tissue samples for drug residues.

Antibiotic use in animals may also contribute to the creation of antibiotic-resistant bacteria. When bacteria are exposed to an antibiotic, those that are resistant to that antibiotic survive and produce offspring that also carry the antibiotic resistance trait. If these resistant bacteria infect humans, the resulting illness cannot be treated with that antibiotic. Since nearly half the antibiotics produced in the United States are used to prevent disease in animals, this use is suspected of being a major contributor to the development of antibiotic-resistant strains of bacteria.[21]

Hormones are used to increase weight gain in sheep and cattle and milk production in dairy cows. Some naturally occurring hormones such as estrogen and testosterone are used in slow-release form, and levels in the treated animals are no higher than in untreated animals. Before synthetic hormones can be used, it must be demonstrated that residues in meat are within the safe limits. A synthetic hormone that has created public concern is genetically engineered bovine somatotropin (bST). Cows naturally produce somatotropin, a hormone that stimulates milk production. Genetically engineered bST is produced by bacteria and injected into cows to increase milk production. Consumer groups contend that genetically engineered bST causes health problems for the cows and for humans who consume milk or meat from the cows. An FDA review of the effect of bST concluded that it causes no serious long-term health effects in cows and that milk and meat from bST-treated cows are not health risks to consumers.[22] The FDA does not require milk from bST-treated cows to be specially labeled, but companies may voluntarily label their products as long as the labeling is truthful and not misleading (**Figure 17.21**).

Contamination from Industrial Wastes

One group of industrial chemicals that pollutes the environment is **polychlorinated biphenyls (PCBs)**. These were used in the past in the manufacture of electrical capacitors and transformers, plasticizers, waxes, and paper. PCBs in runoff from manufacturing plants contaminated water, particularly near the Great Lakes. Although they are no longer produced, these compounds do not degrade and so are still found in the environment. Fish that live and feed in contaminated waters accumulate PCBs in their adipose tissue; humans who consume large quantities of contaminated fish accumulate PCBs in their adipose tissue.

PCB exposure can cause skin conditions, liver damage, and certain kinds of cancer. It is a particular problem for pregnant and lactating women because prenatal exposure and consumption of contaminated breast milk can damage the nervous system and cause learning deficits in children. The American Academy of Pediatrics (AAP) has concluded that the benefits of breast-feeding outweigh the risks of low levels of PCBs.[23] The AAP recommends that breast-feeding women in areas where high exposures of PCBs have occurred check with the local health department for recommendations on fish consumption.

Other contaminants from manufacturing, such as chlordane (used to control termites), radioactive substances such as strontium-90, and toxic metals such as cadmium, lead, arsenic, and mercury have also found their way into fish and shellfish. Cadmium and lead can interfere with the absorption of other minerals, as well as have a direct toxic effect: cadmium can cause kidney damage; lead can impair brain development. Arsenic is believed to contribute to cancer development, and mercury, which has been found in large fish, particularly swordfish, king mackerel, tilefish, and shark, damages nerve cells.[24] Large fish at the top of the food chain are more likely to contain high levels of industrial contaminants, but shellfish also accumulate contaminants because they feed by passing large volumes of water through their bodies (**Figure 17.22**).

Critical Thinking
The Risks and Benefits of Food

Background

After reading a newspaper article about a child who died of foodborne illness contracted by eating an undercooked hamburger, Ron became concerned about the safety of the foods his family was eating. He thought carefully about food safety issues such as eggs and poultry contaminated with *Salmonella*, pesticide residues on fruits and vegetables, and fish contaminated with industrial pollutants, bacteria, viruses, and parasites. He started to think most of the foods his family ate were risky but then decided to see if the benefits they provide are worth the risk.

Data

In general Ron's family eats a healthy diet and is rarely sick, but he knows that a few of the things they like carry risks. He enjoys his meat rare, his son is an athlete who drinks protein shakes containing raw eggs, his young daughter likes to lick cookie dough (containing raw eggs) from the bowl when baking, and he and his wife enjoy eating sushi and raw oysters. Ron makes the following list of foods and records the risks and benefits of each. When he reviews his list, Ron recognizes that although the hamburger may be contaminated, it is an inexpensive source of protein and iron in his family's diet. He decides to continue to eat hamburger but to be sure to cook it to 160 degrees, thereby minimizing the risks.

FOOD	RISK	BENEFIT
Hamburger	Can be contaminated with pathogenic *E. coli*.	A good source of protein and iron in the diet.
Chicken	Is often contaminated with *Salmonella*.	An economical source of protein that is low in fat.
Eggs	Can contain *Salmonella* or *Campylobacter*.	An inexpensive source of protein.
Fish	Can be contaminated with environmental pollutants such as PCBs and toxic metals.	A low-fat source of high-quality protein. Consumption has been associated with a reduced risk of cardiovascular disease.
Raw fish and shellfish	May be a source of bacterial, viral, and parasitic infections.	A low-fat source of high quality protein and omega-3 fatty acids.
Fruits and vegetables	May contain pesticide residues.	An excellent source of fiber and vitamins. They also contain health-promoting phytochemicals.

Critical Thinking Question

Draw a similar risk-benefit conclusion for the other foods on his list. Which foods do you think he should keep in his family's diet? How can he minimize the risks associated with eating them?

▼

Are there any foods on his list that you would suggest he eliminate from the family diet? Why or why not?

 iProfile Use iProfile to compare the omega-3 fatty acid content of varieties of fish and shellfish.

Choosing Wisely to Reduce Risk

Even though individual consumers cannot detect chemicals in food, care in selection and preparation can reduce the amounts that are consumed. One of the easiest ways to reduce risk is to choose a wide variety of foods, thus avoiding excessive consumption of any one food. Although some consumers are concerned about the consumption of pesticide residues, the health risk of eliminating foods from the diet that may contain pesticide residues, such as fresh fruits and vegetables, is probably greater than that of the pesticide exposure. To reduce exposure, consumers can choose locally grown produce. This is likely to have fewer pesticides because it does not contain those applied to prevent spoilage and extend the shelf life during shipping. Foods produced organically or using IPM are also likely to contain fewer pesticide residues.

Pesticides on conventionally grown produce can be removed or reduced by peeling or washing with tap water and scrubbing with a brush if appropriate. For leafy vegetables such as lettuce and cabbage, the outer leaves can be removed and discarded. Some produce, such as cucumbers, apples, eggplant, squash, and tomatoes, is coated with wax to maintain freshness by sealing in moisture, but wax also seals in pesticides. Much of the wax can be removed by rinsing produce in warm water and scrubbing it with a brush, but to eliminate all wax, the produce must be peeled. Although peeling fruits and vegetables eliminates some pesticides, it also eliminates some fiber and micronutrients.

The risk of ingesting chemical pollutants from fish can be minimized by choosing wisely. Smaller species of fish are safer because they are earlier in the food chain, and smaller fish within a species are safer because they are younger and hence have had less time to accumulate contaminants. The safest fish are saltwater varieties caught well offshore, away from polluted waters. Freshwater fish and saltwater fish that live near shore or spend part of their life cycle in freshwater are more likely to contain contaminants. Migratory fish such as striped bass and bluefish are a problem because they may contain contaminants even when they are caught in clean water well offshore. Consuming a variety of fish rather than just one or two kinds can also reduce the risk of ingesting dangerous amounts of contaminants. Most toxins concentrate in adipose tissue, so amounts can be reduced by removing the skin, fatty material, and dark meat from fish (and trimming fat from meat and removing skin from poultry). Use cooking methods such as broiling, poaching, boiling, and baking, which allow the fatty portions of the fish to drain out. Do not eat the "tomale" in lobster. The tomale, a green paste inside the abdominal cavity of a cooked lobster, serves as the liver and pancreas and is the organ in which toxins accumulate. The analogous organ in blue crabs, called the "mustard" because of its yellow color, should also be avoided (see Critical Thinking: The Risks and Benefits of Food).

17.5 Food Technology

Learning Objectives

- Describe how temperature is used to prevent food spoilage.
- Discuss how irradiation preserves food.
- Explain how packaging protects food.
- Compare the risks and benefits of food additives.

Advances in food and agricultural technology have improved the safety and availability of foods. This technology includes techniques to preserve food and develop new food products. It allows food to be stored for long periods, adds nutrients lacking in the diet, and creates disease-resistant high-yield crops. It has helped ensure that food is available even if the local growing season is not ideal. Without technology, the food supply would include only locally grown foods that must be eaten soon after harvest or slaughter. While this has some appeal, it would limit the variety of foods in the diet, particularly during the winter months, and increase the risk for malnutrition if food production were interrupted by a natural or manmade disaster. Despite the many benefits technology offers, it also creates risks.

Food spoilage occurs when the taste, texture, or nutritional value of the food changes as a result of either enzymes that are naturally present in the food or bacteria or mold that grow on the food. For thousands of years, humans have been treating foods in order to protect them from spoilage. Techniques that preserve food slow down or kill microbes or destroy enzymes present in the food. As shown in **Table 17.9**, the acronym FAT TOM reminds us of the factors that affect microbial growth. Most food preservation techniques modify one or more of these factors to stop or slow microbial growth. Many of the oldest methods of food preservation—including drying, smoking, **fermentation**, adding sugar or salt, and heating or cooling—are still used today. In addition, new methods of improving food quality and preventing spoilage and contamination, such as irradiation and specialized packaging have been developed. The newest methods of enhancing and protecting

fermentation A process in which microorganisms metabolize components of a food and therefore change the composition, taste, and storage properties of the food.

Table 17.9 FAT TOM

Food	Provides a growth media for bacteria.
Acidity	Most bacteria grow best at a pH near neutral. Some food additives, such as citric acid and ascorbic acid (vitamin C), are acids, which prevent microbial growth by lowering the pH of food.
Time	The longer a food sets at an optimum growth temperature, the more bacteria it will contain. Preservation methods such as canning and pasteurization kill microbes by heating food to an appropriate temperature for the right amount of time.
Temperature	The high temperatures of canning, cooking, and pasteurization kill microbes, and the low temperatures of freezing and refrigeration slow or stop microbial growth.
Oxygen	In order to grow, most bacteria need oxygen, so packaging that eliminates oxygen prevents their growth.
Moisture	Bacteria need water to grow, so preservation methods such as drying or the use of high concentrations of salt or sugar, which draw water away by osmosis, prevent bacteria from growing.

Source: Adapted from http://www.extension.iastate.edu/foodsafety/Lesson/L4/L4p1.html.

our food supply rely on biotechnology (see Focus on Biotechnology). Food technology often involves adding substances to food. The FDA considers any substance that can be expected to become part of a food a **food additive** and regulates its use. Substances that enter food unexpectedly are considered **accidental contaminants** and are not regulated.

High and Low Temperatures

Cooking food is one of the oldest methods of ensuring food safety. It kills disease-causing organisms and destroys toxins. Cooling food with refrigeration or freezing protects us by slowing or stopping microbial growth. Other preservation techniques that rely on temperature include canning, pasteurization, sterilization, and **aseptic processing**. Aseptic processing heats foods to temperatures that result in sterilization. The sterilized foods are then placed in sterilized packages using sterilized packaging equipment. Aseptic processing is currently used to produce boxes of sterile milk and juices (**Figure 17.23**). These can remain free of microbial growth at room temperature for years (see Science Applied: Pasteurization: From Spoiled Wine to Safe Milk).

Preservation techniques that rely on temperature benefit us by providing appealing, safe food, but they are not risk-free, particularly if used incorrectly. If foods are not heated long enough or to a high enough temperature, or if they are not kept cold enough, there is a risk of microbial foodborne illness. In addition, some types of cooking can also generate hazardous chemicals. These are considered accidental contaminants, so they are not regulated by the FDA. The most familiar group of chemicals produced during cooking is the **polycyclic aromatic hydrocarbons (PAHs)**. These carcinogenic substances are formed when fat drips onto the flame of a grill and burns. They rise with the smoke and are deposited on the surface of the food. Grilled or charred meats are therefore high in PAHs. PAH formation can be minimized by selecting lower-fat meat and using a layer of aluminum foil to prevent fat from dripping on the coals.

Broiled foods, which are cooked with the heat source at the top, are low in PAHs. However, broiling and other methods of high temperature cooking can result in another potential hazard—**heterocyclic amines (HCAs)**, such as benzopyrene. HCAs are formed from the burning of amino acids and other substances in meats. Well-done meat and meat cooked using hotter temperatures contain greater amounts. HCA formation can be reduced by precooking meat, marinating meat before cooking, cooking at lower temperatures, and reducing cooking time by using smaller pieces of meat and avoiding overcooking. The cooking temperatures recommended by the FDA are designed to prevent microbial foodborne illness and minimize the production of PAHs and HCAs.

Another contaminant formed during food preparation is acrylamide. It forms as a result of chemical reactions during high-temperature baking or frying, particularly in

food additives Substances that can reasonably be expected to become a component of a food during processing. The foods that may contain them and the amounts that may be present are regulated by the FDA.

accidental contaminants Substances that unexpectedly enter the food supply. They are not regulated by the FDA.

aseptic processing A method that places sterilized food in a sterilized package using a sterile process.

polycyclic aromatic hydrocarbons (PAHs) A class of mutagenic substances produced during cooking when there is incomplete combustion of organic materials—such as when fat drips on a grill.

heterocyclic amines (HAs) A class of mutagenic substances produced when there is incomplete combustion of amino acids during the cooking of meats—such as when meat is charred.

Figure 17.23 If unopened, milk and juice in aseptic packaging can be stored for long periods without refrigeration. (George Semple)

SCIENCE

ScienceAppliedScienceApplied
Science **AppliedScience** Applied
ScienceAppliedScienceApplied

APPLIED

(DAJ/Getty Images, Inc.)　　(www.victorianoizquierdo.com/Getty Images, Inc.)　　(Elena Schweitzer/Shutterstock)

Pasteurization: From Spoiled Wine to Safe Milk

In 1857, sailors in Napoleon's navy were in mutiny because wine supplies were spoiling after only a few weeks at sea. Napoleon recognized this spoilage problem as a threat to his hopes for world conquest. He turned to Louis Pasteur for help. To study the problem, Pasteur traveled to a vineyard in Arbois, France, where spoilage was causing considerable economic losses for the wine industry. By examining the spoiled wine under a microscope, Pasteur was able to demonstrate the presence of certain strains of microorganisms. He suggested that spoilage could be prevented by heating the wine to a temperature high enough to kill the harmful microbes but low enough that it did not affect the flavor. Experimentation with heating wine for various times and temperatures revealed that as Pasteur had predicted, the microorganisms could be killed without damaging the flavor of the wine. This became the foundation for the modern treatment of bottled liquids to prevent their spoilage, a process known as pasteurization.

Pasteurization had a major public health impact, particularly when applied to the milk industry. Between 1880 and 1907, 500 outbreaks of milk-borne diseases occurred in the United States. Milk from cows suffering from Bang's disease caused undulant fever in humans, a chronic debilitating disease characterized by intermittent fever. Contaminated milk also caused typhoid, scarlet fever, diphtheria, and tuberculosis. Pasteurization eliminated the pathogenic organisms that caused these diseases. By 1900, pasteurized milk was commonly available, but raw milk was still more popular because the high-temperature pasteurization process used at the time left the milk with a cooked taste.

In 1906, Milton J. Rosenau, director of the U.S. Marine Hospital Service Hygienic Laboratory, established a low-temperature, slow pasteurization process (140°F for 20 minutes) that killed pathogens without changing the taste of the milk. This discovery eliminated the primary obstacle to public acceptance of pasteurized milk. By 1936, pasteurized, certified milk was the standard in most large cities, but over half of all milk consumed in the United States was still raw. More progress toward improving milk safety came when the Public Health Service created a document to assist Alabama in developing a statewide milk sanitation program. This document ultimately evolved into the Grade A Milk Pasteurization

This photo depicts Louis Pasteur studying the souring of wine. (Jean Loup Charmet/SPL/Photo Researchers)

Ordinance. This voluntary agreement established uniform sanitation standards for the interstate shipment of Grade A milk. It now serves as the basis of milk safety laws in all 50 states and Puerto Rico.[1]

The milk pasteurization process kills pathogenic bacteria and reduces the total number of microorganisms present, but it allows many microbes to survive. Milk is graded on the basis of bacterial count. A maximum of 20,000 bacteria per milliliter is allowed in Grade A milk. The multiplication of the bacteria that remain eventually causes the milk to spoil. To prevent rapid multiplication after pasteurization, the milk must be cooled immediately and remain refrigerated. In addition to killing microorganisms, the heat also destroys enzymes in the milk; the inactivation of lipase extends the shelf life of homogenized milk by preventing it from becoming rancid. The inactivation of another enzyme called phosphatase is used to gauge the adequacy of pasteurization. Lack of phosphatase activity indicates that the heat treatment has been sufficient, but if phosphatase activity remains, it indicates that the milk was not treated adequately and may not be free of pathogens.

Today almost all milk sold in the United States is pasteurized, and the same techniques are used to prevent spoilage in many other foods. Thanks to the work of Louis Pasteur, we now enjoy the nutritional benefits of milk without the risk of contamination with disease-causing organisms.

[1] U.S. Public Health Service. 1924. United States Proposed Standard Milk Ordinance, Public Health Reports. Washington, D.C.: Public Health Service, November 7, 1924.

carbohydrate-rich foods. The highest levels of acrylamide are found in french fries and snack chips, foods that people should already be eating less of because they are low in nutrients and high in kcalories. High doses of acrylamide have been found to cause cancer and reproductive problems in animals and to act as a neurotoxin in humans. Thus far, dietary exposure to acrylamide has not been associated with cancer in humans, and more research is needed to determine whether long-term, low-level exposure has any cumulative effects.[25] Methods for reducing the amounts and potential toxicity of acrylamide in foods are being investigated.[26]

Food Irradiation

Irradiation, also called *cold pasteurization*, exposes food to a high dose of x-rays, gamma radiation, or high-energy electrons to kill microorganisms and insects and inactivate enzymes that cause germination and ripening of fruits and vegetables. Although irradiated foods must be labeled with the radura symbol (**Figure 17.24**) and the statement "treated with radiation" or "treated by irradiation," foods that contain irradiated spices or other irradiated ingredients do not need to display this symbol.

Irradiation can be used in place of chemical treatments, so it reduces exposure to chemical pesticides and preservatives. It is one of the technologies singled out in the National Food Safety Initiative because of its potential for improving the safety of food and reducing the incidence of foodborne illness.

Food irradiation is used in more than 40 countries to treat everything from frog legs to rice. However, it is used relatively infrequently in the United States. Part of the reason for this is lack of irradiation facilities, but public fear and suspicion of the technology also limit its use. The word "irradiation" fosters the belief that the food itself becomes radioactive. Opponents to food irradiation claim that it introduces carcinogens, depletes the nutritional value of food, and is used to allow the sale of previously contaminated foods. In fact, irradiated food is not radioactive and scientific studies conducted over the past 50 years have found that the benefits of irradiation outweigh the potential risks.[27] It increases the safety and shelf life of foods and does not compromise nutritional quality or noticeably change food texture, taste, or appearance as long as it is properly applied to a suitable product. Irradiation can benefit the environment by reducing the use of chemicals to kill microbes and insects. Irradiation can decrease the amounts of certain nutrients but losses are similar to those that occur with canning or cold storage.[28]

The FDA has approved irradiation to destroy pathogens in red meat and poultry and contaminants in spices; prevent insect infestation in flour and spices; increase the shelf life of potatoes; eliminate *Trichinella* in pork; control insects in fruits, vegetables, and grains; and slow the ripening and spoilage of some produce.[29] Because irradiation produces unique compounds in irradiated foods, it is treated as a food additive, and the level of radiation that may be used is regulated. At the allowed levels of radiation, the amounts of these unique compounds produced are almost negligible and have not been found to be a risk to consumers. Irradiated foods may cost more because of the cost of adding an extra processing step, but in the future this may be offset by a longer shelf life (**Figure 17.25**). Irradiation should be used to complement, not replace, proper food handling by producers, processors, and consumers.

irradiation A process, also called cold pasteurization, that exposes foods to radiation to kill contaminating organisms and retard ripening and spoilage of fruits and vegetables.

TREATED BY IRRADIATION

Figure 17.24 The radura symbol This symbol is used to identify foods that have been treated with irradiation.

NON - IRRADIATED -   IRRADIATED - (0.2 M RAD)

Figure 17.25 After 2 weeks in cold storage, the strawberries treated by irradiation remain free of mold (right), whereas the untreated strawberries picked at the same time are covered with mold (left). (Courtesy Council for Agricultural Science and Technology)

Food Packaging

An open package of cheddar cheese will grow mold in the refrigerator after only a few days. An unopened package will stay fresh for weeks. Packaging plays an important role in food preservation; it keeps molds and bacteria out, keeps moisture in, and protects food from physical damage. Food packaging is continuously being improved.

Consumer demand for fresh, easy-to-prepare foods has led manufacturers to offer partially cooked pasta, vegetables, seafood, fresh and cured meats, and dry products such as whole-bean and ground coffee in packaging that, if unopened, will keep perishable food fresh much longer than will conventional packaging. **Modified atmosphere packaging (MAP)** uses plastics or other packaging materials that are impermeable to oxygen. The air inside the package is vacuumed out in order to remove the oxygen. The product can then remain packaged in a vacuum, or the package can be infused with another gas, such as carbon dioxide or nitrogen. The lack of oxygen prevents the growth of aerobic bacteria, slows the ripening of fruits and vegetables, and slows down oxidation reactions, which cause discoloration in fruits and vegetables and rancidity in fats.

MAP is often used to package cooked entrees such as pasta primavera or beef teriyaki. The raw ingredients are sealed in a plastic pouch, the air is vacuumed out, and the pouch and its contents are partially precooked and immediately refrigerated. This processing eliminates the need for the extreme cold of freezing or the extreme heat of canning, so flavor and nutrients are better preserved. Because these products are not heated to temperatures high enough to kill all bacteria and are not stored at temperatures low enough to prevent all bacteria from growing, they could pose a food safety risk. To ensure safety, fresh refrigerated foods should be purchased only from reputable vendors, used before the expiration date printed on the package, refrigerated until use, and heated according to the time and temperature directions on the package.

Packaging can protect food from spoilage, but even the best packaging can introduce risk if it becomes a part of the food. A variety of substances leach into foods from plastics, paper, and even dishes. One potential contaminant from plastics containers is bisphenol A. The transfer of bisphenol A, a chemical found in polycarbonate plastic used to manufacture hard, transparent water bottles, baby bottles, and food containers as well as the coating inside cans, is a concern for pregnant women and infants (**Figure 17.26**). A review by the U.S. National Toxicology Program found that although there is negligible risk of adverse effects in most adults, exposure of pregnant women to bisphenol A could affect fetal brain development, and exposure of infants and children to the chemical could affect the nervous system and accelerate puberty.[30] Eating fewer canned foods and drinking from glass or aluminum, rather than plastic, containers can minimize exposure.

Substances that are known to contaminate foods are indirect food additives and the amounts and types are regulated by EPA tolerance levels and FDA inspections. However, these regulations apply only to the intended use of the product. When used improperly, packaging can migrate into food. These accidental contaminants are not regulated by the FDA. It is the consumer's responsibility to prevent these substances from entering food. For instance, some plastics migrate into food when heated in a microwave oven. Thus, only packages designed for microwave cooking should be used.

Food Additives

Food additives keep bread from molding, give margarine its yellow color, and keep parmesan cheese from clumping in the shaker (**Figure 17.27**). Some substances are intentionally added to foods and are called **direct food additives**. Other substances unintentionally get into our food. These are referred to as **indirect food additives** and include things like the oil used to lubricate food-processing machinery. The FDA regulates the amounts and types of direct and indirect food additives in food.

Additives that Prevent Spoilage Many substances are added to prevent bacteria and molds from causing food spoilage, to extend shelf life, or to protect the natural color and flavor of food. Sugar and salt are two of the oldest **preservatives**. They prevent microbial growth by decreasing the water availability in the product; without adequate water, microbes cannot grow. For example, the high concentration of sugar in

modified atmosphere packaging (MAP) A preservation technique used to prolong the shelf life of processed or fresh food by changing the gases surrounding the food in the package.

Figure 17.26 Does your water bottle contain bispherol A? (Jupiter Images/Getty Images, Inc.)

direct food additives Substances intentionally added to foods. They are regulated by the FDA.

indirect food additives Substances that are expected to unintentionally enter foods during manufacturing or from packaging. They are regulated by the FDA.

preservatives Compounds that extend the shelf life of a product by retarding chemical, physical, or microbiological changes.

Figure 17.27 The additives in these foods prevent the bread from molding, the fruit snacks from hardening, and the powdered sugar from clumping; they also smooth the texture of the pudding and give color and flavor to soft drinks and candy. (George Semple)

jams and jellies draws water away from the microbial cells and prevents them from growing. Antioxidants such as sulfites and BHT (butylated hydroxytoluene) are also used as preservatives. They prevent fats and oils in baked goods and other foods from becoming rancid or developing an off-flavor and prevent cut fruits such as apples from turning brown when exposed to air. Other preservatives act by blocking the natural ripening and enzymatic processes that continue to occur in foods even after harvest.

Additives that Improve Nutrient Content, Color, Texture, and Flavor

Additives are not just used to make food safer and last longer. They are also used to enhance the nutrient content, texture, color, and flavor of foods (see Off the Label: Should You Avoid Food Additives?).

Additives to Maintain or Improve the Nutritional Quality Nutrients that are added to foods are considered additives. As discussed in Chapter 8, refined grains are enriched with iron and some of the B vitamins that are lost in processing; these are considered additives. Food is also fortified with nutrients, such as calcium, that are typically lacking in the diet. Although the addition of these additives to foods benefits the population by increasing the nutrient content of the diet, it can also increase the risk of nutrient toxicities.

Additives to Improve and Maintain Texture Many different types of additives are used in product processing and preparation. Emulsifiers improve the homogeneity, stability, and consistency of products such as ice cream. Stabilizers, thickeners, and texturizers, such as pectins and gums, are used to improve consistency or texture in pudding and to stabilize emulsions in foods such as salad dressing. Leavening agents are added to incorporate gas into breads and cakes, causing them to rise. Acids are added as flavor enhancers, preservatives, and antioxidants. Humectants, such as propylene glycol, cause moisture to be retained so products stay fresh. Anti-caking agents prevent crystalline products such as powdered sugar from absorbing moisture and caking or lumping.

Additives to Affect Flavor and Color Additives are also used to enhance the flavor and color of foods. For example, both natural and alternative sweeteners are added to sweeten foods such as yogurt and fruit drinks. Color additives enhance the appearance of foods. A color additive is defined as any dye, pigment, or substance that can impart color when added or applied to a food, drug, cosmetic, or to the human body. Color additives are used in foods for many reasons, including to balance color loss due to storage or processing and to even out natural variations in food color. Colors can be used to make foods appear more appetizing; however, they cannot be used as deception to conceal inferiority. Colors permitted for use in foods are classified as certified or exempt from certification. Certified food colors are synthetic dyes that have been tested to ensure safety, quality, consistency, and strength of color. There are nine certified color additives approved for use in the United States. Colors derived from plant, animal, and certain mineral sources are exempt from certification. They must still meet safety standards before they are approved for use in foods. Examples include annatto extract (yellow), dehydrated beets (bluish-red to brown), caramel (yellow to tan), β-carotene (yellow to orange), and grape skin extract (red, green).

Regulating Food Additives Food additives improve food quality and help protect us from disease, but if the wrong additive is used or if the wrong amount is added, it could do more harm than good. To prevent this, the federal Food, Drug, and Cosmetic (FD&C) Act of 1938 gave the FDA authority over food and food ingredients and defined requirements for truthful labeling of ingredients. This act provided exemptions and safe tolerance levels for additives that were necessary or unavoidable in production and established what are called **standards of identity** for certain foods. Standards of identity define exactly the ingredients that can be contained in certain foods such as mayonnaise, jelly, and orange juice. The FD&C Act also gave the FDA the responsibility of testing food additives for safety. Because the FDA could not possibly test all additives, the 1958 Food Additives Amendment transferred the responsibility for testing from the FDA to the manufacturer. Today, when a manufacturer wants to

standards of identity
Regulations that define the allowable ingredients, composition, and other characteristics of foods.

Off the Label
Should You Avoid Food Additives?

Sometimes the ingredients listed on food labels sound like a chemical soup. Calcium propionate is added to bread, disodium EDTA is added to canned kidney beans, and BHA is in potato chips. Are these chemical additives necessary in our food supply? Are they safe? Understanding what these chemicals are used for can help make the ingredient list a source of information rather than a cause for concern. The table on the next page provides some examples of additives, explains what each does, and gives examples of the types of food where they are used.

The FDA does not approve food additives unless they are safe for most consumers, but this doesn't mean they are safe for everyone. For individuals who are sensitive or allergic to certain additives such as preservatives or colors, the ingredient list provides information that can be lifesaving. For example, in sensitive individuals, sulfites can cause symptoms that range from a stomachache and hives to severe asthmatic reactions. The FDA estimates that 1 in 100 people are sulfite-sensitive.[1] Sulfites are used to preserve foods such as baked goods, canned vegetables, condiments, and maraschino cherries. Individuals sensitive to sulfites should read food labels. Foods served in restaurants are also a concern because sulfites are sometimes used in food preparation. For example, a potato dish on the menu may be prepared using potatoes that were peeled and soaked in a sulfite solution before cooking.

Food colors can also cause reactions in sensitive individuals. The color additive FD&C Yellow No. 5, which is listed as tartrazine on medicine labels, may cause itching and hives in sensitive people. It is also found in beverages, desserts, and processed vegetables. Sensitivity to FD&C Yellow No. 5 occurs in fewer than 1 in 10,000 people.[2] All foods that contain FDA-certified color additives must list them by name in the ingredient list. Colors that are exempt from certification, such as dehydrated beets and carotenoids, do not have to be specifically identified and may be listed on the label collectively as "artificial color" (see figure).[2]

There are more additives than you might think in your whipped topping and maraschino cherry. (Comstock Images/Gettyone.com)

INGREDIENTS: Cream, milk, sugar, dextrose, sorbitan monostearate, artificial flavor, carrageenan, mixed tocopherols (vitamin E) to protect flavor, beta carotene (color), propellant: Nitrous oxide

Ingredients: Cherries, water, corn syrup, sugar, citric acid, natural and artificial flavor, potassium sorbate and sodium benzoate added as preservative, fd&c red #40 (artificial color), and sulfur dioxide (preservative).

---

[1]Papazian, R. Sulfites: Safe for most, dangerous for some. *FDA Consumer* 30:11–14, December 1996. Available online at http://www.fda.gov/fdac/features/096_sulf.html. Accessed May 20, 2009.

[2]U.S. Food and Drug Administration. Food Color Facts. January 1993. Available online at www.cfsan.fda.gov/~lrd/colorfac.html/. Accessed May 20, 2009.

---

use a new food additive, a petition must be submitted to the FDA. The petition describes the chemical composition of the additive, how it is manufactured, and how it is detected and measured in food. The manufacturer must prove that the additive will be effective for its intended purpose at the proposed levels, that it is safe for its intended use, and that its use is necessary. Additives may not be used to disguise inferior products or deceive consumers. They cannot be used if they significantly destroy nutrients or where the same effect can be achieved by sound manufacturing processes.

Common food additives

Type of additive	What's on the label	What they do	Where they are used
Preservatives	Ascorbic acid, citric acid, sodium benzoate, calcium propionate, sodium erythorbate, sodium nitrite, calcium sorbate, potassium sorbate, BHA, BHT, EDTA, tocopherols	Maintain freshness; prevent spoilage caused by bacteria, molds, fungi, or yeast; slow or prevent changes in color, flavor, or texture; and delay rancidity	Jellies, beverages, baked goods, cured meats, oils and margarines, cereals, dressings, snack foods, fruits and vegetables
Sweeteners	Sucrose, glucose, fructose, sorbitol, mannitol, corn syrup, high-fructose corn syrup, saccharin, aspartame, sucralose, acesulfame potassium (acesulfame-K), neotame	Add sweetness with or without extra kcalories	Beverages, baked goods, table-top sweeteners, many processed foods
Color additives	FD&C blue nos. 1 and 2, FD&C green no. 3, FD&C red nos. 3 and 40, FD&C yellow nos. 5 and 6, orange B, citrus red no. 2, annatto extract, beta-carotene, grapeskin extract, cochineal extract or carmine, paprika oleoresin, caramel color, fruit and vegetable juices, saffron, colorings or color added	Prevent color loss due to exposure to light, air, temperature extremes, and moisture; enhance colors; give color to colorless and "fun" foods	Processed foods, candies, snack foods, margarine, cheese, soft drinks, jellies, puddings and pie fillings
Flavors, spices, and flavor enhancers	Natural flavoring, artificial flavor, spices, monosodium glutamate (MSG), hydrolyzed soy protein, autolyzed yeast extract, disodium guanylate or inosinate	Add specific flavors or enhance flavors already present in foods	Processed foods, puddings and pie fillings, gelatin mixes, cake mixes, salad dressings, candies, soft drinks, ice cream, BBQ sauce
Nutrients	Thiamine hydrochloride, riboflavin (vitamin B_2), niacin, niacinamide, folate or folic acid, beta-carotene, potassium iodide, iron or ferrous sulfate, alpha-tocopherols, ascorbic acid, vitamin D, amino acids (L-tryptophan, L-lysine, L-leucine, L-methionine)	Replace vitamins and minerals lost in processing; add nutrients that may be lacking in the diet	Flour, breads, cereals, rice, pasta, margarine, salt, milk, fruit beverages, energy bars, breakfast drinks
Emulsifiers	Soy lecithin, mono- and diglycerides, egg yolks, polysorbates, sorbitan monostearate	Allow smooth mixing and prevent separation; reduce stickiness; control crystallization; keep ingredients dispersed	Salad dressings, peanut butter, chocolate, margarine, frozen desserts
Stabilizers and thickeners, binders, and texturizers	Gelatin, pectin, guar gum, carrageenan, xanthan gum, whey	Produce uniform texture, improve "mouth-feel"	Frozen desserts, dairy products, cakes, pudding and gelatin mixes, dressings, jams and jellies, sauces
pH control agents and acidulants	Lactic acid, citric acid, ammonium hydroxide, sodium carbonate	Control acidity and alkalinity, prevent spoilage	Beverages, frozen desserts, chocolate, low-acid canned foods, baking powder
Leavening agents	Baking soda, monocalcium phosphate, calcium carbonate	Promote rising of baked goods	Breads and other baked goods
Anti-caking agents	Calcium silicate, iron ammonium citrate, silicon dioxide	Keep powdered foods free-flowing, prevent moisture absorption	Salt, baking powder, confectioners' sugar
Humectants	Glycerin, sorbitol	Retain moisture	Shredded coconut, marshmallows, soft candies, confections

Additives Used Before 1958 When the 1958 Food Additives Amendment was passed, over 600 chemicals defined as food additives were already in common use. To accommodate these substances, the amendment exempted two groups of substances from the food additive regulation process. One group included substances that the FDA or the USDA had determined were safe; these were designated as **prior-sanctioned substances**. The nitrates and nitrites used to retard the growth of *Clostridium botulinum* in cured meats such as ham and hot dogs are on the prior-sanctioned list. However, the

prior-sanctioned substances Refers to substances that the FDA or the USDA had determined were safe for use in a specific food prior to the 1958 Food Additives Amendment.

nitrosamines Carcinogenic compounds produced by reactions between nitrites and amino acids.

use of these has been controversial because they form carcinogenic **nitrosamines** in the digestive tract. They are still allowed in foods because there is little evidence that they pose a serious risk in the amounts consumed in the human diet.[31] To minimize any risk posed by nitrosamines without increasing the risk of bacterial illness, the FDA has limited the amount of nitrate and nitrite that can be added to food and has required the addition of antioxidants, which reduce nitrosamine formation, to foods containing these additives. Consumers can reduce nitrosamine exposure by limiting cured meat consumption to 3 to 4 oz per week and maintaining adequate intakes of the antioxidant vitamins C and E.

A second category of substances excluded from the food additive regulation process is **generally recognized as safe (GRAS)** substances. GRAS substances are those whose use is generally recognized as safe based on their extensive history of use in food before 1958 or based on published scientific evidence.

generally recognized as safe (GRAS) A group of chemical additives that are generally recognized as safe based on their long-standing presence in the food supply without obvious harmful effects.

Just because a substance is on the prior-sanctioned or GRAS list doesn't mean it is safe or that it will stay on these lists. If new evidence emerges that suggests that a substance in either of these categories is unsafe the FDA may take action to remove the substance from food products.

Delaney Clause A clause added to the 1958 Food Additives Amendment of the Pure Food and Drug Act that prohibits the intentional addition to foods of any compound that has been shown to induce cancer in animals or humans at any dose.

The Delaney Clause The 1958 Food Additives Amendment also included the **Delaney Clause**, which was designed to protect the public from additives found to be carcinogenic. The Delaney Clause states that a substance that induces cancer in either an animal species or humans at any dosage, no matter how large, may not be added to food. Currently, support is growing to amend the Delaney Clause to allow the use of substances that are added at a level so low that they would not represent a significant health risk.

Outcome

How could homemade frozen custard, which sounds so wholesome, make so many people sick? The frozen custard that the fourth graders made contained raw eggs, which sometimes harbor the bacterium *Salmonella enteritidis.* Thoroughly cooking eggs kills the bacteria, but any food that contains uncooked eggs is a risk. Since the ingredients for all the frozen custard were mixed as one large batch, bacteria from even a single infected egg could have contaminated the entire recipe. The low temperatures used for making frozen custard would retard bacterial growth but not kill the organisms. The fourth graders were slow in measuring and mixing ingredients, so the mixture of raw eggs, milk, sugar, and cream sat at room temperature for almost an hour before it was chilled and placed in the ice cream maker. When the inspectors sampled the frozen custard, they found it contained large numbers of *Salmonella.* Tracking the ingredients used to make the frozen custard revealed that the school had purchased the eggs from a distributor in Florida, who had bought them from a farm in Maryland. At next year's celebration the school decided to have homemade ice cream, which is not made with raw eggs. Fortunately, all of the individuals who became ill recovered, but *Salmonella* infection can cause serious illness and even death in the elderly, infants, and persons with impaired immune function.

APPLICATIONS

Personal Nutrition

1. Can your kitchen pass the food safety test? To find out, go to http://vm.cfsan.fda.gov/~dms/fdkitchn.html. After you complete the exercise answer the following questions.

   a. Based on how you answered these questions, what changes should you make in the way you store and handle foods in your kitchen?

   b. Based on how you answered these questions, are there foods that you will eliminate from your diet?

2. What food additives are in your favorite snacks?

   a. Choose a packaged product you like to snack on and write out all the ingredients it contains.

   b. Which of the ingredients are food additives?

   c. Use the table in the Off the Label feature in this chapter to describe the function of each additive.

   d. If these additives could not be used, how would the product differ?

General Nutrition Issues

1. Sixty-seven people became ill after consuming food at a company picnic. Testing of food samples revealed that the tossed salad, the egg salad, and the turkey slices were all contaminated with *Salmonella*. Invent a scenario that would explain how all three became contaminated.

2. What are the risks and benefits for each scenario described below?

   a. A restaurant decides not to replace their old dishwasher even though it no longer heats the water to above 140°F.

   b. A town decides that they can improve the health of their citizens and the environment by banning the production and sale of all but organically produced foods.

3. A train crash spills a load of industrial waste into a river that feeds into a local reservoir. How would this spill affect:

   a. The safety of the drinking water?

   b. The milk from dairy cattle grazing nearby?

   c. The fish that swim in the river?

   d. The crops irrigated by this water?

Summary

17.1 How Can Food Make Us Sick?

- Foodborne illness is any illness that is related to the consumption of food or contaminants or toxins in food.

- Food may become contaminated where it is grown or produced, during processing or storage, or even in the home. Once contaminated, food preparation surfaces can cross-contaminate other foods.

- The harm caused by contaminants in the food supply depends on the type of toxin, the dose, the length of time over which it is consumed, and the size and health status of the consumer.

17.2 Keeping Food Safe

- The safety of the food supply is monitored by agencies at the international, federal, state, and local levels. The government promotes the use of HACCP (Hazard Analysis Critical Control Point) principles to ensure food safety. HACCP systems help prevent or eliminate food contamination and track contaminated foods to prevent foodborne illness.

- It is the job of the food manufacturer to establish and implement a HAACP system for their particular business.

- Consumers play an important role in limiting the risks of developing foodborne illness through the way they store, handle, and prepare food.

17.3 Pathogens in Food

- The pathogens that affect the food supply include bacteria, viruses, molds, parasites, and prions. Some bacteria cause food-borne infection because they are able to grow in the gastrointestinal tract when ingested. Others produce toxins in food, and consumption of the toxin causes food-borne intoxication.

- Viruses do not grow on food, but when consumed in food, they can reproduce in human cells and cause food-borne illness.

- Molds that grow on foods produce toxins that can harm consumers.

- Parasites include microscopic single-celled animals, as well as worms that can be seen with the naked eye. They are consumed in contaminated water or food.

- Improperly folded prion proteins cause bovine spongiform encephalopathy (BSE) in cattle. The risk of acquiring the human form of this deadly degenerative neurological disease is extremely low.

- The risk of food-borne illness can be decreased through proper food selection, preparation, and storage.

17.4 Chemical Contaminants in Food

- Contaminants such as pesticides applied to crops and industrial wastes that leach into water may find their way into the food supply. To decrease the potential risk of pesticides, safer ones are being developed and U.S. farmers are reducing the amounts applied by using integrated pest management and organic methods.

- Antibiotics are given to animals to prevent disease and increase growth. The widespread use of these drugs may be contributing to the emergence of antibiotic resistant strains of bacteria.

- Industrial pollutants such as PCBs, radioactive substances, and toxic metals have contaminated some waterways and the fish that live in them. As these contaminants move through the food chain, their concentrations increase.

- Consumers can reduce the amounts of pesticides and other environmental contaminants in food by careful selection and handling of produce; selection of low-fat saltwater varieties of fish caught well offshore in unpolluted waters; and trimming fat from meat, poultry, and fish before cooking.

17.5 Food Technology

- High and low temperatures are used to prevent food spoilage. Cold temperatures slow or prevent microbial growth. High temperatures used in canning, pasteurization, sterilization, and cooking kill microorganisms. However, cooking can also introduce hazardous substances such as polycyclic aromatic hydrocarbons, heterocyclic amines, and acrylamide.

- Irradiation preserves food by exposing it to x-rays, gamma radiation, or high-energy electrons. It kills microorganisms, destroys insects, and slows the germination and ripening of fruits and vegetables.

- Packaging can help preserve food, but can introduce risk if it leaches into the food. Modified atmosphere packaging reduces the oxygen available for microbial growth.

- Food additives include all substances that can reasonably be expected to find their way into a food during processing. This includes direct food additives, which are used to preserve or enhance the appeal of food, and indirect food additives, which are substances known to find their way into food during cooking, processing, and packaging. Direct and indirect food additives are regulated by the FDA. Accidental contaminants that enter food when it is used or prepared incorrectly are not regulated by the FDA.

Review Questions

1. What is the major cause of foodborne illness in the United States today?

2. List three factors that determine the likelihood that a contaminant will cause foodborne illness in an individual.

3. How is the federal government involved in ensuring a safe food supply?

4. Explain what HACCP is and how it can prevent or eliminate food contamination.

5. What is the difference between a foodborne infection and a foodborne intoxication?

6. List three common bacterial food contaminants. What can be done to avoid the foodborne illnesses caused by them?

7. What temperature range allows the most rapid bacterial growth?

8. Explain how cross-contamination can occur in home kitchens.

9. How do pesticides applied to crops find their way into animal products?

10. List some food-processing and packaging techniques that reduce foodborne illnesses.

11. What is food irradiation? Is it safe?

12. What is the GRAS list?

13. List four reasons for using food additives.

References

1. Mead, P. S., Slutsker, L., Dietz, V., et al. Food-Related Illness and Death in the United States. *Emerg. Infect. Dis.* Available online at www.cdc.gov/ncidod/eid/vol5no5/mead.htm. Accessed October 10, 2009.

2. US Department of Health and Human Services, USFDA, Food Code, 2005. Available online at http://www.cfsan. fda.gov/~dms/fc05-toc.html. Accessed May 20, 2009.

3. U.S. Food and Drug Administration, Department of Agriculture, and Environmental Protection Agency. Food Safety from Farm to Table: A New Strategy for the 21st Century. February 21, 1997. Available online at vm.cfsan. fda.gov/~dms/fs-draft.html/ Accessed October 2, 2009.

4. U.S. Department of Health and Human Services. National Computer Network in Place to Combat Foodborne Illness (press release). May 22, 1998. Available online at www.cdc.gov/od/oc/media/pressrel/r980522.htm/ Accessed August 3, 2005.

5. CSPI Reports. Dine at Your Own Risk—Part II. Available online at www.cspinet.org/reports/dineat2.html/ Accessed February 20, 2006.

6. U.S. Food and Drug Administration, Center for Food Safety and Nutrition. *Foodborne Pathogenic Microorganisms and Natural Toxins Handbook: The "Bad Bug Book."* Available online at www.foodsafety.gov/~mow/intro.html. Accessed August 1, 2008.

7. Centers for Disease Control and Prevention. *CDC Health Update: Multi-State Outbreak of E-coli 0157 Infections, November–December 2006*. Available online at www2a.cdc.gov/HAN/ArchiveSys/ViewMsgV.asp?AlertNum=00255. Accessed August 7, 2008.

8. Samuel, M. C., Vugia, D. J., Shallow, S. et al. Epidemiology of sporadic *Campylobacter* infection in the United States and declining trend in incidence, FoodNet 1996–1999. *Clin. Infect. Dis.* 38(Suppl. 3):S165–S174, 2004.

9. Centers for Disease Control and Prevention, Division of Foodborne, Bacterial, and Mycotic Disease. *Listeriosis*. Available online at www.cdc.gov/nczved/dfbmd/disease_listing/listeriosis_gi.html. Accessed August 6, 2008.

10. Koepke, R., Sobel, J., and Arnon, S. S. Global occurrence of infant botulism, 1976–2006. *Pediatircs* 122:73–82, 2008.

11. Widdowson, M. A., Sulka, A., Bulens, S. N. et al. Norovirus and foodborne disease, United States, 1991–2000. *Emerg. Infect. Dis.* 11:95–102, 2005.

12. Cheng, P. K., Wong, D. K., Chung, T. W., and Lim, W. W. Norovirus contamination found in oysters worldwide. *J. Med. Virol.* 76:593–597, 2005.

13. Outbreaks of *Escherichia coli* O157:H7 infection and cryptosporidosis associated with drinking unpasteurized apple cider—Connecticut and New York, October 1996. *MMWR* 46:4–8, 1997.

14. Centers for Disease Control and Prevention. Cryptospiridium *Infection*. Available online at www.cdc.gov/ncidod/dpd/parasites/cryptosporidiosis/factsht_cryptosporidiosis.htm. Accessed August 1, 2008.

15. Centers for Disease Control and Prevention. *vCJD (Variant Creutzfeldt-Jakob Disease)*. Available online at www.cdc.gov/ncidod/dvrd/vcjd/. Accessed August 7, 2008.

16. U.S. Environmental Protection Agency. *Setting Tolerances for Pesticide Residues in Foods*. www.epa.gov/pesticides/factsheets/stprf.htm. Accessed August 1, 2008.

17. U.S. Food and Drug Administration, Center for Food Safety and Applied Nutrition. *Pesticide Program Residue Monitoring, 2004–2006*. Available online at www.cfsan.fda.gov/~dms/pes04-06.html. Accessed August 8, 2008.

18. U.S. Food and Drug Administration, Center for Food Safety and Applied Nutrition. *Pesticide Program Residue Monitoring, 2002*. Available online at www.cfsan.fda.gov/~dms/pes02rep.html. Accessed August 8, 2008.

19. U.S. Department of Agriculture, Agricultural Marketing Service. *National Organic Program*. Available online at www.ams.usda.gov/AMSv1.0/ams.fetchTemplateData.do?template=TemplateA&navID=NationalOrganicProgram&leftNav=NationalOrganicProgram&page=NOPNationalOrganicProgramHome&acct=nop. Accessed August 1, 2008.

20. International Food Information Council. *Fact Sheet: FDA's Approval Process for Food Animal Antibiotics—A Focus on Human Food Safety*. May 2008. Available online at www.ific.org/publications/factsheets/fdaanimalantifs.cfm. Accessed August 9, 2008.

21. Pew Commission on Industrial Farm Animal Production. *Final Report: Putting Meat on The Table: Industrial Farm Animal Production in America*. Available online at www.ncifap.org/_images/PCIFAPFin.pdf. Accessed August 11, 2008.

22. U.S. Food and Drug Administration, Center for Veterinary Medicine. *Report on the Food and Drug Administration's Review of the Safety of Recombinant Bovine Somatotropin*. Available online at www.fda.gov/cvm/RBRPTFNL.htm. Accessed August 1, 2008.

23. American Academy of Pediatrics, Committee on Environmental Health. PCBs in breast milk. *Pediatrics* 84:122–123, 1994.

24. U.S. Department of Health and Human Services and U.S. Environmental Protection Agency. *What You Need to Know about Mercury in Fish and Shellfish*. EPA-823-R-04–005, March 2004. Available online at www.cfsan.fda.gov/~dms/admehg3.html. Accessed August 1, 2008.

25. Exon, J. H. A review of the toxicology of acrylamide. *J. Toxicol. Environ. Health B. Crit. Rev.* 9:397–412, 2006.

26. Friedman, M., and Levin, C. E. Review of methods for the reduction of dietary content and toxicity of acrylamide. *J. Agric. Food Chem.* 56:6113–6140, 2008.

27. Osterholm, M. T., and Norgan, A. P. The role of irradiation in food safety. *N. Engl. J. Med.* 350:1898–1901, 2004.

28. U.S. Food and Drug Administration. *Food Irradiation: A Safe Measure*. January 2000. Available online at www.fda.gov/opacom/catalog/irradbro.html. Accessed July 31, 2008.

29. U.S. Food and Drug Administration. *Food Irradiation: A Safe Measure*. January 2000. Available online at www.fda.gov/opacom/catalog/irradbro.html. Accessed July 31, 2008.

30. National Toxicology Program, Center for the Evaluation of Risks to Human Reproduction. *NTP-CERHR Monograph on the Potential Human Reproductive and Developmental Effects of Bisphenol A*. National Institutes of Health publication number 08–5994, September 2008. Available online at http://cerhr.niehs.nih.gov/chemicals/bisphenol/bisphenol.pdf. Accessed February 6, 2009.

31. Eichholzer, M., and Gutzwiller, F. Dietary nitrates, nitrites, and N-nitroso compounds and cancer risk: A review of the epidemiologic evidence. *Nutr. Rev.* 56:95–105, 1998.

(©iStockphoto)

Focus On
Biotechnology

Outline

Figure F5.1 Chimera
Boyer and Cohen called the small loops of bacterial DNA that contain DNA from another organism, chimeras, after the mythical fire-breathing beast with the head of a lion and a goat, the body of a goat, and a serpent for a tail.

In 1909, British physician Archibald Garrod hypothesized that genes might be involved in creating proteins. By 1966, investigators had deciphered the genetic code, which links the information in DNA to the synthesis of proteins. The proteins made affect the traits that an organism exhibits. Then, in 1972, a discussion over hot pastrami and corned beef sandwiches between Dr. Stanley Cohen of Stanford University and Dr. Herbert Boyer of the University of California at San Francisco led to the birth of genetic engineering. The collaboration that resulted brought together the information needed to allow genetic instructions from one organism to be inserted into another. Cohen's laboratory had been studying how bacterial cells take up small loops of DNA. Boyer had been studying enzymes that could cut DNA at specific locations and paste it back together again. Cohen and Boyer realized that fragments of DNA, produced by cutting DNA with Boyer's enzymes, could be pasted into the small loops of DNA and introduced into bacterial cells using the procedure developed in Cohen's lab (**Figure F5.1**). As the bacteria multiplied, so would the new piece of DNA—making copies, or clones. These techniques for recombining DNA from different sources and cloning it are the basis for all genetic engineering.[1]

F5.1 How Does Biotechnology Work?

Learning Objectives

- Explain how genetic engineering introduces new traits into plants.
- Compare and contrast traditional breeding methods and modern biotechnology.

Modern **biotechnology** is possible because of the emergence of techniques that allow scientists to alter the DNA of plants, animals, yeast, and bacteria. By modifying DNA, these techniques, referred to as **genetic engineering**, allow scientists to change the proteins that a cell or organism can make, introducing new traits, enhancing desirable ones, or eliminating undesirable ones. Genetic engineering often involves taking the gene for a desired trait from one organism and transferring it to another. It has allowed researchers to create bacteria that make medicines for humans, plants that are disease-resistant, and foods that provide a healthier mix of nutrients. As this new technology has evolved so has the vocabulary to describe it (**Table F5.1**). Crops and other organisms and food products produced using these techniques are often referred to as *genetically modified* or *GM*.

biotechnology The process of manipulating life forms via genetic engineering in order to provide desirable products for human use.

genetic engineering A set of techniques used to manipulate DNA for the purpose of changing the characteristics of an organism or creating a new product.

Table F5.1 Terms Used in Genetic Engineering

Biotechnology	Manipulating life forms via genetic engineering to provide desirable products for human use.
Bioengineered foods	Foods that have been produced using biotechnology.
Chimera	A DNA molecule composed of DNA from two different species, or an organism consisting of tissues of diverse genetic constitution.
Cloning	Producing an exact duplicate of a gene or an organism.
DNA	A long, thread-like molecule that carries the genetic information of an organism.
Gene	A unit of DNA that provides genetic information coding for a trait. It is the physical basis for the transmission of the characteristics of living organisms from one generation to another.
Gene splicing	The precise joining of DNA from different sources to create a new gene structure.
Genetic engineering	Technology used to selectively alter genes. It can be used to manipulate the genetic material of an organism in such a way as to allow it to produce new and different types of proteins. Other terms applicable to the same techniques are gene splicing, gene manipulation, genetic modification, or recombinant DNA technology.
Genome	The total complement of genetic information in an organism.
GM crops	Genetically modified crops.
GMO	Genetically modified organism.
Hybridization	The mating of different plants to enhance favorable characteristics.
Plasmid	An independent, stable, self-replicating piece of circular DNA in bacterial cells. It is not a part of the normal cell genome.
Recombinant DNA	DNA that has been formed by joining the DNA from different sources.
Transgenic	An organism with a gene or group of genes intentionally transferred from another species or breed.

Genetics: From Genes to Traits

The characteristics of a plant or animal are carried in its genes. These genes, which are segments of DNA, are passed from generation to generation. Genes contain the information that directs the synthesis of proteins. The specific proteins that are made then determine the traits that an individual organism displays.

DNA Structure DNA is a long, threadlike molecule consisting of two strands that twist around each other forming a double helix. Each strand has a backbone made up of alternating units of the 5-carbon sugar deoxyribose and phosphate groups. Each deoxyribose sugar is attached to a molecule called a base. The four different bases that occur in DNA—adenine, thymine, cytosine, and guanine—are usually abbreviated as A, T, C, and G, respectively. The bases on adjacent strands bind to one another, connecting the two strands. Each base binds only to its complementary base: adenine to thymine and cytosine to guanine (**Figure F5.2**).

The DNA of all organisms—plants, bacteria, and animals, including humans—is made up of the same DNA bases. The differences in the sequence of bases in DNA are responsible for all of the genetic differences between living things, whether they are differences between species or differences between individuals of the same species. Different individuals of the same species have small differences in the base sequence of their DNA; only identical twins share the same base sequence. Organisms of different species, such as humans and corn plants, have larger differences in the sequences of DNA bases.

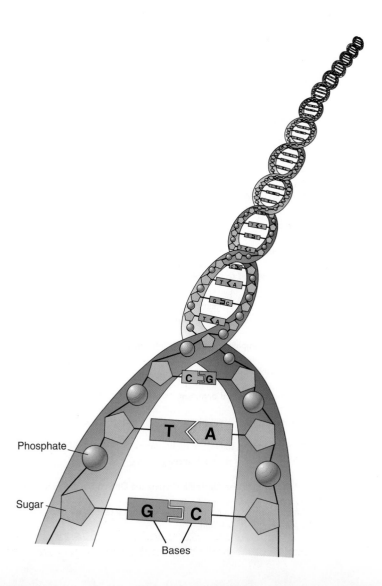

Figure F5.2 DNA: The double helix

DNA is a double-stranded helical molecule. Each strand has a backbone made up of phosphate groups and sugar molecules. Each sugar is attached to adenine (A), thymine (T), cytosine (C), or guanine (G). The two strands of the DNA molecule are bonded together by these bases; A bonds to T, and C bonds to G.

Plant cell
nucleus

Gene

ATGGCCCTGTGGATGCGC

DNA base sequence

Methionine Alanine Leucine Tryptophan Methionine Arginine

Amino acid sequence

Protein

Trait

Figure F5.3 **Relationships among genes, proteins, and traits**
The DNA base sequence in a gene codes for the sequence of amino acids that are joined to form a protein. Which proteins are made determines an organism's traits.

Genes to Proteins to Traits The sequence of bases present in a gene specifies the sequence of amino acids that will be present in a protein (see Chapter 6). In the genetic code, three bases code for a single amino acid. The same three bases will always code for the same amino acid, for example, the DNA base sequence ACC corresponds to the amino acid tryptophan. Because the code is universal among all life on Earth, a particular three-base sequence will code for the same amino acid whether it is in a bacterium, a mosquito, a corn plant, or a human being.

When a gene is expressed, the protein it codes for is made, providing certain characteristics to the organism. For example, if a protein that stimulates growth is made, the organism will grow bigger, and if a protein pigment is made, it will affect the color of the plant or animal. The presence or absence of specific proteins determines the traits that an individual organism displays (**Figure F5.3**).

Even though organisms of different species are very different, they may have genes with similar base sequences if they both need to make the same protein. For example, humans and pigs both rely on the protein hemoglobin to carry oxygen in the blood, so both humans and pigs have a gene with a very similar sequence of bases that codes for the protein hemoglobin. It is estimated that 25% of the genes found in plants are also present in humans, presumably because they code for proteins needed by both organisms.[2]

Passing Traits from Parent to Offspring When an organism reproduces, it passes its genes—and thus the instructions to make the proteins coded for by these genes—to the next generation. When two organisms breed, some genes from each are passed to the offspring. The result is a new combination of genes and the traits for

Figure F5.4 This electron micrograph shows a plasmid, which is a small loop of DNA found in bacterial cells. (Stanley N. Cohen/Photo Researchers)

which they code. Over time, mutations can occur in the sequence of bases that make up the genes. Some of these mutations are harmful, reducing the organism's ability to survive and reproduce. Because the organism dies or cannot reproduce, these harmful mutations are not passed on to the next generation. Other mutations are beneficial and result in traits that allow the organism to survive more easily and thus to reproduce and pass on the altered genes. Over millions of years many genes have been changed by mutations, and those that code for beneficial traits have been passed on because the organisms carrying them thrive and reproduce. The idea behind biotechnology is to speed up the process of introducing beneficial traits that can then be passed from generation to generation.

Methods of Biotechnology

The first step in genetic modification is to identify a stretch of DNA, or gene, for a desired trait, such as resistance to a particular disease. This gene of interest could be from a plant, animal, or bacterial cell. The gene is then clipped out with the specific DNA-cutting enzymes studied by Dr. Boyer, which are called **restriction enzymes** (see Chapter 6: Science Applied: Discovering How to Manipulate Genes).

A number of different techniques can be used to introduce the gene into the host cell. If the host cell is a plant cell the gene can be pasted into, or recombined with, the small loops of bacterial DNA studied by Dr. Cohen, called **plasmids** (**Figure F5.4**). Plasmids have the ability to carry genes from one place to another. The plasmid, containing the gene of interest, can be taken up by a bacterial cell. The bacterial cell can then transfer the gene to a plant cell. Once inside the plant cell, the new DNA can migrate to the nucleus, where the gene for the new trait can be integrated into the plant's DNA. The DNA is then referred to as **recombinant DNA** because the DNA from the plasmid has been combined with the plant's DNA (**Figure F5.5**).

A second method used to get genes into plant cells involves painting the desired segment of DNA onto microscopic metal particles. These are then loaded into a "gene gun" and shot into the plant cells. Once inside the cells, the DNA is washed off the metal particles by cellular fluids and migrates to the nucleus, where it is incorporated into the plant's DNA, forming recombinant DNA.

The modified plant cells produced by either technique are then allowed to multiply. As they do, the new gene is reproduced with them. The cells are then placed in a special culture medium that allows them to differentiate into the different types of cells that make up a whole plant. The new plant is a **transgenic** organism. Each cell in the new plant contains the transferred gene for the desired trait, such as disease resistance (see Figure F5.5).

Genetic engineering is more difficult in animals because animal cells do not take up genes as easily as plant cells do, and making copies of these cells (clones) is also more difficult. However, these techniques have been used to produce cows that yield more milk, cattle and pigs with more meat on them, and sheep that grow more wool.[3]

---

restriction enzyme
A bacterial enzyme used in genetic engineering that has the ability to cut DNA in a specific location.

plasmid A loop of bacterial DNA that is independent of the bacterial chromosome.

recombinant DNA DNA that has been formed by joining DNA from different sources.

transgenic An organism with a gene or group of genes intentionally transferred from another species or breed.

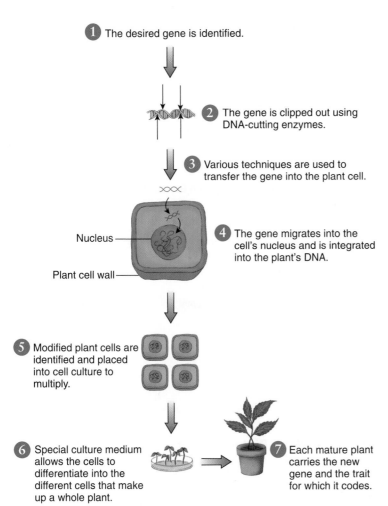

1 The desired gene is identified.

2 The gene is clipped out using DNA-cutting enzymes.

3 Various techniques are used to transfer the gene into the plant cell.

Nucleus

4 The gene migrates into the cell's nucleus and is integrated into the plant's DNA.

Plant cell wall

5 Modified plant cells are identified and placed into cell culture to multiply.

6 Special culture medium allows the cells to differentiate into the different cells that make up a whole plant.

7 Each mature plant carries the new gene and the trait for which it codes.

Figure F5.5 Engineering genetically modified plants Crops developed by using the genetic engineering steps shown here are grown all over the world.

selective breeding Techniques to selectively control mating in plants and animals for the purpose of producing organisms that better serve human needs.

Is Genetic Modification Really New?

Biotechnology methods are new, but humans have been directing the genetic modification of plants and animals for about 10,000 years. Farmers thousands of years ago didn't use gene guns or bacterial plasmids, but they selected seeds from plants with the most desirable characteristics to plant for the next year's crop, bred the animals that grew fastest or produced the most milk to improve the productivity of the next generation of animals, and cross-bred plant varieties to combine the desired traits of each. Almost every fruit, vegetable, or crop grown today has been in some way genetically modified using traditional **selective breeding** techniques. Some of these crops, such as pumpkins, potatoes, sugar beets, and varieties of corn, oats, and rice, would not have developed without human intervention. This intervention has allowed modern farmers to grow plants that produce more food that is more nutritious and can better withstand harsh environments and resist disease.

Traditional Breeding Technology Traditional breeding begins when farmers and ranchers select plants or animals with desired characteristics, such as high yield, palatability, resistance to disease and insects, or aesthetic characteristics. The traits can then be brought together by controlled mating. Plant breeders use a process called **hybridization**, in which two related plants are cross-pollinated or cross-fertilized (**Figure F5.6**). The resulting offspring has characteristics from both parent plants. For example, a breeder who wanted to produce a variety of wheat that was high-yielding and was resistant to cool temperatures would cross plants with these two traits. The breeder would then select the offspring that acquired both of the desired traits.

Cross-breeding of animals has a similar goal. Animal breeders use both inbreeding and outbreeding. Inbreeding involves crosses between closely related animals. It can

Figure F5.6 Cross-pollination or cross-fertilization, as illustrated with these oat seedlings, is a traditional method for breeding new plant varieties. (David Woodfall/Stone/ Getty Images, Inc.)

hybridization The process of cross-fertilizing two related plants with the goal of producing an offspring that has the desirable characteristics of both parent plants.

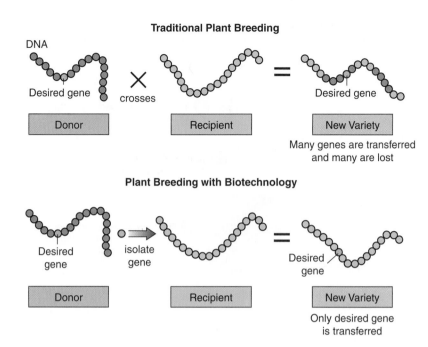

Figure F5.7 Traditional plant breeding versus biotechnology (Top) When traditional genetic modification methods are used thousands of genes are mixed. Not all the new varieties contain the desired gene and it may require many attempts over many years to remove the unwanted traits. (Bottom) Genetic engineering is more precise, more predictable, and faster. It allows the insertion of one or two genes into a plant without the transfer of genes coding for undesirable traits.

intensify desirable traits but may also intensify undesirable traits. Outbreeding crosses unrelated animals to reduce undesirable traits, increase variability, and introduce new traits. Today, inbreeding and outbreeding are carried out by artificial insemination.

Advantages of Modern Biotechnology Traditional breeding techniques work well but they have limitations in terms of both time and outcome. Breeding generations of plants or animals to consistently produce a desired trait is time-consuming; a new trait can only be produced once in the reproductive cycle of the plant or animal. Only plants or animals of the same or closely related species can be interbred. Not every offspring will inherit the desirable traits. Because cross-breeding transfers a set of genes from the parents to the offspring, both desirable and undesirable traits are transferred. Eliminating the undesirable genes while keeping the desirable ones can require many crosses.

Biotechnology, which selects specific genes in the laboratory, has significantly sped up this process and removed certain limitations. It enables breeders to select, modify, and transfer single genes. This speeds up the process by reducing the time and cost of breeding the crosses that are needed to select out the undesirable traits (**Figure F5.7**). In addition, biotechnology is not limited by whether two animals are capable of cross-breeding but, rather, can select desirable genes from any species because the way DNA codes for proteins in plants, animals, yeast, and bacteria is the same. This allows traits from different species and completely different organisms to be used.

F5.2 Applications of Modern Biotechnology

Learning Objectives

- List some ways in which genetic engineering is being used to enhance the food supply.
- Describe how genetic engineering can be used to combat human disease.

The techniques of biotechnology can be used in a variety of ways in both production and processing to alter the quantity, quality, cost, safety, and shelf life of the food supply (**Table F5.2**). This technology also has great potential for addressing the problem of world hunger and malnutrition.

Table F5.2 Characteristics Introduced Using Genetic Engineering

Food	Characteristic
Cherry tomato	Better taste, color, texture
Flavr Savr tomato	Delayed ripening
Tomato	Thicker skin, altered pectin content
Corn	Insect protection, herbicide resistance
Cotton	Insect protection, herbicide resistance
Squash	Virus resistance
Papaya	Virus resistance
Potatoes	Potato beetle resistance, virus resistance
Soybeans	Herbicide resistance, high oleic content to reduce need for hydrogenation
Sugar beets	Herbicide resistance
Sunflower	High oleic acid content to reduce need for hydrogenation

Increasing Crop Yields

Genetic modification of crops can increase yields either directly, by inserting genes that improve the efficiency with which plants convert sunlight into food, or indirectly, by creating plants that are resistant to herbicides, pesticides, and plant diseases, thus reducing crop losses. Scientists are also working to develop plants that can withstand drought, freezing, and high salt concentrations. Many attempts in the last century to increase crop yields in developing countries have failed because they required expensive machinery and chemicals. With genetically engineered crops, simply providing a new type of seed has the potential to increase food production.

Herbicide Resistance Herbicides are chemicals that are sprayed on crops in the field to control weeds. Effective herbicides kill weeds but do not harm crops. A crop such as soybeans is not harmed by a particular herbicide because it contains enzymes that inactivate the herbicide. These enzymes are crop specific so only certain herbicides can be used with certain crops. In some cases the weeds and the crops are resistant to the same herbicide so the farmer has few or no choices for weed control. Genetic engineering allows researchers to transfer genes for herbicide resistance to plants making them resistant to new types of herbicides. Farmers then have more options for weed control so they can use herbicides that are less expensive, more effective, and less environmentally damaging.

Insect Resistance Genetic engineering techniques can increase insect resistance in plants. For example, a gene from the bacterium *Bacillus thuringiensis* produces a protein that is toxic to certain insects but safe for humans and other animals (**Figure F5.8**). By inserting the gene for this protein into plant cells, scientists have created plants that manufacture their own insecticide. The protein produced by this gene, known as Bt, has been used as an insecticide for over 30 years. But when plants manufacture their own insecticide, Bt does not need to be sprayed on the plants. This saves the farmer money, fuel, and time. It also benefits the environment because the Bt affects only insects feeding on the crop of interest and is not spread to surrounding foliage. Corn, potatoes, and cotton have been genetically modified to produce the Bt protein. During the first 3 years of commercial availability, cotton with the Bt gene reduced chemical insecticide use by 2 million pounds.

In addition to creating insect-resistant plants, genetic engineering has been used to create environmentally friendly pesticides. These pesticides are produced by bacteria, which are killed and then sprayed on plants.

Figure F5.8 Genetically engineered corn that produces the Bt protein is toxic to this European corn borer. (Courtesy Marlin E. Rice, Iowa State University)

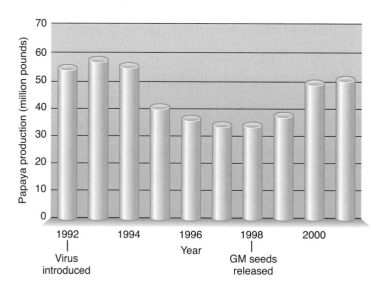

Figure F5.9 **Virus-resistant papaya**
Seeds for papaya that are resistant to the papaya ring-spot virus were released for commercialization in 1998, allowing Hawaiian papaya production to rebound. This was the first genetically enhanced fruit crop on the market.

Disease Resistance Potato, squash, cucumber, watermelon, and papaya have been modified to resist viral infections. The benefits of this technology are illustrated by how it helped to preserve Hawaii's second largest crop. In the mid-1990s the papaya ring-spot virus threatened to wipe out Hawaii's papaya crop. Traditional plant breeding was not able to produce a virus-resistant strain of papaya, but by inserting a gene that acted like a vaccine into the papaya plant DNA, scientists were able to produce papaya plants that were immune to the virus (**Figure F5.9**).[4]

Improving Nutritional Quality

Although the causes of malnutrition are rooted in political, economic, and cultural issues that cannot be resolved by agricultural technology alone, genetically modified crops that target some of the major nutritional deficiencies worldwide are being developed. To address protein deficiency, varieties of corn, soybeans, and sweet potatoes with higher levels of essential amino acids are being developed. To address iron deficiency, rice has been engineered to contain more iron.[5] To address vitamin A deficiency, genes that code for the production of enzymes needed for the synthesis of the vitamin A precursor β-carotene have been inserted into rice.[6] Half of the world's population depends on rice as a dietary staple, but it is a poor source of vitamin A. The genetically modified rice is called Golden Rice for the color imparted by the β-carotene pigment (**Figure F5.10**). One variety of Golden Rice that has been developed contains enough pro-vitamin A in 1/2 cup of dry rice (about 1 cup cooked) to provide over 50% of the RDA for a child.[7] The first field trial of Golden Rice was com-

Figure F5.10 The rice on the (right), called Golden Rice, has genetically modified to produce the vitamin A precursor β-carotene, which gives it a yellow-orange color. The white rice on the left does not contain this genetic modification. (Courtesy Golden Rice Humanitarian Board)

pleted in 2004.[8] When development and testing are finished, Golden Rice could be distributed to public rice breeding institutions where local breeders could incorporate it into rice varieties that are grown for local consumption.

Biotechnology is also being used to provide foods that may help prevent chronic disease. For example, genetic modification has produced a variety of soybeans that has a higher percentage of monounsaturated fat—a type of fat that may help reduce the risk of cardiovascular disease. Vegetable oils that have lower amounts of saturated fat are also being developed, as are soybeans that contain more of the antioxidant vitamin E than the traditional varieties.[9]

Other qualities that affect a food's role in the diet can also be changed by genetic engineering. For example, potatoes that are denser and have less water have been developed because they absorb less oil when fried—lowering the fat content of an order of french fries.

Advancing Food Quality and Processing

Genetic engineering is also being used to improve the appeal and quality of food. The first genetically modified whole food available on the market was the Flavr Savr tomato, introduced in 1994. In this case, rather than adding a gene, an existing gene for an enzyme that controls ripening was inactivated to slow the ripening process and prolong the tomato's shelf life. Unfortunately, the modified tomatoes still softened so they were difficult to harvest and ship. The Flavr Savr tomato was taken off the market because it was not economically feasible.

Biotechnology is also used in food processing. For example, in the past the enzyme preparation rennet, which is used in cheese production, had to be extracted from calf stomachs, but now it can be produced by genetically modified bacteria (**Figure F5.11**). About 60% of the hard cheese made in the United States is made with genetically engineered enzymes.[10] Other enzymes, such as those used in the production of high-fructose corn syrup and the enzyme lactase, which is used to reduce the lactose content of milk, are also produced by genetically modified microorganisms. Many food color and flavor additives are also produced in the laboratory. For example, vanilla can now be produced by plant cells grown in culture, rather than harvested from vanilla orchid plants, which only grow in tropical climates.

Enhancing Food Safety

Biotechnology can improve food safety by engineering foods to reduce or eliminate naturally occurring allergens. For example, people who are allergic to peanuts may someday enjoy peanut butter sandwiches made with peanuts that have been genetically modified to eliminate the proteins or portions of the proteins to which they are allergic.

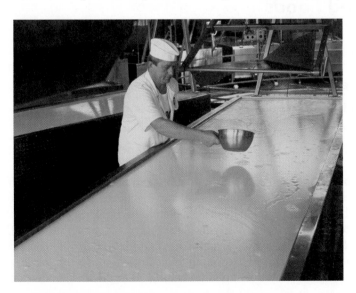

Figure F5.11 During cheese production, an enzyme preparation known as rennet is added to clot the milk. Much of the hard cheese produced in the United States today relies on rennet produced by genetically modified bacteria. (Rosenfeld Images Ltd./Photo Researchers)

Improving Animal and Seafood Production

Genetic engineering is being used to improve methods of preventing, diagnosing, and treating animal disease as well as to enhance growth efficiency and fertility in food animals. The first FDA-approved application of biotechnology in animal production was the use of recombinant bovine somatotropin (bST) in dairy cows. To produce recombinant bST, scientists isolated the gene from cow cells and then inserted it into bacterial cells. The bST, which is produced in large amounts by the bacterial cells, was then isolated, purified, and injected into dairy cows to increase milk production.

Biotechnology is also being applied to **aquaculture**. Aquaculture is the fastest growing sector of animal production worldwide. There is concern about the environmental impact of raising large numbers of fish in a restricted area and the safety of consuming this fish. Today, most of the salmon consumed in the United States is farm-raised. Because farm-raised salmon are fed pellets made of concentrated fish products, they are also fed the toxins that were present in the bodies of other fish. A comparison between wild salmon and farm-raised salmon found that the farm-raised salmon had higher levels of PCB (polychlorinated biphenyl), dioxin, toxaphene, and dieldrin—all of these are suspected to cause cancer in humans.[11] Despite these problems, there is also optimism that aquaculture will help reduce the world's dependence on wild stocks of fish. Biotechnology allows scientists to identify and combine traits in fish and shellfish to increase productivity and improve quality. Scientists are currently investigating genes that will increase production of natural fish growth factors and genes that boost the production of compounds that help marine organisms fight microbial infections. For example, genetic engineering has been used to increase growth rate in a species of Atlantic salmon. These fish grow to market weight in about 18 months, compared to 24 to 30 months for unmodified fish.[12]

aquaculture The controlled cultivation and harvest of aquatic plants or animals.

Combating Human Disease

One of the ways that biotechnology is impacting human health and the treatment of disease is through the production of genetically engineered medicines. In 1978, bacteria were engineered to produce human insulin. Before this, diabetics relied on insulin extracted from pigs or cows. Other engineered proteins used to treat human disease include tissue plasminogen activator to dissolve blood clots in heart attack victims, growth factors to stimulate cell replication in bone marrow transplants, hepatitis B vaccine, and interferon to attack viruses and stimulate the immune system.

F5.3 Safety and Regulation of Genetically Modified Foods

Learning Objectives

- Explain how genetic engineering might create foods that harm consumers.
- Discuss the potential impact of genetic engineering on the environment.
- Describe how genetically modified food and crops are regulated.

The use of biotechnology is expanding rapidly, producing a variety of different products (**Figure F5.12**). Despite the potential benefits of these products there is concern that this technology may create health problems and cause environmental damage. A number of regulations are currently in place to protect consumers and the environment. The National Academy of Sciences has concluded that the risks posed by agricultural products produced by modern biotechnology are the same as those for products produced by traditional plant breeding.[13] Despite this, many consumers and

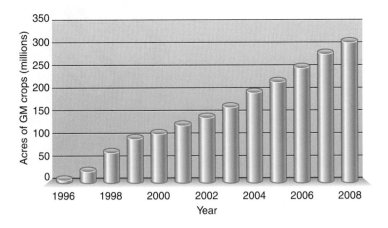

Figure F5.12 Worldwide growth of GM crops, 1996–2008 Despite concerns about the impact of GM crops, the number of acres planted with them has risen steadily. The most common GM crops are soybeans, corn, cotton, and rapeseed (for canola oil).

scientists alike believe that the conclusions regarding the health and environmental effects of these relatively new products are premature and that the impact of this booming technology has not yet become apparent.[14] They urge that this technology be used with caution to avoid introducing health or environmental risks that outweigh the benefits.

Consumer Safety

Consumer safety concerns related to bioengineered foods include the possibility that an allergen or toxin may have inadvertently been introduced into a previously safe food, or that the nutrient content of a food has been negatively affected. Although foods containing ingredients derived from plant biotechnology are not generally required to carry special labels, those that contain potentially harmful allergens or toxins, or that are altered nutritionally, must carry labels (see Off the Label: Should Genetically Modified Foods Carry Special Labels?). Another potential health concern is that the antibiotic resistance genes used in biotechnology may promote the development of antibiotic-resistant strains of bacteria.

Allergens and Toxins Genes code for proteins, so when a new gene is introduced into a food product, a new protein is made. These new proteins may in some cases be allergens or toxins. If a food contains a new protein that is an allergen, allergic individuals will now react to this food, which may previously have been safe for them. For example, if DNA from fish or peanuts—foods that commonly cause allergic reactions—was introduced into tomatoes or corn, these foods would then be dangerous to allergic individuals. To prevent this from happening unintentionally, biotechnology companies have established systems for monitoring the allergenic potential of proteins used for plant genetic engineering.[15] Testing for the transfer of allergens has already proved to be valuable. In 1996 allergy testing successfully prevented soybeans containing a gene from a Brazil nut from entering the market.[16] If these soybeans had entered the food supply they could have caused allergic reactions in people allergic to nuts. However, despite mandatory testing programs, individuals with food allergies cannot assume that new foods are safe.

Likewise, when a product is created using either a donor or recipient organism that is known to produce a toxin, the manufacturer must verify that the resulting product does not have high levels of the toxin. Toxins are also an issue when plants are produced by traditional breeding; toxic varieties of celery and potatoes have resulted from traditional breeding methods.

Changes in Nutrient Content Changing the proteins made by a plant or animal could also affect the nutrient content of foods. For example, tomatoes are an excellent source of vitamin C. If tomatoes were modified to have no vitamin C, people who rely on tomatoes for this vitamin might no longer get enough in their diets. As with foods containing potentially harmful allergens or toxins, foods with altered nutrient content must be labeled to disclose this information.

Off the Label
Should Genetically Modified Foods Carry Special Labels?

Can you identify foods containing ingredients created using genetic engineering? The answer is usually no because the FDA requires special labels only on foods containing genetically modified (GM) ingredients that pose a potential risk to consumers. Some people feel that all foods containing GM ingredients should be labeled as such. Proponents of mandatory labeling argue that consumers have a right to this information and that it will help to ensure that the regulatory measures set up to protect consumer and environmental safety are working. Opponents say such labeling would be misleading, since even foods that are not different in quality, nutrient composition, and safety would be viewed as somehow different from the traditional foods.

Ethical, Philosophical, and Religious Issues

Can a tomato that contains some DNA from a fish be included in a vegan diet? Is corn that contains DNA from a pig appropriate for Jews and Muslims to eat? The FDA currently believes that the answer to these questions is yes, since plants and animals already share some of the same DNA segments. Jewish organizations agree and say that a single gene or even several genes transferred from an animal or shellfish source create no automatic conflict with a kosher diet. Despite this, some have suggested special labeling of GM products for kosher and vegetarian dietary requirements.

Economic Issues

Labeling increases costs at many levels. Hundreds, if not thousands, of food products contain GM ingredients and would therefore need to be labeled if regulations change. DNA-modified plants would need to be segregated during planting and harvesting, and products containing ingredients from them would require different manufacturing, transport, and storage facilities. Despite opposition, however, the need to sell to markets such as the European Union that do not want GM crops is already forcing U.S. farmers to separate and label GM crops.

Current Labeling Policy

When considering the safety and labeling of foods, the FDA traditionally has focused on the characteristics of a food, not on how it is produced. Virtually all plants have been genetically modified through traditional plant breeding, and the FDA does not require declarations regarding those modifications. Under this precedent, labeling decisions are based on whether there are differences between the new food and the traditional food. Labeling of foods containing GM ingredients is therefore required only if the nutritional composition of the food has been altered; if it contains potentially harmful allergens, toxins, pesticides, or herbicides; if it contains ingredients that are new to the food supply; or if the food has been changed significantly enough that its traditional name no longer applies.

What Is an Appropriate Label?

Whether the label is voluntary or mandatory, designing an appropriate label is a complex issue. Some companies are voluntarily labeling foods as "Grown from genetically modified seed." The FDA feels that these simple labels will imply to some people that the product is inherently better than other products, while other people will feel this means that the food is more dangerous than others. However, a more detailed label that describes the way that a particular product was modified would be too lengthy and would not be understood by many consumers.

The Bottom Line

Food labeling allows customers to know what is in their food. They can then use this information to decide whether or not to choose the food. The question remains, are GM ingredients different enough from ingredients produced without genetic engineering to warrant the economic and logistical costs involved in providing this information on food labels?

Antibiotic Resistance There is a concern that the use of genetic engineering will spread antibiotic resistance traits to bacteria in the environment or in the gastrointestinal tract. If pathogenic bacteria were to acquire this trait, it would make some of the antibiotics used to treat disease ineffective. The reason for this concern is that genetic engineering techniques use genes that code for antibiotic-resistance as marker genes. By inserting a marker gene along with the gene they want to transfer, scientists are able to check to see that the gene transfer was successful. Antibiotic-resistant genes are used for this purpose because it is easy to verify that the transfer has occurred by exposing the bacteria to antibiotics—those that survive the antibiotic contain the transferred genes. Current techniques are unlikely to cause problems because the marker genes used are already widespread in the normal bacteria that inhabit the gut and in harmless environmental bacteria. In addition, markers are not used if they confer resistance to clinically important antibiotics. Newer techniques are under development that will remove the antibiotic resistance markers before the plants leave the laboratory.[17]

Environmental Concerns

Some of the arguments against the use of genetically modified crops are that they will reduce diversity, promote the evolution of pesticide-resistant insects, or create "superweeds" that will overgrow our agricultural and forest lands.

Diversity The ability of populations of organisms to adapt to new conditions, diseases, or other hazards depends on the presence of many different species that provide a diversity of genes. When there is diversity, a harmful event, such as the emergence of a new disease strain, does not eliminate all the plants—it might kill one species, but others would have genes that protect them. Likewise a drought might be harmful to some species, while others would have genes that make them drought-resistant.

A concern with biotechnology is that farmers will prefer new, resistant, high-yielding crop varieties and stop planting other varieties, causing certain varieties to eventually become extinct. For example, if every farmer began to use only genetically modified rice, then the varieties of rice that carry other traits would become extinct and those traits would be lost. If a new insect or virus emerged that killed the genetically modified rice, breeders and genetic engineers would not have the other varieties available to search for a gene that allows survival. This problem is not unique to genetically engineered crops. Diversity is also reduced when plants produced by traditional plant breeding are used to the exclusion of others. To preserve diversity and ensure a large supply of traits for use in future breeding, biotechnology techniques are being applied to establish gene banks and seed banks and to identify and characterize the genes in many species.[18] These precautions are designed to help prevent genes from being lost, but they will not prevent our agricultural land from being dominated by only a few varieties of crops.

Superweeds and Superbugs Other environmental concerns that have been raised with regard to genetically modified crops are that they will promote the development of superweeds or superbugs. A superweed might arise if a plant that has been modified to grow faster or to better survive begins growing in areas beyond the farmer's field. Most experts do not feel this is a major concern because domesticated crops depend on a managed agricultural environment and carry traits that make them unable to compete in the wild.

It has also been suggested that the genes inserted to produce hardy, high-yield, fast-growing crops could be transferred to wild relatives by natural cross-breeding. This could result in fast-growing superweeds. Although a possibility, this scenario is unlikely for a number of reasons. First, the probability that a weed growing near a genetically modified plant is closely enough related to cross-breed is small. Even if it does occur, the chances that the new plant will survive and have inherited traits that enhance its survival is even smaller. As a further safeguard to prevent environmental risks, most developers avoid adding traits that could increase the competitiveness or other undesirable properties of weedy relatives.

There is also concern that crops engineered to produce pesticides will promote the evolution of pesticide-resistant insects. Although this is an important concern, the risk of it occurring is no greater when pesticides are engineered into the crops than it is when pesticides are sprayed on crops. An illustration of this problem involves insects that are resistant to the Bt toxin.[18] As more and more of the insect's food supply is made up of plants that produce this pesticide or plants that are sprayed with it, only insects that carry genes making them resistant to Bt can survive and reproduce. This increases the number of Bt-resistant insects and therefore reduces the effectiveness of Bt as a method of pest control. To address this problem, strategies are being developed to prevent the number of Bt-resistant insects from increasing. Farmers who grow pesticide-resistant crops are required to grow nonmodified plants in adjacent fields. This provides

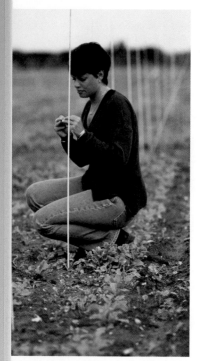

Figure F5.13 Field tests of genetically modified crops attempt to determine the impact of the new crops on the environment and how well the plants function. There is concern, however, that the tests themselves may pose a risk to the environment. (Chris Knapton/Photo Researchers)

a food supply for—and encourages the continued existence of—nonresistant insect pests, thereby reducing the likelihood that the number of pesticide-resistant insects will increase.

Regulation of Genetically Engineered Food Products

Although the United States government does not scrutinize every step of the development of new plant varieties, it is involved in overseeing the process. The government sets guidelines to help researchers address safety and environmental issues at all stages, from the early development of genetically engineered plants through field-testing and, eventually, commercialization. Companies that develop new plant varieties must provide data to support the safety and wholesomeness of the product. Crops created by both traditional breeding and biotechnology methods must be field-tested for several seasons to make sure only desirable changes have been made (**Figure F5.13**). Plants are examined to ensure that they look right, grow right, and produce food that is safe and tastes right. Analytical tests must be performed to determine if the levels of nutrients in the new variety are different and if the food is safe to eat. The FDA, the USDA, and the EPA are all involved in the oversight of plant biotechnology.[19]

The Food and Drug Administration (FDA) The FDA has jurisdiction over the safety of foods in the marketplace and therefore regulates the safety and labeling of all foods and animal feeds derived from crops, including genetically modified crops. The FDA policy is that the safety of a food product should be determined based on the characteristics of the food or food product, not the method used to produce it. Foods developed using biotechnology are therefore evaluated to determine their equivalence to foods produced by traditional plant breeding. Emphasis is placed on whether the food creates a new or increased allergenic risk, has an increased level of a naturally occurring toxin, contains a substance not previously present in the food supply, or is nutritionally different from the traditional plant. Currently, premarket approval is required only when the new food contains substances not commonly found in foods or contains a substance that does not have a history of safe use in foods. Despite this, all new plant varieties developed through biotechnology that are intended for food and animal feed marketed in the United States have thus far completed the FDA's voluntary premarket consultation process before they entered the market. To prevent material from a new plant variety intended for food use from inadvertently entering the food supply without the FDA being consulted, the FDA has asked developers to provide them with information about the safety of the new plants at a relatively early stage of development.[20]

U.S. Department of Agriculture (USDA) The USDA regulates agricultural products and research concerning the development of new plant varieties. The Animal and Plant Health Inspection Service (APHIS) of the USDA helps to ensure that the cultivation of a new plant variety poses no risk to agricultural production or to the environment. For example, if there is a high probability that a new plant variety will cross-breed with a weed and that the transfer of the new trait could allow the weed plant to survive better, APHIS may not allow further development of this plant. If a plant has been studied and tested and does not pose environmental risks, field-testing is allowed. APHIS continues to oversee the testing until it is determined that the plant is safe.

Environmental Protection Agency (EPA) The EPA regulates any pesticides that may be present in foods and sets tolerance levels for these pesticides. This includes genetically modified plants that are able to protect themselves from insects or disease. The EPA assesses the safety of the protein that confers the insect or disease resistance for human consumption, for other organisms, and for the environment.

References

1. Cohen, S. N., Chang, A. C., Boyer, H. W., and Helling, R. B. Construction of biologically functional bacterial plasmids *in vitro. Proc. Natl. Acad. Sci. U.S.A.* 70:3240–3244, 1973.

2. Cook, J. R. Testimony before the U.S. House of Representatives Subcommittee on Basic Research hearing on "Plant Genome Research: From the Lab to the Field to the Market." October 5, 1999, Serial No. 106–60. Washington, D.C.: Government Printing Office, 1999.

3. Margawati, E. T. *Transgenic Animals: Their Benefits to Human Welfare.* Available online at www.actionbioscience.org/ biotech/margawati.html. Accessed March 21, 2009.

4. Gonsalves, D., and Ferreira, S. *Transgenic Papaya: A Case for Managing Risks of Papaya Ringspot Virus in Hawaii.* Available online at www.plantmanagementnetwork.org/pub/ php/review/2003/papaya/. Accessed August 21, 2008.

5. Sautter, C., Poletti, S., Zhang, P., and Gruissem, W. Biofortification of essential nutritional compounds and trace elements in rice and cassava. *Proc. Nutr. Soc.* 65:153–159, 2006.

6. Ye, X., Al-Babili, S., Kloti, A., et al. Engineering the provitamin A (beta-carotene) biosynthetic pathway into (carotenoid-free) rice endosperm. *Science* 287:303–305, 2000.

7. Paine, J. A., Shipton, C. A., Chaggar, S., et al. Improving the nutritional value of Golden Rice through increased pro-vitamin A content. *Nat. Biotechnol.* 23:482–487, 2005.

8. Golden Rice. History of Programme: The Road to the Farm is Bumpy. Available online at www.goldenrice.org/ Content1-Who/who2_history.html/ Accessed February 22, 2006.

9. Sattler, S. E., Cheng, Z., and DellaPenna, D. From *Arabidopsis* to agriculture: Engineering improved vitamin E content in soybean. *Trends Plant Sci.* 9:365–367, 2004.

10. U.S. Department of Agriculture, Agricultural Marketing Service, National Organic Program. Final Rule. Available online at www. ams.usda.gov/nop/nop2000/nop/ finalrulepages/finalrulemap.htm/ Accessed March 1, 2001.

11. Hites, R. A., Foran, J. A., Carpenter, D. O., et al. Global assessment of organic contaminants in farmed salmon. *Science* 303:226–229, 2004.

12. Lewis, C. Kind of fish story: The coming of biotech animals. *FDA Consumer* 35:15–20, Jan/Feb 2001.

13. National Academy of Sciences, National Research Council. *Genetically Modified Pest-Protected Plants: Science and Regulation.* Washington, D.C.: National Academies Press, 2000.

14. Singh, O. V., Ghai, S., Paul, D., and Jain, R. K. Genetically modified crops: Success, safety assessment, and public concern. *Appl. Microbiol. Biotechnol.* 71:598–607, 2006.

15. Goodman, R. E., Vieths, S., Sampson, H. A. et al. Allergenicity assessment of genetically modified crops— what makes sense? *Nat. Biotechnol.* 26:73–81, 2008.

16. Nordlee, J. A., Taylor, S. L., Townsend, J. A., et al. Identification of a Brazil-nut allergen in transgenic soybeans. *N. Engl. J. Med.* 334: 688–692, 1996.

17. Darbani, B., Eimanifar, A., Stewart, C. N. Jr., and Camargo, W. N. Methods to produce marker-free transgenic plants. *Biotechnol. J.* 2:83–90, 2007.

18. Lemaux, P. G. Genetically engineered plants and foods: A scientist's analysis of the issues (Part II). *Annu. Rev. Plant Biol.* 60:511–559, 2009.

19. U.S. Food and Drug Administration. Plant Biotechnology for Food and Feed: FDAs Biotechnology Policy. Available online at www.fda.gov/Food/Biotechnology/default.htm. Accessed October 5, 2009.

20. U.S. Food and Drug Administration. FDA Talk Paper: FDA Proposes Draft Guidance for Industry for New Plant Varieties Intended for Food Use, November 19, 2004. Available online at www.fda.gov/bbs/topics/ANSWERS/ 2004/ANS01327.html/ Accessed October 6, 2005.

18

World Hunger and Malnutrition

Case Study

José wanted to create a poster for the university student union to raise awareness of World Food Day. This event, which commemorates the founding of the Food and Agriculture Organization of the United Nations on October 16, 1945, is observed annually in more than 150 countries. Its goal is to heighten public awareness and understanding of the plight of the world's hungry and malnourished, as well as to promote year-round action to alleviate world hunger. José decided to create a collage of newspaper and magazine headlines to illustrate the inadequate food supply and resulting hunger and malnutrition that plagues most of the world. Some research on the Internet turned up a number of stories from around the globe.

When josé looked at all of this information together, though, he realized that his understanding of malnutrition around the world was not as complete as he had thought. In India, where he had believed hunger was common, there was a grain surplus. In the United States, where the grocery-store shelves were always packed, people were going hungry. José began to realize that hunger and malnutrition are complicated problems and that viewing them as merely the result of a lack of food is an oversimplification.

(Hola Images/Getty Images, Inc.)

(©iStockphoto)

(...umba/AFP/Getty Images, Inc.)

Chapter Outline

18.1 The Two Faces of Malnutrition

Learning Objectives

- Describe the two faces of malnutrition in the world today.
- Explain what is meant by nutrition transition.

For most of us, the image that comes to mind when we think of malnutrition around the world is one of hunger and starvation. The nations at risk change but the soulful eyes and bloated bellies of the starving children remain (**Figure 18.1**). About 923 million people around the world are chronically undernourished; over a third of all deaths in children under 5 years of age are due to undernutrition, which kills nearly 6 million children each year.[1–4] At the same time that global health organizations are struggling with issues of undernutrition, rates of illness related to overcomsumption are soaring. For the first time in human history the number of overweight people rivals the number who are underweight.[5] The overweight and the undernourished both suffer from malnutrition and experience high levels of sickness and disability, shorter life expectancies, and lower levels of productivity. These two faces of malnutrition exist together and complicate the goal of solving the problem of malnutrition worldwide.

Nutrition Transition

nutrition transition A series of changes in diet, physical activity, health and nutrition that occurs as poor countries become more prosperous.

As economic conditions in a country improve changes occur in the way food is grown, produced, and obtained, and traditional diets give way to more modern food intake patterns. This **nutrition transition** begins the shift from concern with undernutrition to concern with overnutrition and, at times, the two exist together in the same population (**Figure 18.2**).

Traditional diets in developing countries are based on a limited number of foods—primarily starchy root vegetables. As incomes increase and food availability improves, the diet becomes more varied and is likely to include more meat, milk, refined grains, fat, and sugar. Along with this dietary transition comes changes in lifestyle that decrease activity. There is a shift toward less physically demanding occupations, an increase in the use of transportation to get to work or school, more labor-saving technology in the home, and more passive leisure time. As a result, nutrition-related chronic diseases such as cardiovascular disease, cancer, diabetes, and obesity are newly appearing, rapidly rising, or already established in every country around the world (**Figure 18.3**).

Some of the effects of this economic and nutrition transition are positive. Shifts in diet are accompanied both by increases in life expectancy and by decreases in the frequency of low birth weight, infectious disease, and nutrient deficiencies. However, at the same time, rates of heart disease, cancer, diabetes, and obesity increase.[6,7] The

Figure 18.1 Undernutrition is more common in developing nations, especially among children because they have high nutrient needs. (Reuters/Bettman/©Corbis)

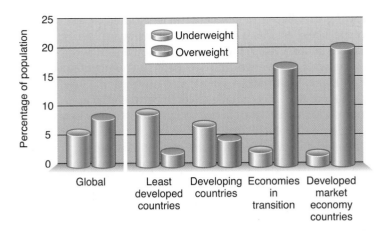

Figure 18.2 Impact of economic development on the incidence of underweight and overweight
As countries develop economically, the incidence of underweight drops, but the percentage of the population that is overweight increases. Higher rates of obesity are found in cities because of greater food availability and more sedentary occupations.

increased reliance on animal proteins as well as on refined and processed foods also increases the amount of energy and natural resources needed to produce the food, which in the long term may damage the environment.

Obesity: A World Health Problem

There are now more than 1 billion adults worldwide who are overweight and 300 million of them carry enough excess body fat to be classified as obese.[5] The prevalence of obesity around the world ranges from less than 5% in rural China, Japan, and some African countries to as high as 75% of the adult population in urban Samoa.[5] In Argentina, Colombia, Mexico, Paraguay, Peru, and Uruguay more than half of the population is overweight, and more than 15% are obese.[8] Countries such as China and India, which have historically been plagued by undernutrition, must now also contend with overnutrition. In China the number of adults who are overweight jumped from 9% in 1989 to 15% in 1992, and rates are almost 20% in some cities.[9] In parts of Africa obesity is now considered a major disease along with AIDS and malnutrition. Because obesity increases the risk of cardiovascular disease, hypertension, stroke, type 2 diabetes, certain cancers, arthritis, and other conditions it is now a major contributor to what has been called the "global burden of chronic disease and disability (Figure 18.3)."[5]

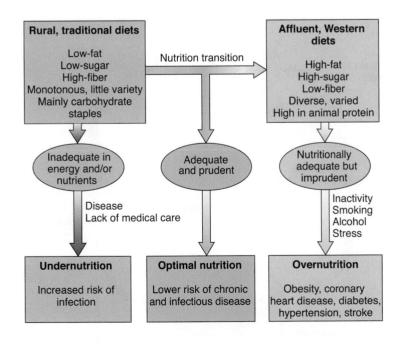

Figure 18.3 Consequences of nutrition transition
A diet that falls somewhere between the traditional rural diet that may be inadequate in energy, protein, or micronutrients and the affluent Western diet that meets nutrient needs but is high in fat and sugar and low in fiber is optimal for health. (Source: Adapted from Vorster. H. H., Bourne, L. T., Venter, C. S., and Oosthuizen, W. Contribution of nutrition to the health transition in developing countries: A framework for research and intervention. Nutr. Rev. 57: 341–349, 1999).

Life Cycle

The growing prevalence of obesity among children is also a major concern. According to the latest estimates from the International Obesity Task Force about 22 million children under 5 years of age are overweight and at least 155 million school-age children worldwide are overweight or obese.[10] The number of overweight children is on the rise in Egypt, South Africa, China, and Australia. In Chile, Peru, and Mexico obesity rates are more than 25% among children between the ages of 4 and 10 years.[8] In some countries a high prevalence of overweight children now exists alongside a high frequency of undernourished children. For example, in northern Africa the percentage of overweight children is over 8% while the percent of wasted children is reported at over 7%; in eastern Asia, 4.3% of preschool children are overweight and 3.4% wasted.[11]

18.2 The Cycle of Malnutrition

Learning Objectives

- Discuss the impact of malnutrition throughout the life cycle.
- Define stunting.
- Describe the relationship between malnutrition and infectious disease.

cycle of malnutrition A cycle in which malnutrition is perpetuated by an inability to meet nutrient needs at all life stages.

In populations where undernutrition is a chronic problem, there is a **cycle of malnutrition** (**Figure 18.4**). The cycle begins when women consume a deficient diet during pregnancy. These women are more likely to give birth to low-birth-weight infants who are susceptible to illness and early death. The children who do survive may be small and weakened physically and mentally. They grow into undernourished adults, who are also susceptible to disease and unable to contribute optimally to economic and social development. The women in this next generation also begin their pregnancies poorly nourished and are therefore likely to give birth to low-birth-weight infants. Interruption of this cycle of malnutrition at any point can benefit the individuals and the society. Healthy children can then grow into healthy adults who produce healthy offspring and can contribute fully to society.

Low Birth Weight and Infant Mortality

infant mortality rate
The number of deaths during the first year of life per 1000 live births.

Low-birth-weight infants—those weighing less than 5.5 lbs (2.5 kg) at birth—are at greater risk of complications, illness, and early death. A higher number of low-birth-weight infants means a higher **infant mortality rate**, the number of deaths per 1000

Figure 18.4 The cycle of malnutrition
Malnutrition affects the health and productivity of individuals at every stage of life. It often begins in the womb, continues through infancy and childhood, and extends into adolescent and adult life.

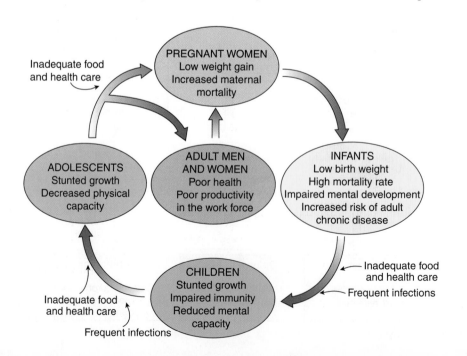

live births in a population. The infant mortality rate and the number of low-birth-weight births are indicators of the health and nutritional status of a population. In industrialized countries like Sweden, the United States, and Japan the infant mortality rate is less than 7 per 1000 live births; in developing countries like Angola, Somalia, and Afghanistan, the rate is over 100 per 1000 live births (**Table 18.1**).[12] Low-birth-weight infants who do survive require extra nutrients, which are usually not available. Malnutrition in infancy and childhood has a profound effect on mental and physical growth and development as well as susceptibility to infectious disease.

Table 18.1 Indicators of Poverty and Malnutrition

	Infant Mortality (deaths per 1000 live births)	Life Expectancy (years)	Illiteracy (percent of population)	Access to Medical Care (people per physician)
More Developed Countries	20	76	3	680
Less Developed Countries				
Sierra Leone	182	37.2	66.7	—
Central Africa	113	44.9	57.6	25,920
Ghana	67	60	33.6	22,970
Ivory Coast	81	46.7	57.4	11,739
El Salvador	31	69.6	23	848
Cuba	7	76	4.1	176
Haiti	71	54.1	54.2	4,000
India	70	62.6	46.5	2,459
Bangladesh	79	58.1	61	12,884

Source: World Bank: www.worldbank.org/data/wdi2000/pdfs/tab2_18.pdf/.

stunting A decrease in linear growth rate, which is an indicator of nutritional well-being in populations of children.

Stunting

Malnourished children grow poorly. The prevalence of decreased growth in height, referred to as **stunting**, is used as an indicator of the well-being of a population's children (**Figure 18.5**). It is estimated that over 30% of children under 5 years of age in developing countries are stunted.[13] Deficiencies of energy, protein, iron, and zinc, as well as prolonged infections, have been implicated as causes. Stunting in childhood produces smaller adults who have a reduced work capacity. Stunted women are more likely to give birth to low-birth-weight babies. In addition, those who had lower birth weights and early childhood stunting are more likely to have abdominal obesity in adulthood.[14] Abdominal obesity increases the risk of morbidity from cardiovascular disease, hypertension, and diabetes.

Infectious Diseases

Infectious diseases are more common in undernourished children (**Figure 18.6**). Undernourished children have depressed immune systems, which reduces their ability to resist infection. Mortality from infections is increased among malnourished children; they may die of infectious diseases that would not be life-threatening in well-nourished children. Well over half of all deaths in children under 5 years are due to infectious disease.[4] It is estimated that 35% of deaths in children under age 5 occurs due to the presence of undernutrition.[3] Mortality is increased even among children with mild to moderate malnutrition. Even immunization programs, designed to reduce the incidence of infectious disease, may be ineffective because the immune systems of undernourished individuals cannot respond normally.

Figure 18.5 Stunted children may never regain the height lost as a result of malnutrition, and most children will never gain the corresponding body weight. Stunting also leads to premature death later in life because vital organs never fully develop. (Jorgen Schytte/Peter Arnold, Inc.)

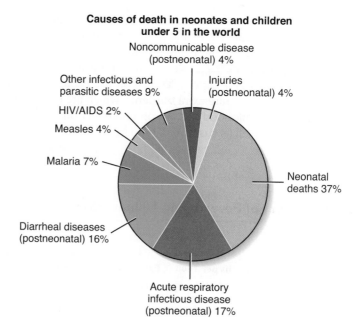

Causes of death in neonates and children under 5 in the world

Noncommunicable disease (postneonatal) 4%

Other infectious and parasitic diseases 9%

Injuries (postneonatal) 4%

HIV/AIDS 2%

Measles 4%

Malaria 7%

Neonatal deaths 37%

Diarrheal diseases (postneonatal) 16%

Acute respiratory infectious disease (postneonatal) 17%

Figure 18.6 Worldwide causes of death in children under five
Infectious diseases such as measles, diarrheal diseases, and respiratory infections, are often fatal for malnourished children. About 35% of deaths in young children might be prevented by adequate nutrition. (Source: World Health Organization. Black, R. E., Allen, L. H., Bhutta, Z. A., et al. Maternal and child undernutrition: Global and regional exposures and health consequences. Lancet 371:243–260, 2008.)

18.3 Causes of Undernutrition

Learning Objectives

- Discuss the factors that cause food shortages for populations and for individuals.
- Explain the concept of food insecurity.
- List three common nutrient deficiencies worldwide and explain the consequences of these deficiencies.

famine A widespread lack of access to food due to a disaster that causes a collapse in the food production and marketing systems.

The specific reasons for hunger vary with the time and location, but the underlying cause is that the food available in the world is not distributed equitably. This inequitable distribution results in either not enough food or the wrong combination of foods to meet nutrient needs. This in turn results in protein-energy malnutrition and micronutrient deficiencies.

Food Shortages

Figure 18.7 In October 2005 an earthquake struck northern Pakistan killing almost 100,000 people, causing widespread damage, and interrupting the production and distribution of food. Without adequate relief efforts widespread famine following such a disaster could kill more people than the earthquake itself. (Reuters/Thierry Roge/Landov)

The most obvious example of a food shortage is **famine**, which is a widespread failure in the food supply due to a collapse in the food production and marketing systems. Drought, floods, earthquakes, and crop destruction by diseases or pests are natural causes of famines. Man-made causes include wars and civil conflicts. Regions that produce barely enough food for survival under normal conditions are vulnerable to the disaster of famine. This situation is analogous to a man standing in water up to his nostrils: if all is calm, he can breathe, but if there is a ripple, he will drown. When a ripple such as a natural or civil disaster occurs, it cuts the margin of survival and creates famine (**Figure 18.7**).

Food shortages due to famine are very visible because they cause many deaths in one area during a short period of time, but chronic food shortages take a greater toll when it comes to the number of hungry people in the world. Chronic shortages occur when economic inequities result in lack of money, health care, and education for individuals or populations; when the food supply is insufficient to feed the population; when cultural and religious practices limit food choices; or when environmental resources are misused, limiting the ability to continue to produce food.

Figure 18.8 Ninety-six percent of the world's undernourished people live the developing world, where poverty is most prevalent. (Per-Anders Pettersson/Getty Images, Inc.)

Poverty and Hunger More than 1.4 billion people in the developing world currently live below the international poverty line, earning less than $1.25 per day.[15] Poverty is central to the problem of hunger and undernutrition; in most parts of the world their incidence is almost identical (**Figure 18.8**). Poverty creates what is called **food insecurity**, or the limited ability to acquire nutritious, safe foods. Food insecurity can occur in countries, in households, and among individuals. In wealthy countries social safety nets, such as soup kitchens, government food assistance programs, and job training programs, help the hungry to obtain food or money to buy food. In poor countries a family that cannot grow enough food or earn enough money to buy food, may have nowhere to turn for help.[16]

Disease and disability are more prevalent among the poor. Poverty reduces access to health care so disease goes untreated (see Table 18.1). When left untreated, illness increases nutrient needs and further limits the ability to obtain an adequate diet, contributing to malnutrition. Lack of immunizations and medical treatment result in an increased incidence of and morbidity from infectious disease and a decrease in survival rates from chronic diseases such as cancer. Lack of health care also increases infant mortality and the incidence of low-birth-weight births.

The poor have less access to education, which reduces the opportunities to escape poverty. It also increases the risk of undernutrition and disease because lack of education leads to inadequate care for infants, children, and pregnant women. A lack of education about food preparation and storage can affect food safety and the health of the household—unsanitary food preparation increases the incidence of gastrointestinal diseases, which contribute to malnutrition.

Overpopulation Overpopulation exists when a region has more people than its natural resources can support. A fertile river valley can support more people per acre than can a desert environment. But even in fertile regions of the world, if the number of people increases too much, resources are overwhelmed and food shortages occur.

The human population is currently growing at a rate of more than 82 million persons per year, and most of this growth is occurring in developing countries (**Figure 18.9**).[17] These countries cannot escape from poverty because their economy cannot keep pace with the rate of population growth. Efforts to produce enough food can damage the soil and deplete environmental resources, further reducing the capacity to produce food in the future. The problem of hunger today is due primarily to the unequal distribution of resources, but it is estimated that, worldwide, food production has begun to lag behind population growth. If this trend continues, there will soon be too little food in the world to feed the population.

Video

food insecurity A situation in which people lack adequate physical, social, or economic access to sufficient, safe, nutritious food that meets their dietary needs and food preferences for an active and healthy life.

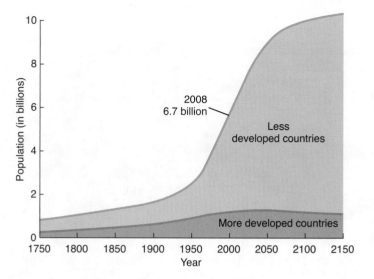

Figure 18.9 World population growth, 1750 to 2150
Since about 1950, most of the increase in world population has occurred in developing countries, and this trend is expected to continue.

Cultural Practices In some cultures, access to food may be limited for certain individuals within households. For example, women and girls may receive less food than men and boys, because culturally they are viewed as less important. How much food is available to an individual within a household depends on gender, control of income, education, age, birth order, and genetic endowments.

The cultural acceptability or unacceptability of foods also contributes to food shortages and malnutrition. If available foods are culturally unacceptable, a food shortage exists unless the population can be educated to use and accept new foods. For example, insects are eaten in some cultures and provide an excellent source of protein, but they are unacceptable to people in other cultures.

Limited Environmental Resources The land and resources available to produce food are limited. Some resources, such as minerals and fossil fuels, are present in the earth in finite amounts and are nonrenewable—that is, once used they cannot be replaced in a reasonable amount of time. Other resources such as soil and water are **renewable resources**, because they will be available indefinitely if they are used at a rate at which the earth can restore them. For example, when agricultural land is used wisely—crops rotated, erosion prevented, contamination limited—it can be reused almost endlessly. However, if this land is not used carefully, soil erosion, nutrient depletion, and accumulation of pollutants in soil and water may exceed the ability to restore and reuse this resource. Sometimes the methods used to increase food production have damaging long-term effects on the environment.

renewable resources
Resources that are restored and replaced by natural processes and that can therefore be used forever.

Crops and Cattle Modern mechanized agricultural methods increase yields, but use more energy and resources and cause more environmental damage than more traditional labor-intensive farming. In industrialized nations about 17% of energy used is for food production.[18]

In general the environmental cost of producing plant-based foods is lower than that of producing animal products, but the cost may still be substantial. Modern large-scale farming can erode the soil and deplete its nutrients. Fertilizers used to restore soil and pesticides used to kill insects can contaminate groundwater and eventually waterways. And if the plant products are shipped long distances, require refrigeration or freezing, or need other types of processing, the environmental costs are increased even more (see Your Choice: Does Choosing Vegetarian Help Alleviate World Hunger?).

Modern cattle production uses rangeland, grain, water, and fossil fuels, and creates both air and water pollution. The animals themselves produce methane gas in their gastrointestinal tracts, which enters the air and contributes to the greenhouse effect. When animal sewage is stored in ponds and heaps, it decomposes, producing more methane. Livestock is responsible for about 18% of greenhouse gas emissions, a larger share than that of all the cars in the world combined.[19]

Does Choosing Vegetarian Help Alleviate World Hunger?

Some people choose to consume a vegetarian diet out of concern for the environment. They argue that producing animal products consumes large amounts of energy, destroys forests and grazing lands, and pollutes the air and water. These problems, in turn limit the amount of food that can be produced and thus contribute to world hunger. Although these arguments are valid in some instances, the impact of food animals on the environment and nutrient intake depends on how these animals are integrated into the ecosystem.

On a traditional small farm, animals can consume crop wastes, kitchen scraps, and grasses that people cannot eat and turn them into meat, milk, and eggs that make important contributions to the human diet. But animals raised in agribusinesses are fed grain rather than grasses and kitchen scraps. Worldwide, 33% of total arable land is used to grow crops to feed animals.[1] Humans who eat these animals then get back only a fraction of the food energy they could have gotten from eating the grain. The energy from fossil fuel used in livestock production is also high, ranging from 4 kcalories of fossil energy to obtain 1 kcalorie of chicken protein to 40 kcalories of fossil fuel to produce 1 kcalorie of beef protein.[2] Livestock production accounts for over 8% of global human water use and 70% of all agricultural land.[1] The world simply would not have enough energy, water, or land to produce enough food if everyone were to adopt the typical American meat-based diet.

Management of animal waste materials also affects the environment. On small farms, manure is used for fertilizer in local fields. On huge farms, thousands of animals are confined to a small area so manure builds up rapidly; runoff can pollute nearby rivers and lakes that supply drinking water. Animal wastes also produce gases that are released into the atmosphere, contributing to acid rain and global warming.

The sheer number of domestic animals is also destructive to the environment. Overstocking of pastures and overgrazing reduce the potential to continue to use those lands, and new grazing land is created by cutting down forests. Deforestation allows carbon dioxide to accumulate in the atmosphere and contributes to global warming.

Is the elimination of animal foods the answer to feeding the world and saving the planet? Not really. In the developing world, small amounts of meat and milk in the diet can mean the difference between survival and starvation. In the United States, animal foods provide important sources of vitamin B_{12}, calcium, and highly absorbable forms of iron and zinc. Eliminating animal products would reduce both the variety and nutrient content of the human diet.

By using sustainable agricultural systems, we could both nourish the world's population and preserve the environment. Fertile land could be used to grow crops for human consumption, and cattle and sheep could be fed only from grazing lands unsuitable for growing crops. To absorb the resultant drop in animal production, developed nations would have to decrease their demand for animal products. Consuming a diet that is higher in grains, vegetables, and fruits and lower in animal products is therefore a goal that is compatible not only with the recommendations for a healthy diet but also with the ecological health of the planet. Completely eliminating animal products is neither necessary nor beneficial.

Grazing cattle on land that is unfit for growing crops preserves arable land for human food production. (USDA/Photo Researchers)

---

[1]Steinfeld, H., Gerber, P., Wassenaar, T. et al. *Livestock's Long Shadow: Environmental Issues and Options* 2006. Available online at http://www.fao.org/docrep/010/a0701e/a0701e00.HTM. Accessed March 17, 2009.

[2]Pimentel, D., and Pimentel, M. Sustainability of meat-based and plant-based diets and the environment. *Am. J. Clin. Nutr.* 78 (Suppl.):660S–663S, 2003.

As more countries undergo nutrition transition, the demand for meat-based diets will increase, as will the use of natural resources and energy. In addition, the demand for grain is increasing as a result of the recent sharp acceleration in the use of grain to produce ethanol to fuel cars.[20] The increased demand has contributed to increases in food prices, which have made it even more challenging for low- and middle-income families worldwide to obtain enough food.

Fishing It is not only the resources of the land that are at risk. Throughout human history fish from the world's oceans have been an important source of protein. However, increases in population have increased demand for fish to the point that the Earth's oceans are being depleted.[21] Because the ocean is open to fishermen from around the world, its use has been difficult to control. Many marine species have been harvested until their numbers are severely reduced. Pollution also threatens the world's fishing grounds. Oil spills and deliberate dumping can occur offshore, and sewage, pesticides, organic pollutants, and sediments from erosion wash into coastal waters where most fish spend at least part of their lives.

Poor Quality Diets

Even when there is enough food, undernutrition can occur if the quality of the diet is poor. The typical diet in developing countries is based on high-fiber grain products and has little variety. Adults who are able to consume a relatively large amount of this diet may be able to meet their nutrient needs. But those with increased needs or a limited capacity to consume these foods are at risk for nutrient deficiencies. Children, pregnant women, the elderly, and the ill may not be able to eat enough of this bulky grain diet to meet their needs. Deficiencies of protein, iron, iodine, and vitamin A are common because of poor-quality diets (**Table 18.2**).

Life Cycle

Table 18.2 Malnutrition at Different Life Stages

Life Stage	Common Deficiencies	Consequence
In utero	Energy	Low birth weight
	Iodine	Brain damage
	Folate	Neural tube defects
Infant/young child	Protein, energy	Growth retardation, increased risk of infection
	Iron	Anemia
	Iodine	Developmental retardation, goiter
	Vitamin A	Infection, blindness
Adolescent	Protein, energy	Stunting, delayed growth
	Iron	Anemia
	Iodine	Impaired intellectual development, goiter
	Vitamin A	Infection, blindness
	Calcium	Inadequate bone mineralization
Pregnant women	Protein, energy	Intrauterine growth retardation, increased mortality of mother and fetus
	Folate	Maternal anemia, neural tube defects in infants
	Iron	Maternal anemia
	Iodine	Cretinism in infant, goiter in mother
	Vitamin A	Infection, blindness
Adult	Energy, protein	Thinness, lethargy
	Iron	Anemia
Elderly adult	Energy	Thinness, lethargy
	Calcium and protein	Osteoporosis fractures, falls

Source: World Health Organization.

Protein-Energy Malnutrition Protein and energy deficiencies usually occur together and are most common in children. When there is a general lack of food marasmus results, but when the diet is limited to starchy grains and vegetables, protein deficiency can predominate, particularly in individuals with high protein needs— those who are growing, developing, or healing (see Chapter 6). Kwashiorkor, a deficiency of protein but not energy, occurs as a result of the wrong combination of foods rather than of a general lack of food. It is common in children over 18 months of age when the main food is a bulky cereal grain low in high-quality protein. Children have small stomachs and are not able to consume enough of this grain to meet their protein needs (**Figure 18.10**). Other factors such as metabolic changes caused by infection may also play a role in the development of kwashiorkor.

Iron Deficiency Iron deficiency is the most common nutritional deficiency worldwide. As many as 4 to 5 billion people, 66% to 80% of the world's population have low body iron stores, an early stage of iron deficiency; 2 billion people worldwide have iron-deficiency anemia, the most severe stage of iron deficiency. Nine out of ten anemia sufferers live in developing countries.[22] Iron deficiency can result from too little dietary iron, an increased need for iron, or a chronic loss of iron due to blood loss (see Chapter 12). Limited meat consumption in the developing world restricts iron intake to poorly absorbed nonheme plant sources. Also, intestinal parasites, especially hookworm infections, cause gastrointestinal blood loss, which leads to iron-deficiency anemia. The greater rates of both acute and chronic infections, such as malaria, in the developing world aggravate dietary iron deficiency.

Iron deficiency can have a major impact on the health and productivity of a population. Anemia during pregnancy increases the risk of maternal and fetal mortality, premature delivery, and low birth weight. Iron deficiency in infants and children can stunt growth, retard mental development, decrease resistance to infection, and increase morbidity due to disease. In older children and adults it causes fatigue and decreases productivity.

Iodine Deficiency Iodine is an essential trace element that is a constituent of the thyroid hormones (see Chapter 12). Globally, over 1.9 billion people, including 285 million school-aged children, have inadequate iodine intake as defined by low urinary iodine excretion.[23] When iodine is deficient in the food supply it affects virtually all members of the community. During pregnancy, iodine deficiency increases the incidence of stillbirths, spontaneous abortions, and developmental abnormalities such as cretinism in the offspring.[24] Although goiter is the most visible symptom of iodine deficiency cretinism is the most severe manifestation (**Figure 18.11**). Cretinism is characterized by impaired cognitive and physical development. It is devastating to individuals and families, but the more subtle effects of iodine deficiency on mental performance and work capacity may have a greater impact on the population as a whole. Iodine-deficient children have lower IQs and impaired school performance. Iodine deficiency in children and adults is associated with apathy and decreased initiative and decision-making capabilities. Worldwide iodine deficiency diseases are believed to be the greatest single cause of preventable brain damage in the fetus and infant, and of retarded psychomotor development in young children.[24]

Iodine deficiency occurs in regions with iodine-deficient soil that rely extensively on locally produced food. The eastern Mediterranean region and Africa have the highest incidence of iodine deficiency disorders. Because soil iodine is low in regions where deficiency is common, the problem can be solved only by importing foods high in iodine or by adding iodine to the local diet through fortification or supplementation. In 1990 it was estimated that 1.6 billion people lived in areas considered to be at risk for iodine deficiency. Since then, as a result of campaigns to introduce iodized salt, this number has been drastically reduced. However, there are still 54 countries where iodine deficiency is a major public health problem.[24]

Vitamin A Deficiency It is estimated that more than 250 million preschool children worldwide suffer from vitamin A deficiency.[25] It causes blindness; depresses immune function, which increases the risk of infections; retards growth; and is often

Figure 18.10 Because they are small, children are often unable to eat enough of a bulky grain diet to meet their protein needs. (Jim Sugar/ © Corbis)

Life Cycle

Figure 18.11 Goiter, which is an enlargement of the thyroid gland, is the most visible symptom of iodine deficiency. (Bruce Coleman, Inc./ Alamy)

(DAJ/Getty Images, Inc.)   (www.victorianoizquierdo.com/Getty Images, Inc.)   (Elena Schweitzer/Shutterstock)

SCIENCE

ScienceAppliedScienceApplied
ScienceAppliedScienceApplied
ScienceAppliedScienceApplied

APPLIED

Vitamin A: The Anti-Infective Vitamin

In 1910, one out of every four U.S. infants died before one year of age. The major causes were infectious diseases: epidemics of diarrhea during the summer and respiratory infections during the winter.[1] Similar problems affected children in Europe. In the early part of the twentieth century, the discovery of vitamins led to observations that nutritional deficiency, particularly vitamin A deficiency, was associated with an increased incidence and severity of infectious disease.[2]

In 1925, an epidemic of pneumonia swept through a colony of dogs in a research laboratory in England. The pneumonia occurred almost exclusively in vitamin A-deficient animals. It was hypothesized that the deficiency increased susceptibility to respiratory infections and that this might be relevant to infections in children.[3] Animal experiments confirmed this hypothesis and vitamin A was dubbed the "anti-infective vitamin."[4]

The theory that vitamin A could prevent infections triggered 20 years of clinical investigations. Clinical trials were conducted to determine if vitamin A, given as cod liver oil, could reduce morbidity and mortality from respiratory diseases, measles, and other infections. Although results were mixed, the pharmaceutical industry began promoting cod liver oil to decrease severity and recovery time in ailments such as whooping cough, measles, mumps, chicken pox, and scarlet fever.[1] The administration of cod liver oil became routine for millions of children in the United States and Europe in the 1940s.

In 1959, the World Health Organization (WHO) published a paper that reviewed the mounting evidence of a relationship between nutritional status and infection.[5] It recognized that poor nutritional status leads to more frequent and more severe infectious illnesses, and infection triggers metabolic responses that cause nutrient losses. To a well-nourished child, common infectious diseases such as measles are usually a passing illness, whereas to a malnourished child, they can result in life-long disabilities or death.

Today, antibiotics, vaccinations, and a nutritious and varied diet have reduced infant morbidity and mortality in the United

As this 1940 ad shows, cod liver oil, which is a good source of vitamin A, was promoted to reduce the incidence and severity of infections in children. (Bettman/©Corbis)

States and other developed nations. Worldwide, though, infections are still responsible for over half of the deaths that occur in children under age 5 every year, and about 35% of these deaths are associated with malnutrition.[6,7] Improved vitamin A status can help reduce the number of child deaths.

The relationship between vitamin A and measles has been studied extensively. Before a vaccine was developed, measles claimed 7 million to 8 million lives a year. Today it remains a major problem in developing nations. A deficiency of vitamin A reduces the ability of the immune system to defend itself against infection, and the infection itself causes loss of vitamin A that could precipitate acute vitamin A deficiency and blindness.[8] Because of these interactions, the WHO and UNICEF currently advise that large doses of vitamin A be provided to children with measles and that vitamin A be supplemented at the time of measles vaccination.[9] Providing vitamin A supplements is a short-term answer that can accompany long-term solutions to vitamin A deficiency and malnutrition, such as changes in dietary intake patterns and fortification of appropriate foods with vitamin A.

[1]Semba, R. D. Vitamin A as "anti-infective" therapy, 1920–1940. *J. Nutr.* 129:783–791, 1999.

[2]Brundtland, G. H. Nutrition and infection: Malnutrition and mortality in public health. *Nutr. Rev.* 58(II):S1–S4, 2000.

[3]Mellanby, E. Diet and disease, with special reference to the teeth, lungs, and prenatal feeding. *Lancet* 1:151–519, 1926.

[4]Green, H. N., and Mellanby, E. Vitamin A as an anti-infective agent. *Br. Med. J.* 2:691–696, 1928.

[5]Scrimshaw, N. S., Taylor, C. E., and Gordon, J. E. Interaction of nutrition and infection. *Am. J. Med. Sci.* 237:367–403, 1959.

[6] World Health Organization. The Global Burden of Disease: 2004 update, 2008. Available online at www.who.int/healthinfo/global_burden_disease/2004_report_update/en/index.html. Accessed May 4, 2009.

[7] Black, R. E., Allen, L. H., Bhutta, Z. A. et al. Maternal and child undernutrition: Global and regional exposures and health consequences. *Lancet* 371:243–260, 2008.

[8]West, C. E., Vitamin A and measles. *Nutr. Rev.* 58 (II): S46–S54, 2000.

[9]WHO/ UNIFEC. Joint Statement. Reducing Measles mortality in emergencies. Available online at www.unicef.at/fileadmin/medien/pdf/Measles_Emergencies.pdf. Accessed May 8, 2009.

accompanied by anemia (see Chapter 9). It is the leading cause of preventable blindness in children. It is estimated that 250,000 to 500,000 children go blind from vitamin A deficiency every year; half die within a year of losing their sight.[25] In communities where vitamin A deficiency exists, supplementation has been shown to significantly reduce childhood deaths due to infection (see Science Applied: Vitamin A: The Anti-Infective Vitamin).[26]

Obtaining sufficient vitamin A is a particular problem during periods of rapid growth and development, such as infancy, early childhood, pregnancy, and lactation. Need is increased by frequent infections, such as those causing diarrhea, and illnesses such as measles. Deficiencies of other nutrients, including fat, protein, and zinc, can contribute to vitamin A deficiency because they are needed to absorb and transport the vitamin in the body.

Life Cycle

Other Nutrients of Concern In addition to deficiencies of protein, iron, iodine, and vitamin A, there are several vitamin and mineral deficiencies that have recently emerged or reemerged as problems throughout the world. Beriberi, pellagra, and scurvy, caused by deficiencies of thiamin, niacin, and vitamin C, respectively, are rare in the developed world but still occur among the extremely poor and underprivileged and in large refugee populations. Folate deficiency is also a problem in many parts of the world. It causes megaloblastic anemia during pregnancy and often compounds existing iron-deficiency anemia. In women of childbearing age low folate intake increases the risk of having a baby with a neural tube defect. Folate deficiency may also contribute to coronary heart disease and stroke by causing elevated homocysteine levels, and low folate status is associated with cancer, especially of the colon.[27] In the United States, enriched grain products are fortified with folic acid to assure adequate intake and to reduce the incidence of neural tube defects.

Deficiencies of the minerals zinc, selenium, and calcium are also of concern.[28] Zinc deficiency affects about one-third of the world's population and is believed to cause as many deaths as vitamin A or iron deficiency.[29] Zinc deficiency can cause growth retardation or failure, diarrhea, immune deficiencies, skin and eye lesions, delayed sexual maturation, night blindness, and behavioral changes. It may also contribute to intrauterine growth retardation and neural tube defects in the fetus, and in the elderly it may affect taste acuity and cause dermatitis and impaired immune function. Selenium deficiency has been identified in population groups in China, New Zealand, and the Russian Federation. Selenium deficiency is associated with an increased incidence of Keshan disease (see Chapter 12), a type of heart disease that affects mainly children and young women.[28] Inadequate calcium intake is also a concern worldwide due to its association with the occurrence of osteoporosis.[28] Although factors other than low calcium intake, such as hormone levels and exercise, play a role in the development of osteoporosis, calcium supplementation has been proposed as a means of combating the high prevalence of spine and hip fractures due to osteoporosis, particularly in postmenopausal women.

18.4 Eliminating World Hunger

Learning Objectives

- Discuss two strategies that can help reduce population growth.
- Explain how international trade can help eliminate hunger.
- Discuss the role of sustainable agriculture in maintaining the food supply.
- List three considerations needed to plan food fortification.

In 1996 the World Food Summit set a goal of cutting world hunger in half by 2015. Progress was made in the late 1990s resulting in a slow, steady decrease in the number of chronically hungry people, but the most recent numbers indicate that the number of hungry people has increased by 80 million since the early 1990s.[1]

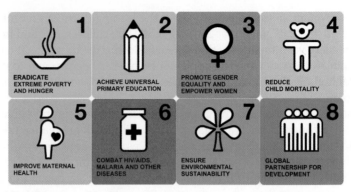

Figure 18.12 Millennium development goals
These eight goals, to be achieved by 2015, were adopted by 189 nations during the United Nations (UN) Millennium Summit in September 2000. They correspond to the world's main development challenges. In order to achieve the first goal, stamping out hunger, most of the others must also be addressed. (Source: United Nations. End Poverty: Millennium Development Goals 2015. Available online at www.un.org/millenniumgoals.)

Solving the problem of world hunger is a daunting task. It involves controlling population growth, meeting the nutritional needs of a large and diverse population with culturally acceptable foods, increasing production of nutrient-dense foods, and maintaining the global ecosystem (**Figure 18.12**). It requires international cooperation, commitment from national and local governments, and the involvement of local populations. The solutions involve economic policies, technical advancement, education, and legislative measures. It requires input from politicians, nutrition scientists, economists, and the food industry. Programs and policies must be in place to provide food in the short term and in the long term establish sustainable programs to allow continued production and distribution of food.

Short-Term Emergency Aid

When people are starving, short-term food and medical aid must be provided right away. The standard approach has been to bring food into the stricken area (**Figure 18.13**). These foods generally consist of agricultural surpluses from other countries and often are not well planned in terms of their nutrient content. Although this type of relief is necessary for a population to survive an immediate crisis such as famine, it does little to prevent future hunger.

There are many international, national, and private organizations working toward the goal of relieving world hunger. The Food and Agriculture Organization (FAO) works to improve the production, intake, and distribution of food worldwide. The World Health Organization (WHO) targets community health centers and emphasizes the prevention of nutrition problems, such as micronutrient deficiencies.

Figure 18.13 Many international relief organizations provide food to hungry people throughout the world. (© AP/Wide World Photos)

The World Bank finances projects such as supplementation and fortification to foster economic development. The United Nations Children's Fund (UNICEF), which relies on volunteer support, distributes food to all countries in need with a goal of assisting developing countries that occasionally suffer periods of starvation. The Red Cross, the UN Disaster Relief Organization, and the UN High Commissioner for Refugees concentrate on famine relief. The Peace Corps focuses more on fostering long-range development. More and more agencies are engaging in both development and relief. A few examples include the U.S. Agency for International Development, Oxfam, the Hunger Project, and Catholic Relief Services (**Table 18.3**).

Table 18.3 Organizations that Work to Alleviate World Hunger

Organization	What They Do	Where to Find Them
Bread for the World Institute	Helps hungry people by engaging in research and education on policies related to hunger and development.	www.bread.org
CARE	Helps fight poverty by providing aid to poor communities.	www.care.org
Food and Agriculture Organization (FAO), Sustainable Development Department	Provides knowledge and advice on biophysical, biological, socioeconomic, and social dimensions of sustainable development. Promotes sustainable methods and concepts and strategies.	www.fao.org
Freedom from Hunger	Provides cash, credit, and education to women in poor rural areas to help them better nourish their children, keep their families healthy, and develop profitable businesses.	www.freefromhunger.org
The International Fund for Agricultural Development (IFAD)	Finances agricultural development projects that improve nutrition and enable the rural poor to enhance food production and overcome poverty.	www.ifad.org
Oxfam America	Works to eliminate the social and economic problems that prevent people from getting the skills and resources they need to be self-sufficient.	www.oxfamamerica.org
The United Nations Children's Fund (UNICEF)	Works to improve the health and lives of children through education and vaccination as well as responding to crisis situations.	www.unicef.org
The World Bank	Provides loans, policy advice, technical assistance, and knowledge-sharing services to low- and middle-income countries to reduce poverty.	www.worldbank.org/
World Health Organization (WHO)	Focuses on all aspects of international health. Targets community health centers and emphasizes the prevention of nutrition problems, such as micronutrient deficiencies.	www.who.org.

Providing Enough Food

In the long term, solving the problem of world hunger requires balancing the number of people with the amount of food that can be produced. The rate of population growth worldwide has slowed from five children per woman in 1950 to 2.6 in 2009.[30] A balance between population and the amount of food available globally and locally is needed to feed the world. Inequities within populations must be addressed by eliminating poverty and providing opportunities for education—both to help people escape poverty and to teach them what constitutes a healthy diet and how to prepare it safely. Long-term solutions need to be based on the cultural and economic needs of the local population.

Controlling Population Growth Population growth can be slowed directly by controlling birth rates through family planning. To be successful, family-planning efforts must be acceptable to the population and compatible with their cultural and religious needs. A number of approaches, such as provision of contraceptives, education, and economic incentives have been used to decrease population growth. In Singapore, Thailand, Colombia, and Costa Rica, programs that provide contraceptive information, services, and supplies have been somewhat successful in slowing population growth. In some countries, population-control education is being integrated into the school curriculum, and family-planning messages are carried by popular television programs.

An indirect way to reduce population growth is to increase the general level of education and provide economic security. Birthrates decrease when the educational level and economic status of women is improved.[31] Women with more education tend to marry later and have fewer children. Education also increases the likelihood that women will have control over their fertility, provides knowledge to improve family health, decreases infant and child mortality rates, and offers options other than having numerous children.

Changes in economic policies can help reduce population growth. In some developing countries higher birth rates are due to the economic and societal roles of children. They are needed to work the farms, support the elders, and otherwise contribute to the economic survival of the family. Another reason for high birth rates is high infant mortality. When infant mortality rates are high people choose to have many children to ensure that some will survive. Programs that foster economic development and ensure access to food, shelter, and medical care have been shown to cause a decline in birthrates because people feel secure having fewer children and because economic development reduces the need for children as workers.

food self-sufficiency
The ability of an area to produce enough food to feed its population.

Growing and Importing Adequate Food **Food self-sufficiency** is a country's capacity to feed its population. Developing manageable systems for producing acceptable, sustainable sources of food can increase the level of food self-sufficiency. In countries with limited agricultural resources imports can increase the food supply and help reduce hunger.

Agricultural Technology Technological advancements in agriculture can help a country boost food production. These include newer varieties of plants, better agricultural techniques, and improvements in irrigation. One type of technology being used to increase the quantity and improve the quality of food is genetic engineering (see Focus on Biotechnology). Crop yields can be increased either directly, by inserting genes that improve plant growth, or indirectly, by creating plants that are resistant to herbicides, insects, and plant diseases, thus reducing crop losses. Genes that impart insect and herbicide resistance also help the environment because they allow farmers to achieve insect-free crops and weed-free fields with fewer pesticides and herbicides. Biotechnology can also affect plant characteristics that are of benefit after harvest, such as ease-of-transport, longer shelf lives, and slower ripening. The availability of older technologies such as freezing and refrigeration and better storage facilities can reduce food losses due to insects and rodents and thus also increase the amount of food available to the population.

International Trade Some countries have the resources to grow enough food to feed their population and others do not. When a country has few natural resources, access to international trade systems can help provide for their population. The newly industrialized countries of Asia, such as Thailand and Korea, are examples of how an increase in food imports can decrease the number of hungry people. In general, the countries of the world are becoming more interdependent on food imports and on exports to pay for this food. This interdependence can increase the availability of food for the world population (see Off the Label: What's on Food Labels Around the World?).

subsistence crops Crops grown as food for the local population.

cash crops Crops grown to be sold for monetary return rather than to be used for food locally.

Whether a country's agricultural emphasis focuses on producing **subsistence crops** for local consumption or producing **cash crops**, which can be sold on the national and international market, influences the availability of food for its people. Shifting to cash crops improves the cash flow of the country but uses local resources to produce crops for export and limits the ability of the local people to produce enough food to feed their families. For example, if a large portion of the arable land in West Africa is used to grow cash crops such as coffee and cotton, little agricultural land remains to grow grains and vegetables that nourish the local population. If, however, the cash from the crop is used to purchase nutritious foods for the local people, this decision may help alleviate undernutrition.

Off the Label
What's on Food Labels Around the World?

Did you know that the information on food labels varies from country to country? Labels reflect differences in national nutrition and food-safety guidelines, as well as economic and political agendas. The United States is one of only a few nations where nutrition labeling is mandatory and the information is presented based on common serving sizes. In most countries nutrition labeling is voluntary unless a product makes nutrition claims, and it often takes higher math to figure out how much of a nutrient is in the portion you consume. For example, in England nutrients are listed per 100 grams of the product. So, if you want to find out how much sodium is in the blob of ketchup next to your fish and chips you better find out what fraction of 100 grams of ketchup is on your plate.

The United States may have some of the most comprehensive nutrition information on labels, but we don't come out on top when it comes to other types of information. For example a can of tomatoes labeled in the, European Union, would show that the product is 80% tomatoes and 20% water.[1] In the United States, we would only know that tomatoes were the most abundant ingredient by weight. The United States also lags behind in freshness dating, which is not mandatory in the United States but is required in most other developed countries. The information provided about how a food is produced also varies among countries. If you want to know if your food is organically produced, irradiated, or made using genetically modified ingredients you need to research the labeling guidelines of the country from which you are purchasing the food.

The best labels provide consumers with the information they need to make informed choices. In the United States, consumers are concerned with over-consumption of saturated fat, cholesterol, sodium, and sugar. They can find information about these nutrients on all food labels, but the amounts of niacin, thiamin, and riboflavin are not required because deficiencies are not a concern in the U.S. population. In countries where niacin, thiamin, and riboflavin deficiencies are still prevalent, however, food labels would ideally include the content of these nutrients. In today's global economy, countries should learn from one another and incorporate the best label components from around the world to help their consumers choose wisely.

(Stefano Bianchetti/© Corbis)

---

[1] Food Labeling for the 21st Century: A Global Agenda for Action. A Report by the Center for Science in the Public Interest, 1998. Available online at http://www.cspinet.org/reports/labelrept.pdf. Accessed May 19, 2009.

Maintaining the Environment The resources needed to support food production depend on the methods used. In developing nations, the resources used by a single person are small, but the number of people is large so it is difficult to produce sufficient food without depleting natural resources such as soil, forests, and water supplies. In developed nations, the population is less dense but the resource demands made by each individual are far greater because of lifestyle and the methods of food production and distribution. A single child born in the United States uses 10 to 1000 times more resources daily than the average child born in Chile, Ghana, or Yemen.[32] Solutions to the problem of providing enough food must assure that natural resources are conserved in both industrialized and developing nations to allow continued food production for future generations.

sustainable agriculture
Agricultural methods that maintain soil productivity and a healthy ecological balance while having minimal long-term impacts.

Sustainable Agriculture **Sustainable agriculture** uses food production methods that prevent damage to the environment and allow the land to restore itself so food can be produced indefinitely. For example, contour plowing and terracing help prevent soil erosion, keeping the soil available for future crops. Rotating the crops grown in a specific field prevents the depletion of nutrients in the soil, reducing the need for added fertilizers. Sustainable agriculture uses environmentally friendly chemicals that degrade quickly and do not persist as residues in the environment. It also relies on diversification. This approach to farming maximizes natural methods of pest control and fertilization and protects farmers from changes in the marketplace (**Figure 18.14**).

Sustainable agriculture is not a single program but involves choosing options that mesh well with the local soil, climate, and farming techniques. In some cases, organic farming, which does not use synthetic pesticides, herbicides, and fertilizers (see Chapter 17), may be the more sustainable option. Organic techniques have a smaller environmental impact because they reduce the use of agricultural chemicals and the release of pollutants into the environment. Organic farming is also advantageous in terms of soil quality and biodiversity, but it is a disadvantage when it comes to land use because crop yields are lower. A combination of organic and conventional techniques, as is used with integrated pest management (see Chapter 17), might be best for improving land use and protecting the environment.

Other sustainable programs include agroforestry, in which techniques from forestry and agriculture are used together to restore degraded areas; natural systems agriculture, which attempts to develop agricultural systems that include many types of plants and therefore function like natural ecosystems; and the technique of reducing fertilizer use by matching nutrient resources with the demands of the particular crop being grown.[31]

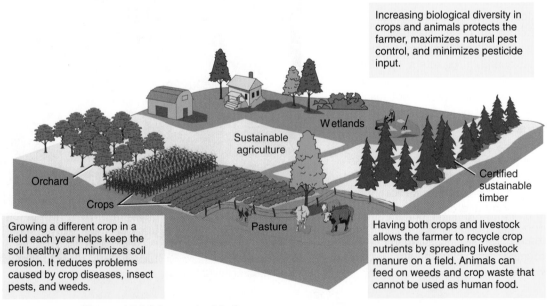

Increasing biological diversity in crops and animals protects the farmer, maximizes natural pest control, and minimizes pesticide input.

Wetlands

Sustainable agriculture

Orchard

Certified sustainable timber

Crops

Growing a different crop in a field each year helps keep the soil healthy and minimizes soil erosion. It reduces problems caused by crop diseases, insect pests, and weeds.

Pasture

Having both crops and livestock allows the farmer to recycle crop nutrients by spreading livestock manure on a field. Animals can feed on weeds and crop waste that cannot be used as human food.

Figure 18.14 A sustainable farm
A sustainable farm consists of a total agricultural ecosystem rather than a single crop. It may include field crops, fruit- and nut-bearing trees, herds of livestock, and forests.

Sustainable Choices The choices individuals make can also influence the environmental impact of food production. Choosing a diet that is primarily plant-based, with smaller amounts of animal products can help to minimize the ecological impact of food production (see Your Choice: Does Choosing Vegetarian Help Alleviate World Hunger?). Choosing locally grown foods in season can minimize the energy costs and pollution due to food transport. Choosing organically grown, minimally processed, and ecologically packaged foods can further minimize the environmental impact of food production (see Critical Thinking: What Can You Do?).

Eliminating Poverty

Although controlling population growth and ensuring adequate food are essential steps in eliminating world hunger, hunger will still exist as long as there is poverty. Even when food is plentiful in a region, the poor do not have access to enough of the right foods to maintain their nutritional health. Economic development that guarantees safe and sanitary housing, access to health care and education, and the resources to acquire enough food are essential to eliminate hunger. Government policies can help to eliminate poverty by increasing the population's income, lowering food prices, or offering feeding programs for the poor, all of which can improve food security.

Ensuring a Nutritious Food Supply

In addition to sufficient energy in the diet, the right mix of nutrients is necessary to ensure the nutritional health of a population. If the foods and crops that are grown or imported do not meet all nutrient needs, the quality of the diet will be poor and malnutrition will occur. If the diet does not provide the right mix of nutrients, deficient nutrients can be added to the diet by changing dietary patterns, fortifying existing foods, or including dietary supplements. Consumers must not only learn how to choose foods that provide the needed nutrients but also how to handle them safely. Strategies to reduce micronutrient deficiencies also need to include strategies to control infectious and parasitic diseases. Genetic engineering can also address nutrient deficiencies by changing the nutrient content of foods. As discussed in Focus on Biotechnology, genes that code for enzymes needed to synthesize β-carotene have been inserted into rice. This new rice may help alleviate vitamin A deficiency in regions where rice is a staple.

Food Fortification Fortification is the process of adding one or more nutrients to commonly consumed foods with the goal of increasing the nutrient intake of a population. Food fortification will not provide energy to a hungry population, but it can increase the protein quality of the diet and eliminate micronutrient deficiencies. Fortification programs have been created by partnerships among industry, academia, and government. Industry and academia can provide the technology for adding nutrients to foods, and government public health policies can promote the consumption of these fortified foods.

In order for fortification to solve a nutritional problem in a population, it must be implemented wisely. Fortification works if vulnerable groups consume foods that are centrally processed. The foods selected for fortification should be among those consistently eaten by the majority of the population so that extensive promotion and reeducation are not needed to encourage their consumption. The nutrient should be added uniformly and in a form that optimizes its utilization. Fortification has been used successfully in preventing health problems in the United States: The fortification of cow's milk to increase vitamin D intake was a major factor in the elimination of infantile rickets, and the enrichment of grains with niacin helped eliminate pellagra. The most recent program is the fortification of grains with folic acid to reduce neural tube defects in newborns (see Chapters 8 and 14).

Fortification has also been used successfully in developing countries. The number of countries with salt-iodization programs doubled over the last decade, rising from 46 to 93, and as a result the global rates of goiter, cognitive disability, and cretinism are falling fast[24] (**Figure 18.15**). Likewise, the fortification of foods with other micronutrients such as vitamin A can help reduce deficiencies.[33]

Figure 18.15 Iodized salt logo
The global iodized salt logo is used around the world as an indicator of iodized salt.

Critical Thinking

What Can You Do?

(©iStockphoto)

Background

Keesha is concerned about the problems of hunger, malnutrition, and global ecology. Although she is a college student who cannot afford to make monetary contributions to relief organizations, she would like to contribute in other ways.

Data

She enjoys working with children, so she arranges to spend one afternoon a week helping with nutrition education programs for children. She also volunteers to spend one evening a week helping to prepare and serve food in a church soup kitchen near campus.

To be more ecological, Keesha buys a canvas bag to take to the grocery store. This will reduce the amount of waste she generates by eliminating the need for a new paper or plastic bag each time she shops. She asks her grocer to wrap the meat and chicken she buys in recyclable paper, and she begins recycling cans, bottles, and paper goods and tries to avoid purchasing products in nonrecyclable containers. This will reduce the amount of nonrecyclable, nonbiodegradable waste she generates. Instead of driving her car the 2 miles from home to campus, she rides her bike, takes the bus, or carpools with a friend. This decreases the use of fossil fuels and reduces air pollution. She contacts her local utility company to arrange an energy audit of her home and make suggestions that will reduce energy usage in her home.

Keesha then makes a list of other thing's she can do to reduce her environmental footprint.

KEESHA'S LIST

Instead of buying nonrecyclable juice boxes for her lunch, she can bring juice in a thermos.

She can begin composting the leftover vegetable scraps and other plant matter from her kitchen.

She can choose organically grown produce.

She can select locally grown foods when possible.

Critical Thinking Question

Looking at Keesha's list, do you think her actions will help? For each item on her list, identify an environmental benefit.

▼

How will each of these actions affect cost to her in dollars?

 iProfile Use iProfile to look up the nutritional composition of some foods availabe at you local farmer's market.

Supplementation Supplementing specific nutrients to at-risk segments of the population can also help reduce the prevalence of malnutrition. Of countries where vitamin A deficiency is a public health problem, 78% have policies supporting regular vitamin A supplementation in children. Many have also adopted the WHO recommendation to provide all breast-feeding women with a high-dose supplement of vitamin A within 8 weeks of delivery. This improves maternal vitamin A status and increases the amount of vitamin A that is in breast milk and therefore passed to the infant. Many countries have adopted programs to supplement children older than 6 months with iron and pregnant women with iron and folate.

Figure 18.16 Replacing white yams, which are a poor source of β-carotene, with yellow yams, which contain enough β-carotene to meet the requirement for vitamin A in a single serving, can improve the quality of the diet. (iStockphoto)

Providing Education

Education can help people improve their nutrient intake by teaching them what foods to eat, how to prepare them safely, and how to grow them. Education must include information about which foods are good nutrient sources so choices made when purchasing foods or growing vegetables at home can meet micronutrient needs. Education is particularly important when introducing a new crop. No matter how nutritious, a new plant variety is not beneficial unless local farmers know how to grow it and the population accepts it as part of their diet and knows how to prepare it. For instance, white yams are common in some regions but are a poor source of β-carotene, which the body can use to make vitamin A. If the yellow yam, which is rich in β-carotene, became an acceptable choice, the vitamin A available to the population would increase (**Figure 18.16**). Food safety is also a concern when changing traditional dietary practices. For example, introducing papaya to the diet as a source of vitamin A will not improve nutritional status if the fruit is washed in unsanitary water and causes dysentery among the people it is meant to nourish.

Education to encourage breast-feeding can also improve nutritional status and health. Breast-feeding reduces the risk of infectious diseases in infants. When infants are not breast-fed, education about nutritious breast milk substitutes and their safe preparation is essential.

18.5 Hunger at Home

Learning Objectives

- Discuss the causes of food insecurity in the United States.
- Describe factors that prevent people from escaping poverty.
- List the population groups that are at greatest risk for undernutrition in the United States.
- Describe five federal programs designed to alleviate hunger in the United States.

In the United States, most of the nutritional problems are related to overnutrition. Sixty-six percent of adults in the United States are overweight or obese.[34] Heart disease, hypertension, and cancer—all related to obesity—are the leading causes of

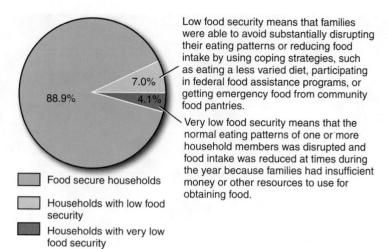

Low food security means that families were able to avoid substantially disrupting their eating patterns or reducing food intake by using coping strategies, such as eating a less varied diet, participating in federal food assistance programs, or getting emergency food from community food pantries.

Very low food security means that the normal eating patterns of one or more household members was disrupted and food intake was reduced at times during the year because families had insufficient money or other resources to use for obtaining food.

88.9%

7.0%

4.1%

- ☐ Food secure households
- ☐ Households with low food security
- ☐ Households with very low food security

Figure 18.17 Food insecurity in the United States
In 2007, approximately 89% of U.S. households were food secure and about 11%, or 13 million households, experienced food insecurity.

death. While much of the population is concerned with consuming a diet to lower the risks for these chronic diseases, hungry families are standing in line at soup kitchens. Problems such as poverty and unemployment lead to food insecurity in a land of plenty. Government food and nutrition policy must be concerned with improving economic security as well as providing food to the hungry and maintaining the food supply at an affordable level—at the same time policy must promote healthy diets to reduce diseases related to overconsumption.

Causes of Food Insecurity

In the United States, general food shortage is not the cause of undernutrition, but food insecurity, hunger, and undernutrition are a growing problem. Today about 13 million American households, experience food insecurity due to a lack of money or other resources (**Figure 18.17**).[35] About 4.7 million households, including 323,000 households with children, experience very low food security. This means that food intake is reduced in one or more household members. Over time this can lead to malnutrition. The incidence of hunger and food insecurity is higher in the poor; the homeless; women, infants, and children; and the elderly; but illness, disability, a sudden decrease in income, or an increase in living expenses can put anyone at risk for food insecurity.

Figure 18.18 Migrant workers are at increased risk of malnutrition due to difficult living and working conditions, low incomes, and limited access to grocery stores. (© AP/Wide World Photos)

Poverty Poverty, the main cause of food insecurity, reduces access to food, education, and health care. About 12.5% of Americans (37.3 million people) live at or below the poverty level (**Table 18.4**).[36] The poor have less money to spend on food and often have less access to affordable food. Lower profits have driven supermarkets out of the cities and into the suburbs. Because many inner city low-income families do not own cars, they must shop at small, expensive corner stores or pay cab fares to take advantage of cheaper prices at more distant, larger stores. Limited income also reduces the chances that healthier foods will be consumed. Choosing leaner meats and dairy products and whole grains costs more—about 35% to 40% of low-income consumers' food budgets.[37] Poverty in rural areas also affects food availability. For example, migrant workers have limited access to food because labor camps are in remote locations and transportation is often unavailable (**Figure 18.18**). Low incomes and difficult working and living conditions further limit these individuals' ability to purchase food and prepare adequate meals. The unemployment and poverty rates are particularly high among Native Americans and Alaska Natives who live in remote locations. Unemployment for Native American communities and Alaska Native villages may be ten times higher than that of the population as a whole.[38]

Table 18.4 2009 Poverty Guidelines in the United States*

Number of Persons in family or Household	Income Limit for Poverty Level (Dollars)
1	10,830
2	14,570
3	18,310
4	22,050
5	25,790
6	29,530
7	33,270
8	37,010
For each additional person, add	3,740

*Includes 48 contiguous states and D.C.

Source: http:aspe.hhs.gov/poverty/09poverty.shtml

Lack of Education Lack of education, a cause and consequence of poverty, also contributes to food insecurity (**Figure 18.19**). For people at or below the poverty level, educational opportunities are fewer and lower in quality. In the short term, lack of knowledge about food selection, food safety, and home economics can contribute to malnutrition. Too little food may cause the diet to be deficient in energy or particular nutrients, but poor food choices also allow food insecurity to coexist with obesity. Lack of education about food safety can also increase the incidence of foodborne illness. In the long term, lack of education prevents people from getting well-paying jobs, which would allow them to escape from poverty.

Limited Health Care Poverty also limits access to health care, leading to poorer health status. Iron deficiency is more than twice as frequent in low-income children, and the incidence of heart disease, cancer, hypertension, and obesity increases with

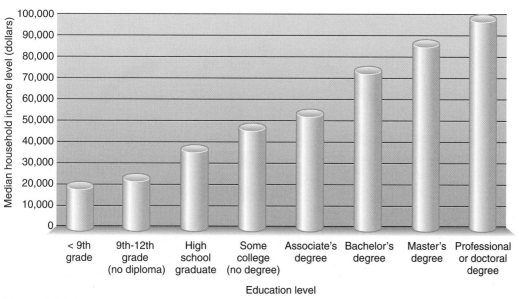

Figure 18.19 Income versus level of education
Income level in the United States is directly correlated with level of education (Source: U.S. Census Bureau. The 2009 Statistical Abstract. Table 670: Money income of households – distribution by income level and selected characteristics: 2006. Available online at www.census.gov/compendia/statab/tables/09s0670.pdf.)

decreasing income. As in developing nations, poverty is reflected in infant mortality rates. Average infant mortality in the U.S. population is about 6.7 per 1000 live births.[39] However, there are groups within the population that have infant mortality rates as high as those in impoverished nations. Among African Americans, the infant mortality rate is 13.6 per 1000 live births—more than twice that of the general population.[39] This difference mirrors the higher poverty rate in this group.

Homelessness The poor must use most of their income to pay for shelter, which seriously reduces the chances that their families will be adequately fed. The high cost of housing not only limits food budgets but also has created a growing problem of homelessness in the United States. It is estimated that between 600,000 and 2.5 million Americans are homeless.[40] The homeless are at high risk of malnutrition and food insecurity because they lack not only money but also cooking and food-storage facilities. Without cooking facilities, they must rely on ready-to-eat foods. Without storage facilities, they cannot use less expensive staples such as rice and dried beans, which can be purchased in bulk. Homeless individuals often rely on soup kitchens and shelters to obtain adequate food.

A Cycle of Poverty Many people find themselves trapped in a cycle of poverty (**Figure 18.20**). As the U.S. economy has shifted from manufacturing to service-based, many factories have closed and manufacturing facilities have moved abroad where labor costs are lower. Former employees often lack the experience or education to move on to other types of work. Unable to find well-paying jobs, they must work longer hours at lower-paying jobs. Low incomes reduce access to transportation and child care, which can also limit access to better jobs. Long work hours reduce the amount of time available to pursue the additional education or training necessary to find better-paying jobs. Limited income and transportation prohibit relocation to areas where better jobs are available.

Life Cycle

High Nutrient Needs The high nutrient needs of pregnant and lactating women and small children put them at particular risk for undernutrition. Almost a third of households with children headed by single women live below the poverty line.[35] Poverty and food insecurity place these women and children at risk of malnutrition, and their special nutritional needs magnify this risk. Because of their increased need for some nutrients, malnutrition may occur in pregnant women, infants, and children even when the

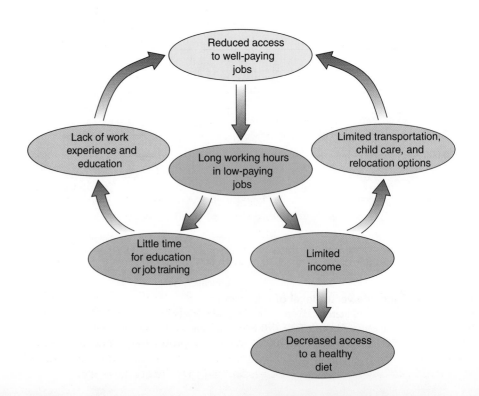

Figure 18.20 Cycle of poverty
Some Americans are trapped in a cycle of poverty because they are unable to acquire the education, training, or resources necessary to obtain better-paying jobs.

rest of the household is adequately fed. For example, the amount of iron in the family diet may be enough to prevent anemia in all but a pregnant teenager.

Disease and Disability Due to diseases and disabilities, the elderly may be limited in their ability to purchase, prepare, and physically ingest food. This puts the elderly, especially the elderly poor, at risk for malnutrition. Greater nutritional risk among older adults is associated with more hospital admissions and, hence, greater health-care costs. The number of individuals over age 85 is expected to quadruple by the year 2050; as the number of elderly increases so will the number at risk of food insecurity.[41] Thus, providing food security for older adults both improves their quality of life and reduces costs for the public health–care system (see Chapter 16).

Life Cycle

Federal Programs to Prevent Malnutrition

Solving the problem of undernutrition in the United States involves improving economic security, keeping food affordable, providing food aid to the hungry, and offering education about healthy diets that will meet nutrient needs and reduce diseases related to overconsumption. Historically, many approaches have been attempted to meet this goal. Some have met with success and others have done little to increase access to a nutritious diet for all. Programs that provide access to affordable food and promote healthy eating have been referred to as a *nutrition safety net* for the American population.

The Nutrition Safety Net The nutrition assistance programs in the United States include a combination of general nutrition assistance with specialized programs targeted to groups with particular nutritional risks: children, seniors, infants, women during and after pregnancy, Native Americans living on reservations, people with disabilities, and homeless people (**Table 18.5**).[42] One of every 5 Americans receives some kind of food assistance, at a total cost of about $54 billion per year.[43]

The largest USDA program designed to make sure that all people have access to an adequate diet is the Supplemental Nutrition Assistance Program (SNAP) (previously known as the Food Stamp Program). SNAP provides monthly benefits in the form of coupons or debit cards that can be used to purchase food, thereby supplementing the food budgets of low-income individuals. Together with SNAP, four other programs that target high-risk populations—the National School Lunch Program, the Special Supplemental Nutrition Program for Women, Infants, and Children (WIC) (**Figure 18.21**), the Child and Adult Care Food Program, and the National School Breakfast Program—account for 95% of the USDA's expenditure for food assistance.

In addition to federal nutrition assistance programs, church, community, and charitable emergency food shelters provide for the basic nutritional needs of many Americans. In the United States, about 150,000 nonprofit food distribution programs help direct food to those in need.[44] The leading hunger-relief charity in the United States is Feeding America, which provides food assistance to over 25 million low-income people per year. It includes a network of food banks across the country and supports thousands of local charitable organizations, such as food pantries and soup kitchens, that distribute food directly to hungry Americans.

Virtually all these food distribution programs use food obtained through food recovery, which involves collecting food that is wasted in fields, commercial kitchens, restaurants, and grocery stores and distributing it to those in need. Field gleaning is a type of food recovery that involves collecting crops that are not harvested because it is not economically profitable to harvest them or that remain in fields after mechanical harvesting. The word *gleaning* means "gathering after the harvest" and dates back at least as far as biblical times. It is estimated that over 25% of America's food—enough to feed 49 million people—goes to waste each year.[45]

Providing Nutrition Education The link between nutrition education and diet quality is strong. People with more nutrition information and more awareness of the relationship between diet and health consume healthier diets.[46] Healthy diets not only improve current health by optimizing growth, productivity, and well-being, but are essential for preventing chronic diseases in the future. Increasing nutrition knowledge can reduce medical care costs and improve the quality of life.

Figure 18.21 WIC provides vouchers that can be used to purchase foods that provide nutrients needed for a healthy pregnancy and childhood. (Tony Freeman/PhotoEdit)

Table 18.5 **Programs to Prevent Undernutrition in the United States**

Program	Target population	Goals and methods
Supplemental Nutrition Assistance Program (SNAP)	Low-income individuals	Increases access to food by providing coupons or debit cards that can be used to purchase food at a grocery store
Commodity Supplemental Food Assistance Program	Low-income pregnant women, breast-feeding and non-breast-feeding postpartum women, infants and children under age 6, and elderly people	Provides food by distributing USDA commodity foods
Special Supplemental Nutrition Program for Women, Infants, and Children (WIC)	Low-income pregnant women, breast-feeding and non-breast-feeding postpartum women, and infants and children under age 5	Provides vouchers for the purchase of foods (including infant formula and infant cereal) high in nutrients that are typically lacking in the program's target population; provides nutrition education and referrals for health care
WIC Farmers' Market Nutrition Program	WIC participants	Increases access to fresh produce by providing vouchers that can be used to purchase produce at authorized local farmers' markets.
National School Breakfast Program	Low-income children	Provides free or low-cost breakfasts to improve the nutritional status of children
National School Lunch Program	Low-income children	Provides free or low-cost lunches at school to improve the nutritional status of children
Special Milk Program	Low-income children	Provides milk for children in schools, camps, and child-care institutions with no federally supported meal program
Summer Food Service Program	Low-income children	Provides free meals and snacks for children when school is not in session
Child and Adult Care Food Program	Children up to age 12 and elderly and disabled adults	Provides nutritious meals to children and adults in day-care settings
Team Nutrition	School-age children	Provides nutrition education, training and technical assistance, and resources to participating schools with the goal of improving children's lifelong eating and physical activity habits
Head Start	Low-income preschool children and their families	Provides education, including nutrition education
Nutrition Program for the Elderly	Individuals age 60 and over and their spouses	Provides free congregate meals in churches, schools, senior centers, or other facilities and delivers food to homebound people
Senior Farmers' Market Program	Low-income seniors	Provides coupons that can be exchanged for eligible foods at farmers' markets, roadside stands, and community-supported agricultural programs
Homeless Children Nutrition Program	Preschoolers living in shelters	Reimburses providers for meals served
Emergency Food Assistance Program	Low-income people	Provides commodities to soup kitchens, food banks, and individuals for home use
Healthy People 2010	U.S. population	Sets national health promotion objectives to improve the health of the U.S. population through health-care system and industry involvement, as well as individual actions
Expanded Food and Nutrition Education Program (EFNEP)	Low-income families	Provides education in all aspects of food preparation and nutrition
Temporary Assistance for Needy Families (TANF)	Low-income households	Provides assistance and work opportunities to needy families by granting states federal funds to implement welfare programs
Food Distribution Program on Indian Reservations	Low-income households living on reservations and Native Americans living near reservations	Provides food by distributing USDA commodity foods

Education can help individuals with lower incomes stretch limited food dollars by making wise choices at the store and reducing food waste at home. Education can promote community gardens to increase the availability of seasonal vegetables. It can teach people how to prepare foods that become available through commodity distribution and food banks. It can explain safe food handling and food preparation methods. Knowing which foods to choose and how to handle them safely is as important in preventing malnutrition as having the money to buy enough food.

A number of government programs are designed to provide nutrition education. One of the goals of Healthy People 2010 is to increase the nutrition education provided by schools as well as by work sites. The Expanded Food and Nutrition Education Program (EFNEP) provides education in all aspects of food preparation and nutrition to low-income families. In addition, the Dietary Guidelines for Americans, MyPyramid, and standardized food labels educate the general public about making wise food choices.

Controlling Food Costs The price of food depends on the amount produced and the consumer demand, so controlling the supply of food is important in determining cost. If the supply is large, prices will be low, but if supply forces prices to drop too much, the profit to the farmer and food industry may be too low to justify harvesting the crop. Government policy has tried to prevent this by controlling agricultural production with programs like the Grain Reserve Program and the Price Support Program. The Grain Reserve Program draws surplus grain off the market when excess is produced or prices decline. This practice keeps grain prices more stable and saves food for times when the harvest is not as plentiful. The Price Support Program also protects farmers from the drop in prices that results from overproduction. While these programs protect farmers, moderate food prices, and limit what reaches the marketplace, they may not provide incentive for farmers to limit production when demand is low. Federal programs also have the potential to support sustainable agriculture by regulating the use of natural resources and agricultural chemicals.

Outcome

José hadn't realized that most hunger is caused by economic, political, sociocultural, and environmental situations that prevent enough food, or the right kinds of food, from reaching people in need. Sometimes, war or natural disaster disrupts food production and distribution, leading to famine, but poverty is one of the most common causes of hunger. To illustrate this in his poster, José tried to highlight articles that focused on the cause of malnutrition in

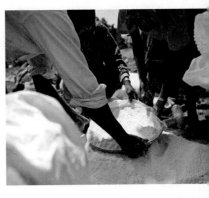

particular areas. He was also shocked to find that obesity was a growing problem even in developing countries. Thus, in his collage he juxtaposed an article about rising worldwide obesity rates and one on malnourished children in Latin America to show that these problems often exist side by side.

José is convinced that a combination of food aid, financial aid, and nutrition education could eliminate malnutrition in the United States, because almost everyone has access to food if he or she has the money to purchase it. The problem is more challenging in other parts of the world. José plans to spend next summer working for a relief organization in Honduras, where malnutrition is widespread.

APPLICATIONS

Personal Nutrition

1. Fill in the table below to help you decide the least expensive way to buy these products:

PRODUCT	COST		
	CORNER STORE ($)	SUPER-MARKET ($)	DISCOUNT/ WAREHOUSE STORE ($)
Orange juice (8 fl oz)			
Orange juice (1/2 gal)			
Brand-name cereal (e.g., Kix or Corn Flakes) (15-oz box)			
Generic brand of a similar cereal (15-oz box)			
White bread (1 loaf)			
Whole-wheat bread (1 loaf)			
Fresh apples (price/lb)			
Bag of chips (1-oz)			
Bag of same brand of chips (15–16-oz)			

a. Calculate the cost per ounce for each item at each type of store.

b. How does the size of the package affect cost?

c. How does the brand name affect cost?

d. Will following the MyPyramid recommendation to make half your grains whole affect food costs?

2. How much money do you spend on food?

a. Keep a record of how much money you spend on food in a day and use this to estimate your monthly food costs.

b. Suggest two or three changes in the foods you choose that will reduce your food costs.

c. How do these changes affect the nutrient content of your diet?

d. What could you eat if your food budget for the day was only $3?

e. Would the $3-a-day diet you put together meet your nutrient needs? Which nutrients are deficient? Which are excessive?

General Nutrition Issues

1. What could you do for World Food Day (October 16)? List some ideas for campus-wide programs to increase awareness of global nutrition issues.

2. What do you know about hunger in various parts of the world?

a. Use the Internet to locate Web sites for organizations such as Worldwatch or Bread for the World Institute.

b. Choose one area of the world where hunger and undernutrition are a major problem and explain the cause of undernutrition in this area.

c. What solutions are in place or proposed to solve these problems?

Summary

18.1 The Two Faces of Malnutrition

- Undernutrition remains a problem around the world.
- Due to changes in diet and lifestyle that occur as economic conditions in a country improve, overnutrition is now also a global health problem that coexists with undernutrition in both developed and developing nations around the world.

18.2 The Cycle of Malnutrition

- In poorly nourished populations, a cycle of malnutrition exists in which undernourished women give birth to low-birth-weight infants at risk of disease and early death. Children who survive grow poorly and become adults who are physically unable to fully contribute to society.

- Malnutrition causes stunting. The prevalence of stunting is used as an indicator of nutritional well-being in populations of children.
- Malnutrition depresses immune function, causing an increase in the frequency and severity of infectious diseases.

18.3 Causes of Undernutrition

- World hunger exists due to the inequitable distribution of available food. Natural and manmade disasters can temporarily disrupt food production and distribution and cause famine.
- Chronic food shortage occurs when economic inequities result in lack of money, health care, and education for individuals or populations; when overpopulation and limited natural resources create a situation in which there are more people than food; when cultural practices limit food choices; and when environmental resources are misused, limiting the ability to continue to produce food.
- Malnutrition occurs when the quality of the diet is poor. High-risk groups with special nutrient needs, such as pregnant women, children, the elderly, and the ill, may not be able to meet their nutrient needs with the available diet. Deficiencies of protein, iron, iodine, vitamin A, and zinc are common worldwide.

18.4 Eliminating World Hunger

- Short-term solutions to undernutrition provide food through relief at the local, national, and international levels.

- Long-term solutions to undernutrition must ensure the availability of food by controlling population growth, increasing the food supply through agricultural technology or importation, developing sustainable systems that will provide food without damaging the environment, and improving economic conditions to eliminate poverty.
- Long-term solutions to undernutrition must ensure a nutritionally adequate food supply. Food fortification and dietary supplementation can be used to increase protein quality and eliminate micronutrient deficiencies and improve the overall quality of the diet.
- Education about what to eat and how to prepare food safely can help eliminate malnutrition.

18.5 Hunger at Home

- Both undernutrition and overnutrition are problems in the United States. Food insecurity is associated with poverty, which limits education and access to health care and adequate housing. High nutrient needs increase the risk of malnutrition in women and children, and disease and disability increase risk in the elderly. Limited access to food increases risk in certain segments of the population.
- Nutrition programs in the United States focus on maintaining a nutrition safety net that will provide access to affordable food and promote healthy eating. Some programs designed to help feed the hungry address the general population, whereas others focus on specific high-risk groups. Most programs provide access to food and some provide nutrition education.

Review Questions

1. What is meant by the statement, "world nutrition policies must address the two faces of malnutrition"?

2. What is meant by nutrition transition?

3. What is the cycle of malnutrition?

4. How does overpopulation contribute to food shortage?

5. How does poverty contribute to world hunger?

6. How are economic growth and population growth related?

7. What segments of the world population are at greatest risk for undernutrition?

8. List three micronutrient deficiencies that are world health problems.

9. Why are environmental issues important in maintaining the world's food supply?

10. How can sustainable agriculture reduce environmental damage?

11. How can food fortification be used to help eliminate malnutrition?

12. List four population groups in the United States who are at risk for undernutrition.

13. List three federal programs that address malnutrition in the United States.

References

1. Food and Agriculture Organization of the United Nations. *The State of Food Insecurity in the World 2008*. Available online at www.fao.org/docrep/011/i0291e/i0291e00.htm. Accessed July 23, 2009.

2. Caulfield, L. E., de Onis, M. Blössner, M., and Black, R. E. Undernutrition as an underlying cause of child deaths associated with diarrhea, pneumonia, malaria, and measles. *Am. J. Clin. Nutr.* 80:193–198, 2004.

3. Black, R. E., Allen, L. H., Bhutta, Z. A. et al. Maternal and child undernutrition: Global and regional exposures and health consequences. *Lancet* 371: 243–260, 2008.

4. World Health Organization. *The Global Burden of Disease: 2004 update, 2008.* Available online at www.who.int/healthinf/global_burden_disease/2004_report_update/en/index.html Accessed May 4, 2009.

5. World Health Organization. *Global Strategy on Diet Physical Activity and Health: Obesity and Overweight.* Available online at www.who.int/dietphysicalactivity/publications/facts/obesity/en/. Accessed August 27, 2008.

6. Kennedy, E. T. The global face of nutrition: What can governments and industry do? *J. Nutr.* 135: 913–915, 2005.

7. Popkin, B. M. The nutrition transition: An overview of world patterns of change. *Nutr. Rev.* 62(7 Pt 2): S140–143, 2004.

8. Eberwine, D., Pan American Health Organization. Globesity: A crisis of growing proportions. Perspective's in Health 7(3):2002. Available online at www.paho.org/English/DPI/Number15_article2_2.htm/ Accessed February 12, 2006.

9. Chen, C. M. Overview of obesity in mainland China. *Obes. Rev.* 9:14–21, 2008.

10. Lobstein, T., Baur, L., and Uauy, R.; IASO International Obesity Task Force. Obesity in children and young people: A crisis in public health. *Obes. Rev.* 5(Suppl 1):4–104, 2004.

11. De Onis, M., and Blössner, M. Prevalence and trends of overweight among pre-schoolchildren in developing countries. *Am. J. Clin. Nutr.* 72:1032–1039, 2000.

12. Infant Mortality Rates. Available online at www.geographyiq.com/ranking/ranking_Infant_Mortality_Rate_aall.htm. Accessed August 28, 2008.

13. UNICEF Progress for Children. A World Fit for Children. Statistical Review. Available online at www.unicef.org/progressforchildren/2007n6/index_41401.htm. Accessed May 4, 2009.

14. James, P. T., Leach, R., Kalamara, E., and Shayeghi, M. The worldwide obesity epidemic. *Obes. Res.* 9(Suppl 4): 228S–233S, 2001.

15. The World Bank. *Global Purchasing Power Parities and Real Expenditures: 2005 International Comparison Program.* Available online at http://siteresources.worldbank.org/ICPINT/Resources/icp-final.pdf. Accessed April 23, 2009.

16. Are We on Track to End Hunger? Hunger Report 2004. Bread for the World Institute. Available online at www.bread.org/institute/ hunger_report/index.html/ Accessed May 7, 2004.

17. Population Reference Bureau. World population highlights: Key findings from PRB's 2008 world population data sheet, *Population Bulletin* 63(3):1–16, 2008. Available online at www.prb.org/pdf08/63.3highlights.pdf. Accessed August 30, 2008.

18. Reijnders, L., and Soret, S. Quantification of the environmental impact of different dietary protein choices. *Am. J. Clin. Nutr.* 78(Suppl):664S–668S, 2003.

19. Steinfeld, H., Gerber, P., Wassenaar, T. et al. *Livestock's Long Shadow: Environmental Issues and Options.* 2006. Available online at http://www.fao.org/docrep/010/a0701e/a0701e00.HTM. Accessed March 17, 2009.

20. Brown, L. R. *World Facing Huge New Challenge on Food Front—Business-as-Usual Not a Viable Option.* April 16, 2008. Available online at www.earthpolicy.org/Updates/2008/Update72.htm. Accessed August 30, 2008.

21. Worm, B., Hilborn, R., Baum, J. K. et al. Rebuilding global fisheries. *Science* 325:578–585, 2009.

22. World Health Organization. Micronutrient Deficiencies. Iron Deficiency Anaemia. Available online at www.who.int/nutrition/ topics/ida/en/index.html/ Accessed April 24, 2009.

23. de Benoist, B., Andersson, M., Takkouche, B., and Egli, I. Prevalence of iodine deficiency worldwide. *Lancet* 362:1859–1860, 2003.

24. World Health Organization. Micronutrient Deficiencies. Iodine Deficiency Disorders. Available online at www.who.int/nutrition/ topics/idd/en/index.html/ Accessed May 20, 2008.

25. World Health Organization. Micronutrient Deficiencies. Vitamin A Deficiency. Available online at www.who.int/nutrition/topics/vad/ en/index.html/ Accessed April 23, 2008.

26. Jones, G., Steketee, R. W., Black, R. E. et al. How many child deaths can we prevent this year? *Lancet* 362:65–71, 2003.

27. Hubner, R. A., and Houlston, R. S. Folate and colorectal cancer prevention. *Br. J. Cancer* 100:233–239, 2009.

28. World Health Organization. *The World Health Report, 1998: Life in the 21st Century—A Vision for All.* Geneva: World Health Organization, 1998. Available online at www.who.int/whr/1998/en/index.html. Accessed April 24, 2009.

29. Lopez, A. Malnutrition and the burden of disease. *Asia Pac. J. Clin. Nutr.* 13(Suppl):S7, 2004.

30. Central Intelligence Agency. *World Fact Book. Country Comparisons: Total Fertility Rate.* Available online at www.cia.gov/library/publications/the-world-factbook/rankorder/2127rank.html. Accessed July 23, 2009.

31. Berg, L. R., and Hager, M. C. *Visualizing Environmental Science.* Hoboken: John Wiley & Sons, 2007.

32. Raloff, J. The human numbers crunch. *Sci. News* 149:396–397, 1996.

33. Bhutta, Z. A. Micronutrient needs of malnourished children. *Curr. Opin. Clin. Nutr. Metab. Care* 11:309–314, 2008.

34. Ogden, C. L., Carroll, M. D., Curtin, L. R. et al. Prevalence of overweight and obesity in the United States 1999–2004, *JAMA* 295:1549–1555, 2006.

35. Nord, M., Andrews, M., and Carlson, S. Household Food Security in the United States, 2007. ERR-66, U.S. Department of Agriculture, Economic Research Service, November, 2008.

36. DeNavas-Walt, C., Proctor, B. D., and Smith, J. C. *Current Population Reports, P60-235, Income, Poverty, and Health Insurance Coverage in the United States: 2007.* Washington, DC: U.S. Government Printing Office, 2008.

37. Jetter, K. M., and Cassady, D. L. The availability and cost of healthier food items. *Am. J. Prev. Med.* 30:38–44, 2006.

38. Native Economic Development Guidance and Empowerment. Available online at www.occ.treas.gov/cdd/edge.pdf/ Accessed February 16, 2006.

39. MacDorman, M. F., and Mathews, T. J. Recent trends in infant mortality in the United States. *NCHS data brief*, no. 9. Hyattsville, MD: National Center for Healthy Statistics, 2008.

40. McCarty, M. *Homelessness: Recent Statistics, Targeted Federal Programs, and Recent Legislation*. May 2005. Available online at www.fas.org/sgp/crs/misc/RL30442.pdf. Accessed March 17, 2009.

41. Federal Interagency Forum on Aging. Older Americans 2004: Key Indicators of Well Being. Available online at www.agingstats.gov/ default.htm/ Accessed April 14, 2009.

42. U.S. Department of Agriculture. Food and Nutrition Service. *The National Nutrition Safety Net: Tools for Community Food Security*. FNS-314, January, 2000.

43. Economic Research Service, U.S. Department of Agriculture. *The Food Assistance Landscape: FY 2007 Annual Report*. Economic Bulletin 6-5, May 2008. Available online at www.ers.usda.gov/Publications/EIB6-5/EIB6-5.pdf. Accessed September 5, 2008.

44. Feeding America. *How We Work*. Available online at http://feedingamerica.org/our-network/how-we-work.aspx. Accessed March 30, 2009.

45. U.S. Department of Agriculture, Food Recovery and Gleaning Initiative. *A Citizen's Guide to Food Recovery*. Available online at www.usda.gov/news/pubs/gleaning/content.htm. Accessed September 5, 2008.

46. U.S. Department of Agriculture, Economic Research Service, USDA Center for Nutrition Policy and Promotion. USDA's Healthy Eating Index and Nutrition Information. Available online at www.usda.gov/cnpp/usda_healthy_eating _index.htm/ Accessed April 5, 2004.

Appendices

(©iStockphoto)

Appendix A
Additional DRI Tables

All other DRI tables are included in the front and back covers of this text

Dietary Reference Intakes: Recommended Intakes for Individuals: Essential Amino Acids

Life Stage Group	Histidine (mg/kg/day)	Isoleucine (mg/kg/day)	Leucine (mg/kg/day)	Lysine (mg/kg/day)	Methionine + Cysteine (mg/kg/day)	Phenylalanine + Tyrosine (mg/kg/day)	Threonine (mg/kg/day)	Tryptophan (mg/kg/day)	Valine (mg/kg/day)
Infants									
0–6 mo*	23	88	156	107	59	135	73	28	87
7–12 mo	32	43	93	89	43	84	49	13	58
Children									
1–3 y	21	28	63	58	28	54	32	8	37
4–8 y	16	22	49	46	22	41	24	6	28
Males									
9–13 y	17	22	49	46	22	41	24	6	28
14–18 y	15	21	47	43	21	38	22	6	27
19–30 y	14	19	42	38	19	33	20	5	24
31–50 y	14	19	42	38	19	33	20	5	24
51–70 y	14	19	42	38	19	33	20	5	24
> 70 y	14	19	42	38	19	33	20	5	24
Females									
9–13 y	15	21	47	43	21	38	22	6	27
14–18 y	14	19	44	40	19	35	21	5	24
19–30 y	14	19	42	38	19	33	20	5	24
31–50 y	14	19	42	38	19	33	20	5	24
51–70 y	14	19	42	38	19	33	20	5	24
> 70 y	14	19	42	38	19	33	20	5	24
Pregnancy	18	25	56	51	25	44	26	7	31
Lactation	19	30	62	52	26	51	30	9	35

*Values for this age group are AI (Adequate Intakes).

Source: Institute of Medicine, Food and Nutrition Board "Dietary Reference Intakes for Energy, Carbohydrates, Fiber, Fat, Protein and Amino Acids." Washington, DC: National Academies Press, 2002.

Dietary Reference Intake Values for Energy: Total Energy Expenditure (TEE) Equations for Overweight and Obese Individuals

Life Stage Group	TEE Prediction Equation	PA Values
Overweight boys aged 3–18 years	TEE = 114 − (50.9 × age in yrs) + PA[(19.5 × weight in kg) + (1161.4 × height in m)]	Sedentary = 1.00 Low active = 1.12 Active = 1.24 Very active = 1.45
Overweight girls aged 3–18 years	TEE = 389 − (41.2 × age in yrs) + PA[(15.0 × weight in kg) + (701.6 × height in m)]	Sedentary = 1.00 Low active = 1.18 Active = 1.35 Very active = 1.60
Overweight and obese men aged 19 years and older	TEE = 1086 − (10.1 × age in yrs) + PA[(13.7 × weight in kg) + (416 × height in m)]	Sedentary = 1.00 Low active = 1.12 Active = 1.29 Very active = 1.59
Overweight and obese women aged 19 years and older	TEE = 448 − (7.95 × age in yrs) + PA[(11.4 × weight in kg) + (619 × height in m)]	Sedentary = 1.00 Low active = 1.16 Active = 1.27 Very active = 1.44

Source: Institute of Medicine, Food and Nutrition Board "Dietary Reference Intakes for Energy, Carbohydrates, Fiber, Fat, Protein and Amino Acids," Washington, DC: National Academies Press, 2002.

Appendix B
Standards for Body Size

Body Mass Index (BMI) and Associated Risk

Body mass index (BMI), is the measurement of choice for determining health risks associated with body weight. To use the table find the appropriate height in the left-hand column. Move across the row to the given weight. The number at the top of the column is the BMI for that height and weight. Use the table above to determine the risks associated with BMI and waist circumference.

BMI (kg/m²)	19	20	21	22	23	24	25	26	27	28	29	30	35	40
Height (in.)	Weight (lb.)													
58	91	96	100	105	110	115	119	124	129	134	138	143	167	191
59	94	99	104	109	114	119	124	128	133	138	143	148	173	198
60	97	102	107	112	118	123	128	133	138	143	148	153	179	204
61	100	106	111	116	122	127	132	137	143	148	153	158	185	211
62	104	109	115	120	126	131	136	142	147	153	158	164	191	218
63	107	113	118	124	130	135	141	146	152	158	163	169	197	225
64	110	116	122	128	134	140	145	151	157	163	169	174	204	232
65	114	120	126	132	138	144	150	156	162	168	174	180	210	240
66	118	124	130	136	142	148	155	161	167	173	179	186	216	247
67	121	127	134	140	146	153	159	166	172	178	185	191	223	255
68	125	131	138	144	151	158	164	171	177	184	190	197	230	262
69	128	135	142	149	155	162	169	176	182	189	196	203	236	270
70	132	139	146	153	160	167	174	181	188	195	202	207	243	278
71	136	143	150	157	165	172	179	186	193	200	208	215	250	286
72	140	147	154	162	169	177	184	191	199	206	213	221	258	294
73	144	151	159	166	174	182	189	197	204	212	219	227	265	302
74	148	155	163	171	179	186	194	202	210	218	225	233	272	311
75	152	160	168	176	184	192	200	208	216	224	232	240	279	319
76	156	164	172	180	189	197	205	213	221	230	238	246	287	328

BMI (kg/m²)		Waist less than or equal to 40 in. (men) or 35 in. (women)	Waist greater than 40 in. (men) or 35 in. (women)
18.5 or less	Underweight	—	N/A
18.5–24.9	Normal	—	N/A
25.0–29.9	Overweight	Increased	High
30.0–34.9	Obese	High	Very High
35.0–39.9	Obese	Very High	Very High
40 or greater	Extremely Obese	Extremely High	Extremely High

Source: Adapted from Partnership for Healthy Weight Management http://www.consumer.gov/weightloss/bmi.htm

Birth to 36 months: Girls
Length-for-age and Weight-for-age percentiles

NAME _____

RECORD # _____

Published May 30, 2000 (modified 4/20/01).

Source: Developed by the National Center for Health Statistics in collaboration with the National Center for Chronic Disease Prevention and Health Promotion (2000). www.cdc.gov/growthcharts

SAFER · HEALTHIER · PEOPLE™

Birth to 36 months: Boys
Length-for-age and Weight-for-age percentiles

NAME _____

RECORD # _____

AGE (MONTHS)

LENGTH

WEIGHT

AGE (MONTHS)

	Mother's Stature _____	Gestational			
	Father's Stature _____	Age: _____ Weeks			Comment
Date	Age	Weight	Length	Head Circ.	
Birth					

Published May 30, 2000 (modified 4/20/01).

Source: Developed by the National Center for Health Statistics in collaboration with the National Center for Chronic Disease Prevention and Health Promotion (2000). www.cdc.gov/growthcharts

CDC

SAFER · HEALTHIER · PEOPLE™

2 to 20 years: Girls
Body mass index-for-age percentiles

NAME _____

RECORD # _____

*To Calculate BMI: Weight (kg) ÷ Stature (cm) ÷ Stature (cm) x 10,000
or Weight (lb) ÷ Stature (in) ÷ Stature (in) x 703

AGE (YEARS)

Published May 30, 2000 (modified 10/16/00).

Source: Developed by the National Center for Health Statistics in collaboration with the National Center for Chronic Disease Prevention and Health Promotion (2000). www.cdc.gov/growthcharts

SAFER · HEALTHIER · PEOPLE™

2 to 20 years: Boys
Body mass index-for-age percentiles

Date	Age	Weight	Stature	BMI*	Comments

*To Calculate BMI: Weight (kg) ÷ Stature (cm) ÷ Stature (cm) x 10,000
or Weight (lb) ÷ Stature (in) ÷ Stature (in) x 703

AGE (YEARS)

Published May 30, 2000 (modified 10/16/00).

Source: Developed by the National Center for Health Statistics in collaboration with the National Center for Chronic Disease Prevention and Health Promotion (2000). www.cdc.gov/growthcharts

SAFER · HEALTHIER · PEOPLE™

Appendix C
Normal Blood Values of Nutritional Relevance

Red blood cells	
Men	4.6–6.2 million/mm^3
Women	4.2–5.2 million/mm^3
White blood cells	5,000–10,000/mm^3
Hematocrit	
Men	40–54 ml/100 ml
Women	36–47 ml/100 ml
Children	35–49 ml/100 ml
Hemoglobin	
Men	14–18 g/100 ml
Women	12–16 g/100 ml
Children	11.2–16.5 g/100 ml
Ferritin	
Men	20–300 ng/ml
Women	20–120 ng/ml
Calcium	9–11 mg/100 ml
Iodine	3.8–8 µg/100 ml
Iron	
Men	75–175 µg/100 ml
Women	65–165 µg/100 ml
Zinc	0.75–1.4 µg/ml
Magnesium	1.8–3.0 mg/100 ml
Potassium	3.5–5.0 mEq/liter
Sodium	136–145 mEq/liter
Chloride	100–108 mEq/liter
Vitamin A	20–80 µg/100 ml
Vitamin B$_{12}$	200–800 pg/100 ml
Vitamin C	0.6–2.0 mg/100 ml
Carotene	48–200 µg/liter
Folate	2–20 ng/ml
pH	7.35–7.45
Total protein	6.6–8.0 g/100 ml
Albumin	3.0–4.0 g/100 ml
Cholesterol	<200 mg/100 ml
Glucose	60–100 mg/100 ml blood, 70–120 mg/100 ml serum

Source: Handbook of Clinical Dietetics, American Dietetic Association, © 1981 by Yale University Press (New Haven, Conn.); and Committee on Dietetics of the Mayo Clinic, *Mayo Clinic Diet Manual* (Philadelphia: W. B. Saunders Company, 1981), pp. 275–277.

Guidelines for Determining Healthy Lipid Levels

Classification of LDL, Total, and HDL Cholesterol and Triglycerides (mg/dL)

LDL Cholesterol

<100	Optimal*
100–129	Near optimal/above optimal
130–159	Borderline high
160–189	High
≥190	Very high

Total Cholesterol

<200	Desirable
200–239	Borderline high
≥240	High

HDL Cholesterol

<40	Increasaes risk
≥60	Decreases risk

Triglycerides

<150	Normal
150–190	Borderline high
200–499	High
≥500	Very high

*For very high-risk people, LDL cholesterol should be < 70.

Source: NCEP, ATP III, 2004 update. Available online at http://www.nhlbi.nih.gov/guidelines/cholesterol/atglance.pdf

Major Risk Factors (Exclusive of LDL Cholesterol) that Increase Heart Disease Risk

Cigarette smoking
Hypertension (BP ≥ 140/90 mmHg or on antihypertensive medication)
Low HDL cholesterol (<40 mg/dL)*
Family history of premature heart disease (heart disease in male first-degree relative < 55 years; or in female first-degree relative < 65 years)
Age (men ≥ 45 years; women ≥ 55 years)

*HDL cholesterol ≥ 60 mg/dL counts as a "negative" risk factor; its presence removes one risk factor from the total count.

Source: National Cholesterol Education Program, ATP III, 2004 update.

High Blood Pressure (Hypertension) Guidelines

Classification

High	140/90 or above
Prehypertension	120–139 / 80–90
Normal	119/79 or below

Source: Joint National Committee on Prevention, Detection, Evaluation, and Treatment of High Blood Pressure (2003). *The seventh report of the Joint National Committee on Prevention, Detection, Evaluation, and Treatment of High Blood Pressure.* NIH Publication No. 03–5233. Bethesda, MD: U.S. Department of Health and Human Services.

Appendix F
World Health Organization Nutrition Recommendations

The Population Nutrient Goals from WHO

	Limits for Population Average Intakes	
	Lower Limit	Upper Limit
Total fat	15% of energy	30% of energy[a]
Saturated fatty acids	0% of energy	10% of energy
Polyunsaturated fatty acids	3% of energy	7% of energy
Dietary cholesterol	0 mg/day	300 mg/day
Total carbohydrate	55% of energy	75% of energy
Complex carbohydrates[b]	50% of energy	75% of energy
Dietary fiber[c]		
As non-starch polysaccharides (NSP)	16 g/day	24 g/day
As total dietary fiber	27 g/day	40 g/day
Free sugars[d]	0% of energy	10% of energy
Protein	10% of energy	15% of energy
Salt	—[e]	6 g/day

Total energy
Energy intake needs to be sufficient to allow for normal childhood growth, for the needs of pregnancy and lactation, and for work and desirable physical activities, and to maintain appropriate body reserves of energy in children and adults. Adult population on average should have a body-mass index (BMI) of 20–22. (BMI = body mass in kg/[height in meters]^2).

The lower limit defines the minimum intake needed to prevent deficiency diseases, while the upper limit expresses the maximum intake compatible with the prevention of chronic diseases.

[a]An interim goal for nations with high fat intakes; further benefits would be expected by reducing fat intake toward 15% of total energy.
[b]A daily minimum intake of 400 g vegetables and fruits, including at least 30 g of legumes, nuts, and seeds, should contribute to this component.
[c]Dietary fiber includes the non-starch polysaccharides (NSP), the goals for which are based on NSP obtained from mixed food sources. Since the definition and measurement of dietary fiber remain uncertain, the goals for total dietary fiber have been estimated from the NSP values.
[d]These sugars include monosaccharides, disaccharides, and other short-chain sugars extracted from carbohydrates by refining. These refined, or purified, sugars do not include the natural sugars consumed when eating fruits and vegetables or drinking milk.
[e]Not defined.
Source: Diet, nutrition and the prevention of chronic diseases. A report of the WHO Study Group on Diet. Nutrition and Prevention of Noncommunicable Diseases. Nutr. Rev. 49:291–301, 1991.

Appendix G
U.S. Nutrition Recommendations

Key Recommendations of the 2005 Dietary Guidelines for Americans

ADEQUATE NUTRIENTS WITHIN CALORIE NEEDS
Key Recommendations
- Consume a variety of nutrient-dense foods and beverages within and among the basic food groups while choosing foods that limit the intake of saturated and *trans* fats, cholesterol, added sugars, salt, and alcohol.
- Meet recommended intakes within energy needs by adopting a balanced eating pattern, such as the USDA Food Guide or the DASH Eating Plan.

Key Recommendations for Specific Population Groups
- People over age 50: Consume vitamin B_{12} in its crystalline form (i.e., fortified foods or supplements).
- Women of childbearing age who may become pregnant: Eat foods high in heme-iron and/or consume iron-rich plant foods or iron-fortified foods with an enhancer of iron absorption, such as vitamin C-rich foods.
- Women of childbearing age who may become pregnant and those in the first trimester of pregnancy: Consume adequate synthetic folic acid daily (from fortified foods or supplements) in addition to food forms of folate from a varied diet.
- Older adults, people with dark skin, and people exposed to insufficient sunlight: Consume extra vitamin D.

WEIGHT MANAGEMENT
Key Recommendations
- To maintain body weight in a healthy range, balance calories from foods and beverages with calories expended.
- To prevent gradual weight gain over time, make small decreases in food and beverage calories and increase physical activity.

Key Recommendations for Specific Population Groups
- Those who need to lose weight: Aim for a slow, steady weight loss by decreasing calorie intake and increasing activity.
- Overweight children: Reduce the rate of body weight gain while allowing growth and development. Consult a healthcare provider.
- Pregnant women: Ensure appropriate weight gain as specified by a healthcare provider.
- Breastfeeding women: Moderate weight reduction is safe and does not compromise weight gain of the nursing infant.
- Overweight adults and overweight children with chronic diseases and/or on medication: Consult a healthcare provider about weight loss strategies prior to starting a weight-reduction program to ensure appropriate management of other health conditions.

PHYSICAL ACTIVITY
Key Recommendations
- Engage in regular physical activity and reduce sedentary activities to promote health, psychological well-being, and a healthy body weight.
  - To reduce the risk of chronic disease in adulthood engage in at least 30 minutes of moderate-intensity physical activity, above usual activity, at work or home on most days of the week.
  - For most people, greater health benefits can be obtained by engaging in physical activity of more vigorous intensity or longer duration.
  - To help manage body weight and prevent gradual, unhealthy body weight gain in adulthood engage in approximately 60 minutes of moderate- to vigorous-intensity activity on most days of the week while not exceeding caloric intake requirements.
  - To sustain weight loss in adulthood participate in at least 60 to 90 minutes of daily moderate-intensity physical activity while not exceeding caloric intake requirements. Some people may need to consult with a healthcare provider before participating in this level of activity.
- Achieve physical fitness by including cardiovascular conditioning, stretching exercises for flexibility, and resistance exercises for muscle strength.

Key Recommendations for Specific Population Groups
- Children and adolescents: Engage in at least 60 minutes of physical activity on most, preferably all, days of the week.
- Pregnant women: In the absence of medical or obstetric complications, incorporate 30 minutes or more of moderate-intensity physical activity on most, if not all, days of the week. Avoid activities with a high risk of falling or abdominal trauma.
- Breastfeeding women: Be aware that neither acute nor regular exercise adversely affects the mother's ability to breastfeed successfully.
- Older adults: Participate in regular physical activity to reduce functional declines associated with aging and to achieve the other benefits.

FOOD GROUPS TO ENCOURAGE
Key Recommendations
- Consume a sufficient amount of fruits and vegetables while staying within energy needs. Two cups of fruit and 2 1/2 cups of vegetables per day are recommended for a reference 2,000-calorie intake, with higher or lower amounts depending on the calorie level.
- Choose a variety of fruits and vegetables each day. In particular, select from all five vegetable subgroups (dark green, orange, legumes, starchy vegetables, and other vegetables) several times a week.
- Consume 3 or more ounce-equivalents of whole-grain products per day, with the rest of the recommended grains coming from enriched or whole-grain products. In general, at least half the grains should come from whole grains.
- Consume 3 cups per day of fat-free or low-fat milk or equivalent milk products.

(continued)

Key Recommendations of the 2005 Dietary Guidelines for Americans (*continued*)

Key Recommendations for Specific Population Groups
- Children and adolescents: Consume whole-grain products often; at least half the grains should be whole grains. Children 2 to 8 years should consume 2 cups per day of fat-free or low-fat milk or equivalent milk products. Children 9 years of age and older should consume 3 cups per day of fat-free or low-fat milk or equivalent milk products.

FATS
Key Recommendations
- Consume less than 10 percent of calories from saturated fat and less than 300 mg/day of cholesterol, and keep *trans* fat as low as possible.
- Keep total fat intake between 20 to 35 percent of calories, with most fats coming from sources of polyunsaturated and monounsaturated fatty acids.
- When selecting and preparing meat, poultry, dry beans, and milk or milk products, make choices that are lean, low-fat, or fat-free.
- Limit intake of fats and oils high in saturated and/or *trans* fatty acids, and choose products low in such fats and oils.

Key Recommendations for Specific Population Groups
- Children and adolescents: Keep total fat intake between 30 to 35 percent of calories for children 2 to 3 years of age and between 25 to 35 percent of calories for children and adolescents 4 to 18 years of age, with most fats coming from sources of polyunsaturated and monounsaturated fatty acids, such as fish, nuts, and vegetable oils.

CARBOHYDRATES
Key Recommendations
- Choose fiber-rich fruits, vegetables, and whole grains often.
- Choose and prepare foods and beverages with little added sugars as suggested by the USDA Food Guide and the DASH Eating Plan.
- Reduce the incidence of dental caries by practicing good oral hygiene and consuming sugar- and starch-containing foods and beverages less frequently.

SODIUM AND POTASSIUM
Key Recommendations
- Consume less than 2,300 mg (approximately 1 tsp of salt) of sodium per day.
- Choose and prepare foods with little salt. At the same time, consume potassium-rich foods, such as fruits and vegetables.

Key Recommendations for Specific Population Groups
- Individuals with hypertension, blacks, and middle-aged and older adults: Aim to consume no more than 1,500 mg of sodium per day, and meet the potassium recommendation (4,700 mg/day) with food.

ALCOHOLIC BEVERAGES
Key Recommendations
- Those who choose to drink alcoholic beverages should do so sensibly and in moderation—defined as the consumption of up to one drink per day for women and up to two drinks per day for men.
- Alcoholic beverages should not be consumed by those who cannot restrict their alcohol intake, women of childbearing age, pregnant and lactating women, children and adolescents, individuals taking medications that interact with alcohol, and those with specific medical conditions.
- Alcoholic beverages should be avoided by individuals engaging in activities that require attention, skill, or coordination, such as driving or operating machinery.

FOOD SAFETY
Key Recommendations
- To avoid microbial foodborne illness:
  - Clean hands, food contact surfaces, and fruits and vegetables. Meat and poultry should not be washed or rinsed.
  - Separate raw, cooked, and ready-to-eat foods while shopping, preparing, or storing foods.
  - Cook foods to a safe temperature to kill microorganisms.
  - Chill (refrigerate) perishable food promptly and defrost foods properly.
  - Avoid raw (unpasteurized) milk or any products made from unpasteurized milk, raw or partially cooked eggs or foods containing raw eggs, raw or undercooked meat and poultry, unpasteurized juices, and raw sprouts.

Key Recommendations for Specific Population Groups
- Infants and young children, pregnant women, older adults, and those who are immunocompromised: Do not eat or drink raw (unpasteurized) milk or any products made from unpasteurized milk, raw or partially cooked eggs or foods containing raw eggs, raw or undercooked meat and poultry, raw or undercooked fish or shellfish, unpasteurized juices, and raw sprouts.
- Pregnant women, older adults, and those who are immunocompromised: Reheat deli meats and frankfurters to steaming hot.

Healthy People 2010

Goals

1. Increase quality and years of healthy life.
2. Eliminate health disparities.

Leading Health Indicators

1. Physical activity
2. Overweight and obesity
3. Tobacco use
4. Substance abuse
5. Responsible sexual behavior
6. Mental health
7. Injury and violence
8. Environmental quality
9. Immunization
10. Access to health care

Focus Areas

Access to quality health services
Arthritis, osteoporosis, and chronic
   back conditions
Cancer
Chronic kidney disease
Diabetes
Disability and secondary conditions
Educational and community-based
   programs
Environmental health
Family planning
Food safety
Health communication
Heart disease and stroke
HIV

Immunization and infectious diseases
Injury and violence prevention
Maternal, infant, and child health
Medical product safety
Mental health and mental disorders
Nutrition and overweight
Occupational safety and health
Oral health
Physical activity and fitness
Public health infrastructure
Respiratory diseases
Sexually transmitted diseases
Substance abuse
Tobacco use
Vision and hearing

Source: Healthy People 2010. Available online at www.health.gov/healthy people.

Macronutrient Recommendations for Lowering Blood Cholesterol

Component	Recommendation
Polyunsaturated fat	Up to 10% of total calories
Monounsaturated fat	Up to 20% of total calories
Total fat	25–35% of total calories† *
Carbohydrate†	50–60% of total calories† *
Dietary fiber	20–30 grams per day
Protein	Approximately 15% of total calories

* An increase of total fat to 35 percent of total calories and a reduction in carbohydrate to 50 percent is allowed for persons with the metabolic syndrome. Any increase in fat intake should be in the form of either polyunsaturated or monounsaturated fat.

† Carbohydrate should derive predominantly from foods rich in complex carbohydrates including grains—especially whole grains—fruits, and vegetables.

Source: National Cholesterol Education Program.

Nutrition and Physical Fitness Recommendations from the American Cancer Society

Maintain a healthy weight throughout life.

• Balance calorie intake with physical activity.

• Avoid excessive weight gain throughout life.

• Achieve and maintain a healthy weight if currently overweight or obese.

Adopt a physically active lifestyle.

• Adults: Engage in at least 30 minutes of moderate to vigorous physical activity, above usual activity, on 5 or more days of the week; 45 to 60 minutes of international physical activity are preferable.

• Children and adolescents: Engage in at least 60 minutes per day of moderate to vigorous physical activity at least 5 days per week.

Eat a healthy diet, with an emphasis on plant sources.

• Choose foods and drinks in amounts that help achieve and maintain a healthy weight.

• Eat 5 or more servings of a variety of vegetables and fruits every day.

• Choose whole grains over processed (refined) grains.

• Limit intake of processed and red meats.

If you drink alcoholic beverages, limit your intake.

• Drink no more than 1 drink per day for women or 2 per day for men.

Source: Some adapted from Complete Guide—Nutrition and Physical Activity for Cancer Prevention. Available online at http://www.cancer.org.

Ethnic and Alternative Pyramids for Diet and Lifestyle Planning

Mediterranean Diet Pyramid
A contemporary approach to delicious, healthy eating

Meats and Sweets
Less often

Poultry and Eggs
*Moderate portions,
every two days or
weekly*

Wine
In moderation

Cheese and Yogurt
*Moderate portions,
daily or weekly*

Fish and Seafood
*Often, at least
two times per week*

Drink Water

**Fruits,
Vegetables,
Grains (mostly
whole), Olive oil,
Beans, Nuts,
Legumes and
Seeds, Herbs
and Spices**
*Base every meal
on these foods*

**Be Physically
Active; Enjoy
Meals with
Others**

Illustration by George Middleton   © 2009 Oldways Preservation and Exchange Trust   www.oldwayspt.org

Source: Oldways Preservation and Exchange Trust. Available online at www.oldwayspt.org

The Traditional Healthy Asian Diet Pyramid

Daily Beverage Recommendations:

6 Glasses of Water or Tea

Sake, Wine, or Beer in moderation

Monthly

MEAT

Weekly

SWEETS

EGGS & POULTRY

Optional Daily

FISH & SHELLFISH or DAIRY

VEGETABLE OILS

Daily

FRUITS

LEGUMES, SEEDS & NUTS

VEGETABLES

RICE, NOODLES, BREADS, MILLET, CORN & OTHER WHOLE GRAINS

Daily Physical Activity

© 2000 Oldways Preservation & Exchange Trust   www.oldwayspt.org

Source: Oldways Preservation and Exchange Trust. Available online at www.oldwayspt.org

Appendix I
Exchange Lists

Starch

Bread

Food	Serving Size
Bagel, large (about 4 oz)	¼ (1 oz)
⚠ Biscuit, 2½ inches across	1
Bread	
☺ reduced-calorie	2 slices (1½ oz)
white, whole-grain, pumpernickel, rye, unfrosted raisin	1 slice (1 oz)
Chapatti, small, 6 inches across	1
⚠ Cornbread, 1¾ inch cube	1 (1½ oz)
English muffin	½
Hot dog bun or hamburger bun	½ (1 oz)
Naan, 8 inches by 2 inches	¼
Pancake, 4 inches across, ¼ inch thick	1
Pita, 6 inches across	½
Roll, plain, small	1 (1 oz)
⚠ Stuffing bread	⅓ cup
⚠ Taco shell, 5 inches across	2
Tortilla, corn, 6 inches across	1
Tortilla, corn, 6 inches across	1
Tortilla, flour, 10 inches across	⅓ tortilla
⚠ Waffle, 4-inch square or 4 inches across	1

☺ = More than 3 grams of dietary fiber per serving.

⚠ = Extra fat, or prepared with added fat. (Count as 1 starch + 1 fat.)

🧂 = 480 milligrams or more of sodium per serving.

The Exchange Lists are the basis of a meal planning system designed by a committee of the American Diabetes Association and The American Dietetic Association. While designed primarily for people with diabetes and others who must follow special diets, the Exchange Lists are based on principles of good nutrition that apply to everyone. Copyright© 2008 by the American Diabetes Association and The American Dietetic Association.

Cereals and Grains

Food	Serving Size
Barley, cooked	⅓ cup
Bran, dry	
☺ oat	¼ cup
☺ wheat	½ cup
☺ Bulgur (cooked)	½ cup
Cereals	
☺ bran	½ cup
cooked (oats, oatmeal)	½ cup
puffed	1½ cups
shredded wheat, plain	½ cup
sugar-coated	½ cup
unsweetened, ready-to-eat	¾ cup
Couscous	⅓ cup
Granola	
low-fat	¼ cup
▽ regular	¼ cup
Grits, cooked	½ cup
Kasha	½ cup
Millet, cooked	⅓ cup
Muesli	¼ cup
Pasta, cooked	⅓ cup
Polenta, cooked	⅓ cup
Quinoa, cooked	⅓ cup
Rice, white or brown, cooked	⅓ cup
Tabbouleh (tabouli), prepared	½ cup
Wheat, germ, dry	3 Tbsp
Wild rice, cooked	½ cup

Starchy Vegetables

Food	Serving Size
Cassava	⅓ cup
Corn	½ cup
on cob, large	½ cup (5 oz)
☺ Hominy, canned	¾ cup
☺ Mixed vegetables with corn, peas, or pasta	1 cup
☺ Parsnips	½ cup
☺ Peas, green	½ cup
Plantain, ripe	⅓ cup
Potato	
baked with skin	¼ large (3 oz)
boiled, all kinds	½ cup or ½ medium (3 oz)
▽ mashed, with milk and fat	½ cup
French fried (oven-baked)	1 cup (2 oz)
☺ Pumpkin, canned, no sugar added	1 cup
Spaghetti/pasta sauce	½ cup
☺ Squash, winter (acorn, butternut)	1 cup
☺ Succotash	½ cup
Yam, sweet potato, plain	½ cup

Crackers and Snacks

Food	Serving Size
Animal crackers	8
Crackers	
⚠️ round-butter type	6
saltine-type	6
⚠️ sandwich-style, cheese or peanut butter filling	3
⚠️ whole-wheat regular	2–5 (¾ oz)
🙂 whole-wheat lower fat or crispbreads	2–5 (¾ oz)
Graham cracker, 2½-inch square	3
Matzoh	¾ oz
Melba toast, about 2-inch by 4-inch piece	4 pieces
Oyster crackers	20
Popcorn	3 cups
⚠️ 🙂 with butter	3 cups
🙂 no fat added	3 cups
🙂 lower fat	3 cups
Pretzels	¾ oz
Rice cakes, 4 inches across	2
Snack chips	
fat-free or baked (tortilla, potato), baked pita chips	15–20 (¾ oz)
⚠️ regular (tortilla, potato)	9–13 (¾ oz)

Beans, Peas, and Lentils

The choices on this list count as 1 starch + 1 lean meat.

Food	Serving Size
🙂 Baked beans	⅓ cup
🙂 Beans, cooked (black, garbanzo, kidney, lima, navy, pinto, white)	½ cup
🙂 Lentils, cooked (brown, green, yellow)	½ cup
🙂 Peas, cooked (black-eyed, split)	½ cup
🧂 🙂 Refried beans, canned	½ cup

Fruits

Fruit

The weight listed includes skin, core, seeds, and rind.

Food	Serving Size
Apple, unpeeled, small	1 (4 oz)
Apples, dried	4 rings
Applesauce, unsweetened	½ cup
Apricots	
canned	½ cup
dried	8 halves
☺ fresh	4 whole (5½ oz)
Banana, extra small	1 (4 oz)
☺ Blackberries	¾ cup
Blueberries	¾ cup
Cantaloupe, small	⅓ melon or 1 cup cubed (11 oz)
Cherries	
sweet, canned	½ cup
sweet fresh	12 (3 oz)
Dates	3
Dried fruits (blueberries, cherries, cranberries, mixed fruit, raisins)	2 Tbsp
Figs	
dried	1½
☺ fresh	1½ large or 2 medium (3½ oz)
Fruit cocktail	½ cup
Grapefruit	
large	½ (11 oz)
sections, canned	¾ cup
Grapes, small	17 (3 oz)
Honeydew melon	1 slice or 1 cup cubed (10 oz)
☺ Kiwi	1 (3½ oz)
Mandarin oranges, canned	¾ cup
Mango, small	½ fruit (5½ oz) or ½ cup
Nectarine, small	1 (5 oz)
☺ Orange, small	1 (6½ oz)
Papaya	½ fruit or 1 cup cubed (8 oz)
Peaches	
canned	½ cup
fresh, medium	1 (6 oz)
Pears	
canned	½ cup
fresh, large	½ (4 oz)
Pineapple	
canned	½ cup
fresh	¾ cup
Plums	
canned	½ cup
dried (prunes)	3
small	2 (5 oz)
☺ Raspberries	1 cup
☺ Strawberries	1¼ cup whole berries
☺ Tangerines, small	2 (8 oz)
Watermelon	1 slice or 1¼ cups cubes (13½ oz)

Fruit Juice

Food	Serving Size
Apple juice/cider	½ cup
Fruit juice blends, 100% juice	⅓ cup
Grape juice	⅓ cup
Grapefruit juice	½ cup
Orange juice	½ cup
Pineapple juice	½ cup
Prune juice	⅓ cup

Milk

Milk and Yogurts

Food	Serving Size	Count as
Fat-free or low-fat (1%)		
Milk, buttermilk, acidophilus milk, Lactaid	1 cup	1 fat-free milk
Evaporated milk	½ cup	1 fat-free milk
Yogurt, plain or flavored with an artificial sweetener	⅔ cup (6 oz)	1 fat-free milk
Reduced-fat (2%)		
Milk, acidophilus milk, kefir, Lactaid	1 cup	1 reduced-fat milk
Yogurt, plain	⅔ cup (6 oz)	1 reduced-fat milk
Whole		
Milk, buttermilk, goat's milk	1 cup	1 whole milk
Evaporated milk	½ cup	1 whole milk
Yogurt, plain	8 oz	1 whole milk

Dairy-Like Foods

Food	Serving Size	Count as
Chocolate milk		
fat-free	1 cup	1 fat-free milk + 1 carbohydrate
whole	1 cup	1 whole milk + 1 carbohydrate
Eggnog, whole milk	½ cup	1 carbohydrate + 2 fats
Rice drink		
flavored, low-fat	1 cup	2 carbohydrates
plain, fat-free	1 cup	1 carbohydrate
Smoothies, flavored, regular	10 oz	1 fat-free milk + 2½ carbohydrates
Soy milk		
light	1 cup	1 carbohydrate + ½ fat
regular, plain	1 cup	1 carbohydrate + 1 fat
Yogurt		
and juice blends	1 cup	1 fat-free milk + 1 carbohydrate
low carbohydrate (less than 6 grams carbohydrate per choice)	⅔ cup (6 oz)	½ fat-free milk
with fruit, low-fat	⅔ cup (6 oz)	1 fat-free milk + 1 carbohydrate

Sweets, Desserts, and Other Carbohydrates

Beverages, Soda, and Energy/Sports Drinks

Food	Serving Size	Count as
Cranberry juice cocktail	½ cup	1 carbohydrate
Energy drink	1 can (8.3 oz)	2 carbohydrates
Fruit drink or lemonade	1 cup (8 oz)	2 carbohydrates
Hot chocolate		
regular	1 envelope added to 8 oz water	1 carbohydrate + 1 fat
sugar-free or light	1 envelope added to 8 oz water	1 carbohydrate
Soft drink (soda), regular	1 can (12 oz)	2½ carbohydrates
Sports drink	1 cup (8 oz)	1 carbohydrate

Brownies, Cake, Cookies, Gelatin, Pie, and Pudding

Food	Serving Size	Count as
Brownie, small, unfrosted	1¼-inch square, ⅞ inch high (about 1 oz)	1 carbohydrate + 1 fat
Cake		
angel food, unfrosted	1/12 of cake (about 2 oz)	2 carbohydrates
frosted	2-inch square (about 2 oz)	2 carbohydrates + 1 fat
unfrosted	2-inch square (about 2 oz)	1 carbohydrate + 1 fat
Cookies		
chocolate chip	2 cookies (2¼ inches across)	1 carbohydrate + 2 fats
gingersnap	3 cookies	1 carbohydrate
sandwich, with crème filling	2 small (about ⅔ oz)	1 carbohydrate + 1 fat
sugar-free	3 small or 1 large (¾ –1 oz)	1 carbohydrate + 1–2 fats
vanilla wafer	5 cookies	1 carbohydrate + 1 fat
Cupcake, frosted	1 small (about 1¾ oz)	2 carbohydrates + 1–1½ fats
Fruit cobbler	½ cup (3½ oz)	3 carbohydrates + 1 fat
Gelatin, regular	½ cup	1 carbohydrate
Pie		
commercially prepared fruit, 2 crusts	⅛ of 8-inch pie	3 carbohydrates + 2 fats
pumpkin or custard	⅛ of 8-inch pie	1½ carbohydrates + 1½ fats
Pudding		
regular (made with reduced-fat milk)	½ cup	2 carbohydrates
sugar-free or sugar-and fat-free (made with fat-free milk)	½ cup	1 carbohydrate

Candy, Spreads, Sweets, Sweeteners, Syrups, and Toppings

Food	Serving Size	Count as
Candy bar, chocolate/peanut	2 "fun size" bars (1 oz)	1½ carbohydrates + 1½ fats
Candy, hard	3 pieces	1 carbohydrate
Chocolate "kisses"	5 pieces	1 carbohydrate + 1 fat
Coffee creamer		
dry, flavored	4 tsp	½ carbohydrate + ½ fat
liquid, flavored	2 Tbsp	1 carbohydrate
Fruit snacks, chewy (pureed fruit concentrate)	1 roll (¾ oz)	1 carbohydrate
Fruit spreads, 100% fruit	1½ Tbsp	1 carbohydrate
Honey	1 Tbsp	1 carbohydrate
Jam or jelly, regular	1 Tbsp	1 carbohydrate
Sugar	1 Tbsp	1 carbohydrate
Syrup		
chocolate	2 Tbsp	2 carbohydrates
light (pancake type)	2 Tbsp	1 carbohydrate
regular (pancake type)	1 Tbsp	1 carbohydrate

Condiments and Sauces

Food	Serving Size	Count as
Barbeque sauce	3 Tbsp	1 carbohydrate
Cranberry sauce, jellied	¼ cup	1½ carbohydrates
Gravy, canned or bottled	½ cup	½ carbohydrate + ½ fat
Salad dressing, fat-free, low-fat, cream-based	3 Tbsp	1 carbohydrate
Sweet and sour sauce	3 Tbsp	1 carbohydrate

Doughnuts, Muffins, Pastries, and Sweet Breads

Food	Serving Size	Count as
Banana nut bread	1-inch slice (1 oz)	2 carbohydrates + 1 fat
Doughnut		
cake, plain	1 medium (1½ oz)	1½ carbohydrates + 2 fats
yeast type, glazed	3¾ inches across (2 oz)	2 carbohydrates + 2 fats
Muffin (4 oz)	¼ muffin (1 oz)	1 carbohydrate + ½ fat
Sweet roll or Danish	1 (2½ oz)	2½ carbohydrates + 2 fats

Frozen Bars, Frozen Desserts, Frozen Yogurt, and Ice Cream

Food	Serving Size	Count as
Frozen pops	1	½ carbohydrate
Fruit juice bars, frozen, 100% juice	1 bar (3 oz)	1 carbohydrate
Ice cream		
fat-free	½ cup	1½ carbohydrates
light	½ cup	1 carbohydrate + 1 fat
no sugar added	½ cup	1 carbohydrate + 1 fat
regular	½ cup	1 carbohydrate + 2 fats
Sherbet, sorbet	½ cup	2 carbohydrates
Yogurt, frozen		
fat-free	⅓ cup	1 carbohydrate
regular	½ cup	1 carbohydrate + 0–1 fat

Granola Bars, Meal Replacement Bars/Shakes, and Trail Mix

Food	Serving Size	Count as
Granola or snack bar, regular or low-fat	1 bar (1 oz)	1½ carbohydrates
Meal replacement bar	1 bar (1⅓ oz)	1½ carbohydrates + 0–1 fat
Meal replacement bar	1 bar (2 oz)	2 carbohydrates + 1 fat
Meal replacement shake, reduced calorie	1 can (10–11 oz)	1½ carbohydrates + 0–1 fat
Trail mix		
candy/nut-based	1 oz	1 carbohydrate + 2 fats
dried fruit-based	1 oz	1 carbohydrate + 1 fat

Nonstarchy Vegetables

Nonstarchy Vegetables

Amaranth or Chinese spinach
Artichoke
Artichoke hearts
Asparagus
Baby corn
Bamboo shoots
Beans (green, wax, Italian)
Bean sprouts
Beets
Borscht
Broccoli
Brussels sprouts
Cabbage (green, bok choy, Chinese)
Carrots
Cauliflower
Celery
Chayote
Coleslaw, packaged, no dressing
Cucumber
Eggplant
Gourds (bitter, bottle, luffa, bitter melon)
Green onions or scallions
Greens (collard, kale, mustard, turnip)
Hearts of palm
Jicama

Kohlrabi
Leeks
Mixed vegetables (without corn, peas, or pasta)
Mung bean sprouts
Mushrooms, all kinds, fresh
Okra
Onions
Oriental radish or daikon
Pea pods
Peppers (all varieties)
Radishes
Rutabaga
Sauerkraut
Soybean sprouts
Spinach
Squash (summer, crookneck, zucchini)
Sugar pea snaps
Swiss chard
Tomato
Tomatoes, canned
Tomato sauce
Tomato/vegetable juice
Turnips
Water chestnuts
Yard-long beans

Meat and Meat Substitutes

Lean Meat and Meat Substitutes

Food	Amount
Beef: Select or Choice grades trimmed of fat: ground round, roast (chuck, rib, rump), round, sirloin, steak (cubed, flank, porterhouse, T-bone), tenderloin	1 oz
ⓢ Beef jerky	1 oz
Cheeses with 3 grams of fat or less per oz	1 oz
Cottage cheese	¼ cup
Egg substitutes, plain	¼ cup
Egg whites	2
Fish, fresh or frozen, plain: catfish, cod, flounder, haddock, halibut, orange roughy, salmon, tilapia, trout, tuna	1 oz
ⓢ Fish, smoked: herring or salmon (lox)	1 oz
Game: buffalo, ostrich, rabbit, venison	1 oz
ⓢ Hot dog with 3 grams of fat or less per oz (8 dogs per 14 oz package) *Note: May be high in carbohydrate.*	1
Lamb: chop, leg, or roast	1 oz
Organ meats: heart, kidney, liver *Note: May be high in cholesterol.*	1 oz
Oysters, fresh or frozen	6 medium
Pork, lean	
ⓢ Canadian bacon	1 oz
rib or loin chop/roast, ham, tenderloin	1 oz

Medium-Fat Meat and Meat Substitutes

Food	Amount
Beef: corned beef, ground beef, meatloaf, Prime grades trimmed of fat (prime rib), short ribs, tongue	1 oz
Cheeses with 4–7 grams of fat per oz: feta, mozzarella, pasteurized processed cheese spread, reduced-fat cheeses, string	1 oz
Egg *Note: High in cholesterol, so limit to 3 per week.*	1
Fish, any fried product	1 oz
Lamb: ground, rib roast	1 oz
Pork: cutlet, shoulder roast	1 oz
Poultry: chicken with skin; dove, pheasant, wild duck, or goose; fried chicken; ground turkey	1 oz
Ricotta cheese	2 oz or ¼ cup
ⓢ Sausage with 4–7 grams of fat per oz	1 oz
Veal, cutlet (no breading)	1 oz
Poultry, without skin: Cornish hen, chicken, domestic duck or goose (well-drained of fat), turkey	1 oz
Processed sandwich meats with 3 grams of fat or less per oz: chipped beef, deli thin-sliced meats, turkey ham, turkey kielbasa, turkey pastrami	1 oz
Salmon, canned	1 oz
Sardines, canned	2 medium
ⓢ Sausage with 3 grams of fat or less per oz	1 oz
Shellfish: clams, crab, imitation shellfish, lobster, scallops, shrimp	1 oz
Tuna, canned in water or oil, drained	1 oz
Veal, lean chop, roast	1 oz

High-Fat Meat and Meat Substitutes

These foods are high in saturated fat, cholesterol, and calories and may raise blood cholesterol levels if eaten on a regular basis. Try to eat 3 or fewer servings from this group per week.

Food	Amount
Bacon	
[s] pork	2 slices (16 slices per lb or 1 oz each, before cooking)
[s] turkey	3 slices (½ oz each before cooking)
Cheese, regular: American, bleu, brie, cheddar, hard goat, Monterey jack, queso, and Swiss	1 oz
[s] [!] Hot dog: beef, pork, or combination (10 per lb-sized package)	1
[s] Hot dog: turkey or chicken (10 per lb-sized package)	1
Pork: ground, sausage, spareribs	1 oz
Processed sandwich meats with 8 grams of fat or more per oz: bologna, pastrami, hard salami	1 oz
[s] Sausage with 8 grams fat or more per oz: bratwurst, chorizo: Italian, knockwurst, Polish, smoked, summer	1 oz

Plant-Based Proteins

Because carbohydrate content varies among plant-based proteins, you should read the food label.

Food	Amount	Count as
"Bacon" strips, soy-based	3 strips	1 medium-fat meat
Baked beans	⅓ cup	1 starch + 1 lean meat
Beans, cooked: black, garbanzo, kidney, lima, navy, pinto, white	½ cup	1 starch + 1 lean meat
"Beef" or "sausage" crumbles, soy-based	2 oz	½ carbohydrate + 1 lean meat
"Chicken" nuggets, soy-based	2 nuggets (1½ oz)	½ carbohydrate + 1 medium-fat meat
Edamame	½ cup	½ carbohydrate + 1 lean meat
Falafel (spiced chickpea and wheat patties)	3 patties (about 2 inches across)	1 carbohydrate + 1 high-fat meat
Hot dog, soy-based	1 (1½ oz)	½ carbohydrate + 1 lean meat
Hummus	⅓ cup	1 carbohydrate + 1 high-fat meat
Lentils, brown, green, or yellow	½ cup	1 carbohydrate + 1 lean meat
Meatless burger, soy-based	3 oz	½ carbohydrate + 2 lean meats
Meatless burger, vegetable- and starch-based	1 patty (about 2½ oz)	1 carbohydrate + 2 lean meats
Nut spreads: almond butter, cashew butter, peanut butter, soy nut butter	1 Tbsp	1 high-fat meat
Peas, cooked: black-eyed and split peas	½ cup	1 starch + 1 lean meat
Refried beans, canned	½ cup	1 starch + 1 lean meat
"Sausage" patties, soy-based	1 (1½ oz)	1 medium-fat meat
Soy nuts, unsalted	¾ oz	½ carbohydrate + 1 medium-fat meat
Tempeh	¼ cup	1 medium-fat meat
Tofu	4 oz (½ cup)	1 medium-fat meat
Tofu, light	4 oz (½ cup)	1 lean meat

Fats

Fats and oils have mixtures of unsaturated (polyunsaturated and monounsaturated) and saturated fats. Foods on the Fats list are grouped together based on the major type of fat they contain. In general, 1 fat choice equals:

- 1 teaspoon of regular margarine, vegetable oil, or butter
- 1 tablespoon of regular salad dressing

Unsaturated—Monounsaturated Fats

Food	Serving Size
Avocado, medium	2 Tbsp (1 oz)
Nut butters (*trans* fat-free): almond butter, cashew butter, peanut butter (smooth or crunchy)	1½ tsp
Nuts	
almonds	6 nuts
Brazil	2 nuts
cashews	6 nuts
filberts (hazelnuts)	5 nuts
macadamia	3 nuts
mixed (50% peanuts)	6 nuts
peanuts	10 nuts
pecans	4 halves
pistachios	16 nuts
Oil: canola, olive, peanut	1 tsp
Olives	
black (ripe)	8 large
green, stuffed	10 large

Polyunsaturated Fats

Food	Serving Size
Margarine: lower-fat spread (30%–50% vegetable oil, *trans* fat-free)	1 Tbsp
Margarine: stick, tub (*trans* fat-free), or squeeze (*trans* fat-free)	1 tsp
Mayonnaise	
reduced-fat	1 Tbsp
regular	1 tsp
Mayonnaise-style salad dressing	
reduced-fat	1 Tbsp
regular	2 tsp
Nuts	
Pignolia (pine nuts)	1 Tbsp
walnuts, English	4 halves
Oil: corn, cottonseed, flaxseed, grape seed, safflower, soybean, sunflower	1 tsp
Oil: made from soybean and canola oil—Enova	1 tsp
Plant stanol esters	
light	1 Tbsp
regular	2 tsp
Salad dressing	
🧂 reduced-fat	2 Tbsp
Note: May be high in carbohydrate.	
🧂 regular	1 Tbsp
Seeds	
flaxseed, whole	1 Tbsp
pumpkin, sunflower	1 Tbsp
sesame seeds	1 Tbsp
Tahini or sesame paste	2 tsp

Saturated Fats

Food	Serving Size
Bacon, cooked, regular or turkey	1 slice
Butter	
reduced-fat	1 Tbsp
stick	1 tsp
whipped	2 tsp
Butter blends made with oil	
reduced-fat or light	1 Tbsp
regular	1½ tsp
Chitterlings, boiled	2 Tbsp (½ oz)
Coconut, sweetened, shredded	2 Tbsp
Coconut milk	
light	⅓ cup
regular	1½ Tbsp
Cream	
half and half	2 Tbsp
heavy	1 Tbsp
light	1½ Tbsp
whipped	2 Tbsp
whipped, pressurized	¼ cup
Cream cheese	
reduced-fat	1½ Tbsp (¾ oz)
regular	1 Tbsp (½ oz)
Lard	1 tsp
Oil: coconut, palm, palm kernel	1 tsp
Salt pork	¼ oz
Shortening, solid	1 tsp
Sour cream	
reduced-fat or light	3 Tbsp
regular	2 Tbsp

Free Foods

A "free" food is any food or drink choice that has less than 20 calories and 5 grams or less of carbohydrate per serving.

Selection Tips

- Most foods on this list should be limited to 3 servings (as listed here) per day. Spread out the servings throughout the day. If you eat all 3 servings at once, it could raise your blood glucose level.

- Food and drink choices listed here without a serving size can be eaten whenever you like.

Low Carbohydrate Foods

Food	Serving Size
Cabbage, raw	½ cup
Candy, hard (regular or sugar-free)	1 piece
Carrots, cauliflower, or green beans, cooked	¼ cup
Cranberries, sweetened with sugar substitute	½ cup
Cucumber, sliced	½ cup
Gelatin	
dessert, sugar-free	
unflavored	
Gum	
Jam or jelly, light or no sugar added	2 tsp
Rhubarb, sweetened with sugar substitute	½ cup
Salad greens	
Sugar substitutes (artificial sweeteners)	
Syrup, sugar-free	2 Tbsp

Modified Fat Foods with Carbohydrate

Food	Serving Size
Cream cheese, fat-free	1 Tbsp (½ oz)
Creamers	
nondairy, liquid	1 Tbsp
nondairy, powdered	2 tsp
Margarine spread	
fat-free	1 Tbsp
reduced-fat	1 tsp
Mayonnaise	
fat-free	1 Tbsp
reduced-fat	1 tsp
Mayonnaise-style salad dressing	
fat-free	1 Tbsp
reduced-fat	1 tsp
Salad dressing	
fat-free or low-fat	1 Tbsp
fat-free, Italian	2 Tbsp
Sour cream, fat-free or reduced-fat	1 Tbsp
Whipped topping	
light or fat-free	2 Tbsp
regular	1 Tbsp

Condiments

Food	Serving Size
Barbecue sauce	2 tsp
Catsup (ketchup)	1 Tbsp
Honey mustard	1 Tbsp
Horseradish	
Lemon juice	
Miso	1½ tsp
Mustard	
Parmesan cheese, freshly grated	1 Tbsp
Pickle relish	1 Tbsp
Pickles	
dill	1½ medium
sweet, bread and butter	2 slices
sweet, gherkin	¾ oz
Salsa	¼ cup
Soy sauce, light or regular	1 Tbsp
Sweet and sour sauce	2 tsp
Sweet chili sauce	2 tsp
Taco sauce	1 Tbsp
Vinegar	
Yogurt, any type	2 Tbsp

Drinks/Mixes

Any food on this list—without a serving size listed—can be consumed in any moderate amount.

- Bouillon, broth, consomme
- Bouillon or broth, low-sodium
- Carbonated or mineral water
- Club soda
- Cocoa powder, unsweetened (1 Tbsp)
- Coffee, unsweetened or with sugar substitute
- Diet soft drinks, sugar-free
- Drink mixes, sugar-free
- Tea, unsweetened or with sugar substitute
- Tonic water, diet
- Water
- Water, flavored, carbohydrate free

Seasonings

Any food on this list can be consumed in any moderate amount.

- Flavoring extracts (for example, vanilla, almond, peppermint)
- Garlic
- Herbs, fresh or dried
- Nonstick cooking spray
- Pimento
- Spices
- Hot pepper sauce
- Wine, used in cooking
- Worcestershire sauce

Combination Foods

Many of the foods you eat are mixed together in various combinations, such as casseroles. These "combination" foods do not fit into any one choice list. This is a list of choices for some typical combination foods. This list will help you fit these foods into your meal plan. Ask your RD for nutrient information about other combination foods you would like to eat, including your own recipes.

Entrees

	Food	Serving Size	Count as
Ⓢ	Casserole type (tuna noodle, lasagna, spaghetti with meatballs, chili with beans, macaroni and cheese)	1 cup (8 oz)	2 carbohydrates + 2 medium-fat meats
Ⓢ	Stews (beef/other meats and vegetables)	1 cup (8 oz)	1 carbohydrate + 1 medium-fat meat + 0–3 fats
	Tuna salad or chicken salad	½ cup (3½ oz)	½ carbohydrate + 2 lean meats + 1 fat

Frozen Meals/Entrees

	Food	Serving Size	Count as
Ⓢ ☺	Burrito (beef and bean)	1 (5 oz)	3 carbohydrates + 1 lean meat + 2 fats
Ⓢ	Dinner-type meal	generally 14–17 oz	3 carbohydrates + 3 medium-fat meats + 3 fats
Ⓢ	Entree or meal with less than 340 calories	about 8–11 oz	2–3 carbohydrates + 1–2 lean meats
	Pizza		
Ⓢ	cheese/vegetarian, thin crust	¼ of a 12 inch (4½–5 oz)	2 carbohydrates + 2 medium-fat meats
Ⓢ	meat topping, thin crust	¼ of a 12 inch (5 oz)	2 carbohydrates + 2 medium-fat meats + 1½ fats
Ⓢ	Pocket sandwich	1 (4½ oz)	3 carbohydrates + 1 lean meat + 1–2 fats
Ⓢ	Pot pie	1 (7 oz)	2½ carbohydrates + 1 medium-fat meat + 3 fats

Salads (Deli-Style)

	Food	Serving Size	Count as
	Coleslaw	½ cup	1 carbohydrate + 1½ fats
	Macaroni/pasta salad	½ cup	2 carbohydrates + 3 fats
Ⓢ	Potato salad	½ cup	1½–2 carbohydrates + 1–2 fats

Soups

	Food	Serving Size	Count as
⑤	Bean, lentil, or split pea	I cup	I carbohydrate + I lean meat
⑤	Chowder (made with milk)	I cup (8 oz)	I carbohydrate + I lean meat + 1½ fats
⑤	Cream (made with water)	I cup (8 oz)	I carbohydrate + I fat
⑤	Instant	6 oz prepared	I carbohydrate
⑤	with beans or lentils	8 oz prepared	2½ carbohydrates + I lean meat
⑤	Miso soup	I cup	½ carbohydrate + I fat
⑤	Oriental noodle	I cup	2 carbohydrates + 2 fats
	Rice (congee)	I cup	I carbohydrate
⑤	Tomato (made with water)	I cup (8 oz)	I carbohydrate
⑤	Vegetable beef, chicken noodle, or other broth-type	I cup (8 oz)	I carbohydrate

Fast Foods

The choices in the Fast Foods list are not specific fast food meals or items, but are estimates based on popular foods. You can get specific nutrition information for almost every fast food or restaurant chain. Ask the restaurant or check its website for nutrition information about your favorite fast foots.

Breakfast Sandwiches

	Food	Serving Size	Count as
⑤	Egg, cheese, meat, English muffin	I sandwich	2 carbohydrates + 2 medium-fat meats
⑤	Sausage biscuit sandwich	I sandwich	2 carbohydrates + 2 high-fat meats + 3½ fats

Main Dishes/Entrees

	Food	Serving Size	Count as
⑤ ☺	Burrito (beef and beans)	I (about 8 oz)	3 carbohydrates + 3 medium-fat meats + 3 fats
⑤	Chicken breast, breaded and fried	I (about 5 oz)	I carbohydrate + 4 medium-fat meats
⑤	Chicken drumstick, breaded and fried	I (about 2 oz)	2 medium-fat meats
⑤	Chicken nuggets	6 (about 3½ oz)	I carbohydrate + 2 medium-fat meats + I fat
⑤	Chicken thigh, breaded and fried	I (about 4 oz)	½ carbohydrate + 3 medium-fat meats + 1½ fats
⑤	Chicken wings, hot	6 (5 oz)	5 medium-fat meats + 1½ fats

Oriental

	Food	Serving Size	Count as
🧂	Beef/chicken/shrimp with vegetables in sauce	I cup (about 5 oz)	I carbohydrate + I lean meat + I fat
🧂	Egg roll, meat	I (about 3 oz)	I carbohydrate + I lean meat + I fat
	Fried rice, meatless	½ cup	I½ carbohydrates + I½ fats
🧂	Meat and sweet sauce (orange chicken)	I cup	3 carbohydrates + 3 medium-fat meats + 2 fats
🧂 ☺	Noodles and vegetables in sauce (chow mein, lo mein)	I cup	2 carbohydrates + I fat

Pizza

	Food	Serving Size	Count as
	Pizza		
🧂	cheese, pepperoni, regular crust	⅛ of a 14 inch (about 4 oz)	2½ carbohydrates + I medium-fat meat + I½ fats
🧂	cheese/vegetarian, thin crust	¼ of a 12 inch (about 6 oz)	2½ carbohydrates + 2 medium-fat meats + 1% fats

Sandwiches

	Food	Serving Size	Count as
🧂	Chicken sandwich, grilled	I	3 carbohydrates + 4 lean meats
🧂	Chicken sandwich, crispy	I	3½ carbohydrates + 3 medium-fat meats + I fat
	Fish sandwich with tartar sauce	I	2½ carbohydrates + 2 medium-fat meats + 2 fats
	Hamburger		
🧂	large with cheese	I	2½ carbohydrates + 4 medium-fat meats + I fat
	regular	I	2 carbohydrates + I medium-fat meat + I fat
🧂	Hot dog with bun	I	I carbohydrate + I high-fat meat + I fat
	Submarine sandwich		
🧂	less than 6 grams fat	6-inch sub	3 carbohydrates + 2 lean meats
🧂	regular	6-inch sub	3½ carbohydrates + 2 medium-fat meats + I fat
	Taco, hard or soft shell (meat and cheese)	I small	I carbohydrate + I medium-fat meat + I½ fats

Salads

	Food	Serving Size	Count as
🧂 ⊍	Salad, main dish (grilled chicken type, no dressing or croutons)	Salad	1 carbohydrate + 4 lean meats
	Salad, side, no dressing or cheese	Small (about 5 oz)	1 vegetable

Sides/Appetizers

	Food	Serving Size	Count as
▽!	French fries, restaurant style	small	3 carbohydrates + 3 fats
		medium	4 carbohydrates + 4 fats
		large	5 carbohydrates + 6 fats
🧂	Nachos with cheese	small (about 4½ oz)	2½ carbohydrates + 4 fats
🧂	Onion rings	1 serving (about 3 oz)	2½ carbohydrates + 3 fats

Desserts

Food	Serving Size	Count as
Milkshake, any flavor	12 oz	6 carbohydrates + 2 fats
Soft-serve ice cream cone	1 small	2½ carbohydrates + 1 fat

Alcohol

Nutrition Tips

- In general, 1 alcohol choice (½ oz absolute alcohol) has about 100 calories.

Selection Tips

- If you choose to drink alcohol, you should limit it to 1 drink or less per day for women, and 2 drinks or less per day for men.
- To reduce your risk of low blood glucose (hypoglycemia), especially if you take insulin or a diabetes pill that increases insulin, always drink alcohol with food.
- While alcohol, by itself, does not directly affect blood glucose, be aware of the carbohydrate (for example, in mixed drinks, beer, and wine) that may raise your blood glucose.
- Check with your RD if you would like to fit alcohol into your meal plan.

Alcoholic Beverage	Serving Size	Count as
Beer		
light (4.2%)	12 fl oz	1 alcohol equivalent + ½ carbohydrate
regular (4.9%)	12 fl oz	1 alcohol equivalent + 1 carbohydrate
Distilled spirits: vodka, rum, gin, whiskey 80 or 86 proof	1½ fl oz	1 alcohol equivalent
Liqueur, coffee (53 proof)	1 fl oz	1 alcohol equivalent + 1 carbohydrate
Sake	1 fl oz	½ alcohol equivalent
Wine		
dessert (sherry) dry,	3½ fl oz	1 alcohol equivalent + 1 carbohydrate
red or white (10%)	5 fl oz	1 alcohol equivalent

Appendix J
Food Labeling Information

Nutrition Facts

Serving Size 1 bar (24g)
Servings Per Container 12

Amount Per Serving

Calories 120   Calories from Fat 45

	% Daily Value*
Total Fat 5g	8%
Saturated Fat 1g	5%
Trans Fat 1g	
Cholesterol 0mg	0%
Sodium 65mg	3%
Total Carbohydrate 17g	6%
Dietary Fiber 1g	4%
Sugars 6g	
Protein 2g	

Vitamin A 0%	•	Vitamin C 0%
Calcium 0%	•	Iron 4%

* Percent Daily Values are based on a 2,000
calorie diet. Your daily values may be higher
or lower depending on your calorie needs:

	Calories:	2,000	2,500
Total Fat	Less than	65g	80g
Sat Fat	Less than	20g	25g
Cholesterol	Less than	300mg	300mg
Sodium	Less than	2,400mg	2,400mg
Total Carbohydrate		300g	375g
Dietary Fiber		25g	30g

Calories per gram:
Fat 9 • Carbohydrate 4 • Protein 4

Ingredients: Rolled oats, sugar, sunflower oil,
brown sugar syrup, honey, salt, soy lecithin

Statement of identity

Net quantity of contents

Structure-function claim

Directions

Supplement Facts panel

Other ingredients in descending order of predominance and by common name of proprietary blend

Name and place of business of manufacturer packer or distributor. This is the address to write for more product information

Daily Reference Values Used to Establish Daily Values

Food Component	Daily Reference Value (2000 Kcal)
Total fat	Less than 65 g (30% of energy)
Saturated fat	Less than 20 g (10% of energy)
Cholesterol	Less than 300 mg
Total carbohydrate	300 g (60% of energy)
Dietary fiber	25 g (11.5 g/1000 Kcal)
Sodium	Less than 2400 mg
Potassium	3500 mg
Protein	50 g (10% of energy)

Recommended Dietary Intakes (RDIs)* Used to Establish Daily Values

Vitamins and Minerals	Units of Measurement	Adults and Children 4 or more Years of Age	Infants	Children Under 4 Years of Age	Pregnant or Lactating Women
Vitamin A	International Units[†]	5000 (1000 μg)	1500	2500	8000
Vitamin D	International Units[†]	400 (10 μg)	400	400	400
Vitamin E	International Units[†]	30 (10 μg)	5	10	30
Vitamin C	Milligrams	60	35	40	60
Folic acid	Micrograms	400	0.1	0.2	0.8
Thiamin	Milligrams	1.5	0.5	0.7	1.7
Riboflavin	Milligrams	1.7	0.6	0.8	2.0
Niacin	Milligrams	20	8	9	20
Vitamin B_6	Milligrams	2.0	0.4	0.7	2.5
Vitamin B_{12}	Micrograms	6.0	2	3	8
Biotin	Micrograms	300	0.05	0.15	0.30
Pantothenic acid	Milligrams	10	3	5	10
Calcium	Milligrams	1000	0.6	0.8	1.3
Phosphorous	Milligrams	1000	0.5	0.8	1.3
Iodine	Micrograms	150	45	70	150
Iron	Milligrams	18	15	10	18
Magnesium	Milligrams	400	70	200	450
Copper	Milligrams	2.0	0.6	1.0	2.0
Zinc	Milligrams	15	5	8	15
Vitamin K	Micrograms	80	—[‡]	—[‡]	—[‡]
Chromium	Micrograms	120	—	—	—
Selenium	Micrograms	70	—	—	—
Molybenum	Micrograms	75	—	—	—
Manganese	Milligrams	2	—	—	—
Chloride	Milligrams	3400	—	—	—

* Based on National Academy of Sciences' 1968 Recommended Dietary Allowances.

[†] The RDIs for fat-soluble vitamins are expressed in International Units (IU). Values that are approximately equivalent in micrograms are given in parentheses.

[‡] No values yet established for vitamin K, chromium, selenium, molybdenum, manganese, or chloride for this population.

Health Claims Permitted on Food or Supplement Labels

Health Claims that Meet Significant Scientific Agreement

These are authorized by the FDA based on an extensive review of the scientific literature or information from a scientific body of the U.S. government or the National Academy of Sciences that supports the nutrient/disease relationship.

- Calcium and osteoporosis

- Dietary fat and cancer

- Dietary saturated fat and cholesterol and risk of coronary heart disease

- Dietary non-carcinogenic carbohydrate sweeteners and dental caries

- Fiber-containing grain products, fruits, and vegetables and cancer

- Folic acid and neural tube defects

- Fluoridated water and reduced risk of dental caries

- Fruits, vegetables and grain products and cancer

- Fruits, vegetables, and grain products that contain fiber, particularly soluble fiber, and risk of coronary heart disease

- Plant sterol/stanol and coronary heart disease

- Potassium and the risk of high blood pressure and stroke

- Saturated fat, cholesterol and trans fat and reduced risk of heart disease

- Sodium and hypertension

- Soluble fiber from certain foods and risk of coronary heart disease

- Soy protein and risk of coronary heart disease

- Stanols/sterols and risk of coronary heart disease

- Whole grain foods and the risk of heart disease and certain cancers

Qualified Health Claims

These are used when there is emerging evidence for a relationship between a food, food component, or dietary supplement and reduced risk of a disease or health-related condition but there is not enough scientific support for the FDA to issue an authorizing regulation.

- Qualified claims about cancer risk: selenium and cancer, antioxidant vitamins and cancer, green tea and cancer, tomatoes and cancer.

- Qualified claims about cardiovascular disease risk: nuts and heart disease, walnuts and heart disease, omega-3 fatty acids and coronary heart disease, B vitamins and vascular disease, monounsaturated fatty acids from olive oil and reduced coronary heart disease risk, unsaturated fatty acids from canola oil and coronary heart disease risk, corn oil and coronary heart disease.

- Qualified claims about chromium picolinate and diabetes.

- Qualified claims about calcium and colorectal cancer and colon/rectal polyps, calcium and hypertension and preeclampsia.

- Qualified claims about cognitive function: phosphatidylserine and cognitive dysfunction and dementia.

- Qualified claims about neural tube birth defects: 0.8 mg folic acid and neural tube birth defects.

Source: U.S. Food and Drug Administration. Center for Food Safety and Applied Nutrition. Label Claims. Available online at http://www.cfsan.fda.gov/~dms/2lg-xc.html

Nutrient Content Descriptors Commonly Used on Food Labels

Free	Means that a product contains no amount of, or a trivial amount of, fat, saturated fat, cholesterol, sodium, sugars, or kcalories. For example, "sugar free" and "fat free" both mean less than 0.5 g per serving. Synonyms for "free" include "without," "no," and "zero."
Low	Used for foods that can be eaten frequently without exceeding the Daily Value for fat, saturated fat, cholesterol, sodium, or kcalories. Specific definitions have been established for each of these nutrients. For example, "low fat" means that the food contains 3 g or less per serving, and "low cholesterol" means that the food contains less than 20 mg of cholesterol per serving. Synonyms for "low" include "little," "few," and "low source of."
Lean and extra lean	Used to describe the fat content of meat, poultry, seafood, and game meats. "Lean" means that the food contains less than 10 g fat, less than 4.5 g saturated fat, and less than 95 mg of cholesterol per serving and per 100 g. "Extra lean" means that the food contains less than 5 g fat, less than 2 g saturated fat, and less than 95 mg of cholesterol per serving and per 100 g.
High	Can be used if a food contains 20% or more of the Daily Value for a particular nutrient. Synonyms for "high" include "rich in" and "excellent source of."
Good source	Means that a food contains 10 to 19% of the Daily Value for a particular nutrient per serving.
Reduced	Means that a nutritionally altered product contains 25% less of a nutrient or of energy than the regular or reference product.
Less	Means that a food, whether altered or not, contains 25% less of a nutrient or of energy than the reference food. For example, pretzels may claim to have "less fat" than potato chips. "Fewer" may be used as a synonym for "less."
Light	May be used in different ways. First, it can be used on a nutritionally altered product that contains one-third fewer kcalories or half the fat of a reference food. Second, it can be used when the sodium content of a low-calorie, low-fat food has been reduced by 50%. The term "light" can be used to describe properties such as texture and color as long as the label explains the intent—for example, "light and fluffy."
More	Means that a serving of food, whether altered or not, contains a nutrient that is at least 10% of the Daily Value more than the reference food. This definition also applies to foods using the terms "fortified," "enriched," or "added."
Healthy	May be used to describe foods that are low in fat and saturated fat and contain no more than 360 mg of sodium and no more than 60 mg of cholesterol per serving and provide at least 10% of the Daily Value for vitamins A or C, or iron, calcium, protein, or fiber.
Fresh	May be used on foods that are raw and have never been frozen or heated and contain no preservatives.

Source: USDA. A food Labeling Guide Appendix A. Available online at http://www.cfsan.fda.gov/~dms/2lg-xa.html

Appendix K
Energy Expenditure for Various Activities

Type of Activity	Calories per Hour (by body weight)				
	100 lb	120 lb	150 lb	180 lb	200 lb
Aerobics, high impact	318	381	476	572	635
Aerobics, low impact	227	272	340	408	454
Backpacking, general	318	381	476	572	635
Ballroom dancing, fast (disco, folk, square)	249	299	374	449	499
Ballroom dancing, slow (waltz, foxtrot)	136	163	204	245	272
Badminton, social singles and doubles, general	204	245	306	367	408
Baseball, playing catch	113	136	170	204	227
Basketball, game, structured	363	435	544	653	726
Basketball, shooting baskets	204	245	306	367	408
Boxing, punching bag	272	327	408	490	544
Boxing, sparring	408	490	612	735	816
Basketball, wheelchair	295	354	442	531	590
Bowling	136	163	204	245	272
Calisthenics, heavy, vigorous (pushups, pullups)	363	435	544	653	726
Calisthenics, light/moderate	159	191	238	286	318
Circuit training, general	363	435	544	653	726
Cleaning, heavy (wash car, wash windows, mop)	136	163	204	245	272
Cycling, <10 mph, leisure	181	218	272	327	363
Cycling, 10–12 mph, light	272	327	408	490	544
Cycling, 12–14 mph, moderate	363	435	544	653	726
Dancing, general	204	245	306	367	408
Fencing	272	327	408	490	544
Fishing, general	136	163	204	245	272
Football, competition	408	490	612	735	816
Football, playing catch	113	136	170	204	227
Golf, pulling clubs	227	272	340	408	454
Golf, using power cart	159	191	238	286	318
Gymnastics, general	181	218	272	327	363
Hacky sack	181	218	272	327	363
Handball, general	544	653	816	980	1089
Hiking, cross country	272	327	408	490	544

(continued)

Type of Activity	100 lb	120 lb	150 lb	180 lb	200 lb
Horseback riding, trotting	295	354	442	531	590
Ice hockey	363	435	544	653	726
Ice or in-line skating, general	318	381	476	572	635
Ice or in-line skating, speed, competition	680	816	1021	1225	1361
Jai alai	544	653	816	980	1089
Jog/walk combination	272	327	408	490	544
Jumping rope, moderate, general	454	544	680	816	907
Kayaking	227	272	340	408	454
Mowing lawn, general	249	299	374	449	499
Playing with children, heavy (walk/run)	227	272	340	408	454
Playing with children, light (standing)	127	152	191	229	254
Racquetball, casual, general	318	381	476	572	635
Rowing or canoeing, 4.0 to 5.9 mph	318	381	476	572	635
Running, 10 mph (6 min/mile)	726	871	1089	1306	1451
Running, 7.5 mph (8 min/mile}	567	680	850	1021	1134
Running, 8.6 mph (7 min/mile)	635	762	953	1143	1270
Sailing, Sunfish/Laser/Hobby Cat, keel boat, ocean	136	163	204	245	272
Skateboarding	227	272	340	408	454
Skiing, cross country, vigorous downhill	363	435	544	653	726
Skiing, downhill, moderate effort	272	327	408	490	544
Soccer, casual, general	318	381	476	572	635
Softball, fast or slow pitch	227	272	340	408	454
Surfing, body or board	136	163	204	245	272
Swimming, laps, freestyle, fast	454	544	680	816	907
Swimming, laps, freestyle, slow	363	435	544	653	726
Table tennis (Ping Pong)	181	218	272	327	363
Tae kwan do, judo, juijitsu, karate, kick boxing	454	544	680	816	907
Tai chi	181	218	272	327	363
Tennis general	318	381	476	572	635
Volleyball, noncompetitive, general	136	163	204	245	272
Walking, 2.5 mph, firm surface	136	163	204	245	272
Walking, 4 mph, level, firm surface	227	272	340	408	454
Weight lifting, free or machine	272	327	408	490	544
Yoga, hatha	113	136	170	204	227

Data provided by Axxya Systems—Nutritionist Pro.

Appendix L
Chemistry, Metabolism, and Structures

A Review of Basic Chemistry

Chemistry is the science of the structure and interactions of matter. All living and nonliving things consist of matter, which is anything that occupies space and has mass. Mass is the amount of matter in any object, which does not change.

Chemical Elements

All forms of matter—both living and nonliving—are made up of a limited number of building blocks called chemical elements. Each element is a substance that cannot be split into a simpler substance by ordinary chemical means. Scientists now recognize 112 elements. Of these, 92 occur naturally on Earth. The rest have been produced from the natural elements using particle accelerators or nuclear reactors. Each element is designated by a chemical symbol, one or two letters of the element's name in English, Latin, or another language. Examples of chemical symbols are H for hydrogen, C for carbon, O for oxygen, N for nitrogen, Ca for calcium, and Na for sodium.

Twenty-six different elements normally are present in the human body. Just four elements, called the major elements, constitute about 96% of the body's mass: oxygen (O), carbon (C), hydrogen (H), and nitrogen (N). Eight others, the lesser elements, contribute 3.8% of the body's mass: calcium, phosphorus (P), potassium (K), sulfur (S), sodium, chlorine (Cl), magnesium (Mg), and iron (Fe). An additional 14 elements—the trace elements—are present in tiny amounts. Together, they account for the remaining 0.2% of the body's mass.

Structure of Atoms

Each element is made up of atoms, the smallest units of matter that retain the properties and characteristics of the element. Atoms are extremely small. Hydrogen atoms, the smallest atoms, have a diameter less than 0.1 nanometer, and the largest atoms are only five times larger.

Dozens of different subatomic particles compose individual atoms. However, only three types of subatomic particles are important for understanding the chemical reactions in the human body: protons, neutrons, and electrons (**Figure L.1**). The dense central core of an atom is its nucleus. Within the nucleus are positively charged protons and uncharged (neutral) neutrons. The tiny, negatively charged electrons move about in a large space surrounding the nucleus. They do not follow a fixed path or orbit but instead form a negatively charged "cloud" that envelops the nucleus.

Even though their exact positions cannot be predicted, specific groups of electrons are most likely to move about within certain regions around the nucleus. These regions, called **electron shells**, are depicted as simple circles around the nucleus. Because each electron shell can hold a specific number of electrons, the electron shell model best conveys this aspect of atomic structure (see Figure L.1). The first electron shell (nearest the nucleus) never holds more than 2 electrons. The second shell holds a maximum of 8 electrons, and the third can hold up to 18 electrons. The electron shells fill with electrons in a specific order, beginning with the first shell. For example, notice in **Figure L.2** that sodium (Na), which has 11 electrons total, contains 2 electrons in the first shell, 8 electrons in the second shell, and 1 electron in the third shell. The number of electrons in an atom of an element always equals the number of protons. Because each electron and proton carries one charge, the negatively charged electrons and the positively charged protons balance each other. Thus, each atom is electrically neural; its total charge is zero.

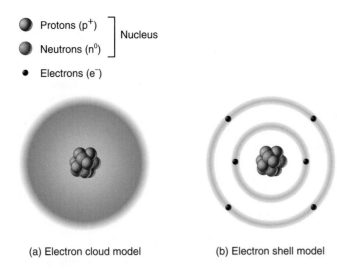

Figure L.1 Two representations of the structure of an atom. Electrons move about the nucleus, which contains neutrons and protons. (a) In the electron cloud model of an atom, the shading represents the chance of finding an electron in regions outside the nucleus. (b) In the electron shell model, filled circles represent individual electrons, which are grouped into concentric circles according to the shells they occupy. Both models depict a carbon atom, with six protons, six neutrons, and six electrons.

The *number of protons* in the nucleus of an atom is an atom's **atomic number**. For example, hydrogen has an atomic number of 1 because its nucleus has one proton, whereas sodium has an atomic number of 11 because its nucleus has 11 protons (see **Figure L.2**).

The **mass number** of an atom is the sum of its protons and neutrons. Because sodium has 11 protons and 12 neutrons, its mass number is 23 (see Figure L.2). Although all atoms of one element have the same number of protons, they may have different numbers of neutrons and thus different mass numbers. **Isotopes** are atoms of an element that have different numbers of neutrons and therefore different mass numbers. In a sample of oxygen, for example, most atoms have 8 neutrons, and a few have 9 or 10, but all have 8 protons and 8 electrons. Most isotopes are stable, which means that their nuclear structure does not change over time. The stable isotopes of oxygen are designated ^{16}O, ^{17}O, and ^{18}O (or O-16, O-17, and O-18). As you may already have determined, the numbers indicate the mass number of each

Atomic number = number of protons in an atom
Mass number = number of protons and neutrons in an atom (boldface indicates most common isotope)
Atomic mass = average mass of all stable atoms of a given element in daltons

Figure L.2 Atomic structures of several stable atoms. The atoms of different elements have different atomic numbers because they have different numbers of protons.

isotope. As you will discover shortly, the number of electrons of an atom determines its chemical properties. Although the isotopes of an element have different numbers of neutrons, they have identical chemical properties because they have the same number of electrons.

Certain isotopes, called **radioactive isotopes**, are unstable; their nuclei decay into a stable configuration. As they decay, these atoms emit radiation and in the process often transform into a different element. For example, the radioactive isotope of carbon, C-14, decays to N-14. The decay of a radioisotope may be as fast as a fraction of a second or as slow as millions of years. The **half-life** of an isotope is the time required for half of the radioactive atoms in a sample of that isotope to decay into a more stable form. The half-life of C-14, which is used to determine the age of organic samples, is 5600 years, whereas the half-life of I-131, an important clinical tool, is 8 days.

Ions, Molecules, and Compounds

The atoms of each element have a characteristic way of losing, gaining, or sharing their electrons when interacting with other atoms to achieve stability. The way that electrons behave enables atoms in the body to exist in electrically charged forms called ions, or to join with each other into the complex combinations called molecules. If an atom either *gives up* or *gains* electrons, it becomes an ion. An **ion** is an atom that has a positive or negative charge because it has unequal numbers of protons and electrons. An ion of an atom is symbolized by writing its chemical symbol followed by the number of its positive or negative charges. Thus, Ca^{2+} stands for a calcium ion that has two positive charges because it has lost two electrons.

When two or more atoms *share* electrons, the resulting combination is called a **molecule**. A *molecular formula* indicates the elements and the number of atoms of each element that make up a molecule. A molecule may consist of two atoms of the same kind, such as an oxygen molecule. The molecular formula for a molecule of oxygen is O_2. The subscript 2 indicates that the molecule contains two atoms of oxygen. Two or more different kinds of atoms may also form a molecule, as in a water molecule (H_2O). In H_2O one atom of oxygen shares electrons with two atoms of hydrogen.

A **compound** is a substance that contains atoms of two or more different elements. Most of the atoms in the body are joined into compounds. Water (H_2O) and sodium chloride (NaCl), common table salt, are compounds. A molecule of oxygen (O_2) is not a compound because it consists of atoms of only one element. Thus, while all compounds are molecules, not all molecules are compounds.

A **free radical** is an electrically charged atom or group of atoms with an unpaired electron in the outermost shell. A common example is superoxide, which is formed by the addition of an electron to an oxygen molecule. Having an unpaired electron makes a free radical unstable, highly reactive, and destructive to nearby molecules.

Chemical Bonds

The forces that hold together the atoms of a molecule or a compound are **chemical bonds**. The likelihood that an atom will form a chemical bond with another atom depends on the number of electrons in its outermost shell, also called the **valence shell**. An atom with a valence shell holding eight electrons is *chemically stable*, which means it is unlikely to form chemical bonds with other atoms. Two or more atoms that do not have 8 electrons in their valence shells can interact in ways that produce a chemically stable arrangement of eight valence electrons for each atom. For this to happen, an atom either empties its partially filled valence shell, fills it with donated electrons, or shares electrons with other atoms. The way that valence electrons are distributed determines what kind of chemical bond results. An **ionic bond** is formed when positively and negatively charged ions are attracted to one another. As shown in **Figure L.3**, sodium has one valence electron and chlorine has seven valence electrons. When an atom of sodium donates its sole valence electron to an atom of chlorine, the resulting positive and negative charges pull both ions tightly together, forming an ionic bond. The resulting compound is sodium chloride, written NaCl.

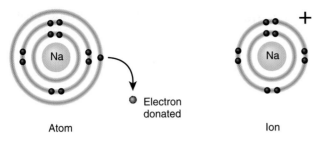

(a) Sodium: 1 valence electron

(b) Chlorine: 7 valence electrons

(c) Ionic bond in sodium chloride (NaCl)

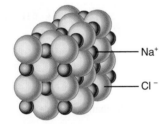

Na⁺

Cl⁻

(d) Packing of ions in a crystal
of sodium chloride

Figure L.3 Ions and ionic bond formation. (a) A sodium atom can have a complete octet of electrons in its outermost shell by losing one electron. (b) A chlorine atom can have a complete octet by gaining one electron. (c) An ionic bond may form between oppositely charged ions.

A **covalent bond** forms when two or more atoms *share* electrons rather than gaining or losing them. Atoms form a covalently bonded molecule by sharing one, two, or three pairs of valence electrons (**Figure L.4**). They are the most common chemical bonds in the body, and the compounds that result from them form most of the body's structures. In a **polar covalent bond**, the sharing of electrons between two atoms is unequal: the nucleus of one atom attracts the shared electrons more strongly than the nucleus of the other atom. When polar covalent bonds form, the resulting molecule has a partial negative charge near the atom that attracts electrons more strongly (**Figure L.5**).

Chemical Reactions

A **chemical reaction** occurs when new bonds form or old bonds break between atoms. Chemical reactions are the foundation of all life processes. Each chemical reaction involves energy changes. **Chemical energy** is a form of energy that is stored in the bonds of compounds and molecules. The total amount of energy present at the beginning and end of a chemical reaction is the same. Although energy can be neither created nor destroyed, it may be converted from one form to another.

DIAGRAMS OF ATOMIC AND MOLECULAR STRUCTURE

STRUCTURAL
FORMULA

MOLECULAR
FORMULA

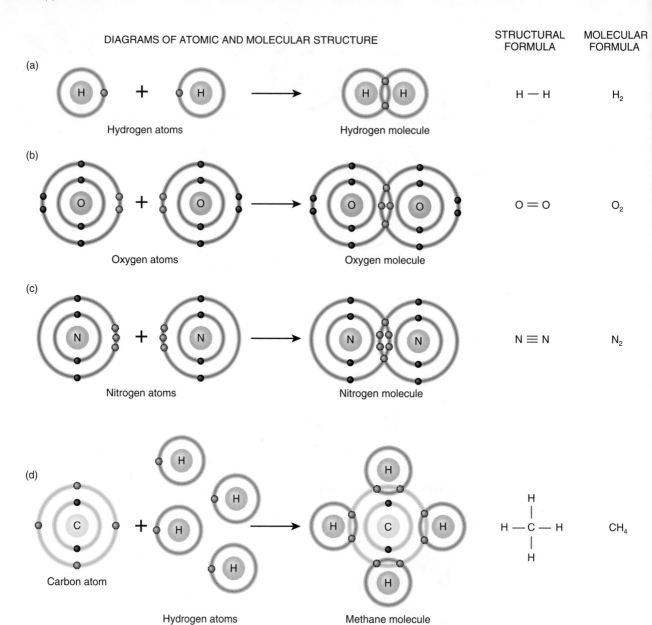

(a) Hydrogen atoms → Hydrogen molecule   H — H H_2

(b) Oxygen atoms → Oxygen molecule   O = O O_2

(c) Nitrogen atoms → Nitrogen molecule   N ≡ N N_2

(d) Carbon atom + Hydrogen atoms → Methane molecule

$$H - \overset{\overset{\textstyle H}{|}}{\underset{\underset{\textstyle H}{|}}{C}} - H$$

CH_4

Figure L.4 Covalent bond formation. The red electrons are shared equally. In writing the structural formula of a covalently bonded molecule, each straight line between the chemical symbols for two atoms denotes a pair of shared electrons. In molecular formulas, the number of atoms in each molecule is noted by subscripts.

Oxygen atom   Hydrogen atoms   Water molecule

Figure L.5 Polar covalent bonds between oxygen and hydrogen atoms in a water molecule. The red electrons are shared unequally. Because the oxygen nucleus attracts the shared electrons more strongly, the oxygen end of a water molecule has a partial negative charge, written δ^-, and the hydrogen ends have partial positive charges, written δ^+.

After a chemical reaction takes place, the atoms of the reactants are rearranged to yield products with new chemical properties. When two or more atoms, ions, or molecules combine to form new and larger molecules, the processes are called **synthesis reactions**. One example of a synthesis reaction is the reaction between two hydrogen molecules and one oxygen molecule to form two molecules of water (see **Figure L.6**). **Decomposition reactions** split up large molecules into smaller atoms, ions, or molecules. For instance, the series of reactions that break down glucose to pyruvic acid, with the net production of two molecules of ATP, are important catabolic reactions in the body. Many reactions in the body are **exchange reactions**; they consist of both synthesis and decomposition reactions. Some chemical reactions may be reversible. In a **reversible reaction**, the products can revert to the original reactants.

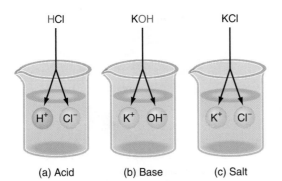

2 H₂   O₂   2 H₂O

Reactants   Products

Figure L.6 The chemical reaction between two hydrogen molecules (H_2) and one oxygen molecule (O_2) to form two molecules of water (H_2O). Note that the reaction occurs by breaking old bonds and making new bonds.

Inorganic Compounds and Solutions

Most of the chemicals in your body exist in the form of compounds. **Inorganic compounds** contain no more than one carbon atom. They include water and many salts, acids, and bases. Inorganic compounds may have either ionic or covalent bonds. **Organic compounds** always contain carbon and always have covalent bonds. Most are large molecules and many are made up of long chains of carbon atoms.

Inorganic Acids, Bases, and Salts When inorganic acids, bases, or salts dissolve in water, they **dissociate**; they separate into ions and become surrounded by water molecules. An **acid (Figure L.7a)** is a substance that dissociates into one or more **hydrogen ions (H)** and one or more negatively charged anions. Because H is a single proton with one positive charge, an acid is also referred to as a **proton donor**. A **base**, by contrast **(Figure L.7b)**, removes H+ from a solution and is therefore a **proton acceptor**.

To ensure homeostasis, intracellular and extracellular fluids must contain almost balanced quantities of acids and bases. The more hydrogen ions (H^+) dissolved in a solution, the more acidic the solution; the more hydroxide ions (OH^-), the more basic (alkaline) the solution. The chemical reactions that take place in the body are very sensitive to even small changes in the acidity or alkalinity of the body fluids in which they occur. Any departure from the narrow limits of normal H^+ and OH^- concentrations greatly disrupts body functions.

A solution's acidity or alkalinity is expressed on the **pH scale**, which extends from 0 to 14. This scale is based on the concentration of H^+ in moles per liter. The midpoint of the pH scale is 7, where the concentrations of H^+ and OH^- are equal. A substance with a pH of 7, such as pure water, is neutral. A solution that has more H^+ than OH^- is an **acidic solution** and has a pH below 7. A solution that has more OH^- than H^+ is a **basic (alkaline) solution** and has a pH above 7. Although the pH of body fluids may differ, as we have discussed, the normal limits for each fluid are quite narrow. Homeostatic mechanisms maintain the pH of blood between 7.35 and 7.45, which is slightly more basic than pure water. If the pH of blood falls below 7.35, a condition called acidosis occurs, and if the pH rises above 7.45, it results in a condition called alkalosis; both conditions can seriously compromise homeostasis. Even though strong acids and bases are continually taken into and formed by the body, the pH of fluids inside and outside cells remains almost constant. One important reason for this is the presence of **buffer systems**, which function to convert strong acids or bases into weak acids or bases.

HCl   KOH   KCl

H⁺   Cl⁻   K⁺   OH⁻   K⁺   Cl⁻

(a) Acid   (b) Base   (c) Salt

Figure L.7 Dissociation of inorganic acids, bases, and salts. Dissociation is the separation of inorganic acids, bases, and salts into ions in a solution.

Organic Compounds

Organic compounds are usually held together by covalent bonds. Carbon has four electrons in its outermost (valence) shell. It can bond covalently with a variety of atoms, including other carbon atoms, to form rings and straight or branched chains. Other elements that most often bond with carbon in organic compounds are hydrogen, oxygen, and nitrogen. Sulfur and phosphorus are also present in organic compounds.

The chain of carbon atoms in an organic molecule is called the **carbon skeleton**. Many of the carbons are bonded to hydrogen atoms, yielding a hydrocarbon. Also attached to the carbon skeleton are distinctive **functional groups**, other atoms or molecules bound to the hydrocarbon skeleton. Each type of functional group has a specific arrangement of atoms that confers characteristic chemical properties upon the organic molecule attached to it.

Nucleic Acids: Deoxyribonucleic Acid (DNA) and Ribonucleic Acid (RNA)

Nucleic acids, so named because they were first discovered in the nuclei of cells, are huge organic molecules that contain carbon, hydrogen, oxygen, nitrogen, and phosphorus. Nucleic acids are of two varieties. The first, **deoxyribonucleic acid (DNA)**, forms the

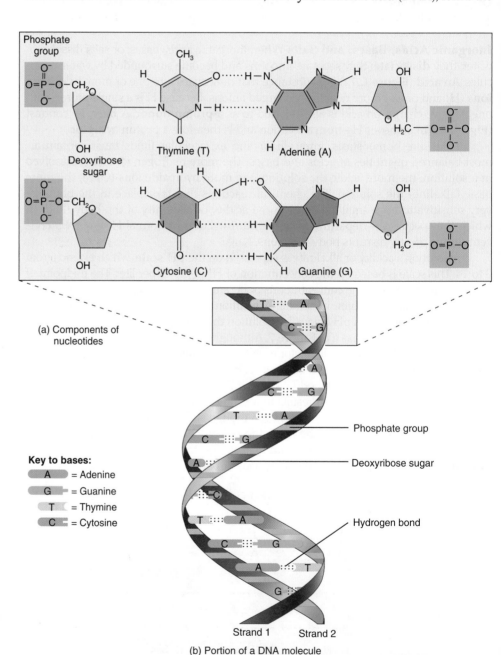

Figure L.8 DNA molecule.
(a) A nucleotide consists of a base, a pentose sugar, and a phosphate group. (b) The paired bases project toward the center of the double helix. The structure is stabilized by hydrogen bonds (dotted lines) between each base pair. There are two hydrogen bonds between adenine and thymine and three between cytosine and guanine. Hydrogen bonds result from the attraction of oppositely charged parts of molecules and are weak compared to ionic or covalent bonds.

Key to bases:
A = Adenine
G = Guanine
T = Thymine
C = Cytosine

(a) Components of nucleotides

Phosphate group

Deoxyribose sugar

Hydrogen bond

Strand 1   Strand 2

(b) Portion of a DNA molecule

inherited genetic material inside each human cell (**Figure L.8**). In humans, each **gene** is a segment of a DNA molecule. Our genes determine the traits we inherit, and by controlling protein synthesis they regulate most of the activities that take place in body cells throughout a lifetime. When a cell divides, its hereditary information passes on to the next generation of cells. **Ribonucleic acid (RNA)**, the second type of nucleic acid, relays instructions from the genes to guide each cell's synthesis of proteins from amino acids.

DNA and RNA molecules consist of a chain of repeating **nucleotides**. Each nucleotide consists of three parts: a nitrogenous base, a pentose sugar, and a phosphate group. DNA contains the sugar deoxyribose and four different nitrogenous bases: adenine (A), thymine (T), cytosine (C), and guanine (G). Adenine and guanine are larger, double-ring bases called **purines**; thymine and cytosine are smaller, single-ring bases called **pyrimidines**. RNA contains the sugar ribose and instead of thymine it contains the pyrimidine base uracil (U).

Adenosine Triphosphate Adenosine triphosphate or **ATP** is the "energy currency" of living systems (**Figure L.9**). ATP transfers the energy liberated in exergonic catabolic reactions to power cellular activities that require energy (endergonic reactions). Among these cellular activities are muscular contractions, movement of chromosomes during cell division, movement of structures within cells, transport of substances across cell membranes, and synthesis of larger molecules from smaller ones. As its name implies, ATP consists of three phosphate groups attached to adenosine, a unit composed of adenine and the five-carbon sugar ribose.

A Review of Metabolism

Metabolism refers to all of the chemical reactions that occur in the body. Those chemical reactions that break down complex organic molecules into simpler ones are collectively known as **catabolism**. Overall, catabolic (decomposition) reactions are *exergonic*; they produce more energy than they consume, releasing the chemical energy stored in organic molecules. Important sets of catabolic reactions occur in glycolysis, the citric acid cycle, and the electron transport chain, each of which is reviewed below.

Chemical reactions that combine simple molecules to form the body's complex structural and functional components are collectively known as **anabolism**. Examples of anabolic (synthesis) reactions are the formation of peptide bonds between amino acids during protein synthesis, the building of fatty acids into phospholipids that form the plasma membrane bilayer, and the linkage of glucose molecules to form glycogen. Anabolic reactions are *endergonic*; they consume more energy than they produce.

Figure L.9 Structures of ATP and ADP. "Squiggles" (~) indicate the two phosphate bonds that can be used to transfer energy. Energy transfer typically involves hydrolysis of the last phosphate bond of ATP.

Carbohydrate Metabolism

As you learned in Chapter 4, both polysaccharides and disaccharides are hydrolyzed into the monosaccharides glucose (about 80%), fructose, and galactose during the digestion of carbohydrates. Hepatocytes (liver cells) convert most of the remaining fructose and practically all the galactose to glucose. So the story of carbohydrate metabolism is really the story of glucose metabolism.

Glucose Catabolism The oxidation of glucose to produce ATP is also known as **cellular respiration**, and it involves four sets of reactions: glycolysis, the formation of acetyl coenzyme A, the citric cycle, and the electron transport chain (**Figure L.10**).

1. **Glycolysis** is a set of reactions in which one glucose molecule is oxidized and two molecules of pyruvic acid are produced (**Figure L.11**). The reactions also produce two molecules of ATP and two energy-containing NADH + H$^+$. Because glycolysis does not require oxygen, it is a way to produce ATP anaerobically (without oxygen) and is known as **anaerobic cellular respiration**.
2. **Formation of acetyl coenzyme A** is a transition step that prepares pyruvic acid for entrance into the citric acid cycle. This step also produces energy-containing NADH + H$^+$ plus carbon dioxide (CO_2).
3. **Citric acid cycle reactions** oxidize acetyl coenzyme A and produce CO_2, ATP, energy-containing NADH + H$^+$, and FADH$_2$. (**Figures L.12 and L.13**)
4. **Electron transport chain reactions** oxidize NADH + H$^+$ and FADH$_2$ and transfer their electrons through a series of electron carriers. The citric acid cycle and the electron transport chain both require oxygen to produce ATP and are collectively known as **aerobic cellular respiration**.

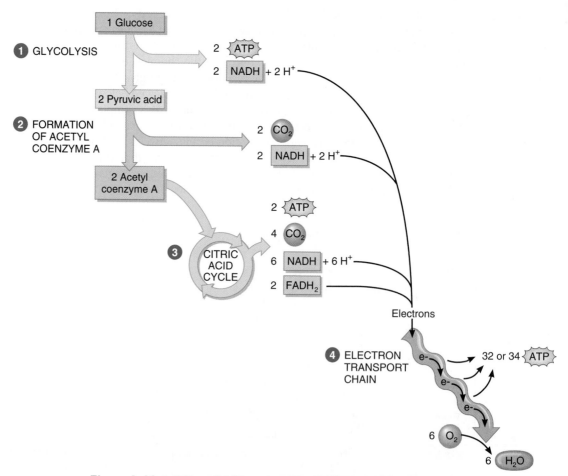

Figure L.10 Overview of cellular respiration (oxidation of glucose). A modified version of this figure appears in several places in this appendix to indicate the relationships of particular reactions to the overall process of cellular respiration. The oxidation of glucose involves glycolysis, the formation of acetyl coenzyme A, the citric acid cycle, and the electron transport chain.

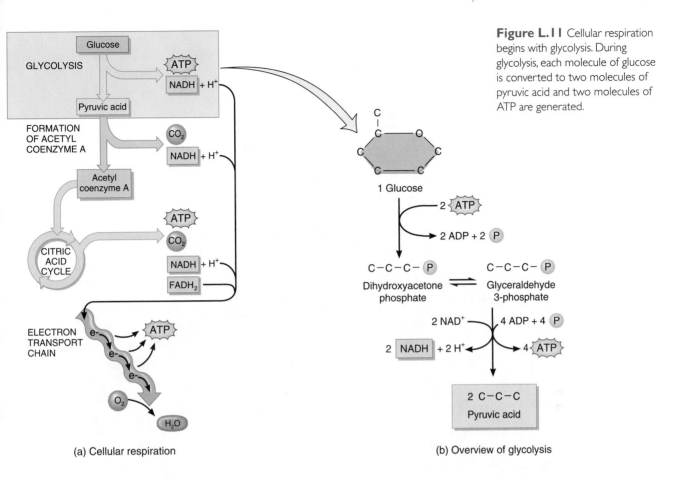

Figure L.11 Cellular respiration begins with glycolysis. During glycolysis, each molecule of glucose is converted to two molecules of pyruvic acid and two molecules of ATP are generated.

(a) Cellular respiration

(b) Overview of glycolysis

Figure L.12 After formation of acetyl coenzyme A, the next stage of cellular respiration is the citric acid cycle. Reactions of the citric acid cycle occur in the matrix of mitochondria.

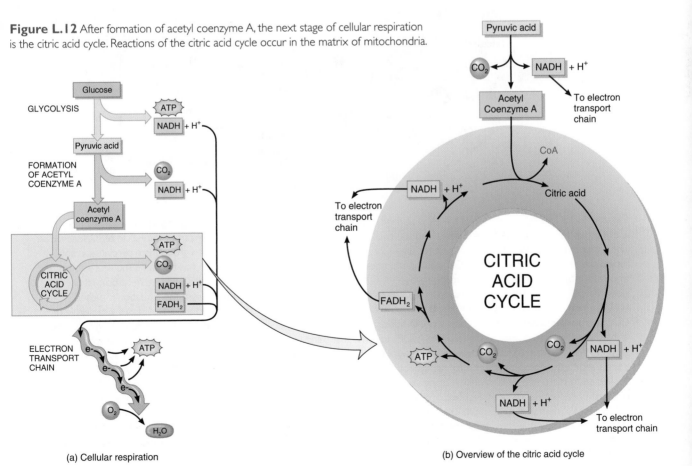

(a) Cellular respiration

(b) Overview of the citric acid cycle

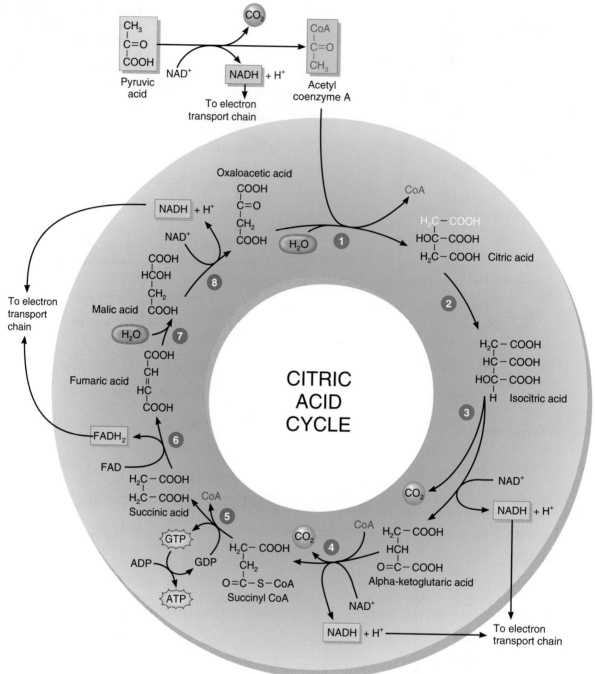

Figure L.13 The eight reactions of the citric acid cycle. ❶ Entry of the acetyl group. The chemical bond that attaches the acetyl group to coenzyme A (CoA) breaks, and the two-carbon acetyl group attaches to a four-carbon molecule of oxaloacetic acid to form a six-carbon molecule called citric acid. CoA is free to combine with another acetyl group from pyruvic acid and repeat the process. ❷ Isomerization. Citric acid undergoes isomerization to isocitric acid, which has the same molecular formula as citrate. Notice, however, that the hydroxyl group (—OH) is attached to a different carbon. ❸ Oxidative decarboxylation. Isocitric acid is oxidized and loses a molecule of CO_2, forming alpha-ketoglutaric acid. The H^+ from the oxidation is passed on to NAD^+, which is reduced to $NADH + H^+$. ❹ Oxidative decarboxylation. Alpha-ketoglutaric acid is oxidized, loses a molecule of CO_2, and picks up CoA to form succinyl CoA. ❺ Substrate-level phosphorylation. CoA is displaced by a phosphate group, which is then transferred to guanosine diphosphate (GDP) to form guanosine triphosphate (GTP). GTP can donate a phosphate group to ADP to form ATP. ❻ Dehydrogenation. Succinic acid is oxidized to fumaric acid as two of its hydrogen atoms are transferred to the coenzyme flavin adenine nucleotide (FAD), which is reduced to $FADH_2$. ❼ Hydration. Fumaric acid is converted to malic acid by the addition of a molecule of water. ❽ Dehydrogenation. In the final step in the cycle, malic acid is oxidized to re-form oxaloacetic acid. Two hydrogen atoms are removed and one is transferred to NAD^+, which is reduced to $NADH + H^+$. The regenerated oxaloacetic acid can combine with another molecule of acetyl CoA, beginning a new cycle. The three main results of the citric acid cycle are the production of reduced coenzymes ($NADH + H^+$ and $FADH_2$), which contain stored energy; the generation of GTP, a high-energy compound that is used to produce ATP; and the formation of CO_2, which is transported to the lungs and exhaled.

Figure L.14 Glycogenesis and glycogenolysis. The glycogenesis pathway converts glucose into glycogen; the glycogenolysis pathway breaks down glycogen into glucose.

Glucose Anabolism Even though most of the glucose in the body is catabolized to generate ATP, glucose may take part in or be formed via several anabolic reactions. One is the synthesis of glycogen (**Figure L.14**); another is the synthesis of new glucose molecules via gluconeogenesis (**Figure L.15**) from some of the products of protein and lipid breakdown.

Lipid Metabolism

Lipids, like carbohydrates, may be oxidized to product ATP. In order for muscle, liver, and adipose tissue to oxidize the fatty acids derived from triglycerides to produce ATP, the triglycerides must first be split into glycerol and fatty acids, a process called **lipolysis**. Liver cells and adipose cells can synthesize lipids from glucose or amino acids through **lipogenesis** (**Figure L.16**).

Protein Metabolism

During digestion, proteins are broken down into amino acids. Unlike carbohydrates and triglycerides, which are stored, proteins are not warehoused for future use. Instead, amino acids are either oxidized to produce ATP via the citric acid cycle (**Figure L.17**) or used to synthesize new proteins for body growth and repair. Excess dietary amino acids are not excreted in the urine or feces but instead are converted into glucose (gluconeogenesis) or triglycerides (lipogenesis).

Figure L.15 Gluconeogenesis, the conversion of noncarbohydrate molecules (amino aids, lactic acid, and glycerol) into glucose.

Figure L.16 Pathways of lipid metabolism. Glycerol may be converted to glyceraldehyde 3-phosphate, which can then be converted to glucose or enter the citric acid cycle for oxidation. Fatty acids undergo beta oxidation and enter the citric acid cycle via acetyl coenzyme A. The synthesis of lipids from glucose or amino acids is called lipogenesis.

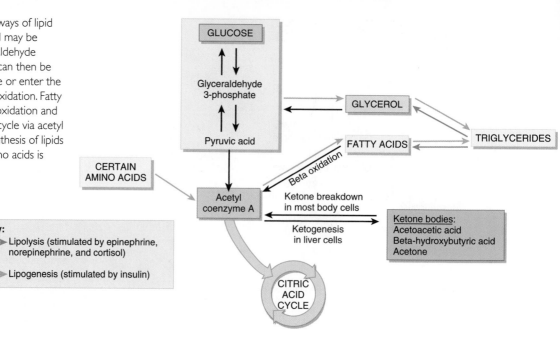

Figure L.17 Various points at which amino acids (shown in yellow boxes) enter the citric acid cycle for oxidation.

Amino Acid Structures

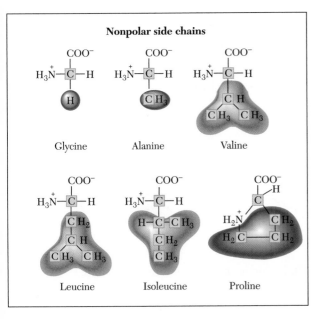

Nonpolar side chains

Glycine Alanine Valine

Leucine Isoleucine Proline

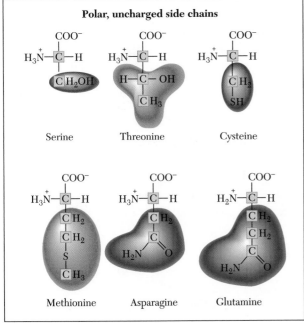

Polar, uncharged side chains

Serine Threonine Cysteine

Methionine Asparagine Glutamine

⬭ Essential amino acids side chain
⬭ Nonessential amino acids side chain

Aromatic side chains

Phenylalanine Tyrosine Tryptophan

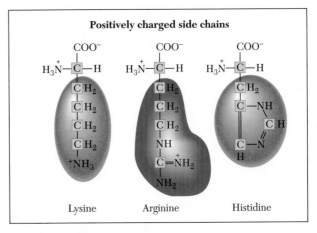

Positively charged side chains

Lysine Arginine Histidine

Negatively charged side chains

Aspartate Glutamate

Vitamin Structures

Water-Soluble Vitamins

Thiamin

Thiamin structure

Thiamin pyrophosphate (TPP): The active coenzyme form of thiamin.

Riboflavin

Oxidized
form

Reduced
form

Riboflavin structure: In riboflavin coenzymes the nitrogens can pick up hydrogen atoms.

Flavin mononucleotide (FMN): One of the active coenzyme forms of riboflavin.

Flavin adenine dinucleotide (FAD): One of the active coenzyme forms of riboflavin.

Niacin

Nicotinic acid   Nicotinamide

Forms of niacin: Both nicotinic acid and nicotinamide can provide a source of niacin in the diet. Both can be used to make niacin coenzymes.

Nicotinamide adenine dinucleotide (NAD⁺) and nicotinamide adenine dinu-cleotide phosphate (NADP⁺): The active coenzyme forms of niacin. NADP has the same structure as NAD except a phosphate group is attached to the oxygen instead of the highlighted ⓗ. These niacin coenzymes can pick up a hydrogen and two electrons to form NADH or NADPH.

Biotin

Biotin structure

Pantothenic acid

Pantothenic acid: This molecule is part of the structure of coenzyme A (CoA).

Coenzyme A: This coenzyme includes partothenic acid as part of its structure.

Vitamin B$_6$

Pyridoxine   Pyridoxal   Pyridoxamine

Forms of vitamin B$_6$: Pyridoxine, pyridoxal, and pyridoxamine are all converted into the active form of vitamin B$_6$.

Pyridoxal Phosphate: The active coenzyme form of vitamin B$_6$.

Folate

Pteridine ring   Para-amino benzoic acid   Glutamate

Folate structure: Folate consists of a pteridine ring combined with para-amino benzoic acid and at least one glutamate (a nonessential amino acid). The monoglutamate form is called folic acid. The folate naturally occurring in foods is the polyglutamate form.

Tetrahydrofolate: The active coenzyme form of folate has four added hydrogens. Derivatives of this form of folate carry and transfer different types of one-carbon units during synthetic reactions.

Vitamin B₁₂

Vitamin B₁₂ structure: Cobalamin, commonly known as vitamin B₁₂, is composed of a complex ring structure with a cobalt ion in the center.

Vitamin C

Ascorbic acid
(reduced form)

Dehydroascorbic acid
(oxidized form)

Vitamin C: Ascorbic acid can donate two hydrogen atoms with their electrons.

Fat-Soluble Vitamins
Vitamin A

Retinol: The alcohol form of vitamin A.

Retinal: The aldehyde form of vitamin A.

Retinoic acid: The acid form of vitamin A.

β-Carotene: A vitamin A precursor.

Vitamin D

Vitamin D synthesis and metabolism: Vitamin D is synthesized in the skin during exposure to sunlight. Hydroxylation in the liver and kidneys converts it to its active form, 1,25-dihydroxy-vitamin D_3.

Vitamin E

Vitamin E: The alpha-tocopherol form is shown here. In other tocopherol isomers the number and positions of the methyl groups differ. In other vitamin E isomers, called tocotrienols, the carbon chains contain double bonds.

Vitamin K

Phylloquinone

$$R = -CH_2-CH=C-CH_2-(CH_2-CH_2-CH-CH_2)_3-H$$

Menaquinone

$$R = -(CH_2-CH=C-CH_2)_n-H$$

Menadione

$$R = -H$$

Vitamin K: Phylloquinone (from plants) and menaquinones (from bacteria) are naturally occurring compounds with vitamin K activity. Menadion is a synthetic compound with vitamin K activity.

Appendix M
Critical Thinking Answers

Chapter 1
Using the Scientific Method

Review the 2 experiments discussed here. Which hypothesis is supported? Which is refuted? The second hypothesis has been supported because the Japanese Americans consuming a traditional Japanese diet had a lower incidence of colon cancer than those consuming a typical American diet. The first hypothesis has been refuted. Japanese Americans are not genetically different from Japanese living in Japan, so the difference in colon cancer incidence between these two groups cannot be due to genetic differences.

Could you propose other experiments to obtain more information about the causes of colon cancer in the United States? Epidemiological observations could be used to look for correlations between dietary factors in the American diet and the incidence of colon cancer. Case controlled studies could be done to identify dietary factors that are unique to the cancer group. Finally, intervention studies could be done to test different hypotheses. For example, if epidemiology suggested that a high fiber diet reduced colon cancer risk an intervention trial could be designed to compare people on high and low fiber diets. An intervention study could also be done in Japan comparing the incidence of colon cancer of Japanese people who consume a western diet with those who consume a traditional diet.

Based on the evidence presented here, propose a theory to explain the difference in the incidence of colon cancer in the U.S. and Japan. Some component of the typical American diet contributes to the development of colon cancer.

Chapter 2
The Personalized Pyramid

How does Jarad's diet compare to the MyPyramid recommendations? Does he eat enough whole grains? Do his vegetable choices meet the recommendations for types of vegetables?

Food Group	Jarad's MyPyramid Recommendations	Jarad's Typical Diet
Grains	9 ounce equivalents	8
Vegetables	3.5 cups	2
Fruits	2 cups	I
Milk	3 cups	2.5
Meat and Beans	6.5 ounce equivalents	6

Jarad consumes less-than recommended amounts from all the food groups. Only 1 of his 9 grains is whole grain. Half his grains should be whole. His only vegetables are potatoes, tomato sauce, and some chopped onions and lettuce. He consumes no dark green vegetables or orange vegetables.

Based on the foods he chooses, why do you think he is gaining weight? Many of the foods he chooses are high in solid fats or added sugar, which add discretionary kcalories. He also drinks soda, which contributes only discretionary kcalories. Therefore, although he does not consume enough food from all the food groups to meet his nutrient needs, the foods he chooses are high in kcalories leading to weight gain.

Use the MyPyramid Web site to determine how Jarad's kcalorie needs would change if he begins exercising for 50 minutes per day. His energy needs would increase by about 200 kcalories per day.

Assessing Nutritional Health

Do you think Darra has iron deficiency anemia? Evaluate this by looking up the normal values for hemoglobin and hematocrit in Appendix C. Yes, both her hemoglobin and hematocrit are below normal: Darra's hemoglobin is 11.2 g/100 mL blood and the normal range is 12–16 g/100 mL Darra's hematocrit is 35 ml/100 mL blood and the normal range is 36–47 ml/100 mL.

What about her iron intake? Compare her iron intake to the recommendations for a woman her age. She consumes only 6 mg of iron, which is 33% of the recommended 18 mg/day.

Should Darra be concerned about the nutrients she is consuming in excess of the recommended amount? Use the DRI tables to determine if they are likely to pose a risk. Although she exceeds the recommendations for vitamins A and C and calcium, she does not exceed the UL for any of these nutrients so she does not need to be concerned.

Chapter 3
Gastrointestinal Problems Can Affect Nutrition

What effect would this have on his nutrition and health? If he doesn't have enough saliva, he will have difficulty swallowing and tasting his food. This will decrease the appeal of food and may reduce his food intake. Also because saliva helps protect the teeth, the likelihood that he will develop cavities will increase.

How will this affect the digestion and absorption of nutrients in the carrots? If he can't chew the carrots well, the enzymes needed to digest them will not have access to all of the carrot. As a result, pieces will remain undigested and pass through the GI tract and the vitamins and minerals they contain will not be available for absorption.

Which person's stomach will empty faster? Why? The stomach of the student who ate just the cereal with skim milk and black coffee will empty faster because the meal is smaller and is much lower in fat. The amount of food and the high fat content of the eggs, sausage, biscuits with butter, and whole milk will cause this meal to remain in the stomach longer.

How will this affect food consumption and nutrient absorption? The surgery reduces the size of her stomach so she can only consume small amounts of food at any one time. Small meals are also important because the surgery bypasses the sphincter that regulates the entry of food into the small intestine. A large meal would cause too much material to enter the small intestine too quickly and would cause diarrhea. She does not absorb all the nutrients from her food because a section of the small intestine has been bypassed, reducing the area available for absorption. In addition, the smaller stomach may reduce the efficiency of both mechanical and chemical digestion in the stomach. Undigested food cannot be absorbed.

What effect would this have on her ability to digest and absorb proteins? Pancreatic enzymes are needed to digest carbohydrate, fat, and protein. If these enzymes are lacking, digestion will be incomplete, and nutrient absorption will be compromised. Protein-digesting enzymes in the stomach and mucosal cells can partially compensate for her reduction in pancreatic enzymes.

What type of foods should be avoided and why? She should avoid fatty foods. Bile is needed for fat absorption. Fat entering the small intestine causes the gallbladder to contract and release bile. A low-fat diet will minimize gallbladder contraction and therefore pain.

How would this affect fluid needs? The large intestine absorbs much of the water that enters with the contents of the small intestine. If most of his large intestine is removed he will lose more water and will need to consume more than before to prevent dehydration.

How might this affect the feces? The amount of intestinal gas? His feces will be larger and softer assuming he consumes additional fluid with his fiber. If he doesn't consume more fluid, this additional fiber could make him constipated. The added fiber provides a plentiful food supply for the intestinal microflora so it will cause an increase in the amount of intestinal gas produced.

Chapter 4
Becoming Less Refined

Determine whether Emma eats enough carbohydrate by calculating her percent of kcalories from carbohydrate in her diet (see Table 4.3). (350 g of carbohydrate × 4 kcal/g) ÷ 2340 kcalories × 100 = 59.8% of kcalories

This is within the recommended range of 45 to 65 percent of kcalories.

Now consider her fiber intake. Does it meet recommendations? If not, list specific changes she could make in her diet to increase her fiber intake to the recommended level. She only consumes 19.6 grams of fiber, which is below the recommended 25 grams per day for adult women. She could increase her fiber intake by having oatmeal or another whole grain cereal for breakfast and adding a high fiber vegetable such as broccoli to her dinner.

What about added refined sugars? Which food adds the most sugar to her diet? Identify other foods in her diet that are high in added sugar. Suggest foods she could substitute for these to reduce her added sugar intake. The soda adds the most sugar to her diet, but the fruit punch, candy bar, ice cream, and cherry syrup are also high in added sugar. The milk and apple contribute sugar, but these are unrefined sources. To reduce the amount of added sugar she can replace the soda and candy bar with a glass of low-fat milk and 2 oatmeal raisin cookies or some peanut butter and whole grain crackers and a glass of orange juice. For her evening snack she could top her ice cream with fresh berries instead of cherry syrup. These substitutions will also increase her fiber intake.

Chapter 5
Lowering the Risk of Heart Disease

Is Rafael at risk for a heart attack? Review his risk factor questionnaire and list the factors that increase his risk. He has a family history of heart disease because his mother died of a heart attack before the age of 65. He is a smoker and is inactive, so his lifestyle further increases his risk. His blood pressure is elevated and his total blood cholesterol of 210 mg/dL is over the recommendation of less than 200 mg/dL. His LDL cholesterol of 160 mg/dL is also above the recommended level and his HDL cholesterol is less than recommended. His triglycerides are in the healthy range.

What about his diet? Based on the information from his typical intake, how does his fat intake compare with recommendations? Are there any other food choices he makes that increase his risk? The percent of energy from fat in his diet is within the AMDR, but he consumes less polyunsaturated fat and more saturated fat and cholesterol than recommended and his diet is high in *trans* fat. His choices of whole-fat dairy products and red meat increase his saturated fat and cholesterol intake. He does not consume enough whole grains and does not eat any legumes or nuts so his intake of fiber is less than that recommended. By not consuming legumes he is missing out on soluble fiber that can help lower blood cholesterol and by avoiding nuts he is missing the heart healthy monounsaturated and omega-3 fatty acids that they provide.

Suggest some diet and lifestyle changes that would reduce Rafael's risk of developing heart disease. To reduce his saturated and *trans* fat intake he can use low-fat dairy products and reduce his intake of red meat and solid fats. To increase the amounts of unsaturated fat in his diet he can use liquid oils for cooking and eat more nuts, seeds, and fish. To increase his fiber intake he can choose more whole grains and add some legumes to his diet. Lifestyle changes that will help reduce his risk of heart disease include increasing his activity to at least 30 minutes most days of the week and stopping smoking.

Eating Healthier Fats

Assuming Isabel is eating 2250 kcalories per day, calculate the percent of energy from fat and saturated fat (sat fat) in her original diet. How do these percentages compare to recommendations? What foods are the biggest contributors to her saturated fat intake? To her *trans* fat intake? To her cholesterol intake? Her original diet contains 45% of kcalories from total fat and 15% of kcalories from saturated fat. It is recommended that total fat intake be 20 to 35% of kcalorie intake and that the amount of saturated fat be limited to less than 10% of kcalories. The biggest contributor to her saturated fat intake is the Big Mac. The biggest contributors to her *trans* fat intake are the French fries, tater tots and coconut cookies. The bran muffin, whole milk, Big Mac, and fish sticks all add significant amounts of cholesterol.

Now look at the changes she has made. Assuming her kcalorie intake stayed the same, calculate the percent of energy from fat and saturated fat in her modified diet. Her modified diet contains 17% of kcalories from total fat and 4% of kcalories from saturated fat.

Fat is not the only concern in choosing a healthy diet. How does her modified diet stack up to the MyPyramid recommendations in terms of grains, fruits, and vegetables?

The MyPyramid recommendations for a 2200 kcalorie diet are 7 ounces of grains, 3 cups of vegetables, and 2 cups of fruit. Her diet meets these recommendations. It includes 7 ounces of grains, assuming the large bran muffin is 4 ounce-equivalents. The muffin is made with bran, but none of her other grains are whole. Her diet contains 3 cups of vegetables from the stir fry, the baked potato, the green beans, and the salad. It also contains 2 cups of fruit from the orange and the apple.

Chapter 6
What Does Nitrogen Balance Tell Us?

Subject A is in negative nitrogen balance. List some possible reasons that would explain this. She is losing nitrogen and therefore losing protein. This would occur if she was losing weight, if her diet was not providing enough protein to meet her needs, or if she was experiencing a stress such as illness, injury, or surgery that caused her body to breakdown protein.

Calculate Subject B's nitrogen balance. What can you determine about subject B based on your answer? Nitrogen balance = $11.2 - 11.2 = 0$

Subject B is in nitrogen balance and therefore he is consuming enough protein to meet body needs and the total amount of protein in his body is not changing.

What would you predict about Subject C's nitrogen balance based on the fact that she is pregnant? Calculate her nitrogen balance. Explain whether it supports your prediction. If she is pregnant she should be building new tissue. This new tissue is mostly protein so she would retain some of the nitrogen in her diet. Her nitrogen balance of $12.8 - 10.4 = +2.4$ confirms this.

Choosing a Healthy Vegetarian Diet

Does Ajay get enough protein? Compare his intake with the RDA for someone his age and size. The RDA is 0.8 grams per kilogram of body weight. Ajay weighs 154 pounds, which is 70 kilograms (154 lbs ÷ 2.2 lbs/kg = 70 kg). Therefore his recommended protein intake is 56 g per day (70 kg × 0.8 g/kg = 56 g). His diet provides 70.5 grams, more than enough to meet his RDA.

Does his diet contain complementary proteins? List the protein sources in his diet and explain how they complement each other. At breakfast the wheat protein in the toast complements the protein in the peanut butter. At lunch the legume (lentils) protein in the dahl complements the protein in the rice. At dinner the protein in the chick-peas complements the protein in the rice and the wheat protein in the poori. The milk he has at breakfast and the yogurt (and ice cream) he has at dinner provide animal proteins that further complement the plant proteins in his diet.

If Ajay decided to become a vegan, what could he substitute for his dairy foods in order to meet his protein needs? At breakfast he could put soymilk on his cereal, which would provide 2 grams per half cup and compliment the wheat protein in the Grape Nuts cereal. At dinner he could substitute soy yogurt, which would provide about 6 grams of protein. Instead of ice cream for dessert he could have a smoothie made with bananas, strawberries and soymilk, which would add about 4 grams of protein.

How could he make sure his vegan diet meets his need for calcium and vitamin D (see Table 6.5)? To increase his calcium intake he could eat more leafy green vegetables, which are a good source of calcium, and use calcium-fortified products like orange juice, soy milk, and breakfast cereal. To meet his need for vitamin D he could spend plenty of time outdoors in the sun to ensure adequate vitamin D synthesis and use vitamin D-fortified breakfast cereal and soymilk to boost his vitamin D intake.

Chapter 7
Balancing Energy: Genetics and Lifestyle

Is Aysha overweight? Calculate her BMI. Aysha is 64 inches tall and weighs 155 lbs: Her BMI is equal to 155 lbs ÷ (64 inches)^2 × 703 = 26.6 kg/m^2, which is in the overweight range.

Is she in energy balance? Calculate her EER. How do her energy needs compare with her typical intake?
Aysha is 64 inches tall and weighs 155 lbs:

> 64 in. × 0.0254 m/in. = 1.63 m
> 155 lbs ÷ 2.2 lbs/kg = 70.4 kg
> Aysha is in the low active activity category,
> so PA = 1.12

Using the equation in table 7.6 Aysha's EER is equal to:

$$EER = 354 - (6.91 \times 23 \text{ yrs}) + 1.12(9.36 \times 70.4 \text{ kg}) + (726 \times 1.63 \text{ m}) = 2259 \text{ kcal}$$

note: This answer uses the EER equations in table 7.6. Because Aysha is overweight, it is technically correct to use the equations in Appendix A for calculating the energy expenditure of individuals who are overweight or obese:

$$TEE = 448 - (7.95 \times 23 \text{ yrs}) + 1.16(11.4 \times 70.4 \text{ kg}) + (619 \times 1.63 \text{ m}) = 2367 \text{ kcal}$$

She consumes about 2450 kcal per day but is expending only 2259 kcal per day, so she is not in energy balance. She is consuming 191 kcal per day more than she is expending.

If Aysha's weight does not change, but she increases her activity to 60 minutes per day, what will her new EER be? This will boost Aysha into the active physical activity category (PA = 1.27) and her EER will increase to:

$$EER = 354 - (6.91 \times 23 \text{ yrs}) + 1.27(9.36 \times 70.4 \text{ kg}) + (726 \times 1.63 \text{ m}) = 2535 \text{ kcal}$$

If the equation from Appendix A for calculating the energy expenditure of individuals who are overweight or obese is used:

$$TEE = 448 - (7.95 \times 23 \text{ yrs}) + 1.27(11.4 \times 70.4 \text{ kg}) + (619 \times 1.63 \text{ m}) = 2566 \text{ kcal}$$

If she maintains her higher activity level, but doesn't change her intake, how long will it take her to lose 10 pounds (assume 3500 kcalories/pound)? Her new energy balance = 2450 kcal consumed − 2535 kcal expended = −85 kcal/day. To lose 10 pounds she will need to shift energy balance by 35,000 kcalories:

> 35,000 ÷ 85 kcal/day = 412 days

It will take her a little over a year to lose 10 pounds. If she reduces her intake, the weight will come off faster.

Is she destined to be overweight based on her family history? Ashya is not destined to be overweight, but to maintain her weight in a healthy range she probably needs to monitor her energy intake more carefully and exercise more than an individual with no genetic tendency to store excess body fat. If she makes small changes in her diet and exercise patterns that she can stick with, she is more likely to succeed.

Choosing a Weight Loss Plan that Works for You

Would Rose benefit from weight loss based on the data given about her in the table? Yes. Her BMI is in the obese category, her waist circumference is greater than 35 inches, and she has high blood pressure and elevated total and LDL blood cholesterol. Weight loss will help lower her blood pressure and blood cholesterol levels and reduce her risk of type 2 diabetes.

Evaluate the programs she is considering: Are the diets nutritionally sound? Do they recommend activity and include social support? What about cost? The low-carbohydrate plan lacks variety and may be low in certain nutrients because it limits choices from grains, vegetables, fruits, and milk. The liquid formula is adequate nutritionally because the formula is fortified with nutrients. The one meal that is allowed adds additional nutrients as well as fiber and phytochemicals if nutrient-dense foods are selected. The exchange plan is also nutritionally sound. Allowing varied choices from multiple food groups at each meal helps ensure that all nutrient needs are met.

The only plan that includes any exercise or social support is the exchange plan, which includes a walking group that meets 5 days a week. The cost of the 3 plans is similar. Low-carbohydrate diets include a lot of animal products so they tend to be expensive—about 3 times the cost of a standard diet. The exchange plan carries a fee of $25.00 per week in addition to food, which makes the cost comparable to the low carbohydrate plan. The liquid formula is about $10 per week for the formula plus the costs of one meal a day, so it is probably the least expensive.

Which plan do you think would benefit Rose in the long term? The exchange plan is best in the long term because it is easy to follow and will teach her diet planning skills that will help her maintain her weight loss in the long term. It will integrate well into her current lifestyle and will also address the need to increase her activity level.

Chapter 8

Folate Recommendations

Why is folate a concern for Mercedes when planning a pregnancy? Research has shown that consuming extra folic acid during the month before conception and during early pregnancy can reduce the incidence of neural tube defects in the baby.

Look at Mercedes' diet. Which foods are highest in folate? Of these, which are fortified with folic acid? The orange juice, refried beans, white rice, flour tortilla, and salad each provide over 50 μg of folate. The white rice and flour tortilla are fortified with folic acid because they are processed, enriched grains.

Mercedes has oatmeal for breakfast because it is a whole grain, but why is it low in folate? If she replaced her white rice with brown rice and her tortilla and hamburger bun with whole wheat products, how would this affect her total folate intake? Oatmeal is a whole grain, so it has not been fortified with folic acid. The other grain products in her diet, such as the white rice, hamburger bun, and tortilla are refined and fortified so they contain added folic acid. Replacing her white rice with brown rice and her hamburger bun and tortilla with whole-wheat products

would reduce her total folate intake (see table) and would reduce her intake of the folic acid form of folate. Despite this she should not pass up whole grains – they are good sources of most B vitamins, minerals, and fiber. It is recommended that half her grains be whole.

Grain product	Folate (μg)
White flour tortilla	98
Whole-wheat tortilla	10
White rice	110
Brown rice	13
White hamburger bun	61
Whole-wheat hamburger bun	13

Would you recommend Mercedes take a folic acid supplement? Yes, she is not meeting her need for folic acid.

Supplemental Choices

Review the ingredients in Hazel's supplements. If she takes all these products at the frequency recommended in the table, will she be exceeding the UL for any nutrients? She will exceed the UL for vitamin C, niacin, and vitamin B_6.

The amount of vitamin C from the Vitamin C supplement and Prevention plus totals 2500 mg, which exceeds the UL of 2000 mg per day. For niacin, three tablets of B50 per day provide 150 mg, which exceeds the UL of 35 mg per day. For vitamin B_6, three tablets of B50 per day provide 180 mg, which exceeds the UL of 100 mg per day.

Did you find a UL for echinacea? Why not? No. Echinacea is not a nutrient, therefore it has no UL.

Would you recommend that Hazel take these supplements? Why or why not? No. She should stop taking these supplements because the amounts of nutrients are so high that she is exceeding the UL for some. In addition, there is little evidence that the echinacea in the supplement will prevent her from getting colds. To ensure she meets all her nutrient needs it would be better to take a multivitamin/mineral supplement that contains no more than 100% of the Daily Value for any nutrient. She can also increase her nutrient intake by improving her diet. By consuming the recommended amounts of foods from each group of MyPyramid and making nutrient-dense choices from these groups she can meet all her micronutrient needs. She could also select a fortified breakfast cereal to help ensure she meets her needs.

Chapter 9

How Much Vitamin A Is In Your Fast-Food Meal?

Looking at his fast food options, John notices that pizza has lots of vitamin A. What ingredients in pizza make it so much higher in vitamin A than the other choices? The pizza is a good source of vitamin A because it has cheese, which is a source of preformed vitamin A, and tomato sauce, tomatoes, and peppers, which provide provitamin A carotenoids. Meats, such as the hamburger and chicken, as well as the bun and potatoes in the other meals are all poor sources of vitamin A.

Should John be concerned about his vitamin A intake? Use iProfile to estimate how much vitamin A he is getting in his breakfast and lunch. How much vitamin C is provided by

these meals? His breakfast and lunch provide about 534 μg (RDA = 900 μg) of vitamin A and 22 mg of vitamin C (RDA = 90 mg).

How could John's breakfast and lunch be modified to increase his intake of vitamin A and vitamin C? He could increase his intake of preformed vitamin A by replacing the soda he has at lunch with a glass of milk. He could boost his provitamin A and vitamin C intake by increasing his fruit and vegetable intake. Adding cantaloupe, mango, or grapefruit to his breakfast will increase his provitamin A and vitamin C intake. Strawberries, orange juice, and kiwis can add additional vitamin C to his breakfast or lunch. Adding vegetables to his lunch can also boost both provitamin A and vitamin C intake. For example, he could put some spinach on his sandwich and bring a bag of baby carrots to munch on to add provitamin A. Including raw broccoli florets with his lunch will provide a source of vitamin C and if he chooses sliced sweet peppers, it will add both vitamin A and vitamin C to his lunch.

Chapter 10

A Diet for Health

How healthy is Rashamel's current diet? Does it meet the recommendations of MyPyramid for grains, fruits, and vegetables for someone who needs 2600 kcalories per day (see MyPyramid.gov)? As seen in the table Rashamel consumes the recommended 9 ounces of grains, but only 3 ounces are from whole grains, less than the recommended half of all grains. He eats only one cup of vegetables, which is below the recommendations of 3.5 cups per day. He eats 3 cups of fruits, which exceeds the recommended 2 cups.

	MyPyramid Recommendations (2600 kcals)	Rashamel's Current Diet
Grains	9 ounce equivalents	9
Vegetables	3.5 cups	1
Fruits	2 cups	3
Milk	3 cups	3
Meats and beans	6.5 ounce equivalents	2

Now compare his diet to the recommendations of the DASH Eating Plan (see Table 10.3). Does he meet these recommendations? How many additional servings from grains, fruits, and vegetables would he need to add? As seen in the table below Rashamel's current diet provides fewer servings of grains, fruits, vegetables, and beans, nuts, and seeds than recommended by the DASH Eating Plan.

	Dash Eating Plan (2600 kcals)(servings/day)	Rashamel's Current diet (servings/day)
Grains	10–11	9
Vegetables	5–6	1
Fruits	5–6	3
Low-fat dairy	2–3	3
Meats, fish, poultry	2	2
Beans, nuts, and seeds	1	0
Fat and oils	3	3.5

Rashamel's wife is concerned about her risk for osteoporosis. Use Table 10.3 and iProfile to plan a day's meals that follow a 1600-kcalorie DASH Eating Plan and meet her calcium needs.

She could choose:

Meal	Serving	DASH serving
Breakfast		
Fortified cereal	1 cup	2 grains (100 mg calcium)
Low fat milk	1 cup	1 milk (300mg calcium)
Banana	1 medium	2 fruits
Calcium-fortified orange Juice	3/4 cup	1 fruit (400 mg calcium)
Lunch		
Chef salad	2 cups	2 vegetables
with egg	1	1 oz meat
and chopped ham	1 oz	1 oz meat
and salad dressing	2 tb	1 fat and oils
Whole wheat crackers	6	1 grain
Low-fat yogurt	1 cup	1 milk (300 mg calcium)
Snack		
Sunflower seeds	1/3 cup	1 beans, nuts and seeds
Dinner		
Chicken breast	3 oz	3 oz
Brown rice	1 cup	2 grains
Steamed spinach	1 cup	2 vegetables (100 mg calcium)
Apple	1	1 fruit
Low-fat milk	1 cup	1 milk (300 mg calcium)

Chapter 11

Osteoporosis Risk

Evaluate Mika's risk for osteoporosis by looking at her answers on the questionnaire. Why would her milk intake and activity level as a child affect her risk now? Her risk is increased by the fact that she is a female, drank little milk as a child, and still typically consumes less than the recommended amount of milk. Her risk is further increased because she smokes, gets little exercise, and has a family history of osteoporosis. Her intake of calcium and the amount of exercise she got as a child affect her risk now because there are factors that determine peak bone mass, which is usually established by about age 30. Less calcium and exercise in childhood lead to lower peak bone mass, which increased her risk of osteoporosis as an adult.

How does Mika's calcium intake compare with the recommendations? Suggest changes she could make in her diet to increase her calcium without increasing her kcalorie intake. Her intake of 695 mg is below the AI of 1000 mg for women age 31 to 50 years. For breakfast she could drink calcium fortified orange juice. At lunch she could replace a slice of bologna with a slice of cheese on her sandwich. For a snack she could have low-fat yogurt instead of chips. For dinner she could have a leafy green vegetable such as Swiss chard instead of green beans and drink milk instead of iced tea.

Do you think Mika should take a calcium supplement? Why or why not? Yes, without major changes in her diet, Mika is unlikely to meet her calcium needs. In addition, she is approaching menopause, when the risk of osteoporosis increases, and she does not meet exercise recommendations. The benefits of a supplement outweigh the risks.

Chapter 12

Increasing Iron Intake and Uptake

Does Hanna's iron intake meet the RDA for a young female vegetarian? No, she consumes only 12 mg of iron. The RDA is 32 mg of iron per day for vegetarian women of childbearing age.

How could Hanna increase her iron intake without adding iron to her diet? She could go back to using iron cookware – the iron leaches into food. Cooking acidic foods in iron cookware further increases the amount of iron that leaches into the food. She can also include more iron-fortified foods in her diet, such as breakfast cereals and soymilk.

What could Hanna do to increase the absorption of the iron in her meals? Vitamin C-rich foods enhance iron absorption, so Hanna could increase her vitamin C intake by replacing her apple juice at breakfast with orange juice and substituting strawberries for the apple juice at dinner. Since tannins interfere with the absorption of iron she could have her tea between meals.

Does Hanna's diet provide good vegetarian sources of calcium? Are there other nutrient deficiencies for which she may be at risk? Good vegan sources of calcium include calcium-fortified cereals, tofu, almonds, legumes, and green leafy vegetables. For lacto and lacto-ovo vegetarians dairy products provide a good calcium source. Hanna's diet includes kale and yogurt, which are good sources of calcium. Since she does consume dairy products she is unlikely to be at risk for calcium, vitamin D, or B_{12} deficiency but the lack of meat in her diet puts her at risk of zinc deficiency.

Chapter 13

Incorporating Exercise Sensibly

List 3 things that are wrong with Nicole's exercise program. She started with too much exercise, she included strength training 5 days per week rather than the recommended 2–3 times per week, and she did not plan her exercise to fit well into her lifestyle.

What should her heart rate be to be in the aerobic zone?

Maximum heart rate	= 220 − age = 220 − 45	
	= 175 beats per minute	
60% of maximum	= 175 × 0.6	
	= 105 beats per minute	
85% of maximum	= 175 × 0.85	
	= 149 beats per minute	

To stay in her aerobic range she should exercise at a heart rate of at least 105 but no more than 149 beats per minute.

Calculate Nicole's EER before and after the addition of her exercise regimen. Do you think she will lose weight? Before her activity change, Nicole's physical activity level was in the sedentary category. Her estimated energy requirement (EER) can be calculated using the following equation for an adult woman (see inside cover):

EER = 354 − (6.91 × age in yrs) + PA [(9.36
      × weight in kg) + (726 × height in m)]
Age = 45 yrs, PA = 1.0, weight = 70.4 kg,
height = 1.7 meters
EER = 354 − (6.91 × 45) + 1.0[(9.36 × 70.4)
      + (726 × 1.7)] = 1936 kcalories/day

Her exercise program put her in the active physical activity category so her EER increases as follows:

EER = 354 − (6.91 × 45) + 1.27[(9.36 × 70.4) + (726 ×
      1.7)] = 2447 kcalories/day

If she could stick with this and not increase her food intake she would lose weight. Her energy expenditure has increased by over 500 kcalories a day. This would result in a weight loss of about a pound a week.

Suggest some modifications to her exercise program that will keep her from getting sore and keep her family happy. She should start slowly – perhaps 20 minutes of walking and build up to 45 minutes of walking 3 days a week. She could combine this with going to the gym twice a week for 30 minutes of weight lifting and light callisthenics. She needs to plan these activities so they do not interfere with family time.

Evaluating Supplements

Use the questions in Table 13.4 to help Paulo evaluate these claims. Since Paulo is a sprinter the claims made by these supplements would be beneficial to his performance. Based on the question in Table 13.4 he explores the scientific evidence to support these claims, whether there are any dangerous side effects, and considers how much each will cost.

Based on the information given in this chapter, explain the advantages and risks of these products. Creatine is a precursor for creatine phosphate, which is a source of ATP for short-term exercise. Supplements increase creatine phosphate levels in the muscle, which provides more energy for short bursts of activity such as sprinting. The risks of taking creatine are low, but there is little information on the long-term effects of this supplement. Creatine ingestion is not recommended and the FDA has advised consumers to consult with a physician before using it.

Chromium is a mineral that is needed for insulin to perform optimally. Insulin has many essential roles, including getting glucose into cells, turning on protein synthesis, and stimulating the synthesis of fat. The claim that it will increase lean tissue makes some sense metabolically, but supplements have not been found to increase lean tissue or enhance performance. The risk of taking chromium picolinate is low.

Suggest places Paulo could get additional information he can trust. In order to find sound scientific studies he should look for articles in well-respected, peer-reviewed journals in the field of nutrition and sports, such as the *International Journal of Sport Nutrition*, and *Medicine and Science in Sports and Exercise*. He should then focus on studies that include athletes involved in the types of activities he performs. He can also look at the government nutrition site at www.nutrition.gov for links to information on dietary supplements.

Would you recommend Paulo take these supplements? Why or why not? If Paulo participates in sprint events requiring short bursts of activity, creatine might improve his performance. To have this benefit he needs to continue to take the supplement, and there are no good long-term studies on creatine safety. There is little risk if Paulo wants to try creatine to see if his performance is improved, but he should be cautious about taking it over the long term. The evidence supporting the benefits of chromium picolinate is questionable so, although the risks of taking it are small, they still outweigh the benefits.

Chapter 14
Nutrient Needs for a Successful Pregnancy

Once Tina is in her second trimester, how many extra kcalories will she need? What about protein and iron? She will need 340 extra kcalories during her second trimester. Her RDA for protein is increased above the nonpregnant RDA by 25 grams per day during her second trimester; this would be a total of about 71 grams per day. Her diet already provides more than this amount. During her second trimester her RDA for iron increases by 9 mg to 27 mg of iron per day, well above the 13.5 mg she currently consumes.

Compare Tina's intake to the recommendations of MyPyramid for Moms shown in Table 14.13. Does she meet the food group recommendations for her first trimester? What should she add during her second trimester? No she doesn't consume enough dairy servings even for her first trimester. In addition to including more milk, during her second trimester she will need an additional serving of grains and an extra 1/2 ounce from the meats and beans group.

Suggest a snack that will meet these food group recommendations and provide the additional kcalories she needs. She could have a half of a ham sandwich on whole wheat bread. This will add 200 kcalories and along with the additional glass of milk she needs, she will provide the extra 340 kcalories.

What about iron? Does her current diet meet her needs without the supplement? How much iron does the snack you suggested provide? No, her diet does not even come close to meeting iron needs without the supplement. This snack would add 2.5 mg of iron.

Chapter 15
At Risk for Malnutrition

Why is Jamar's energy balance out of balance? Does he get the amount of daily activity recommended for a child his age? Evaluate his diet by comparing the number of servings per day he consumes from the various food groups to the MyPyramid recommendations for an 8-year-old boy. His energy balance is out of balance because he is consuming more energy than he is expending. His high intake is due to a diet that is very high in discretionary kcalories from high-fat dairy products and snack foods. His low expenditure is due to a lack of physical activity. Children should get at least an hour of moderate intensity exercise each day. Jamar only gets 25 minutes of exercise during recess at school 5 days a week. Most of his leisure time is spent in sedentary activities.

The MyPyramid recommendations for an 8-year-old sedentary boy are 5 ounces of grains, 1.5 cups of fruit, 1.5 cups of vegetables, 2 cups of milk, and 4 ounces of meat and beans. Jamar consumes about 3 times more milk as recommended, and consumes enough fruit, but falls short on the amounts of grains, vegetables, and meat and beans he includes in his diet.

Why is he anemic? What foods does he consume that are good sources of iron? How would his intake of dairy products affect his iron status? Jamar is anemic because his diet is low in heme and nonheme iron and in foods that promote iron absorption. He consumes little red meat, which is a good source or absorbable heme iron. Chicken and fish are also good sources of heme iron, but he does not consume these everyday. He consumes both enriched and whole grains, which provide nonheme iron, but his intake of nonheme iron from vegetables is low. Citrus fruit and other sources of vitamin C enhance absorption of nonheme iron, but his diet is low in these. His high intake of dairy products provides lots of calcium but large amounts of calcium consumed with iron can reduce iron absorption.

How might Jamar's iron deficiency anemia have contributed to his weight gain? Iron deficiency anemia causes lethargy, which would decrease his activity level and contribute to a positive energy balance.

Suggest some dietary changes that could increase his iron intake and decrease his energy intake. He could have a serving of red meat in spaghetti sauce or as a pizza topping, he could have iron fortified breakfast cereal and dried fruit for snacks. To further increase iron intake, Jamar's food could be cooked in iron cookware. To increase iron absorption he could consume dietary iron sources with foods that are high in vitamin C. For instance, having a glass of orange juice with his iron-fortified breakfast cereal would provide iron and enhance its absorption. To reduce his energy intake he could switch to low-fat milk and snack on fruit and whole-grain crackers, rather than candy and chips.

Less Food May Not Mean Fewer Kcalories

Why is Jenny continuing to gain weight on her new diet despite eating a smaller breakfast and skipping lunch? Even though Jenny seems to be eating less food, the foods she has chosen are high in fat and so contain more kcalories per gram than the foods in her original diet. Her new diet provides about 100 kcalories more than her original diet.

How could Jenny modify her new diet to reduce her kcalorie intake and still fit her busy schedule? The bagel she chose for breakfast is fine, but she should have a whole grain variety and add some fruit or juice as well as some cheese or peanut butter to make sure she is not hungry before lunch. For a quick lunch, she could have a turkey sandwich from a nearby deli. She won't be as hungry in the afternoon so she could have a carton of low-fat yogurt for an afternoon snack, rather than frozen yogurt, a candy bar, and potato chips. For dinner, she could have the pizza she snacked on in her original diet, and top it with vegetables such as mushrooms, peppers, broccoli, and tomatoes. Including a salad and a glass of low-fat milk with her pizza at dinner will fill her up and be much lower in kcalories than a double burger, fries, and a shake.

Chapter 16
Averting Malnutrition

How is Shirley doing? Does she meet the recommendations of MyPyramid for someone of her age who gets less than 30 minutes of activity per day? No. Her intake compared to MyPyramid recommendations is shown in the table below (assuming her soup contains about 1/2 ounce of noodles and an ounce of chicken). Her intake of grain products is slightly below the recommended amount, and she consumes no whole grains other than the bran cereal. She also consumes fewer fruits and vegetables and less milk and meat than recommended.

Food Group	Recommended Amount	Amount Shirley Consumes
Grains	5 ounces	4.5 ounces
Vegetables	2 cups	1 cup
Fruits	1.5 cups	1 cup
Milk	3 cups	2 cups
Meat & Beans	5 ounces	4 ounces

Suggest foods Shirley could add to improve her diet. She could increase her fiber intake by adding some whole wheat toast with breakfast and switching to brown rice with dinner. She could add fiber and increase her fruit and fluid intake by adding fruit to her breakfast cereal and having a glass of orange juice. She could add fiber and boost her vegetable intake by adding vegetables to the soup she has for lunch or by having a salad with lunch. She could add fiber and an ounce from the meat and beans group by adding some beans to her soup. She could increase her fluid and dairy intake by including a glass of milk at lunch or some tea with milk after dinner.

What factors other than nutrient content need to be considered when recommending food that will improve Shirley's diet? Other factors that need to be considered include the time it takes to cook the meals and the texture of her foods. If she is still having dental problems she might have difficulty chewing fresh fruits and vegetables and meats. Having to carry groceries from the store, and food costs may also affect the foods she can choose.

Would you recommend any dietary supplements for Shirley? Yes. Due to her age her absorption of vitamin B_{12} is likely to be limited and that from a supplement is better absorbed. Her low milk intake means she is probably not getting enough calcium or vitamin D. Since her energy intake is generally low this will make it even more difficult to meet micronutrient needs, so both a multivitamin/mineral supplement and a calcium supplement with vitamin D would be beneficial.

Chapter 17

Safe Picnic Choices

Is this picnic safe? It is safe only if none of the foods were contaminated with pathogens that can cause foodborne illness, or if they were prepared in ways that killed any pathogens that were present, or were stored in ways that prevented or slowed the growth of pathogens.

Which foods are the least risky? The safest foods are those that involve no preparation and are intended to be served at room temperature such as the chips, cookies, and cheese and crackers. Store-bought dips are a good choice because they can remain unopened until the picnic begins. Acidic dips such as tomato-based salsa are safe because the acid inhibits bacterial growth. The apple pie is also probably safe during the picnic as long as it has been refrigerated beforehand. The raw fruits and vegetables are safe as long as they are washed before they are prepared and served.

Which foods carry the highest risks? The more food is handled, the more likely it is to be contaminated. The chicken salad, tamales, and stuffed mushrooms pose a risk because they are handled extensively in preparation. The fried chicken, tamales, and stuffed mushrooms are cooked, but when left at room temperature, the inside may stay warm enough to provide a good environment for microbial growth.

What can Tamika do to reduce the risk of foodborne illness? She can bring ice and coolers to keep foods like the chicken salad, onion dip, fruit salad, and vegetables at cool temperatures below the danger zone. There is no way to keep hot foods hot but she can encourage people to eat the hot foods first so they do not cool off and then sit in the warm sun for hours.

After the picnic is over, what foods would you consider safe to keep as leftovers and what would you throw out? The fruit salad, raw vegetables, chips, crackers and cheese, and cookies would be the safest to keep. The chicken salad and cooked items that were left at room temperature for hours (fried chicken, stuffed mushrooms, and tamales) should be discarded, as should the chicken salad and onion dip.

The Risks and Benefits of Food

Draw a similar risk-benefit conclusion for the other foods on his list. Which foods do you think he should keep in his family's diet? How can he minimize the risks associated with eating them? To decrease the risks associated with using raw eggs, he can advise his son that he does not need protein shakes but that if he wants to drink them, he should use nonfat dry milk rather than raw eggs to add protein. He can have his daughter wait for the cookies to bake before tasting them. To decrease the risk of consuming high levels of contaminants from fish, he can eat a wider variety of fresh and saltwater fish to avoid consuming high levels of any one contaminant. Because the risks of eating raw fish are greater, he can limit sushi to a rare treat purchased only from a restaurant that he knows buys the fish fresh daily. The pesticide risks from consuming produce are small compared with the benefits of a diet high in fruits and vegetables. To reduce the amounts of pesticides ingested, fruits and vegetables can be washed thoroughly or consumed without skins. He can also reduce pesticide consumption by purchasing organic produce, but he must consider that it is more expensive. He can also buy locally grown produce and grow some of his own vegetables in the summer.

Are there any foods on his list that you would suggest he eliminate from the family diet? Why or why not? The riskiest food on Ron's list is raw shellfish. When raw clams and oysters are eaten, so are the contents of their digestive tracts, which can include any bacteria, viruses, chemical contaminants, and other impurities that are present in the water where they feed. The risk of foodborne infection can be reduced by cooking the shellfish, but they still may contain chemical contaminants, and other impurities that are not destroyed by heat.

Chapter 18

What Can You Do?

Looking at Keesha's list, do you think her actions will help? For each item on her list, identify an environmental benefit. Bringing her juice in a thermos reduces the amount of garbage (packaging, disposable cups, etc.) she generates from her meals; composting reduces the amount of garbage sent to the landfill; buying organically grown produce supports agricultural techniques that reduce the amount of chemical fertilizers and pesticides used and therefore introduced into the environment; and buying locally grown foods reduces the energy cost of transporting and storing produce grown at distant locations.

How will each of these actions affect the cost to her in dollars? Bringing her juice in a thermos reduces her costs because it is more expensive to buy individual juice boxes than to buy juice in a large container. This savings will soon offset the cost of the thermos. Composting will save money because she will have less garbage to take to the landfill and she will not have to purchase fertilizer for her garden. Buying organically grown produce will cost more, but the cost of locally grown foods is usually less than the cost of foods imported from other locations.

Appendix N
Calculations and Conversions

Weights and Measures

Measure	Abbreviation	Equivalent
1 gram	g	1000 milligrams
1 milligram	mg	1000 micrograms
1 microgram	μg	1/1000000 of a gram
1 nanogram	ng	1/1000000000 of a gram
1 picogram	pg	1/1000000000000 of a gram
1 kilogram	kg	1000 grams
		2.2 lb
1 pound	lb	454 grams
		16 ounces
1 teaspoon	tsp	approximately 5 grams
1 tablespoon	Tbsp	3 teaspoons
1 ounce	oz	28.4 grams
1 cup	c	8 fluid ounces
		16 tablespoons
1 pint	pt	2 cups
		16 fluid ounces
1 quart	qt	2 pints
		32 fluid ounces
1 gallon	gal	128 fluid ounces
		4 quarts
1 liter	l	1.06 quarts
		1000 milliliters
1 milliliter	ml	1000 microliters
1 deciliter	dl	100 milliliters
1 kcalorie	kcal, Cal	1000 calories
		4.167 kilojoules
1 kilojoule	kJ	1000 joules

Glossary

A

absorption The process of taking substances from the gastrointestinal tract into the interior of the body.

Acceptable Macronutrient Distribution Ranges (AMDRs) Ranges of intake for carbohydrate, fat, and protein, expressed as a percentage of total energy intake, that are associated with reduced risk of chronic disease while providing adequate intakes of essential nutrients.

accidental contaminants Substances that unexpectedly enter the food supply. They are not regulated by the FDA.

Accutane A drug that is used orally to treat severe acne. It is a derivative of vitamin A.

acesulfame K (Acesulfame potassium) An alternative sweetener that contains no energy and is 200 times as sweet as sugar.

acetyl-CoA A metabolic intermediate consisting of a 2-carbon compound attached to a molecule of CoA that is produced during the breakdown of glucose, fatty acids, and amino acids.

acetylcholine A neurotransmitter that functions in the brain and other parts of the nervous system.

acid A substance that releases hydrogen ions (H^1) in solution.

acrodermatitis enteropathica An inherited defect in zinc absorption and metabolism that leads to severe zinc deficiency.

active transport The transport of substances across a cell membrane with the aid of a carrier molecule and the expenditure of energy. This may occur against a concentration gradient.

acute Refers to effects that develop rapidly.

adaptive thermogenesis Adjustments in energy expenditure induced by factors such as changes in ambient temperature and food intake.

added sugars Sugars and syrups that have been added to foods during processing or preparation.

Adequate Intake (AI) A DRI value used as a goal for intake when no RDA can be determined. These values are an approximation of the average nutrient intake that appears to sustain a desired indicator of health.

ADI (Acceptable Daily Intake) The amount of a substance in food or drinking water that can be safely consumed daily over a lifetime without adverse effects.

adipocytes Fat-storing cells.

adipose tissue Tissue found under the skin and around body organs that is composed of fat-storing cells.

adolescent growth spurt An 18- to 24-month period of peak growth velocity that begins at about ages 10 to 13 in girls and 12 to 15 in boys.

adrenaline A hormone secreted by the adrenal gland in response to stress that causes changes, such as an increase in heart rate, that prepare the body for "fight or flight"; also called epinephrine.

aerobic capacity or **VO₂ max** The maximum amount of oxygen that can be consumed by the tissues during exercise. This is also called maximal oxygen consumption.

aerobic exercise Endurance exercise such as jogging, swimming, or cycling that increases heart rate and requires oxygen in metabolism. This type of exercise improves cardiovascular fitness.

aerobic metabolism Metabolism in the presence of oxygen. In aerobic metabolism glucose, fatty acids, and amino acids are completely broken down to form carbon dioxide and water and produce ATP.

aflatoxin An extremely potent carcinogen that is produced by a mold that grows on peanuts, corn, and grains.

agar A polysaccharide extract of seaweed that is used in foods as an emulsifier, stabilizer, and gel.

age-related bone loss The bone loss that occurs in both cortical and trabecular bone of men and women as they advance in age.

AIDS (acquired immune deficiency syndrome) The syndrome caused by HIV infection that causes the immune system to fail, resulting in frequent recurrent infections that ultimately result in death.

alcohol An energy-containing molecule that provides 7 kcalories per gram and is produced by the fermentation of carbohydrates; the type of alcohol that is consumed in the diet is called ethanol.

alcohol dehydrogenase (ADH) An enzyme found primarily in the liver and stomach that helps break down alcohol into acetaldehyde, which is then converted to acetyl-CoA.

alcohol intoxication or **alcohol poisoning** A condition that occurs when the quantity of alcohol consumed exceeds the individual's tolerance for alcohol and impairs mental and physical abilities.

alcoholic hepatitis Inflammation of the liver caused by alcohol consumption.

alcoholism A chronic disorder characterized by dependence on alcohol and development of withdrawal symptoms when alcohol intake is reduced.

alcohol-related birth defects Malformations in the skeleton or major organ systems in a child due to maternal alcohol consumption during pregnancy.

alcohol-related neurodevelopmental disorders (ARND) A spectrum of abnormalities such as learning and developmental disabilities and behavioral abnormalities in a child due to maternal alcohol consumption during pregnancy.

aldosterone A hormone secreted by the adrenal glands that increases sodium reabsorption by the kidney and therefore enhances water retention.

alginate A polysaccharide extract of brown algae used in the processing of food, primarily dairy products.

alimentary canal See gastrointestinal tract.

allergen A substance, usually a protein, that stimulates an immune response.

allergy An adverse reaction involving the immune system that results from exposure to a specific allergen.

alpha-carotene (α-carotene) A carotenoid, some of which can be converted into vitamin A, that is found in leafy green vegetables, carrots, and squash.

alpha-linolenic acid (α-linolenic acid) An 18-carbon omega-3 polyunsaturated fatty acid known to be essential in humans.

alpha-tocopherol (α-tocopherol) The form of tocopherol that provides vitamin E activity in humans.

alveoli (singular, alveolus) Milk-producing glands in the breast.

Alzheimer's disease A disease that results in the relentless and irreversible loss of mental function.

amenorrhea Delayed onset of menstruation or the absence of three or more consecutive menstrual cycles.

amino acid A building block of protein. Contains a central carbon atom bound to a hydrogen atom, an amino group, an acid group, and a side chain that is unique to each amino acid.

amino acid pool All of the amino acids in body tissues and fluids that are available for use by the body.

amino acid score See chemical score.

amniotic fluid The liquid in the amniotic sac that surrounds and protects the fetus during development.

amniotic sac A membrane surrounding the fetus that contains the amniotic fluid.

amylopectin A plant starch that is composed of long, branched chains of glucose molecules.

amylose A plant starch that is composed of long unbranched chains of glucose molecules.

anabolic Energy-requiring processes in which simpler molecules are combined to form more complex substances.

anabolic steroids Synthetic fat-soluble hormones that mimic testosterone and are used by some athletes to increase muscle strength and mass.

anaerobic metabolism or **anaerobic glycolysis** Metabolism in the absence of oxygen. Each molecule of glucose is broken apart, generating two molecules of ATP. Glucose is metabolized in this way when the blood cannot deliver oxygen to the tissues quickly enough to support aerobic metabolism.

anaerobic threshold or **lactate threshold** The exercise intensity at which the reliance on anaerobic metabolism results in the accumulation of lactic acid.

anaphalaxis An immediate and severe allergic reaction to a substance (e.g., food or drugs). Symptoms include breathing difficulty, loss of consciousness, and a drop in blood pressure. This condition requires immediate medical attention and can be fatal.

androstenedione A compound (known as andro) that can be converted into testosterone and estrogen inside the body. It is a dietary supplement used by athletes to increase muscle mass and strength.

anecdotal Information based on a story of personal experience.

anemia A condition in which there is a reduced number of red blood cells or a reduced amount of hemoglobin, which reduces the oxygen-carrying capacity of the blood.

anencephaly A birth defect due to failure of the neural tube to close that results in the absence of a major portion of the brain, skull, and scalp.

angiotensin II A compound that causes blood vessel walls to constrict and stimulates the release of the hormone aldosterone.

Anisakis disease A disease caused by infection of the gastrointestinal tract with the Anisakis roundworm, which can contaminate raw fish.

anorexia athletica A type of eating disorder that is characterized by engaging in compulsive exercise to eliminate excess kcalories.

anorexia nervosa An eating disorder characterized by self-starvation, a distorted body image, and below normal body weight.

antacid A drug used to neutralize acidity in the gastrointestinal tract.

anthropometric measurements External measurements of the body, such as height, weight, limb circumference, and skinfold thickness.

antibiotic A substance that inhibits the growth of or destroys microorganisms; used to treat or prevent infection.

antibiotic resistance When bacteria or other microbes that cause disease evolve into forms that can no longer be killed by antibiotics.

antibodies Proteins produced by cells of the immune system that destroy or inactivate foreign substances in the body.

anticaking agent A substance added to dry food products to prevent clumping.

anticarcinogen A compound that can counteract the effect of cancer-causing substances.

anticoagulant A substance that delays or prevents blood clotting.

antidiuretic hormone (ADH) A hormone secreted by the pituitary gland that increases the amount of water reabsorbed by the kidney and therefore retained in the body.

antigen A foreign substance (almost always a protein) that, when introduced into the body, stimulates an immune response.

antioxidant A substance that is able to neutralize reactive oxygen molecules and thereby reduce oxidative damage.

antithiamin factors Substances in food that destroy the vitamin thiamin. Some are enzymes and are destroyed by cooking; others are not inactivated by cooking.

anus The lower opening of the digestive tract through which the feces leave the body.

apolipoprotein B A protein embedded in the outer shell of low-density lipoprotein (LDL) particles that binds to LDL receptor proteins on body cells.

appetite The desire to consume specific foods that is independent of hunger.

aquaculture The controlled cultivation and harvest of aquatic plants or animals.

arachidonic acid A 20-carbon omega-6 polyunsaturated fatty acid that can be synthesized from linoleic acid.

arginine A nonessential amino acid found in protein.

ariboflavinosis The condition resulting from a deficiency of riboflavin.

arteries Vessels that carry blood away from the heart.

arteriole A small artery that carries blood to capillaries.

arthritis A disease characterized by inflammation of the joints, joint pain, and sometimes changes in joint structure.

ascorbic acid or **ascorbate** The chemical term for vitamin C.

aseptic processing A method that places sterilized food in a sterilized package using a sterile process.

asparagine A nonessential amino acid found in protein.

aspartame An alternative sweetener that is 200 times as sweet as sugar and is composed of the amino acids phenylalanine and aspartic acid.

aspartic acid A nonessential amino acid found in protein.

atherosclerosis A type of cardiovascular disease that involves the buildup of fatty material in the artery walls.

atherosclerotic plaque The cholesterol-rich material that is deposited in the blood vessels of individuals with atherosclerosis. It consists of cholesterol, smooth muscle cells, fibrous tissue, and eventually calcium.

atoms The smallest units of an element that still retain the properties of that element.

ATP (adenosine triphosphate) The high-energy molecule used by the body to perform energy-requiring activities.

atrophic gastritis An inflammation of the stomach lining that causes a reduction in stomach acid and allows bacterial overgrowth.

atrophy Wasting or decrease in the size of a muscle or other tissue caused by lack of use.

attention deficit hyperactivity disorder (ADHD) A condition that is characterized by a short attention span, acting without thinking, and a high level of activity, excitability, and distractibility.

authoritative statement Refers to a means of authorizing health claims that involves a statement of support from an appropriate scientific body of the United States government such as the National Academy of Sciences.

autoimmune disease A disease that results from immune reactions that destroy normal body cells.

avidin A protein found in raw egg whites that binds biotin, preventing its absorption.

B

bacteria (singular, **bacterium**) Tiny single-celled organisms found throughout the environment. Most are harmless or beneficial, but a few types can cause disease in humans.

balance study A study that compares the total amount of a nutrient that enters the body with the total amount that leaves the body.

basal metabolic rate (BMR) The rate of energy expenditure under resting conditions. BMR measurements are performed in a warm room in the morning before the subject rises, and at least 12 hours after the last food or activity.

basal metabolism The energy expended to maintain an awake resting body that is not digesting food.

base A substance that accepts hydrogen ions in solution.

bee pollen A mixture of pollen, bee saliva, and plant nectar that collects on the legs of bees; sold as an ergogenic aid.

behavior modification A process used to gradually and permanently change habitual behaviors.

beriberi A thiamin-deficiency disease that is characterized by muscle weakness, loss of appetite, nerve degeneration, and heart changes.

beta-carotene (β-carotene) An orange-colored carotenoid found in many yellow and red-orange fruits and vegetables that has more provitamin A activity than other carotenoids. It also acts as an antioxidant.

beta-cryptoxanthin (β-cryptoxanthin) A carotenoid found in corn, green peppers, and lemons that can provide some vitamin A activity.

beta-oxidation (β-oxidation) The first step in the production of ATP from fatty acids. This pathway breaks the carbon chain of fatty acids into two-carbon units that form acetyl-CoA and release high-energy electrons that are passed to the electron transport chain.

bile A substance made in the liver and stored in the gallbladder. It is released into the small intestine to aid in fat digestion and absorption.

bile acids Emulsifiers present in bile that are synthesized by the liver from cholesterol.

binge drinking When five or more drinks are consumed by a man or 4 or more by a woman in a row on a single occasion.

binge-eating disorder An eating disorder characterized by recurrent episodes of binge eating in the absence of purging behavior.

bingeing or **binge eating** The rapid consumption of a large amount of food in a discrete period of time associated with a feeling that eating is out of control.

bioavailability A general term that refers to how well a nutrient can be absorbed and used by the body.

bioelectric impedance analysis A technique for estimating body composition that measures body fat by directing a low-energy electric current through the body and calculating resistance to flow.

biological value A measure of protein quality determined by comparing the amount of nitrogen retained in the body with the amount absorbed from the diet.

biotechnology The process of manipulating life forms via genetic engineering in order to provide desirable products for human use.

blood pressure The amount of force exerted by the blood against the artery walls.

body image The way a person perceives and imagines their body.

body mass index (BMI) An index of weight in relation to height that is used to compare body size with a standard; it is equal to body weight (in kilograms) divided by height (in meters) squared.

bomb calorimeter An instrument used to determine the energy content of food. It measures the heat energy released when a dried food is combusted.

bone remodeling The process whereby bone is continuously broken down and re-formed to allow for growth and maintenance.

botulism A severe food-borne intoxication that results from consuming the toxin produced by the bacterium *Colostridium botulinum.*

bovine somatotropin (bST) A hormone naturally produced by cows that stimulates the production of milk. A synthetic version of this hormone is now being produced by genetic engineering.

bovine spongiform encephalopathy (BSE) A fatal neurological disease, also known as mad cow disease, that affects cattle and may be transmitted to humans by consuming beef by-products.

bran The protective outer layers of whole grains. It is a concentrated source of dietary fiber.

Brewer's yeast The type of yeast used in brewing beer; a good source of B vitamins and often used as a nutritional supplement.

brown adipose tissue A type of fat tissue that has a greater number of mitochondria than the more common white adipose tissue. It can waste energy by producing heat and is responsible for some of the change in energy expenditure in adaptive thermogenesis in rodents.

brush border Refers to the microvilli surface of the intestinal mucosa, which contains some digestive enzymes.

buffer A substance that reacts with an acid or base by picking up or releasing hydrogen ions to prevent changes in pH.

bulimia nervosa An eating disorder characterized by the consumption of large amounts of food at one time (binge eating), followed by purging behaviors such as vomiting or the use of laxatives to eliminate kcalories from the body.

C

caffeine A bitter white substance found in coffee, tea, chocolate, and other foods; a stimulant and a diuretic.

calcitonin A hormone secreted by the thyroid gland that reduces blood calcium levels.

calorie The amount of heat required to raise the temperature of 1 g of water 1 degree Celsius; equal to 4.18 joules. Typically used to refer to the number of kilocalories in food or expended by the body.

calorimetry A technique for measuring energy expenditure.

Campylobactor jejuni A bacterium common in raw milk and undercooked meat that causes food-borne illness.

cancer A disease characterized by cells that grow and divide without restraint and have the ability to grow in areas of the body reserved for other cells.

capillaries Small, thin-walled blood vessels where the exchange of gases and nutrients between blood and cells occurs.

carbohydrate A compound containing carbon, hydrogen, and oxygen in the same proportions as in water; includes sugars, starches, and most fibers.

carbohydrate loading See Glycogen supercompensation.

carbon dioxide A waste product produced by cellular respiration that is eliminated from the body by the lungs.

carcinogen A substance that causes cancer.

cardiorespiratory system The circulatory and respiratory systems, which together deliver oxygen and nutrients to cells.

cardiovascular Refers to the heart and blood vessels.

cardiovascular disease Any disease affecting the heart and blood vessels.

caries or **dental caries** Cavities, or decay of the tooth enamel caused by acid produced when bacteria growing on the teeth metabolize carbohydrate.

carnitine A molecule synthesized in the body that is needed to transport fatty acids and some amino acids into the mitochondria for metabolism. Supplements of carnitine are marketed to athletes to enhance performance.

carotenoids Natural pigments synthesized by plants and many microorganisms. They give yellow and red-orange fruits and vegetables their color.

carpal tunnel syndrome Numbness, tingling, weakness, and pain in the hand caused by pressure on the nerves.

carrageenan A seaweed polysaccharide extracted from the algae Irish moss and used as a thickener, mainly in dairy products.

case-control study A type of observational study that compares individuals with a particular condition under study with individuals of the same age, sex, and background who do not have the condition.

casein The predominant protein in cow's milk.

cash crops Crops grown to be sold for monetary return rather than to be used for food locally.

cassava A starchy root that is the staple of the diet in many parts of Africa.

catabolic The processes by which substances are broken down into simpler molecules releasing energy.

catalase An iron-containing enzyme that destroys peroxides.

cataracts A disease of the eye that results in cloudy spots on the lens (and sometimes the cornea), which obscure vision.

celiac disease A disorder that causes damage to the intestines when the protein gluten is eaten.

cell The basic structural and functional unit of plant and animal life.

cell differentiation Structural and functional changes that cause cells to mature into specialized cells.

cell membrane The membrane that surrounds the cell contents.

cellular respiration The reactions that break down carbohydrates, fats, and proteins in the presence of oxygen to produce carbon dioxide, water, and energy in the form of ATP.

cellulite Subcutaneous fat that has a lumpy appearance because strands of connective tissue connect it to underlying structures.

cellulose An insoluble fiber that is the most prevalent structural material of plant cell walls.

cephalic response The stimulation of gastric secretion by the sight, smell, and sound of food preparation.

certified food color A food color that has been tested and certified for safety, quality, consistency, and strength of color.

ceruloplasmin A copper-containing plasma protein that converts iron to the ferric form, which can bind to transferrin for transport in the blood.

cesarean section The surgical removal of the fetus from the uterus.

chemical bonds Forces that hold atoms together.

chemical or **amino acid score** A measure of protein quality determined by comparing the essential amino acid content of the protein in a food with that in a reference protein. The lowest amino acid ratio calculated is the chemical score.

Chinese restaurant syndrome See MSG symptom complex.

cholecalciferol The chemical name for vitamin D_3. It can be formed in the skin of animals by the action of sunlight on a form of cholesterol called 7-dehydrocholesterol.

cholecystokinin (CCK) A hormone released by the duodenum that signals the pancreas to secrete digestive enzymes and causes the gallbladder to contract and release bile into the duodenum.

cholesterol A lipid that consists of multiple chemical rings and is made only by animal cells.

cholic acid A bile acid.

choline A compound needed for the synthesis of the phospholipid phosphatidylcholine (lecithin) and the neurotransmitter acetylcholine. It is important for a number of biochemical reactions, and there is evidence that it is essential in the diet during certain stages of life.

chromium picolinate A form of chromium sold as a supplement promoted to change body composition. Chromium is involved in insulin action, and supplements claim to increase lean body mass, decrease body fat, and delay fatigue. There is little evidence of their effectiveness as an ergogenic aid.

chronic Refers to effects that develop slowly over a long period.

chylomicron A lipoprotein that transports lipids from the mucosal cells of the small intestine and delivers triglycerides to body cells.

chyme A mixture of partially digested food and stomach secretions.

chymotrypsin A protein-digesting enzyme produced in an inactive form in the pancreas and activated in the small intestine, where it aids digestion.

circulatory system The organ system consisting of the heart, blood, and blood vessels, which transports material to and from cells.

cirrhosis Chronic liver disease characterized by the loss of functioning liver cells and the accumulation of fibrous connective tissue.

citric acid cycle Also known as the Krebs cycle or the tricarboxylic acid cycle, this is the stage of cellular respiration in which two carbons of acetyl-CoA are oxidized, producing two molecules of carbon dioxide.

clinical trial or **human intervention study** A study of a population in which there is an experimental manipulation of some members of the population; observations and measurements are made to determine the effects of this manipulation.

clones Copies that are identical to the original.

Clostridium botulinum A bacterium that produces a deadly toxin and grows in a low-acid, low-oxygen environment, such as inside certain canned goods.

Clostridium perfringens A bacterium found in meat and poultry that can cause food-borne illness.

coagulation The process of blood clotting.

cobalamin The chemical term for vitamin B_{12}.

coenzyme A small organic molecule (not a protein but sometimes a vitamin) that is necessary for the proper functioning of many enzymes.

coenzyme Q or **ubiquinone** A coenzyme that transfers electrons from one molecule to another in the electron transport chain of cellular respiration.

cofactor An inorganic ion or coenzyme required for enzyme activity.

colic A condition in young infants characterized by inconsolable crying. It is believed to be due to pain from gas buildup in the gastrointestinal tract or immaturity of the central nervous system

collagen The major protein in connective tissue.

colon The largest portion of the large intestine.

colostrum The first milk, which is secreted in late pregnancy and up to a week after birth. It is rich in protein and immune factors.

complete dietary protein Protein that provides essential amino acids in the proportions needed to support protein synthesis.

complex carbohydrates Carbohydrates composed of sugar molecules linked together in straight or branching chains. They include glycogen, starches, and fibers.

compression of morbidity The postponement of the onset of chronic disease such that disability occupies a smaller and smaller proportion of the life span.

concentration gradient A condition that exists when the amount of a dissolved substance is greater in one area than it is in another.

conception The union of sperm and egg (ovum) that results in pregnancy.

condensation reaction A type of chemical reaction in which two molecules are joined to form a larger molecule and water is released.

conditionally essential amino acid An amino acid that is essential in the diet only under certain conditions or at certain times of life; also called semiessential amino acid.

connective tissue One of the four human tissue types; includes cartilage, bone, blood, adipose tissue, and the coverings of some organs.

constipation Infrequent or difficult defecation.

control group A group of participants in an experiment that are identical to the experimental group except that no experimental treatment is used. They are used as a basis of comparison.

cornea The clear, transparent fibrous outer surface of the eye.

coronary heart disease A disease of the heart and blood vessels that supply blood to the heart.

correlation Two or more factors occurring together.

cortical or **compact bone** Dense, compact bone that makes up the sturdy outer surface layer of bones.

creatine A compound that can be converted into creatine phosphate, which replenishes muscle ATP during short bursts of activity. Creatine is a dietary supplement used by athletes to increase muscle mass and delay fatigue during short intense exercise.

creatine phosphate A compound found in muscle that can be broken down quickly to convert ADP to ATP.

cretinism A condition resulting from poor maternal iodine intake during pregnancy that causes stunted growth and poor mental development in offspring.

criteria of adequacy Functional indicators, such as the level of a nutrient in the blood or the appearance of a deficiency symptom, that can be measured to determine the biological effect of a level of nutrient intake; established for each nutrient and gender and life-stage group when developing Dietary Reference Intakes.

critical control points Possible points in food production, manufacturing, and transportation at which contamination could occur or be prevented.

critical periods Times in growth and development when an organism is more susceptible to harm from poor nutrition or other environmental factors.

cross-contamination The transfer of contaminants from one food or object to another.

cross-sectional data Information obtained by a single broad sampling of many different individuals in a population.

cruciferous A group of vegetables (also called crucifers) named for the cross shape of their four-petal flowers. They include broccoli, brussels sprouts, cabbage, cauliflower, kale, kohlrabi, mustard greens, rutabagas, and turnips. Their consumption is linked with lower rates of cancer.

cyclamate An alternative sweetener that was common in the United States in the 1960s; banned after it was found to cause cancer in laboratory animals.

cycle of malnutrition A cycle in which malnutrition is perpetuated by an inability to meet nutrient needs at all life stages.

cysteine A conditionally essential sulfur-containing amino acid; when methionine is available in sufficient quantities, cysteine is not essential in the diet.

cytoplasm The cellular material outside the nucleus that is contained by the cell membrane.

cytosol The liquid found within cells.

D

Daily Reference Values (DRVs) Reference values established for protein and seven nutrients for which no original RDAs were established. The values are based on dietary recommendations for reducing the risk of chronic disease.

daily value A nutrient reference value used on food labels to help consumers see how foods fit into their overall diets.

DASH diet A dietary pattern that is plentiful in fruits and vegetables and low-fat dairy products and therefore high in potassium, magnesium, calcium, and fiber, and low in saturated fat and cholesterol.

deamination The removal of the amino group from an amino acid.

dehydration A condition that results when the output of water exceeds water intake, due to either low water intake or excessive loss.

Delaney Clause A clause added to the 1958 Food Additives Amendment of the Pure Food and Drug Act that prohibits the intentional addition to foods of any compound that has been shown to induce cancer in animals or humans at any dose.

dementia A deterioration of mental state resulting in impaired memory, thinking, and/or judgment.

denaturation The alteration of a protein's three-dimensional structure.

dental caries The decay and deterioration of teeth caused by acid produced when bacteria on the teeth metabolize carbohydrate.

deoxyribose The 5-carbon sugar that is part of DNA.

depletion-repletion study A study that feeds a diet devoid of a nutrient until signs of deficiency appear, and then adds the nutrient back to the diet to a level at which symptoms disappear.

dermatitis An inflammation of the skin.

DHA See Docosahexaenoic acid.

DHEA (dehydroepiandosterone) A precursor of the sex hormones testosterone, estrogen, and progesterone; sold as a dietary supplement to slow aging and to increase muscle mass.

diabetes mellitus A disease caused by either insufficient insulin production or decreased sensitivity of cells to insulin. It results in elevated blood glucose levels.

diacylglycerol or **diglyceride** A molecule of glycerol with two fatty acids attached.

diaphragm A muscular wall separating the abdomen from the thoracic cavity containing the heart and lungs.

diarrhea An intestinal disorder characterized by frequent or watery stools.

dicumarol An anticoagulant that was isolated from moldy clover.

diet history Information about dietary habits and patterns. It may include a 24-hour recall, a food record, or a food frequency questionnaire to provide information about current intake patterns.

dietary antioxidant A substance in food that significantly decreases the adverse effects of reactive species on normal physiological function in humans.

dietary fiber A mixture of indigestible carbohydrates and lignin that is found intact in plants.

dietary folate equivalent (DFE) The unit used to express the amount of folate present in food. One DFE is equivalent to 1 μg of folate naturally occurring in food, 0.6 μg of synthetic folic acid from fortified food or supplements consumed with food, or 0.5 μg of synthetic folic acid consumed on an empty stomach.

Dietary Guidelines for Americans A set of nutrition recommendations designed to promote population-wide dietary changes to reduce the incidence of nutrition-related chronic disease.

Dietary Reference Intakes (DRIs) A set of reference values for the intake of energy, nutrients, and food components that can be used for planning and assessing the diets of healthy people in the United States and Canada.

dietary supplement A product intended for ingestion in the diet that contains one or more of the following ingredients: vitamins, minerals, herbs, botanicals, or other plant-derived substance; amino acids; concentrates or extracts.

diet-induced thermogenesis See Thermic effect of food (TEF).

diffusion The movement of molecules from an area of higher concentration to an area of lower concentration without the expenditure of energy.

digestion The process of breaking food into components small enough to be absorbed into the body.

digestive system The organ system responsible for the ingestion of food, the digestion and absorption of nutrients and the elimination of food residues; includes the gastrointestinal tract as well as a number of accessory organs.

digestive tract See Gastrointestinal tract.

diglyceride See Diacylglycerol.

dipeptide Two amino acids linked by a peptide bond.

direct calorimetry A method of calculating energy use that measures the amount of energy released as heat.

direct food additives Substances intentionally added to foods. They are regulated by the FDA.

disaccharide A sugar formed by linking two monosaccharides.

discretionary kcalories The balance of energy remaining in a person's energy allowance after consuming all the food needed to meet their nutrient needs.

dissociate To separate two charged ions.

diuretic A drug that promotes fluid excretion.

diverticula Sacs or pouches that protrude from the wall of the large intestine.

diverticulitis A condition in which diverticula in the large intestine become inflamed.

diverticulosis A condition in which outpouchings (or sacs) form in the wall of the large intestine.

DNA (deoxyribonucleic acid) The genetic material found in the nucleus that codes for the synthesis of proteins.

docosahexaenoic acid (DHA) A 22-carbon omega-3 polyunsaturated fatty acid found in fish that may be needed in the diet of newborns. It can be synthesized from alpha-linolenic acid.

double-blind study An experiment in which neither the study participants nor the researchers know who is in a control or an experimental group.

doubly-labeled water method A technique for measuring energy expenditure based on measuring the disappearance of isotopes of hydrogen and oxygen in body fluids after consumption of a defined amount of water labeled with both isotopes.

Down syndrome A disorder caused by extra genetic material that results in distinctive facial characteristics, mental retardation, and other abnormalities.

duodenum The upper segment of the small intestine that connects to the stomach.

E

eating disorder A persistent disturbance in eating behavior or other behaviors intended to control weight that affects physical health and psychosocial functioning.

eating disorders not otherwise specified (EDNOS) A category of eating disorders that includes abnormal eating behaviors that don't fit into the anorexia or bulimia nervosa categories

eclampsia A hypertensive disorder of pregnancy characterized by high blood pressure, protein in the urine, convulsions, and coma.

edema Swelling due to the buildup of extracellular fluid in the tissues.

eicosanoids Regulatory molecules, including prostaglandins and related compounds, that can be synthesized from omega-3 and omega-6 fatty acids.

eicosapentaenoic acid (EPA) A 20-carbon omega-3 polyunsaturated fatty acid found in fish that can be synthesized from alpha-linolenic acid but may be essential in humans under some conditions.

electrolytes Positively and negatively charged ions that conduct an electrical current in solution. Commonly refers to sodium, potassium, and chloride.

electron High-energy particle carrying a negative charge that orbits the nucleus of an atom.

electron transport chain The final stage of cellular respiration in which electrons are passed down a chain of molecules to oxygen to form water and produce ATP.

elements Substances that cannot be broken down into products with different properties.

elimination diet A program that eliminates potential allergy-causing foods from an individual's diet. It is used in combination with a food challenge, which then systematically adds these foods back to identify any that cause an allergic reaction.

embryo The developing human from 2 to 8 weeks after fertilization. All organ systems are formed during this time.

empty kcalories Refers to foods that contribute energy but few other nutrients.

emulsifier A substance that allows water and fat to mix by breaking large fat globules into smaller ones.

endocrine system Organ system composed of cells, tissues, and organs that secrete hormones to help control body functions.

endoplasmic reticulum A cellular organelle involved in the synthesis of proteins and lipids and composed of a system of membranous tubules, channels, and sacs in the cytosol; rough endoplasmic reticulum has ribosomes on its outside surface.

endorphins Compounds that cause a natural euphoria and reduce the perception of pain under certain stressful conditions.

endosperm The largest portion of a kernel of grain. It is primarily starch and serves as a food supply for the sprouting seed.

endurance The length of time one can perform a task.

energy The capacity to do work.

energy balance The amount of energy consumed in the diet compared with the amount expended by the body over a given period.

energy-yielding nutrients Nutrients that can be metabolized to produce energy in the body.

enriched Refers to a food that has had nutrients added to restore those lost in processing to a level equal to or higher than originally present. It is a type of fortification that is typically used to refer to refined grain products.

enteral or tube feeding A method of feeding by providing a liquid diet directly into the stomach or intestine through a tube placed down the throat or through the wall of the GI tract.

Environmental Protection Agency (EPA) U.S. government agency responsible for determining acceptable levels of environmental contaminants in the food supply and for establishing water quality standards.

enzymes Protein molecules that accelerate the rate of specific chemical reactions without being changed themselves.

EPA See Environmental Protection Agency

epidemiology The study of the interrelationships between health and disease and other factors in the environment or lifestyle of different populations.

epiglottis A piece of elastic connective tissue at the back of the throat that covers the opening of the passageway to the lungs during swallowing.

epinephrine A hormone secreted by the adrenal gland in response to stress that causes changes, such as an increase in heart rate, in preparation for "fight or flight"; also called adrenaline.

epithelial tissue One of the four human tissue types; includes the cells that cover external body surfaces and line internal cavities and tubes.

ergogenic aid Anything designed to increase work or improve performance.

ergot A toxin produced by a mold that grows on grains, particularly rye.

erythropoietin a protein hormone made by the kidneys that stimulates bone marrow stem cells to produce red blood cells. It can manufactured using genetic engineering and is taken by endurance athletes as an ergogenic aid known as EPO.

esophagus A portion of the GI tract that extends from the pharynx to the stomach.

essential amino acid or indispensable amino acid An amino acid that cannot be synthesized by the human body in sufficient amounts to meet needs and therefore must be included in the diet.

essential fatty acid A fatty acid that must be consumed in the diet because it cannot be made by the body or cannot be made in sufficient quantities to meet needs.

essential fatty acid deficiency A condition characterized by dry scaly skin and poor growth that results when the diet does not supply sufficient amounts of the essential fatty acids.

essential hypertension High blood pressure that has no obvious external cause.

essential nutrients Nutrients that must be provided in the diet because the body either cannot make them or cannot make them in sufficient quantities to satisfy its needs.

Estimated Average Requirements (EARs) Intakes that meet the estimated nutrient needs (as defined by a specific indicator of adequacy) of 50% of individuals in a gender and life-stage group.

Estimated Energy Requirements (EER) The amount of energy calculated to maintain body weight in a healthy person based on age, gender, size, and activity level.

estrogen A steroid hormone secreted by the ovaries and by the placenta that is involved in the maintenance of pregnancy and the maintenance and development of female sex organs and secondary sex characteristics.

ethanol The type of alcohol in alcoholic beverages. It is produced by yeast fermentation of sugar.

Exchange Lists A food group system that groups foods according to energy and macronutrient content. It is used extensively in planning diabetic and weight loss diets.

excretory system Organ system involved in the elimination of metabolic waste products; includes the lungs, skin, and kidneys.

experimental controls Factors included in an experimental design that limit the number of variables, allowing an investigator to examine the effect of only the parameters of interest.

experimental groups Groups of participants in an experiment who are subjected to an experimental treatment.

extracellular fluid The fluid located outside cells. It includes fluid found in

F

the blood, lymph, gastrointestinal tract, spinal column, eyes, joints, and that found between cells and tissues.

facilitated diffusion The movement of substances across a cell membrane from an area of higher concentration to an area of lower concentration with the aid of a carrier molecule. No energy is required.

failure to thrive The inability of a child's growth to keep up with normal growth curves.

fallopian tubes or **oviducts** Narrow ducts leading from the ovaries to the uterus.

famine A widespread lack of access to food due to a disaster that causes a collapse in the food production and marketing systems.

fasting hypoglycemia Low blood sugar that is not related to food intake; often caused by an insulin-secreting tumor.

fat A lipid that is solid at room temperature; commonly used to refer to all lipids or specifically to triglycerides.

fat-free mass Body mass composed of all tissue except adipose tissue.

fatigue The inability to continue an activity at an optimal level.

fat-soluble vitamins vitamins that do not dissolve in water; includes vitamins A, D, E, and K.

fatty acids Organic molecules made up of a chain of carbons linked to hydrogen atoms with an acid group at one end.

fatty liver The accumulation of fat in the liver.

fatty streak A cholesterol deposit in the artery wall.

FDA See Food and Drug Administration.

feces Body waste, including unabsorbed food residue, bacteria, mucus, and dead cells, which is excreted from the gastrointestinal tract by passing through the anus.

female athlete triad The combination of disordered eating, amenorrhea, and osteoporosis that occurs in some female athletes, particularly those involved in sports in which low body weight and appearance are important.

fermentation A process in which microorganisms metabolize components of a food and therefore change the composition, taste, and storage properties of the food.

ferritin The major iron storage protein.

fertilization The union of sperm and egg (ovum).

fetal alcohol syndrome A characteristic group of physical and mental abnormalities in an infant resulting from maternal alcohol consumption during pregnancy.

fetus The developing human from the ninth week to birth. Growth and refinement of structures occur during this time.

fiber See Dietary fiber.

fitness The ability to perform routine physical activity without undue fatigue.

flavin adenine dinucleotide (FAD) and **flavin mononucleotide (FMN)** The active coenzyme forms of riboflavin. The structure of these molecules allows them to pick up and donate hydrogens and electrons in chemical reactions.

flexibility Range of motion.

fluorosis Mottling of the tooth enamel caused by chronic overconsumption of fluoride.

foam cell A cholesterol-filled white blood cell.

folate and folacin General terms for the many forms of this vitamin. The majority of the folate found naturally in foods is in the polyglutamate form, which contains a string of glutamate molecules that must be removed before it can be absorbed.

folic acid The monoglutamate form of folate, which is present in the diet in fortified foods and supplements.

food additives Substances that can reasonably be expected to become a component of a food during processing. The foods that may contain them and the amounts that may be present are regulated by the FDA.

Food and Drug Administration (FDA) U.S. government agency responsible for the safety and wholesomeness of all food except red meat, poultry, and eggs; also sets standards and enforces regulations for food labeling and for food and color additives.

food challenge The introduction of foods into the diet one at a time to determine if allergy symptoms occur. It is used in combination with an elimination diet to identify foods that cause an allergic reaction.

Food Code A set of recommendations published by the FDA for the handling and service of food sold in restaurants and other establishments that serve food.

food diary A method of assessing dietary intake that involves an individual keeping a written record of all food and drink consumed during a defined period.

food disappearance surveys Surveys that estimate the food use of a population by monitoring the amount of food that leaves the marketplace.

food frequency questionnaire A method of assessing dietary intake that gathers information about how often certain categories of food are consumed.

food insecurity An inability to consistently acquire foods that are nutritionally adequate and individually, socially, and culturally acceptable.

food intolerance An adverse reaction to a food that does not involve antibody production by the immune system.

food jag When a child will only eat one food item meal after meal.

food processing Any alteration of food from the way it is found in nature.

food self-sufficiency The ability of an area to produce enough food to feed its population.

food shortage Insufficient food to feed a population.

food-borne illness An illness caused by consumption of food containing a toxin or disease-causing microorganism.

food-borne infection Illness produced by the ingestion of food containing microorganisms that can multiply inside the body and cause injurious effects.

food-borne intoxication Illness caused by consuming a food containing a toxin.

fortification A term used generally to describe the process of adding nutrients to foods, such as the addition of vitamin D to milk.

fortified foods Foods to which one or more nutrients have been added.

free radical One type of highly reactive molecule that causes oxidative damage.

fructose A monosaccharide found in fruits and honey that is composed of six carbon atoms arranged in a ring structure; commonly called fruit sugar.

functional fiber Isolated indigestible carbohydrates that have been shown to have beneficial physiological effects in humans.

functional foods Foods that provide a health benefit beyond that attributed to the nutrients they contain.

G

galactose A monosaccharide that combines with glucose to form lactose or milk sugar.

gallbladder An organ of the digestive system that stores bile, which is produced by the liver.

gastric banding A surgical procedure in which an adjustable band is placed around the upper portion of the stomach to limit the volume that the stomach can hold and the rate of stomach emptying.

gastric bypass A surgical procedure to treat morbid obesity that both reduces the size of the stomach and bypasses a portion of the small intestine.

gastric juice A collection of secretions including hydrochloric acid and pepsinogen, released by the gastric glands into the stomach.

gastrin A hormone secreted by the stomach mucosa that stimulates the secretion of gastric juice.

gastroesophageal reflux disease (GERD) A chronic condition in which acidic stomach contents leak back up into the esophagus causing pain and damaging the esophagus.

gastroesophageal sphincter The muscular valve at the top of the stomach that allows food to enter the stomach from the esophagus and then keeps the food and digestive juice from leaking back up into the esophagus.

gastrointestinal tract A hollow tube consisting of the mouth, pharynx, esophagus, stomach, small intestine, and large intestine, in which digestion and absorption of nutrients occur.

gel A jelly-like suspension of a liquid in a solid system that is semisolid in consistency.

gelatin A protein derived from collagen that is deficient in the amino acid tryptophan.

gene A length of DNA containing the information needed to synthesize RNA or a polypeptide chain.

gene expression The events of protein synthesis in which the information coded in a gene is used to synthesize a product; either a protein or a molecule of RNA.

generally recognized as safe (GRAS) A group of chemical additives that are generally recognized as safe based on their long-standing presence in the food supply without obvious harmful effects.

genes Units of a larger molecule called DNA that are responsible for inherited traits.

genetic engineering A set of techniques used to manipulate DNA for the purpose of changing the characteristics of an organism or creating a new product.

germ The embryo or sprouting portion of a kernel of grain. It contains vegetable oil, protein, fiber, and vitamins.

gestation The time between conception and birth, which lasts about 9 months (or about 40 weeks) in humans.

gestational diabetes mellitus A consistently elevated blood glucose level that develops during pregnancy and returns to normal after delivery.

gestational hypertension The development of high blood pressure after the twentieth week of pregnancy.

ghrelin A hormone produced by the stomach that stimulates food intake.

ginseng An herb used in traditional Chinese medicine; claims are made that it improves athletic performance and increases sexual potency.

glomerulus A ball of capillaries in the nephron that filters blood during urine formation.

glucagon A hormone made in the pancreas that stimulates the breakdown of liver glycogen and the synthesis of glucose to increase blood sugar.

gluconeogenesis The synthesis of glucose from simple noncarbohydrate molecules. Amino acids from protein are the primary source of carbons for glucose synthesis.

glucose A monosaccharide that is the primary form of carbohydrate used to provide energy in the body. It is the sugar referred to as blood sugar.

glutamic acid A nonessential amino acid that is found in protein and in monosodium glutamate (MSG).

glutathione peroxidase A selenium-containing enzyme that protects cells from oxidative damage by neutralizing peroxides.

glycemic index A ranking of the effect on blood glucose of a food of a certain carbohydrate content relative to an equal amount of carbohydrate from a reference food such as white bread or glucose.

glycemic load An index of the glycemic response that occurs after eating specific foods. It is calculated by multiplying a food's glycemic index by the amount of available carbohydrate in a serving of the food.

glycemic response The rate, magnitude, and duration of the rise in blood glucose that occurs after a particular food or meal is consumed.

glyceride The most common type of lipid; consists of one, two, or three fatty acids attached to a molecule of glycerol.

glycerol A 3-carbon molecule that forms the backbone of triglycerides and phosphoglycerides; also used as a humectant in food.

glycogen A carbohydrate made of many glucose molecules linked together in a highly branched structure. It is the storage form of carbohydrate in animals.

glycogen supercompensation or **carbohydrate loading** A regimen of diet and exercise training designed to maximize muscle glycogen stores before an athletic event.

glycolysis also called **anaerobic metabolism** Metabolic reactions in the cytosol of the cell that split glucose into two 3-carbon pyruvate molecules. The energy released from one molecule of glucose is used to make two ATP molecules.

goiter An enlargement of the thyroid gland caused by a deficiency of iodine.

goitrogens Substances that interfere with the utilization of iodine or the function of the thyroid gland.

gout Disorder in which crystals of uric acid deposit in and around joints, especially of the big toe and foot, causing pain and arthritis.

GRAS See Generally recognized as safe.

growth hormone A hormone secreted by the pituitary gland that stimulates growth.

guar gum A branched polysaccharide from guar plants used as an additive to increase the viscosity of food.

gum A plant polysaccharide and its derivatives that can dissolve in water and swell to form viscous solutions.

gum arabic A branched polysaccharide from acacia trees; it is colorless, odorless, and tasteless, and is used as an additive to increase the viscosity of food.

gum tragacanth A branched polysaccharide from thorny shrubs that grow in the semidesert of the Near East; used as an additive to thicken foods and to stabilize emulsions.

H

hazard analysis critical control point (HACCP) A food safety system that focuses on identifying and preventing hazards that could cause foodborne illness.

health claim A statement made about the relationship between a nutrient or food and a disease or health condition.

Healthy Eating Index A system developed to evaluate the adequacy of the American diet. It is based on how well a person's diet meets current dietary recommendations.

Healthy People Initiative A set of national health promotion and disease prevention objectives for the U.S. population.

heart attack A condition in which an artery supplying blood to the heart becomes blocked, cutting off blood flow and hence oxygen and nutrients to a segment of the heart muscle, resulting in tissue death.

heartburn A burning sensation in the chest caused when acidic stomach contents leak into the esophagus through the gastroesophageal sphincter.

heat cramp A muscle cramp caused by an imbalance of sodium and potassium at the muscle cell membrane as a result of excessive exercise without adequate fluid and electrolyte replacement.

heat exhaustion Low blood pressure, rapid pulse, fainting, and sweating caused when dehydration decreases blood volume so much that blood can no longer both cool the body and provide oxygen to the muscles.

heat stroke Elevated body temperature as a result of fluid loss and the failure of the temperature regulatory center of the brain.

heat-related illness Conditions, including heat cramps, heat exhaustion, and heat stroke, that can occur due to an unfavorable combination of exercise, hydration status, and climatic conditions.

heavy drinker Someone who consumes five or more drinks per occasion on at least five different days.

Heimlich maneuver A procedure used to dislodge an object blocking an air passage; involves the application of sharp, firm pressure to the abdomen just below the rib cage.

heme iron A readily absorbed form of iron found in animal products that is chemically associated with proteins such as hemoglobin and myoglobin.

hemicellulose An insoluble fiber that is a structural component of plant cell walls.

hemochromatosis An inherited condition that results in increased iron absorption and leads to iron deposits throughout the body and tissue damage.

hemoglobin An iron-containing protein in red blood cells that binds oxygen and transports it through the bloodstream to cells.

hemolytic anemia Anemia that results when red blood cells break open.

hemorrhoids Swollen veins in the anal or rectal area.

hemosiderin An insoluble iron storage compound that stores iron when the amount of iron in the body exceeds the storage capacity of ferritin.

hepatic portal circulation The system of blood vessels that collects nutrient-laden blood from the digestive organs and delivers it to the liver.

hepatic portal vein The vein that transports blood from the GI tract to the liver.

hepatitis Inflammation of the liver.

herb The leaves, flowers, stems, roots, seeds, or any other part of a nonwoody seed-bearing plant that dies down to the ground after flowering.

herbicide An agent that kills weeds.

heterocyclic amines (HCAs) A class of mutagenic substances produced when there is incomplete combustion of amino acids during the cooking of meats—such as when meat is charred.

hiatal hernia When the upper part of the stomach bulges through the opening in the diaphragm into the chest cavity.

high-density lipoproteins (HDLs) Lipoproteins that pick up cholesterol from cells and transport it to the liver so that it can be eliminated from the body. A high level of HDL decreases the risk of cardiovascular disease.

high-fructose corn syrup A sweetener made from corn syrup that is composed of approximately half fructose and half glucose.

histamine A substance produced by cells of the immune system as part of a nonspecific response that leads to inflammation.

HIV (Human Immunodeficiency Virus) A virus that infects cells of the immune system and eventually leads to AIDS.

homeostasis A physiological state in which a stable internal body environment is maintained.

homocysteine A sulfur-containing amino acid that is produced from the metabolism of methionine. Elevated blood levels increase the risk of cardiovascular disease.

hormone A chemical messenger that is produced in one location, released into the blood, and elicits responses at other locations in the body.

hormone sensitive lipase An enzyme present in adipose cells that responds to chemical signals by breaking down triglycerides into fatty acids and glycerol for release into the bloodstream.

human intervention study or **clinical trial** A study of a population in which there is an experimental manipulation of some members of the population; observations and measurements are made to determine the effects of this manipulation.

humectant A substance added to foods to retain moisture.

hunger Internal signals that stimulate one to acquire and consume food.

hybridization The process of cross-fertilizing two related plants with the goal of producing offspring that have the desirable characteristics of both parent plants.

hydrochloric acid An acid secreted by the gastric glands of the stomach to aid in digestion.

hydrogen peroxide A reactive oxygen-containing compound that can form free radicals and cause oxidative damage. It can be eliminated by the selenium-containing enzyme glutathione peroxidase.

hydrogenation The process whereby hydrogen atoms are added to the carbon-carbon double bonds of unsaturated fatty acids, making them more saturated.

hydrolysis reaction A type of chemical reaction in which a large molecule is broken into two smaller molecules by the addition of water.

hydrolyzed protein See Protein hydrolysate.

hydroxyapatite A crystalline compound composed of calcium and phosphorus that is deposited in the protein matrix of bone to give it strength and rigidity.

hyperactivity Overactive, excitable, distractible behavior that is characteristic of attention deficit hyperactivity disorder.

hypercarotenemia A condition caused by an accumulation of carotenoids in the adipose tissue, causing the skin to appear yellow-orange.

hyperemesis gravidarum A severe and intractable form of nausea and vomiting that affects some women during pregnancy.

hypertension Blood pressure that is consistently elevated to 140/90 mm Hg or greater.

hypertensive disorders of pregnancy High blood pressure during pregnancy that is due to chronic hypertension, gestational hypertension, preeclampsia-eclampsia, or preeclampsia superimposed on chronic hypertension.

hypertrophy An increase in the size of a muscle or organ.

hypoglycemia A low blood glucose level, usually below 40 to 50 mg of glucose per 100 mL of blood.

hyponatremia Abnormally low concentration of sodium in the blood.

hypothalamus The region of the brain that monitors and regulates conditions and activities in the body, including food intake and energy expenditure.

hypothermia A condition in which body temperature drops below normal. Hypothermia depresses the central nervous system, resulting in the inability to shiver, sleepiness, and eventually coma.

hypothesis An educated guess made to explain an observation or to answer a question.

I

ileocecal valve The structure that separates the ileum of the small intestine from the large intestine.

ileum The 11-foot segment of the small intestine that connects the jejunum with the large intestine.

immunization An injection of a killed or inactivated organism into the body to stimulate the immune system to develop antibodies against the active disease-causing organism.

impaired glucose tolerance or **pre-diabetes** A fasting blood sugar level above the normal range but not high enough to be classified as diabetes (100–125 mg/dL).

implantation The process by which the developing embryo embeds in the uterine lining.

incomplete dietary protein Protein that is deficient in one or more essential amino acids relative to body needs.

indirect calorimetry A method of estimating energy use that compares the amount of oxygen consumed to the amount of carbon dioxide expired.

indirect food additives Substances that are expected to unintentionally enter foods during manufacturing or from packaging. They are regulated by the FDA.

infant mortality rate The number of deaths during the first year of life per 1000 live births.

inflammation A protective response to injury or destruction of tissues; signs of acute inflammation include pain, heat, redness, swelling and loss of function.

inorganic molecules Those containing no carbon hydrogen bonds.

inositol A compound that is often included in B vitamin supplements; functions as part of a phospholipid in the human brain but is not a dietary essential; also called myo-inositol.

insensible losses Fluid losses that are not perceived by the senses, such as evaporation of water through the skin and lungs.

insoluble fiber Fiber that, for the most part, does not dissolve in water and cannot be broken down by bacteria in the large intestine. It includes cellulose, some hemicelluloses, and lignin.

insulin A hormone made in the pancreas that allows the uptake of glucose by body cells and has other metabolic effects such as stimulating protein and fat synthesis and the synthesis of glycogen in liver and muscle.

insulin-dependent diabetes See Type 1 diabetes.

integrated pest management (IPM) A method of agricultural pest control that integrates nonchemical and chemical techniques.

intermediate-density lipoprotein (IDL) A lipoprotein produced by the removal of triglycerides from VLDLs, most of which are then transformed to LDLs.

International Unit (IU) A unit of measure that has been used to express requirements of some vitamins.

interstitial fluid The portion of the extracellular fluid located in the spaces between cells and tissues.

intervention study See Clinical trial.

intestinal microflora Microorganisms that inhabit the large intestine.

intracellular fluid The fluid located inside cells.

intrinsic factor A protein produced in the stomach that is needed for the absorption of adequate amounts of vitamin B_{12}.

ion An atom or group of atoms that carries an electrical charge.

iron deficiency anemia A condition that occurs when the oxygen-carrying capacity of the blood is decreased because there is insufficient iron to make hemoglobin. It is diagnosed clinically when red blood cells are small and pale and hemoglobin concentration is below normal.

irradiation A process, also called cold pasteurization, that exposes foods to radiation to kill contaminating organisms and retard ripening and spoilage of fruits and vegetables.

isoleucine An essential amino acid found in protein.

isomers Molecules with the same molecular formula but a different arrangement of the atoms.

isotopes Alternative forms of an element that have different atomic masses, which may or may not be radioactive.

J

jejunum The 8-foot-long section of the small intestine lying between the duodenum and the ileum.

juvenile-onset diabetes See Type 1 diabetes.

K

kcalories An abbreviation for kilocalories, the unit of heat that is used to express the amount of energy provided by food. The term *calorie* is commonly used to refer to kcalories.

keratin A hard protein that makes up hair and nails.

keratomalacia Softening and drying and ulceration of the cornea resulting from vitamin A deficiency.

Keshan disease A type of heart disease that occurs in areas of China where the soil is very low in selenium. It is believed to be caused by a combination of a viral infection and selenium deficiency.

ketoacidosis A life-threatening increase in the acidity of the blood due to high ketone levels.

ketones or **ketone bodies** Molecules formed in the liver when there is not sufficient carbohydrate to completely metabolize the 2-carbon units produced from fat breakdown.

ketosis High levels of ketones in the blood.

kilocalorie (kcalorie, kcal) The unit of heat that is used to express the amount of energy provided by foods. It is the amount of heat required to raise the temperature of 1 kilogram of water 1 degree Celsius (1 kcalorie = 4.18 kjoules).

kilojoule (kjoule, kJ) A unit of work that can be used to express energy intake and energy output. It is the amount of work required to move an object weighing 1 kilogram a distance of 1 meter under the force of gravity (4.18 kjoules = 1 kcalorie).

kinky hair disease An inherited defect in copper transport that results in copper deficiency. Symptoms include poor growth, neurological symptoms, and coarse, kinky, colorless, brittle hair. Also called Menkes disease.

kwashiorkor A form of protein-energy malnutrition in which only protein is deficient.

L

lactase An enzyme located in the brush border of the small intestine that breaks the disaccharide lactose into glucose and galactose.

lactate threshold or **anaerobic threshold** The exercise intensity at which the reliance on anaerobic metabolism results in the accumulation of lactic acid.

lactation Milk production and secretion.

lacteal Lymph vessel in the villi of the small intestine that transports the products of fat digestion.

lactic acid A compound produced from the breakdown of glucose in the absence of oxygen. It is also an additive used in food to maintain acidity or form curds.

lactitol The sugar alcohol formed from lactose.

lacto-ovo vegetarian One who eats no animal flesh but eats eggs and dairy products such as milk and cheese.

lactose A disaccharide that is formed by linking galactose and glucose. It is commonly known as milk sugar.

lactose intolerance The inability to digest lactose because of a reduction in the levels of the enzyme lactase. It causes symptoms including intestinal gas and bloating after dairy products are consumed.

lacto-vegetarian One who eats no animal flesh or eggs but eats dairy products.

large intestine The portion of the gastrointestinal tract that includes the colon and rectum; some water and vitamins are absorbed, and bacteria act on food residues here.

large-for-gestational-age An infant weighing greater than 4 kg (8.8 lb) at birth.

laxative A substance that eases the excretion of feces.

LDL receptor A protein on the surface of cells that binds to LDL particles and allows their contents to be taken up for use by the cell.

lean body mass Body mass attributed to nonfat body components such as bone, muscle, and internal organs. It is also called *fat-free mass*.

leavening agent A substance added to food that causes the production of gas, resulting in an increase in volume.

lecithin A phosphoglyceride composed of a glycerol backbone, two fatty acids, a phosphate group, and a molecule of choline.

legumes The starchy seeds of plants belonging to the pea family; includes peas, peanuts, beans, soybeans, and lentils.

leptin A protein hormone produced by adipocytes that signals information about the amount of body fat.

leptin receptors Proteins that bind the hormone leptin. In response to this binding, they trigger events that cause changes in food intake and energy expenditure.

let-down A hormonal reflex triggered by the infant's suckling that causes milk to be released from the milk glands and flow through the duct system to the nipple.

leucine An essential amino acid found in protein.

life expectancy The average length of life for a population of individuals.

life span The maximum age to which members of a species can live.

life-stage groups Groupings of individuals based on stages of growth and development, pregnancy, and lactation that have similar nutrient needs.

lignin An insoluble fiber responsible for the hard woody nature of plant stems.

limiting amino acid The essential amino acid that is available in the lowest concentration in relation to the body's needs.

linoleic acid An essential omega-6 essential fatty acid with 18 carbons and 2 double bonds.

lipases Fat-digesting enzymes.

lipid bilayer Two layers of phosphoglyceride molecules oriented so that the fat-soluble fatty acid tails are sandwiched between the water-soluble phosphate-containing heads.

lipids Organic molecules, most of which do not dissolve in water, that provide energy and insulation and serve as precursors in the synthesis of certain hormones; include fatty acids, glycerides, phospholipids, and sterols.

lipoic acid A coenzyme needed in the reaction that forms acetyl-CoA; not a dietary essential.

lipoprotein lipase An enzyme that breaks down triglycerides into fatty acids and glycerol; attached to the cell membranes of cells that line the blood vessels.

lipoproteins Particles containing a core of triglycerides and cholesterol surrounded by a shell of protein, phospholipids, and cholesterol that transport lipids in blood and lymph.

liposuction A procedure that suctions out adipose tissue from under the skin; used to decrease the size of local fat deposits such as on the abdomen or hips.

locust bean gum A branched polysaccharide that is produced from the endosperm of the seed of the carob plant; used as an additive to increase viscosity in cheese products and sausages.

longevity The duration of an individual's life.

longitudinal data Information obtained by repeatedly sampling the same individuals in a population over time.

low birth weight A birth weight less than 2.5 kg (5.5 lbs).

low-density lipoprotein (LDL) A lipoprotein that transports cholesterol to cells. Elevated LDL cholesterol increases the risk of cardiovascular disease.

low-density lipoprotein receptor A protein on the surface of cells that binds to LDL particles and allows their contents to be taken up for use by the cell.

lumen The inside cavity of a tube, such as the gastrointestinal tract.

lutein A carotenoid found in corn and green peppers that has no vitamin A activity but provides some protection against macular degeneration.

lycopene A carotenoid that gives the red color to tomatoes. It cannot be converted to vitamin A.

lymph vessel A tubular component of the lymphatic system that carries fluid away from body tissues. Lymph vessels in the intestine are known as lacteals and can transport large particles such as the products of fat digestion.

lymphatic system The system of vessels, organs, and tissues that drains excess fluid from the spaces between cells, transports fat-soluble substances from the digestive tract, and contributes to immune function.

lysosome A cellular organelle containing degradative enzymes.

lysozyme An enzyme in saliva, tears, and sweat that is capable of destroying certain types of bacteria.

M

macrocytes Larger-than-normal mature red blood cells that have a shortened life span.

macronutrients Nutrients needed by the body in large amounts. These include water and the energy-yielding nutrients carbohydrates, lipids, and proteins.

macular degeneration An incurable eye disorder that is caused by deterioration of the retina of the eye. It is the leading cause of blindness in adults over the age of 55 years.

mad cow disease The common name for bovine spongiform encephalopathy, a cattle disease that causes the brain to degenerate.

major minerals Minerals needed in the diet in amounts greater than 100 mg per day or present in the body in amounts greater than 0.01% of body weight.

malignancy A mass of cells showing uncontrolled growth, a tendency to invade and damage surrounding tissues, and an ability to seed daughter growths to sites remote from the original growth.

malnutrition Any condition resulting from an energy or nutrient intake either above or below that which is optimal.

maltase An enzyme found in the brush border of the small intestine that breaks maltose into two molecules of glucose.

maltose A disaccharide made up of 2 molecules of glucose. It is formed in the intestines during starch digestion.

mannitol The sugar alcohol formed from the sugar mannose.

marasmus A form of protein-energy malnutrition in which a deficiency of energy in the diet causes severe body wasting.

maturity-onset diabetes See Type 2 diabetes.

maximal oxygen consumption or **VO$_2$ max** The maximum amount of oxygen that can be consumed by the tissues during exercise. Also called aerobic capacity.

maximum heart rate The maximum number of beats per minute that the heart can attain. It declines with age and can be estimated by subtracting age in years from 220.

megaloblastic or **macrocytic anemia** A condition in which there are abnormally large immature and mature red blood cells in the bloodstream and a reduction in the total number of red blood cells and the oxygen-carrying capacity of the blood.

megaloblasts Large, immature red blood cells that are formed when developing red blood cells are unable to divide normally.

melatonin A hormone involved in regulating the body's cycles of sleep and wakefulness. Levels decline with age. Supplements are claimed to boost antioxidant defenses, improve immune function, and slow aging.

menaquinones The forms of vitamin K synthesized by bacteria and found in animals.

menarche The onset of menstruation, which occurs normally between the ages of 10 and 15 years.

Menkes disease An inherited defect in copper transport that results in copper deficiency. Symptoms include poor growth, neurological symptoms, and coarse, kinky, colorless, brittle hair. Also called kinky hair disease.

menopause The physiological changes that mark the end of a woman's capacity to bear children.

menstruation The cyclic discharge of the uterine lining that, in the absence of pregnancy, occurs about every four weeks during the reproductive years of female humans.

metabolic pathway A series of chemical reactions inside of a living organism that results in the transformation of one molecule into another.

metabolic syndrome A collection of health risks, including excess fat in the abdominal region, high blood pressure, elevated blood triglycerides, low high-density lipoprotein (HDL) cholesterol, and high blood glucose that increases the chance of developing heart disease, stroke, and diabetes. The condition is also known by other names including Syndrome X, insulin resistance syndrome, and dysmetabolic syndrome.

metabolism The sum of all the chemical reactions that take place in a living organism.

metallothionein Refers to proteins that bind minerals. One such protein binds zinc and copper in intestinal cells limiting their absorption into the blood.

methionine An essential sulfur-containing amino acid found in protein.

methyl group A chemical group consisting of a carbon atom bound to three hydrogen atoms.

micelles Particles formed in the small intestine when the products of fat digestion are surrounded by bile acids. They facilitate the absorption of fat.

microbe An organism too small to be seen without a microscope; also called a microorganism.

microflora See Intestinal microflora.

micronutrients Nutrients needed by the body in small amounts. These include vitamins and minerals.

microorganism An organism such as a bacterium, too small to be seen without a microscope.

microsomal ethanol oxidizing system (MEOS) A liver enzyme system located in microsomes that converts alcohol to acetaldehyde. Activity increase with increases in alcohol consumption.

microvilli or **brush border** Minute brush-like projections on the mucosal cell membrane that increase the absorptive surface area in the small intestine.

minerals In nutrition, elements needed by the body in small amounts for structure and to regulate chemical reactions and body processes.

miscarriage or **spontaneous abortion** Interruption of pregnancy prior to the seventh month.

mitochondrion (mitochondria) The cellular organelle that is responsible for producing ATP via aerobic metabolism; the citric acid cycle and electron transport chain are located here.

modified atmosphere packaging (MAP) A type of food packaging in which the gases inside the package control or retard chemical, physical, and microbiological changes.

modified starch or **modified food starch** Starch that has been treated to enhance its ability to thicken or form a gel.

mold Multicellular fungi that form a filamentous branching growth.

molecular biology The study of cellular function at the molecular level.

molecules Units of two or more atoms of the same or different elements bonded together.

monoacylglycerol or **monoglyceride** A molecule of glycerol with one fatty acid attached.

monosaccharide A single sugar unit, such as glucose.

monosodium glutamate (MSG) An additive used as a flavor enhancer, commonly used in Chinese food; made up of the amino acid glutamate bound to sodium.

monounsaturated fatty acid A fatty acid containing one carbon-carbon double bond.

morbid obesity A body mass index greater than 40 kg/m^2.

morbidity The incidence or state of disease or disability.

morning sickness Nausea and vomiting that affects many women during the first few months of pregnancy and in some women can continue throughout the pregnancy.

mRNA (messenger RNA) A molecule that carries the information in a gene to ribosomes in the cytosol so polypeptides can be synthesized.

MSG symptom complex Symptoms of headache, flushing, tingling, burning sensations, and chest pain reported by some individuals after consuming monosodium glutamate (MSG); commonly referred to as Chinese restaurant syndrome.

mucosa The layer of tissue lining the GI tract and other body cavities.

mucus A viscous fluid secreted by glands in the gastrointestinal tract and other parts of the body. It acts to lubricate, moisten, and protect cells from harsh environments.

mutagen Any agent that causes a change in a cell's genetic material.

mutations Changes in DNA caused by chemical or physical agents.

myelin A soft, white fatty substance that covers nerve fibers and aids in nerve transmission.

myocardial infarction Heart attack.

myoglobin An iron-containing protein in muscle cells that binds oxygen.

myo-inositol See Inositol.

N

National Health and Nutrition Examination Survey (NHANES) An ongoing set of surveys designed to monitor the overall nutritional status of the U.S. population; combines food consumption information with medical histories, physical examinations, and laboratory measurements.

National Organic Program A USDA program that provides guidelines and certification for organic food production.

nephron The functional unit of the kidney which performs the job of filtering the blood and maintaining fluid balance.

nervous system A system of nerve cells organized in message sending, message receiving, and information processing pathways.

net protein utilization A measure of protein quality determined by comparing the amount of nitrogen retained in the body with the amount eaten in the diet.

neural tube The portion of the embryo that develops into the brain and spinal cord.

neural tube closure A developmental event in which neural tissue forms a groove and the sides fold together to form a tube; is completed about 28 days after fertilization.

neural tube defect A defect in the formation of the neural tube that occurs early in development and results in defects of the brain and spinal cord such as anencephaly and spina bifida.

neurotransmitter A chemical substance produced by a nerve cell that can stimulate or inhibit another cell.

niacin equivalent (NE) A unit used to express the amount of niacin present in food including that which can be made from its precursor, tryptophan. One NE is equal to 1 mg of niacin or 60 mg of tryptophan.

nicotinamide A form of niacin.

nicotinamide adenine dinucleotide (NAD) and nicotinamide adenine dinucleotide phosphate (NADP) The active coenzyme forms of niacin that are able to pick up and donate hydrogens and electrons. They are important in the transfer of electrons to oxygen in (cellular) respiration and in many synthetic reactions.

nicotinic acid A form of niacin.

night blindness The inability of the eye to adapt to reduced light causing poor vision in dim light.

nitrogen balance The amount of nitrogen consumed in the diet compared with the amount excreted by the body over a given period.

nitrosamines Carcinogenic compounds produced by reactions between nitrites and amino acids.

nonessential or **dispensable amino acids** Amino acids that can be synthesized by the human body in sufficient amounts to meet needs.

nonexercise activity thermogenesis (NEAT) The energy expended for everything we do other than sleeping, eating, or sports-like exercise.

nonheme iron A poorly absorbed form of iron found in both plant and animal foods that is not part of the iron complex found in hemoglobin and myoglobin.

noninsulin-dependent diabetes See Type 2 diabetes.

nucleus The central core of an atom, consisting of positively charged protons and electrically neutral neutrons. In cells, it is an organelle containing DNA.

nursing bottle syndrome Extreme tooth decay in the upper teeth resulting from putting a child to bed with a bottle containing milk or other sweet liquids.

nutrient density An evaluation of the nutrient content of a food in comparison to the kcalories it provides.

nutrients Chemical substances in foods that provide energy and structure and help regulate body processes.

nutrition A science that studies the interactions that occur between living organisms and food.

nutrition transition The shift in dietary pattern that occurs as incomes increase—from a diet high in complex carbohydrates and fiber to a more varied diet adequate in protein and micronutrients but higher in fat, saturated fat, and sugar.

nutritional assessment The process of determining the nutritional status of individuals or groups for the purpose of identifying nutritional needs and planning personal healthcare or community programs to meet those needs.

nutritional genomics or **nutrigenomics** The study of how diet affects our genes and how individual genetic variation can affect the impact of nutrients or other food components on health.

nutritional status State of health as it is influenced by the intake and utilization of nutrients.

O

obese A condition characterized by excess body fat. It is defined as a body mass index of 30 kg/m² or greater.

obesity genes Genes that code for proteins involved in the regulation of food intake, energy expenditure, or the deposition of body fat. When they are abnormal, the result is abnormal amounts of body fat.

oil A lipid that is liquid at room temperature.

oleic acid A monounsaturated fatty acid with 18 carbons.

Olestra (sucrose polyester) An artificial fat made of sucrose with fatty acids linked to it. It cannot be digested or absorbed. It has been approved by the FDA for use in certain snack foods.

oligosaccharides Short chain carbohydrates containing 3 to 10 sugar units.

omega-3 (ω-3) fatty acid A fatty acid containing a carbon-carbon double bond between the third and fourth carbons from the omega end; includes alpha-linolenic acid found in vegetable oils and eicosapentaenoic acid (EPA) and docosahexaenoic acid (DHA) found in fish oils.

omega-6 (ω-6) fatty acid A fatty acid containing a carbon-carbon double bond between the sixth and seventh carbons from the omega end; includes linoleic and arachidonic acid.

opsin A protein in the retina of the eye involved in the visual cycle.

organ A discrete structure composed of more than one tissue that performs a specialized function.

organ system A group of cooperative organs.

organelles Cellular organs that carry out specific metabolic functions.

organic food Food produced without the use of synthetic fertilizers or pesticides, sewage sludge, irradiation, or genetically modified ingredients according to the production and handling standards of the USDA's National Organic Program.

organic molecules Those containing carbon hydrogen bonds.

osmosis The passive movement of water across a semipermeable membrane in a direction that will equalize the concentration of dissolved substances on both sides.

osteoarthritis The form of arthritis common in the elderly that is characterized by a wearing down of the joint surfaces and pain when the joint is moved.

osteoblasts Cells responsible for the deposition of bone.

osteoclasts Large cells responsible for bone breakdown.

osteomalacia A vitamin D deficiency disease in adults characterized by a loss of minerals from bones. It causes bone pain, muscle aches, and an increase in bone fractures.

osteoporosis A bone disorder characterized by a decrease in bone mass, an increase in bone fragility, and an increased risk of fractures.

overload principle The concept that the body will adapt to the stresses placed on it.

overnutrition Poor nutritional status resulting from an energy or nutrient intake in excess of that which is optimal for health.

overtraining syndrome A collection of emotional, behavioral, and physical symptoms that occurs when training without sufficient rest persists for weeks to months.

overweight Being too heavy for one's height. It is defined as having a body mass index (a ratio of weight to height squared) of 25 to 29.9 kg/m².

oviduct See Fallopian tubes.

ovum The female reproductive cell.

oxalates Organic acids found in spinach and other leafy green vegetables that can bind certain minerals and decrease their absorption.

oxaloacetate A 4-carbon compound derived from carbohydrate that combines with acetyl-CoA in the first step of the citric acid cycle.

oxidation The loss of electrons.

oxidative damage Damage caused by highly reactive oxygen molecules that steal electrons from other compounds, causing changes in structure and function.

oxidative stress A condition that occurs when there are more reactive oxygen molecules than can be neutralized by available antioxidant defenses. It occurs either because excessive amounts of reactive oxygen molecules are generated or because antioxidant defenses are deficient.

oxidized LDL cholesterol A substance formed when the cholesterol in LDL particles is oxidized by reactive oxygen molecules. It is key in the development of atherosclerosis because it contributes to the inflammatory process.

oxidized Refers to a compound that has lost an electron or undergone a chemical reaction with oxygen.

oxytocin A hormone produced by the posterior pituitary gland that acts on the uterus to cause uterine contractions and on the breast to cause the movement of milk into the secretory ducts that lead to the nipple.

P

PA (Physical Activity) Value A numeric value associated with activity level that is a variable in the EER equations used to calculate energy needs.

palmitic acid A saturated fatty acid containing 16 carbons.

pancreas An organ that secretes digestive enzymes and bicarbonate ions into the small intestine during digestion. It also secretes the hormones insulin and glucagon into the blood.

pancreatic amylase A starch-digesting enzyme found in pancreatic juice.

pancreatic juice The secretion of the pancreas containing bicarbonate to neutralize acid and enzymes for the digestion of carbohydrates, fats, and proteins.

papain A protein-digesting enzyme found in papaya.

para-aminobenzoic acid (PABA) A chemical that is part of the folic acid molecule but that alone has no vitamin activity and cannot be used by the body to synthesize folic acid; effective at blocking ultraviolet (UV) light and thus is used in topical sunscreens.

parasites Organisms that live at the expense of others without contributing to the survival of the host.

parathyroid hormone (PTH) A hormone released by the parathyroid gland that acts to increase blood calcium levels.

parietal cells Cells in the stomach lining that make hydrochloric acid and intrinsic factor in response to nervous or hormonal stimulation.

partially hydrogenated vegetable oil Vegetable oil that has been modified by hydrogenation to decrease the number of unsaturated bonds, therefore raising the melting point and improving the storage characteristics.

pasteurization The process of heating food products to kill disease-causing organisms.

pathogen A biological agent that causes disease.

peak bone mass The maximum bone density attained at any time in life, usually occurring in young adulthood.

pectin A soluble fiber found in plant cell walls that forms a gel when mixed with acid and sugar.

peer review Review of the design and validity of a research experiment by experts in the field of study who did not participate in the research.

pellagra A niacin deficiency disease that is characterized by dermatitis, dementia, diarrhea, and, ultimately, death.

pepsin A protein-digesting enzyme produced by the gastric glands. It is secreted in the gastric juice in an inactive form and activated by acid in the stomach.

pepsinogen An inactive protein-digesting enzyme produced by gastric glands and activated to pepsin by acid in the stomach.

peptic ulcer An open sore in the lining of the stomach, esophagus, or small intestine.

peptide Two or more amino acids joined by peptide bonds.

peptide bond A chemical linkage between the amino group of one amino acid and the acid group of another.

peptide PYY An appetite-suppressing peptide hormone that is released from the gastrointestinal tract after a meal.

periodontal disease A degeneration of the area surrounding the teeth, specifically the gum and supporting bone.

peristalsis Coordinated muscular contractions that move food through the gastrointestinal tract.

pernicious anemia An anemia resulting from vitamin B_{12} deficiency that occurs when dietary vitamin B_{12} cannot be absorbed due to a lack of intrinsic factor. If not treated with vitamin B_{12} injections or large oral doses, the condition will result in nerve damage.

peroxide A reactive chemical that can form free radicals and cause cellular damage.

pesticide A substance used to prevent or decrease damage to plants from insects and microorganisms.

pH A measure of the level of acidity or alkalinity of a solution.

pharynx A funnel-shaped opening that connects the nasal passages and mouth to the respiratory passages and esophagus. It is a common passageway for food and air and is responsible for swallowing.

phenylalanine An essential amino acid found in protein that cannot be metabolized by individuals with phenylketonuria (PKU).

phenylketone The product of phenylalanine breakdown produced when phenylalanine cannot be converted to tyrosine; when blood levels get too high, brain damage may result.

phenylketonuria (PKU) An inherited disease in which the body cannot metabolize the amino acid phenylalanine. If the disease is untreated, toxic by-products called *phenylketones* accumulate in the blood and cause brain damage.

phosphate group A chemical group consisting of one phosphorus atom and four oxygen atoms.

phosphoglyceride A phospholipid composed of a glycerol backbone with two fatty acids and a phosphate group

attached; mixes well with both watery and oily substances and is an important component of cell membranes.

phospholipids Types of lipids containing phosphorous. The most common are the phosphoglycerides, which are composed of a glycerol backbone with two fatty acids and a phosphate group attached.

photosynthesis The metabolic process by which plants trap energy from the sun and use it to make sugars from carbon dioxide and water.

phylloquinone The form of vitamin K found in plants.

physical frailty Impairment in function and reduction in physiological reserves severe enough to cause limitations in the basic activities of daily living.

phytic acid or **phytate** A phosphorus-containing storage compound found in seeds and grains that can bind minerals and decrease their absorption.

phytochemicals Substances found in plant foods (*phyto* means plant) that are not essential nutrients but may have health-promoting properties.

phytoestrogen An estrogen-like molecule produced by plants.

phytosterol Compound produced by plants that has a structure similar to cholesterol.

pica An abnormal craving for and ingestion of unusual food and nonfood substances.

placebo A fake medicine or supplement that is indistinguishable in appearance from the real thing. It is used to disguise the control and experimental groups in an experiment.

placenta An organ produced from both maternal and embryonic tissues. It secretes hormones, transfers nutrients and oxygen from the mother's blood to the fetus, and removes wastes.

plant sterols and **stanols** Compounds found in plant cell membranes that resemble cholesterol in structure. They can lower blood cholesterol by competing with cholesterol for absorption in the gastrointestinal tract.

plaque The cholesterol-rich material that is deposited in the blood vessels of individuals with atherosclerosis. It consists of cholesterol, smooth muscle cells, fibrous tissue and, eventually, calcium. Also refers to deposits on the teeth composed of mucus and bacteria that contribute to dental caries.

plasma The liquid portion of the blood that remains when the blood cells are removed.

plasmid A loop of bacterial DNA that is independent of the bacterial chromosome.

platelet A cell fragment found in blood that is involved in blood clotting.

polar Having a positive charge at one end and a negative charge at the other.

polychlorinated biphenyls (PCBs) Carcinogenic industrial compounds that have found their way into the environment and, subsequently, the food supply. Repeated ingestion causes them to accumulate in biological tissues over time.

polycyclic aromatic hydrocarbons (PAHs) A class of mutagenic substances produced during cooking when there is incomplete combustion of organic materials—such as when fat drips on a grill.

polypeptide A chain of three or more amino acids joined together by peptide bonds.

polysaccharides Carbohydrates containing many sugar units linked together.

polyunsaturated fatty acid A fatty acid that contains two or more carbon-carbon double bonds.

postmenopausal bone loss The accelerated bone loss that occurs in women for about 5 years after estrogen production decreases.

prebiotics Substances that pass undigested into the colon and stimulate the growth and/or activity of certain types of bacteria.

precursor Inactive form of a substance that can be converted into the active form.

pre-diabetes or **impaired glucose tolerance** A fasting blood glucose level above the normal range but not high enough to be classified as diabetes (100–125 mg/dl).

preeclampsia A hypertensive disorder of pregnancy characterized by an increase in body weight, elevated blood pressure, protein in the urine, and edema. It can progress to *eclampsia*, which can be life-threatening to mother and fetus.

pregnancy-induced hypertension See hypertensive disorders of pregnancy

premature or **preterm infant** An infant born before 37 weeks of gestation.

premenstrual syndrome (PMS) A syndrome of mood swings, food cravings, bloating, tension and depression, headaches, acne, and anxiety, among other symptoms, that results from the hormonal changes during the days prior to menstruation.

preservative A compound that prevents spoilage and extends the shelf life of a product by retarding chemical, physical, or microbiological changes.

preterm or **premature** An infant born before 37 weeks of gestation.

prion A pathogenic protein that is the cause of degenerative brain diseases called spongiform encephalopathies. *Prion* is short for *proteinaceous infectious particle*.

prior-sanctioned substances Refers to substances that the FDA or the U.S. Department of Agriculture (USDA) had determined were safe for use in a specific food prior to the 1958 Food Additives Amendment.

probiotics Products that contain live bacteria, which when consumed live temporarily in the colon and confer health benefits on the host.

processed foods Foods that have been specially treated or changed from their natural state.

progesterone A female sex hormone needed for development and function of the uterus and mammary glands.

programmed cell death The death of cells at specific predictable times.

prolactin A hormone released by the anterior pituitary that acts on the milk-producing glands in the breast to stimulate and sustain milk production.

pro-oxidant A substance that promotes oxidative damage.

protein An organic molecule made up of one or more intertwining chains of amino acids.

protein complementation The process of combining proteins from different sources so that they collectively provide the proportions of amino acids required to meet needs.

protein digestibility-corrected amino acid score (PDCAAS) A measure of protein quality that reflects a protein's digestibility as well as the proportions of amino acids it provides.

protein efficiency ratio A measure of protein quality determined by comparing the weight gain of a laboratory animal fed a test protein with the weight gain of an animal fed a reference protein.

protein hydrolysate or **hydrolyzed protein** A mixture of amino acids or amino acids and polypeptides that results when a protein is completely or partially broken down by treatment with acid or enzymes.

protein quality A measure of how efficiently a protein in the diet can be used to make body proteins.

protein turnover The continuous synthesis and breakdown of body proteins.

protein-energy malnutrition (PEM) A condition characterized by wasting and an increased susceptibility to infection that results from the long-term consumption of insufficient amounts of energy and protein to meet needs.

protein-sparing modified fast A very-low-kcalorie diet with a high proportion of protein designed to maximize the loss of fat and minimize the loss of protein from the body.

prothrombin A blood protein required for blood clotting.

provitamin or **vitamin precursor** A compound that can be converted into the active form of a vitamin in the body.

psyllium A plant product high in soluble fiber that is used in over-the-counter bulk-forming laxatives.

puberty A period of rapid growth and physical changes that ends in the attainment of sexual maturity.

purging Behaviors such as self-induced vomiting and misuse of laxatives, diuretics, or enemas to rid the body of kcalories.

pyloric sphincter A muscular valve that helps regulate the rate at which food leaves the stomach and enters the small intestine.

pyridoxal phosphate The major coenzyme form of vitamin B_6 that functions in more than 100 enzymatic reactions, many of which involve amino acid metabolism.

pyridoxamine A form of vitamin B_6.

pyridoxine A form of vitamin B_6; a general name used to refer to vitamin B_6, including pyridoxal, pyridoxine, and pyridoxamine.

pyruvate A 3-carbon molecule produced when glucose is broken down by glycolysis.

Q

qualified health claims Health claims on food labels that have been approved based on emerging but not well-established evidence for a relationship between a food, food component, or dietary supplement and reduced risk of a disease or health-related condition.

R

raffinose An oligosaccharide found in beans and other legumes that cannot be digested by human enzymes in the stomach and small intestine.

reactive hypoglycemia Low blood sugar that occurs an hour or so after the consumption of high-carbohydrate foods; results from an overproduction of insulin.

recombinant DNA DNA that is produced by joining DNA from different sources to create a unique combination of genes.

Recommended Dietary Allowances (RDAs) Intakes that are sufficient to meet the nutrient needs of almost all healthy people in a specific life-stage and gender group.

rectum The portion of the large intestine that connects the colon and anus.

reduced Refers to a substance that has gained an electron.

Reference Daily Intakes (RDIs) Reference values established for vitamins and minerals that are based on the highest amount of each nutrient recommended for any adult age group by the 1968 RDAs.

refined Refers to foods that have undergone processes that change or remove various components of the original food.

renewable resources Resources that are restored and replaced by natural processes and that can therefore be used forever.

renin An enzyme produced by the kidneys that aids in the conversion of angiotensin to its active form, angiotensin II.

reserve capacity The amount of functional capacity that an organ has above and beyond what is needed to sustain life.

resistant starch Starch that escapes digestion in the small intestine of healthy people.

respiratory system Organ system that includes the lungs and air passageways involved in the exchange of oxygen from the environment with carbon dioxide waste from cells by way of the bloodstream.

resting energy expenditure (REE) Energy expenditure at rest. It is measured after 5 or 6 hours without food or exercise.

resting heart rate The number of times that the heart beats per minute while a person is at rest.

resting metabolic rate (RMR) An estimate of basal metabolic rate that is determined by measuring energy utilization after 5 to 6 hours without food or exercise.

restriction enzyme A bacterial enzyme used in genetic engineering that has the ability to cut DNA in a specific location.

Retin-A A drug that is a vitamin A derivative used topically to treat acne.

retinal The aldehyde form of vitamin A, which is needed for the visual cycle.

retinoic acid The acid form of vitamin A, which is needed for cell differentiation, growth, and reproduction.

retinoids The chemical forms of preformed vitamin A: retinol, retinal, and retinoic acid.

retinol activity equivalent (RAE) The amount of retinol, β-carotene, α-carotene, or β-cryptoxanthin that provides vitamin A activity equal to 1 μg of retinol.

retinol The alcohol form of vitamin A, which can be interconverted with retinal.

retinol-binding protein A protein that is necessary to transport vitamin A from the liver to other tissues.

rhodopsin A light-sensitive compound found in the retina of the eye that is composed of the protein opsin loosely bound to retinal.

ribose The 5-carbon sugar that is part of RNA.

ribosome The cell organelle where protein synthesis occurs.

rickets A vitamin D deficiency disease in children that is characterized by poor bone development because of inadequate calcium absorption.

risk factor A characteristic or circumstance that is associated with the occurrence of a particular disease.

risk-benefit analysis The process of weighing the risk of a substance against the benefits it provides; if the risk is small and the benefits great, small amounts of this substance may be acceptable.

RNA (ribonucleic acid) A single-stranded nucleic acid. It carries information in DNA from the nucleus to the cytosol, is a component of ribosomes, and delivers amino acids for protein synthesis.

s

saccharin An alternative sweetener that contains no energy and is about 300 times sweeter than sugar.

saliva A watery fluid produced and secreted into the mouth by the salivary glands. It contains lubricants, enzymes, and other substances.

salivary amylase An enzyme secreted by the salivary glands that breaks down starch.

salivary glands The internal structures located at the sides of and below the face and in front of the ears; secrete saliva into the mouth.

Salmonella A bacterium that commonly causes food-borne illness.

sarcopenia Progressive decrease in skeletal muscle mass and strength that occurs with age.

satiety The feeling of fullness and satisfaction, caused by food consumption, that eliminates the desire to eat.

saturated fatty acid A fatty acid in which the carbon atoms are bound to as many hydrogen atoms as possible and which therefore contains no carbon-carbon double bonds.

scavenger receptors Proteins on the surface of macrophages that bind to oxidized LDL cholesterol and allow it to be taken up by the cell.

scientific method The general approach of science that is used to explain observations about the world around us.

scurvy The vitamin C deficiency disease.

secondary lactose intolerance Lactase deficiency that occurs as a result of disease and may resolve after the disease has ended.

secretin A hormone released by the duodenum that signals the pancreas to secrete bicarbonate ions and stimulates the liver to secrete bile into the gallbladder.

segmentation Rhythmic local constrictions of the intestine that mix food with digestive juices and speed absorption by repeatedly moving the food mass over the intestinal wall.

selective breeding Techniques to selectively control mating in plants and animals for the purpose of producing organisms that better serve human needs.

selectively permeable Describes a membrane or barrier that will allow some substances to pass freely but will restrict the passage of others.

selenoproteins Proteins that contain selenium as a structural component of their amino acids. Selenium is most often found as selenocysteine, which contains an atom of selenium in place of the sulfur atom.

self-esteem The general attitude of approval or disapproval that people make and maintain about themselves.

semiessential amino acid See Conditionally essential amino acid.

semivegetarian One who avoids only certain types of meat, fish, or poultry; e.g., an individual who avoids all red meat but continues to consume poultry and fish.

serotonin A neurotransmitter that functions in the sleep center of the brain.

set point A level at which body fat or body weight seems to resist change despite changes in energy intake or output.

set point theory The theory that when people finish growing, they have a stable weight range, known as their set-point. Weight will tend to return to this set point despite periodic changes in energy intake or output.

sickle cell anemia An inherited disease in which hemoglobin structure is altered. Red blood cells containing the altered hemoglobin are sickle-shaped; rupture easily, causing anemia; and block small blood vessels, causing inflammation and pain.

significant scientific agreement Refers to a means of authorizing health claims on food labels that involves extensive review of the scientific evidence.

simple carbohydrates Carbohydrates known as sugars that include monosaccharides and disaccharides.

simple diffusion The movement of substances from an area of higher concentration to an area of lower concentration. No energy is required.

simple sugar See Simple carbohydrates.

Simplesse An artificial fat made from egg and milk proteins that provides about 1.3 kcalories per gram.

single-blind study An experiment in which either the study participants or the researchers are unaware of who is in a control or an experimental group.

skinfold thickness A measurement of subcutaneous fat used to estimate total body fat.

small intestine A tube-shaped organ of the digestive tract where digestion of ingested food is completed and most of the absorption occurs.

small-for-gestational-age An infant born at term weighing less than 2.5 kg (5.5 lbs).

smooth muscle Involuntary muscles that cause constriction of the gastrointestinal tract, blood vessels, and glands.

sodium bicarbonate A compound that is part of an important buffer system in pancreatic juice and in the bloodstream.

sodium caseinate A form of the milk protein casein that is frequently used as a food additive.

sodium-potassium ATPase An energy-requiring protein pump in the cell membrane that pumps sodium out of the cell and potassium into the cell.

soluble fiber Fiber that dissolves in water or absorbs water to form viscous solutions and can be broken down by the intestinal microflora. It includes pectins, gums, and some hemicelluloses.

solutes Dissolved substances.

solution A solvent containing a dissolved substance.

solvent A fluid in which one or more substances dissolve.

sorbitol A sugar alcohol formed from the sugar sorbose; used as a sweetener or humectant in food.

sperm The male reproductive cell.

sphincter A muscular valve that helps control the flow of materials in the gastrointestinal tract.

spina bifida A birth defect resulting from the incorrect development of the spinal cord that can leave the spinal cord exposed.

spontaneous abortion or **miscarriage** Interruption of pregnancy prior to the seventh month.

spore A dormant state of some bacteria that is resistant to heat but can germinate and produce a new organism when environmental conditions are favorable.

sports anemia A temporary decrease in hemoglobin concentration that occurs during exercise training. It occurs as an adaptation to training in which expanded plasma volume dilutes red blood cells, but it does not impair delivery of oxygen to tissues.

stabilizer A substance added to food to stabilize its consistency.

standards of identity Regulations that define the allowable ingredients, composition, and other characteristics of foods.

Staphylococcus A bacterium, commonly found in the nasal passages, that can contaminate food and cause food-borne illness.

starch A carbohydrate made of many glucose molecules linked in straight or branching chains. The bonds that hold the glucose molecules together can be broken by human digestive enzymes.

starchyose An oligosaccharide found in beans and other legumes that cannot be digested by human enzymes in the stomach and small intestine.

starvation The condition that occurs when insufficient food is ingested to maintain health.

stearic acid An 18-carbon saturated fatty acid that, unlike other saturated fats, does not raise blood cholesterol levels.

steroid hormone A hormone that is made from cholesterol; includes the male and female sex hormones.

sterol A type of lipid with a structure composed of multiple chemical rings.

stomach A muscular pouchlike organ of the digestive tract that mixes food and secretes gastric juice into the lumen and the hormone gastrin into the blood.

stroke A blood clot or bleeding in the brain that causes brain tissue death.

stroke volume The volume of blood pumped by each beat of the heart.

structure/function claims Claims on food and supplement labels that describe the role of a nutrient or dietary ingredient in maintaining normal structure or function in humans.

stunting A decrease in linear growth rate, which is an indicator of the nutritional well-being in populations of children.

subcutaneous fat Adipose tissue located under the skin which is not associated with a great increase in the risk of chronic diseases.

subscapular The region just below the shoulder blade that is a common location for measuring skinfold thickness.

subsistence crops Crops grown as food for the local population.

sucralose An alternative sweetener made from sucrose that is about 600 times sweeter than sucrose; trichlorogalactosucrose. It is heat stable, and so can be used in baked products.

sucrase An enzyme in the brush border of the small intestine that breaks sucrose into glucose and fructose.

sucrose A disaccharide that is formed by linking fructose and glucose. It is commonly known as table sugar or white sugar.

sudden infant death syndrome (SIDS) or **crib death** The unexplained death of an infant, usually during sleep.

sugar alcohols Sweeteners that are structurally related to sugars but provide less energy than monosaccharides and disaccharides because they are not well absorbed.

sulfites Sulfur-containing compounds used as preservatives to prevent oxidation in dried fruits and vegetables and to prevent bacterial growth in wine.

superoxide dismutase (SOD) An enzyme that protects the cell from oxidative damage by neutralizing superoxide free radicals. One form of the enzyme requires zinc and copper for activity, and another form requires manganese.

superoxide radical A type of reactive oxygen molecule that can form free radicals leading to oxidative damage. They can be neutralized by the enzyme superoxide dismutase.

sustainable agriculture Environmentally friendly methods of farming that allow the production of crops or live-stock without damage to soil, water, biodiversity, or other natural resources.

T

tannins Substances found in tea and some grains that can bind certain minerals and decrease their absorption.

taurine An amino acid found only in animal foods that is not used in protein synthesis but is necessary for nerve function and vision and the synthesis of bile acids; made in the adult human in sufficient quantities but may be essential in premature infants.

teratogen A chemical, biological, or physical agent that causes birth defects.

testosterone A steroid hormone secreted by the testes that is involved in the maintenance and development of male sex organs and secondary sex characteristics.

texturizer A substance added to food to change its texture.

theory An explanation based on scientific study and reasoning.

thermic effect of food (TEF) or **diet-induced thermogenesis** The energy required for the digestion of food and the absorption, metabolism, and storage of nutrients. It is equal to approximately 10% of daily energy intake.

thiamin pyrophosphate The active coenzyme form of thiamin. It is the predominant form found inside cells, where it aids reactions in which a carbon-containing group is lost as CO_2.

threshold effect A reaction that occurs at a certain level of ingestion and increases as the dose increases. Below that level there is no reaction.

thyroid gland A gland located in the neck that produces thyroid hormones and calcitonin.

thyroid hormones Hormones produced by the thyroid gland that regulate metabolic rate.

thyroid stimulating hormone A hormone that stimulates the synthesis and secretion of thyroid hormones from the thyroid gland.

tocopherol The chemical name for vitamin E.

Tolerable Upper Intake Levels (ULs) Maximum daily intakes that are unlikely to pose a risks of adverse health effects to almost all individuals in the specified life-stage and gender group.

tolerances The maximum amount of pesticide residues that may legally remain in food, set by the EPA.

total energy expenditure (TEE) The sum of basal energy expenditure, the thermic effect of food, and the energy used in physical activity, regulation of body temperature, deposition of new tissue, and production of milk.

total fiber The sum of dietary fiber and functional fiber.

total parenteral nutrition (TPN) A method of providing complete nutrition without use of the gastrointestinal tract by infusing a nutrient-rich solution directly into the bloodstream.

toxic The capacity to produce injury at some level of intake.

toxin A substance with the ability to cause harm at some level of exposure; also called toxicant.

trabecular or **spongy bone** The type of bone that forms the inner spongy lattice that lines the bone marrow cavity and supports the cortical shell.

trace elements or **trace minerals** Minerals required in the diet in amounts of 100 mg or less per day or present in the body in amounts of 0.01% of body weight or less.

***trans* fatty acid** An unsaturated fatty acid in which the hydrogen atoms are on opposite sides of the double bond.

transamination The process by which an amino group from one amino acid is transferred to a carbon compound to form a new amino acid.

transcription The process of copying the information in DNA to a molecule of mRNA.

transferrin An iron transport protein in the blood.

transferrin receptor Protein found in cell membranes that binds to the iron-transferrin complex and allows it to be taken up by cells.

transit time The time between the ingestion of food and the elimination of the solid waste from that food.

translation The process of translating the mRNA code into the amino acid sequence of a polypeptide chain.

treatment groups See Experimental groups.

triacylglycerol See Triglyceride.

triceps Region at the back of the upper arm that is a common site for measuring skin-fold thickness.

trichinosis The disease caused by infection with the roundworm *Trichinella spiralis* after eating undercooked contaminated pork or game meats; the juvenile form of this roundworm migrates to the muscles and causes flu-like symptoms and muscle pain and weakness.

triglyceride (Triacylglycerol) The major form of lipid in food and in the body; consisting of three fatty acids attached to a glycerol molecule.

trimester A term used to describe each third, or 3-month period, of a pregnancy.

tripeptide Three amino acids linked together by peptide bonds.

tropical oils A term used in the popular press to refer to the saturated oils—coconut, palm, and palm kernel oil—that are derived from plants grown in tropical regions.

trypsin A protein-digesting enzyme that is secreted from the pancreas in inactive form and activated in the small intestine.

tuber The starchy underground storage organ of plants.

tumor initiator A substance that causes mutations and therefore may predispose a cell to becoming cancerous.

tumor promoter A substance that contributes to cancer formation by stimulating cells to divide.

twenty-four-hour recall A method of assessing dietary intake in which a trained interviewer helps an individual remember what he or she ate during the previous day.

type 1 diabetes A form of diabetes that most commonly develops during childhood and is caused by the autoimmune destruction of insulin-producing cells in the pancreas, usually leading to absolute insulin deficiency; previously known as insulin-dependent diabetes mellitus or juvenile-onset diabetes.

type 2 diabetes A form of diabetes that most commonly occurs in overweight adults and is characterized by insulin resistance and relative (rather than absolute) insulin deficiency; previously known as noninsulin-dependent diabetes mellitus or adult-onset diabetes

tyrosine A conditionally essential amino acid; when phenylalanine is available in sufficient quantities, tyrosine is not essential in the diet.

U

U.S. Department of Agriculture (USDA) U.S. government agency responsible for monitoring the safety and wholesomeness of meat, poultry, and eggs.

ubiquinone A compound that transports electrons in the electron transport chain but that is not essential in the diet; also called coenzyme Q.

UL See Tolerable Upper Intake Level (UL).

ulcer An open sore.

undernutrition Any condition resulting from an energy or nutrient intake below that which meets nutritional needs.

underwater weighing A technique that uses the difference between body weight underwater and body weight on land to estimate body composition.

underweight A body mass index of less than 18.5 kg/m², or a body weight 10% or more below the desirable body weight standard.

unsaturated fatty acid A fatty acid that contains one or more carbon-carbon double bonds.

urea A nitrogen-containing waste product formed from the breakdown of amino acids that is excreted in the urine.

urine A fluid produced by the kidneys consisting of metabolic wastes, excess water, and dissolved substances.

uterus A female organ for containing and nourishing the embryo and fetus from the time of implantation to the time of birth.

V

variable A factor or condition that is changed in an experimental setting.

vegan A pattern of food intake that eliminates all animal products.

vegetarian A pattern of food intake that eliminates some or all animal products.

veins Vessels that carry blood toward the heart.

venule A small vein that drains blood from capillaries and passes it to larger veins for return to the heart.

very low birth weight A birthweight less than 1.5 kg (3.3 lb).

very-low-density lipoproteins (VLDLs) Lipoproteins assembled by the liver that carry lipids from the liver and deliver triglycerides to body cells.

very-low-kcalorie diet A weight-loss diet that provides fewer than 800 kcalories per day.

villi (villus) Finger-like protrusions of the lining of the small intestine that participate in the digestion and absorption of nutrients.

viruses Minute particles not visible under an ordinary microscope that depend on cells for their metabolic and reproductive needs.

visceral fat Adipose tissue deposited in the abdominal cavity around the internal organs. High levels are associated with an increased risk of heart disease, high blood pressure, stroke, diabetes, and breast cancer.

vitamins Organic compounds needed in the diet in small amounts to promote and regulate the chemical reactions and processes needed for growth, reproduction, and maintenance of health.

W

warfarin An anticoagulant drug that acts by inhibiting the action of vitamin K. It is a derivative of dicumarol; also used as rat poison.

water A molecule composed of two hydrogen atoms and one oxygen atom; essential nutrient needed by the human body in large amounts.

water-soluble vitamin A vitamin that dissolves in water; includes the B vitamins and vitamin C.

wear and tear hypothesis A hypothesis that proposes that the changes that occur with age result from the accumulation of cellular damage over time.

weight cycling or **yo yo dieting** The repeated loss and regain of body weight.

Wernicke-Korsakoff syndrome A form of thiamin deficiency associated with alcohol abuse that is characterized by mental confusion, disorientation, loss of memory, and a staggering gait.

whole grain The entire kernel of grain including the bran layers, the germ, and the endosperm.

whole-wheat flour A flour that contains all components of the wheat kernel: the bran, the germ, and the endosperm.

Wilson's disease An inherited defect in copper metabolism that leads to excessive accumulation of copper in the body and can cause neurological symptoms and liver disease.

X

xanthan gum A plant extract used as a stabilizer in processed foods.

xanthomas Cholesterol deposits that form under the skin.

xerophthalmia A spectrum of eye conditions resulting from vitamin A deficiency that may lead to blindness. An early symptom is night blindness, and as deficiency worsens, lack of mucus leaves the eye dry and vulnerable to cracking and infection.

xylitol The sugar alcohol formed from the sugar xylose; used in sugarless gum.

Y

yo-yo diet syndrome See Weight cycling.

Z

zeaxanthin A carotenoid found in corn and green peppers that has no vitamin A activity but provides some protection against macular degeneration.

zoochemicals Substances found in animal foods (*zoo* means animal) that are not essential nutrients but may have health-promoting properties.

zygote The cell produced by the union of sperm and ovum during fertilization.

Index

LIFE STAGE GROUP	EER PREDICTION EQUATION	EER FOR ACTIVE PHYSICAL ACTIVITY LEVEL (KCAL/DAY)[a]	
		MALE	FEMALE
0–3 mo	EER = (89 × weight of infant in kg − 100) + 175	538	493 (2 mo)[c]
4–6 mo	EER = (89 × weight of infant in kg − 100) + 56	606	543 (5 mo)[c]
7–12 mo	EER = (89 × weight of infant in kg − 100) + 22	743	676 (9 mo)[c]
1–2 y	EER = (89 × weight of infant in kg − 100) + 20	1046	992 (2 y)[c]
3–8 y			
Male	EER = 88.5 − (61.9 × Age in yrs) + PA[b][(26.7 × Weight in kg) + (903 × Height in m)] + 20	1742 (6 y)[c]	
Female	EER = 135.3 − (30.8 × Age in yrs) + PA[b][(10.0 × Weight in kg) + (934 × Height in m)] + 20		1642 (6 y)[c]
9–13 y			
Male	EER = 88.5 − (61.9 × Age in yrs) + PA[b][(26.7 × Weight in kg) + (903 × Height in m)] + 25	2279 (11 y)[c]	
Female	EER = 135.3 − (30.8 × Age in yrs) + PA[b][(10.0 × Weight in kg) + (934 × Height in m)] + 25		2071 (11 y)[c]
14–18 y			
Male	EER = 88.5 − (61.9 × Age in yrs) + PA[b][(26.7 × Weight in kg) + (903 × Height in m)] + 25	3152 (16 y)[c]	
Female	EER = 135.3 − (30.8 × Age in yrs) + PA[b][(10.0 × Weight in kg) + (934 × Height in m)] + 25		2368 (16 y)[c]
19 and older			
Males	EER = 662 − (9.53 × Age in yrs) + PA[b][(15.91 × Weight in kg) + (539.6 × Height in m)]	3067 (19 y)[c]	
Females	EER = 354 − (6.91 × Age in yrs) + PA[b][(9.36 × Weight in kg) + (726 × Height in m)]		2403 (19 y)[c]
PREGNANCY			
14–18 y			
1st trimester	Adolescent EER + 0		2368 (16 y)[c]
2nd trimester	Adolescent EER + 340 kcal		2708 (16 y)[c]
3rd trimester	Adolescent EER + 452 kcal		2820 (16 y)[c]
19–50 y			
1st trimester	Adult EER + 0		2403 (19 y)[c]
2nd trimester	Adult EER + 340 kcal		2743 (19 y)[c]
3rd trimester	Adult EER + 452 kcal		2855 (19 y)[c]
LACTATION			
14–18 y			
1st 6 mo	Adolescent EER + 330 kcal		2698 (16 y)[c]
2nd 6 mo	Adolescent EER + 400 kcal		2768 (16 y)[c]
19–50 y			
1st 6 mo	Adult EER + 330 kcal		2733 (19 y)[c]
2nd 6 mo	Adult EER + 400 kcal		2803 (19 y)[c]

[a]The intake that meets the average energy expenditure of active individuals at a reference height, weight, and age.

[b]See table entitled "Physical Activity Coefficients (PA Values) for Use in EER Equations" to determine the PA value for various ages, genders, and activity levels.

[c]Value is calculated for an individual at the age in parentheses.

PHYSICAL ACTIVITY COEFFICIENTS (PA VALUES) FOR USE IN EER EQUATIONS

AGE AND GENDER	SEDENTARY	LOW ACTIVE	ACTIVE	VERY ACTIVE
3 to 18 y				
Boys	1.00	1.13	1.26	1.42
Girls	1.00	1.16	1.31	1.56
≥ 19 y				
Men	1.00	1.11	1.25	1.48
Women	1.00	1.12	1.27	1.45

Source: Institute of Medicine, Food and Nutrition Board. "Dietary Reference Intakes for Energy, Carbohydrates, Fiber, Fat, Protein, and Amino Acids." Washington, D.C.: National Academies Press, 2002.

DIETARY REFERENCE INTAKES: TOLERABLE UPPER INTAKE LEVELS (UL[a]): VITAMINS

Life Stage Group	Vitamin A (µg/day)[b]	Vitamin C (mg/day)	Vitamin D (µg/day)	Vitamin E (mg/day)[c,d]	Vitamin K	Thiamin	Riboflavin	Niacin (mg/day)[d]	Vitamin B$_6$ (mg/day)	Folate (µg/day)[d]	Vitamin B$_{12}$	Pantothenic Acid	Biotin	Choline (mg/day)	Carotenoids[e]
INFANTS															
0–6 mo	600	ND[f]	25	ND	ND	ND	ND	ND	ND	ND	ND	ND	ND	ND	ND
7–12 mo	600	ND	25	ND	ND	ND	ND	ND	ND	ND	ND	ND	ND	ND	ND
CHILDREN															
1–3 y	600	400	50	200	ND	ND	ND	10	30	300	ND	ND	ND	1.0	ND
4–8 y	900	650	50	300	ND	ND	ND	15	40	400	ND	ND	ND	1.0	ND
MALES, FEMALES															
9–13 y	1,700	1,200	50	600	ND	ND	ND	20	60	600	ND	ND	ND	2.0	ND
14–18 y	2,800	1,800	50	800	ND	ND	ND	30	80	800	ND	ND	ND	3.0	ND
19–70 y	3,000	2,000	50	1,000	ND	ND	ND	35	100	1,000	ND	ND	ND	3.5	ND
> 70 y	3,000	2,000	50	1,000	ND	ND	ND	35	100	1,000	ND	ND	ND	3.5	ND
PREGNANCY															
≤ 18 y	2,800	1,800	50	800	ND	ND	ND	30	80	800	ND	ND	ND	3.0	ND
19–50 y	3,000	2,000	50	1,000	ND	ND	ND	35	100	1,000	ND	ND	ND	3.5	ND
LACTATION															
≤ 18 y	2,800	1,800	50	800	ND	ND	ND	30	80	800	ND	ND	ND	3.0	ND
19–50 y	3,000	2,000	50	1,000	ND	ND	ND	35	100	1,000	ND	ND	ND	3.5	ND

[a] UL = The maximum level of daily nutrient intake that is likely to pose no risk of adverse effects. Unless otherwise specified, the UL represents total intake from food, water, and supplements. Due to lack of suitable data, ULs could not be established for vitamin K, thiamin, riboflavin, vitamin B$_{12}$, pantothenic acid, biotin, or carotenoids. In the absence of ULs, extra caution may be warranted in consuming levels above recommended intakes.

[b] As preformed vitamin A only.

[c] As α-tocopherol; applies to any form of supplemental α-tocopherol.

[d] The ULs for vitamin E, niacin, and folate apply to synthetic forms obtained from supplements, fortified foods, or a combination of the two.

[e] β-Carotene supplements are advised only to serve as a provitamin A source for individuals at risk of vitamin A deficiency.

[f] ND = Not determinable due to lack of data of adverse effects in this age group and concern with regard to lack of ability to handle excess amounts. Source of intakes should be from food only to prevent high levels of intake.

Source: Dietary Reference Intake Tables: The Complete Set. Institute of Medicine, National Academies of Sciences. Available online at www.nap.edu

Dietary Reference Intakes: Tolerable Upper Intake Levels (UL[a]): Minerals

Life Stage Group	Arsenic[b]	Boron (mg/day)	Calcium (g/day)	Chromium	Copper (µg/day)	Fluoride (mg/day)	Iodine (µg/day)	Iron (mg/day)	Magnesium (mg/day)[c]	Manganese (mg/day)	Molybdenum (µg/day)	Nickel (mg/day)	Phosphorus (g/day)	Selenium (µg/day)	Silicon[d]	Vanadium (mg/day)[e]	Zinc (mg/day)	Sodium (g/day)	Chloride (g/day)	Potassium
INFANTS																				
0–6 mo	ND[f]	ND	ND	ND	ND	0.7	ND	40	ND	ND	ND	ND	ND	45	ND	ND	4	ND	ND	ND
7–12 mo	ND	ND	ND	ND	ND	0.9	ND	40	ND	ND	ND	ND	ND	60	ND	ND	5	ND	ND	ND
CHILDREN																				
1–3 y	ND	3	2.5	ND	1,000	1.3	200	40	65	2	300	0.2	3	90	ND	ND	7	1.5	2.3	ND
4–8 y	ND	6	2.5	ND	3,000	2.2	300	40	110	3	600	0.3	3	150	ND	ND	12	1.9	2.9	ND
MALES, FEMALES																				
9–13 y	ND	11	2.5	ND	5,000	10	600	40	350	6	1,100	0.6	4	280	ND	ND	23	2.2	3.4	ND
14–18 y	ND	17	2.5	ND	8,000	10	900	45	350	9	1,700	1.0	4	400	ND	ND	34	2.3	3.6	ND
19–70 y	ND	20	2.5	ND	10,000	10	1,100	45	350	11	2,000	1.0	4	400	ND	1.8	40	2.3	3.6	ND
> 70 y	ND	20	2.5	ND	10,000	10	1,100	45	350	11	2,000	1.0	3	400	ND	1.8	40	2.3	3.6	ND
PREGNANCY																				
≤ 18 y	ND	17	2.5	ND	8,000	10	900	45	350	9	1,700	1.0	3.5	400	ND	ND	34	2.3	3.6	ND
19–50 y	ND	20	2.5	ND	10,000	10	1,100	45	350	11	2,000	1.0	3.5	400	ND	ND	40	2.3	3.6	ND
LACTATION																				
≤ 18 y	ND	17	2.5	ND	8,000	10	900	45	350	9	1,700	1.0	4	400	ND	ND	34	2.3	3.6	ND
19–50 y	ND	20	2.5	ND	10,000	10	1,100	45	350	11	2,000	1.0	4	400	ND	ND	40	2.3	3.6	ND

[a]UL = the maximum level of daily nutrient intake that is likely to pose no risk of adverse effects. Unless otherwise specified, the UL represents total intake from food, water, and supplements. Due to lack of suitable data, ULs could not be established for arsenic, chromium, silicon, and potassium. In the absence of ULs, extra caution may be warranted in consuming levels above recommended intakes.

[b]Although the UL was not determined for arsenic, there is no justification for adding arsenic to food or supplements.

[c]The ULs for magnesium represent intake from a pharmacological agent only and do not include intake from food and water.

[d]Although silicon has not been shown to cause adverse effects in humans, there is no justification for adding silicon to supplements.

[e]Although vanadium in food has not been shown to cause adverse effects in humans, there is no justification for adding vanadium to food and vanadium supplements should be used with caution. The UL is based on adverse effects in laboratory animals and this data could be used to set a UL for adults but not children and adolescents.

[f]ND = Not determinable due to lack of data of adverse effects in this age group and concern with regard to lack of ability to handle excess amounts. Source of intake should be from food only to prevent high levels of intake.

Source: Dietary Reference Intake Tables: The Complete Set. Institute of Medicine, National Academies of Sciences. Available online at www.nap.edu